BIOLOGICAL SCIENCE:

An Ecological Approach

BIOLOGICAL SCIENCE:

An Ecological Approach

Sixth Edition

BSCS Green Version

BSCS
The Colorado College
Colorado Springs, Colorado 80903

Revision Team

Jean P. Milani, BSCS, Revision Coordinator
Frank C. Erk, State University of New York at Stony Brook
Joseph D. McInerney, Director, BSCS
Paul D. McIver, Englewood High School, Englewood, Colorado
William V. Mayer, President Emeritus, BSCS
Fran Slowiczek, San Diego County Office of Education
Carol Leth Stone, Science Writer, Alameda, California
Gordon E. Uno, University of Oklahoma, Norman

KENDALL/HUNT PUBLISHING COMPANY
2460 Kerper Boulevard P.O. Box 539 Dubuque, Iowa 52004-0539

Cover photo by Ken DeQuaine, Middleton, Wisconsin

ISBN 0–8403–4033–8

Revised Printing, 1988

Printed in the United States of America
10 9 8 7

Contributors

Charles R. Barman, Indiana University at Kokomo
Edward Drexler, Pius XI High School, Milwaukee
Donald P. Kelley, South Burlington, Vermont
James L. Koevenig, University of Central Florida, Orlando
William H. Leonard, Clemson University, Clemson, South Carolina
Don E. Meyer, Boulder, Colorado
Kenneth G. Rainis, Ward's Natural Science Establishment
Richard R. Tolman, Brigham Young University, Provo, Utah
William L. Wissinger, Saint Bonaventure University, Saint Bonaventure, New York
David A. Zegers, Millersville University, Millersville, Pennsylvania

Content Reviewers

Kenneth Andrews, The Colorado College, Colorado Springs
Robert Blystone, Trinity University, San Antonio
William Cairney, United States Air Force Academy
Jack L. Carter, The Colorado College, Colorado Springs
Garrett Hardin, University of California, Santa Barbara
Werner G. Heim, The Colorado College, Colorado Springs
Pat Huwa, Cherry Creek High School, Englewood, Colorado
James L. Koevenig, University of Central Florida, Orlando
Ivo Lindauer, University of Northern Colorado, Greeley
Lynn Margulis, Boston University
Raylene Owen, Cherry Creek High School, Englewood, Colorado
R. Craig Postlewaite, United States Air Force Academy
Richard Storey, The Colorado College, Colorado Springs
Sally Swartz, Cherry Creek High School, Englewood, Colorado
Gordon E. Uno, University of Oklahoma, Norman
E. Peter Volpe, Mercer University, Macon, Georgia
Barbara Winternitz, The Colorado College, Colorado Springs

BSCS Production Staff

Lynne A. Chase
Anthony A. Hauk
Thelma G. Hyson
Robin J. Miyahara
Douglas J. Robert
Doug Sokell
Brenda L. Vance
Katherine A. Winternitz

Artists

Carl J. Bandy
Bill Border
Randall E. Kochevar
Marjorie C. Leggitt
Yates Malmin
Paula Nicholas

BSCS Administrative Staff

Jane Butler Kahle, Chair, Board of Directors
Joseph D. McInerney, Director

Acknowledgments

The following teachers contributed comments and suggestions for this edition: Richard Benz, Wickliffe, OH; Richard Bergholz, Montesano, WA; R. W. Bolin, Wheatridge, CO; Donald Burger, Shillington, PA; Charlotte Candelaria, Sitka, AK; Stuart M. Caudill, Gastonia, NC; R. Chapel, San Diego, CA; Robert Cripps, Vicksburg, MS; Kermit J. Daum, Kerby, KS; Ray Deiss, Bergenfield, NJ; Linda de Kort, Kalispell, MT; Matilda Dunn, Sewanee, TN; James Enderson, Colorado Springs, CO; Charlotte Freeman, Chattanooga, TN; Vernon L. Gilliland, Liberal, KS; Margaret Graber, Sylvania, OH; Charles R. Gruentzel, Gillett, WI; Richard Guckert, Marietta, GA; Susan Heberle, Lodi, CA; Orville Heitkamp, Belle Plaine, MN; Douglass Herman, Sioux City, IA; Karl Hoffman, Rego Park, NY; Michael Hoffman, Colorado Springs, CO; Patrick Hollis, New Braunfels, TX; Pat Huwa, Englewood, CO; William E. Jurney, Roseville, MN; W. H. Leonard, Baton Rouge, LA; J. Kenneth Long, Jr., Shippensburg, PA; Darrel McClelland, Simla, CO; Paul McIver, Englewood, CO; Del McNally, Arvada, CO; Richard Miller, Gardner, KS; Richard Myers, Portland, OR; Ron Nilson, Morton, WA; Jeffrey Noblett, Colorado Springs, CO; Joseph Novak, Cornell, NY; Janet O'Leary, Silverton, CO; Raylene Owen, Englewood, CO; Suresh Pathiki, Andhra Pradesh, India; James Petrait, Ogden, UT; Roger Popple, Reedsburg, WI; Syed Razvi, Westland, MI; Melinda Reed, Arvada, CO; Lou Rollenhagen, Palisade, CO; Eugene Schmidt, Fairbanks, AK; Wendy Senger, Kalispell, MT; Fran Slowiczek, San Diego, CA: Glenn Snyder, Wheat Ridge, CO; M. Southall, Scottsdale, AZ; Edgar Stuhr, Lexington, MA; Don Tatge, Bloomington, MN, Penny Teeters, Grand Junction, CO; Frank Turner, Canton, OH; Jack Whitney, Littleton, CO; and Clark Wilder, Colorado Springs, CO.

Contents

Detailed Contents

Foreword

This we know.
The earth does not belong to man;
man belongs to the earth . . .
All things are connected,
like the blood which unites one family . . .
Man did not weave the web of life;
he is merely a strand in it.
Whatever he does to the web,
he does to himself.

Chief Seattle 1854
Suquamish Tribe
Washington Territory

Chief Seattle's eloquent, farsighted statement, written almost 125 years before the publication of this book, captures well the intent of the course you are about to begin. Like many people who have lived close to nature, Chief Seattle understood that "all things are connected." The source and the implications of those connections are the subject of this book.

Chief Seattle's closing statement is a warning: we humans do not stand apart from nature—we are part of it. In 1854, the population of North America was approximately 50 million, and the total population of the world was 1.075 billion. Today, the population of North America is 260 million; the population of the world is 4.7 billion. By virtue of our numbers and our ever more powerful technology, we have the ability to disturb the fragile strands of the web of life to an alarming degree.

The five major sections of *Biological Science: An Ecological Approach* are organized to provide you with information about the structure of the web of life—its sources of energy, its seemingly endless diversity, its development through evolutionary processes, its elegant simplicity, and the often stunning beauty of its complexity.

We hope that the information you encounter in this book will help you understand more completely the interrelationships among all living things, and the place of *Homo sapiens* in the web of life. Equally important, we hope that this book will help you understand that science is a unique and powerful way of knowing about the natural world. It relies on curiosity, creativity, observation, analysis, continuous questioning, and, perhaps most important, critical thinking. Facts and information mean little if we cannot apply them to the solution of personal or societal problems and to the improvement and protection of the web of life.

Chief Seattle knew quite well that each generation shoulders anew the responsibility for the quality of life on this fragile planet. We hope this book will provide you with some of the knowledge and skills required to help you with that important task.

Jean P. Milani
Coordinator, Green Version 6th Edition

Richard R. Tolman
Supervisor, Green Version 5th Edition

Gordon E. Uno
Supervisor, Green Version 4th Edition

Haven Kolb
Supervisor, Green Versions 1st, 2nd, and 3rd Editions

December 1986

BIOLOGICAL SCIENCE:

An Ecological Approach

Alan D. Briere / TOM STACK & ASSOCIATES

Section One

The World of Life: The Biosphere

How shall we begin to study biology—the science of life?

We might start with the abundance of life that lives in a lake and discuss the many relationships among the individuals. We might look into some living thing and examine its smallest parts under our microscope to see how those parts are put together. Or we might study chemistry, because chemical processes occur in all living things. We might even take a historical approach, searching for clues to the beginning of life and examining the fossil record to trace the development of living things.

There are many ways to start a biology course. Let us begin by looking at the many relationships among familiar living things around us.

Rod Planck / TOM STACK & ASSOCIATES

Food webs are a major part of the web of life. What role is played by the white-footed mouse, *Peromyscus leucopus*?

CHAPTER 1

The Web of Life

Introduction

You are one of many **organisms** (OR guh niz umz)—living things—in the web of life. Because all organisms depend on other organisms for their source of energy and matter, there are many connections in this web. All organisms need energy to live, to grow, and to reproduce. All organisms need matter to make up their bodies. In the web of life there are many direct connections between organisms that eat each other. There also are countless, indirect relationships between any individual and the organisms that affect its life. All this activity happens in the **biosphere** (BY oh sfir), the living part of the world. The biosphere exists in a delicate balance, which may change from day to day or year to year, but which remains relatively stable for long periods of time. The people who study the biosphere are **biologists** (by OL uh jists), scientists who study living things. In this chapter we will introduce the biosphere and the bases for all living things—matter and energy.

Interactions

Guidepost: Why is it difficult to study an organism apart from its environment?

1.1 Organisms Interact with the Organisms They Eat

A brightly colored grasshopper sits on a young plant and chews a leaf. The grasshopper is blue, red, and black, and it is as long as your fingernail. After several minutes the leaf is completely eaten. The grasshopper jumps toward another plant, but lands on a sticky thread instead. The thread is just one of many that are carefully woven together into a large, shiny trap—a web. As the grasshopper struggles to free itself, more threads stick to it. With each movement, the grasshopper sends a vibration from thread to thread and finally to the maker of the trap. In

Figure 1.1 Grasshopper feeding on a plant.

C. Allan Morgan

Figure 1.2 What activity is illustrated here?

Milton Rand/TOM STACK & ASSOCIATES

the blink of an eye, a large brown and yellow spider seizes the grasshopper and kills it with poison injected from its fangs. Digestive fluid from the spider's mouth liquefies the grasshopper's body, and the spider sucks up the resulting broth. Later, the spider drops the remains of the grasshopper on the ground and begins to wait for another insect.

This story is repeated every day all around the world. An insect eats a plant, and a spider eats the insect. Like the threads of the web, these three organisms are connected to each other in the web of life. They are connected to each other by their shared need for energy to grow and to reproduce. Some animals eat plants to get their energy, and some animals eat other animals. Plants, such as the poppies in figure 1.3, get their energy from the sun and make their own food. No matter where the energy comes from, without it an organism soon dies. If grasshoppers eat all the leaves of the young plant, the plant can no longer make its own food, and it dies. If the spider web is torn by a falling twig, the web must be repaired, or the trap can no longer catch food for the spider. The link to the supply of energy cannot be broken.

Many things can change the relationships between the plant, the grasshopper, and the spider. Caterpillars may eat the plant, which means less food for the grasshoppers. Without enough rain, the plant may die before it can reproduce or provide food for an animal. The spider may catch flies and moths as well as grasshoppers in its trap. A bird may eat the grasshopper, and it may even eat the spider and the caterpillar. The spider web has many threads, and in the web of life many organisms are connected to each other. The more closely we view the world, the more complex this web becomes.

Figure 1.3 Poppies in the sun.

BSCS by Carlye Calvin

Figure 1.4 Gypsy moth caterpillar eating a leaf. How is the food supply of other organisms affected?

USDA-APHIS

Figure 1.5 Bird eating a caterpillar.

David C. Fritts

We have seen how plants and animals interact within the web of life. The nonliving parts of the world such as temperature, sunlight, and rainfall influence the growth of plants and animals. The study of the living and nonliving parts of the environment and how they affect organisms is called **ecology** (ee KOL uh jee). Scientists who study ecology are **ecologists** (ee KOL uh jists). Ecology is only one aspect of biology. In this text, we will study many areas of biology, but we will focus on ecology. Let us begin our study by observing some organisms in investigation 1.1

Investigation 1.1 THE POWERS OF OBSERVATION

Introduction

There are many ways of exploring the world around us. In this investigation you will begin your exploration by doing some of the things scientists do: observing, reporting, and verifying observations.

Materials (per class)

labeled specimens of organisms
hand lens or stereomicroscope
millimeter rulers

Procedure

1. Located around the room are groups of organisms or parts of organisms. Each group contains 4 specimens of an organism. A **specimen** is a sample individual or, in the case of large plants, a characteristic part (a leaf, for example). Each group is labeled with the name of the organism and a number. Each specimen is labeled with a letter.
2. Work in teams of 2 to 4. Each team will begin with a different group of specimens. You will have approximately 10 minutes to observe and describe the specimens.
3. Select one person to take notes. Observe the 4 specimens and make notes on differences you see among the specimens. Take measurements, if appropriate. Remember, the differences must be in the organisms, not the containers they are in.
4. When your team has decided on the differences among the 4 specimens, choose 1 specimen and, on a separate sheet of paper, write a description of it. Make this description as complete as possible. Other teams will use it to try to pick out which of the specimens you were describing. Do not indicate the letter of the specimen on your description sheet. Write this information (group number and letter of specimen described) on a slip of paper and give it to your teacher.
5. When your teacher signals that the time is up, place your team description with the group of specimens so that other teams can use it for step 6.
6. When your teacher tells you, move to the group with the next highest number. The group with the highest number will go to group 1. You will have several minutes to observe each group. Select another team member to take notes. Read the description and decide as a team which of the specimens it describes.
7. Make up a chart with these headings:

Group Number	Specimen Fitting Description

Record the letter of the specimen on your chart.

8. When your teacher signals, move to the group with the next highest number. Move from each group to the next in this way. Continue until you return to your starting point.
9. Your teacher will list each group and the letter of the specimen described on the chalkboard. Check your chart of observations against this list. If your conclusions do not agree with the list, recheck that group of specimens. Did you miss anything? Was the description complete?

Discussion

1. Which was easier, writing a clear description or selecting the described specimen? Why?
2. (a) What information could be added to each description to make it clearer?
   (b) Does everyone in the class agree on what could be added? Why or why not?
3. (a) What information could be removed and still leave each description clear?
   (b) Does everyone agree on what information to remove? Why or why not?
4. Was there a group that you would have liked to describe? Why?
5. In what ways did reporting and verifying observation in this investigation increase your knowledge of these organisms?

1.2 Plants, Animals, and Other Organisms Make Up a Food Chain

Not far from the spider's web is a raspberry bush, and beneath the bush is a rabbit. The rabbit needs shelter and a place to hide from animals that may kill it. The raspberry bush is an ideal place to hide because its thorns can tear clothes or dig into the flesh of larger animals.

Figure 1.6 Describe all the relationships you see among the plants and animals and their environment.

The rabbit needs food, so it eats the low-hanging red fruit of the bush. A small brown bird feasts on the fruit near the top of the bush. The raspberry leaves are not very tasty to the rabbit, so after the berries are gone, it ventures out of its hiding place to look for grasses to eat. The rabbit moves quietly to a small patch of tender grass, but its movement is seen by a hungry fox. The fox creeps slowly toward the grass and suddenly leaps for the rabbit. The rabbit looks up just in time to avoid the teeth of the fox, and a wild chase begins. This time the rabbit reaches safety in a nearby raspberry bush.

A young rabbit the week before was not as lucky. Not far from the raspberry bush is the den of the fox. Near the den are scraps of fur and flesh that were last week's rabbit. The fox had carried this rabbit back here and eaten most of it. The next day flies buzzing around the rabbit carcass laid eggs on the dead flesh. The eggs hatched into wormlike maggots that fed on the flesh. At the same time, **microorganisms** (my kroh OR guh niz umz) such as bacteria, organisms too small to be seen with the naked eye, began to break down the flesh, causing it to decay.

There are many interrelationships among the rabbits and raspberries and the other plants and animals living near them. They all play roles in the web of life. Green plants, such as the raspberry bush and the grasses, use light energy to make their own food. Therefore, they are called **producers.** Animals, on the other hand, cannot make their own food, so they must eat plants or other animals or both. They are called **consumers.** Consumers that break down the bodies of dead plants and

Figure 1.7 Decomposers such as flies are an essential part of a food web.

animals in the process of decay are called **decomposers** (dee kum POHZ erz). Examples are bacteria and mushrooms, such as those in figure 1.8. All of these organisms, living and interacting in one place, form a **community.**

We can describe the interrelationships among the raspberry bush, the rabbit, and the fox in a **food chain.** This pathway tells us who eats what. In this case, the rabbit eats raspberries from the bush, and the fox eats the rabbit, as shown in figure 1.9a. A shorter food chain is the bird that eats the raspberries (figure 1.9b). These two food chains are connected to each other by the raspberry bush. Earlier, we described yet another food chain in which a spider ate a grasshopper that ate a plant (figure 1.9c). If the bird that eats raspberries also eats the spider, two more food chains are connected (figure 1.9d). When all the food chains in a community are joined together, a **food web** is formed.

The food web represents the web of life, but it is not the whole web of life. We have not included decomposers or all the plants a rabbit might eat or all the animals that might eat a rabbit. What would the web look like if there were two spiders instead of just one? Figure 1.10 shows a simplified food web that involves the organisms we have been discussing in this chapter. You can see that a complete food web can be very large and very complex.

Figure 1.8 Mushrooms are important decomposers. Their underground parts absorb food from dead organisms.

Gordon E. Uno

Figure 1.9 There is more than one food chain here. How many can you find?

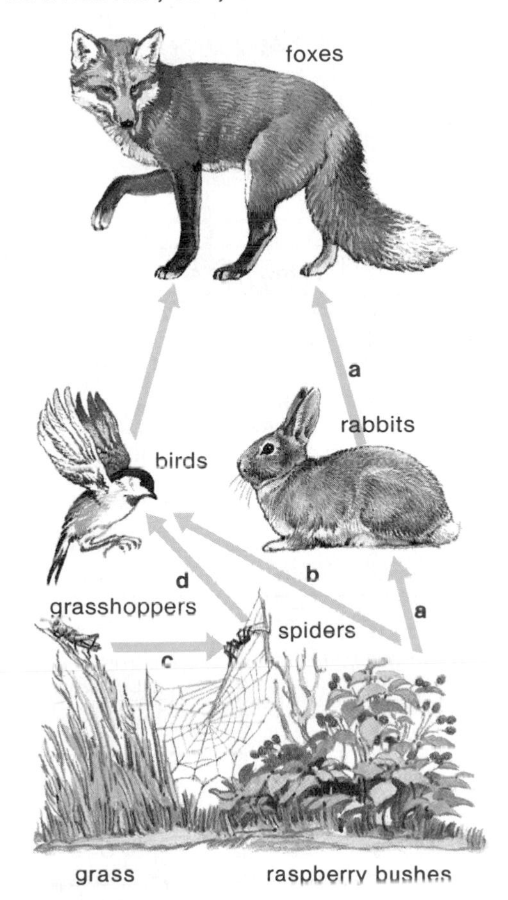

Figure 1.10 How many food chains can you trace in this simplified food web?

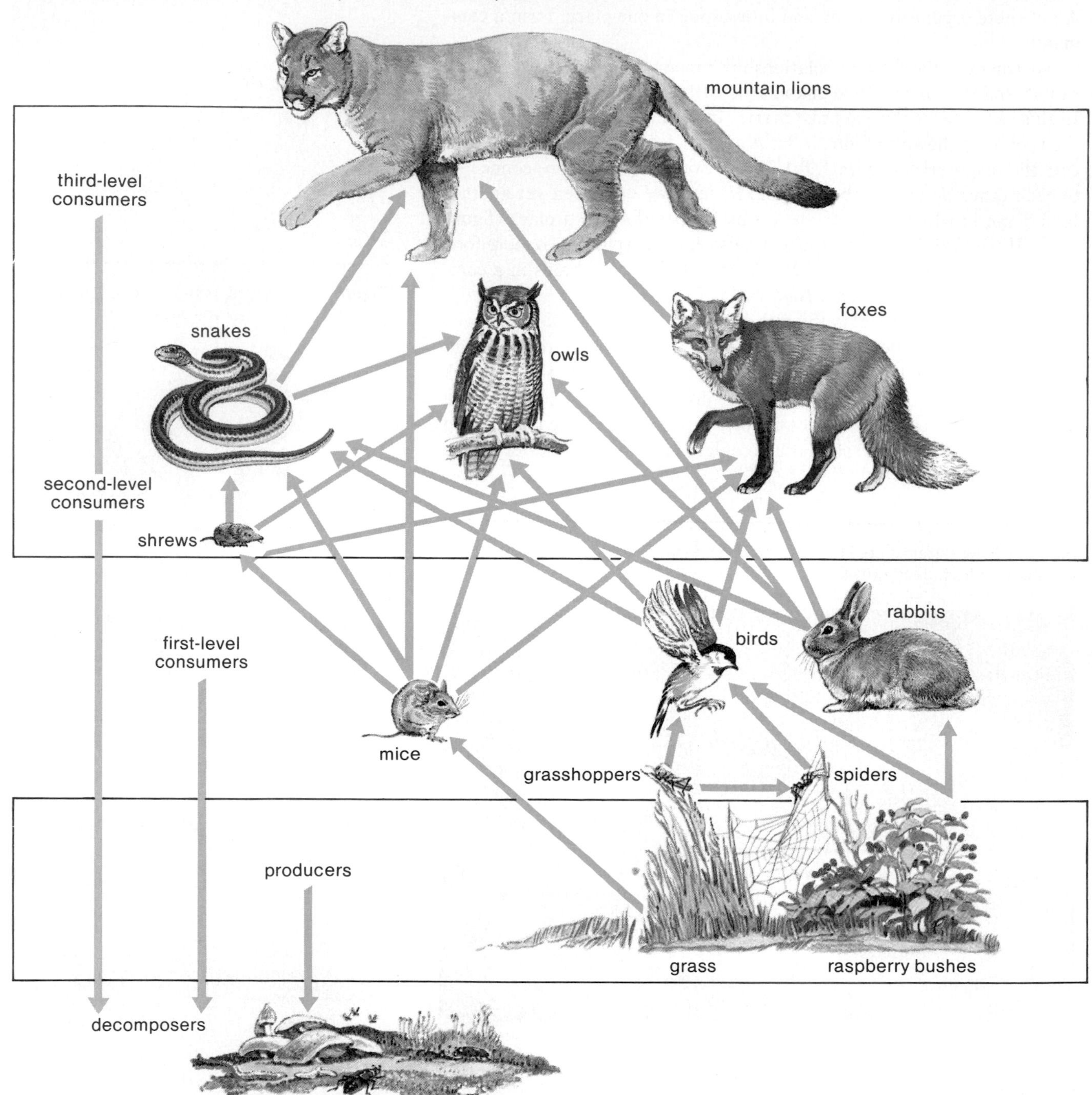

Biology Today C

Ecologist

Barbara Winternitz is an ecologist who teaches at Colorado College. Teaching classes is only a small part of her work in ecology. She conducts field research on birds in aspen forests and on Scrub Jays in the pinon-juniper woodland. At the same time she shows students how to do such research. She and her students work with state and local agencies in assessing and designing parks and open space areas for wildlife, and they inventory wildlife present in areas soon to be changed. As more of the land near cities is developed for human uses, the wildlife living there can be badly disturbed by roadbuilding, powerline construction and bulldozing. Sometimes these impacts can be reduced by knowing in advance the trails used by large animals, and where and when small animals are breeding and therefore most easily destroyed. By planting vegetation the animals like to eat in places that are safe for them, the developer can help maintain normal wildlife populations.

All across the country dams are being built, coal and other minerals strip-mined, and fields and farms converted to suburban development All of this destroys habitats (homes) for fish and wildlife. The impact of development must be assessed for each group of animals, and ways must be found to reduce this impact.

On one day, Barbara may work with a private company wanting to develop homes. Where would be the best land to set aside for parks and wildlife? How can a major road be built so it does not affect the movement of mule deer, and reduces the chances of serious car and deer collisions? On another day she may assess wildlife use of a city park scheduled for change. How can the changes be made so they are least disruptive for wildlife? Where should trails be located for both humans and wildlife to use? She also speaks to citizens' groups or school groups to alert them to changes that soon will happen.

All organisms need a place to live. For humans, not only living space and food, but the energy to produce other necessities must be extracted from the natural environment. The interrelationships of fish and wildlife with water, land, people, and industry are very complex. Ecologists attempt to ensure that the development of our nation's resources is in the best interests of all our people and takes into account all the many kinds of wildlife. State fish and game departments, conservation organizations, private consulting firms and other industries hire ecologists to assist in their operations. There are many pressures on ecologists, especially when a developer wants to destroy the habitat of an endangered species. The ecologist must be a true diplomat and negotiator in order to achieve the best solutions for all concerned.

Katherine A. Winternitz

Katherine A. Winternitz

1.3 The Living World Tends to Be Balanced

The world changes all the time. Some change seems rapid. You can see the world change with seasons. Trees lose their leaves in winter, and swarms of houseflies and mosquitoes may pester you in summer. You can see change in your world and in yourself through the years. Change also occurs over very long periods of time. The dinosaurs and flying reptiles of the past have given way to the mammals and birds of today. Yet the living world tends toward a balance at any given time.

That balance depends on many interacting factors. The rabbits live off the green plants, and many other animals, including humans, live off the rabbits. This might appear to be hard on the rabbits, but rabbits produce many offspring in a short time. Imagine how many rabbits there would be if they reproduced without control. They soon would be so numerous that they would eat all the plants; all the rabbits then would die. Foxes and other animals that eat rabbits may help keep the rabbit population under control. Disease or lack of food also may keep the rabbit population from growing too large. These controls, or checks, apply to all living organisms and are just one part of the balance of nature. Much of ecology deals with the study of the checks and balances in nature.

Self-Review

1. What parts of the environment does an ecologist study?
2. How do producers differ from consumers?
3. How is a food chain related to a food web?
4. Explain how reproduction and death are part of the balance of nature.
5. In what way do decomposers differ from other consumers?

Guidepost: Where do organisms obtain the matter and energy they require?

The Foundations of Life

1.4 All Biological Activity Requires Energy

When we look at food chains and food webs, we find that they involve the flow of energy and matter from one organism to another. The details of that flow will be developed throughout the rest of this biology course. Here, we will look at just the broad outline.

All the activities of an organism require energy. Imagine a marathon runner trying to run 26 miles without first eating high-energy foods. The activity does not have to be great to require energy. Even the movement of a tiny one-celled organism across a drop of water requires energy. Whenever you see biological activity, you need to ask, "Where does the energy come from to support this activity?"

Where do you get *your* energy? It may take some imagination to see energy in a hamburger and a pile of french fries. But there is energy in this food: it is **chemical energy.** Such energy is found in the structure of the molecules that make up the meat and the potatoes. Other forms of energy include electrical, mechanical, heat, light, and nuclear energy.

Figure 1.11 Where do these organisms get their energy?

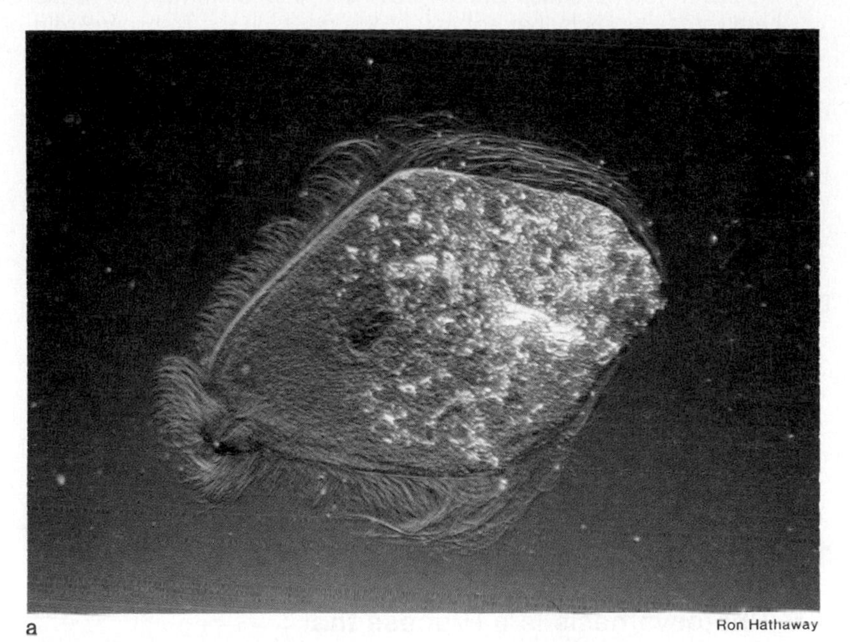

a Ron Hathaway

b BSCS by Carlye Calvin

The most important form of energy for you is the chemical energy stored in the food you eat. You begin to release this energy as you digest your food. Most of the energy from your food, however, is released within your cells in a complex series of chemical reactions known as **cellular respiration** (SEL yoo ler res pih RAY shun). This energy then can be used by you to grow and develop. Investigation 1.2 may help you understand how you are involved in the flow of energy and matter.

Investigation 1.2 YOU AND THE WEB OF LIFE

Introduction

How do *you* fit in the web of life? By relating your food for one day to the plants and animals from which it came, and to the other organisms with which those plants and animals interact, you may begin to form a picture of your role in the biosphere.

Materials

pencil and paper

Procedure

1. List the food that you ate yesterday. Separate these items into foods that came from animals and those that came from plants.
2. Many foods are combinations of different foods. List the ingredients of each food separately. Then indicate whether each was from a plant or animal—and the type of plant or animal. For instance, if you had cake for lunch you should list: flour—plant, wheat; sugar—plant, sugar cane or sugar beets; eggs—animal, chicken. For every animal that you have listed, list several foods that it eats. For example, if you had milk with your cake, list cow as the producer of the milk, and list grass and corn as food the cow eats.

3. Across the bottom of a clean sheet of paper, write the names of all the plants you have mentioned. Above this, in another row, list all the herbivores—animals that eat any of the plants in the first row. From each plant, draw a line to every animal that eats it. (Use figure 1.10 as a model.)
4. Above the herbivore line, enter the names of all the carnivores—animals from your list that eat other animals. From each herbivore, draw a line to the carnivores that eat that herbivore. The food web you have drawn shows some of the relationships between the plants and animals that provided your food for one day.

Discussion

1. (a) Are any of the items you listed as food for animals also foods that you could eat?
   (b) Which ones?
2. Did you include in your food web organisms that might compete with you for your food? Add as many as you can to your food web.
3. What about the role of decomposers in your food web? Indicate with lines how they might be involved.

1.5 Photosynthesis Is a Process that Supplies Food Energy

Remember that you are part of many food chains and one giant food web. Your hamburger came from a cow, but cows eat only plants such as grasses and grains. A grass plant or a potato does not eat other organisms. Where do they get their energy? All green plants grow in light. In the process of **photosynthesis** (foh toh SIN thuh sis), they absorb light energy from the sun and convert it to the chemical energy of sugars. The plant can use the energy in the sugars to grow and reproduce, or it can store some of the energy in the form of starch to be used at a later time. The potato plant does that. When we harvest and eat the potato, we benefit from the chemical energy stored in it.

Figure 1.12 For a hamburger with french fries these are your main sources of energy. But where did they get *their* energy?

Gordon E. Uno

BSCS by Carlye Calvin

Photosynthesis supplies almost all the food energy in the world. Only certain bacteria are able to make their own food in other ways. After grass makes its own food in photosynthesis, it uses some of that food to grow. Thus, some of the energy that is captured from sunlight is used before it reaches the cow, even if the cow eats the whole plant. Because no animal can make its own food, it must get its energy from plants or other animals. The cow eats the grasses and uses the energy in them to grow, to produce milk, and to move across the pasture. However, some of the energy is not used by the cow and remains in the waste products dropped in the pasture. This energy is not completely lost to all organisms. Decomposers break down the cow dung and use the energy from it for their own growth and reproduction. Decomposers also get energy from the bodies of the cows and plants that die.

No matter where energy comes from, almost all energy that enters a food web eventually is lost from the community in the form of heat. The conversion of chemical energy to the energy used by living organisms is not efficient. Whenever an organism breaks down its food, some of the energy escapes as heat. However, no organism can use this heat energy for growth. If you touch your arm, it feels warm. That is because some of the chemical energy once stored in the hamburger and fries you ate is converted to heat energy. The rest of the energy is used to keep you alive and for your growth.

Energy enters a food web through its producers and then is transferred from one consumer to another. Decomposers break down dead organisms and wastes to get their own energy. Eventually, however, all the energy that was once captured by plants in photosynthesis leaves a food web as heat—heat from your arm, from decomposers, and even from plants. This means that energy must continually enter a community, beginning with photosynthesis, or the community will die. The source of this energy for almost all communities in the world is the sun. If the sun were to burn out, life on earth would cease.

We have seen that energy flows one way through a food web. The flow of matter is very different.

1.6 Matter Is Used to Build the Bodies of Living Things

Living things get their energy from the sun, but they get their matter, or substance, from the earth and the air around them. You probably know something about matter. An **atom** is the smallest unit of an element. An **element** is matter that is made of a single kind of atom. Most elements occur as **molecules** (MOL uh kyoolz), which usually are combinations of two or more atoms. A **compound** is matter that has more than one kind of atom, chemically combined. Plants and animals are made up of many different compounds. But the atoms used to make up these compounds can be found all around you in the nonliving world.

Living things are very different from nonliving things. For a long time scientists thought that there must be special elements in organisms that were not found in nonliving matter. We now know this is not the case. Of more than 100 different elements found in the earth, only about 30 are used in the makeup of organisms. Most of these are very common.

Examples are the hydrogen found in a water molecule and the carbon found in the carbon dioxide of the air. Figure 1.13 shows the proportion of elements in humans, and table 1.1 compares elements present in organisms and in the earth.

The movement of matter through the food web begins with plants. Plants take in **inorganic** (IN or GAN ik) compounds, such as carbon dioxide and water. Inorganic compounds contain no carbon at all or just one carbon atom per molecule. Only small amounts of chemical energy are present in inorganic compounds.

During photosynthesis, plants build larger, carbon-containing **organic** (or GAN ik) compounds. Using light energy, they link together many carbon atoms to make sugars. Both energy and matter are stored in organic compounds. A plant can use sugars as a source of energy, as we learned in section 1.5. Or the plant can use the sugar molecules to

Figure 1.13 The human body contains the same elements that are found in air, water, rocks, and other nonliving substances.

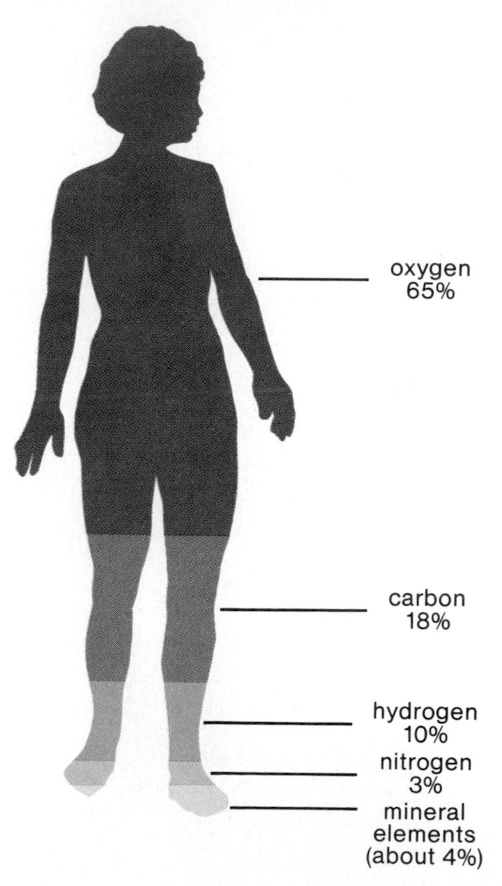

Table 1.1 A comparison of elements in organisms and the earth

Element	Symbol	Approximate % (by Weight) of a Human	Approximate % (by Dry Weight) of a Corn Shoot	Approximate % (by Weight) of the Earth's Crust
Oxygen	O	65.0	44.4	49.0
Carbon	C	18.0	43.6	0.09
Hydrogen	H	10.0	6.2	0.88
Nitrogen	N	3.3	1.5	0.03
Calcium	Ca	1.5	0.23	3.4
Chlorine	Cl	0.19	0.14	0.19
Copper	Cu	0.00015	—	0.01
Iodine	I	0.00004	—	variable
Iron	Fe	0.005	0.08	4.7
Magnesium	Mg	0.05	0.18	1.9
Manganese	Mn	0.0003	0.04	0.08
Phosphorus	P	1.0	0.20	0.12
Potassium	K	0.35	0.92	2.4
Selenium	Se	0.0003	—	0.02
Silicon	Si	trace	1.2	25.0
Sodium	Na	0.24	—	2.6
Sulphur	S	0.25	0.17	0.05
Zinc	Zn	0.002	—	trace

Other trace elements in the human body: arsenic, boron, chromium, cobalt, fluorine, molybdenum, nickel, tin and vanadium.

make other molecules needed to build its body. To do this, a plant rearranges the atoms in the sugar molecules and adds new atoms. Thus sugars are a food. A **food** is an organic substance that an organism can break down to get energy for growth, maintenance, and repair. Food is also matter that can be used to build the structure of the body.

An animal eats a plant, using it as a food. In this way both energy and matter are passed from one organism to another in a food web. However, unlike the flow of energy in a food web, the flow of matter is not one-way. Matter cycles within a community. Plants use carbon dioxide, water, and other substances in photosynthesis. These are the same substances that are given off by organisms when they use the food.

Producers build large molecules and store energy and matter in them. After a consumer organism uses those molecules as food, the matter in them—carbon dioxide, water, and other molecules—is returned to the environment. Plants then can use these materials to continue the process of photosynthesis. In a community the same matter is used again and again. Matter travels in cycles from the nonliving environment to living plants through food webs, and back to the nonliving environment. It then enters the food webs once again in photosynthesis. The relationship between matter and energy in the biosphere is summarized in figure 1.14.

Figure 1.14 Energy flows one way through the biosphere, from producers to consumers to decomposers. Matter, however, cycles from the nonliving to the living environment, through food webs.

Self-Review

1. What is the source of energy for almost all living things?
2. How are light and chemical energy related in photosynthesis?
3. How does matter get from the soil and air to animals?
4. How does the flow of energy through a community differ from that of matter?
5. In what way does an inorganic compound differ from an organic compound?

The Living World and How We Study It

1.7 The Biosphere Is Home to All Living Things

After studying many different food webs, biologists have concluded that the spider, the rabbit, and you are all part of one worldwide web of life. All organisms are part of this web, and they are tied together by the energy and the matter that they need for life. The living world forms only a thin layer around the nonliving world. This layer is called the

Guidepost: How do humans fit into the biosphere?

biosphere, and it includes all the organisms and the air, soil, and water surrounding them. The biosphere extends from the bottom of the oceans into the air above the earth, as can be seen in figure 1.15.

Because you are a living organism, you, too, are part of the biosphere. You have interrelationships with your family, friends, and teachers. Because you are part of the web of life, you also have relationships with all other organisms. Some relationships are obvious, such as those with the plants and animals that you eat. However, you often do not see the relationships with the animals that eat the same foods you eat. The relationship between you and a grasshopper that eats and damages lettuce is indirect. Any damage to your food plants can affect your food supply, however.

Humans also have long-term effects on the biosphere. Data being gathered today show that many human activities strain and destroy the delicate balance of nature in the biosphere. That happens when people behave as though they were independent of the rest of the living world.

Figure 1.15 The world of life—the biosphere. All life on earth is limited to this thin shell of air, land and water. Living organisms can be found from the highest point above sea level to almost 11,000 m below sea level.

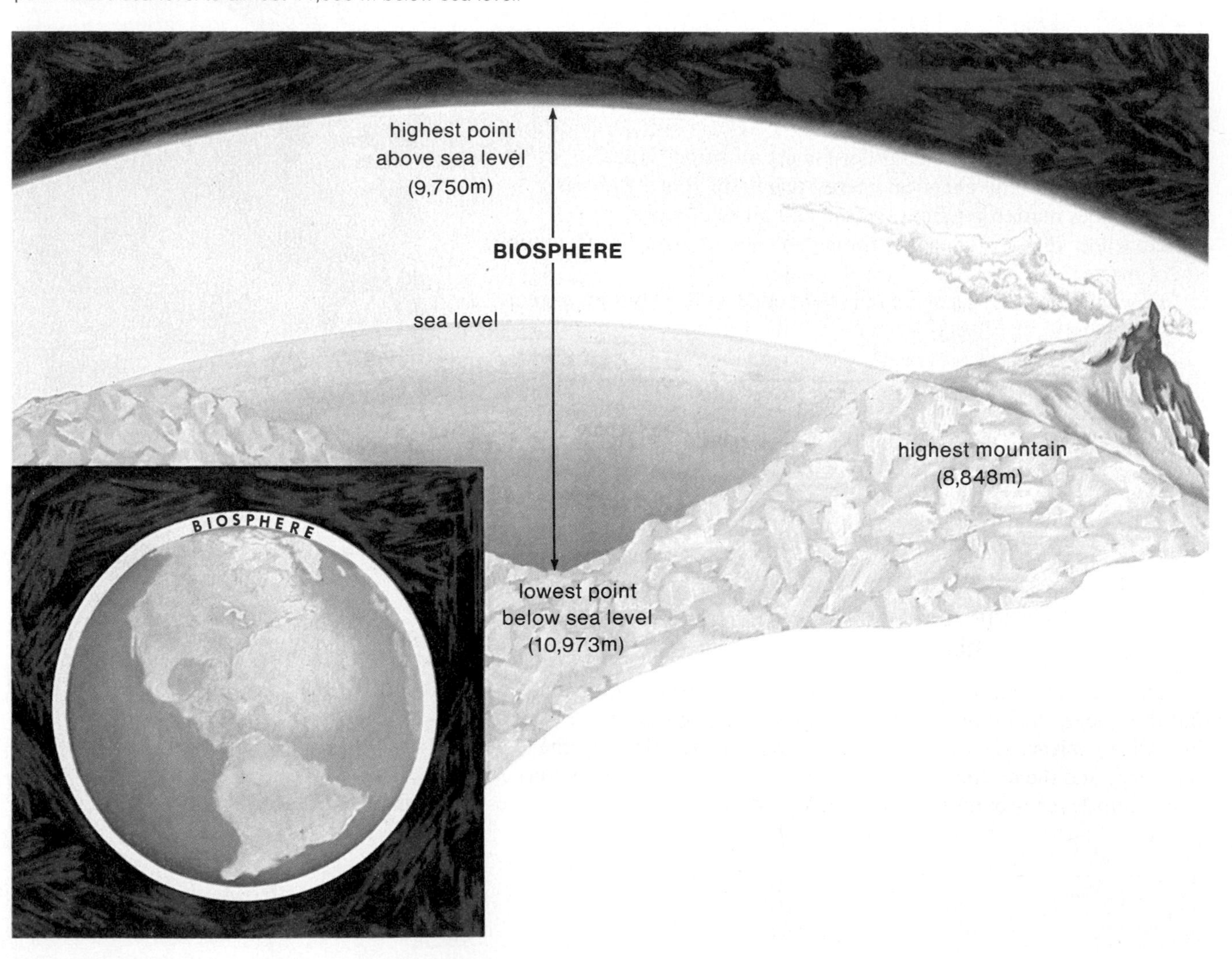

In the spider's web, one torn thread weakens the entire web. So, too, do your actions affect the world. What you, your friends, and your family do affect the rest of the biosphere in many subtle ways.

1.8 A Hypothesis Is an "Educated Guess" that Explains an Observation

The biosphere is a complex, living world. We look at the biosphere from many different viewpoints, but each viewpoint reveals only a small part of the whole. An artist might look at living things for their beauty of color and form. A farmer might look for ways to manage the growth of living things. A biologist might view the world scientifically.

As a science, biology does not deal with value judgments such as what is beautiful. Beliefs and value judgments differ from person to person. For instance, in figure 1.16a and b, some members of your class might prefer the fawn, others the puppy. Biology is concerned with facts—information that does not differ from one person to another. The Steller's jay in figure 1.16d is blue—a fact that can be agreed on by everyone

Figure 1.16 The question, "Which animal is nicer—the fawn or the puppy?" involves a value judgment. "Which bird is blue?" deals with a fact—color.

a Staley Studio

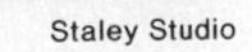

b BSCS

c Staley Studio

d Staley Studio

with normal color vision. Biologists collect and organize facts about organisms, and they use the facts in ways to gain more information. Science, though, is much more than just the collection of facts. It is a systematic way of looking at the world and of obtaining the facts. It is an ongoing process of inquiry, the product of which is a body of knowledge. This body of knowledge is subject to change and revision as we acquire new information. Above all, science is a human endeavor because *people* are involved in the process of inquiry.

Science is one way of obtaining knowledge about the world around us. The method of obtaining scientific knowledge involves a series of steps that begins with an **observation** of the living world. In the field with the spider and the rabbit, there may be many flowers with insects buzzing around them. A scientist may observe this field and ask the question, "What attracts bees to the bright red flowers in the field?" Library research may provide information about previous investigations of the question, or it may suggest appropriate approaches to the problem. Reading and thinking about the question may produce thoughts such as "Bees may be attracted to this kind of flower because of its red color." This thought is a **hypothesis** (hy POTH uh sis). A hypothesis is a statement that explains an observation. A good hypothesis leads to predictions and can be tested by experimentation. An experiment is usually designed to collect evidence that would either support or not support the hypothesis.

The hypothesis about the bees makes possible a prediction. *If* bees are attracted to the flower by its red color, *then* an artificial flower cut out of red paper may attract the same bees to it when placed in the field. To test this hypothesis you could cut out paper flowers, some yellow and some red. Suppose you carried out this experiment and observed that a bee landed on a red paper flower but not a yellow one. Have you proved that the bees are attracted to red flowers by the color? No, you have only provided evidence to support the hypothesis. Perhaps the bee became tired after flying and landed on the red paper flower because it was

Figure 1.17 What attracted the bee to this flower?

C. Allan Morgan

the nearest resting place. Perhaps you made the red flower out of paper more flimsy than the yellow one, and it fluttered in the wind. The fluttering, rather than the color, may have attracted the bee to your paper flower.

You can see that flowers may differ in many ways. These differences are called **variables** (VAIR ee uh bulz). Some of the variables for the flowers in the field are size, shape, odor, movement of petals, and color. A good experiment tries to control all variables except for the one you are studying—the experimental variable. In this experiment, color is the experimental variable, so it is important that the flowers be made of paper that differs *only* in color. The yellow flowers are included as a **control,** to make certain that it is the red color that attracts the bees. If no bees ever land on red paper flowers, you can reject the hypothesis. You must think of other possible reasons why bees visit the flowers. Perhaps it is the odor of the flowers. Many experiments may be necessary before you have enough information to answer the question, but each one of your experiments provides certain facts, or **data.** A scientist uses data to make conclusions about the hypothesis. In this example, the data are observations of what the bees do and what they do not do under the conditions of the experiment. In investigation 1.3 you will have a chance to use some of these processes.

Self-Review

1. What parts of the earth make up the biosphere?
2. How does a value judgment differ from a fact?
3. What is the role of observation, hypothesis, data, control, and a variable in a scientific investigation?

Investigation 1.3 HOW DO FLOWERS ATTRACT BEES? A STUDY OF EXPERIMENTAL VARIABLES

Introduction

You will recall from the previous reading that a hypothesis focuses a question to something that can be tested by an experiment. Observations from the experiment will either support or not support the hypothesis. There are usually many variables that can affect the outcome of an experiment. The experimental variable is the specific one being studied. Other variables are usually controlled or made the same in an experiment. If other variables are, in fact, controlled, there is a better chance that the experimental variable alone is responsible for the differences in results of the experiment. In this investigation you will try to determine what variables are responsible for the observations and why experimental controls are useful.

Procedure

1. Study the observation and hypothesis in the diagram immediately below about what attracts bees to flowers.

   Observation: Bees are attracted to flower 1.

Figure 1.18a

   Hypothesis: If bees are attracted to flower 1 by scent, then addition of scent to a flower that does not attract bees should cause bees to be attracted to that flower.

2. Examine experiment 1 immediately below. Here the scent of a flower that attracts bees is added to a flower that does not attract bees.

   Experiment 1: Scent of flower 1 is added to flower 2.

Figure 1.18b

   (a) What does experiment 1 lack?
   (b) Is the scent the only variable?
   (c) Identify as many variables as you can think of between these two types of flowers.

3. Study carefully experiment 2 immediately below. Be prepared to defend or criticize it. A, B, and C show different possible outcomes.

   Experiment 2: This is a redesign of experiment 1 to consider other variables that might be responsible for the original observation. Flower 2 in this case is a different type from flower 1, although both appear similar.

Outcome A

Figure 1.19a

Outcome B

Figure 1.19b

Outcome C

Figure 1.19c

Discussion

1. Compare the results of flower 2 in experiment 1 with flower 2 in experiment 2. What variables are being controlled in the design of experiment 2?
2. In experiment 2, the scent-producing substance from flower 1 is dissolved in a liquid (water or another solvent harmless to flowers) to produce a spray. What is the purpose of the control flowers with nothing sprayed on them?
3. What is the purpose of the control flowers sprayed with unscented spray?
4. What hypothesis would account for outcome A in experiment 2?
5. What hypothesis would account for outcome B?
6. What hypothesis would account for outcome C?
7. How does outcome B illustrate the difference between the two sets of control plants?
8. What other variables can you think of that might be helpful to control?
9. Why would it be useful to try a similar experiment with more than one group of the same kind of bees?
10. Why would it be useful to repeat it with more of the same kind of flowers?
11. How would you interpret the results if the *numbers* of bees visiting each kind of flower differed noticeably?
12. How would results similar to outcome A with different kinds of flowers strengthen your conclusions?

Summary

No organism is isolated from other living things. All organisms are part of a large, complex web of life. Plants are producers. They use the energy from the sun and inorganic material from the soil and air to produce the organic molecules of life. Because animals are consumers and cannot do this, all of them depend on plants, directly or indirectly, as their source of energy and matter. Humans also rely on plants and animals for food. Humans, though, have a greater effect on the biosphere than other organisms because our activities often result in permanent changes in the environment. Using the techniques of observation, hypothesis formation, and experimentation, we are becoming more aware of how those changes affect the lives of all organisms in the biosphere.

Application Questions

1. What might happen to the balance in the food web of life in a pond if the number of one kind of organism suddenly increased greatly? How long do you think such an increase would last?
2. Consider the pond in question 1. Is your prediction affected by the kind of organism involved? Consider first a producer; then, a consumer.
3. Look at the fawn and the puppy in figure 1.16. Draw a food web for each animal. Explain the role each animal plays in a food web.
4. After drawing a food web for the fawn and the puppy in question 3, has your value judgment changed about which one you like better? Why or why not?
5. What is the relationship between hypotheses and facts?

Problems

Some of the following problems involve applications of your understanding of the text and the laboratory. Others require further study.

1. In making a trip to outer space, astronauts must take along a part of our biosphere. Try to design an efficient "package" of the biosphere for such a trip.
2. Some people have careers related to biology. How does the career of the nutritionist in your school cafeteria relate to energy flow and materials cycles in a food web?

Suggested Readings

F. Graham, "Durward Allen: A Clear-Eyed View of the Natural World" *Audubon* (February, 1985). Although the article concentrates on this famous ecologist, it illustrates the methods employed by all ecologists and biologists to study wildlife.

C. P. Hickman, L. S. Roberts, and F. M. Hickman, 1984, *Integrated Principles of Zoology* (St. Louis: Times Mirror/Mosby College). The first two chapters contain discussions pertaining to chapter 1.

G. T. Miller, Jr., 1982, *Living in the Environment* (Belmont, CA: Wadsworth Publishing). Excellent resource, with several chapters relating to the foundations and interactions of life.

Scientific American (September 1970). The entire issue deals with the biosphere.

C. Starr and R. Taggart, 1981, *Biology: The Unity and Diversity of Life* (Belmont, CA: Wadsworth Publishing). See Chapter 28: Community Interactions.

C. Allan Morgan

A population of lady bird beetles. Notice the variation in spots. Such genetic variation is the raw material of evolution.

CHAPTER 2

Populations

Introduction

An individual is one organism. An organism always lives with other organisms, some like itself and some different from it. Individuals of the same kind make up a population, and populations grow or decrease in size in response to many environmental factors. Some factors are nonliving and some are living, but all interact to affect the size of a population. When some factor affects one population, the other populations connected to it within the web of life also are affected. Humans affect other populations more than other organisms because we change the environment to suit our needs. Our needs, however, might not be the needs of other organisms.

Individuals and Populations

Guidepost: How do populations change?

2.1 Individuals Are Separate Packages

In general, life processes occur in separate "packages." You are such a package, an individual. You carry on the activities of life within your body apart from the life processes in the bodies of your parents, brothers, or sisters. Each person is an individual. So, too, is each cow in a herd or each corn plant in a field. In most cases it is easy to distinguish individuals. Sometimes, however, plants are connected to each other underground. What looks like two separate plants above ground is really only one. With some careful digging you can determine that the two aboveground parts are connected, as with the iris in figure 2.1.

Rarely is an individual totally isolated from all others of its kind. A group of similar individuals living in one particular area is called a **population.** To define a population, you need to identify the kind of individuals, the time, and the place. Thus, you can refer to the population of pigeons in Denver in 1987, the number of spring beauty flowers in Oklahoma in March, or the geese in figure 2.2. You also can refer to the number of *Brontosaurus* dinosaurs throughout their entire history.

Populations are very important to scientists. To test a hypothesis, a scientist needs to observe not just one individual, but many individuals from a population. This is to make sure the observations made for one hold true for all. If not, the hypothesis might have to be changed.

A population is also very important because as it increases or decreases in size, it can affect many other populations. The more we know about one population, the more we can predict about others.

2.2 Population Size Depends on Interactions Among Four Factors

The size of a population changes over a period of time. Suppose a biologist counted 700 ponderosa pine trees on a hill in Colorado in 1976. In 1986 there were only 500 trees on the same hill. That means that there were 200 fewer trees in 1986 than in 1976, a decrease in the population of ponderosa pines. We can express that change as a **rate.** A rate is the amount of change divided by the amount of time for the change to take place. In this example, the rate is the change in the number of trees divided by the change in time: -200 trees/10 years = -20 trees per year. In other words, there was an average of 20 fewer trees each year in the population.

Figure 2.1 From above ground how many iris plants do these seem to be? How many when the soil is removed?

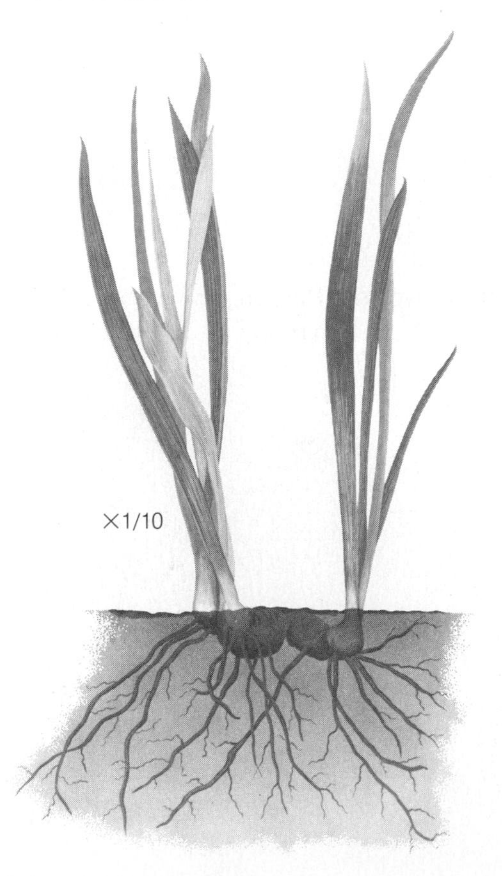

Figure 2.2 Population of Canada geese.

Dominique Braud/TOM STACK & ASSOCIATES

What might explain the decrease of 200 pine trees in the 10 years between 1976 and 1986? Because pines cannot wander away, or emigrate, they must have died. That decrease represents the death rate, or **mortality** (mor TAL ih tee), of the pine population. The number of deaths in the pine population per unit of time is the death rate. Mortality is not the only change that can affect a population, however. While some pines might have died, some young pine trees might have started to grow from seed. Death decreases a population size; reproduction increases it. Rabbits are born, birds are hatched, and seeds of plants germinate. For all of these, the rate at which reproduction increases the population is called the birthrate, or **natality** (nay TAL ih tee).

Figure 2.3 Ponderosa pine forest in Colorado.

Doug Sokell

Figure 2.4 Dead ponderosa pines.

Alexandra Vargo

Figure 2.5 Spruce seedlings

Doug Sokell

Figure 2.6 Dandelion seeds. Do dandelions immigrate or emigrate?

Dwight R. Kuhn

Pine trees are rooted in place, but for organisms that can move, there are two other ways a population size may change. **Immigration** (im uh GRAY shun) occurs when one or more organisms move into an area where others of their kind can be found. Immigration increases the population. **Emigration** (em uh GRAY shun) occurs when organisms leave the area. Emigration decreases the population.

Suppose you are studying the pigeon population in your city or town. Last year a certain number of pigeons hatched, and some died. Some pigeons flew into the city, and some flew out. Natality and immigration increase the population of pigeons; mortality and emigration decrease the population. Thus, the size of any population is the result of the relationships among these opposing rates. These four rates—natality, mortality, immigration, and emigration—are the factors that determine population size. They apply to every population, including the human population. In investigation 2.1 you will see how these factors interact in the growth of two populations.

Investigation 2.1 POPULATION GROWTH

Introduction

In the past section you have learned how four rates—natality, mortality, immigration, and emigration—determine population size. Carrying capacity is the maximum population a given environment can support on a long-term basis. Doubling time is the number of years required for a population to double its size. In this investigation, you will compare the growth of two populations and examine the roles played by carrying capacity, doubling time, and the four rates on that growth.

Materials:

pocket calculator
graph paper

Part A—Reindeer Population

Procedure

In 1911, 25 reindeer—4 males and 21 females—were introduced onto Saint Paul Island, one of the Pribilof Islands in the Bering Sea near Alaska. Saint Paul Island is approximately 106 square kilometers in size (41 square miles), and is more than 200 miles from the mainland. On Saint Paul Island there were no predators of the reindeer, and no hunting of the reindeer was allowed. The graph below indicates what happened to the reindeer population on the island between 1911 and 1950. Use the graph to answer the following questions.

Figure 2.7

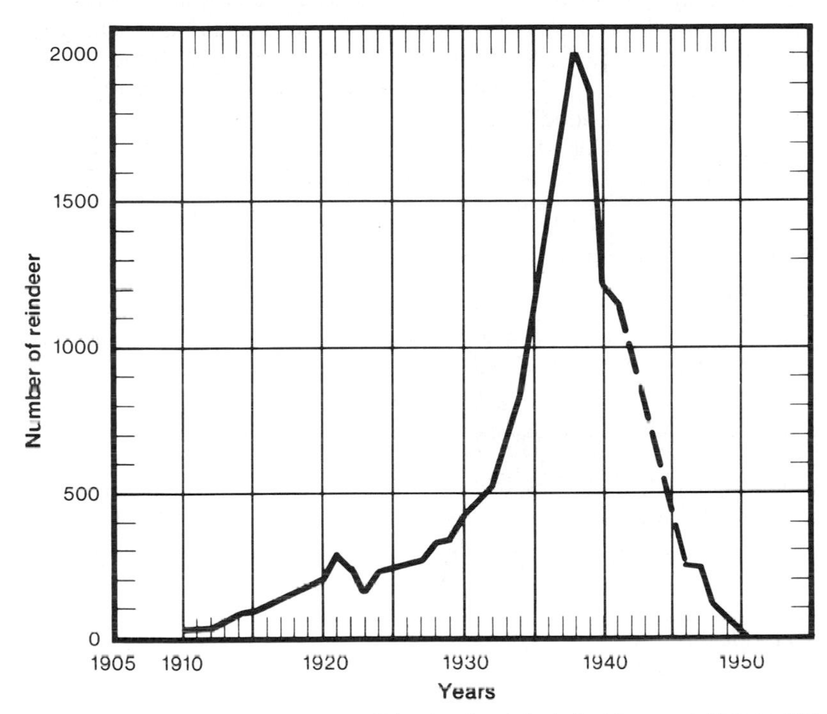

1. (a) What was the size of the population at the beginning of the study?
   (b) In 1920?
   (c) What was the difference in the number of reindeer between 1911 and 1920?
   (d) What was the average annual increase in the number of reindeer each year between 1911 and 1920?
2. (a) What was the difference in population size between the years 1920 and 1930?
   (b) What was the average annual increase in the number of reindeer in each of the years between 1920 and 1930?
3. What was the average annual increase in the number of reindeer in each of the years between 1930 and 1938?
4. During which of the three periods—1911–1920, 1920–1930, or 1930–1938—was the increase in the population of reindeer greatest?
5. (a) What was the greatest number of reindeer found on Saint Paul Island between 1910 and 1950?
   (b) In what year did this occur?
6. In 1950, only 8 reindeer were still alive. What is the average annual *decrease* in the number of reindeer in each of the years between 1938 and 1950?

Discussion

1. Could emigration or immigration have played a major role in determining the size of the reindeer population? Explain your answer.
2. What might account for the tremendous increase in the population of reindeer between 1930 and 1938 as compared to the rate of growth during the first years the reindeer were on the island?
3. What effect might 2000 reindeer have had on the island and its vegetation?
4. Consider all the factors an organism requires to live. What might have happened on the island to cause the change in population size from 1938 to 1950?
5. In 1950, 8 reindeer were still alive. If some of those were males and some females, what do you predict would happen to the population of reindeer in the next few years?
6. (a) Beginning in 1911, in which years did the population double?
   (b) How many years did it take each of those doublings to occur?
   (c) What happened to the doubling time between 1911 and 1938?
7. What evidence is there that the carrying capacity for reindeer on this island was exceeded?
8. (a) What does this study tell you about unchecked population growth?
   (b) What difference might hunting or predators have made?

Part B—Human Population

Procedure

1. On a sheet of graph paper, plot the growth of the human population using the data below.

Table 2.1 Human population growth between A.D. 1000 and 1985

Date A.D.	Human Population (Millions)	Date A.D.	Human Population (Millions)
1	250	1920	1800
1000	280	1930	2070
1200	384	1940	2300
1500	427	1950	2500
1650	470 (Black Death)	1960	3000
1750	694	1975	4080
1850	1100	1980	4450
1900	1600	1985	4850

2. Use your graph to determine the doubling times for the human population between A.D. 1 and 1985.
   (a) How much time elapsed before the human population of A.D. 1 doubled?
   (b) Is the amount of time needed for the human population to double increasing or decreasing?
   (c) What does that indicate about how fast the human population is growing?
3. Extend your graph to the year 2000. What do you estimate the human population will be in that year?

4. Using the equations below, estimate the doubling time for the current population based on the rate of growth from 1980 to 1985. In what year will the present population double?

Rate of growth (in percent) =

$$\frac{(\text{population in 1985} - \text{population in 1980}) \times 100}{\text{population in 1980} \times \text{number of years}}$$

$$\text{Doubling time} = \frac{70}{\text{rate of growth}}$$

Discussion

1. What similarities do you see between the graph of the reindeer population and the graph of the human population you just constructed?
2. What are the 3 or 4 most important factors required to sustain a population?
3. (a) In what ways is the earth as a whole similar to an island such as Saint Paul Island?
   (b) Does the earth have a carrying capacity? Explain your answer.
4. What might happen to the population of humans on the earth if the present growth rate continues?
5. (a) What methods could be used to reduce the rate of growth of the human population?
   (b) In your opinion, which of those methods would be most acceptable?
6. Cite a place in the world where population growth is a problem today. How is it a problem?
7. Cite a place in the world where population growth is *not* a problem today. Why is it not a problem?
8. What problems in your country are related to the size of the human population?
9. What are the most important 3 or 4 factors to think about with regard to the world population?

2.3 The Human Population Uses Huge Amounts of Resources

All the humans on the earth make up one large population. This population is especially important because it can affect all the plants and animals on the earth. There are many reasons for this impact, but two are particularly significant. First, because our population is large, we use huge amounts of the world's resources—such as food, clean water, fuels, and building materials. After we use these resources, we return many to the earth as waste materials that cannot be used again in that form. Second, the number of people on earth is increasing at a tremendous and alarming rate. That means that though we use up many resources now, we will use even more in the future. Is there a limit to the size of the human population?

Figure 2.8 How many people can you count?

BSCS

You are one of more than 4.8 billion living human beings on the earth today. About 358,000 babies are born each day. About 146,000 people die each day around the world. The human population grows by about 80 million people each year. That is more people than live in California, New York, Texas, and Pennsylvania combined.

Experts estimate that at the current rate of growth, the human population will double in less than 40 years. Think about what would happen if the student population in your school were to double, but the resources were to remain the same. You would have the same number of teachers, classrooms, desks, and lunches, but twice as many people would be trying to use them. Could your school handle the increase? Now, suppose the student population doubled again. What do you think would happen?

Just like the student population in the crowded school, the human population on the earth increases, but the resources do not. Why is the human population growing so rapidly? Simply put, natality exceeds mortality. The mortality rate was high in the early history of humans. Some of our early ancestors were killed and eaten by large animals, but most died at an early age from diseases. Today in most countries humans no longer have to worry about predators, and we have reduced the danger of death due to disease. Thus, the population grows.

All organisms need certain things for life. We now know that genetic background, diet, behavior, and environment play important roles in health. There is a long list of resources that we require to live normal, healthy lives, however. These are the necessities of life.

Is the population problem one that concerns just other countries? The answer to that is an emphatic "No!" Human beings, like all other living things, have certain basic needs. No matter where we live, we all need

Figure 2.9 The necessities of life: clean air, water, food, and shelter from cold.

Carlye Calvin

Doug Sokell

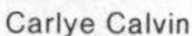

Carlye Calvin

Katherine A. Winternitz

food, clean water, and oxygen to breathe. We need living space, shelter from cold or harmful weather, and protection from other organisms that might harm us, including disease-causing organisms.

It is difficult to provide all the necessities of life to a growing population. Energy is required to grow the food needed to feed all the hungry people. Energy and resources are needed to make and run tractors, irrigation pumps, and harvesters. Energy also is needed to transport the food into cities and towns from distant farms. Already there are many towns that must ration water. Water for drinking, washing, and irrigation often is piped for thousands of kilometers; resources and labor are required to make and install the pipes. In some places local industries must take action to keep the air clean and breathable. In a number of cities people may become ill from breathing unclean air. When any of the necessities of life are reduced or spoiled, the human population is affected. In investigation 2.2, you will have a chance to learn just how much of one of these necessities of life you need.

Figure 2.10 Energy is used to make and run this harvester, and to transport the wheat for processing and distribution to grocery stores.

Bill Keck / CSU Extension

Figure 2.11 What abiotic environmental factors can you identify in this photo? What potential effects could these factors have on the human population?

Dave Baird / TOM STACK & ASSOCIATES

Self-Review

1. What three things define a population?
2. When is it difficult to distinguish an individual from a population?
3. What four factors determine population size, and how does each affect the population?
4. How does the human population affect other populations?

Investigation 2.2 WATER—A NECESSITY OF LIFE

Introduction

In this investigation you will calculate how much water you use individually on a daily basis, and then calculate the water needs for your family, your class, your school, your town, and your state. You also will discover some of the ways in which you use water indirectly.

Materials

graph paper
calculators (optional)

Procedure

1. Record how many gallons of water you think you use individually in an average day. Later you will compare this *estimated* daily water use with your *calculated* daily water use.
2. As a group, list all the ways members of your class use water on a day-to-day basis.
3. Using the data in table 2.2, Domestic Uses of Water, determine your *individual* water use per day for each activity that your class listed in procedure 2. Include your share of general family uses such as dishwasher and clothes washer. Then determine your individual *total* water use per day.
4. Compare the individual water use you calculated in procedure 3 with the water use you estimated in procedure 1. Is your calculated figure higher or lower than your estimated figure?
5. Find out how many people are in your school, including teachers and students. Find out how many people live in your town or city and your state.
6. Calculate the amount of water used per day by your family, your class, your school, your town, and your state, for each of the activities listed in procedure 2.
7. Calculate total water use per day for all the activities combined, for your family, your class, your school, your town, and your state.
8. Draw a bar graph to illustrate how much water is used by your class for each activity. Which activities require the most water?

Table 2.2 Domestic uses of water

Activity	Amount Used—in Gallons
Brushing teeth	2–10
Washing hands	2
Shaving	20 (2/min)
Showering	20–25 (5/min)
Tub bathing	25–35
Flushing toilet	3.5–8
Getting a drink	0.25
Cooking a meal	5–7
Washing dishes	30 (8–10/meal)
Automatic dishwasher	15
House cleaning	7
Washing machine	24–50
Watering lawn	10/min (102/1000 m^2)
Leaking faucet	25–50/day
Faucet and toilet leaks in New York City = 757 million/day	

(From *Living in the Environment*, Third Ed., by G. Tyler Miller, Jr. © 1982 by Wadsworth, Inc. Used by permission.)

Discussion

1. There are many water uses that are not obvious to most people. Consider, for example, how much water is necessary to raise one calf until it is fully grown. (See table 2.3, How to make a cow.) Why do you think so much water is needed to raise a calf?

Table 2.3 How to make a cow

Ingredients

1	80-lb calf
8	acres grazing land
12,000	lbs forage
125	gals gasoline and various petroleum byproducts
305	lbs fertilizer
1.5	acres farmland
2,500	lbs corn
350	lbs soybeans
	insecticides
	herbicides
	antibiotics
	hormones
1.2	million gals water, to be added regularly throughout

Fertilizer Recipe

Combine:

170	lbs nitrogen
45	lbs phosphorus
90	lbs potassium

Take one 80-lb calf—allow to nurse and eat grass for 6 months, then wean. Over next 10 months, feed 12,000 pounds of forage. Use about 25 gallons of petroleum to make fertilizer to add to the 1.5 acres of land. Set aside rest of gasoline to power machinery, produce electricity, and pump water. Plant corn and soybeans—apply insecticides and herbicides. At 24 months, feed cow small amounts of crop and transfer to feedlot. Add antibiotics to prevent disease and hormones to speed up fattening. During next 4 months, feed remaining crop mixed with roughage. Recipe yields about 440 usable pounds of meat—1000 7-ounce servings. Option: Bake the 2500 pounds of grain and 350 pounds of soybeans into bread and casseroles—18,000 8-ounce servings.

(Excerpt from *The Cousteau Almanac* by Jacques-Yves Cousteau. Copyright © 1980, 1981 by the Cousteau Society, Inc. Reprinted by permission of Doubleday & Company, Inc.)

Table 2.4 Indirect uses of water

Agricultural

Item	Gallons Used
1 egg	40
1 orange	100
1 ear corn	76
1 loaf bread	142
1 kg flour	165
1 kg sugar	275
1 kg rice	1,101
1 kg beef	5,507

Industrial

Item	Gallons Used
Industrial mining and manufacturing	183/person/day
Cooling water for electric power plants	700/person/day
1 gallon gasoline	26–95
1 kg steel	77
Sunday newspaper	280
1 kg synthetic rubber	660
1 kg aluminum	2,202
1 car	94,825

(From *Living in the Environment*, Third Ed., by G. Tyler Miller, Jr. © 1982 by Wadsworth, Inc. Used by permission.)

2. Make a list of the ways you use water indirectly, for example, in the production of the food you eat or materials you use.
3. Compare your list with table 2.4, "Indirect Uses of Water." How many of these uses did you list?
4. How could you reduce your indirect use of water?
5. What could you do to reduce your direct use of water?
6. Is there any evidence that the water supply you use daily is decreasing in size or is being contaminated by pollutants? How could you go about obtaining this information?

For Further Investigation

1. Research actual water use for one of the items you listed in discussion question 2.
2. Examine your family utility bills for the past year and note the amount of water used in each month. Each unit represents 1 m^3 of water. Calculate your family's average monthly water use in gallons. (A gallon equals 0.004 m^3.) How does actual use compare with your calculations in this investigation?

The Environment and Populations

Guidepost: How do environmental factors affect population size?

2.4 The Environment Is Made Up of Biotic and Abiotic Factors

Factors that affect the human population also affect all other populations. Everything that surrounds and affects an organism is its **environment** (en VY run munt). The environment may slow the growth of an individual and may even kill it. Or the environment may stimulate the growth and reproduction of an individual. In either case, the environment affects the size of a population.

We can divide the environment into two parts. There is the living part and the nonliving part of an organism's surroundings. The living or recently living part is called the **biotic** (by OT ik) environment. This includes your neighbors, houseplants, and dog, the fleas on your dog, and all the organisms you eat. The nonliving part is called the **abiotic** (AY by OT ik) environment, which includes things such as living space, sunlight, soil, wind, and rain. Both biotic and abiotic factors affect the size of a population. If all the environmental conditions are not optimal, a population might not grow. An environmental factor that slows the growth of a population is called a **limiting factor.** We will discuss some of those limiting factors in the following sections, and you can observe their effects on a specific population in investigation 2.3.

Figure 2.12 Jeffrey pine growing out of a crevice in rock. What biotic and abiotic factors affect this tree?

Doug Sokell

Investigation 2.3 STUDY OF A POPULATION

Introduction

Yeast organisms are useful for studying populations. They reproduce rapidly and are conveniently small. You will observe a population of yeast cells growing in a broth **medium** (plural, media). How do populations change over a period of time? Before going any further with this investigation, think of three hypotheses that might be possible answers to this question. Write these hypotheses in your data book and evaluate them with the data you collect during this investigation.

Materials (per team)

125 ml flasks (2)
aluminum foil
glass marking crayon
250 ml beaker
balance (sensitive to 0.1 g)
250 ml graduated cylinder
stirring rod
Bunsen burner or hot plate
spatula
microscope slides
cover slips
microscope
dropping pipets
distilled water
nutrient materials
- bacto-yeast extract
- potassium phosphate-monobasic
- peptone
- glucose

Procedure

Day 1

1. Measure 200 ml of distilled water and place it in the 250 ml beaker.
2. Weigh the four sources of nutrients in the amounts shown below and add them to the 200 ml of distilled water.

bacto-yeast extract	0.5 g
potassium phosphate-monobasic	0.4 g
peptone	1.0 g
glucose	8.0 g

3. Heat over a low flame or low heat until the materials are dissolved. Stir constantly while heating. When properly dissolved, the medium is sparkling clear and slightly yellow.
4. Pour 49 ml of your prepared medium into each of the 125 ml flasks. Shape an aluminum-foil cap over the mouth of each flask.
5. Label each flask with your team identification. Label one flask A and the other B.
6. Your teacher will sterilize the flasks and the medium. Why is sterilizing necessary?

Day 2

1. Your teacher will transfer 1 ml of a yeast stock culture to your flask A. Nothing will be added to flask B. Keep the two flasks in the same environment during the investigation. What is the purpose of flask B?
2. You now have a start of a new population in flask A. Review your hypotheses as to what you think might happen over the next ten days.
3. Before you go any further, prepare a table like table 2.5 below in your data book.

Table 2.5 Number of yeast cells

Count	Day 0	Day 1	Day 2	Day 3	Day 4	Day 5	Day 6	Day 7	Day 8	Day 9	Day 10
First sample											
Second sample											
Third sample											
Fourth sample											
Fifth sample											
Total											
Average											
Dilution											
Total × Dilutions											

4. You need to know the number of yeast cells with which your new population began. The number is so small that it would be hard to find them in your flask A. Instead, you will make a count from the yeast stock culture that was used to start your population in flask A. Your teacher will place a drop of material from the yeast stock culture on a slide, and you will use the following counting method.
   (a) Place a clean cover slip over the drop of material on your slide. Position the slide on your microscope stage (be careful not to tilt the stage). Focus with low power; then switch to high power.
   (b) Count the number of individual organisms in five different high-power fields, as shown in figure 2.13. (Note: Yeast organisms are difficult to see if the light is too bright.) Refer to figure 2.14 for the appearance of yeast organisms. The cells often stick together, but count each cell in any clump separately. Buds also count as individuals. Now have your partner make five counts of a new sample provided by your teacher. Record your five counts on the table in your data book under Day 0.
5. But wait. Is that an accurate count of the yeast population in flask A? Remember you made the counts from the stock culture flask. Only 1 ml of that stock culture was added to the 49 ml of the yeast growth medium in your flask for a total of 50 ml. You must do a little mathematics with the number you got in procedure 4 (b). What calculations must you do to get a count for Day 0 for your population in flask A?
6. Do the calculations and record this number on the Total × Dilutions line on your table for Day 0.

Figure 2.13 Approximate positions of fields for counts.

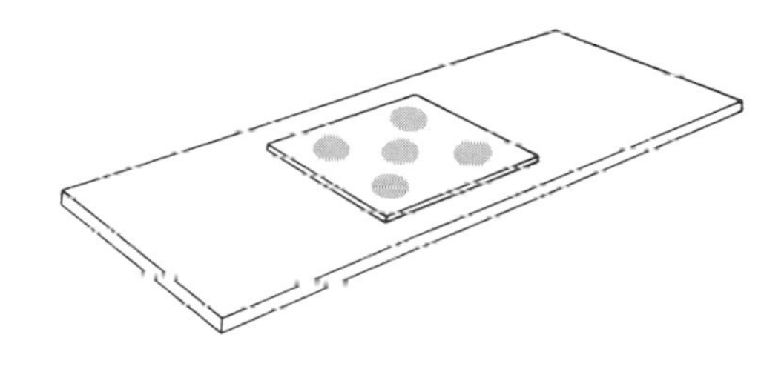

Figure 2.14 Yeast. Note the buds still attached to the yeast cells. These will become new individuals. ×600

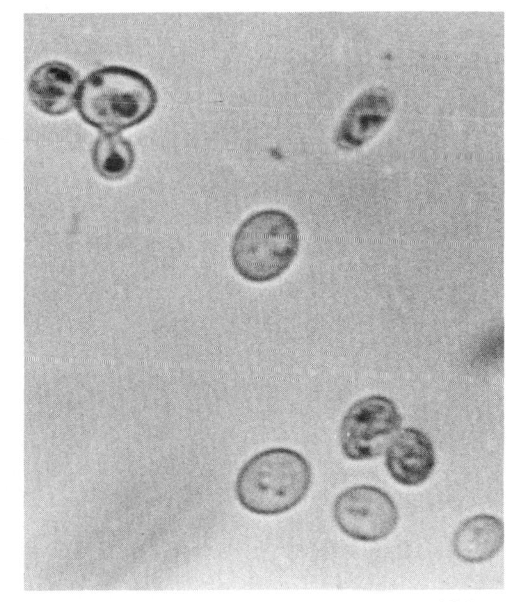

BSCS by Richard Tolman

Days 3–12

1. Shake flask A thoroughly to distribute the yeast organisms evenly. Use a clean medicine dropper and immediately place a drop of the culture on a clean microscope slide. Place a clean cover slip over the drop. As you did yesterday, position the slide on the microscope stage, focus with low power, and then switch to high power. Use the same counting method as you did in procedure 4(b) yesterday.
2. Record your data under Day 1 on the table in your data book.
3. Follow the same procedure for Day 2, Day 3, and so forth.

Figure 2.15 Diluting a yeast culture 10 and 100 times.

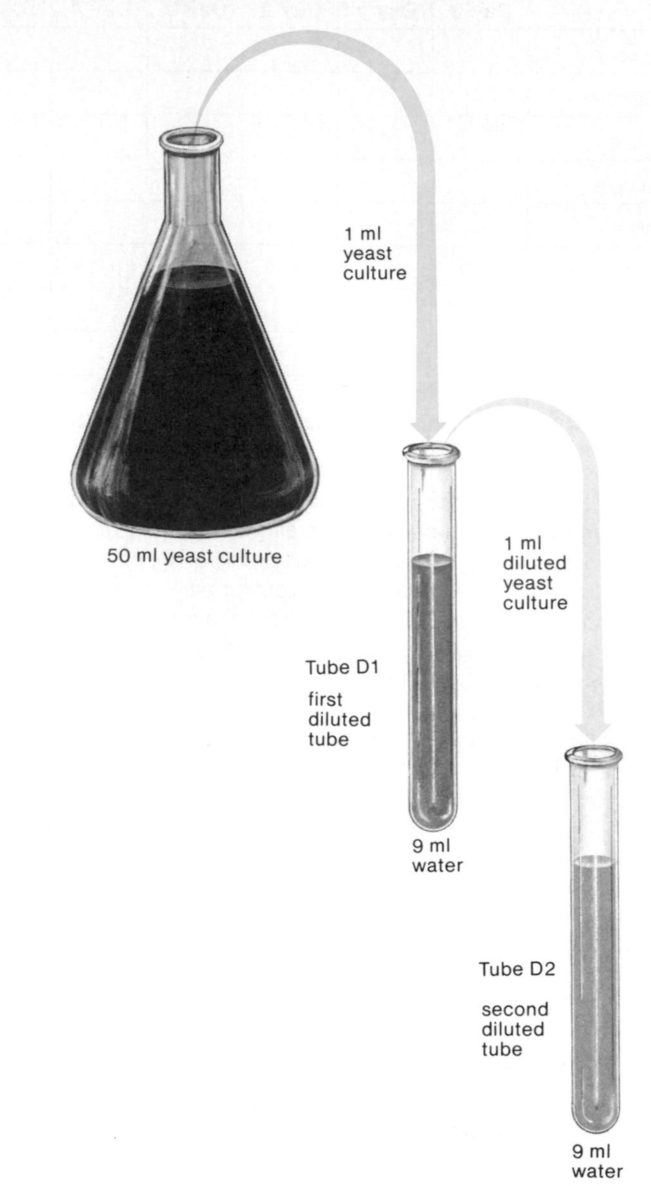

4. There is the possibility that as the population grows older, the fields will be too crowded to get an accurate count. If that happens you must dilute the culture. Obtain a test tube containing 9 ml of water; label this tube with your team number and D1 (Dilution 1). Shake the yeast culture until the organisms are evenly distributed. Use a pipette and immediately transfer 1 ml of the culture into the dilution tube. Mix the contents of the dilution tube thoroughly. Place 1 drop from the dilution tube on a slide as directed above and count the yeast organisms.

5. If the field is still too crowded for easy counting, transfer 1 ml of the contents of tube D1 to another test tube containing 9 ml of water. Mark this dilution D2. It may even be necessary to use a third dilution (see figure 2.15).
6. In tube D1, the culture is diluted 10 times, in tube D2, 100 times. If you make dilutions during counting, record the proper number (10, 100, or 1000) after Dilution on the data table. If you make no dilutions, the dilution is 1.

Discussion

In this investigation, you obtained an estimate of the population in the flask by counting the individuals in a small sample, a method called **sampling.** To increase the accuracy of your estimate, you took certain precautions. You shook the flask to distribute the organisms evenly. You counted the organisms in five different fields of view. Averaging those five fields smoothed out chance differences. On the master table you averaged the figures obtained by all teams. That further smoothed out chance differences among the flasks. The final count for each day's population is the average number of organisms per high-power field.

1. On a sheet of graph paper, list the ages of the cultures (in days) on the horizontal axis. Then, list the number of organisms per high-power field on the vertical axis. Plot your data and then use a different color to plot the average data of all teams.
2. On the basis of your discussions of this investigation, explain similarities and differences among the graph lines representing data from different teams.
3. Is there any general trend in the graph line representing the average data of all teams? If so, describe it.
4. Review the three hypotheses you developed before starting this investigation. Are any of them supported by the data? Are any not supported? Explain.
5. What limiting factors influenced the growth of the yeast population?

For Further Investigation

1. Does temperature affect the growth of a yeast population? Repeat the procedures, but incubate the cultures at a constant temperature 15° C above or below the average temperature at which the tubes were incubated before.
2. Does the amount of food energy available affect the growth of a yeast population? The medium you used in this investigation contained 4 percent glucose, a sugar that is used as food by yeast. Your teacher has directions for making a 1 percent and a 2 percent glucose medium. Repeat the procedures using one of these media.

2.5 Many Abiotic Factors Make Up the Weather

The weather is a group of abiotic factors that affects all plants and animals. Weather factors include temperature, sunlight intensity, precipitation (rainfall, snowfall, fog), humidity (amount of moisture in the air), and wind. Each factor may be measured alone, but they all affect each other, and they all affect population size.

In the northern part of the United States, the first heavy frost kills almost all adult mosquitoes: frost is a limiting factor for the mosquito population. In the autumn, swallows fly south, and their population in the north drops. Both those population decreases are related to one weather factor—temperature. However, temperature affects the mosquito population through mortality and the swallow population through emigration.

Wind is often a limiting factor for organisms. The trees in figure 2.16 grow one-sided or very low because the prevailing winds always blow from one direction. Low humidity in the desert results in a high rate of evaporation. The high evaporation, coupled with low rainfall, permits only plants with special adaptations to survive.

Long-term weather—climate—determines what kinds of plants can grow in a particular area. Throughout the world, characteristic associations of plants and the animals they support are found in each climate. We will examine those associations in detail in chapter 22.

2.6 Living Things Require Space to Live

Each individual needs living space. Some organisms need less space than others. For instance, individual corn plants often touch each other in the field and grow very well. Mountain lions, on the other hand, usually stay several kilometers away from each other. In general, **motile** (MOH til), or moving, organisms, such as animals, need more space than nonmotile ones, such as plants. Large organisms need more space than small ones.

Figure 2.16 Most of the branches on these trees point in one direction. Can you think of a reason why?

Gordon Uno

You might predict that the amount of space an organism needs is related to the availability of nutrients. That is true to some degree, but another factor that affects organisms in a population is their **density**—the number of individuals in relation to the space the population occupies (figure 2.17). For example, in the experiment shown in figure 2.18, mice in cages were given more than enough food every day. As the mice

Figure 2.17 (a) Plan of an orchard. Each dot represents one tree. What is the density of trees in the orchard? (b) Under natural conditions, organisms are rarely distributed evenly. Calculate the density of dusty clover in the field as a whole and then only in the northwest quarter. Compare.

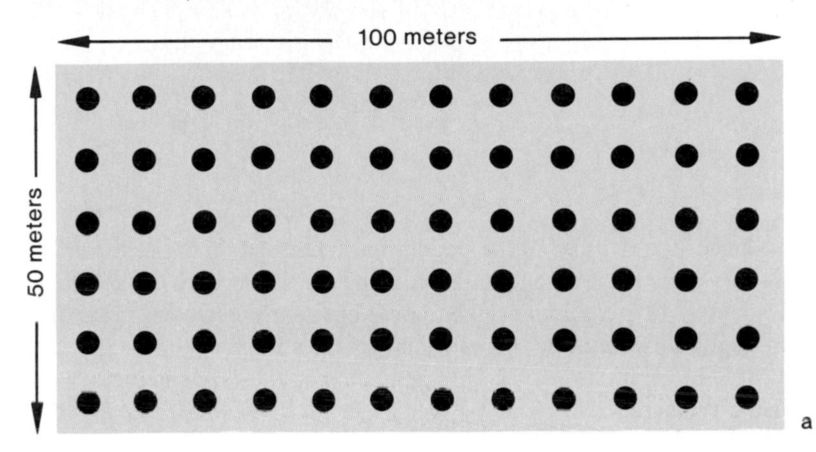

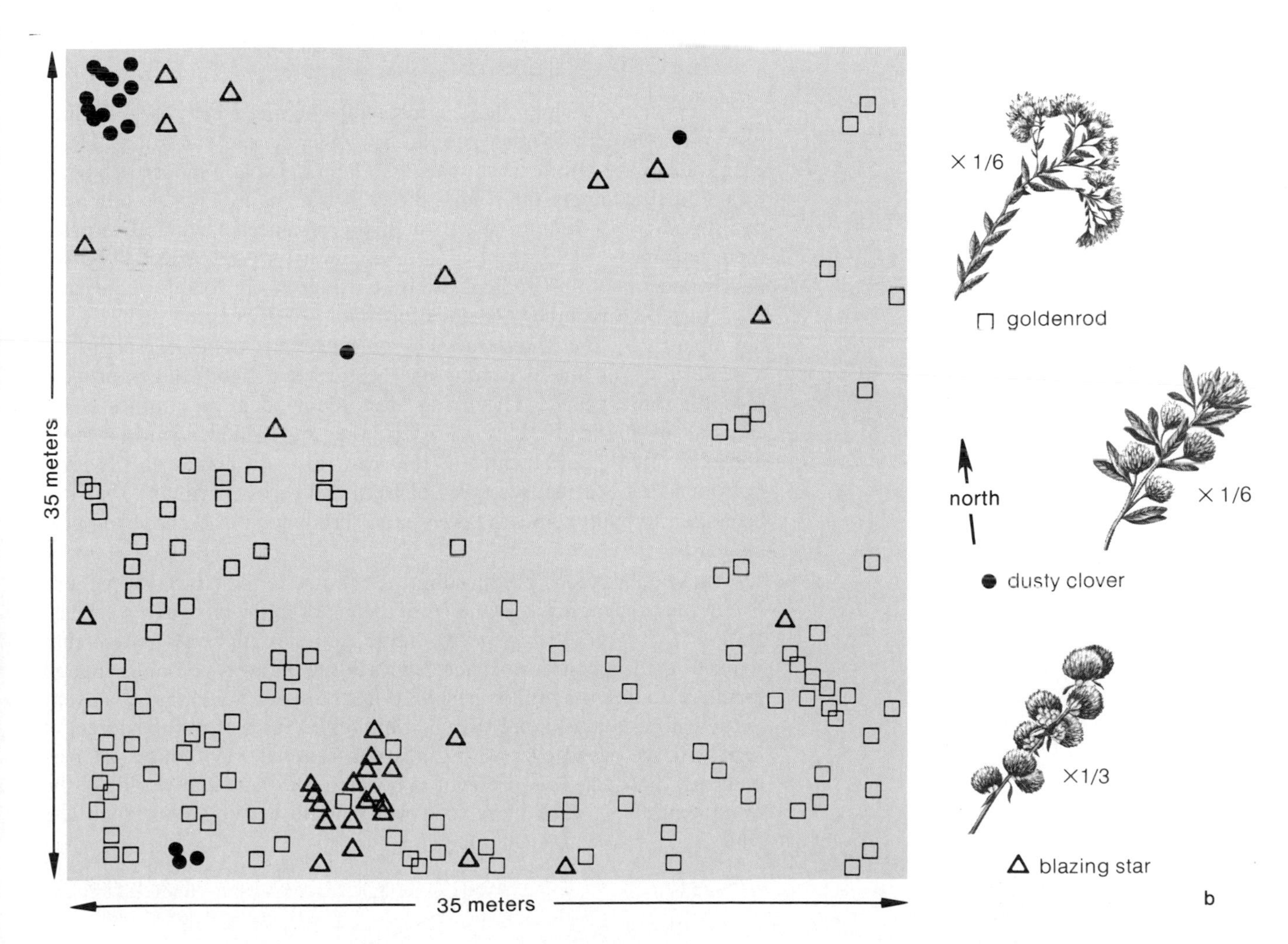

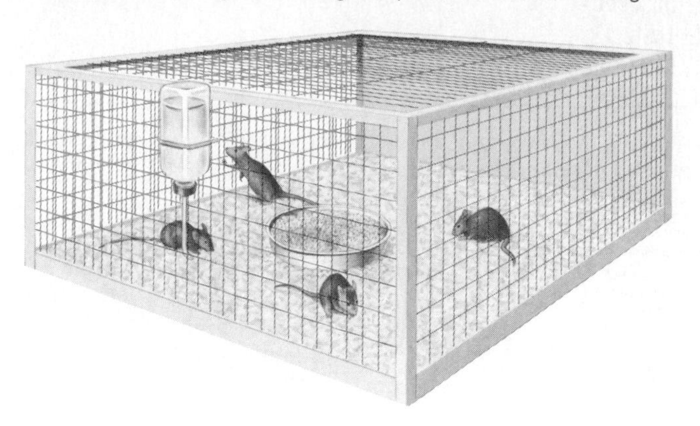

Figure 2.18 In this experiment, mice were provided with more than enough food (left). As a result (right), the population has grown dramatically. What will happen if the mice in the cage on the right experience a food shortage?

reproduced, the density of the population increased, and the cages became very crowded. Some female mice stopped taking care of their nests and young. Mice continued to be born, but many newborn mice died from neglect. Eventually, mortality of young mice reached nearly 100 percent. The high infant mortality kept the population density from increasing further.

2.7 Humans Use Much Farmland for Other Purposes

Experiments, such as the one involving the mice, help us to predict what might happen to other populations under similar conditions. However, though the mice experiments may help to explain mouse behavior, it is difficult to apply the results directly to humans. Like all other organisms, humans require space for living. We need farmland to grow food, but most people who live in cities never see that space. Unfortunately, the amount of land on which we can grow our food is decreasing each year because other demands for space are increasing: people want more places for their houses. Each house occupies about one-eighth of a hectare. Eight houses occupy one hectare, sufficient land to provide food for three people. The living space demanded by families is increasing dramatically. Unfortunately, the space on which they build homes is often prime farmland. It is easy to build homes on the level farmland that is already cleared of trees and rocks. Farmland that has been used to build homes is taken out of production of crops, often permanently.

Trucks deliver food produced in the country to the cities. People who live in the suburbs drive to and from their jobs in the city each weekday. Both of these activities require a large, complex highway system that requires great amounts of space. Beneath the highways alone is enough farmland to feed 0.5 million people. It has been estimated that each year in the United States, more than 0.4 million hectares (1 million acres) of farmland are paved over with highways, covered with houses, or permanently flooded. This problem is occurring around the world. If the trend continues, much more food will have to be grown on much less land.

Figure 2.19 Much of our productive farmland is being threatened by suburban growth.

John D. Cunningham/VISUALS UNLIMITED ©

Figure 2.20 Each year, more than 1 million acres of farmland are paved for highways.

Doug Sokell

2.8 Water Is a Necessity of Life

All living organisms need water. In almost all places on earth where you find water, you also will find living organisms. In all living organisms you will find water. In fact, between 50 and 95 percent of the weight of a plant or animal is water. If you weigh 140 pounds, about 100 pounds of you is water. Almost all of the chemical reactions needed to keep an organism alive take place in water. Water molecules, in fact, are part of many chemical reactions. Although a few organisms can become inactive when there is no water in their environment, most organisms die.

Figure 2.21 Natality in the desert increases after a heavy rainfall.

a John D. Cunningham/VISUALS UNLIMITED ©

b Rod Allin/TOM STACK & ASSOCIATES

It rarely rains in the deserts of southern Arizona, but a few weeks after a heavy rainfall, thousands of small, bright, flowering plants quickly grow and blanket the once bare and baked desert soil. Rain provides the moisture needed for seeds to sprout, thus increasing natality. After a heavy rainstorm in Texas, small pools of water may be formed. Those pools may attract frogs to feed on insects and to mate there. At least for a short time, the frog population increases through immigration to the pool.

2.9 Poor Sanitation Is Responsible for the Spread of Disease in Many Parts of the World

A source of pure drinking water is vital to the health of humans and other animals. Many diseases are spread by water, and unclean living conditions increase the risk of exposure to such diseases. In some parts of the world the only water available for drinking contains traces of human wastes. Disease-causing organisms carried in polluted drinking water are the cause of many serious illnesses around the world. Toxic

Figure 2.22 What might be responsible for this warning?

Gary Milburn/TOM STACK & ASSOCIATES

chemicals that seep into wells and reservoirs of drinking water also can cause illnesses. As we will see in chapter 23, the purity of the water in some parts of the United States is threatened by such problems.

In 1900 the chief causes of death in the United States were influenza, pneumonia, and tuberculosis. Today, as you can see in figure 2.23 the chief causes of death are heart disease and cancer, both of which have been linked, at least in part, to environmental problems and aging. Much of the decrease in fatal diseases has come about through the discovery and use of vaccines and antibiotics. Equally helpful has been an increase in sanitation and public health practices that control the spread of disease-causing organisms.

Fewer babies die in infancy now than ever before. In 1915, 100 out of every 1000 infants born in the United States died in their first year of life. In 1985 this figure dropped to only 10.5 deaths out of every 1000. A baby born in the United States today has a life expectancy of more than 70 years. In some countries the life expectancy is less than 50 years. Poor sanitary conditions are largely the cause of this difference. The death of children accounts for the low life-expectancy figures. Nearly all the childhood deaths in those countries are caused by a combination of undernutrition, parasites, and infections spread by air and water. Both the chance of contracting a disease and its severity are much greater if you do not get enough food of the right kind. A simple case of diarrhea or a cold can become a fatal disease.

Figure 2.23 In 1900, infectious diseases such as pneumonia, influenza, and tuberculosis were the major causes of death. Today, heart disease and cancer head the list. What changes since 1900 might account for these trends?

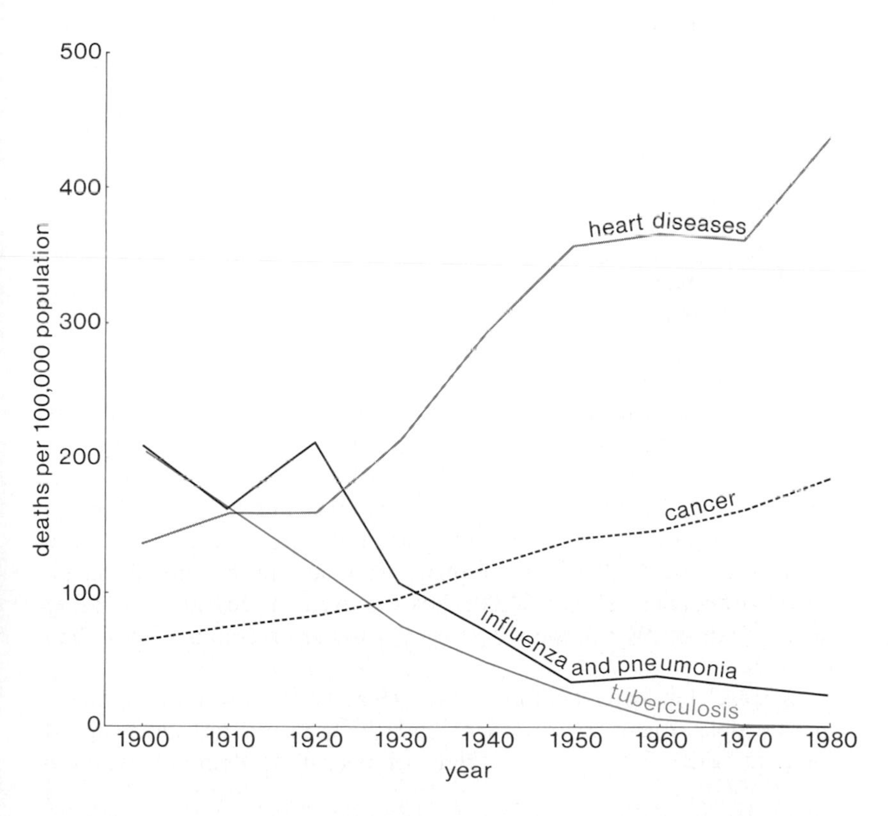

2.10 Nutrients Are Used to Make an Organism's Body

Living organisms need nutrients for maintenance and growth. Consumers obtain their nutrients from the foods they eat. These foods—plants and animals—are part of the biotic environment. Producers get their nutrients from the soil, part of the abiotic environment. Both plants and animals need a broad range of nutrients. When a nutrient is available in adequate amounts in the environment, a population may grow. Excess amounts of certain nutrients can be harmful, and scarcity of a nutrient may limit the growth of the population. That is why farmers must add fertilizers to their crops if they expect their harvest to be good. Table 2.6 lists the nutrients most plants need for growth.

Table 2.6 Essential elements for plants

Element	Relative No. of Atoms Compared to Molybdenum
Molybdenum	1
Copper	100
Zinc	300
Manganese	1,000
Boron	2,000
Iron	2,000
Chlorine	3,000
Sulfur	30,000
Phosphorus	60,000
Magnesium	80,000
Calcium	125,000
Potassium	250,000
Nitrogen	1,000,000
Oxygen	30,000,000
Carbon	35,000,000
Hydrogen	60,000,000

Adapted from *Plant Physiology,* Third Edition, p. 103, by F. B. Salisbury and C. E. Ross, © 1985 by Wadsworth, Inc. Reprinted by permission of the publisher.

2.11 Getting Enough of the Right Kind of Food Is Not Easy

Food is a necessity of life. In many parts of the world today, the food supply is a major limiting factor for humans. The lack of food slows growth or even causes death. Hungry people can be found even in the United States. Many places in the world experience periodic times of **famine** (FAM in), a great shortage of food. In places such as Asia, Africa, and Latin America, the number of people that must be fed is increasing much more quickly than food can be grown to feed them.

A common and useful measure of energy is the **calorie.** A calorie is the amount of energy required to raise the temperature of one gram of water one degree Celsius. The calorie you are probably familiar with, however, is the food calorie, which is really a kilocalorie, or kcal—1000 calories. Teenage females need 1200 to 3000 kcals per day, depending on how active they are. Teenage males need 2100 to 3900 kcals, and a football player may use more than 6000 kcals.

In industrialized countries life-styles have changed greatly in the past 100 years, and humans have become less physically active. Because intake of kcals has remained fairly constant, many people consume more kcals than they need. In other places in the world, however, people are not able to get enough kcals to maintain normal activity levels. Such people are **undernourished.** Without a continuous and sufficient supply of kcals, activity level drops, and eventually muscles are broken down to supply the cells with nutrients.

The number of kcals is not the only factor that is measured when judging the nutritional value of food. Humans need certain nutrients that are not abundant in plants. A meal of only corn bread or white rice is not nutritious. Animal products have the essential nutrients in sufficient amounts, but animals are costly to produce and to buy. To provide an American 3000 kcals of food supplying all required nutrients, a farmer must raise about 30,000 kcals in plant substance. In the United States, almost 90 percent of that 30,000 kcals is used to feed animals being raised for meat. Worldwide, 40 percent of the grain crop is used to feed livestock.

Because they cannot afford to buy meat or to raise meat animals, many people around the world lack both the kcals and nutrients needed for good health. Ironically, children with poor diets often have *swollen*

Figure 2.24 Many people from poorer countries are unable to obtain adequate amounts of energy.

John Isaac/UNICEF

bellies due to the low levels of nutrients in the food they can find to eat. Such a condition is seen in children suffering from **kwashiorkor** (kwah shee OR kor). That disease occurs when children eat a diet high in carbohydrates but low in protein. These children are **malnourished**—they may get enough kcals in their diet, but their food lacks essential nutrients needed for growth and good health. Lack of adequate protein also may cause mental retardation.

Africa has the fastest growth rate of any continent in the world. Widespread famine has plagued parts of Africa in the 1970s and the 1980s. Millions of people have died or will die from lack of food. A severe drought is partly to blame for the food shortage. Without water at the right time, the crops in the field die. However, other factors also are responsible. Much of the fertile soil has been blown away by the wind

Figure 2.25 The child on the left has kwashiorkor, the most common form of protein deficiency malnutrition. Note the swollen abdomen, a common symptom of this disease.

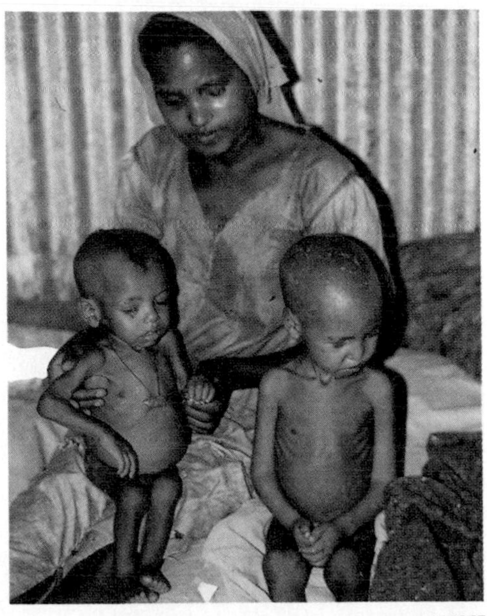

John Isaac/UNICEF

or washed away by infrequent and violent rainstorms (figure 2.26). Soil erosion leaves less farmland on which to grow crops. A population explosion and thè inability to grow food have added to the catastrophe in Africa.

This problem is not limited to just one part of the earth. The number of people living today in the world is so large that if all the farmland were divided equally, each person would have only one-half hectare for growing his or her share of food. The amount of land that can be farmed is limited, however, so that as the population increases, the amount of farmland per person decreases. Although it is true that most farmland in the United States is very productive, this high productivity can be maintained only by using huge amounts of fuel energy and fertilizers.

Compare the so-called primitive way of getting food with the so-called modern way. There are only a few hunting-gathering tribes left in the world today. Those people hunt and fish and gather berries, nuts, leaves, roots, and insect larvae. Hunters and gatherers use energy as they walk

Figure 2.26 Soil erosion has compounded the malnutrition and population problems in Ethiopia.

Robert Maust

Figure 2.27 The game provides enough energy for the hunters to continue living.

Warren Garst/TOM STACK & ASSOCIATES

about and chase after animals (figure 2.27). For every kcal of energy that tribesmen use up, they get back an average of 5 to 10 kcals of food energy.

Nonmechanized farming practices in tropical and warm climates may return 16 to 20 kcals in food per kcal of energy spent. Compare this to food production in the United States. For each kcal of energy we use to grow our food, we get back only 0.1 kcal of energy—an energy-losing system. In other words, we use more energy to grow and transport the food we eat than we can get back from the food itself. The only way we can keep up this losing battle is to use our precious supply of oil and gas. Oil and gas, however, are nonrenewable resources—materials used by humans that can never be produced again. Once nonrenewable resources are used, they are gone forever. If we use these resources now, we will not be able to support our agricultural system in the future. In other words, we cannot keep growing food indefinitely with an energy-losing system.

Self-Review

1. How does a limiting factor affect a population?
2. How are space and population density related?
3. In what ways is water important to living things?
4. Why is sanitation important to the health of humans?
5. In a famine, are people undernourished, malnourished, or both? Explain.
6. How does a so-called primitive way of getting food compare with so-called modern methods in terms of energy spent and energy returned?

Interaction of Environmental Factors

Guidepost: What limits the size of a population?

2.12 A Population Is Affected by Many Factors

The populations of both producers and consumers can be affected greatly by other organisms. In a single field, snakes, foxes, and hawks catch and eat mice. Microscopic disease-causing organisms or parasites that live inside the mice may weaken them so much that the mice die. A poisonous plant mistaken for food may kill unsuspecting rabbits. In all these cases, one organism affects another. Because of this interaction, the size of both populations is affected.

Figure 2.28 (a) Normal tomato plants and (b) tomatoes affected by fungus. What factors are involved?

a Don & Pat Valenti/TOM STACK & ASSOCIATES

b Doug Sokell

When we study changes in a population, we usually find they involve the interaction of many factors. Consider tomato plants in a southern New Jersey field (figure 2.28a). In some years, all of the plants that are planted in April survive until July when bright red, juicy tomatoes can be harvested. In other years all the plants may die. With enough sunlight and good soil conditions, tomato plants usually grow well when temperature, rainfall, and humidity are high and the wind is light. There are many biotic factors that also affect the life of the tomato plants. For example, various fungi thrive in hot, humid weather. They may attack the tomato plants (figure 2.28b) and greatly reduce their population. That, of course, is a disaster for the tomato grower.

Although there are many environmental factors that affect the size of a population, a population can affect many parts of the environment. In turn, other populations are affected because populations are connected to each other in the web of life.

2.13 Any Space Can Support Only a Limited Number of Individuals

Populations in nature vary between some upper and lower limits. Each population is like a swing, moving back and forth between two points or between a high and low number. The lowest limit is, of course, zero. At that point the population no longer exists. Once that occurs, a new population can be established only through immigration.

What limits the size of a population on the upper side? There are many factors that may cause a population to stop growing. In the long run, however, the size of a population is limited by the amount of matter and energy, the **resources** that are available to it. If a population is so large that it uses all the available water, nutrients, or food, it can no longer grow. At this point, it will probably decrease in size, sometimes with many individuals dying all at once. The greatest number of individuals that a space can support with its available resources is called its **carrying capacity.** Each area has a carrying capacity. In any given space, even under the best conditions, there is a limit to energy and matter. In other words, resources are finite.

Figure 2.29 A muledeer herd in South Dakota.

Gary Randall/TOM STACK & ASSOCIATES

Consider this example. Suppose a deer population in a valley in the Rocky Mountains is increasing. Gradually the kinds of plants that the deer eat become scarce. A few deer may emigrate and look for food in other places. Those that stay in the valley will be undernourished and may become weak. They may easily be caught by mountain lions, or a disease may kill them. Because of this emigration and mortality, the deer population decreases. Fewer plants are now eaten. As the remaining plants continue to grow, more food becomes available for the surviving deer. Deer stop emigrating, and a few hungry deer may even immigrate into the valley from the surrounding hills. All the deer now find plenty of food and become healthy. Mountain lions cannot catch these healthy deer as easily and must search for other sources of food. With less mortality and more immigration, the deer population increases in size. We are back where we started.

The deer population example illustrates the process of **homeostasis** (hoh mee oh STAY sis). In ecology, homeostasis is the tendency for populations to remain relatively stable. In this case, the deer population remains within some upper and lower limits even though many different factors affect it. Environmental factors tend to keep a population either from becoming too large or from disappearing. For instance, if too many deer survive, there will not be enough food for all to eat. Some deer die, and the population returns to a more stable level. Why did homeostasis apparently not work for the reindeer population you studied in investigation 2.1?

We have disrupted homeostasis for the human population. Our ability to control many diseases has resulted in a decrease in mortality for humans. More people produce more babies, and the human population continues to grow. Like all areas, however, the earth as a whole has a carrying capacity. Scientists do not agree about the carrying capacity of the earth. If food were the only factor, some claim the earth could support 7 to 8 billion people. Others think that the current population cannot be maintained for very long. All agree, however, that the human population cannot grow forever. We have already seen dramatic population crashes in different areas of the world. For those areas, the carrying capacity for humans has already been reached. There, population demands for the necessities of life exceeded the supply.

Figure 2.30 Factors limiting growth: oil, irrigation and drinking water, and space.

a Carlye Calvin

b David M. Doody/TOM STACK & ASSOCIATES

c John D. Cunningham/VISUALS UNLIMITED ©

Even in the United States we must find answers to the problem of increased demand on limited resources. A rancher knows that he or she can raise a limited number of cattle on pasture land of a certain size. How many more people can we feed using food from farms of limited size? Petroleum is used not only for gasoline and heating fuels, but also for medicines, cosmetics, plastics, records, styrofoam cups, fertilizers, synthetic rubber, and human-made fibers such as polyester and nylon. If more oil and gas are used now, what will people use in the future? Many people get their drinking and irrigation water from underground reservoirs. What happens if people use up this stored water? Suppose your town or city needs a new highway, and the highway is planned to run through your neighborhood. How should the land be used? Should you keep your house, should the demand for highways be met, or should you work to reduce the need for the highway?

Like all populations, the one made up of humans has many limiting factors. As more and more people are born, these limiting factors become apparent in different parts of the world. However, because we are all part of the same population on the same planet—Earth—we are all in the same boat, and the boat is filling up very fast with people who have many needs.

Self-Review

1. How does the amount of resources affect the carrying capacity of an area?
2. How do environmental factors affect population size?
3. How have humans disrupted homeostasis for their population?

Summary

We are all part of a population, the human population. Like all others, the human population is affected by both biotic and abiotic factors. Some of those factors help to increase a population's size, and other factors cause it to decrease. Among the needs of the human population is space for farmland, homes, and highways. These uses all compete for the same space, but only one use is possible. The need for food is great, but in this world where some countries grow large amounts of food, others have starving people. The countries with starving people have reached their carrying capacity. How long will it take before the carrying capacity of the earth is reached? The human population is huge and growing, and it affects other organisms because of the amount of resources we use in our daily lives. Think about what each person uses and multiply it by the people in your city, state, or country. The figures are huge. In our use of resources and the environment, we change the world around us. When these changes occur, other populations are affected—and not always for the better. The changes occur because all populations are linked together in the biosphere.

Application Questions

1. Do you think space is a biotic or an abiotic factor? Explain.
2. Why are the terms "mortality" and "natality"—as defined in this text—not applicable to individuals?
3. Discuss the present relationship between the human population and the earth's carrying capacity.
4. Name as many ways as you can that humans continue to change the biosphere.
5. Why is it difficult for people to see the effects they have on the biosphere?
6. It is seldom possible to count all the individuals in a natural population. How can a biologist study populations without such data?
7. A team of biologists studied a population of box turtles in an Ohio woodlot for a period of 10 years. They determined that the natality averaged 40 per year, the mortality 30 per year, immigration 3 per year, and emigration 8 per year. Was the population increasing or decreasing? Was the area supplying box turtles to other places or vice versa?
8. In question 7 what was the average annual change due to immigration and emigration? If the initial population was 15 turtles, what was the population at the end of 10 years?

Problems

1. Obtain the census data for your state. Make a graph of these data, beginning with the first census after your state entered the Union. How does the form of this graph compare with that for the population of the United States as a whole? Try to explain any differences.
2. Obtain some duckweed, an aquatic plant that grows on the surface of ponds. Tap the mass of plants with your finger to separate a single individual. Place the single duckweed plant in pond or aquarium water in a petri dish. Make counts of the numbers of individuals at intervals of 2 to 4 days. Keep a record of dates and numbers. Construct a graph to show the growth of the duckweed population.
3. Grains, such as wheat and rice, are a basic food throughout the world. The 1985 worldwide production of grains was approximately 1.7 billion tons. This was enough grain to provide 4.6 billion people with enough food energy for normal activity for a year. Still, hundreds of thousands of people in Asia, Africa, and South America were malnourished and thousands of others starved to death. How can you explain this? *The World Almanac* and books such as L. Brown, 1974, *By Bread Alone* (New York: Praeger), may give you some insights.

Suggested Readings

Almanac and Book of Facts (New York: Newspaper Enterprise Assoc.). Published yearly; contains up-to-date population data.

L. R. Brown, W. U. Chandler, and S. Postel, "State of the Earth" *Natural History* (April, 1985). The effects of the earth's rapidly expanding population are discussed in reference to soil erosion, water quality, deforestation and pollution's effects on forests, overfishing, climatic changes, energy use, birth control, and population policies.

J. M. Moran, M. D. Morgan, and J. H. Wiersma, 1980, *Introduction to Environmental Science* (San Francisco: W. H. Freeman). Several chapters deal with animal and human populations.

C. H. Southwick, 1985, *Global Ecology* (Sunderland, MA: Sinauer Assoc.). Articles deal with stabilizing human population, and improving worldwide health and nutrition.

E. P. Volpe, 1984, *Biology and Human Concerns* (Dubuque, IA: Wm. C. Brown Company Publishers). Several chapters are devoted to various aspects of populations.

R. A. Wallace, J. L. King, and G. P. Sanders, 1984, *Biosphere: The Realm of Life* (Glenview, IL: Scott, Foresman). Includes well-illustrated discussions of population.

CARRIBEAN COLLECTION/Nancy Sefton

A coral reef is a rich ecosystem that supports many communities.

CHAPTER 3

Communities and Ecosystems

Introduction

Many populations live and interact within a community. In relationships between organisms of two or more populations, some benefit and some do not. Whatever the case, relationships tie a community together. Because of the relationships, large communities with many interacting organisms tend to be stable through time. Humans can disrupt that stability when they cause other populations within the community to become extinct. However, humans also can preserve communities and help maintain their stability.

Life in a Community

Guidepost: How do different populations affect each other?

3.1 Many Interactions Are Indirect

The human population is not isolated from other populations. In fact, all populations interact with each other in a complex web of relationships. The set of interacting populations at one place and time is called a community. In your community there are dogs, cats, trees, weeds, and humans that all interact. Sometimes the interaction is very direct, such as when you mow a lawn or the dog next door barks at you. Most of the time, however, the interactions are indirect, and people tend to ignore them. Suppose, for instance, that you had soup for lunch and threw the can away. The garbage truck hauled the can to the dump, where it filled with rainwater. A female mosquito laid her eggs in the water and her offspring matured, flew from the dump, and bit a person or other animal. Perhaps neither would have been bitten if you had not eaten the soup in the first place. Thus, you have had an indirect relationship with the mosquitoes and their victims.

Figure 3.1 A typical neighborhood community.

BSCS

Each community is affected by the abiotic environment—by the sunlight, soil, wind, rain, and temperature. A community with its abiotic environment is called an **ecosystem** (EE koh sis tum). We can use the two words, community and ecosystem, to describe the same group of organisms. However, the term ecosystem refers to both the biotic and abiotic environments of an area. Although the biosphere is too big to study as a whole, we can study a part of the biosphere—an ecosystem. In investigation 3.1, you can observe two of the abiotic factors that affect an ecosystem.

Investigation 3.1 ABIOTIC ENVIRONMENT: A COMPARATIVE STUDY

Introduction

The abiotic factors you will investigate are temperature and **relative humidity.** Relative humidity is a measure of the moistness of air. It is defined as the percentage of water vapor actually in the air at any given temperature, compared with the amount of water vapor that the air could hold at that temperature. In general, organisms lose water faster in an atmosphere with low relative humidity than in an atmosphere with high relative humidity. Therefore, this environmental factor is important to land organisms.

Materials (per team)

3 watches
3 metersticks
3 thermometers (−10° to +100° C)
3 thermometers (of same range, with cotton sleeves over the bulbs)
3 bottles (with screw tops) containing 30–50 ml distilled water
3 pieces stiff cardboard
3 umbrellas or other shade devices
table of relative humidities

Procedure

1. Each team will work in 3 groups. One member of each group will read the instruments. Another will fan the thermometer with stiff cardboard and record the data. Before starting, the 3 recorders should synchronize their watches and agree on the time at which each measurement is to be made.
2. Record your data on a form similar to this one.

Location				
	Height			
	0 cm	30 cm	90 cm	150 cm
Time				
Dry-bulb temperature				
Wet-bulb temperature				
Relative humidity				

3. Each team will make measurements in 3 kinds of environment. One group of students will work in a dense cover of vegetation. Choose a woods, preferably, or a thicket, or a mass of shrubbery in a park. A second group will work in a place that has a single layer of herbaceous vegetation. Select a meadow or a lawn (preferably not cut close to the ground). A third group will work in a place that has no vegetation. Find some bare ground or a tennis court. The 3 environments should be as close together as possible.
4. Each group will make 4 sets of measurements: at ground level, at 30 cm above the ground, at 90 cm above, and at 150 cm above.
5. Take readings on both types of thermometers at the same time. Position the thermometers as described in steps 3 and 4 at least 5 minutes before readings are to be taken. (If the first reading is to be taken at 1:30 P.M., both thermometers should be in the first position at 1:25 P.M.) To make the wet-bulb reading, soak the sleeve of a thermometer in water and fan it vigorously for at least 2 minutes; then read the thermometer. (For the first reading, fan the thermometer from 1:28 P.M. to 1:30 P.M.) Schedule at least 8 minutes between readings. You will need time to move both thermometers to the next position and leave them there for 5 minutes. Use the umbrellas to shield the thermometers from the direct rays of the sun.
6. Your teacher will supply a relative-humidity table. To find the relative humidity on the table, you will need both your dry-bulb and wet-bulb thermometer readings. When you know these 2 temperatures, you can determine the amount of water vapor actually in the air compared with the amount that the air could hold at that temperature. The necessary calculations were made when the table was constructed.

Discussion

1. At ground level which environment is coolest and most humid?
2. At ground level which is warmest and least humid?
3. How do these 2 environments (items 1 and 2) compare in temperature and humidity at higher levels above the ground?
4. At which level above the ground are all 3 environments most alike in temperature and humidity?

5. How does the greatest temperature difference *within* the same environment compare with the greatest temperature difference *among* the environments?
6. What differences among the 3 environments may account for differences in temperatures and relative humidities?
7. How does this show interaction of biotic and abiotic factors in an ecosystem?
8. You have been examining the differences among environments. Now turn to differences within an environment.
   (a) How does the temperature in each environment vary with respect to elevations?
   (b) Is the variation the same for each environment? If not, in which is the variation greatest?
   (c) How does the humidity in each environment vary with respect to elevation?
   (d) Is the variation the same for each environment?
9. In weather forecasts, temperatures predicted for the center of a city often differ from those predicted for the suburbs. Relate that fact to the situations you have been observing.
10. What differences in temperature and humidity would be experienced by a beetle crawling on the ground in a meadow and a gnat hovering at 1.5 m above the meadow?
11. In a general sense, we may say the beetle and the gnat are in the same environment, but small differences within an environment are often important to the existence of some organisms. We can, therefore, distinguish small environments within larger ones on the basis of measurements such as those you have made in this investigation. Would it be useful to measure such differences if you were studying the ecological relationships among cows in a meadow? Explain.

3.2 The Florida River Community Has Many Interacting Populations

An interesting aquatic community lives in the short rivers along the west coast of Florida (figure 3.2). One of the largest members of this community is the river turtle. Adult turtles eat many of the plants that grow in the rivers, but their favorite food is the long, narrow blades of the tape grass. Consumers that eat only plants are called **herbivores** (HER

Figure 3.2 A Florida river.

Florida Department of Natural Resources

bih vorz). Unlike the adults, young river turtles are **carnivores** (KAR nih vorz): they are consumers that eat other animals. These young turtles feast on snails, aquatic insects, and worms.

Many carnivorous animals eat river turtles (figure 3.3). The highest mortality strikes turtle eggs. Because female turtles lay their eggs in a hole they dig on land, the eggs can be dug up and eaten by skunks, raccoons, or snakes. Unhatched turtles also are killed by molds that live in the soil and grow through the thin shells into the eggs. If the eggs survive, the young turtles that hatch from the eggs may be eaten by snakes or raccoons before they reach the river. Even if the young turtles reach the river, they are still vulnerable. Large fish, alligators, herons, and snapping turtles may eat them in the river. For the young turtles, mats of floating plants, tangled tree roots, and sunken logs all provide hiding places from carnivores.

When river turtles are larger, few organisms can kill them directly. Leeches attach themselves to turtles and suck their blood, but that does not usually kill the turtles. However, turtles do die of disease, accidents, and old age. After they die, their bodies become food for decomposers that return all the substances in the turtle's body back to the abiotic world.

Each of the relationships we have described so far is a direct one between a river turtle and another kind of organism. River turtles also have many indirect relationships with other organisms. For instance, plants provide not only food and hiding places but also the oxygen in the water for the fish that might eat young turtles. Snails eat tape grass. Therefore, they compete with the river turtles for the same food supply. However,

Figure 3.3 Four animals that eat young river turtles. Describe the direct and indirect relationships shown here.

Figure 3.4 Tape grass, spiral-shelled snails, musk turtle (left), adult river turtle (right), and pond turtle (below).

another kind of turtle, the musk turtle, eats nothing but snails. By reducing the number of snails that eat tape grass, musk turtles have an indirect effect on the river turtles. In addition, many carnivores that eat young river turtles also eat musk turtles. Thus, the more musk turtles there are in the river, the less likely it is that young river turtles will be eaten.

3.3 A Niche Represents All the Activities of an Organism

We have been looking at the community as it affects river turtles. We have described the **niche** (NITCH) of the river turtle. The niche of any organism is its role in the community: what it eats, what organisms eat it, and what indirect relationships it has with other organisms. A niche also describes how an organism affects and is affected by its **habitat** (HAB ih tat)—the place where it lives. Thus, a niche includes both the biotic and the abiotic environments of the organism. If we had started with some other organism, we might see the community in a different way because we would have focused on the niche of that organism. No two types, or **species** (SPEE sheez), of organisms occupy the same niche within a community. For instance, there are many species of turtles living in a Florida river. They occupy diverse niches, but each species lives in a manner distinct from the other turtles and has different relationships with the other members of the community. To understand the community fully, we would have to look at all the relationships among all the organisms and describe all the niches. That would not be easy even for a small community.

Consider the effect of adding just one more population, such as humans, to the study. Humans trap skunks, kill snakes, and catch fish that eat young river turtles. That indirectly reduces the mortality of river turtles. Humans also may dredge the rivers and thus kill the tape grass, which would then increase turtle mortality.

3.4 Organisms Can Benefit from or Be Harmed by Other Organisms

Organisms play different roles within their community at different times. You could easily see some of the roles in the description of the Florida river community. For example, tape grass, algae, and other green plants are producers. River turtles, snails, skunks, and fish are all consumers. Other kinds of relationships that help to form the community's web of life include predation, parasitism, competition, commensalism, and mutualism. Each of these five relationships involves two different organisms, but in the first three at least one of the organisms is affected negatively by the interaction.

Predation (preh DAY shun) occurs when one organism eats another. Snapping turtles eat young river turtles. Musk turtles eat snails. Spiders eat grasshoppers, and you eat cows. A consumer that kills another consumer organism and eats it is called a **predator** (PRED uh tor). The organism that is eaten is called the **prey** (PRAY). The predator may kill its prey before or while it eats it. The predator is affected positively by this interaction: it gets food (matter and energy) from its prey. However, the prey is affected negatively because it loses its life.

Figure 3.5 A black-crowned night heron with its prey.

Paul Ayick/TOM STACK & ASSOCIATES

Figure 3.6 The mistletoe, a parasitic plant, makes its living off a ponderosa pine.

Carlye Calvin

In **parasitism** (PAIR uh sih tiz um), one organism lives on or in another organism and uses that organism as its food source. The food source usually remains alive during the interaction. A leech clings to a turtle's skin and sucks its blood. Microorganisms in the turtle absorb food directly from its blood. Your dog may have worms in its intestines or fleas in its hair. You may have disease organisms in your lungs or a tick on your skin. An organism that lives on or in another living organism and obtains food from it is a **parasite** (PAIR uh syt). The organism from which a parasite obtains its food is a **host.** Plants also can have parasites, which may include molds, microorganisms, or even other plants, such as mistletoe (figure 3.6). Large microorganisms can have smaller parasitic

Figure 3.7 Competition does not always involve food. Both bluebirds and starlings nest in holes in trees, poles and fence posts. Since neither is able to dig holes for itself, both are dependent on holes already available. The presence of either of these birds may be harmful to the other.

microorganisms in them. A predator kills its prey outright: a parasite may indirectly kill its host by weakening it. The weakened host is then more susceptible to disease or becomes an easier prey for predators.

In **competition,** usually neither of the interacting organisms benefits. Both snails and river turtles eat tape grass. The tape grass eaten by a turtle cannot be eaten by a snail, or vice versa. Therefore, the presence of one of these herbivores is harmful to the other. A relationship where both organisms are affected in a negative way is an example of competition. Organisms may compete for things such as food, space, sunlight, nutrients, or water. There is no competition for factors such as temperature or humidity. The competition is always for something in short supply, as seen in figure 3.7. In the Florida rivers, if both tape grass and other plants are scarce, competition for tape grass by herbivores is intense. If plants are abundant, competition is reduced.

Other kinds of relationships occur in a community that were not discussed in the Florida river community. In commensalism and mutualism, at least one of the organisms benefits. In **commensalism** (kuh MEN suh liz um), one organism in the relationships benefits, and the other is unaffected. An example is the relationship between the remora and the shark that can be seen in figure 3.8. A remora is a fish that has a suction disk on the top of its head. Using that disk, the remora attaches itself to some large sea animal, most often a shark. Because the shark pulls it along, the remora uses very little energy to move about. In addition, it eats small pieces of the shark's prey that float by. Thus, the remora benefits from the relationship, and its effect on the shark seems to be neutral.

Many of the relationships we have described pit one organism against another. An animal eats a plant. Two animals compete for the same food. There are, however, many relationships in which both organisms are

Figure 3.8 Remoras on a shark.

Brian Parker/TOM STACK & ASSOCIATES

Figure 3.9 Lichens on a tree trunk.

Doug Sokell

affected positively. These are **mutualistic** (MYOO choo uh LIS tik) relationships. **Lichens** (LY kenz) are leaflike, hairlike, or crustlike structures that grow on rocks or the bark of trees (figure 3.9). Lichens may be gray-green, black, yellow, or orange, and the structure you see is really made up of two different organisms that live in very close association. One is an alga, a microscopic producer that makes food by photosynthesis. The other is a fungus, a consumer that gets its food from the alga, but in return provides moisture for the alga. Thus, both organisms benefit from the relationship. In most cases of mutualism, neither organism could live without the other.

Frequently, an organism plays more than one role in a community. For instance, snapping turtles are predators of young river turtles, but they are also **scavengers** (SKAV en jerz): they eat the flesh of dead animals that they did not kill. When you eat a salad, you are an herbivore. If you also eat a hamburger, you eat meat and plants, and so you are an **omnivore** (OM nih vor). Because every community includes many different kinds of organisms, an individual can have many kinds of relationships. The more we study a community, the more interactions we see. You can study an example of one kind of interaction—competition—in investigation 3.2.

Self-Review

1. Give an example of a direct and an indirect interaction between two organisms.
2. Distinguish between a community and an ecosystem.
3. How does an organism's niche differ from its habitat?
4. In what ways are predation and parasitism alike?
5. Distinguish between commensalism and mutualism.

Investigation 3.2 COMPETITION AMONG SPECIES

Introduction

You will recall that competition occurs when resources are in short supply. These resources may include food, water, minerals, light, breeding space, mates, and other substances needed for survival and reproduction. Remember that no two species can occupy the same niche within a community. Competition between two species can be so intense that species A outcompetes species B because the former is better equipped to use the resource or because it is able to prevent species B from utilizing the resource. This phenomenon is called competitive exclusion. In these situations, the second species (1) moves to some other place where competition is less intense, or it is a better competitor, or (2) becomes extinct.

Rather than going to wilderness areas to find examples of competition and its results, we will use an analogy involving things more familiar to both eye and stomach. Our "species" are fast-food restaurants (FFRs), and the resource in short supply is the consumer's money. FFRs are defined as those restaurants where service is quick, carryout is available, and neither waiter nor waitress comes to your table. This definition eliminates some establishments. However, it reduces the "species" to a manageable number and restricts our sample to a group of FFRs that compete intensely.

Procedure

Part A—Fast-Food Restaurant Competition

1. Obviously, FFRs do coexist, often in close proximity to one another. Develop several hypotheses to answer the question: How might these FFRs avoid extinction? Another way of asking the same question is: What might individual FFRs do to increase their own chances of survival?
2. For this investigation we will use the hypothesis that entrée specialization might explain coexistence. Study the entrées from 4 nationally franchised FFRs in table 3.1. These generic categories are necessary because each FFR has its own set of unique names for many entrées. For example, different types of hamburgers were placed into categories on the basis of size (quarter-pound hamburgers were categorized as large and anything smaller was labeled regular).

Table 3.1 Entrées of four nationally franchised fast-food restaurants

	A	B	C	D
Roast beef sandwich	X			
Turkey sandwich	X			
Chicken pieces		X	X	X
Chicken sandwich	X		X	X
Fish sandwich	X	X	X	
Breakfast	X	X	X	
Children's meal		X	X	X
Regular hamburger	X	X	X	
Regular cheeseburger	X		X	
Large hamburger		X	X	X
Large cheeseburger		X	X	X
Extra-large hamburger		X	X	X
Extra-large cheeseburger			X	X
Salad bar	X		X	X
Baked potato				X
Chili				X
Hot dog	X			
Ham and cheese sandwich			X	
Bacon hamburger	X		X	X

3. Construct 3 diagrams such as the one in figure 3.10 to compare these "species" of similar FFRs.

Figure 3.10

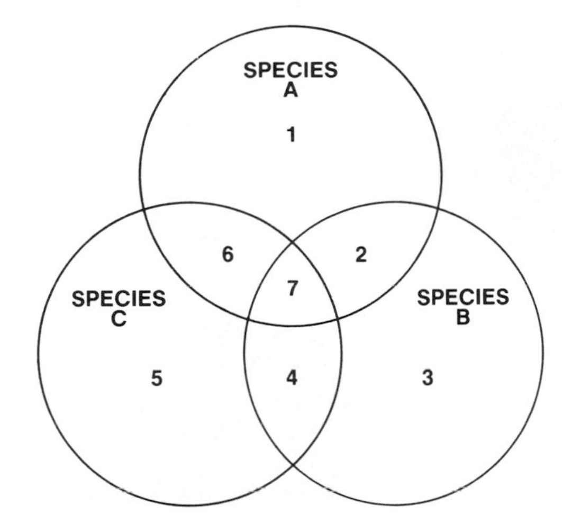

4. Follow the directions in the table below and write the name of the entrée that fits each category in the proper numbered area on the diagrams.

Table 3.2 Comparison of FFR species

	A-B-D	A-C-D	B-C-D
	Entrées unique to	Entrées unique to	Entrées unique to
Areas 1, 3, & 5	A, B, & D	A, C, & D	B, C, & D
	Entrées common to	Entrées common to	Entrées common to
Area 2	A & B, not D	A & C, not D	B & C, not D
Area 4	B & D, not A	C & D, not A	C & D, not B
Area 6	A & D, not B	A & D, not C	B & D, not C
Area 7	A, B, & D	A, C, & D	B, C, & D

5. How is coexistence possible for each set of FFRs?
6. The hypothesis being tested by these data was: Entrée specialization might explain coexistence. Do these data support this hypothesis?

Part B—Competition Between Birds

In the short-grass prairie of the Great Plains, yellow-headed and red-winged blackbirds live together in the same marshes. Studies of these two species indicate that both species use basically the same niches. The only difference between the species is that the red-wing is a generalist and can nest in a variety of habitats ranging from moist brushy habitats to moist meadows. Red-wings do, however, prefer to nest in extremely moist marshes at the edge of the open water of ponds and lakes. The yellow-head is more of a specialist and requires the extremely wet part of the

Figure 3.11 Overlapping niches of red-winged and yellow-headed blackbirds.

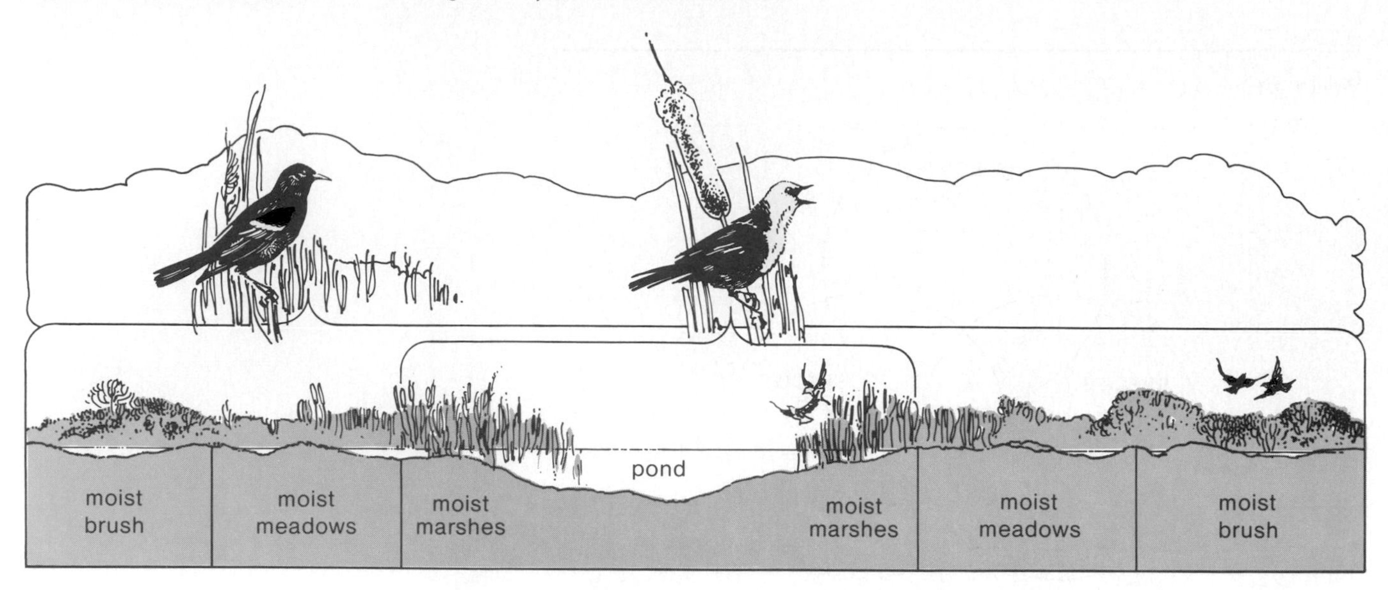

marsh, next to open water, to nest successfully. In fact, yellow-headed blackbirds, because of their larger size and more aggressive nature, will displace red-wings in that open wet marsh. Thus, the yellow-headed blackbird has a niche totally included within that of the red-wing, as shown in figure 3.11.

1. How do the competitive abilities of red-wings compare to those of yellow-heads?
2. Why are all red-wings not displaced by yellow-heads?
3. Compare FFRs B and C. Using what you have learned about blackbirds, how is coexistence possible between these 2 FFRs?

Discussion

1. (a) A new FFR chain, E, opens a restaurant one block from an established B. E offers exactly the same menu and service as B. What do you think would happen, and why?
   (b) What does this suggest to you about the chances that a fish species not established in a lake could swim up a river into that lake and establish itself there?
2. Five very similar species of small, insectivorous birds live in the same spruce forest and apparently coexist. What variables might you investigate to explain this?
3. From the investigation you have learned that competitive exclusion does not always occur among competing species. How do the species coexist?
4. How can two species coexist when one has a niche included within that of the other?
5. How can the concepts of competition, specialization, and included niches be applied to other aspects of urban life?

Figure 3.12 What is the boundary of the ecosystem?

George Silk, Life Magazine © Time, Inc.

Ecosystem Structure

Guidepost: How are biotic and abiotic environmental factors related to each other in an ecosystem?

3.5 The Boundaries of an Ecosystem Are Difficult to Determine

What are the boundaries of an ecosystem? You might think that the boundary in the Florida river example is easy to define—the edge of the water. However, turtles crawl onto the river banks to lay their eggs. Herons get most of their food from the river, but they nest in tall trees near the water. Frogs are caught and eaten by raccoons on land. Although some organisms such as fish spend all of their lives in the river, other organisms in our example do not.

When we consider abiotic factors, the question of boundaries becomes more complex. Energy for the entire ecosystem comes from the sun, which is a great distance from the river's shoreline. Rain falls from the sky and may carry soil from the riverbanks to the river. The wind may blow seeds into the river from communities many kilometers away. Thus, we could keep expanding the boundaries of this one ecosystem to include many more ecosystems.

The Florida river is not a special case. All ecosystems are connected to others around them. A river ecosystem is linked to a forest. A forest ecosystem is linked to the grassland, and so on. In fact, all ecosystems on earth are connected to each other to form the biosphere. Because of this connection, a change in one ecosystem may affect many others.

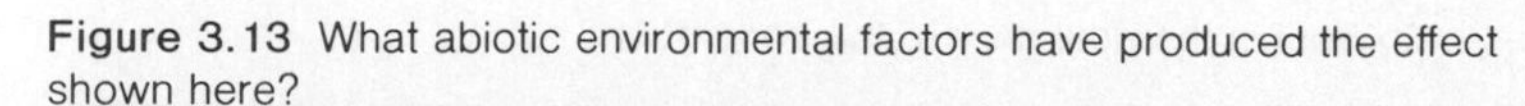

Figure 3.13 What abiotic environmental factors have produced the effect shown here?

Katherine A. Winternitz

3.6 A Change in the Abiotic Environment Causes Many Changes in the Biotic Community

Many of the interactions in a community involve abiotic factors. In chapter 2 we saw how one population is affected by abiotic factors. However, when one population is affected, many others in the same community are affected at the same time because of the web of relationships. If the temperature drops to abnormal lows in Florida, river turtle eggs and young river turtles could be killed while they are still on land. With fewer river turtles, more tape grass will grow, but there will be less food for the snapping turtles. If a heavy rainfall washes mud into the river, light will not penetrate as deeply in the water, and fewer plants will be able to photosynthesize. That, in turn, means less oxygen and less food for herbivores. So each environmental change has many effects: one change causes many others. Investigation 3.3 examines the effects of one environmental change on the germination of seeds.

Investigation 3.3 EFFECTS OF ACID RAIN ON SEED GERMINATION

Introduction

Acid rain is something of a misnomer, because rain is naturally acidic, with a pH of about 5.6. When we speak of acid rain, therefore, we refer to rain with a pH lower than 5.6. Acid rain is produced when sulfur and nitrogen compounds are released into the atmosphere, where they combine with water to form sulfuric and nitric acids. Sulfur compounds may come from natural sources such as decomposing organic matter, volcanos, and geysers. The environmental problem called acid rain does not arise from natural sources, however. Acid rain is caused primarily by fossil fuel combustion. When coal, oil, and gas are burned, large amounts of sulfur and nitrogen are released as gases and combine with water to make the rain more acid. Acid rain has many effects on an ecosystem. In this investigation, you will examine just one of those effects.

Materials

petri dish
4 bean seeds
water solutions ranging in pH from 2 to 7
rainwater
absorbent paper towels
scissors
transparent metric ruler
graph paper
colored chalk or magic markers
glass marking pencil

Procedure

Part A—Day 1

1. Cut 4 paper discs the size of the petri dish from the absorbent paper towel.
2. Dampen the paper discs with the water assigned to you by your teacher. Make note of the pH of your assigned water.
3. Place 2 of the paper discs on the bottom of the petri dish.
4. Measure the length of your 4 seeds and determine the average length. Sketch the shapes of the seeds and note their color.
5. Record the average length in millimeters at Day 0 in your data book.
6. Arrange the seeds in the petri dish and cover with the 2 remaining discs. Make sure the discs are still moist. If not, add more of your assigned pH solution.
7. Replace lid on petri dish and label it with your name.
8. Make a hypothesis as to the ideal pH for bean seed growth. Record your hypothesis in your data book.

Part B—Days 2-10

1. Remove the lid from the petri dish and remove the paper discs covering the four seeds.
2. Use the transparent ruler to measure the length of the seeds in millimeters. Average the lengths and record the average in your data book.
3. Sketch the shape of the seeds and note their color.
4. Cover the seeds with the paper discs. Moisten the paper if necessary with the assigned pH solution and replace the lid.
5. On a piece of graph paper, set up a graph with age in days on the horizontal axis and length of the seeds in millimeters on the vertical axis.
6. Plot the average length of your seeds for the 2 measurements (Day 0 and Day 1) you have made.
7. Repeat procedures 1–6 each day for the length of the investigation. If the seeds begin to germinate during this time, include the length of any growth in your measurement.
8. Students who are working with the same pH solution should combine their data and determine the average.
9. One student representing each pH should record data on the class graph. Use the color assigned to your particular pH.

Discussion

1. Observe the data on the completed class graph. What appears to be the optimal pH solution for successful bean seed germination?
2. What appears to be the least ideal pH solution for successful bean seed germination?
3. What pH do you think the rainwater has, based on the data gathered? Determine its pH.
4. What impact on local crops might an increased rain acidity have?
5. Do you think there is reason for concern?

This investigation was adapted from E. Johnson and R. Bybee, supervisors, "Acid Rain: Activities for Science Teachers" *The American Biology Teacher* 45:4 (April/May 1983) © National Association of Biology Teachers, Reston, Virginia. Reprinted by permission.

3.7 Within a Community There Are Generally More Producers Than Consumers

One of the most important abiotic factors that affects relationships in a community is energy. As we discussed in chapter 1, organisms in an ecosystem are tied together by the flow of energy and matter from one organism to another. A herbivore eats a plant, and a carnivore eats a herbivore. This food chain depends on the energy from the sun. Without the sun, there would be no green plants. Without the green plants, there would be no herbivores, and without them, no carnivores. That is true for almost all ecosystems on the earth. There are a few ecosystems that do not get their energy from the sun by way of photosynthesis. The deep-sea vent communities found in the Pacific Ocean and the Gulf of Mexico are examples of such ecosystems. In these communities, the producers are bacteria that use sulfur compounds welling up from vents in the earth as a source of energy. Consumers in these vent communities include eight-foot long worms, king-sized clams, and blind crabs. In chapter 23 you will find out more about these unusual communities.

Most communities, however, depend on green plants as the source of all food. The size of a community is, therefore, limited by the amount of energy entering it through its producers. The total amount of chemical energy stored by photosynthesis is the **gross primary productivity** of the community. Much of that energy is used by the producers to grow and to maintain themselves. The remaining energy, that which is available as food for the consumers, is the **net primary productivity** of the community. One way to measure net primary productivity of a community is to find the **mass** of all producers. Mass is a measure of the amount of matter in an object. Because much of the mass of living organisms is water, the producers first must be dried for a truer estimate of their mass. For instance, the energy found in a fresh apricot and a dried apricot is the same, though the mass of the dried fruit is much less.

The greater the net primary productivity of a community, the greater the amount of food that is available to consumers. When net primary productivity is high, more consumers can live in the community. No matter how great the productivity, however, there is always some limit

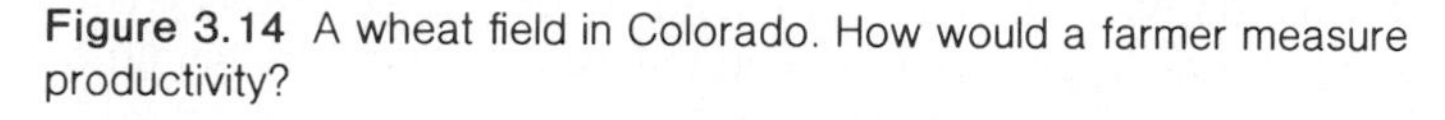

Figure 3.14 A wheat field in Colorado. How would a farmer measure productivity?

BSCS by Bert Kempers

Figure 3.15 A food energy pyramid. Each level is one tenth the equivalent of the level below it. Every organism carries on activities that use or release most of the energy it obtains. Only a fraction of the energy is passed along in a food chain.

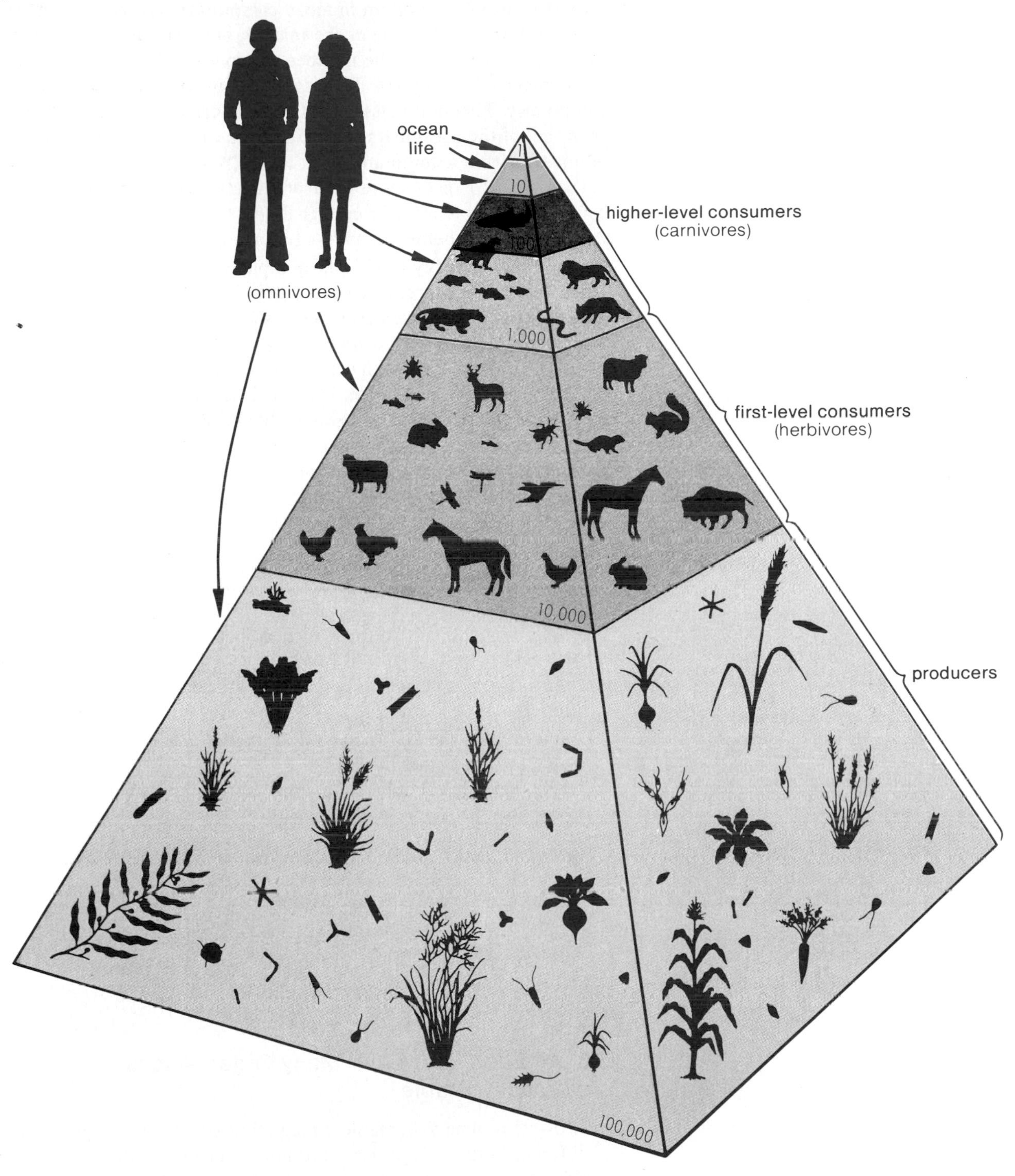

to the number of organisms that can be found in any community—the carrying capacity for each kind of organism. If we weigh the mass or count the number of each kind of organism, we will find an important pattern that helps to describe a community. Like a pyramid, which decreases in size from bottom to top, a community has many producers at its base, fewer herbivores in the middle, and even fewer carnivores at the top. In most cases, the number of producers is much greater than the number of consumers. That describes the **pyramid of numbers** in a community. The total mass of all the producers is usually much greater than that of the consumers. That describes the **pyramid of biomass** (BY oh mass) within a community.

You would expect more food producers than food consumers in a community. There must be enough food to go around, or consumers die. As we discussed before, as plants live, they use up much of the energy they produce. Energy used to keep a plant alive cannot be taken in by a herbivore. Therefore, a large number of plants is needed to support a few herbivores. Because herbivores also use some of the energy to keep themselves alive, not all of the energy they take in is available to carnivores. Thus, we would expect to find fewer carnivores than herbivores in a community. For instance, in a small valley there may be millions of individual producers, such as grasses, but only a few hundred herbivores, such as rabbits. In this same valley, you may have to search carefully to find just one or two carnivores, such as foxes.

Self-Review

1. Why is it difficult to draw distinct boundaries between most ecosystems?
2. How are gross and net primary productivity of a community related?
3. Why is only part of the chemical energy produced by plants available for use by herbivores?
4. What one idea about a community is shown by the pyramid of numbers and the pyramid of biomass?

Guidepost: How do the complex activities of humans affect ecosystems?

Ecosystem Stability and Human Influences

3.8 An Ecosystem with Many Organisms Is Usually Stable

Ecosystems tend to be stable through time because of the great number of different kinds of organisms and interconnecting relationships found in them. In general, the greater the number of kinds of organisms—and, thus, the greater the number of links in the food web—the more stable the community is thought to be. A large community is like a web with many threads. If only one of the threads is broken, the web may still function normally. If a disease kills many of the rabbits in a community, the foxes can eat mice and squirrels until rabbits reproduce or immigrate into the community. Even though many rabbits have died, the rest of the ecosystem remains intact: it may be changed, but it is not destroyed. This is the process of homeostasis, discussed in chapter 2.

3.9 Humans Upset the Stability of Ecosystems

Ecosystems can be greatly changed by humans. We can have positive effects on other members of the community or we can have dramatic, negative effects. As we have mentioned before, humans disrupt homeostatic processes. For instance, farmers eliminate many members of a food web when they raise crops to meet human needs. To feed the human population, large fields of producers are planted. To use machinery efficiently, a single crop is planted in a large field. One cornfield may be 16 hectares, contain 76,000 plants, and yield 7258 m^3 of corn. In a normal food web, these corn plants would provide energy for a great number of consumers—birds, insects, and animals that eat birds and insects. Because corn-eating birds and insects compete with humans for the crop, they are eliminated by humans, as are other plants that compete with the corn for light, water, and nutrients. With such a large population of plants, there is also opportunity for the spread of disease. The disease might be a parasite of the corn. If the farmer is to grow crops economically for humans to eat, he must control the food web and reduce the pests and diseases. Often such control involves widespread spraying of crops, which may have unplanned side effects.

Humans also suffer from parasitic diseases, such as malaria and African sleeping sickness, which are carried by insects. Because such parasitic diseases cause many deaths as well as illness and lost work time, we try to eliminate the insects that carry them. One way to control pests is to use a poison. Such poisons are called insecticides, herbicides, and fungicides. All of these can be included in the term **biocides.** The United States alone produces more than 636 million kg of biocides each year. What are all these poisons used for, and what effect do they have on the relationships in a community?

Figure 3.16 A corn field.

USDA-APHIS

Figure 3.17 Spraying crops with pesticides helps control destructive insects and disease.

USDA-Office of Communication

Many biocides act in a way similar to DDT in the environment, so we can use DDT as an example. Although the use of DDT has been banned in the United States, U.S. chemical companies make DDT and export it to other nations that still use this biocide. An example shows how a food chain can be affected, unexpectedly, by the use of biocides. Marshes along the north shore of Long Island, New York, were sprayed with DDT to control mosquitoes. Later, microscopic organisms in the water were found to have about 0.04 ppm (parts per million) of DDT in their cells. This is a very low level of poison, but no one expected to find any poison in these organisms. The minnows, clams, and snails that ate these organisms had levels of DDT more than ten times higher—between 0.5 and 0.9 ppm. The eels, flukes, and billfish that ate the snails and small fish had levels of DDT ranging from 1.3 to 2.0 ppm. The ospreys, herons, and gulls that ate the eels and minnows had levels of DDT

Figure 3.18 As DDT is passed from organism to organism in the Long Island Sound food chain, the concentration is magnified about 10 million times. Dots represent DDT, and arrows show small amounts lost in the daily activities of the organisms.

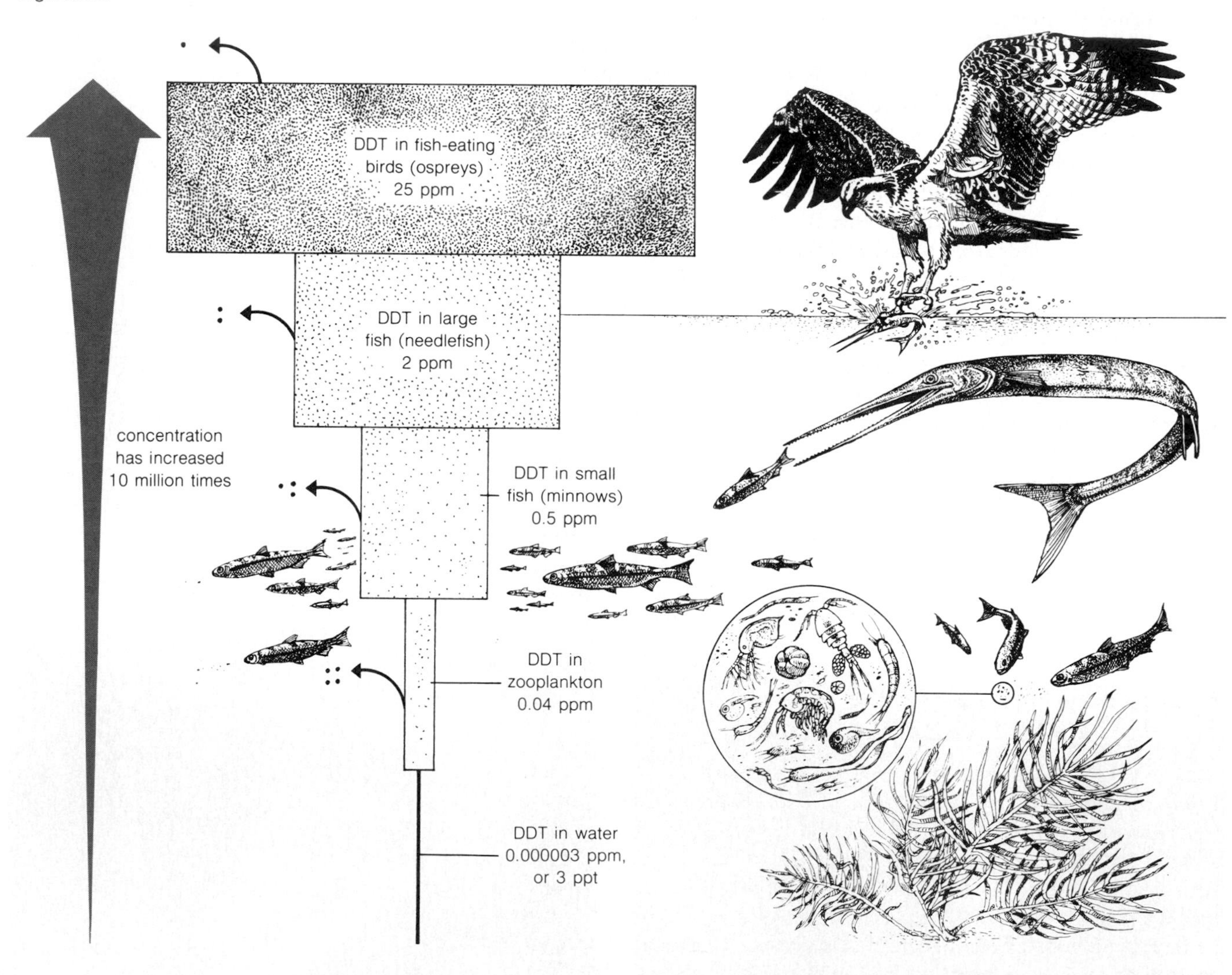

between 10 and 25 ppm. Thus, the concentration of DDT in the tissues of the organisms in this food chain increased almost 10 million times from the amount in seawater, and nearly 625 times from the producer level at the bottom of the pyramid to the consumer level at the top. That relationship is shown in figure 3.18.

DDT and other chemicals become concentrated in fewer individuals within a food chain. Each consumer eats a large number of producers. Although the body of the producer may be broken down and used by the consumer, the DDT in the producer's body is not broken down. Each of the producers contains a little DDT, and these small amounts are concentrated within the consumer. The greater the concentration of DDT in an organism, the greater the damage. Ospreys and pelicans are adversely affected by DDT, which prevents them from producing normal eggs. The egg shells are so thin that the eggs and the developing young inside are crushed by the nesting parent. At one time, some of the osprey and pelican populations became nearly extinct because of the effects of DDT. No one expected that the DDT used to control pests could affect so many other organisms far from the area where the poison was sprayed. The intended victims of the DDT were mosquitoes, but many other organisms were harmed.

Malaria is a disease carried from one person to another by mosquitoes. A person with malaria experiences successive bouts of chills followed by high fever and, in some cases, may die. Many people in the tropics suffer from malaria. At one time, malaria was a major health problem on the island of Borneo in Indonesia. To help the people of Borneo, workers from the World Health Organization sprayed remote villages and nearby areas with DDT. Most of the mosquitoes in the sprayed area died, but because organisms are connected to each other in the web of life, other organisms also were affected. Flies and cockroaches, the favorite food of lizards that lived in the remote villages, died from the DDT. The lizards gorged themselves on the DDT-poisoned insects, and they, too, began to die. Local cats ate the infected lizards and died. After the cats died, the rat population grew unchecked.

The malaria-carrying mosquitoes were killed by the DDT, but the rats in the villages carried another disease that affected humans. Although the people on the island no longer had to worry about malaria, they began to die from the other disease. To restore the balance in the community, cats were parachuted into the remote villages so they could eat the rats. This is another example of the unplanned effects that humans have on other organisms and on themselves, because of the interaction of many organisms in a community.

Figure 3.19 Borneo rat patrol.

3.10 Human Activity Creates Biocide-Resistant Organisms

Some pest populations include individuals that are resistant to a biocide. These individuals vary in their ability to tolerate, detoxify, or avoid the poison. Most of the pests are killed by the spray, but a few individuals survive and reproduce. They pass their biocide resistance to their offspring. When people try to kill these offspring with the same biocide, the poison has little effect. The strength or the amount of the spray must be increased to be effective, but in some cases no amount of spray will control the pests. A different pesticide may or may not be effective. Today, one can find many resistant disease-causing and disease-carrying organisms in places where biocides have been used often. DDT-resistant mosquitoes, herbicide-resistant weeds, and antibiotic-resistant bacteria are not uncommon.

3.11 Humans Cause the Extinction of Many Species

There are many different types of organisms in the world. Each type of organism is called a species. At the same time that biocide-resistant pest organisms are on the rise, many species of useful or potentially important organisms have lost or are losing the battle against human influence. As our human population grows and we expand our activities, we occupy more land. This process destroys the habitats of many organisms. Sometimes this is good for humans, as when we drain a pond that is a breeding ground for mosquitoes. Other times the damage extends to beneficial and desirable species. The smog created by automobiles and industry is killing trees of many species over a wide area of Southern California (figure 3.21). The needles of ponderosa pines grad-

Figure 3.20 These two illustrations show a change in a population involving a single characteristic, the ability to tolerate a pesticide.

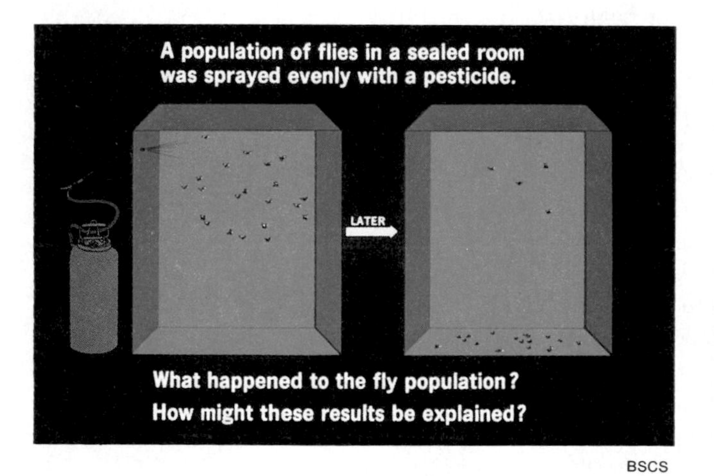

A population of flies in a sealed room was sprayed evenly with a pesticide.
LATER
What happened to the fly population?
How might these results be explained?
After several weeks, the fly population had increased in size.
The flies were sprayed for a second time.
LATER
What happened to the fly population after the second spraying?
Account for these results.

BSCS

BSCS

Figure 3.21 An entire forest has been killed by smog in southern California.

John D. Cunningham/VISUALS UNLIMITED ©

ually turn brown, and palm trees have only a small tuft of fronds at their tops. In these cases, photosynthesis is reduced, and the plants soon die.

The Everglades National Park is a delicate area in south Florida that depends on a slowly moving sheet of water flowing from north to south. Drainage ditches built at the northern edge of the Everglades have decreased the flow of water over the entire area. As a result, many alligator holes (figure 3.22a), which helped to contain fires in the Everglades, have dried up. Destructive fires are now more frequent in this national park (figure 3.22b).

Because of human activities, plants and animals in heavily populated areas such as Florida and Southern California are threatened. Unfortunately, these are not the only two areas where this occurs. For certain organisms, human-caused changes in the environment have been tragic. On the average, the earth has lost one species of mammal every year since 1900. When such an event occurs, we say the species has become **extinct** (ek STINKT). There are hundreds of plants and animals with

Figure 3.22 (a) Alligator holes once were abundant in the Everglades. (b) Today, fires often are destructive.

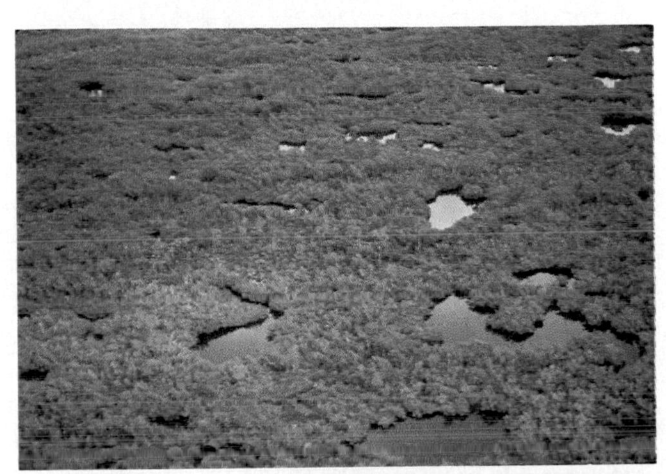

a Richard Frear/National Park Service

b Jack Boucher/National Park Service

very small populations that seem threatened with extinction. Examples include the whooping crane and some rare pitcher plants (figure 3.23). Extinction is, of course, a natural process. The process has been greatly accelerated, however, because humans have changed whole ecosystems. What difference does it make that passenger pigeons and dodo birds have become extinct?

First, there are some good biological arguments against extinction in general. One comes from genetics. As long as wild populations exist, a vast resource of genetic characteristics remains available. That is vital to prevent widespread death among the genetically similar individuals of our crops and domesticated animals. If all the crop plants in a field are genetically similar and one individual gets a disease, all the plants may die. The extinction of each wild population erases genetic material that could mean healthy crops and animals. Once extinction occurs, the genetic material is gone—forever.

Figure 3.23 Whooping cranes and pitcher plants may be threatened with extinction.

Kerry T. Givens/TOM STACK & ASSOCIATES

A second argument against human-caused extinction is related to the instability of simplified ecosystems. Think of a field of corn as a simplified ecosystem. If something should happen to the corn, the whole ecosystem would collapse. To prevent such a collapse in a natural ecosystem, it is vital for a community to have a wide diversity of species. The fewer the species in a community, the easier it is for homeostasis to be completely disrupted. Although new species are evolving all the time, the process is very slow compared to the rate at which humans are able to cause species to become extinct. Each time a species becomes extinct, the biosphere is simplified a little more, and it becomes more difficult to maintain the stable biosphere on which all life depends.

Figure 3.24 Some animals that have been completely exterminated through human activities.

A third argument comes from research on plants that are important to medicine. The island of Madagascar, off the east coast of Africa, is the only known habitat of the Madagascar periwinkle (figure 3.25). This relative of the common garden periwinkle produces two chemicals not produced by other plants—vincristine and vinblastine. Both of these chemicals are used to help combat Hodgkin disease—a leukemia-like disease that affects thousands of people each year. As the human population on Madagascar grew, the habitat for the periwinkle shrank. It almost shrank to the point of making the periwinkle extinct. Fortunately, foresighted botanists collected and grew some of these plants before they were gone forever. The medicines made from the Madagascar periwinkle are worth millions of dollars each year, and help many people with Hodgkin disease to live longer. These medicines would never have been known to us if we had destroyed the habitat of this plant.

How many more organisms are there in the world that we know very little about? Almost 800,000 species of insects alone have been described, but at least twice that many are thought to exist. If extinction occurs, we will never know anything about them or the many other undiscovered species. Even as you read this page, thousands of organisms are being destroyed to meet the needs of a growing human population around the world.

3.12 Humans Can Preserve Natural Areas for the Future

Humans also can have a positive influence on communities. To ensure that some ecosystems are maintained in their natural state, Congress sets aside wilderness areas. In these areas only foot and horse travel is allowed, and camping may be restricted to designated campsites. In some wilderness areas a permit system is used. What good are these places if

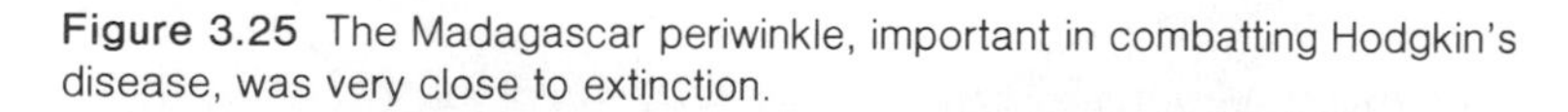

Figure 3.25 The Madagascar periwinkle, important in combatting Hodgkin's disease, was very close to extinction.

G. Prance/VISUALS UNLIMITED ©

Biology Today C

Naturalist / Interpreter

Dave Marshall is a naturalist/interpreter for the Bear Creek Nature Center in Colorado. He grew up in Colorado Springs, which is very close to the Rocky Mountains. His father was an outdoorsman, and he took Dave on many fishing trips to the nearby streams and lakes. This, along with his father's interest in birds, sparked Dave's interest in nature, and he decided to pursue a career related to natural history. Originally, he planned to study forest management and ecology, but after discovering a program in environmental interpretation in a college catalog, he decided that this career "seemed to fit," and he went on to obtain degrees in Environmental Education and in Resource and Recreation Management.

One of Dave's major duties is conducting natural history programs for elementary school students at the Nature Center. He leads the children on a short walk on the nearby trails, shows them the exhibits at the Nature Center, introduces them to a display animal, such as a turtle or garter snake, and gives a short talk on the specific program. Dave is also in charge of the mammal natural history records, the insect collection, and the Nature Center library. Dave also leads frequent nature hikes to various types of nearby natural areas.

Dave's favorite part of being a naturalist/interpreter is leading programs and being with the public. He especially enjoys working with children, and he feels a special satisfaction when he sees that their curiosity and imagination have been stimulated by his program. Dave feels that being a good communicator—both oral and written—is the most important quality for a naturalist/interpreter. Being a good naturalist is not as important as being able to communicate what you know and to stimulate people's curiosity about the natural world.

Other duties of a naturalist/interpreter include exhibit design and construction, preparation of brochures and educational materials, providing information for visitors, natural history research, plant and animal identification, small animal care, and training volunteers. Because naturalist/

El Paso County Parks Department's Bear Creek Nature Center

interpreters sometimes lead hikes into the back country, good physical health is important.

Many people interested in natural history become trained volunteers, or docents. Docents assist in all the duties of the naturalist/interpreter, and often present programs and lead walks themselves. Volunteers also may become involved in programs with senior citizens and scouts. Docents with special skills or interests such as photography and art often are able to use these skills.

No special education is required to become a volunteer—just a strong interest in natural history and a desire to share this knowledge with others. Positions such as naturalist volunteers and naturalist/interpreters can be very rewarding because they provide a service. This service will be needed more in the future, as the relationship between humans and the environment becomes more critical.

El Paso County Parks Department's Bear Creek Nature Center

Figure 3.26 Three Sisters wilderness area in Oregon.

Doug Sokell

more people cannot use them? Although human activity in parks is controlled, bears feeding out of garbage cans and chipmunks eating out of your hand are not part of normal food chains. Wherever you find many humans, the normal stability of a community is changed.

To learn about the community as a whole and its individual organisms, scientists must study a community that has not been changed by humans. Wilderness areas serve to protect communities from human influence. By studying these areas, we can learn about the many different relationships in a community. We also can save such areas for the future.

Self-Review

1. How does the number of kinds of organisms in an ecosystem relate to the stability of that ecosystem?
2. For what purpose are biocides used?
3. What happens to the concentration of a biocide in the members of a food chain?
4. Why should human-caused extinction of organisms be avoided?

Summary

There are many kinds of relationships in a community, some of which are direct but most of which are indirect. Relationships include predation, parasitism, competition, commensalism, and mutualism. A single organism may have many kinds of relationships with other organisms, and these relationships define the organism's niche. The organism's habitat, on the other hand, is the abiotic environment in which it lives. The niches of organisms are distinct, but the boundaries between ecosystems are not clear, because energy and matter pass easily from one ecosystem to another. In most ecosystems, there are far more producers than consumers, and there is stability through time. Humans can affect the populations of producers or consumers by what they do. Sometimes, as when DDT is sprayed, the results are many, surprising, and undesirable. In some cases, human activity can lead to the extinction of another species. This may have negative consequences for humans in the future. One way to prevent this is to preserve communities in wilderness areas for future generations to enjoy.

Application Questions

1. How does the concept of ecosystems help us to understand the biosphere?
2. What do you think would happen if all of the turtles were killed within the Florida river community?
3. What do you think would happen to a community if the number of carnivores suddenly doubled?
4. A predator affects the population of its prey, but a parasite may not have the same effect on its host population. Explain.
5. How can organisms living in the same habitat occupy different niches?
6. Explain why organisms can compete for space but not for temperature.

Problems

1. How might an ecologist find out whether the effect of one kind of organism on another is beneficial, harmful, or neutral?
2. Study a community in your city or town. Gather information to answer these questions: (1) How does the community get its energy? (2) Which organisms would be present and which would be absent if humans were not part of the community?
3. Here are two parasite-host relationships: (1) chestnut tree and chestnut blight; (2) whooping cough and humans. Investigate these two relationships. How are the hosts affected, and how have humans tried to control the parasites?

Suggested Readings

P. R. Ehrlich and A. H. Ehrlich, 1981, *Extinction: The Causes and Consequences of the Disappearance of Species* (New York: Random House, Inc.). Discusses the impact that extinction of species has on the human population of earth.

C. P. Hickman, L. S. Roberts, and F. M. Hickman, 1984, *Integrated Principles of Zoology* (St. Louis: Times Mirror/ Mosby College). The last two chapters in this well-written text deal with animal ecology and animals in the human environment.

H. W. Menard, 1986, *Islands* (New York: W. H. Freeman). One chapter looks at island ecosystems from a geological viewpoint.

E. P. Volpe, 1984, *Biology and Human Concerns* (Dubuque, IA: Wm. C. Brown Company Publishers). Includes an interesting discussion about human modification of the environment.

D. H. S. Wehle and F. C. Coleman, "Plastics at Sea" *Natural History* (February 1983). The pollution of oceans and beaches with plastic materials is increasing, and sea birds, marine turtles, whales, and seals are suffering as a result.

Doug Sokell

The crashing wave displays some of the energy of water.

CHAPTER 4

Matter and Energy in the Web of Life

Introduction

Living things are intimately tied together by the need of all organisms for matter and energy. Producer organisms such as green plants make their own food, using energy from the sun and absorbing matter from the surrounding soil and air. Consumer organisms, on the other hand, must obtain their energy and matter from other organisms. Humans, for instance, eat plants and animals to get their food. This food is made up of the biological molecules—the molecules of life—found in all living things. We eat the biological molecules of plants and animals and rearrange them to make our own biological molecules. In this chapter we will look at these important molecules and investigate some characteristics of matter and energy.

Matter and Energy

Guidepost: How are matter and energy related in the biosphere?

4.1 Atoms Are the Basic Units of Matter

We have learned that a biological community includes producers, consumers, and decomposers. These organisms are tied together in the web of life because matter and energy pass from one organism to another. To understand how this occurs, we need to look more closely at some characteristics of matter and energy.

There are many kinds of matter in the biosphere. Compounds can be broken down into the elements from which they were formed. The compound water, for example, can be broken down into the elements oxygen and hydrogen, as shown in figure 4.1. Elements cannot be broken down into other kinds of substances. Carbon, iron, nitrogen, gold, silver, calcium, and chlorine are elements with which you are probably familiar. Carbon is especially important to life, as we will see later in the chapter.

Figure 4.1 The compound water can be broken down into two elements—hydrogen and oxygen.

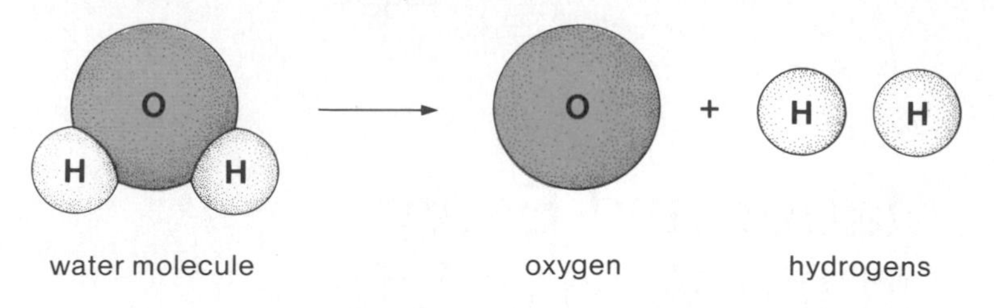

Figure 4.2 (a) Simplified atomic models of hydrogen, carbon and oxygen. Electrons are shown where they are most likely to move around the nucleus. (b) The "cloud model" of a hydrogen atom. The dots represent possible positions for a single electron. The circle represents the area in which the electron probably will be located 90 percent of the time.

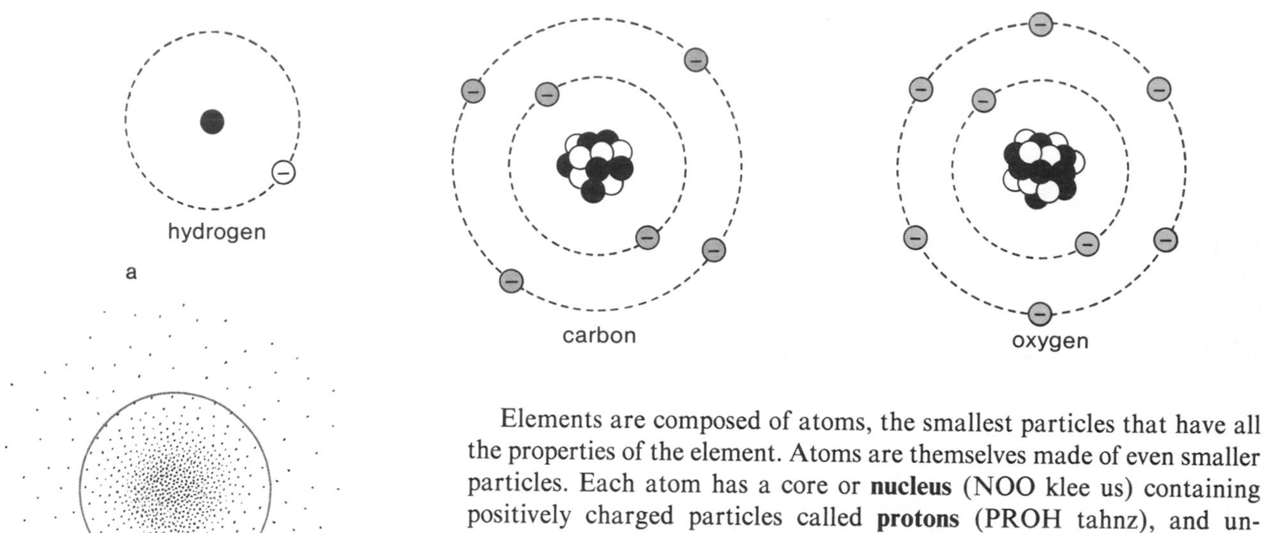

Elements are composed of atoms, the smallest particles that have all the properties of the element. Atoms are themselves made of even smaller particles. Each atom has a core or **nucleus** (NOO klee us) containing positively charged particles called **protons** (PROH tahnz), and uncharged particles called **neutrons** (NOO trahnz). Rapidly orbiting the atomic nucleus are one or more **electrons** (ee LEK trahnz), negatively charged particles. The number of electrons is the same as the number of protons, so an atom is electrically neutral.

Elements differ in the numbers of particles their atoms contain. For example, an atom of hydrogen is made up of one proton and one electron. (Hydrogen is the only element that does not have neutrons in its atoms.) An atom of carbon contains six protons, six neutrons, and six electrons. Oxygen atoms are composed of eight protons, eight neutrons, and eight electrons. Models of these atoms are shown in figure 4.2.

Reactions between atoms depend on the number of electrons the atoms have. Reactions may involve an electron moving from one atom to another. That is what happens when atoms of sodium and chlorine react to form table salt. Each sodium atom gives up an electron to a chlorine atom, as shown in figure 4.3. As a result, the number of protons and the number of electrons in the sodium atom are no longer equal. The sodium atom has a positive charge, because it has one less electron than protons. Such a charged particle is called an **ion** (EYE un).

The electron from the sodium has been captured by the chlorine atom, which now has one more electron than it originally had. The chlorine atom has become an ion with a negative charge—a chloride ion.

Figure 4.3 When one atom of sodium and one of chlorine react to form a molecule, a single electron from sodium is transferred to chlorine. The compound formed is sodium chloride, or $NaCl$. By losing one electron, sodium becomes a positive ion, and by gaining one electron, chlorine (chloride) becomes a negative ion.

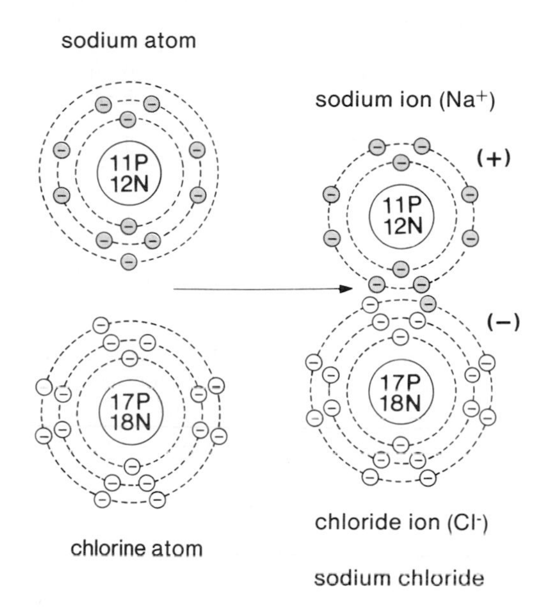

Figure 4.4 In a molecule of water, the oxygen atom forms an electron-sharing bond with each hydrogen atom. Compare this model with figure 4.1.

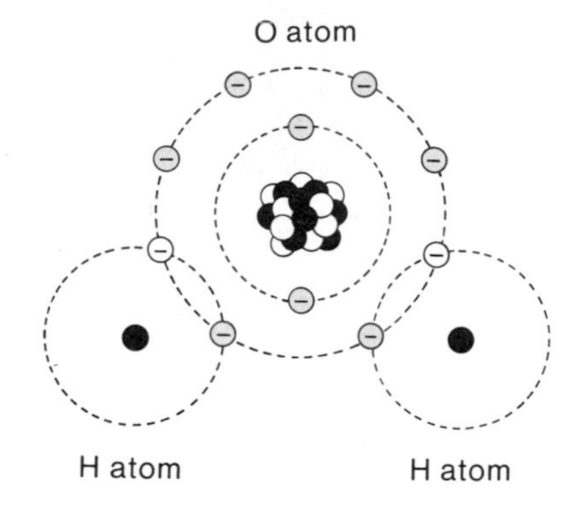

The positively charged sodium ions and the negatively charged chloride ions are attracted to each other. When these particles of unlike charge come together, they form molecules of sodium chloride, or table salt. The forces that hold the atoms together in a molecule are called **chemical bonds.**

Often, when atoms react, they do not gain or lose electrons. Intead, they form a chemical bond by sharing electrons. For example, in a molecule of water, an atom of oxygen shares electrons with two atoms of hydrogen (figure 4.4). Molecules of carbon dioxide, hydrogen gas, and oxygen gas also are formed by shared electrons.

4.2 Chemical Reactions Are Essential to Life

There are two basic types of chemical reactions in living cells. We have seen how sodium and chlorine combine to form salt, and how oxygen and hydrogen combine to form water. These are examples of **synthesis** (SIN thuh sis) reactions, in which compounds are built up. Compounds also may be broken down, in **decomposition** (de kom poh ZISH un) reactions. Digestion of foods involves decomposition reactions.

In order for chemical reactions to take place, the reacting substances must come in contact with each other. That happens most easily when they are in solution, that is, dissolved in water. Water is such a common compound that we give it little thought, yet it has unique properties that make it essential for life. Our bodies, in fact, are about 67 percent water. Cucumbers and watermelons are more than 90 percent water, and even seeds contain about 10 percent.

Figure 4.5 Water molecules ionize into hydrogen and hydroxide ions.

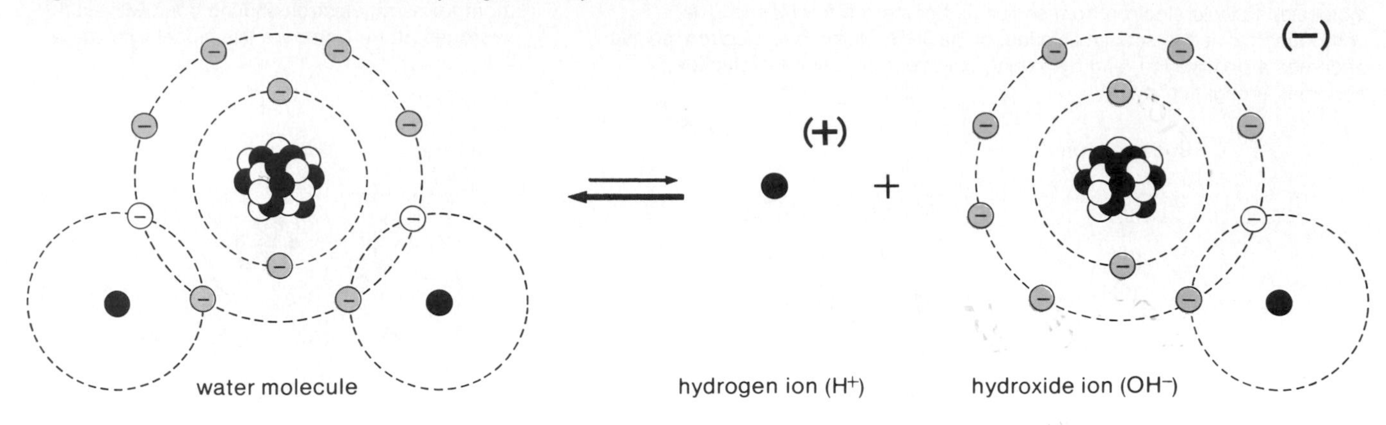

Figure 4.6a. pH of several common substances.

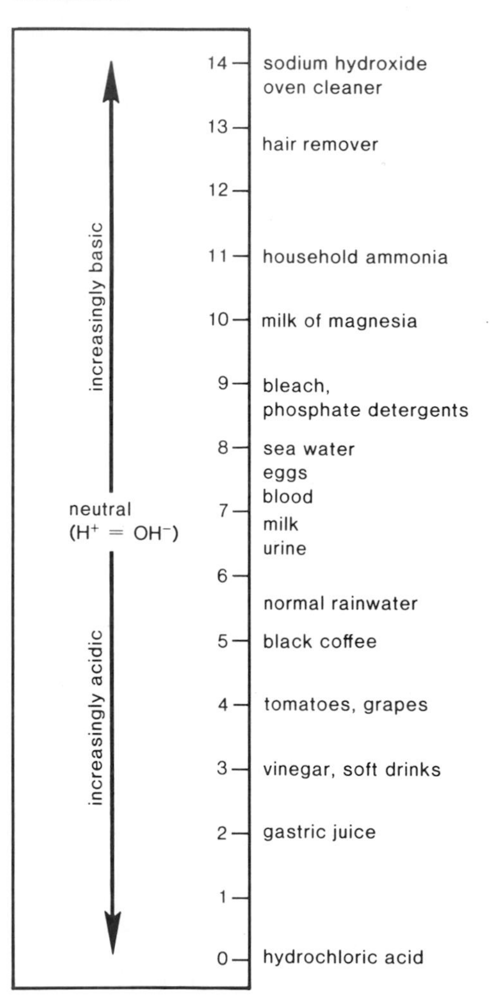

When salt dissolves in water, the sodium and chloride ions separate from each other, or **ionize** (EYE uh nyz). Many other compounds also ionize in solution. Even water itself ionizes to a small extent. Only about 1 in 10 million molecules of water ionizes, but all life processes depend on this small percentage.

A water molecule ionizes into hydrogen and hydroxide ions. The hydrogen ion is a single proton—a hydrogen atom that has lost its only electron. The missing electron is held by the hydroxide ion, which consists of an oxygen atom, a hydrogen atom, and the extra electron.

Hydrogen and hydroxide ions are involved in most of the reactions that occur in organisms. If, as a result of such reactions, more hydrogen ions than hydroxide ions remain in solution, we say the solution is **acidic** (uh SID ik). If more hydroxide than hydrogen ions remain, the solution is **basic** or **alkaline** (AL kuh lin). The relative levels of hydrogen and hydroxide ions are very important to organisms because of their effects on chemical reactions.

We measure the hydrogen ion level of a solution by means of the **pH** (PEE AYTCH) **scale.** As you can see in figure 4.6b, the scale ranges from 0 to 14. A solution with a pH of 7 is said to be **neutral,** because it has equal amounts of hydrogen and hydroxide ions. As the hydrogen ion level rises, the solution becomes more acidic, and the pH drops. Thus, a solution with a pH of 2 is highly acidic. Solutions with a pH above 7 are basic. They have relatively low levels of hydrogen ions, with correspondingly high levels of hydroxide ions. The pH of several common substances is shown in figure 4.6a.

Organisms have an internal pH that must remain fairly stable. Certain environmental factors affect that stability in a variety of ways. In investigation 4.1 you will discover how that internal pH is regulated by the use of chemicals called **buffers.**

Even when dissolved in water, most atoms and molecules react extremely slowly, if at all. Substances do exist, however, that promote chemical reactions. Such substances are called **catalysts** (KAT uh lists). They are present in very small amounts, and although they participate in the reactions, they are not themselves changed or used up in the reactions. Catalysts make it possible for reactions to occur at rates high enough to sustain life. The specialized and highly specific catalysts present in organisms are called **enzymes** (EN zymz). We will learn more about enzymes in section 4.13.

Figure 4.6b. The pH scale. Any pH below 7 is acidic and any pH above 7 is basic.

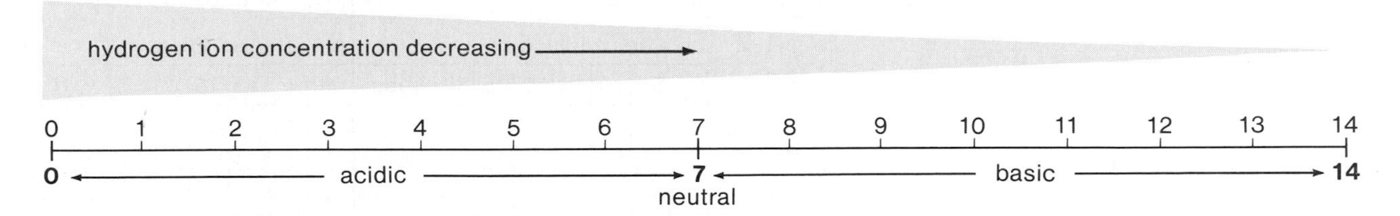

Investigation 4.1 ORGANISMS AND pH

Introduction

In chapter 2 you learned that there is a tendency for populations to remain relatively stable. That process of stability is called homeostasis. Individual organisms must maintain an internal homeostasis. There are many environmental factors to which organisms and cells must respond as a part of maintaining that internal homeostasis. One of those is the relative concentrations of hydrogen (H^+) and hydroxide (OH^-) ions. Biochemical activities of living tissues frequently tend to change the pH. Yet life depends on maintaining the pH that is normal for each tissue or system. How do organisms survive and maintain themselves in spite of metabolic activities that tend to shift pH either toward acidic or basic ends of the scale?

Materials

pH meter or narrow range pH paper
tap water
small beakers or jars, 50 ml
graduated cylinder, 50 ml
dropping pipets
0.1 *N* HCl (**CAUTION:** *hydrochloric acid is harmful to living tissue and clothes.*)
0.1 *N* NaOH (**CAUTION:** *sodium hydroxide is harmful to living tissue and clothes.*)
liver and potato homogenates, 10 g/ 100 ml of water
egg white (diluted 1:5 with water)
2% solution of warm gelatin
sodium phosphate pH 7 buffer solution

Procedure

Part A—Water and pH

In order to compare the reaction of living substances to that of nonliving materials in relation to pH changes, you will first use tap water as the solution to be tested.

1. Prepare a table in your data book like the one below.

Tests with 0.1 *N* HCl								Tests with 0.1 *N* NaOH						
Solution Tested	pH after addition of							pH after addition of						
	0	5	10	15	20	25	30 drops	0	5	10	15	20	25	30 drops
Tap water														
Liver														
(etc.)														

2. Pour 25 ml of tap water into a 50 ml beaker.
3. Record its initial pH by using the pH meter or dipping strips of pH paper into the water and comparing the color change to a standard color chart.
4. Add 0.1 *N* HCl a drop at a time, swirling to mix after each drop. Determine the pH after each 5 drops have been added until 30 drops have been used. Record the pH measurements in your table. Rinse the beaker thoroughly and pour into it another 25 ml of tap water. Record its initial pH and add 0.1 *N* NaOH drop by drop, recording the pH changes in exactly the same way as for the 0.1 *N* HCl.
5. Make a simple graph, plotting 2 lines for the change of pH in tap water against the drops of acid and base solutions added. Use a solid line for acid changes and a dash line for changes with NaOH.
6. Summarize the effects of HCl and NaOH on tap water.

Part B—Tissues from Organisms and pH

1. Use the tissue homogenate assigned to your team by your teacher.
2. Repeat procedures 1–4 in part A but substitute your assigned tissue homogenate for tap water. Record all your data.
3. What was the total pH change for the 30 drops of acid added to the tissue homogenate?
4. For the 30 drops of base added?
5. How do these data compare with the changes in tap water?
6. Graph the results for your tissue homogenate on the same graph as for tap water, using solid and dash lines of a different colored pencil for each line representing a change in pH for your tissue.
7. Examine your graph and the graphs of teams who used a tissue homogenate different from yours.
8. How do biological materials respond to changes in pH?
9. What patterns do the graphs indicate for biological materials?

Part C—Buffers and pH

What accounts for the behavior of living tissues in response to changes in pH? Why are the changes not as great as when nonliving material, such as tap water, was used in the investigation? Frequently in biological investigations, it is difficult to study living tissue. Investigators have found that they can learn as much, and sometimes more, by substituting a model for the real thing. We will use a model to get data to help us answer the questions asked at the beginning of this part of this investigation.

1. Test the buffer solution (a nonliving chemical solution—a model) using the same techniques as used in parts A and B. The only difference will be to substitute the buffer solution for the tap water and the tissue homogenate. Record all your data.
2. Graph the reaction of the buffer solution on the same graph used for tap water and the tissue homogenate. Different colored solid and dash lines should be used for clarity.
3. How does this nonliving system respond to the HCl and NaOH?

Discussion

1. Is the response of the nonliving system to change in pH more like that of water or of the biological material?
2. How does the reaction of the buffer solution to change in pH serve as a model for the response of biological materials to pH changes?
3. Would buffers aid or hinder the maintenance of homeostasis within a living cell in a changing environment?

4.3 Energy Is Used to Do Work and to Make and Maintain Order

Chemical reactions usually involve energy. In general, synthesis reactions require an input of energy. Decomposition reactions usually release energy. What is energy, and how is it used in living systems?

Matter is easy to understand because we can see it, touch it, and weigh it. **Energy** is more difficult to understand. We define energy as the ability to do work or cause change. It is work to move an arm, play tennis, heat a house, or build a skyscraper. We also can call growing a leaf or a wing

Figure 4.7 Is this person working?

BSCS by Bob Wilson

"work" because energy is used in these processes. In a cell, energy is used to move substances and to build organic molecules. This, too, is work. Energy also is required to make and maintain order.

Living things are extremely complex. Their atoms and molecules are arranged into highly organized systems. High levels of organization, however, are very unstable. If left to themselves, all systems tend to become simple and random, or disorganized. Buildings crumble, weeds grow in the garden, and dead organisms decay. Organization can be maintained only by continual input of energy.

Think about your room. When it is clean and neat, it is a very organized system. How long does it stay that way? The tendency is for your room to become disorganized—for your books and clothes to become spread out in a random fashion. To get your room organized again requires energy and work.

Like your clean room, a living organism is an organized system. A living frog, for instance, is highly organized. The frog remains that way because it eats flies and other insects that contain energy. The energy from the frog's food keeps the frog alive. The energy also allows the frog to grow and to reproduce. If the frog does not get enough food, it dies. Then the frog's body becomes disorganized as soil decomposers break down its body, converting cells into molecules. The decomposers live by using the matter and energy remaining in the frog's body cells.

All life processes work toward an organized state and against randomness. That requires energy, just as it takes energy for you to keep your room clean and neat. Where does the energy come from?

Self-Review

1. How is matter different from energy?
2. How are protons, neutrons, and electrons related within an atom?
3. How are chemical bonds formed?
4. In terms of pH values, what is the difference between neutral, acidic, and alkaline solutions?
5. What is a catalyst?
6. Why do all organisms need energy?

Figure 4.8 The tendency toward increasing disorder of a system and its surroundings.

Energy for Life

Guidepost: What is the source of energy for living organisms and how is it used?

4.4 Photosynthesis Is the Source of Your Energy

Biological activity, like all other activity, requires energy. Consumer organisms get their energy from the food they eat, but what about producers? Their energy comes from the sun. You remember from chapter 1 that energy can be found in different forms, such as light, heat, electricity, and mechanical, chemical, and nuclear energy. Energy also can be changed from one of those forms to another. In the process of photosynthesis, green plants use light energy from the sun to form complex organic molecules that store energy. The energy stored in those molecules—chemical energy—is used by the plants and by organisms that eat the plants. Because no animal can make its own food, all animals depend on plants for their source of energy as well as matter. Directly or indirectly, therefore, the source of energy for biological activity in almost all organisms on the earth is photosynthesis.

In photosynthesis, plant cells convert light energy from the sun to the chemical energy stored in sugar molecules. The first step in this process is the absorption of light energy by a green plant. The energy is absorbed primarily by **chlorophyll** (KLOR uh fil), a green pigment that gives plants their color. A plant also takes in carbon dioxide molecules from the air and water molecules from the soil. These are the raw materials used to make sugars. The plant uses the light energy it has absorbed to break down the water molecules into hydrogen and oxygen. The hydrogen is combined with carbon dioxide to form sugar molecules. The oxygen is released into the air as oxygen gas. Some of the light energy absorbed by the plant is thus stored in the sugar molecules as chemical energy. These events are highlighted in figure 4.9.

In the formation of sugars, several small molecules are linked together by chemical bonds. The energy used to form the sugars is stored in the structure of the molecules. Light energy is thus converted to chemical energy. When sugars are broken down in a cell, the energy stored in the structure of the molecules is released. That energy then is used by the cell to do cellular work.

Life requires suitable temperatures, a source of water, and a source of energy. The sun is our energy source. However, no organism can use light energy directly from the sun as a source of food energy. First it must be converted to chemical energy by a plant. Only green plants and other photosynthetic organisms can use light energy to make their own food out of materials from the nonliving world. Thus, all organisms depend on green plants as their source of energy and matter.

4.5 Energy Is Released as Food Is Broken Down

After sugars are made during photosynthesis, how is the energy in the structure of the molecules released? The major energy-releasing process is cellular respiration, a series of chemical reactions that occurs in all living cells. In these reactions, sugars made during photosynthesis are broken down, and energy is released.

Figure 4.9 The energy in sunlight is converted to chemical energy during photosynthesis.

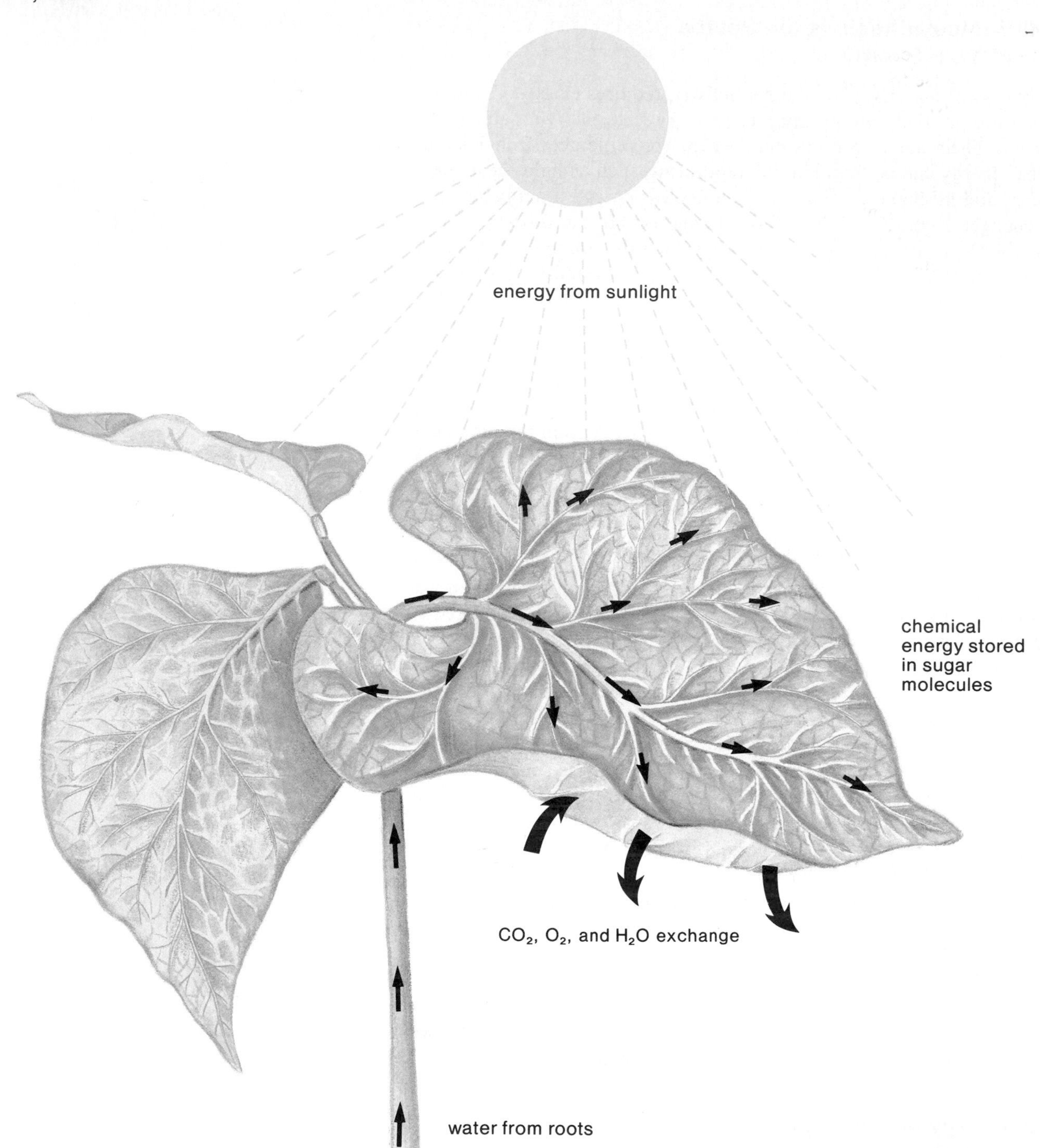

Energy to carry on a cell's work comes from the chemical energy in food. The way in which energy is released from food is remarkably similar among different organisms. Foods are carbon compounds that also contain hydrogen, oxygen, and often other elements. Chemically, foods are similar to fuels such as wood, coal, and oil. These substances serve as fuels because they contain chemical energy. During the chemical reactions of burning, fuels are reduced to simpler compounds. The chemical energy from the fuel is released in the form of heat and light energy.

Chemical energy in food is likewise released by chemical reactions. In a cell, however, the chemical reactions are quite different from those in a fire. During burning, a large amount of energy is released from fuels in a short time. The sudden release of energy produces high temperatures—high enough to provide heat for cooking. Cells would be destroyed by such high temperatures. Energy-releasing chemical reactions occur in cells at low temperatures. The same amount of energy is released as in burning, but it is released gradually, in many small steps. The gradual release of energy is made possible by enzymes.

Suppose you just ate a hamburger for lunch. How is the energy released from it? First, your food must be broken down by enzymes into molecules that are small enough to pass into your cells. This is what your digestive system does, as you will learn in chapter 15. Once inside the cells, these smaller molecules are broken down further by other enzymes. The energy stored in the molecules of your food is released by your cells through respiration.

Figure 4.10 A comparison of energy released during burning and during cellular respiration. How are they the same? How are they different?

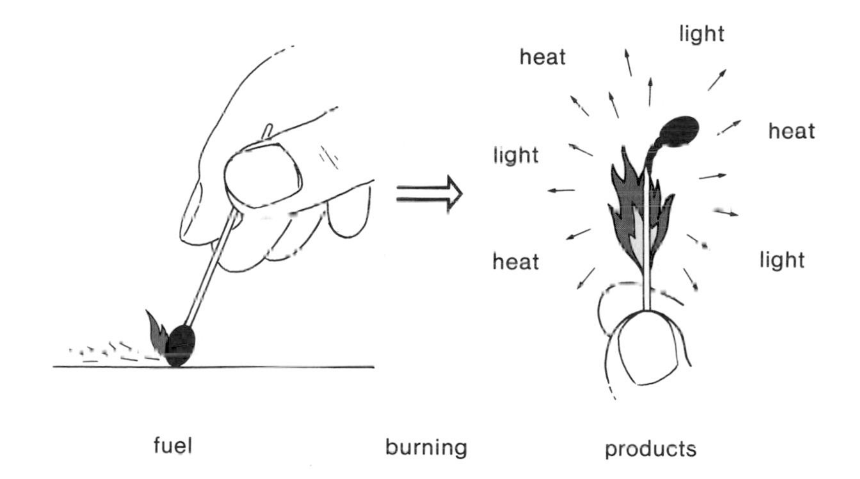

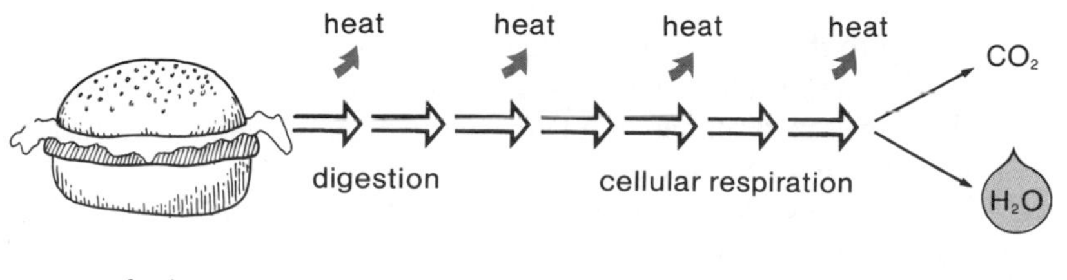

Figure 4.11 The structure of ATP.

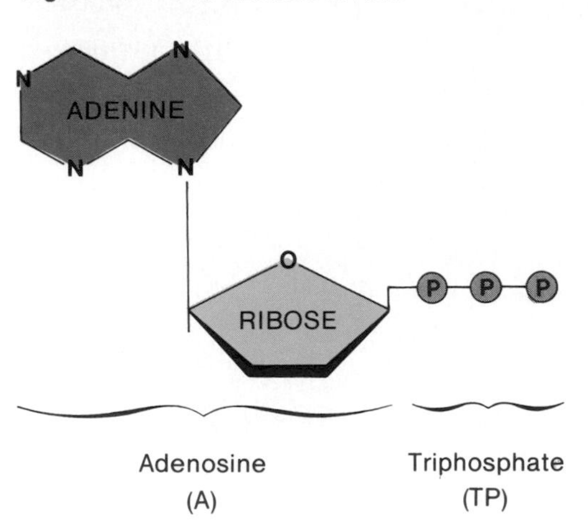

During respiration, the chemical energy in food molecules is released in a series of reactions controlled by enzymes. This energy can be used by the cell to move substances and to carry out other cell work. Carbon dioxide and water molecules are the by-products formed as the food molecules are broken down. Notice that these are the same molecules that the plant used to make sugars in photosynthesis.

4.6 Energy Is Used in Small Packets

A firecracker quickly releases a great deal of energy with light, heat, and a loud bang. The release of energy by a cell does not occur in such an explosion, however. If it did, your cells would burst. Energy release in a cell is a gradual, stepwise process.

If you had a hundred-dollar bill, you might find it difficult to buy small things such as a hamburger, a pack of notebook paper, or a comb. It would be much easier if you had 100 one-dollar bills. So, too, with the energy in a cell. The big bursts of energy from food molecules are put into "small change." This "small change" is the chemical energy stored in compounds such as **adenosine triphosphate** (uh DEN oh seen try FOS fayt), or **ATP.**

ATP is the most important of several energy-transfer compounds found in all organisms. These compounds are involved in all the energy processes of living cells. The energy released during respiration is temporarily transferred to ATP. Each ATP molecule is made up of a main section to which are attached three identical groups of atoms called phosphates (figure 4.11). As food molecules are broken down to simpler compounds, much energy is released. This energy is used to make many ATP molecules. Energy is stored in ATP until its release from ATP by reactions that remove the third phosphate group. This energy then is used to help the cell do its work. This work might be to move a muscle, to send a nerve impulse, to grow, or to form new compounds. ATP is thus a carrier of chemical energy in the cell.

Each ATP molecule releases a bit of energy whenever a phosphate group is broken off. The remaining molecule, which has only two phosphate groups, is called **adenosine diphosphate** (uh DEN oh seen dy FOS fayt), or **ADP.** You cannot keep spending money from your pocket without eventually putting more money in. Likewise, a cell cannot continue to "spend" its ATP without rebuilding that ATP. There is a continual ADP-ATP cycle (figure 4.12). To make ATP molecules, an ADP molecule and a phosphate group are needed, plus chemical energy to combine the two. The energy comes from the breakdown of food molecules. That is one reason you need to eat food every day.

Figure 4.12 The ADP-ATP cycle. ATP molecules are continually rebuilt from ADP molecules, phosphates and chemical energy.

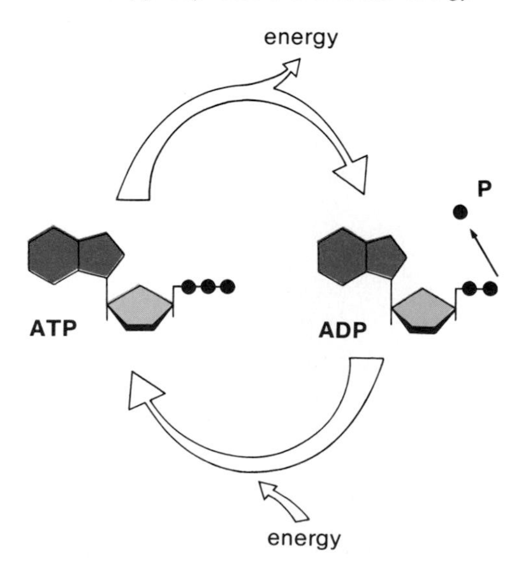

Self-Review

1. What are the two products of photosynthesis?
2. In what way is photosynthesis important for all living organisms?
3. How are the reactions of photosynthesis and cellular respiration similar? How are they different?
4. Is there more energy in one molecule of ATP or one molecule of sugar? How do you know?

Life Is Based on Carbon

Guidepost: What is the source of matter for living things, and what happens to the matter?

4.7 Carbon Is Found in All Living Things

In chapter 1 we said that energy goes one way through a community, but that matter cycles. In other words, the chemical substances that make up the bodies of producers and consumers are exchanged between the living and nonliving parts of the ecosystem. Although organisms are made up of many different chemical elements, we can follow the flow of matter through a community by focusing on the element most important to life—carbon.

Four basic kinds of carbon-containing molecules are found in all organisms. These biological molecules are carbohydrates, proteins, lipids, and nucleic acids. Biological molecules are essential to the life processes of all cells. They also can serve as food.

Carbohydrates (kar boh HY drayts) and **lipids** (LIP idz) are important energy-storing compounds and also form part of the cell structure. The sugars produced in photosynthesis and used in respiration are carbohydrates. Oils and fats are examples of lipids. **Proteins** (PROH teenz) serve as enzymes and form part of the cell structure. Muscles ("meat") are composed largely of protein. **Nucleic** (noo KLEE ik) **acids** are the hereditary, or genetic, material for all organisms. They also coordinate the activities of the cell. We will look at these biological molecules in more detail later in the chapter.

Carbon is the central atom in all living systems. All biological molecules are built of chains or rings of carbon and other atoms such as hydrogen and oxygen (figure 4.13). Proteins and nucleic acids also include nitrogen in their chains and rings.

Because all living organisms contain the same kinds of biological molecules, you can get the molecules you need for life from another organism. In fact, that is the only way you can get the molecules you need for life. You must eat a plant or an animal and rearrange their molecules and atoms into your own.

Figure 4.13 Carbon atoms can bond together in several ways. The unconnected lines protruding from the carbon atoms show that any one of a number of elements can bond with the carbon in these positions.

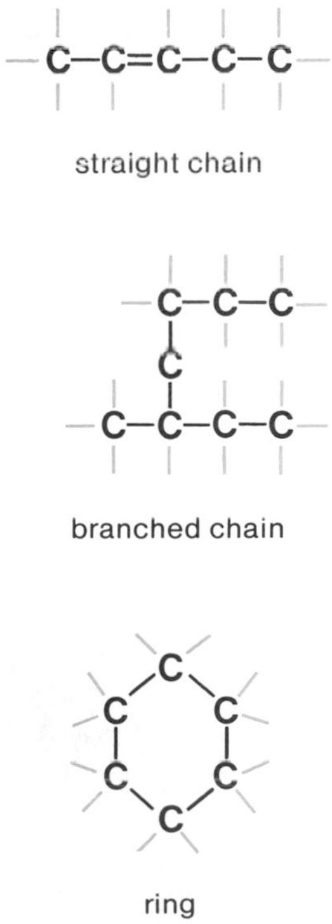

straight chain

branched chain

ring

4.8 Plants Make and Use Carbon-Containing Sugars

Plants take up carbon atoms in the form of carbon dioxide from the air. During photosynthesis, they use the energy of the sun to make sugars from the carbon dioxide (and the hydrogen from water), as shown in figure 4.9. In this way the energy from sunlight and the carbon from carbon dioxide are both stored in the sugars. The sugars can be used in four general ways by the plant.

First, the plant may break down the sugar molecules immediately to release the stored energy. This happens during respiration. The energy that is released from the sugars then may be used by plant cells to continue all the activities of life. Second, a plant may use sugar molecules for growth. The plant connects many sugar molecules together to make the building material necessary for more cells. **Cellulose** (SEL yoo lohs) is a major building material in plants. Third, the plant may store sugars for future use. An important storage compound found in many parts of a plant is starch. Starch is a large carbohydrate molecule made by putting together many individual sugar molecules. When energy is needed by the plant, starch is first broken down to individual sugar molecules. Then during respiration the sugars are broken down to release energy. Fourth, sugar molecules may be converted to the other biological molecules needed for life.

4.9 Carbon Cycles within an Ecosystem

As a plant grows, its body becomes larger. If the plant is eaten, the carbon in the plant is passed from producer to consumer. As the consumer uses the food, it first breaks down the plant body. The carbon-containing molecules are broken apart, releasing both carbon atoms and energy. Much of the energy is used for the activities of the consumer. Some of the carbon from the body of the plant is used to make up the body of the consumer. The rest of the carbon is exhaled as carbon dioxide back into the air. For example, you take in carbon in all the foods you eat. You return carbon dioxide back into the air every time you exhale. A plant also returns carbon dioxide to the air when it uses its own sugars as a source of energy. In both these ways, carbon is returned to the air from which it originally came. When another plant takes in this carbon dioxide during photosynthesis, the cycle of carbon through the community is complete.

Carbon dioxide also is returned to the air by decomposers. When producers or consumers die, decomposers begin their work. As its source of energy, a decomposer uses the energy locked in the bodies of dead organisms. It uses the carbon from the bodies to build its own body. As with consumers, carbon that is not used this way is returned to the air as carbon dioxide. Eventually, almost all the carbon that is taken in by plants during photosynthesis is returned to the air because of the activity

Figure 4.14 The carbon cycle. Use the text to explain the diagram. Where would you place humans in this cycle?

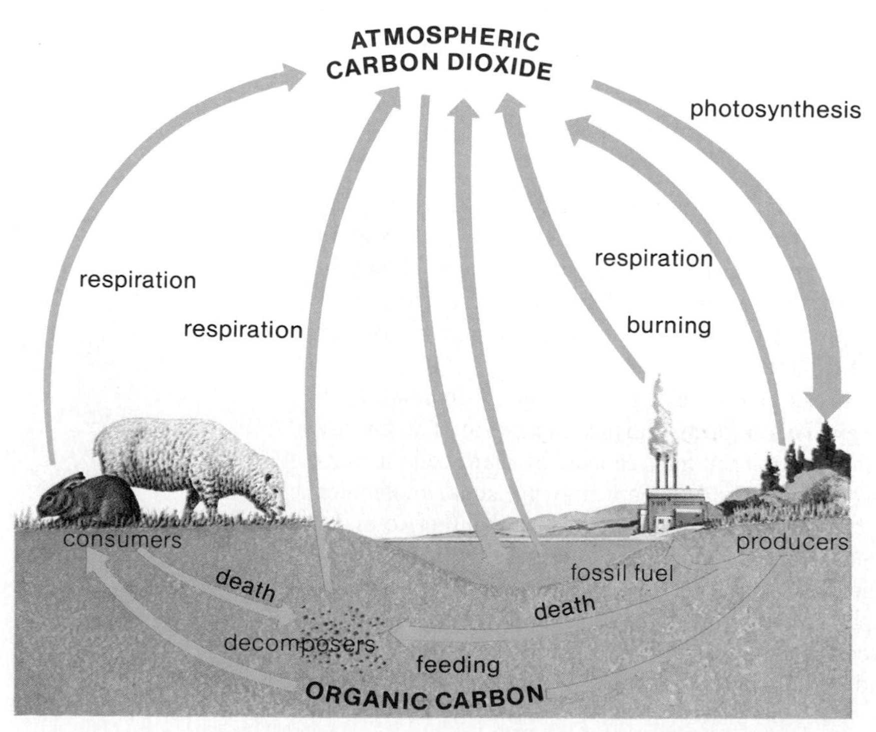

of the decomposers. Long ago, however, many energy-rich plant bodies were buried before decomposers could get to them. When that happened the bodies slowly changed over very long periods of time. They became a source of fuels—coal, oil, and natural gas. Today, when these fuels are dug up and burned by humans, energy is released. The carbon in the fuels is returned to the air as carbon dioxide. Thus, we see that even the energy we get from fuels is a result of photosynthesis.

The process in which carbon is passed from one organism to another, then to the abiotic community, and finally back to plants is called a **carbon cycle.** There are other cycles within ecosystems, including a water cycle, a sulfur cycle, and a nitrogen cycle, that you will learn about in later chapters.

Self-Review

1. Why is the element carbon so important to living things?
2. Of the four ways a plant uses the sugars it makes, which is the only way that does not add material to the plant?
3. How are producers, consumers, and decomposers involved in the carbon cycle?

Investigation 4.2 COMPOUNDS OF LIVING ORGANISMS

Introduction

The compounds your body needs for energy and building materials are carbohydrates, proteins, fats, vitamins, and minerals. These compounds are present in the plants and animals you use as food. In this investigation you will observe the tests for specific compounds. Then you will use those tests to determine the compounds in ordinary foods.

Part A—Test Demonstration

Materials

10% gelatin solution
10% glucose solution
10% starch solution
vitamin C solution
2% sodium chloride solution
butter or vegetable oil
1% silver nitrate
Biuret solution and powder (**CAUTION:** *caustic solution*)
Benedict's solution
Lugol's iodine
0.1% indophenol solution
brown wrapping paper

Procedure

1. Prepare a table similar to the one below in your data book.

Food Substance	Reagent Test	Results
Gelatin solution	Biuret reagent	
Glucose solution	Benedict's solution	
Starch solution	Lugol's iodine	
Vitamin C solution	Indophenol	
Sodium chloride solution	Silver nitrate	
Butter or vegetable oil	Brown paper	

2. Scientists use reagents to detect the presence of certain compounds. Observe the six reagent tests your teacher will perform. After each test, record the results in your table.

Part B—Compounds in Food

Materials (per team)

- 6 test tubes, 13 × 100 ml
- 250 ml beaker
- 10 ml graduated cylinder
- Bunsen burner or other heat source
- Reagents in dropper bottles:
  - Biuret solution
  - Benedict's solution
  - Lugol's iodine
  - indophenol solution
  - 1% silver nitrate
  - brown wrapping paper
  - egg white, liver, apple, orange, onion, potato, or other foods of your choice

Procedure

1. Prepare a table similar to the one below in your data book. Test the foods you are assigned by your teacher for the six different chemical substances. Indicate the presence (+) or absence (−) of each substance.

Substance		Protein	Glucose	Starch	VitaminC	Chloride	Fat
Egg	Prediction						
	Test results						
Potato	Prediction						
	Test results						
Etc.	Prediction						
	Test results						

2. For each food you will test predict what substances you think you will find by placing a (+) in the proper space in the table you just prepared.
3. Protein test: Place 5 ml of the assigned food in a test tube. Add 10 drops of Biuret reagent. Record a (+) or (−).
4. Glucose test: Add 3 ml of Benedict's solution to 5 ml of the assigned food. Place the test tube in a beaker of boiling water and heat for 5 minutes. Record a (+) or (−).
5. Starch test: Add 5 drops of Lugol's iodine to 5 ml of the assigned food. Record a (+) or (−).
6. Vitamin C test: Add 8 drops of indophenol to 5 ml of the assigned food. Record a (+) or (−).
7. Chloride test: Add 5 drops of silver nitrate to 5 ml of the assigned food. Record a (+) or (−).
8. Fat test: Rub the assigned food on a piece of brown wrapping paper. Hold the paper up to the light to detect a grease spot. Record a (+) or (−). When food contains a very small amount of fat, it may not be removed by the method just described. If no fat has been detected, place the assigned food in 10 ml of a fat solvent such as isopropyl alcohol. Allow the fat to dissolve in the solvent for about 5 minutes. Then pour the solvent on brown paper. The spot should dry in about 10 minutes. Then check the paper for a grease spot.

Discussion

1. Which of your predictions was totally correct?
2. Which food contains all the compounds for which you tested?
3. How might the original colors of the tested materials affect the results?
4. On the basis of your tests, which food could be used as a source of protein? glucose? starch? vitamin C? sodium chloride? fat?

The Molecules of Life

Guidepost: How are carbon-containing molecules important to living things?

4.10 Carbohydrates Are Used for Energy, Storage, and Building

The biological molecules contain many of the same kinds of atoms, but they are present in different proportions. Simple carbohydrates contain only the elements carbon, hydrogen, and oxygen. Sugars, starches, and cellulose are some examples of carbohydrates. Glucose and fructose are simple sugars, or **monosaccharides** (MON oh SAK uh rydz). Monosaccharides are sugars that contain only seven or fewer carbon atoms in each molecule (figure 4.15a). Glucose molecules can be changed into other biological molecules within the cell. Another carbohydrate is sucrose, or table sugar. Sucrose has twelve carbon atoms and is formed in a chemical reaction that combines a glucose and a fructose molecule (figure 4.15b). Sucrose is a **disaccharide** (DY SAK uh ryd), because it is built with two simple-sugar units.

Figure 4.15 Monosaccharides (a) can combine together to form disaccharides (b). Starch and cellulose (c) are polysaccharides formed by linking together many monosaccharide subunits.

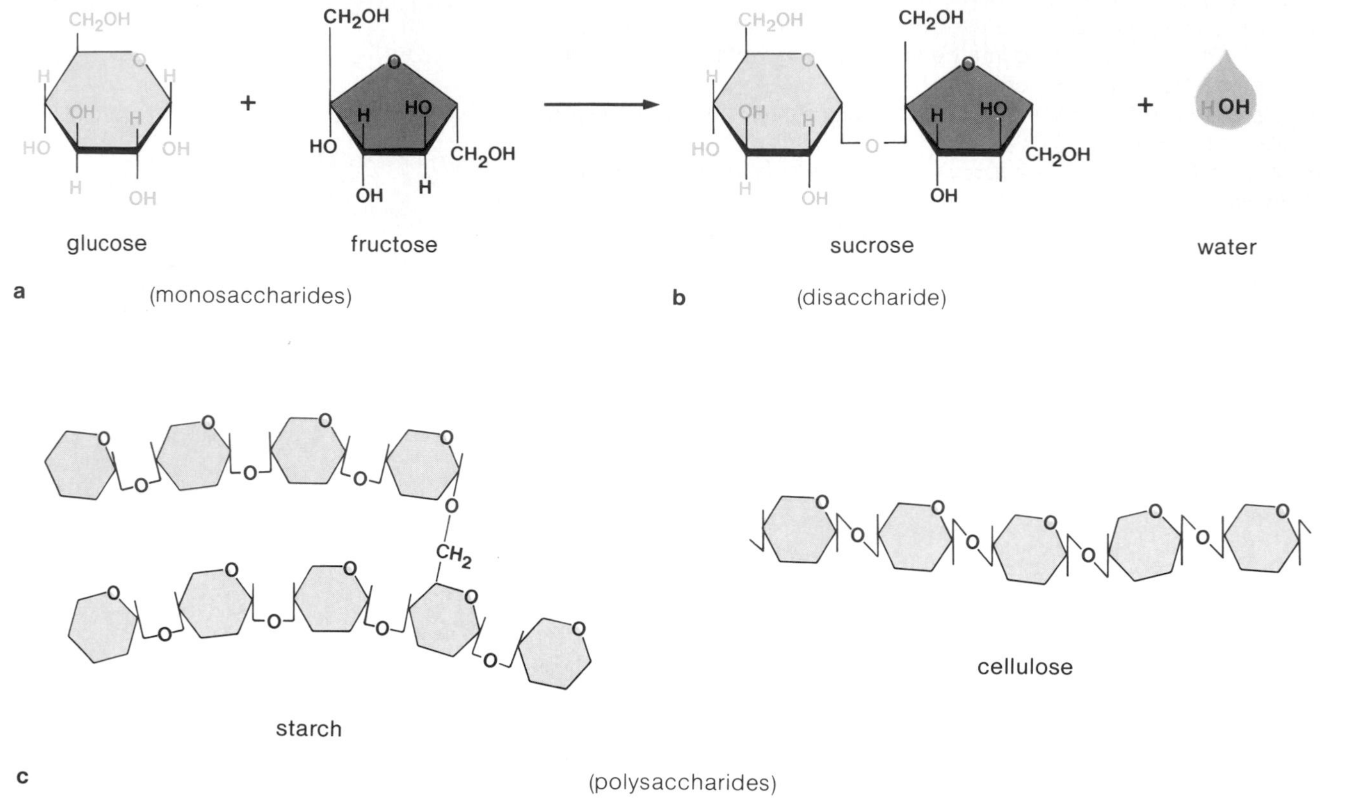

CH_2OH CH_2OH CH_2OH CH_2OH

glucose + fructose → sucrose + water (H OH)

a (monosaccharides) b (disaccharide)

starch cellulose

c (polysaccharides)

Figure 4.16 Cellulose fibers.

J. D. Litvay/VISUALS UNLIMITED

Larger carbohydrate molecules are formed in synthesis reactions in which many simple-sugar molecules of the same kind are linked together. Each of the sugar molecules is a **subunit,** or building block of the larger molecule. Compounds with many sugar subunits linked together are called **polysaccharides** (POL ee SAK uh rydz) (figure 4.15c). The polysaccharide starch is an important storage compound in plants. As a plant grows larger, the polysaccharide cellulose is used to make the rigid walls of new plant cells.

Figure 4.17 A fat molecule consists of fatty acids joined to a glycerol molecule. To form a fat, one molecule of glycerol combines with three molecules of fatty acids. The fatty acids in one fat may be alike or different. The joining of these fatty acids to glycerol releases three molecules of water.

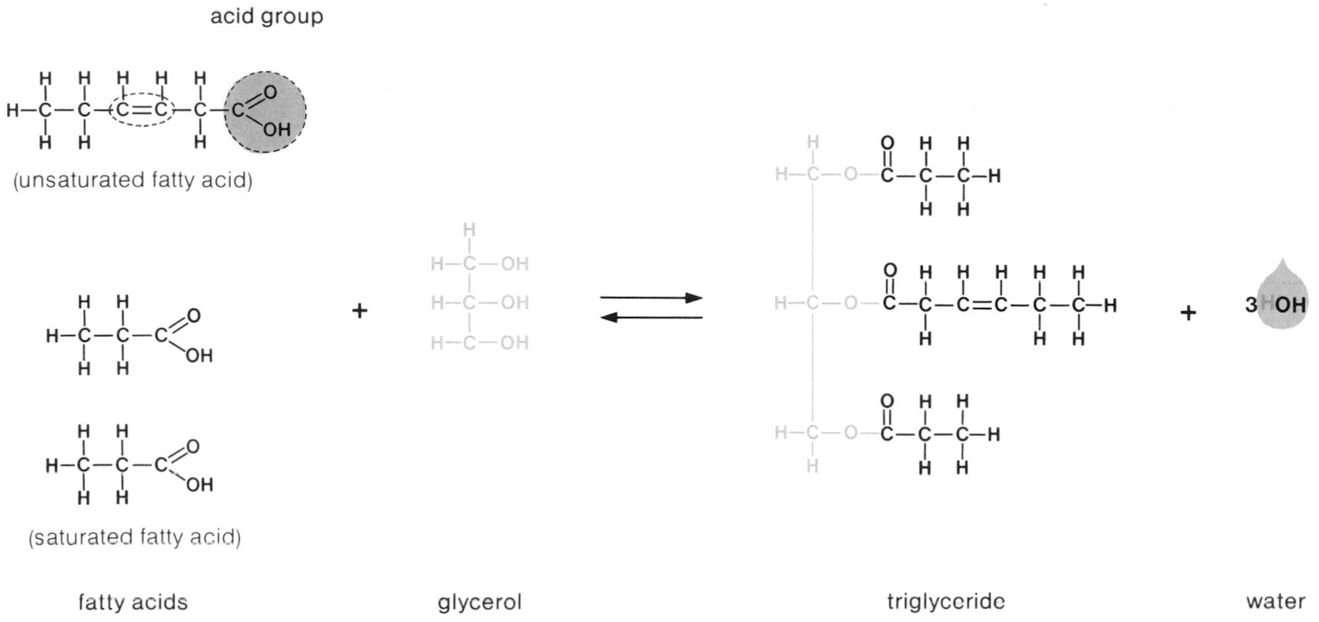

acid group

(unsaturated fatty acid)

(saturated fatty acid)

fatty acids + glycerol ⇌ triglyceride + 3 HOH (water)

4.11 Lipids Are Efficient Energy Storage Compounds

Like carbohydrates, lipids are composed only of carbon, hydrogen, and oxygen atoms. Lipids, however, contain fewer oxygen atoms than do carbohydrates. A fat is one kind of lipid. Fats are synthesized from two smaller molecules, glycerol (a carbohydrate) and fatty acids. Fatty acids are chains of carbon and hydrogen with an acid group on one end. Formation of a fat is shown in figure 4.17. Both glycerol and fatty acids can be formed in cells from glucose. All lipids are formed from fatty acids, but not necessarily in combination with glycerol.

Both carbohydrates and fats are found in organisms as storage compounds. A gram of fat contains more than twice as much chemical energy as a gram of carbohydrate. Hence, fats are better storage compounds. As animals prepare for winter when food is scarce, they eat large amounts of food. Much of this food energy is converted into fat, and the fat level in their bodies increases dramatically. Lipids also are important parts of the normal cell structure in all organisms. Plant waxes and **cholesterol** (koh LES ter ol) are examples of lipids. Excess cholesterol, though, has been linked to heart disease, as you will learn in chapter 15.

Figure 4.18 Diagram of cholesterol.

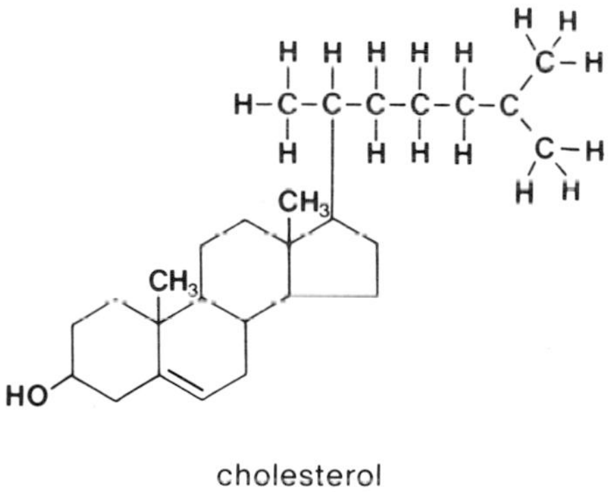

cholesterol

Figure 4.19 (a) The formation of a dipeptide from two amino acids. (b) Polypeptide chains are formed from long strings of amino acids. (c) The polypeptide chain in a myoglobin molecule is coiled and folded into a three dimensional structure.

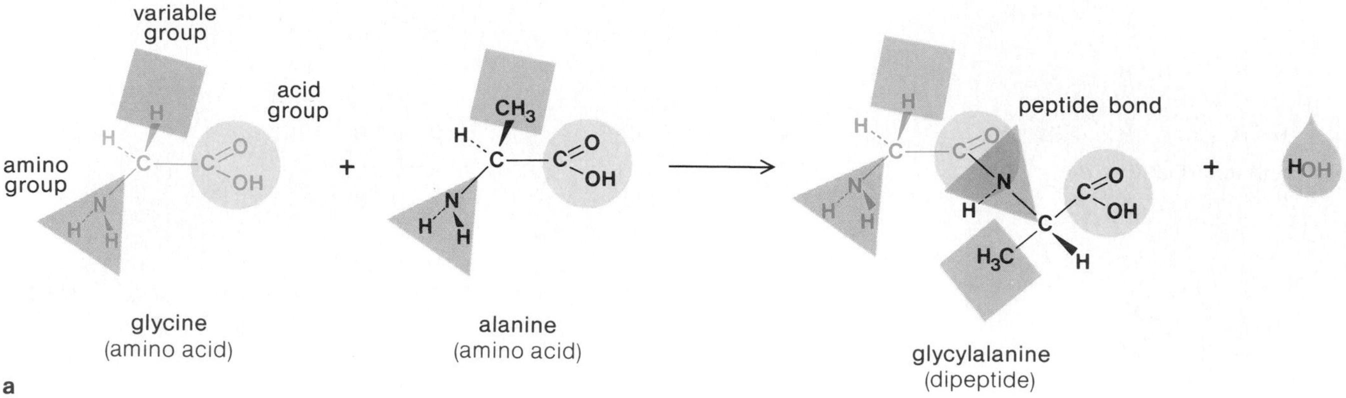

4.12 Muscles, Enzymes, and Many Cell Parts Are Made of Protein

Proteins form part of the structure of each cell. In addition, proteins form enzymes, and muscles are formed largely of proteins. Usually, protein molecules contain thousands of atoms—sometimes tens of thousands. The subunit of a protein molecule is an **amino** (uh MEEN oh) **acid** (figure 4.19a). Amino acids always contain at least four kinds of atoms: carbon, hydrogen, oxygen, and nitrogen. Two amino acids also contain sulfur. There are 20 different kinds of amino acids that can be found in a protein molecule. Green plants can synthesize all of these from inorganic materials. Animals, on the other hand, cannot make all their amino acids and must get some of them ready-made in the food they eat. Unfortunately, not every kind of food contains all the amino acids needed by animals. Therefore, animals such as humans need a balanced diet of protein sources. If we do not get all the amino acids we need, protein-deficiency diseases may occur.

To synthesize a protein, amino acids must be linked together. First two amino acids are linked together to form a **dipeptide** (DY PEP tyd), as shown in figure 4.19a. When another amino acid is added to a dipeptide, a **tripeptide** (TRY PEP tyd) molecule is formed. A long chain of amino acids is a **polypeptide** (POL ee PEP tyd). Some proteins are made of only one polypeptide, but most are made of two or more polypeptides bonded together. Polypeptide chains are coiled and folded into a complex three-dimensional structure to form proteins such as myoglobin (figure 4.19c). This structure is essential to the functioning of the protein, as we will see in the structure of a special kind of protein, the enzyme. Thousands of kinds of proteins can be made. The 20 different kinds of amino acids can be combined in many ways. It is as if you were to combine 20 different letters of the alphabet in as many ways as you could. The possibilities are almost beyond imagination. Not all combinations would make sense, but thousands do. Variety is important, because each kind of chemical reaction in a living organism is controlled by a different kind of enzyme. There are thousands of chemical reactions made possible by the production of many different enzymes.

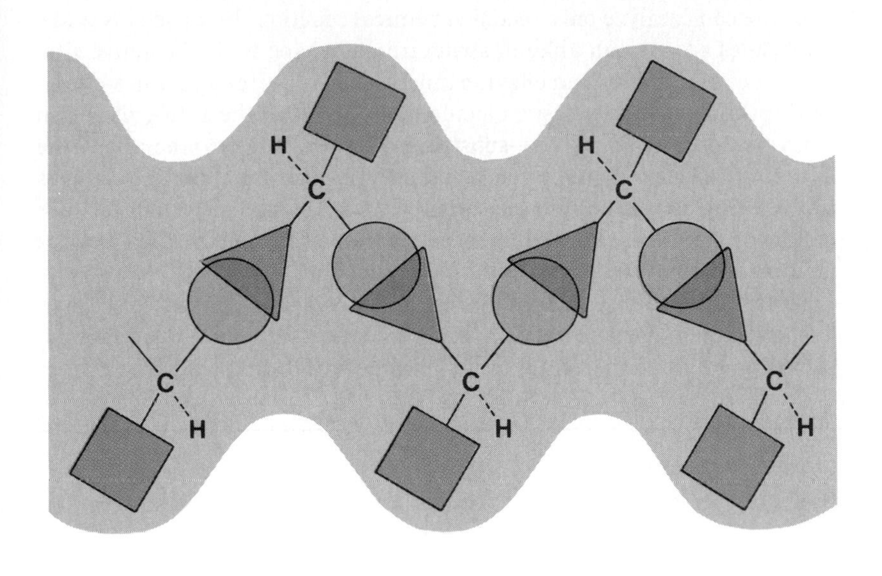

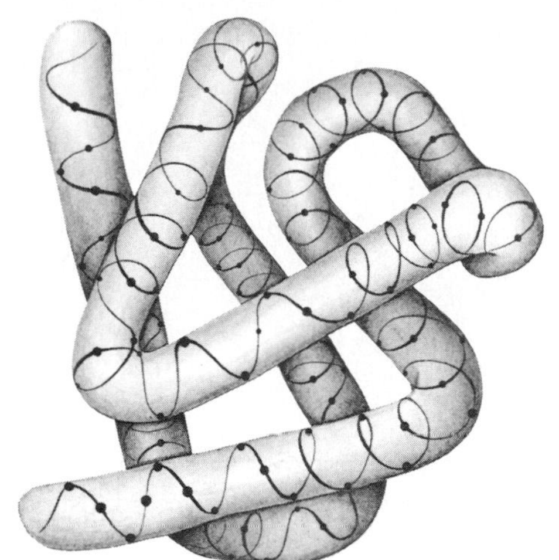

b. polypeptide chain

c myoglobin

4.13 Enzymes Catalyze Cell Reactions

Enzymes are large, complex proteins made by the cell. Like other catalysts, enzymes promote reactions but are not used up in the reaction. They allow chemical reactions to take place at the temperature of the cell. Enzymes are needed in only very small amounts, because one enzyme molecule can complete the same reaction thousands of times in a single minute.

The specific reaction catalyzed by an enzyme depends on the molecular structure and shape of a small area of the enzyme called the **active site.** The active site can attract and hold only specific molecules. An enzyme and the molecules on which it acts—the **substrates** (SUB strayts)—must fit together closely, as shown in figure 4.20. Sometimes

Figure 4.20 Substrates and enzymes combine at the active site to form an enzyme-substrate complex.

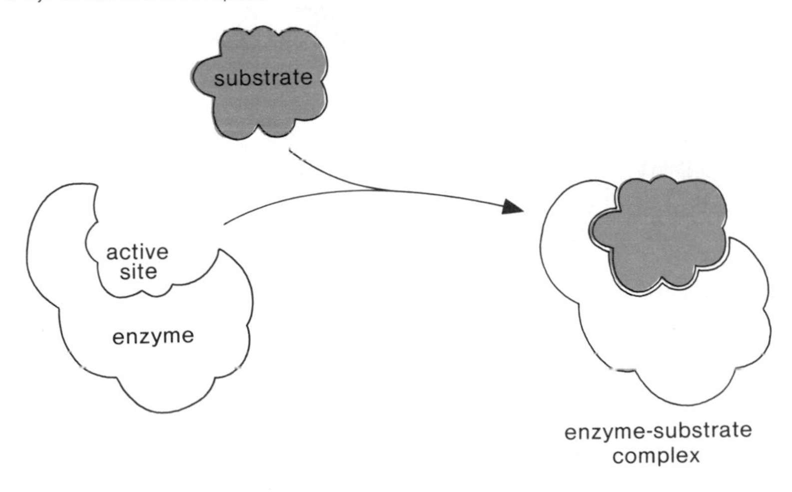

the enzyme changes shape slightly to bring about the necessary fit. Each enzyme can catalyze only specific chemical reactions because only a few molecules are enough alike in structure and shape to fit the active site.

To act as a catalyst, an enzyme must temporarily take part in a chemical reaction. The reacting molecules combine with the active site of an enzyme, forming an **enzyme-substrate complex.** The enzyme aligns the reacting molecules precisely and makes it possible for chemical changes to be completed rapidly at low temperatures. Once the reactions are complete, the newly formed molecules break away, leaving the enzymes the same as they were before the reaction.

Enzymes catalyze both synthesis and decomposition reactions. Usually a different enzyme catalyzes each reaction. In a synthesis reaction, two or more small molecules first combine with the enzyme. The proper

Figure 4.21 In synthesis, two or more substrate molecules join at the active site, forming one larger molecule. In decomposition, the substrate combines with the enzyme and is split into two or more smaller molecules.

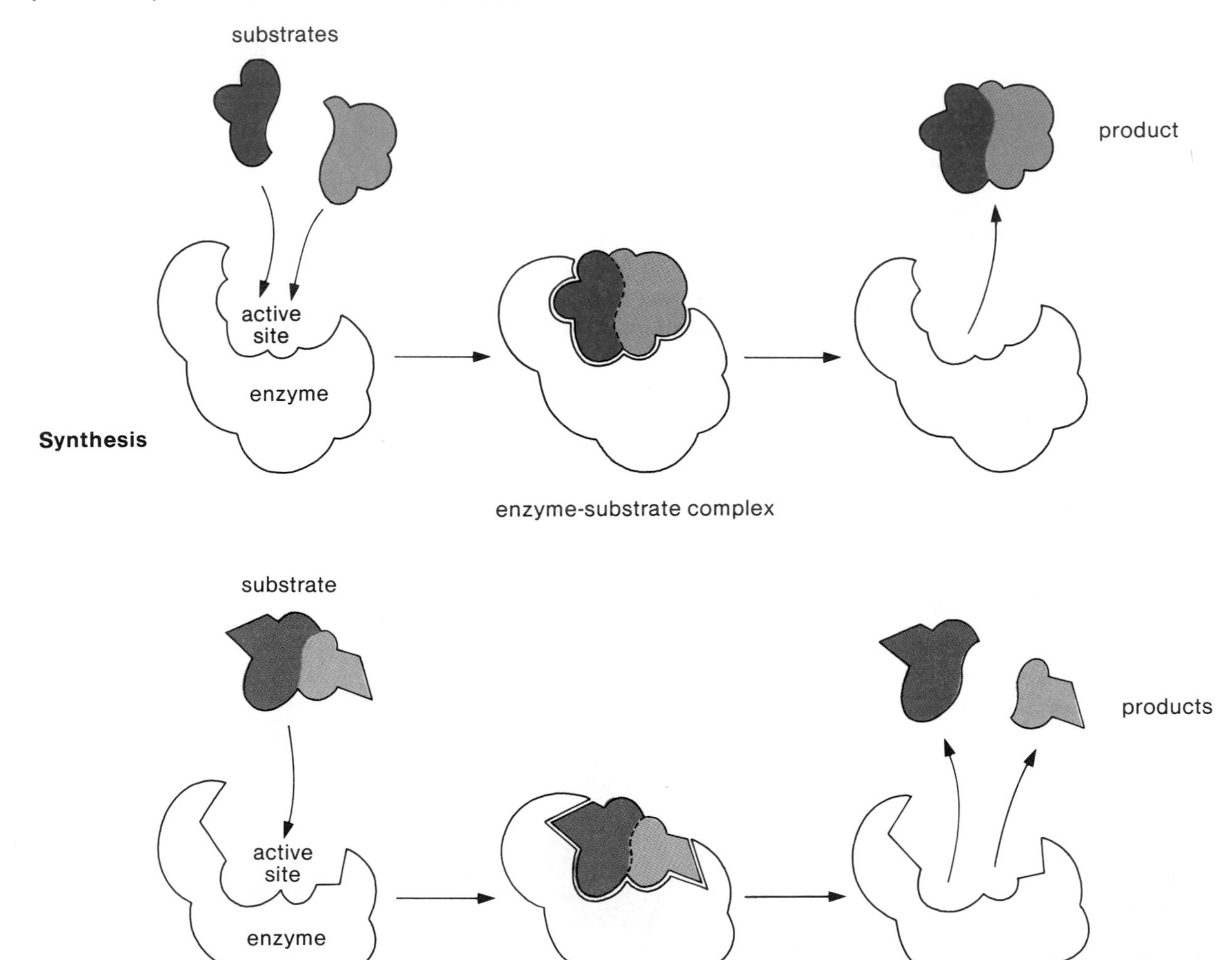

alignment provided by the enzyme enables these small molecules to join into one large molecule. In a decomposition reaction, the substrate combines with the enzyme and then is split into two or more smaller molecules. Both of these reactions are shown in figure 4.21.

Two aspects of enzyme activity are very important to cells. Enzyme reactions are faster at higher temperatures but only within a narrow temperature range. Above certain temperatures, the enzymes begin to lose their shape. Because fit is so important for proper enzyme action, enzymes that lose their shape no longer function. Enzyme activity also varies with the acidity of the solution. Thus, the temperature and the pH must be at the right level for enzymes to act effectively. In investigation 4.3 you will observe some of the characteristics of enzyme-controlled reactions.

Investigation 4.3 A STUDY OF BIOCHEMICAL REACTIONS

Introduction

Hydrogen peroxide (H_2O_2) is a highly active chemical, often used for bleaching. It also is used for cleaning minor wounds. H_2O_2 is formed as a by-product of chemical reactions in cells. Because it is toxic to cells, it would soon kill them if not immediately removed or broken down. In the presence of an enzyme, the cells break down hydrogen peroxide into two harmless substances.

In this investigation you will observe the activity of two substances, both of which break down hydrogen peroxide. One of these is manganese dioxide, an inorganic catalyst. The other is an enzyme, catalase, an organic compound.

Materials (per team)

pieces of fresh liver, each about 6 mm in diameter
pieces of fresh potato
100 ml of 3% hydrogen peroxide solution (**WARNING:** *irritant; avoid skin and eye contact*)
manganese dioxide powder
distilled water
fine sand
2 test tubes, 18 × 150 mm
small test tube rack
forceps
mortar and pestle
hot plate
250 ml beaker
metric ruler
glass-marking pencil

Procedure

1. Prepare a table similar to the one below in your data book.

Test No.	Substance Tested	Reaction		
		Fast	Slow	None
1	Sand and water			
2	Sand and H_2O_2			
3	MnO_2 and water			
4	MnO_2 and H_2O_2			
5	Boiled MnO_2 and H_2O_2			
6	Whole liver and H_2O_2			
7	Ground liver and H_2O_2			
8	Boiled liver and H_2O_2			
9	Whole potato and H_2O_2			
10	Ground potato and H_2O_2			
11	Boiled potato and H_2O_2			

2. Label the test tubes A and B. With a marking pencil draw a line 2 cm from the bottom of each test tube.
3. Pour distilled water up to the mark in tube A and hydrogen peroxide up to the mark in tube B.
4. Add a pinch of fine sand to both tubes. Indicate the reaction in your table for tests 1 and 2.
5. Add a pinch of manganese dioxide (MnO_2) powder to tubes A and B. Indicate the reaction in your table for tests 3 and 4.
6. Boil the contents of tube A (MnO_2 and water) and then add 5 ml of H_2O_2 to this tube. Indicate the reaction in your table for test 5.
7. Clean out both test tubes. Pour fresh hydrogen peroxide up to the 2 cm mark in both tubes.
8. Add a pinch of sand to both tubes. Using forceps, drop a small piece of liver into tube A. Indicate the reaction in your table for test 6.
9. Take another piece of liver of about the same size. Put it in a mortar with a pinch of sand and 2 ml of distilled water. Grind the liver in the mortar with the pestle.
10. Pour a sample of the ground liver (with sand) into tube B. Indicate the reaction in your table for test 7. Go back and look at the data you recorded earlier. Do you want to change any of your earlier reactions? Do so if this is the case.
11. Clean out both test tubes. Pour fresh hydrogen peroxide into tube A up to the 2 cm mark. Add a pinch of sand.
12. Put another piece of liver into boiling water for about 5 minutes. Drop the boiled liver into tube A. Indicate the reaction in your table for test 8.
13. If time permits, repeat steps 7 through 11, using raw potato instead of liver.

Discussion

1. What was the purpose of adding MnO_2 to water in test 3?
2. Do you have any evidence that manganese dioxide is breaking down the hydrogen peroxide instead of reacting with it?
3. What additional steps in the procedure would be needed to confirm this?
4. Consider the formula of hydrogen peroxide and the kind of reaction you observed in tests 6 and 7. What are the most likely products of the breakdown of hydrogen peroxide?
5. How might you confirm your answer?
6. What caused the reaction when you put the liver into the test tubes for tests 6 and 7?
7. How do you explain the difference in activity resulting from the whole piece of liver and from the ground liver?
8. Why is test 2 necessary for this explanation?
9. How do you explain the difference in activity resulting from fresh and boiled liver?
10. Suppose that someone compared test 4 and tests 6 and 7 and concluded that liver contains manganese dioxide. What evidence do you have either for or against this conclusion? (Conside the reaction in test 5.)
11. If you did the tests with potato, what additional information do the results from tests 9 and 10 provide?
12. Why was test 2 necessary?

4.14 Nucleic Acids Control the Activities of the Cell

There are two kinds of nucleic acids: **ribonucleic** (ry boh noo KLEE ik) **acid,** or **RNA,** and **deoxyribonucleic** (dee OK sih ry boh noo KLEE ik) **acid,** or **DNA.** Both of these nucleic acids are present in all cells and are vital to cell function. An organism may be made up of billions of cells, but each living cell has its own DNA and RNA. Information stored in DNA controls all cell activities and also determines the genetic characteristics of the cell and the organism. RNA is required for the synthesis of proteins, including enzymes.

Information stored in DNA determines the sequence of amino acids in proteins and controls when each protein is made. By thus controlling the synthesis of enzymes necessary for chemical reactions in the cell, DNA controls the activities of the cell. Before a cell divides into two cells, it makes a copy of its DNA. During cell division, each new cell receives one copy. Thus, each new cell has all the DNA of the original cell. This ensures that all body cells in an organism have the same DNA. During sexual reproduction, DNA from each of two parents is combined within one cell. Thus the offspring receives genetic information from both parents.

Both DNA and RNA are made up of individual subunits called **nucleotides** (NOO klee oh tydz). Each nucleotide, in turn, is made up of three small molecules linked together: a phosphate group, a five-carbon sugar, and a nitrogen base (figure 4.22). The base may be one of five

Figure 4.22 The parts of a nucleotide.

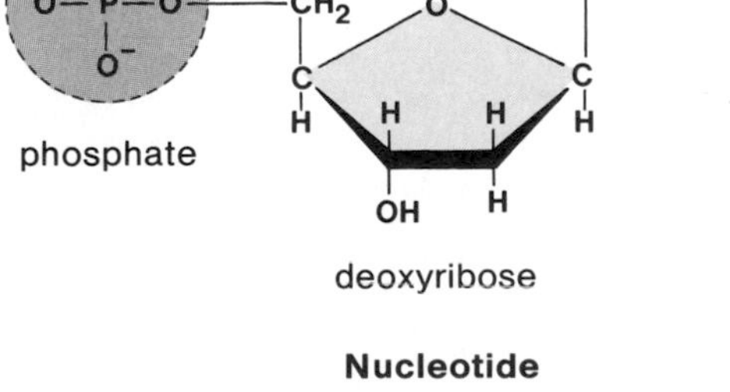

nitrogen base

phosphate

deoxyribose

Nucleotide

different kinds, each kind being made up of carbon, hydrogen, oxygen, and nitrogen atoms. RNA nucleotides contain a monosaccharide called **ribose** (RY bohs). DNA contains a slightly different sugar called **deoxyribose** (dee OK sih RY bohs), which has one less oxygen atom than ribose. DNA molecules are made of two strands with thousands of linked nucleotides. The two strands are attached in a very specific way and coiled to form a double helix. RNA molecules are usually smaller, and may be single-stranded.

These four biological molecules—carbohydrates, lipids, proteins, and nucleic acids—are found in all living organisms. As we will see in the next few chapters, they play very important roles within each cell.

Figure 4.23 A chain of nucleotides with sugars and phosphates forming the backbone and the bases off to the side.

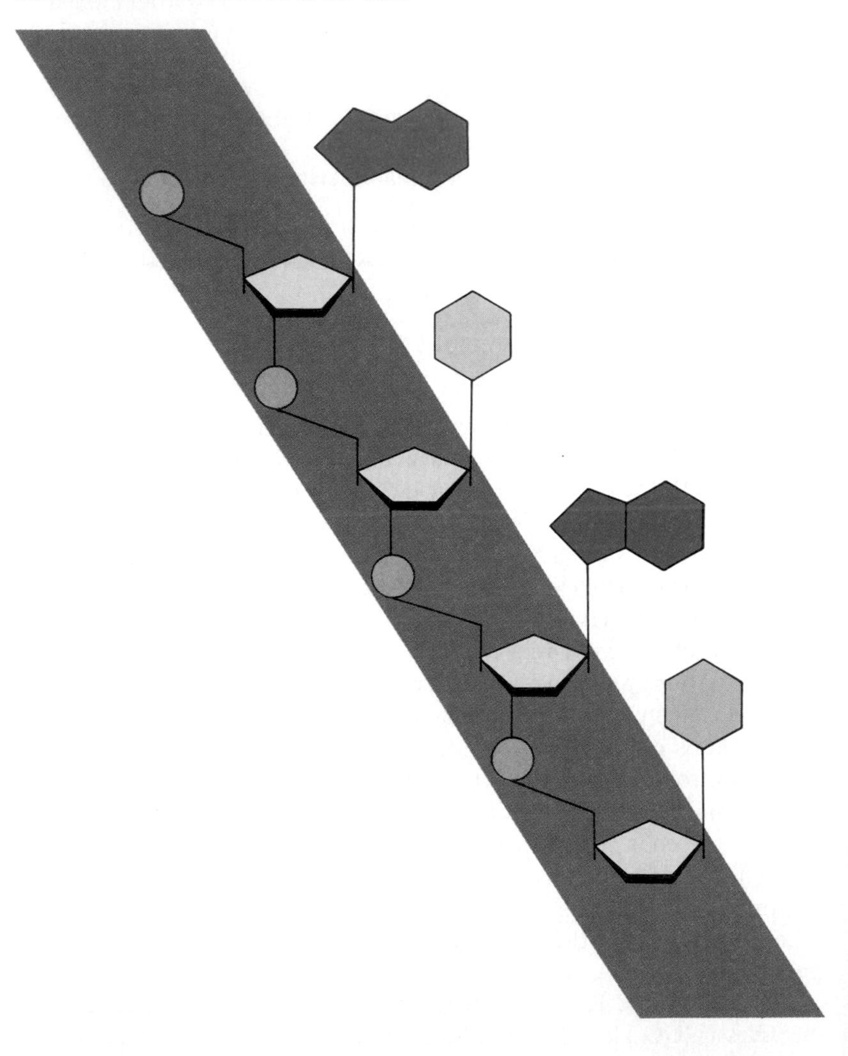

Figure 4.24 Diagram of a small part of a DNA molecule, showing the double helix.

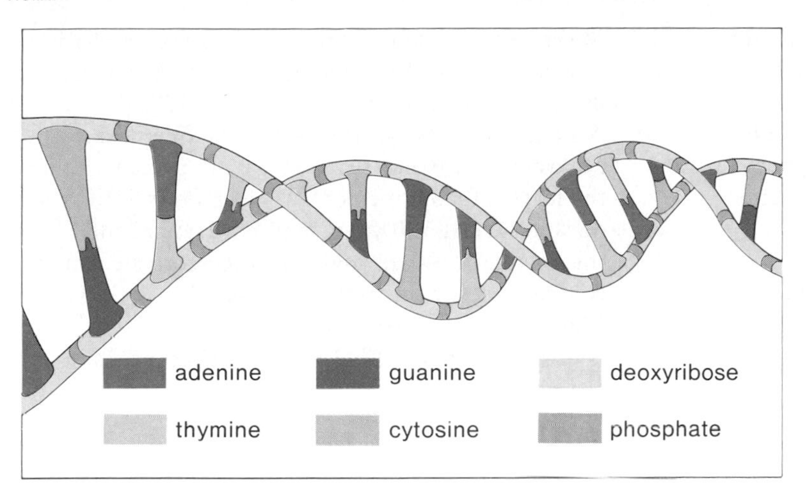

Self-Review

1. What are the subunits of carbohydrates? of proteins? of fats? of nucleic acids?
2. Name one important function of each of the four biological molecules named in question 1.
3. How do enzymes work to catalyze a chemical reaction?
4. Why is fat a better storage compound than starch?
5. How is it possible for so many different kinds of proteins to be made with only 20 different kinds of amino acids?

Summary

Energy is needed to do work and to make order. Without energy, highly organized systems such as living things could not exist. The need for energy is continuous, and therefore organisms must obtain and use energy throughout their lives. Organisms also must obtain matter to build up their bodies: without matter, no organism would grow. Plants make sugars from inorganic molecules in the process of photosynthesis. They convert this carbohydrate into other biological molecules, including proteins, lipids, and nucleic acids, all of which contain carbon. These biological molecules are used by consumers as food that provides their matter and energy. Biological molecules are built up and broken down in many different chemical reactions. All chemical reactions are catalyzed by enzymes, and many of them produce ATP as a temporary energy-transfer molecule.

Application Questions

1. How would the carbon cycle be useful to biologists in making a study of food chains in food webs?
2. The proteins in the cells of a wheat plant are different from the proteins in your cells. How can the differences be explained? What must happen when you use wheat as a nutrient for the formation of your proteins?
3. Many botanists believe that the concentration of carbon dioxide in the air was much greater during the Carboniferous period, when most of the large coal deposits were being formed, than it is at present. What might be the basis for their belief?
4. In what ways do you contribute to the carbon cycle?

Problems

1. Make two lists: (1) all the ways you use energy in a day; and (2) all the different kinds of energy you use (light, heat, mechanical, chemical).
2. A hundred years ago the carbon dioxide in the atmosphere was measured at 0.0283 percent. Today the level is 0.0330 percent. What human activities during the last 100 years may have contributed to this increase? What might be some possible future consequences if this trend continues?
3. Many fats and cooking oils are called "polyunsaturated." Find out what that means in chemical terms.

Suggested Readings

B. Alberts, D. Bray, J. Lewis, M. Raff, K. Roberts, and J. D. Watson, 1983, *Molecular Biology of the Cell* (New York: Garland Publishing). Explains the role of carbon compounds on a cellular level.

H. Curtis, 1983, *Biology* (New York: Worth Publishers). An entire section is devoted to the flow of energy in the web of life.

C. P. Hickman, L. S. Roberts, and F. M. Hickman, 1984, *Integrated Principles of Zoology* (St. Louis: Times Mirror/Mosby College). Contains discussions pertaining to all topics in this chapter.

C. Starr and R. Taggart, 1981, *Biology: The Unity and Diversity of Life* (Belmont, CA: Wadsworth Publishing). A more advanced discussion of carbohydrates, lipids, and proteins.

C. A. Villee, W. F. Walker, and R. D. Barnes, 1984, *General Zoology* (Philadelphia: Saunders College Publishing). Good summary of the organization of matter (atoms and molecules).

Tom J. Ulrich/VISUALS UNLIMITED

Section Two

Continuity in the Biosphere

Individual organisms exist in populations. Through birth and death individuals come and go, but populations of organisms exist for ages. Evidence from fossils indicates that the biosphere itself has endured for more than 3.5 billion years. Thus there is continuity in the biosphere. There is also change. The fossil record indicates that change has been slow and, in general, orderly—that homeostasis exists between organisms and their abiotic environment.

How do populations achieve continuity? How are individuals replaced? How are characteristics maintained generation after generation? And how do characteristics change over many generations, so that ecosystems of today are recognizably different from those of past ages? Those are some of the questions we will consider in Section Two.

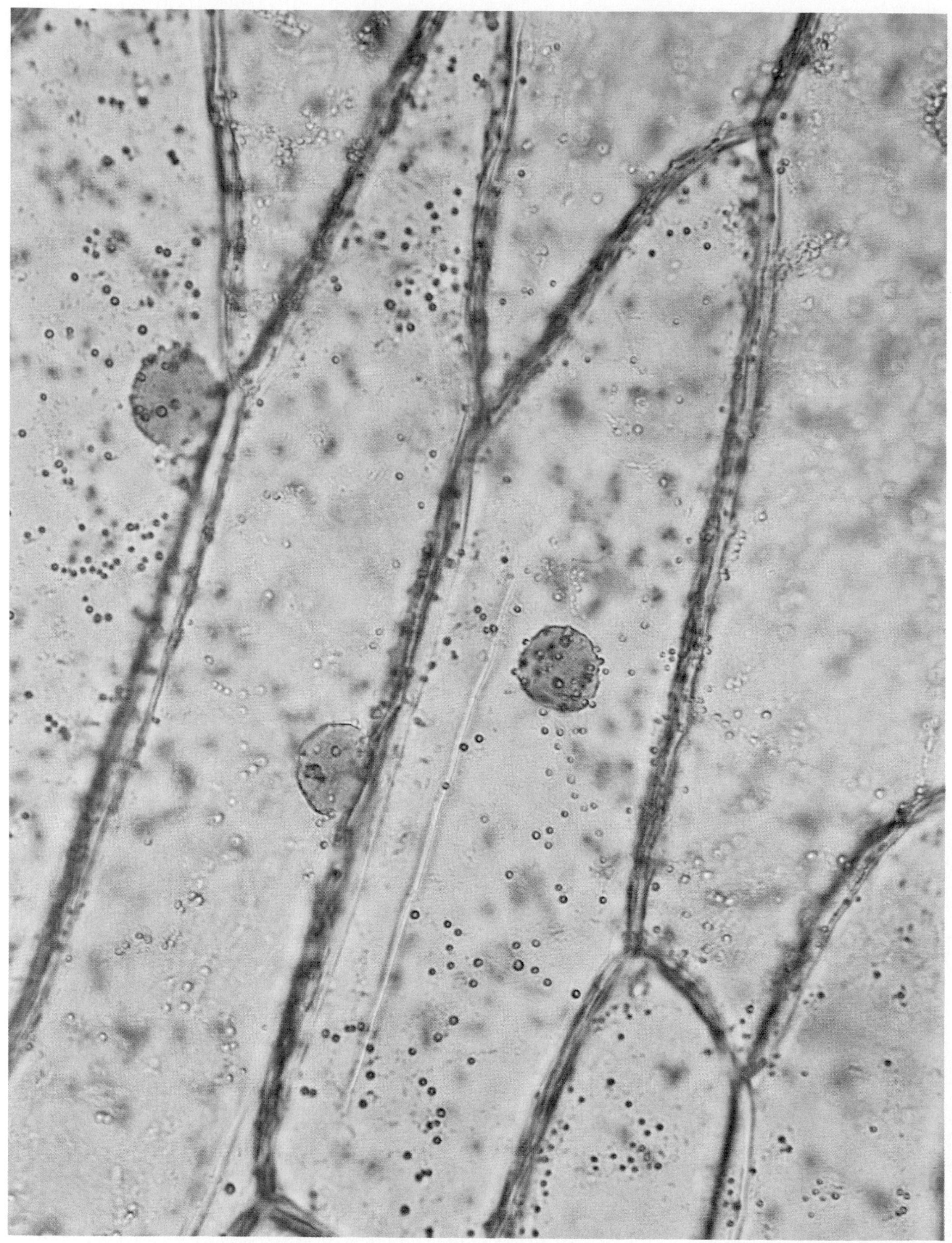

Ed Reschke

These onion cells are typical of many plant cells. What cell structures can you identify?

CHAPTER 5

Continuity in Cells

Introduction

We have been looking at large-scale living systems—populations, communities, ecosystems, and the entire biosphere. In order to learn more about these complex systems, we have also gone to the other end of the scale of life. In the last chapter we were introduced to some of the important biological molecules that make up organisms.

We already know that there are many different types of living beings, called species. Biologists have described more than 3 million different species. No one knows exactly how many there are, for new species are being discovered each year. Each species is distinctive in its own ways, and each species is made up of a number of individuals at any particular time.

Each individual is an organism. Organisms are organized to solve the problems of staying alive and of passing on their distinctive natures to their offspring. At least some of them must be successful in reproduction if a species is to persist.

One does not have to be a biologist to realize that an organism (such as yourself) is made up of many different kinds of parts, each doing a special job. Some parts function to take in food, others to permit movement, others to detect our environment, still others to permit us to reproduce.

Thus, there are many different parts, and many different activities among these parts of an organism. Biologists study all these different parts. They try to learn how they function, how they interact, and how they permit life to continue.

In this chapter we will learn about cells—the basic units of life. We will see how they are constructed, how they work, and how they reproduce themselves.

Guidepost: How did scientists come to understand the microscopic structure of organisms?

Cells

5.1 Cells Are Studied with Special Equipment

Humans and all other organisms are made of tiny units that are too small to be seen by the naked eye. Lenses, built into microscopes, have been used since the seventeenth century to study these otherwise invisible structures.

Lenses have been known for hundreds of years. By 1650 the art of grinding and polishing pieces of glass into lenses had greatly improved, making it possible to build good telescopes and microscopes. Even though these microscopes were simple (see figure 5.1), the best ones could magnify objects more than 200 times. (What magnification can be obtained through the lenses of microscopes used in your classroom?)

Antony van Leeuwenhoek (1632–1723), a Dutch civil servant, learned how to make excellent lenses as a hobby. He placed these into simple microscopes. He had no scientific training, but he was very curious. He looked at everything he could think of with his microscopes—pond water, circulating blood in frogs and rabbits, plant and animal tissues, hairs, and sperm cells. Van Leeuwenhoek found an amazing, invisible world

Figure 5.1 Antony van Leeuwenhoek using one of his microscopes.

Parke-Davis Division of Warner-Lambert Co. Morris Plains, NJ 07950

through his new "eyes." He not only studied the little "wretched beasties" (as he called them), but he made careful drawings as well. Over a period of 50 years, he described bacteria, some tiny creatures that lived between his own teeth, detailed structures in small insects, and even sperm cells from humans, dogs, frogs, and insects. Pictures of parts of living organisms have always been useful to biologists. Drawings are still made today, but photographs and motion pictures are often more accurate and provide more information.

During the late 1600s, an Englishman, Robert Hooke, also made microscopes (figure 5.2) and looked at tiny objects. He studied the cork layer of bark from an oak tree. He made thin layers of cork with a sharp knife, and observed neat rows of thickwalled compartments. They reminded him of the small cells where monks lived in medieval monasteries. Hooke therefore called the compartments cells. Figure 5.3a shows cork cells as Hooke drew them. Compare his drawing with the scanning electron micrograph in b.

Even though many scientists studied these cells and van Leeuwenhoek's "little animals," few understood them. What did they tell about living creatures? At one time cork was living, but now was dead. In living substance, however, some biologists observed that cells were filled with fluid. What was this fluid in living cells? Were the walls of cork cells the remains from once living substance?

5.2 The Cell Theory Unified Information about Cells

It was not long before scientists began to realize that cells are the fundamental units of living organisms. Plant cells were somewhat easier to study than animal cells, because of their thicker cell boundaries. By 1838, however, both animal and plant biologists agreed on an important principle. In that year two German biologists, Matthias Schleiden, a plant biologist or **botanist** (BOT un ist), and Theodor Schwann, an animal biologist or **zoologist** (zoh OL uh jist), proposed the cell theory.

Figure 5.2 One of Robert Hooke's microscopes. Try to determine the function of each component of this instrument.

Trustees of the British Museum (London)

Figure 5.3 (a) Cork cells as seen and drawn by Hooke, and (b) scanning electron micrograph of cork cells.

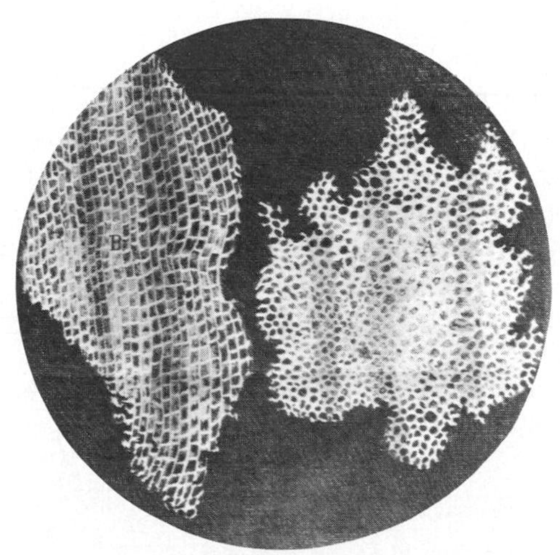

a Linda Hall Library

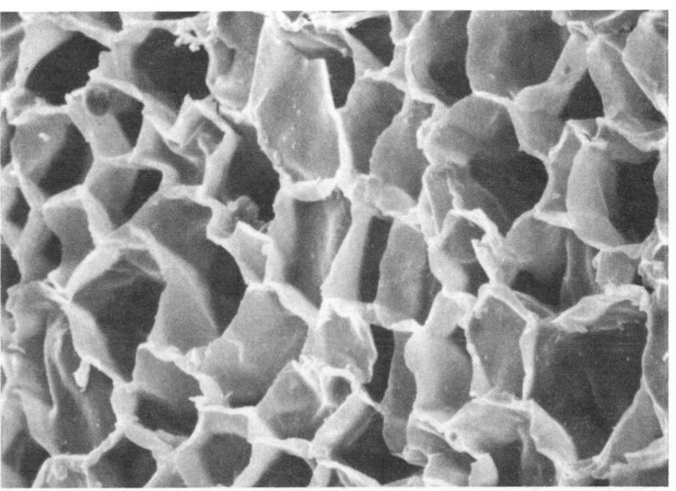

b Dr. Delbert E. Philpott, NASA, Ames Research Center, Moffett Field, CA 94035.

Figure 5.4 The microscope structure of small parts of animals as seen by Schwann. The group of six cells at the right is from a fish. The oval cell is from the nervous system of a frog. The long cell at the bottom is from the muscle of an unborn pig. The spindle-shaped cell at the left also is from an unborn pig.

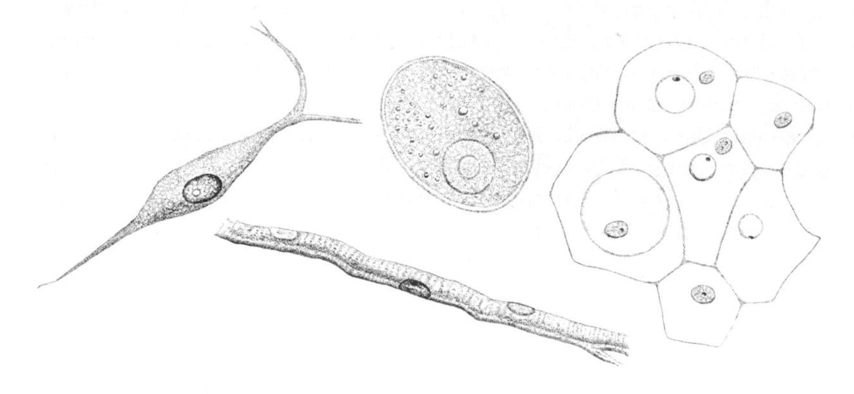

Figure 5.5 The diversity of cells: (a) human nerve cells, (b) red blood cells from a frog, (c) cells of an elodea leaf.

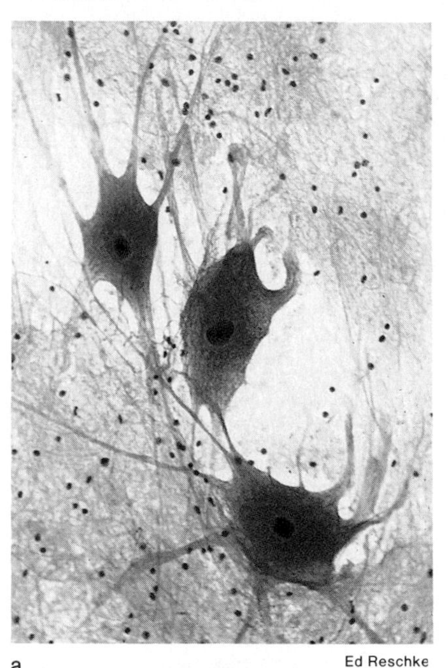

a Ed Reschke

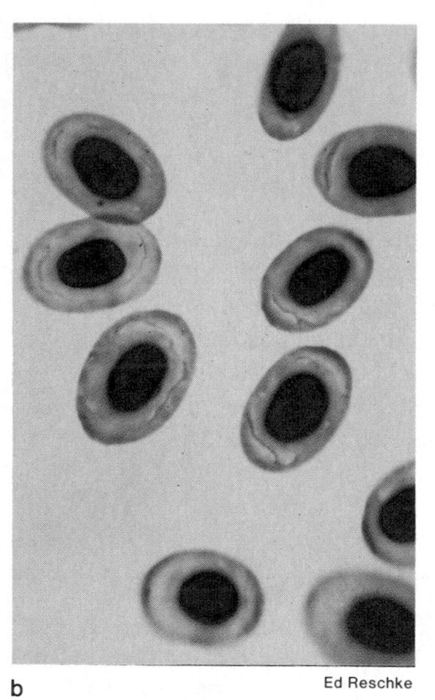

b Ed Reschke

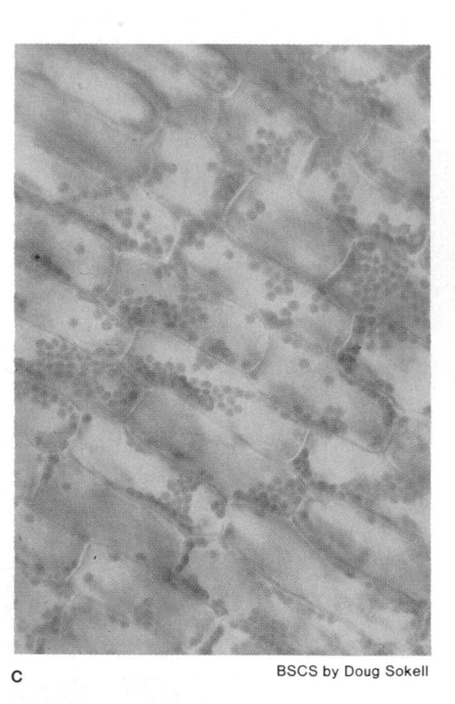

c BSCS by Doug Sokell

The cell theory stated that all organisms consisted of cells and cell products. It held that one could understand how living creatures are built and how they function, if the cells themselves could be understood. Biologists have been pursuing that goal for about 150 years. Even today we are still trying to understand the very complicated ways in which cells live and reproduce.

After the cell theory became a part of biology, studies of organisms advanced rapidly. No longer were plants and animals thought to live by different rules. Schwann wrote: "We have overthrown a great barrier of separation between the animal and vegetable kingdoms."

The fluid that filled cells, however, was colorless and difficult to study. Then it was discovered that certain dyes made from plants would stain the interiors of cells. With these dyes one could see that there were even smaller structures within cells. In fact, there were many different kinds of these little organs within cells. They were named **organelles** (or guh NELZ). In the 1880s, the work of French and German scientists showed how new cells arise from existing cells. If all cells arise from cells already living, then it must follow that there has been no break in the continuous line of descent of cells from other cells, ever since the beginning of life.

Today the cell theory is summarized in three main ideas: (1) cells are the units of structure in living organisms; (2) cells are the units of function in living organisms; and (3) all new cells come from cells that already exist.

Self-Review

1. In what ways did van Leeuwenhoek contribute to the study of the invisible world of life?
2. How has the meaning of the word cell changed since the time of Robert Hooke?
3. What are the main ideas of the cell theory?
4. How did the discovery of staining techniques advance the study of cells?

Cell Structure

Guidepost: What main features do cells have in common?

5.3 Microscopes Enable Biologists to Study Cell Structure

Cell biologists use many different techniques to study cell structure. Dyes of various kinds are often used to stain certain organelles, which then can be studied through a microscope. Many dyes kill cells, however, so other methods are used to study living cells.

The light microscope, based on those invented hundreds of years ago, is still used in laboratories for many basic tasks (see figure 5.6). The light waves pass through a small organism, or thin slices of a larger organism, and the structures are magnified through the lens system.

Very small organisms, such as protozoa and some algae and bacteria, can be studied in the living state. The many interesting creatures you can find in a drop of pond water illustrate the complexity of life in an aquatic ecosystem. Colonies of bacteria and many organisms used in studies of inheritance can be identified or counted with a low-power light microscope. The better light microscopes, with fine quality lenses, can magnify structures up to 1500 times.

The phase contrast microscope is a special light microscope used to study living cells. This microscope depends on differences in the way light waves pass through objects in cells. Some light waves are slowed by passing through structures within cells. The phase contrast microscope can modify these differences in light waves, so that transparent cell structures appear as light and dark regions. Figure 5.7 shows the same cells as seen under an ordinary light microscope and through a phase-contrast microscope.

Electron microscopes enable us to see cell parts at very high magnifications. They use an electron beam instead of a light beam to illuminate the object. On modern transmission electron microscopes, cell

Figure 5.6 This modern light microscope works on the same principles as the microscopes used by Leeuwenhoek and Hooke.

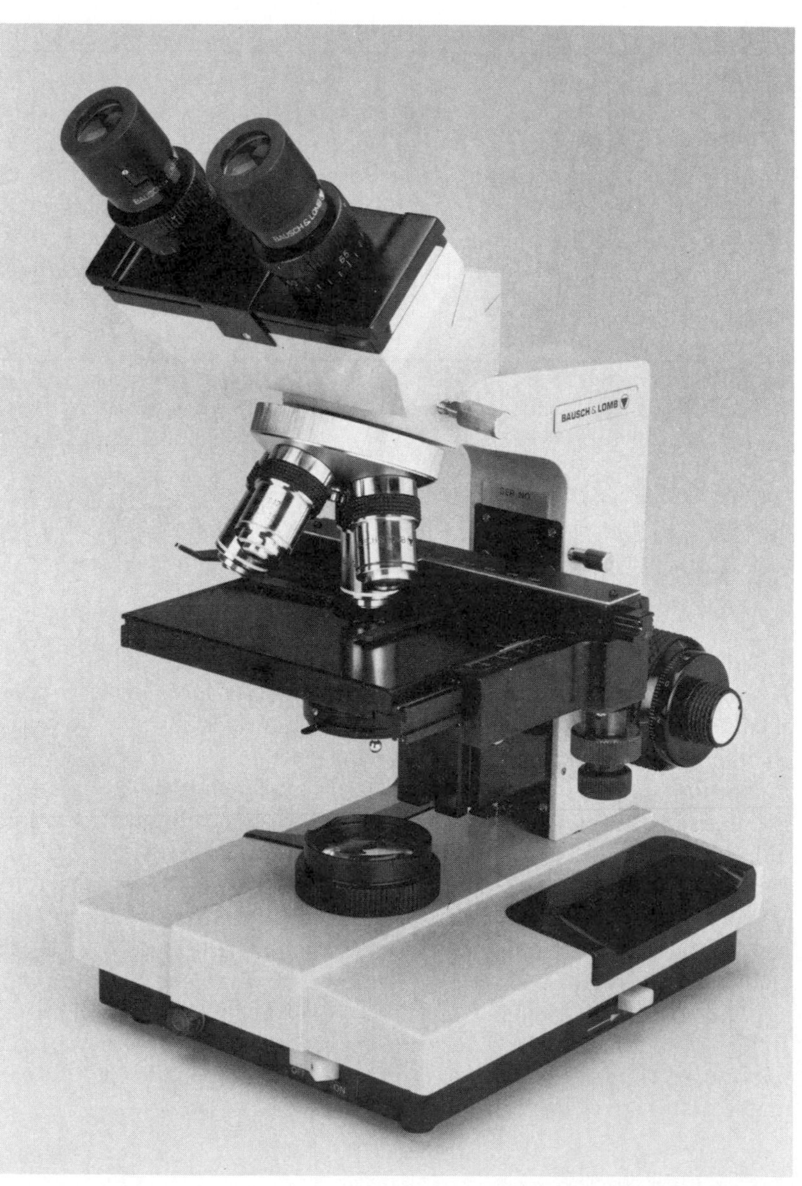

Bausch & Lomb, Rochester, NY

Figure 5.7 Cells from a human cheek lining as seen through (a) ordinary light microscope, and (b) phase contrast microscope.

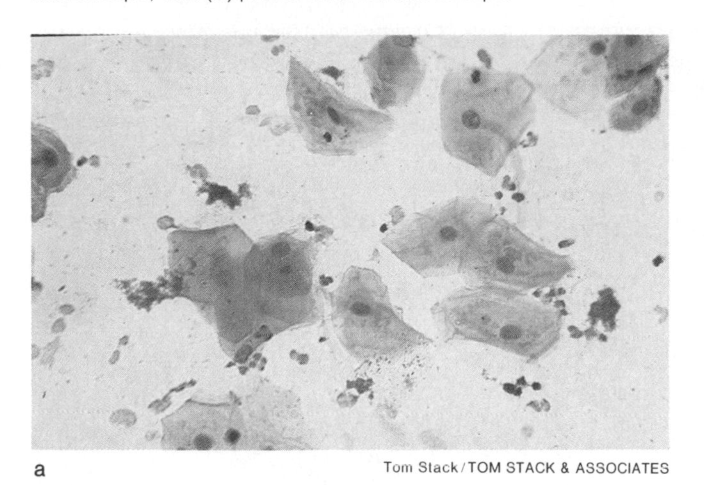

a Tom Stack/TOM STACK & ASSOCIATES

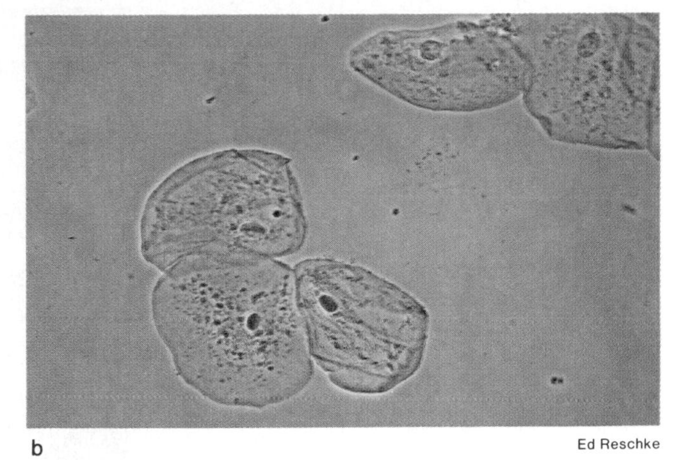

b Ed Reschke

Figure 5.8 (a) Transmission electron microscope (TEM), (b) scanning electron microscope (SEM).

a BSCS

b BSCS

Figure 5.9 Scanning electron micrograph of the surface of a coleus leaf, ×161,000. Note the many hairs and the stomates.

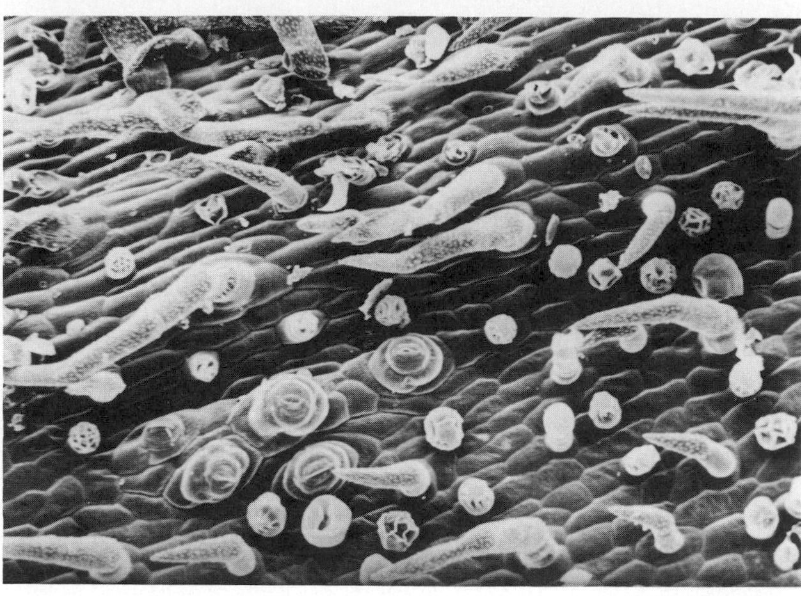

Carolyn Noble Armstrong

structures can be enlarged as much as one million times, and provide photographs that show remarkable detail (see figures 5.11 through 5.15). Scanning electron microscopes allow detailed observations of the surface of biological objects, such as the coleus leaf in figure 5.9.

5.4 Cells Have both Outer and Inner Membranes

A **unicellular** (yoo nih SEL yoo ler) organism consists of a single cell, which carries out all the many activities of that organism. Other organisms are **multicellular** (mul tih SEL yoo ler) and contain from dozens to billions of cells. Most multicellular plants and animals have a number of different types of cells; each type of cell has a certain role to play. Together these cells cooperate to make life possible for a complicated organism, which must solve the problems of living in a changing environment. In a large animal such as a human being, for example, there are at least 200 different types of cells.

Although there are many types of cells, they are similar in basic pattern. Depending on their roles, however, they may differ in some details from other cells. Figure 5.10 shows the basic structures present in most plant and animal cells. Refer to it as you read the descriptions of those structures.

An important feature of all cells is their outer membrane. This **plasma membrane** encloses the cell contents. It is a very thin but very active structure. It controls the passage of materials in and out of a cell. The plasma membrane has a particular chemical nature. It is made of two thin layers of lipid molecules, arranged in a definite way. In addition, protein molecules floating on and within the lipid layers perform special functions, such as helping molecules move in and out of the cell. These proteins, as well as their functions, vary quite a bit in different types of cells.

The electron microscope has revealed the detailed structure of the plasma membrane (see figure 5.10a). The plasma membrane encloses the **cytoplasm** (SYT oh plaz um), which in turn contains the organelles. Organelles often have their own membrane structures. The cytoplasm thus has a very complex structure with many membranes. There is much in the cytoplasm that we still do not understand at all, including the mechanisms that allow communication between the various compartments of the cell. There is evidence that small structures called **vesicles** (VES ih kulz) provide a sort of shuttle service between cell compartments.

The fluid portion of the cytoplasm is called the **cytosol** (SYT oh sol). It is somewhat jellylike. Within the cytosol (figure 5.10j) are suspended the organelles, some of which also are complex, as we will soon see. Many of the chemical reactions of a cell take place in the cytosol, which makes up about half the cell's volume.

5.5 Cells Contain Different Kinds of Organelles

In many cells the most obvious organelle is a rounded body, the **nucleus** (figures 5.10b and 5.11). The entire nucleus can be seen most easily between cell divisions. During cell division, however, the nucleus changes dramatically. Later in this chapter we will study those changes.

In cells that have a nucleus, the nucleus is surrounded by a double membrane called the **nuclear envelope.** It is continuous at several points with a complex network of other membranes in the cytoplasm called the **endoplasmic reticulum** (en doh PLAZ mik reh TIK yoo lum). That long term simply means the network (reticulum) within (endo) the plasm, or living substance, of the cell. The endoplasmic reticulum (figure 5.10h) is often called the **ER** for short. Along the membranes of the ER are often found large numbers of tiny bodies called **ribosomes** (RY boh sohmz), which can be seen in the electron micrograph in figure 5.12. Proteins are made on the ribosomes.

The nucleus contains most of the **genes** of a cell, organized into long strands called **chromosomes** (KROH moh sohmz), which are visible only during nuclear division. The genes control the basic functions of the cell. For that reason the nucleus is considered the control center of the cell. The chromosomes contain DNA and proteins. As we have just seen in chapter 4 (review section 4.14, p. 119), DNA consists of long chains of nucleotides. Those nucleotides contain the basic instructions that tell the cell how to function. The nucleotides direct the synthesis of protein molecules in each cell.

Figure 5.10 An animal cell and a plant cell, and enlargements of the major organelles.

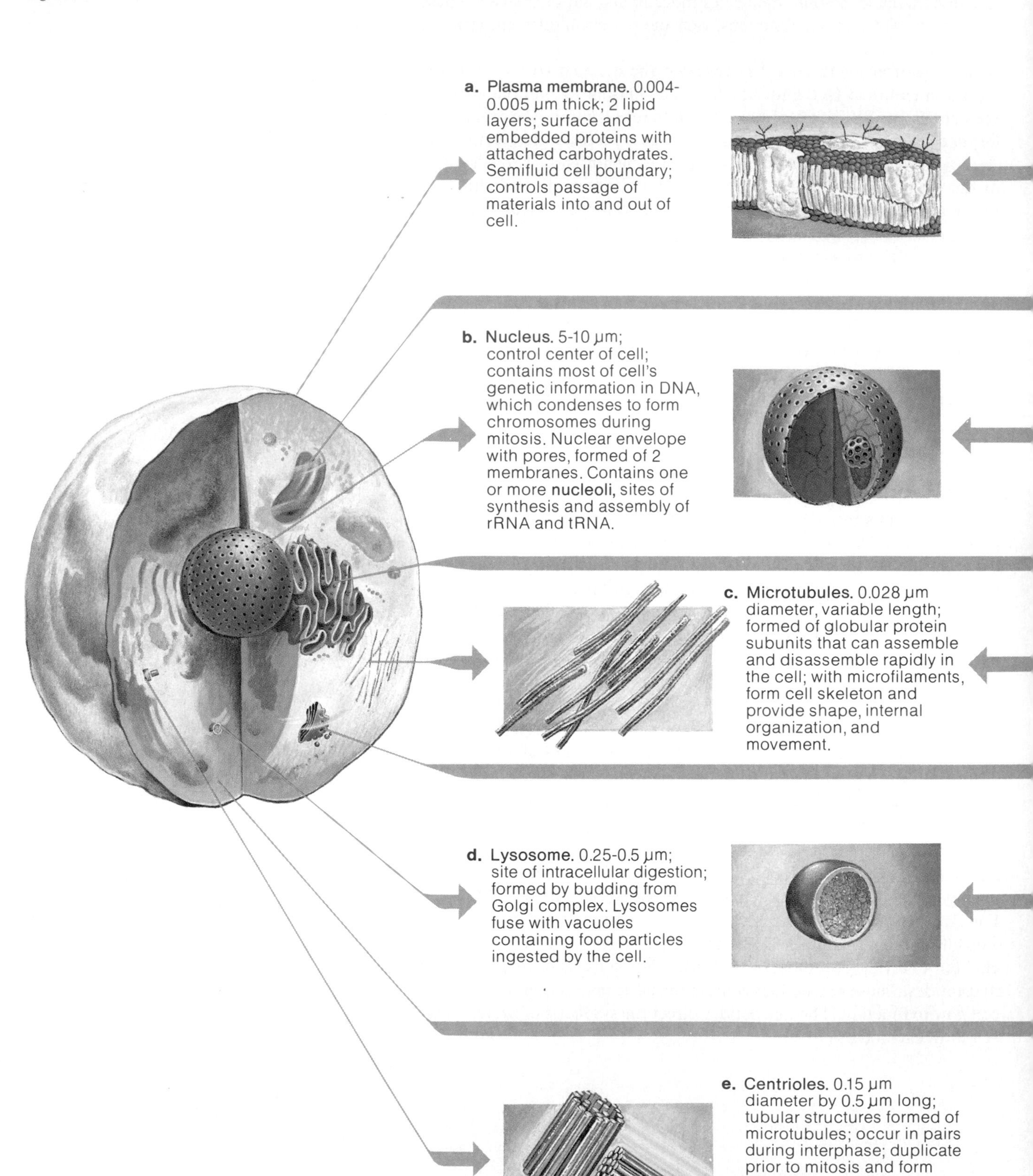

a. Plasma membrane. 0.004-0.005 µm thick; 2 lipid layers; surface and embedded proteins with attached carbohydrates. Semifluid cell boundary; controls passage of materials into and out of cell.
b. Nucleus. 5-10 µm; control center of cell; contains most of cell's genetic information in DNA, which condenses to form chromosomes during mitosis. Nuclear envelope with pores, formed of 2 membranes. Contains one or more nucleoli, sites of synthesis and assembly of rRNA and tRNA.
c. Microtubules. 0.028 µm diameter, variable length; formed of globular protein subunits that can assemble and disassemble rapidly in the cell; with microfilaments, form cell skeleton and provide shape, internal organization, and movement.
d. Lysosome. 0.25-0.5 µm; site of intracellular digestion; formed by budding from Golgi complex. Lysosomes fuse with vacuoles containing food particles ingested by the cell.
e. Centrioles. 0.15 µm diameter by 0.5 µm long; tubular structures formed of microtubules; occur in pairs during interphase; duplicate prior to mitosis and form organizing centers for mitotic spindles in protist and animal cells.

f. Cell wall. 0.1-10 μm thick; formed by living plant cells of cellulose fibers embedded in a matrix of protein and polysaccharides; provides rigidity to plant cells and allows for development of turgor pressure.

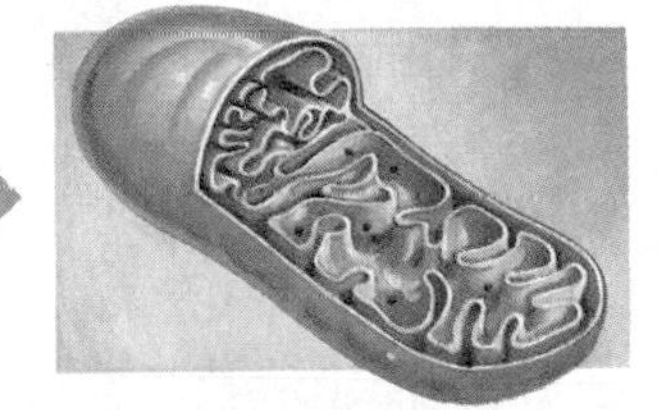

g. Mitochondrion. 2-10 μm long by 0.5-1 μm thick; enclosed in double membrane; inner membrane much folded; most reactions of cellular respiration occur in mitochondrion; contains small amounts of DNA and RNA; several hundred per cell.

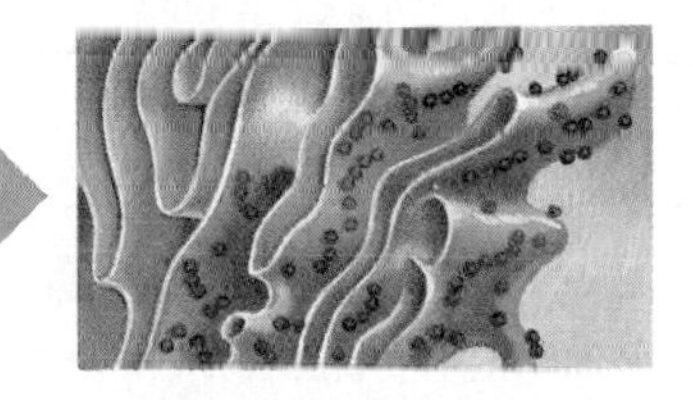

h. Endoplasmic reticulum (ER). 0.005 μm diameter; tubular membrane system that compartmentalizes the cytosol; plays a central role in biosynthesis reactions. Rough ER is studded with **ribosomes**, the site of protein synthesis; smooth ER lacks ribosomes.

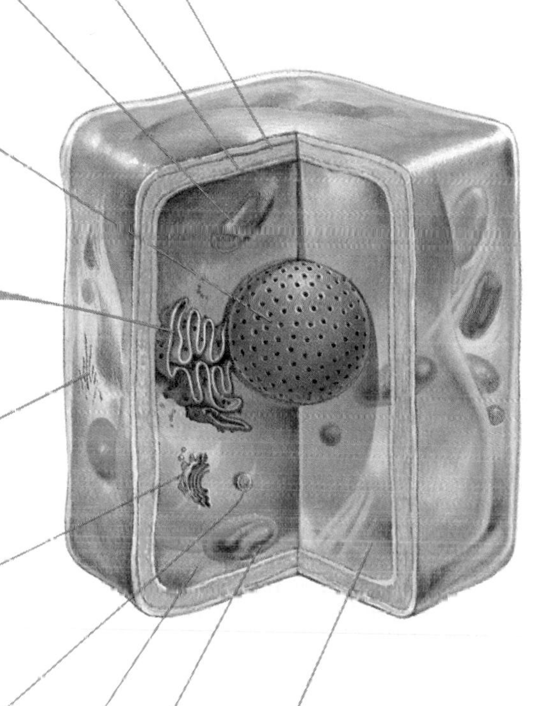

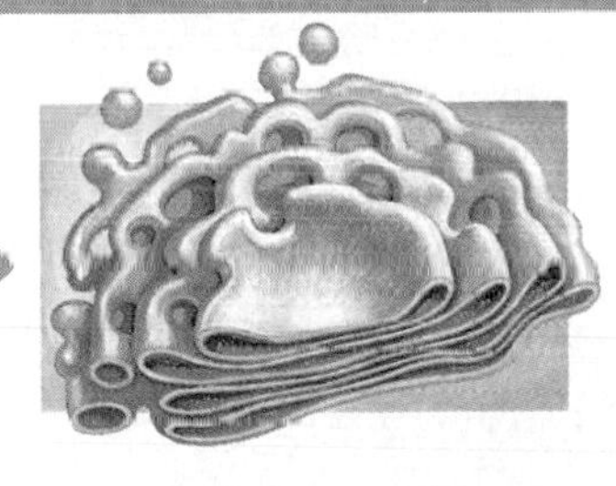

i. Golgi complex. 1 μm diameter; system of flattened sacs that modifies, sorts, and packages macromolecules for secretion or for delivery to other organelles.

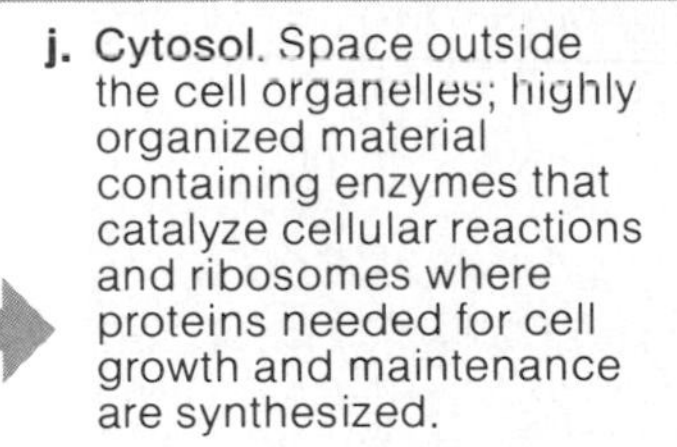

j. Cytosol. Space outside the cell organelles; highly organized material containing enzymes that catalyze cellular reactions and ribosomes where proteins needed for cell growth and maintenance are synthesized.

k. Chloroplast. 5 μm long by 0.5-1 μm thick; enclosed by double membrane, with third membrane system forming thylakoids; thylakoids stacked to form grana. All reactions of photosynthesis occur in chloroplasts.

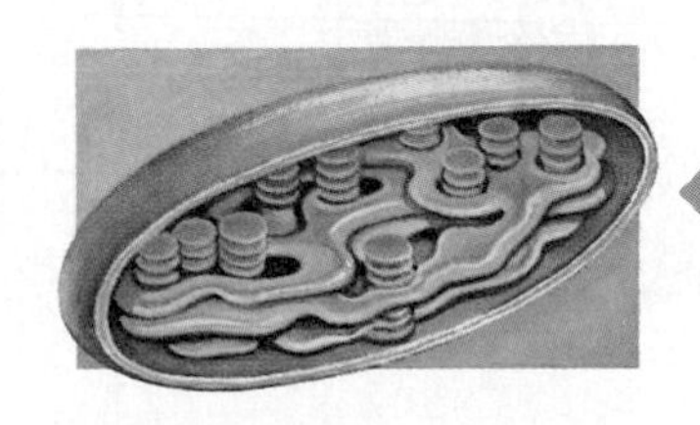

l. Vacuole. Variable size; large vesicle enclosed in single membrane; usually occupies more than 50% of volume in plant cells; stores nutrients and waste products.

Figure 5.11 Transmission electron micrograph of a mouse liver cell nucleus, ×10,640. Note the double membrane that makes up the nuclear envelope. The dark round body at the right is the nucleolus.

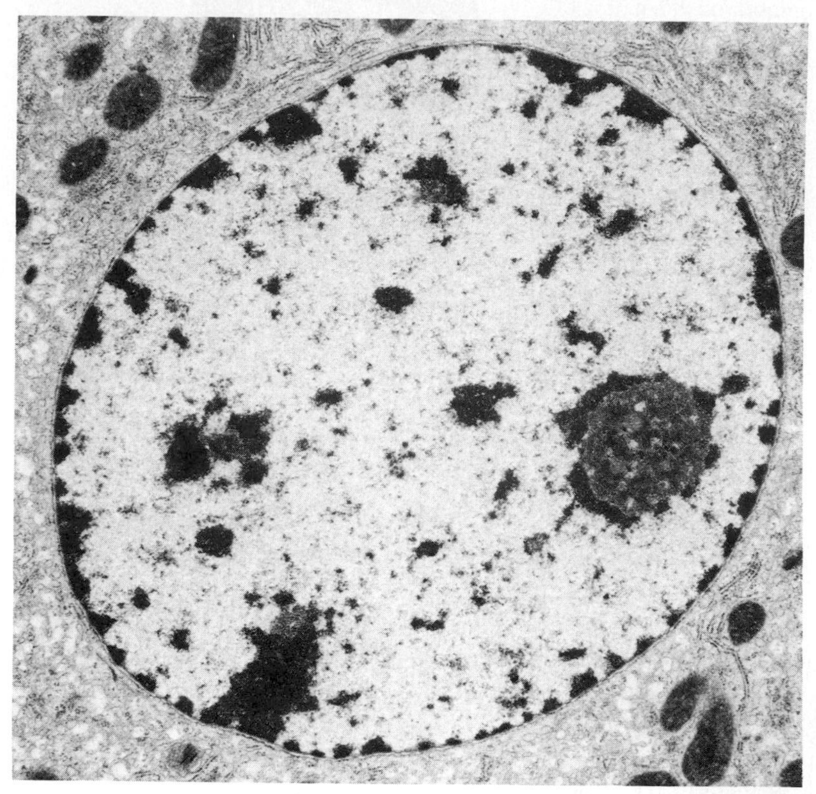

K. G. Murti/VISUALS UNLIMITED

Figure 5.12 Rough endoplasmic reticulum in a mouse liver cell. The dark bodies are mitochondria. Note the ribosomes free in the cytosol at the bottom. Transmission electron micrograph, ×43,500.

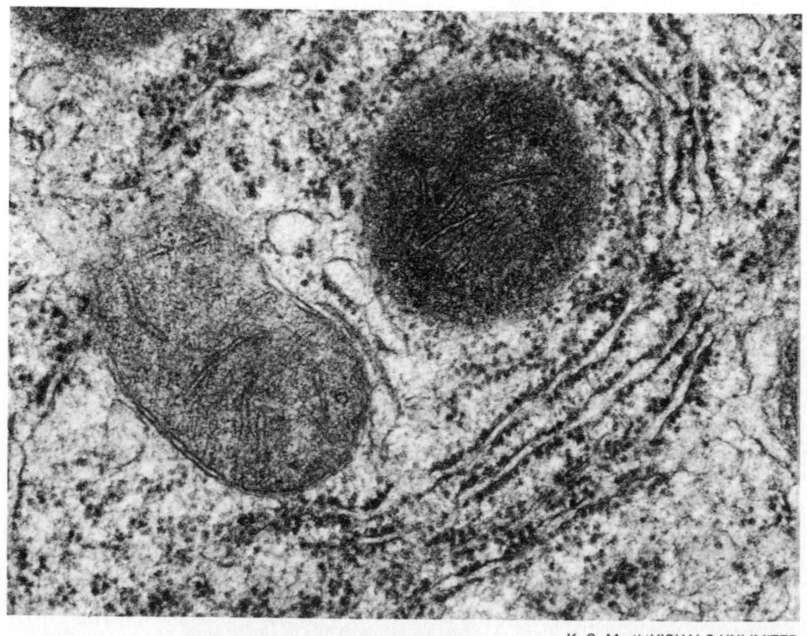

K. G. Murti/VISUALS UNLIMITED

Within the cytosol also are found other kinds of organelles, each with a particular job to do. The **mitochondria** (my toh KON dree uh) (singular, mitochondrion (my toh KON dree uhn)) are often called the powerhouses of the cell. They function in the very important task of releasing energy from nutrients. A whole series of important chemical reactions occurs within the mitochondria. As you learned in the last chapter, those reactions provide new supplies of ATP, the energy "currency" molecules of the cell. This ATP "small change" then can be "spent" on all kinds of cell activities.

Mitochondria are rounded structures about as large as bacterial cells. They have different shapes in different cells, but their basic structures are similar. They consist of two layers of membranes, an outer membrane and a folded inner membrane. You can see their structure in figure 5.10g.

In plant cells there is another important kind of organelle, the **chloroplast** (KLOR oh plast). These structures contain the pigment—chlorophyll—essential for capturing the light energy of the sun. Chloroplasts (figure 5.10k) have an even more complicated membrane structure than do mitochondria. It is in these membranes that photosynthesis takes place. You may remember that photosynthesis is the process whereby the energy of the sun is captured and stored in the structure of biological molecules. It is this chemical energy that is later released for use by cells.

Most plant cells also contain a large central **vacuole** (VAK yoo ohl) surrounded by a single membrane (figure 5.10 l). The vacuole is filled with fluid and may occupy as much as 95 percent of the cell's volume. Vacuoles store and transport nutrients and waste products.

The **Golgi** (GOHL jee) **complex** (figures 5.10i and 5.13) helps package cell products for export from the cell. Materials synthesized on the ER

Figure 5.13 Transmission electron micrograph of a Golgi complex, ×21,930. Part of the nucleus shows at lower left. Note the vesicles around the complex to the right.

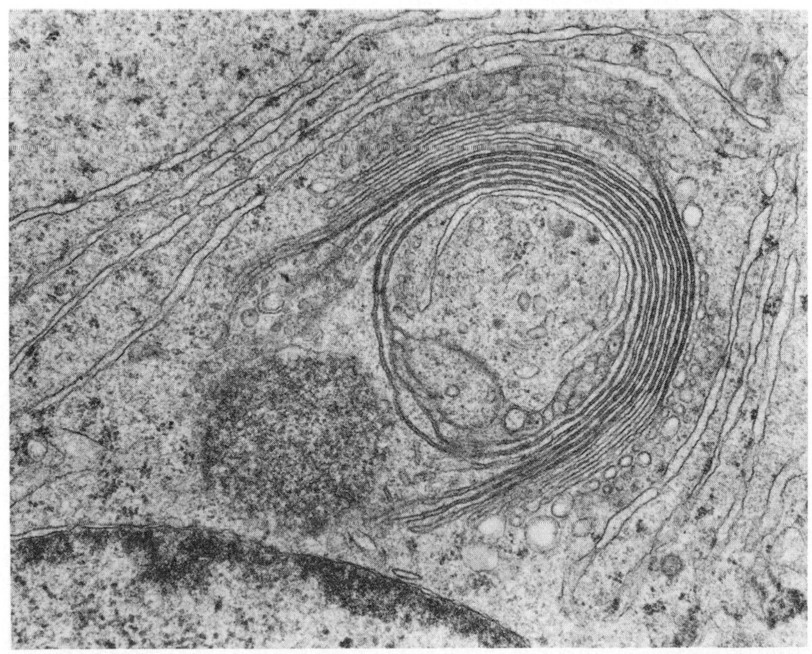

David M. Phillips/VISUALS UNLIMITED

Figure 5.14 Transmission electron micrograph of lysosomes from a mouse kidney cell, ×45,000.

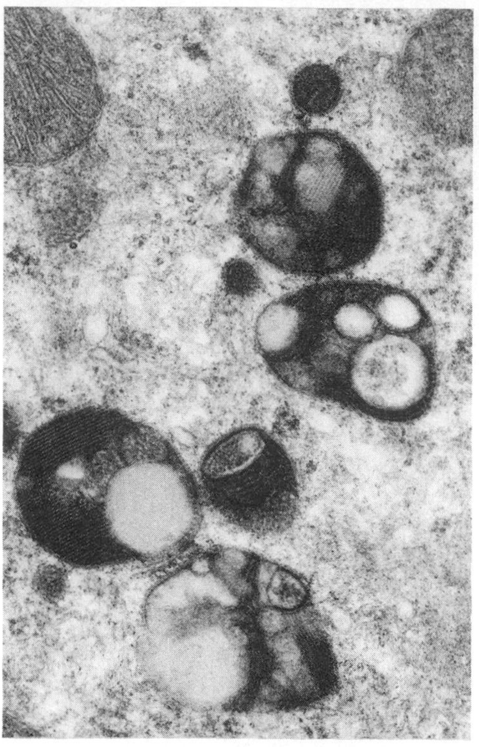

K. G. Murti/VISUALS UNLIMITED

Figure 5.15 Cross section of a centriole, ×210,000. The nine microtubule triplets that form the centriole show clearly in this transmission electron micrograph.

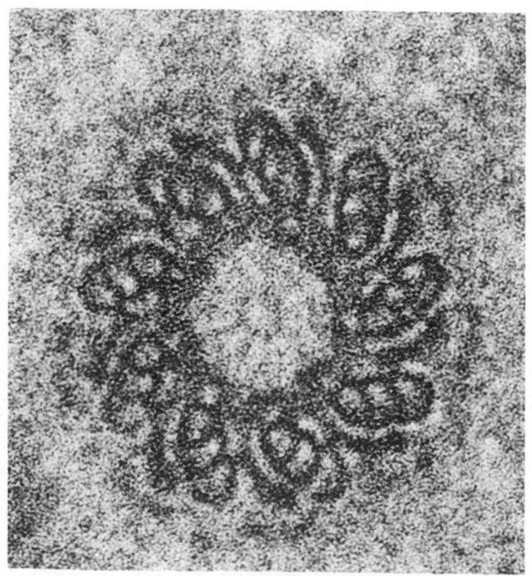

David M. Phillips/VISUALS UNLIMITED

are transferred to saclike structures that are formed by the membranes of the Golgi complex. These products are then packaged in tiny secretory vesicles. The vesicles then make their way to the plasma membrane where they release their products to the extracellular environment, or environment outside of the cell.

Other kinds of vesicles remain within the cell. These are called **lysosomes** (LY soh zohms), and they contain digestive enzymes of various kinds. These enzymes help break down large molecules and worn-out cell parts. Lysosomes are shown in figures 5.10d and 5.14.

Microtubules (MY kroh TOO byoolz) are tiny tubes composed of proteins. They are organized in a complex network that forms the cell's skeleton. Microtubules (figure 5.10c) enable the cell to maintain its distinct shape and internal organization, and they are important in many kinds of cell movements.

Centrioles (SEN tree ohlz) are present in the cells of animals and protists. These tubular structures (figures 5.10e and 5.15) are formed of microtubules. They are present in pairs and play an important role in mitosis, as we shall see.

By now you should begin to see how important membranes are in cells. The cell can be viewed as a highly organized system, divided by membranes into smaller compartments. Each compartment has its own job to do. Molecules pass back and forth across these membranes within a cell, and also move between the cell and its outside environment.

Some kinds of cells have still other kinds of organelles. You have been studying the major kinds of organelles in figure 5.10, which also summarizes their main functions. A somewhat different view of a cell is shown in figure 5.16.

Not all cell structures lie within the plasma membrane. In plant cells and in some other cells there is also a **cell wall** (figure 5.10f) outside the plasma membrane. That is what made plant cells easier to see than animal cells for early biologists. The cell wall is made of materials secreted by the cell while it grows. That is done largely with the help of the membranous Golgi complex. The cell wall provides strength and protection. When the cell dies, the cell wall often remains behind.

When Robert Hooke looked at thin slices of cork under his microscope, he was actually observing the cell walls of the bark of a cork oak. Most of the trunk of a large tree consists of nonliving cell walls. The living cells of the tree are found in a thin band just underneath the bark of the trunk.

Self-Review

1. What is the function of the plasma membrane?
2. What is an advantage of the phase contrast microscope?
3. What is the role of the nucleus?
4. Name two organelles of a cell besides the nucleus and describe their functions.

Figure 5.16 The organelles of a cell must communicate and work together. This is one artist's view of the inner workings of a cell.

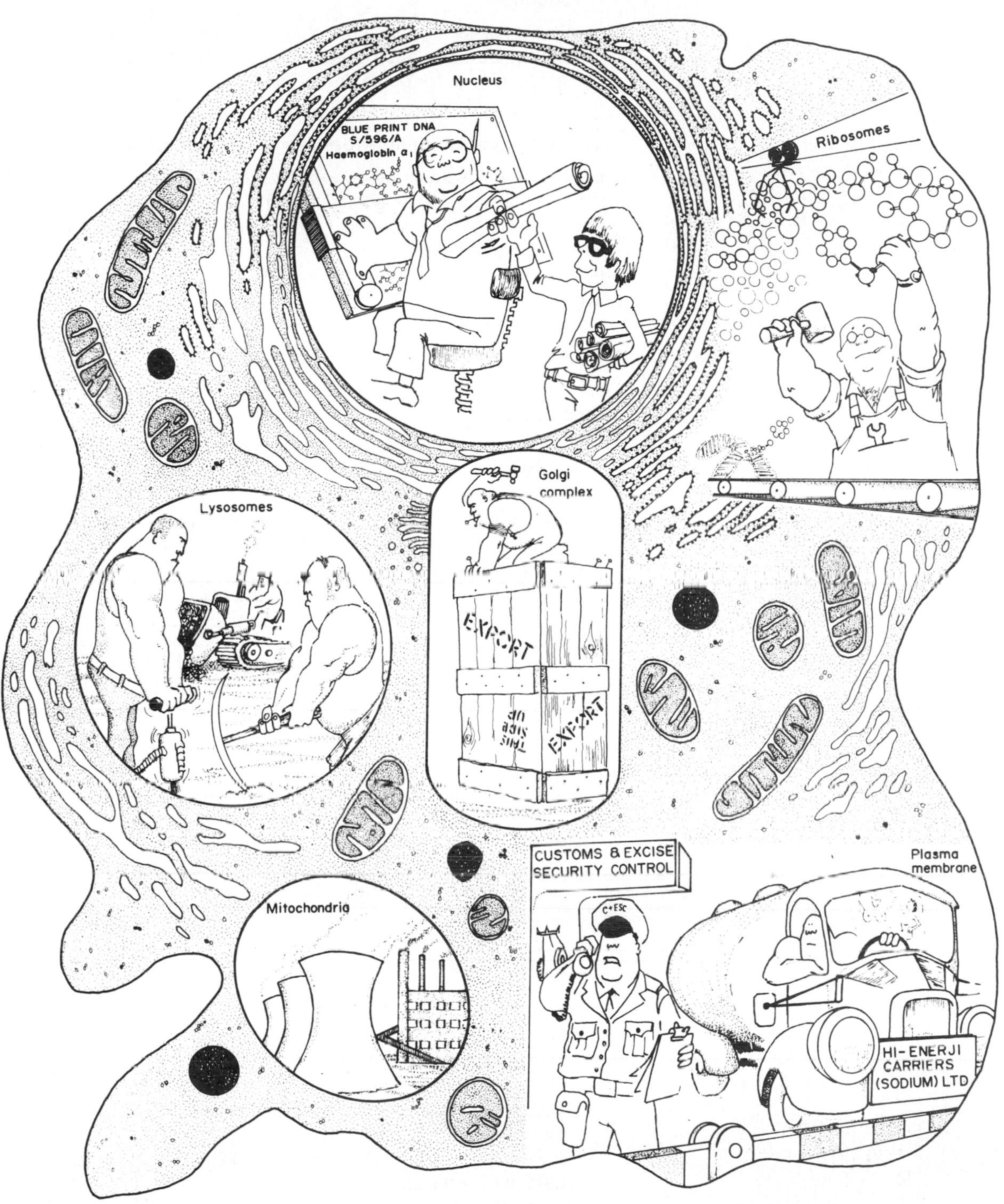

Investigation 5.1 OBSERVING CELLS

Introduction

Although scientists have not observed all kinds of cells, many cells have been described and photographed. In this investigation you will use some of the techniques for observing cells.

Materials (per student or per pair of students)

several 1-cm^2 pieces of onion
iodine-potassium-iodide solution (I_2KI)
physiological saline solution
methylene blue solution
elodea leaves
frog blood
monocular microscope
microscope slides
coverslips
fine-pointed forceps
scalpel
4 dropping pipets
2 dissecting needles
paper towels
toothpicks

Procedure

1. On the inner, concave side of each piece of onion, the **epidermis** (ep ih DER mis)—skin—is easily peeled off with forceps. Place a small piece of epidermis (much smaller than a coverslip) on a slide. Avoid overlapping or wrinkling it. Add 1 or 2 drops of water and a coverslip.
2. Examine the onion epidermis under low power of your microscope. Look for cell boundaries. Draw a small part of the field of view to show the shapes and arrangements of the cells.
3. Place a drop of iodine stain along one edge of the coverslip. Pull it under the coverslip, using the technique shown in figure A-6 (page 967). Record any changes that occur as the stain spreads across the onion epidermis.
4. Switch to high power and draw a single cell. Include as much detail as you can see. Save your drawing for reference in the next text section on cell structure.
5. With forceps remove a young leaf from the tip of an elodea plant. Place it upside down on a clean slide. Add a drop of water and coverslip.
6. (a) Observe the leaf under low power. By slowly turning the fine adjustment back and forth, determine the number of cell layers in the leaf.
   (b) Switch to high power. Select an "average" cell and focus on it carefully. Is there any evidence that the cell is living? If there is, what is the evidence?
7. Make a drawing of the leaf cell, including as much detail as you can see. Label any parts you can identify. Keep this drawing too for later reference.
8. Using the blunt end of a toothpick, *gently* scrape the inside surface of your cheek. You should obtain a small amount of cloudy material. Rub this material on a clean slide.
9. Add a drop or two of methylene blue and a coverslip. Find several cells, well separated from the others, and draw 1 or 2 of them. Include as much detail as you can see. Label any parts you can identify.
10. Place a drop of diluted frog blood on a clean slide. Add a drop of methylene blue and a coverslip.
11. Examine under low power. Find an area where the cells are neither too crowded nor too scarce. Center it in the field of view. Switch to high power. Draw 1 or 2 cells and label any parts you can identify.

Discussion

Construct a chart in your data book. In the first column, list all the kinds of cells you observed. Head the other columns with the names of cell parts that you identified. Review your sketches and notes. For each kind of cell examined, place an X beneath the name of each cell structure observed.

1. Does the lack of an X indicate that the structure was not present in the cells observed? Why or why not?
2. On the basis of your observations, which kind of cell (plant or animal) seems to have more angular, less-rounded shapes? Which has more clearly defined boundaries?
3. What structure may be involved in determining a cell's shape?

Cell Functions

Guidepost: What principles from the physical sciences help explain the functions of organisms?

5.6 Cell Activities Require Energy

All the different cell parts introduced in the last section are important in the life of the cells. Each part has a particular role to play, but biologists cannot always tell what that role is just by looking at a structure. To understand how each cell part fits into the life of a cell, biologists use many different methods, some of which come directly from the physical sciences.

Let us suppose that you take a watch apart (the type with hour, minute, and second hands), and spread all the cogs, wheels, springs and bearings on a table. Just by looking at its parts, you might have trouble in understanding exactly how that watch works.

Biologists are in much the same position. They can describe the various parts of a cell and even separate them, but they might not be able to figure out how the parts all fit together, or how they enable the cell to work. That is a challenge of modern biology. In tackling these problems, it is often more useful to study living cells than nonliving ones.

All cells have the ability to release energy from certain organic molecules, such as sugars. The energy of a molecule is released in many small steps. As mentioned in section 5.5, mitochondria are the organelles mainly involved in energy release. After a cell has taken in energy-rich molecules that can be used as fuel, they are channeled into pathways that lead to the release of that energy. The more active a cell is, the more mitochondria it needs to provide enough energy.

Metabolism (meh TAB oh liz um) is the sum of all the chemical reactions in a cell or organism. Biologically important molecules are processed, energy is transferred to ATP, and the waste materials are released from the cell. Excess carbon atoms may be released as carbon dioxide (CO_2). Extra nitrogen atoms are often released in ammonia molecules (NH_3), or as parts of urea molecules. Such wastes must be expelled, in fact, because they become toxic to the cell.

Some cells, for example those in green plants, also are able to store energy directly in organic molecules such as sugars. These molecules then can be transformed into other kinds of useful molecules such as amino acids, lipids, or nucleotides. Such molecules are used to maintain the life of the cell. They also are used for growth, and they can help build new living substance.

5.7 Substances Move In and Out of Cells in Several Ways

Even though living organisms have complex rules of their own, they also abide by all the rules of physics and chemistry that apply to the nonliving world. Atoms and molecules and small particles, for instance, tend to wander about from places where they are highly concentrated to places where they are less concentrated. That happens in gases, liquids, and even solids in some cases. Such movement, which is completely random, is called **diffusion** (dih FYOO zhun).

Scientists summarize the movements of diffusion in a rule: substances tend to move from areas of higher concentration to areas of lower concentration. This difference in concentration between two places is called a **diffusion gradient**—a measure of the steepness of the difference.

Many substances can move in and out of cells by diffusion alone. Once they have passed into a cell through the plasma membrane, they continue to diffuse throughout the cytosol. Because diffusion is a random process, it aids in the even distribution of materials within a cell, as diagrammed in figure 5.17.

It is important to realize that a living cell is about 70 percent water. Therefore, living substance is essentially an aqueous (watery) system. Many kinds of molecules may be dissolved in this aqueous cell interior. Others that cannot dissolve may be suspended in the cytosol.

The cell wall, if present, allows free diffusion of most substances. The plasma membrane, however, permits only certain molecules to diffuse freely. Oxygen and carbon dioxide are examples.

Figure 5.17 Diffusion (a) without, and (b) with a differentially permeable membrane. In (a), the large particles can move freely and become evenly distributed in the water. In (b), the particles are too large to diffuse through the plasma membrane. At first there is a lower concentration of water inside the cell than outside. Water molecules then move to the inside, causing the cell to expand.

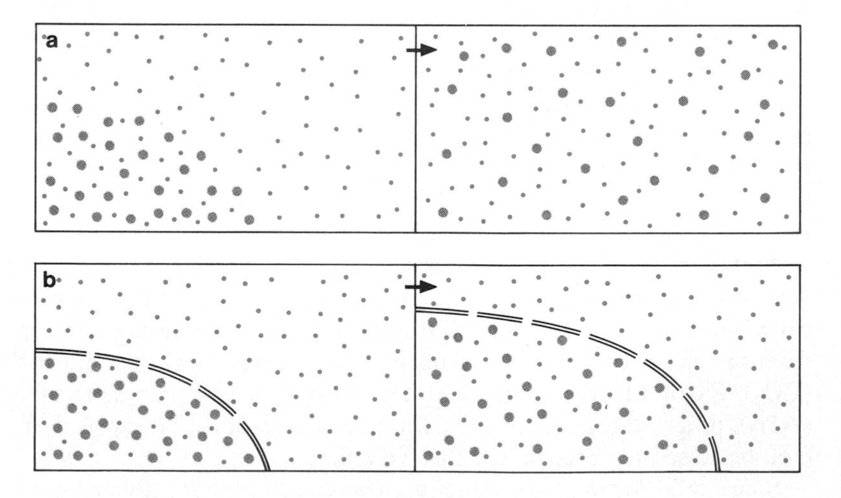

The environment outside a cell also must be aqueous. Otherwise the water in the cell would diffuse out, and the cell would dry out and die. Many cells live in an aqueous environment all their lives. Other cells are usually bathed in a film of water. The amount of water surrounding cells must be sufficient to prevent water within the cell from diffusing outward.

Because water is essential for living cells, life can exist only where there is enough water. Some animals and plants, however, are able to live in dry environments, such as deserts, where water is scarce. They have special means of conserving water. Some of these methods will be discussed in later chapters. Seeds and spores of some organisms have very hard capsules that prevent loss of water for long periods, sometimes years.

When a substance is able to pass through a membrane, we say that the membrane is **permeable** (PER mee uh bul) to that substance. Membranes may be more permeable to some substances than to others: they are said to be differentially permeable. In other words, these membranes have different permeabilities to different substances: perhaps a small urea molecule will pass easily, but not a large starch molecule. Sometimes membranes do not permit substances to pass through at all: then they are said to be **impermeable** (im PER mee uh bul) to that substance.

Some substances are just too large to pass through a membrane. Others have an electrical charge that makes diffusion impossible. That is because the plasma membrane itself is electrically charged. Other ways are used to admit such substances to a cell, or to get rid of them.

One important method a cell uses to transport such substances across a membrane is **active transport.** In other words, the cell actively moves these substances across its membrane by using energy. Sometimes a substance can be moved across a membrane, even though the structure is already more concentrated within the cell than it is outside (see figure 5.18). Thus, the substance is actively transported against a diffusion gradient.

A good example of such active transport is seen in root cells. Minerals the plants require for growth may be present in the soil in very low amounts. Root cells use active transport to accumulate the minerals in relatively high amounts. Because of active transport, the minerals are available to be transported to all parts of the plant.

Figure 5.18 Comparison of diffusion and active transport. By using active transport, a cell can continue to accumulate particles even though their concentration is already greater inside the cell.

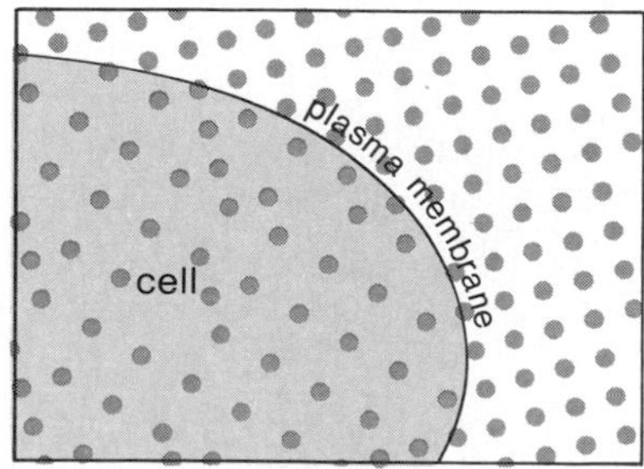

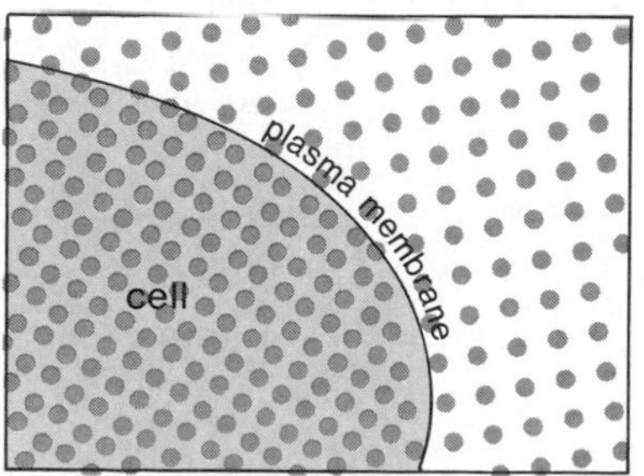

a. Diffusion

b. Active Transport

5.8 Water Follows the Rule of Diffusion

To understand the movement of water in and out of cells, it helps to remember that water also follows the basic rule of diffusion. It moves from the side of the plasma membrane where it is more concentrated to the side where it is less concentrated.

Water is a **solvent**—a substance in which other substances can dissolve. The movement of a solvent through a plasma membrane, when the concentrations of substances are different on its two sides, is called **osmosis** (os MOH sis). Figure 5.19 shows how osmosis works.

The concentration of water outside a cell depends on many factors. Primarily it depends on the concentration of **solutes** (SOL yoots)—salts or other substances—in the water. If water contains only salt, and the salt concentration is 1 percent, for example, then the water concentration is 99 percent.

Cells normally have an inside salt concentration (mainly sodium chloride) of about 0.9 percent. If the outside concentration of water is lower than the concentration of water inside the cell, then water will diffuse out of a cell, and the cell will shrink. On the other hand, if the concentration of water is higher outside the cell, water will diffuse into the cell (study figure 5.19 again).

Distilled water contains no salts at all; it is 100 percent water. Therefore, cells immersed in distilled water will take in water. Sometimes so much water flows into the cell that the pressure on the plasma membrane increases, and the cells may even burst. Red blood cells, for instance, will burst if they are left in distilled water. The hemoglobin pours out, leaving behind the empty plasma membranes. In the blood vessels, the salt concentration of the liquid portion of blood is maintained at about 0.9 percent. The blood cells, therefore, maintain their normal shape and function, because the concentration of salt is the same both outside and inside the cells.

Figure 5.19 A diagram of osmosis. When water concentration is higher inside the cell (left), the cell loses water and shrinks. When water concentration is higher outside the cell (right), the cell takes in water and swells. In the diagram, salt is represented by one kind of particle for simplicity, but in water it ionizes into two kinds of particles, sodium ions and chloride ions.

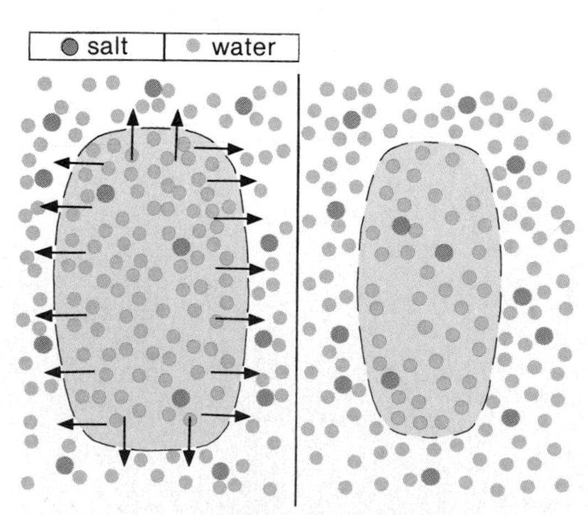
salt
water
if concentration of water is higher inside the cell, water passes out of the cell

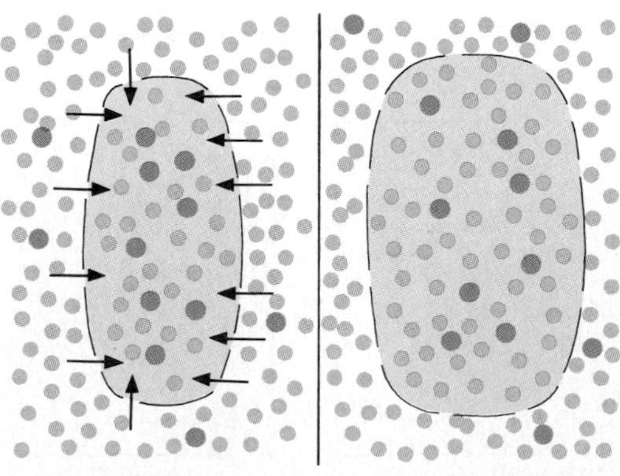
if concentration of water is higher outside the cell, water passes into the cell

Biology Today C

High School Biology Teacher

Pat Huwa is a biology teacher at Cherry Creek High School in Colorado. She is the Colorado recipient of the Outstanding Biology Teacher Award for 1986.

Pat was raised in Milliken, Colorado, where her parents owned a small grocery store. She graduated from high school in a class of eight graduates. That was quite different from the school in which she currently teaches, with an enrollment of more than 3400 students.

A high school counselor recommended that Pat study science because of the varied employment opportunities available to scientists. Pat had studied biology and physics in high school but her small high school had not offered her the opportunity to study chemistry. She decided to major in biology, and earned a bachelor's and a master's degree in biological science. She feels very lucky to be in a profession she enjoys so much.

Pat knows that it is very important for teachers to be aware of current trends and changes in biology and education. In addition to taking college and university classes, Pat feels one of the best ways to keep up to date is to be active in professional organizations, such as the National Association of Biology Teachers, the National Science Teachers Association, Colorado Biology Teachers Association, and Colorado Association of Science Teachers.

At Cherry Creek Pat teaches with Russ Doren, Raylene Owen, and Sally Swartz in a modified team teaching situation. Although they teach their own classes individually, they have found it very economical, both in time and in expenses, to prepare labs, tests, computer assignments, and other activities as a team. All of the team members feel that the quality of their work improves from the direct input of four people. Referring to the team members, Pat says that Raylene is the organizer, Russ the computer whiz, and that Sally makes sure materials are ordered and available. Students have the advantage of knowing all four teachers, and if they have a question or a problem, they go to any of the team members for assistance.

Biology teachers can take any area of biology and make it relevant to the everyday world the students live in. Examples of this include having students investigate why cities ask people to restrict driving and to refrain from using fireplaces during high pollution days, and having students identify risk and preventive factors of heart disease, sexually transmitted diseases, and various genetic diseases.

Because being in class and working with students is Pat's first priority, at times she becomes frustrated with record keeping, classroom interruptions, and grading papers. However, she realizes that these activities are vital to her interaction with students in the classroom. She feels very fortunate to be teaching in a school where she has the support of other teachers, the science coordinator, the administration, the parents, and the students, and she enjoys teaching as much today as when she first started.

BSCS by Doug Sokell

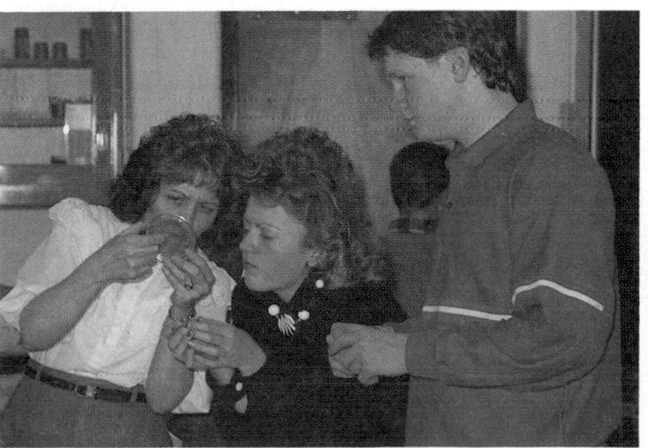

BSCS by Doug Sokell

Cell walls help protect plant cells from bursting due to the inward movement of water by osmosis. The cells simply become rigid. This is what causes well-watered plants to stand upright. Many plants wilt and droop when their cells have lost water.

It is not hard to see, therefore, that when a cell is in balance with its environment, the salt concentration inside the cell is about the same as the salt concentration outside the cell. Cells removed from our bodies, such as blood cells, must be suspended in a salt salution that is the same as that within the cells. This concentration is said to be "normal." The solution into which the cells are collected is called normal saline, that is, the concentration of salt that is normal for the interiors of those cells.

Self-Review

1. What is metabolism?
2. What do cells use for fuel?
3. Why do cells constantly take in and get rid of substances?
4. How does an understanding of physics and chemistry help explain diffusion?
5. Why are membranes said to be differentially permeable?

Investigation 5.2 DIFFUSION THROUGH A MEMBRANE

Introduction

How do things get in and out of cells? In this investigation you will use a model of a plasma membrane (cellulose tubing) to observe the movement of water.

Materials (per team)

15 ml soluble-starch solution
15 ml glucose solution
iodine solution
Tes-tape or piece of Clinitest tablet in test tube
2 lengths of cellulose tubing, 20 cm each
2 beakers, 1000 ml, with water
glass-marking pencil
string

Procedure

1. To open the cellulose tubing, first moisten it and then rub it between your thumb and forefinger. Tie each piece of tubing tightly with string about 1 cm from 1 end.
2. Into 1 tube, pour soluble-starch solution to within 5 cm of the top. Pinch the top of the tube together tightly. Rinse the tube under running water to remove any starch from the outside. Tie the top of the tube tightly with string not more than 2 cm above the top of the liquid.

Figure 5.20

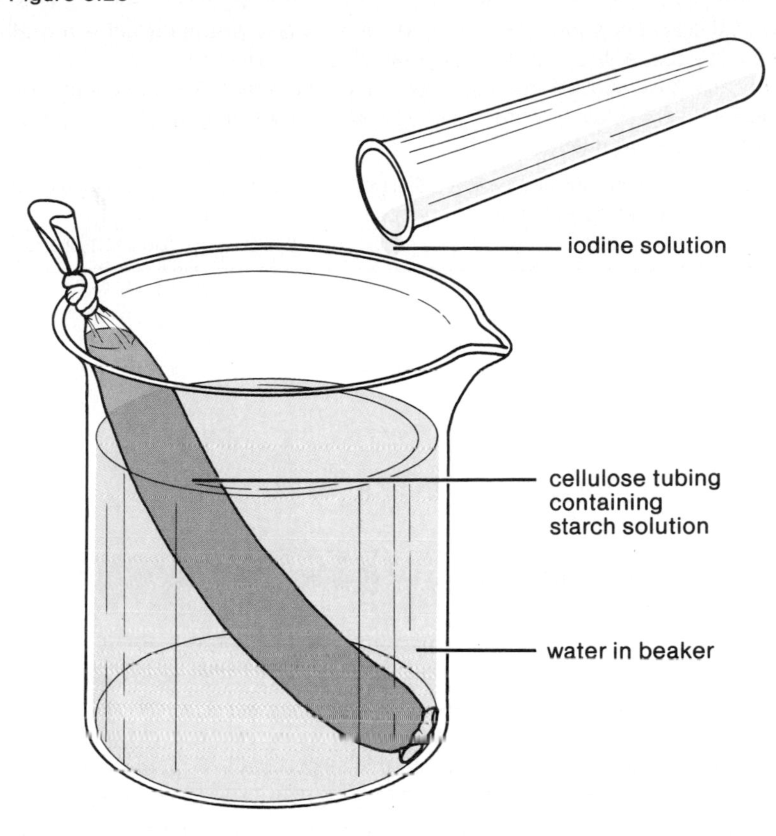

3. Place the tube in a beaker of water. Mark the beaker A. Add enough iodine solution to give the water a distinct yellowish color. See figure 5.20.
4. Into the 2nd tube pour glucose solution to within 5 cm of the top.
5. Repeat procedure 2. Place the tube in a beaker of water. Mark this beaker B.
6. Allow the tubes to stand for about 20 minutes. Dip a piece of Tes-tape into the water in beaker B (or pour a small quantity of the water into a test tube containing a fragment of Clinitest tablet). Record the color of the tape.
7. Observe the tube in beaker A. Record any changes, including color, that you see in either the tube or the water in the beaker.
8. Let beakers A and B stand overnight. The next day record any changes observed.

Discussion

1. On the basis of the chemical test for starch, what must have happened to the iodine molecules in beaker A?
2. On the basis of the chemical test for glucose, what must have happened to the glucose molecules in beaker B?
3. From the evidence obtained by allowing the beakers to stand overnight, what other substances must pass through the membrane in beaker B?

4. Which substance did not pass through a membrane? How do you know that it did not?

Physicists can show that the molecules of any one substance are all about the same size but that the molecules of different substances are different in size. Measurements show that iodine molecules and water molecules are very small, glucose molecules are considerably larger, and starch molecules are very large.

5. On this basis, suggest a hypothesis to account for the observations that were made in this investigation.
6. What assumption did you make about the structure of the membrane?

Guidepost: How do cells duplicate themselves?

Cell Reproduction

5.9 The Rate of Diffusion Limits the Size of Cells

The third major idea of the cell theory is that cells arise from cells that already exist. At one time scientists thought that organisms could come from nonliving matter. Three hundred years ago it was not hard to believe that worms, insects, and molds might have come from decaying or other nonliving matter.

It was not until the 19th century that Louis Pasteur (figure 5.21), working with yeast cells, was able to prove that microorganisms cannot arise from completely nonliving matter. Soon his conclusions were shown to apply to all other kinds of organisms as well. Organisms come from existing organisms, and their cells arise from existing cells.

In the last section we studied how substances diffuse. Diffusion is very helpful in supplying the interiors of cells with the materials they require.

Figure 5.21 (a) Louis Pasteur at work in his laboratory. (b) In his experiments, which showed that microorganisms do not arise from nonliving matter, Pasteur used flasks such as these. No microorganisms grew in the sterilized yeast infusions even though they were open to the air.

Parke-Davis Division of Warner-Lambert Co. Morris Plains, NJ 07950

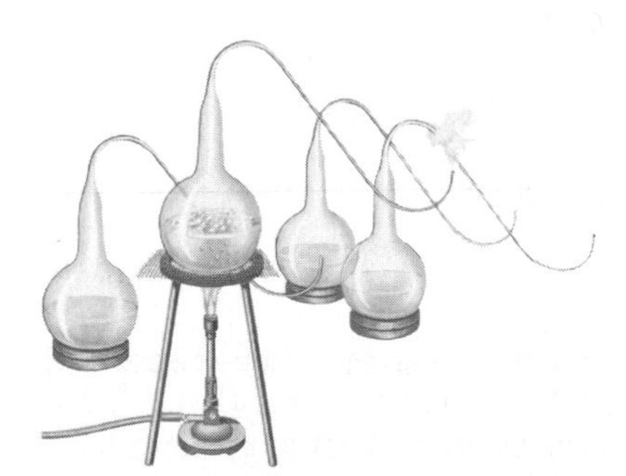

a. Pasteur prepared and boiled four yeast infusions in flasks to which he had given long S-curved necks to trap particles entering the open end.

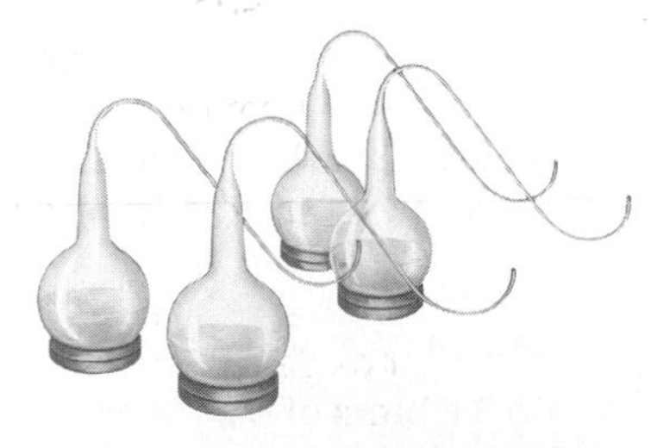

b. He left all the flasks open, yet all remained sterile indefinitely. Air without its impurities did not affect the infusions.

It also helps to rid the cell of unwanted waste products such as carbon dioxide and urea. It is important to note, however, that diffusion is effective only over short distances. It takes a long time for substances to diffuse great distances.

If a cell is to function well, then, it cannot be too large. There is a limit to cell size if diffusion is to work well. When a cell reaches a certain size, it begins a series of changes that permits it to divide into two cells.

Actually, some cells are quite large and are visible with the naked eye. A hen's egg is actually a single cell, but the living part of a bird's egg is very tiny indeed. The rest of the egg consists of stored food in the form of yolk.

Investigation 5.3 CELL SIZE AND DIFFUSION

Introduction

When cells reach a certain size, their rate of growth slows down. Then they stop growing. Each cell divides into two smaller cells, which begin to grow. What causes cells to stop growing and then to divide? One way to investigate questions such as this is to build a model. A model is often a small copy of something large. In this investigation we will reverse the process and build a large model of something small.

Materials (per team of 2 students)

block of phenolphthalein agar
100 ml 0.4% sodium hydroxide (**CAUTION:** *corrosive; avoid contact with skin or eyes*)
250 ml beaker, or culture dish
mm ruler
razor blade
plastic spoon
plastic knife
paper towel

Part A

Procedure

1. With the razor blade, cut the block of phenolphthalein agar into 3 cubes. The 1st should be 3 cm on each side, the 2nd, 2 cm on each side, and the 3rd, 1 cm on each side. Measure carefully and trim away any excess agar. Think of the cubes as large models of microscopic cells. Which of your 3 model cells do you think would be most likely to survive? Why?
2. Place the cubes in the beaker or culture dish and pour in enough sodium hydroxide to cover them.
3. Record your starting time and use the plastic spoon to turn the cubes often for the next 10 minutes. Be careful not to cut or scratch the surface of the cubes.

Discussion

During the 10 minute period consider the following:

1. Materials used during cell activity and growth enter the cell from the outside. Waste products go through the cell surface to the outside. Do you think the cell with the greatest total surface area will do the best job of moving materials in and out of the cell? Explain your answer.

2. Calculate the total surface area of each of your 3 models by using the following formula:

surface area = length × width × number of surfaces

3. Which cell model—the 3-cm cube, the 2-cm cube, or the 1-cm cube—has the greatest surface area?
4. Calculate the volume of each cube.

volume of cube = length × width × height

5. Do these calculations change your answer to question 1? Why or why not?

Part B

Procedure

1. At the end of 10 minutes, use the spoon to remove the cubes from the beaker or culture dish.
2. Blot them dry with the paper towel. Allow them to dry completely.
3. Slice each cube in half with the plastic knife.
4. Measure the outer colored zones with the mm ruler.

Discussion

1. What similarities did you notice when you measured the colored zone of each cube?
2. Which "cell" was apparently most efficient in receiving materials from the outside?
3. Recall your calculations of surface area and volume. Does either calculation explain what you have observed in your cell models? Why or why not?
4. Calculate a ratio of surface area to volume for each cube. To do this, for each cube, divide its surface area by its volume. For example, a surface area of 24 cm^2 divided by a volume of 3 cm^3 $= \frac{24}{3} = \frac{8}{1} =$ 8:1 (a ratio of 8 to 1). Record the ratio of surface area to volume for each cube.
5. Relate your calculated ratios to what you observed with the cell models.
6. How do your observations and your calculations relate to the question of why cells are usually very small?
7. Calculate the ratio of surface area to volume in a cell model that is 0.1 cm^3.
8. What predictions can you make about the cell model in question 7?
9. In what other ways could models be used in scientific research?

5.10 One Cell Divides into Two Cells

In preparation for cell reproduction, special events take place both in the nucleus and in the cytosol. These occur only when the cell is about ready to divide. First, most cells increase in size.

New cells usually contain the same structures as their parent cells. That means that the chromosomes, the organelles in the cytosol, and the plasma membrane all must be duplicated. Otherwise the offspring cells would be incomplete and unable to survive. The duplication of organelles takes place before the nucleus divides.

First the nucleus reproduces, by a complicated series of events called **mitosis** (my TOH sis). The word mitosis is derived from the Greek word for thread. The chromosomes are very threadlike in appearance, especially between cell divisions. Toward the end of mitosis the cytosol, with its organelles, divides. That part of cell division is called **cytokinesis** (syt oh kin NEE sus), which means cell motion.

A cell spends most of its life between divisions in **interphase** (INT er fayz). Cells appear to be inactive in interphase. Appearances can be misleading, however, for these cells are chemically very active. Much is going on, in both the nucleus and the cytosol.

In the nucleus the long, thin chromosomes are being duplicated. This duplication results when new nucleotide molecules (look again at section 4.14) are fitted together with the old ones in a special way. Thus, the genetic information in the chromosomes is copied exactly. This new information is exactly the same as the original information—a replica, in other words. This key process of making a copy of the genetic information is called **replication** (rep lih KAY shun).

You can think of this information, replicated each cell generation, as a program that the cell can call on as needed. Not all genetic information is needed or used by all cells in a higher organism, but all of it is replicated in all cells. In unicellular organisms, each new cell generation needs all the information.

Other events are taking place in the cytosol. New proteins are being made. Other molecules needed for the new cells are being gathered. The organelles are also duplicated in preparation for cell division. The mitochondria and chloroplasts, in addition to their complicated membrane structures, also have some genes of their own. These are replicated. All these activities require energy, raw materials, and enzymes.

Thus in its life a cell passes through two main stages: interphase and cell division. In interphase cells carry on their normal metabolic activities. They also prepare for the next division. During the preparatory time, the chromosomes, the organelles, and the cytosol become very active. After a complex set of events, cell division results in two offspring cells. The new offspring cells then enter interphase again and begin to prepare for the next division.

This repeated drama of cell division, over and over, is called the **cell cycle.** In a multicellular organism it continues until each cell achieves its final role in development. In unicellular organisms the cell cycle could be repeated forever, or until the species becomes extinct.

5.11 Cell Division Is a Continuous Process

Once it begins, cell division is a continuous process, beginning with mitosis and ending with cytokinesis. In studying cell division, however, we freeze the action at intervals. This is similar to looking at a single frame in a motion picture film. Biologists have given a special name to each phase of cell division.

The details of cell reproduction are described and shown in figure 5.22.

Figure 5.22 The cell cycle.

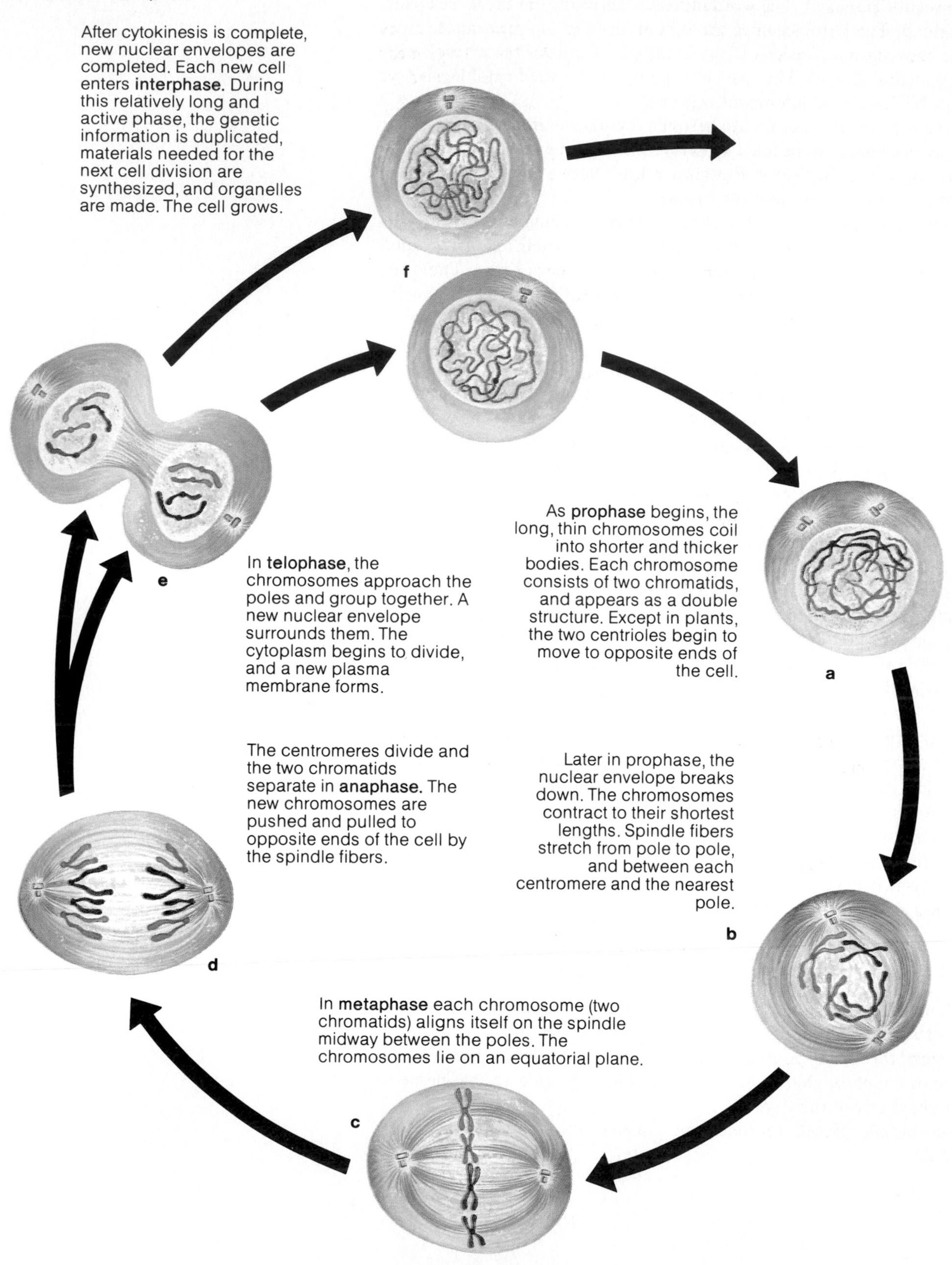

After cytokinesis is complete, new nuclear envelopes are completed. Each new cell enters **interphase.** During this relatively long and active phase, the genetic information is duplicated, materials needed for the next cell division are synthesized, and organelles are made. The cell grows.
f
As **prophase** begins, the long, thin chromosomes coil into shorter and thicker bodies. Each chromosome consists of two chromatids, and appears as a double structure. Except in plants, the two centrioles begin to move to opposite ends of the cell.
a
Later in prophase, the nuclear envelope breaks down. The chromosomes contract to their shortest lengths. Spindle fibers stretch from pole to pole, and between each centromere and the nearest pole.
b
In **metaphase** each chromosome (two chromatids) aligns itself on the spindle midway between the poles. The chromosomes lie on an equatorial plane.
c
The centromeres divide and the two chromatids separate in **anaphase.** The new chromosomes are pushed and pulled to opposite ends of the cell by the spindle fibers.
d
In **telophase**, the chromosomes approach the poles and group together. A new nuclear envelope surrounds them. The cytoplasm begins to divide, and a new plasma membrane forms.
e

The first stage of mitosis is called **prophase** (PROH fayz). Compared to the other stages, it can last for quite a long time. In the nucleus the chromosome strands slowly begin to coil, like tiny springs. In this way they gradually become shorter and thicker (figure 5.22a). The nuclear envelope begins to disappear. At this time, the thin chromosome strands are just barely visible under the microscope. Only then can we see that the chromosomes are double structures (figure 5.22b). This shows that the chromosomes have already replicated.

In the cytosol, meanwhile, the centrioles have duplicated and have started moving to opposite ends of the cell. They provide an organizing center from which a diamond-shaped structure of microtubules forms. This is called the spindle, because it resembles the spindle on old spinning wheels of the past. The spindle determines the direction of the future cell division. Some microtubules stretch from pole to pole. Others attach to the chromosomes and later guide them to opposite ends of the cell.

The rest of mitosis involves the orderly separation of the two strands of each chromosome. After the chromosomes have reached their shortest length, they move to the center of the cell. This stage (figure 5.22c) is called **metaphase** (MET uh fayz). You can imagine that the chromosomes lie in a plane perpendicular to the spindle. Each chromosome strand becomes attached to the spindle at the **centromere** (SEN troh meer), the special region of the chromosome that holds the strands together.

Eventually the cell enters **anaphase** (AN uh fayz), shown in figure 5.22d. The centromeres divide and the chromosome strands separate. They are pulled in opposite directions along the spindle toward the two poles of the dividing cell.

Now the final events of mitosis occur. This last stage (figure 5.22e) is called **telophase** (TEL oh fayz). The chromosomes gather at the poles. Two new nuclear envelopes form, surrounding each group of chromosomes. Thus, two new nuclei are formed.

Meanwhile, the other organelles, which reproduced themselves during interphase, segregate. The cytosol now divides into two parts, more or less equal in size. The new offspring cells become separated by a new plasma membrane that forms between them. Cell reproduction has been completed. The two new cells now have exactly the same genetic information as their parent cell.

The events of cell division in plants are about the same as in animals, as you can see in figures 5.23 and 5.24. The presence of a cell wall in many plant cells does complicate the process. The old cell wall must grow with the cell before division, and a new cell wall must be formed between the two offspring cells.

Figure 5.23 Dividing cells in onion root tip (×600).

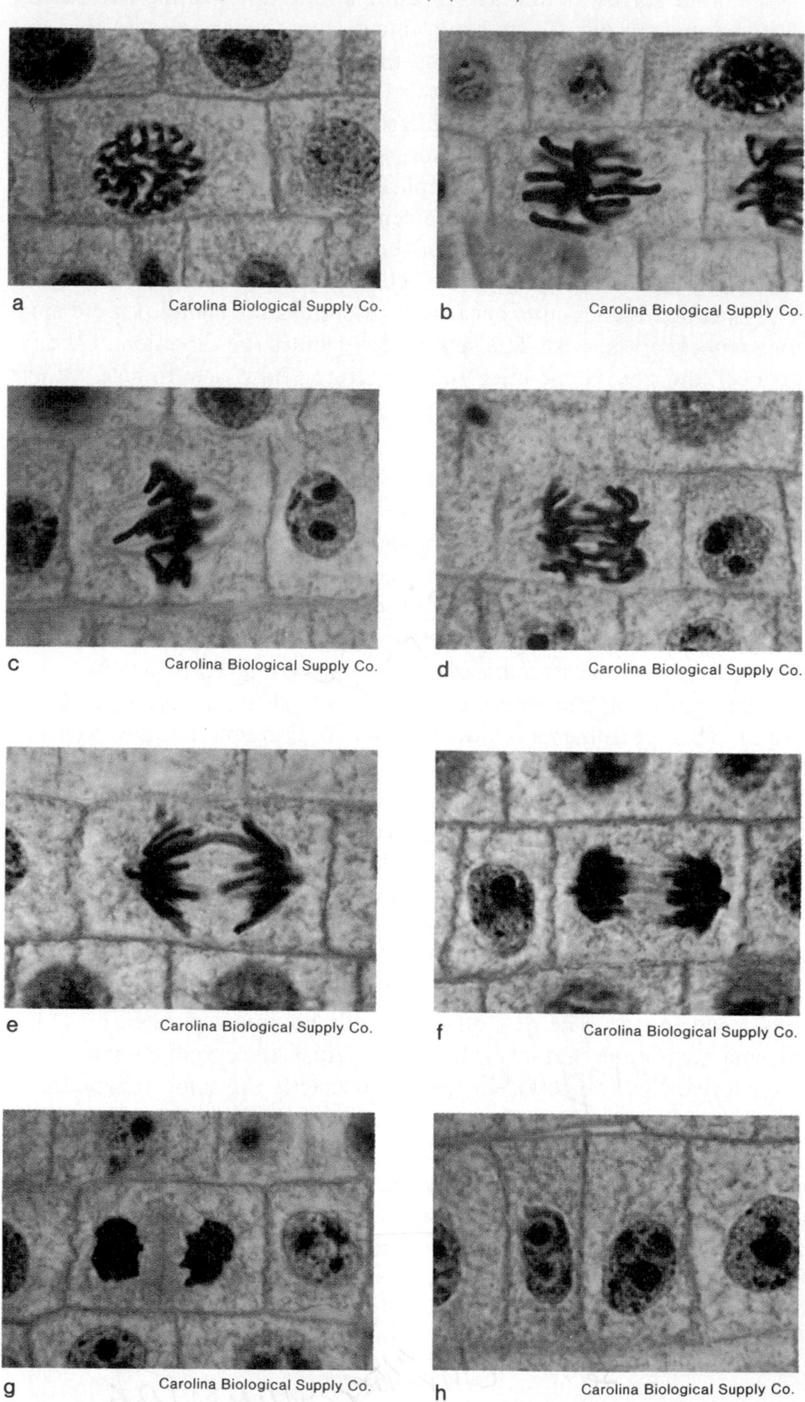

Figure 5.24 Mitosis in cells of whitefish embryos.

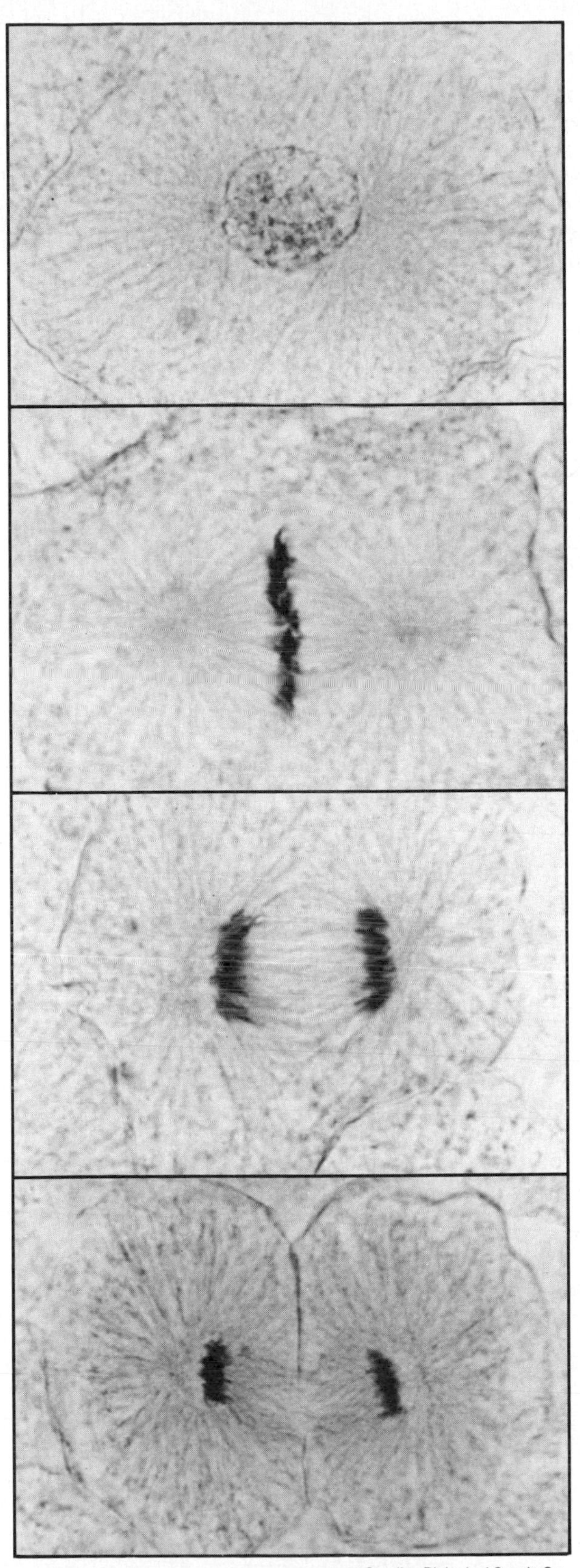

Carolina Biological Supply Co.

Investigation 5.4 MITOSIS AND CELL DIVISION IN PLANTS

Introduction

If an onion is placed in water and kept in the dark for several days, slender white roots sprout from it and grow into the water. This growth occurs partly by repeated duplication of cells. You might expect, therefore, to see cells in mitosis at the end of a root. Because mitosis is only a small segment of the cell cycle, cells in the root tip are not always dividing. It is easiest, therefore, to examine the stages of mitosis in stained, prepared slides that have been sliced very thin longitudinally.

Materials

prepared slides of *Allium* root tip
microscope

Procedure

1. Scan the entire length of the slide. Study each section first under low power, and then under high power.
   (a) In what region of the root tip are most of the cells that are undergoing mitosis?
   (b) How does the shape of cells undergoing mitosis compare with that of cells in other parts of the sections?
2. Study a number of cells in different stages of mitosis, plus several which do not appear to be dividing. Sketch at least 5 entire cells, each in a different stage of mitosis. Number your drawings in the order in which you think the stages occur during mitosis.

Discussion

1. Refer to the illustrations of dividing animal and plant cells on pages 156 and 157. What differences, if any, can you find in the ways mitosis and cell division occur in animal and plant cells?

For Further Investigation

1. Suppose you suspected that frequency of mitosis in onion roots varied with the time of day. How would you go about getting data to confirm or refute your suspicion?
2. Do all the events in mitosis take about the same time, or do some of them occur faster than others? Design an experiment to answer the question.

5.12 Cells Become Specialized in Development

Complex organisms, such as yourself, develop from a single cell, as we shall see in the next chapter. The cell divides, forming a tiny **embryo.** As the embryo grows and develops, the cells increase in number and become more and more different during development. This process is called **differentiation** (dif er en chee AY shun). During development, a human being may form some 200 different kinds of cells by differentiation. Each kind of cell has a specialized function.

As cells become specialized, their divisions may become more distinctive. For instance, different kinds of cells may require different amounts of time to complete cell division. Some bacteria divide very rapidly and produce a new cell generation every 20 minutes or so under ideal conditions. In complex organisms, however, cell divisions take much longer. Some cells divide about every eight hours, but others divide only once every several months. Certain kinds of cells—such as muscle and nerve cells—almost never divide in adults. You have all the nerve cells you will ever get.

Almost all normal cells give rise to a limited number of divisions—usually no more than 50. There appears to be a brake on cell division, although the reason is not known. Some cells seem to lose this control, however, and divide rapidly and abnormally, often at the expense of the organism. These are cancer cells, shown in figure 5.25. They have lost their control over growth and cell division and divide again and again. If cancer cells are not controlled or removed, they may cause the death of the entire organism.

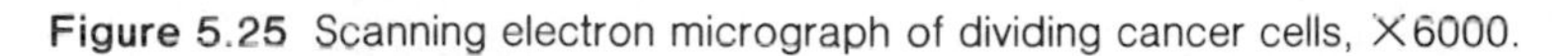

Figure 5.25 Scanning electron micrograph of dividing cancer cells, ×6000.

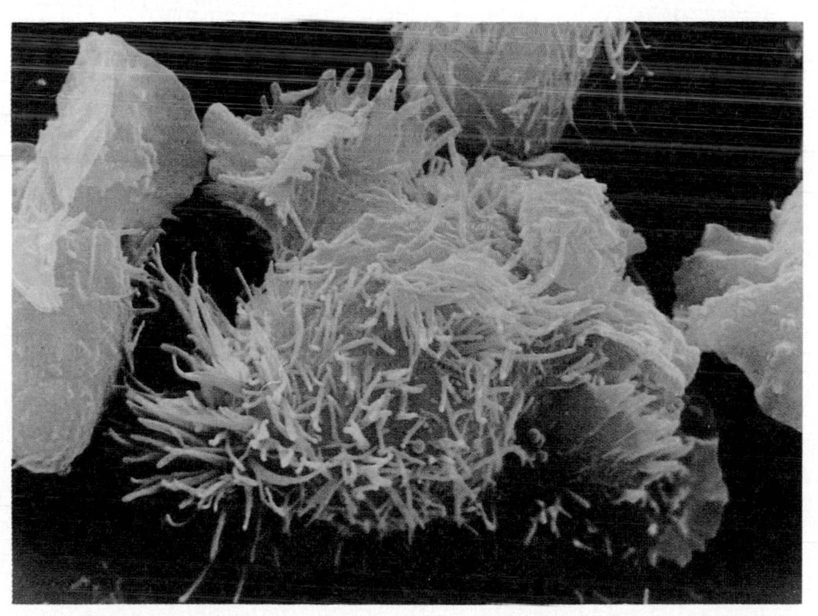

David M. Phillips/VISUALS UNLIMITED

5.13 Cell Division Is Essential to Life

Cells live for a limited time, and life can continue on earth only through repeated cell division. The complex events of cell division ensure that there is accurate reproduction of chromosomes, including their genes. Chloroplasts and mitochondria and their genes also must be reproduced and transmitted to the next cell generation. Although accidents do happen, most cells receive complete and correct genetic information. The genes of both chromosomes and organelles help regulate the activities of a cell.

We can conclude, therefore, that accurate cell division is essential for the continuation of life. When the processes of cell reproduction are interrupted or interfered with, abnormal cell activities (such as are seen in cancer cells) result, or death of cells occurs.

Self-Review

1. What is one factor that limits the size of cells?
2. What is the role of the spindle in mitosis?
3. In cell division, what does the term replication mean?
4. What are the two main events of cell division?
5. What happens to the new chromosomes at the end of mitosis?
6. In your own words, describe the whole process of mitosis.
7. What do you think is the biological importance of cell division?

Summary

Cells are the basic units of organisms. Knowing about cells helps us to understand how organisms are built and how they work. Since most cells are invisible to the naked eye, microscopes are used to study their structures in detail.

A cell is surrounded by a plasma membrane that helps control the passage of materials in and out of the cytoplasm. Substances move by diffusion, or by active transport, which requires energy. Within the cell is its control center, the nucleus. There are also a number of other kinds of organelles, each with a certain job to do. Metabolism, the chemical reactions of a cell, takes place both in the organelles and in the cytosol, the fluid part of the cytoplasm.

The nucleus contains most of the genes, which control the basic functions of a cell. The genes in the nucleus are located in long, thin chromosomes. Each chromosome replicates itself in interphase of the cell cycle. During mitosis and cell division the doubled chromosomes separate, the cytoplasm divides, and two new cells are formed from one existing cell.

All cells arise from existing cells. Each cell thus receives genetic instructions from its parent cell. In the development of complex organisms many different types of cells are formed. Each type of cell has a specific structure and function. Life continues through cell division.

Application Questions

1. During the late 19th century most knowledge of detailed cell structure was gained by studying dead cells. Some biologists objected to many conclusions drawn from such observation. They argued that the processes of killing, staining, and mounting slides might cause cell structure to appear very different from that in living cells. What kinds of evidence are available today to meet at least some of these objections?
2. While working in a police laboratory, you are given a tiny sample of material and asked to identify it as either plant or animal matter. How could you decide which it is?
3. On the basis of your understanding of the diffusion of water, describe what would happen to (a) a marine jellyfish placed in a freshwater stream and (b) a frog placed in ocean water. Some fish (for example, shad and striped bass) annually swim from the ocean into freshwater rivers and back. How are they able to do this?
4. One standard form of therapy for cancer is radiation. Why is radiation effective against cancer cells? (Hint: radiation is also harmful to a developing human in the uterus.)

Problems

1. Examine various kinds of cells from multicellular organisms, either under the microscope or by means of photomicrographs in books. Discuss the relationships between the structural forms of the different cells and their functions.
2. This chapter describes mitosis in cells that have single, well-defined nuclei. Investigate what is known about what happens to nuclear material (chromatin) during division in (a) a cell that lacks a nucleus (a cyanobacterium, for example), and (b) a cell with more than one nucleus (*Paramecium*, for example).
3. In unicellular organisms, cells usually separate shortly after division. In some, however, they remain attached, forming colonies. In multicellular organisms they remain attached, but more strongly in some cases than in others. Investigate the ways in which the cells are held together.

Suggested Readings

C. deDuve, "Microbodies in the Living Cell" *Scientific American* (May 1983). Describes the several different types of subcellular organelles that are linked by superficial structural similarities.

L. Hayflick, "The Cell Biology of Human Aging" *Scientific American* (January 1980). Cell cultures reveal the processes that limit the human lifespan.

K. R. Porter and J. B. Tucker, "The Ground Substance of the Living Cell" *Scientific American* (March 1981). High-resolution electron microscopy has revealed the microtrabecular lattice: a system of filaments that support and move the cell organelles.

E. Rubenstein, "Diseases Caused by Impaired Communication among Cells" *Scientific American* (March 1980). Good explanations of mediators and receptors, how substances enter and affect cells, and how mediators produce their effects.

Scientific American (October 1985). This issue, entitled "The Molecules of Life," contains several articles relating to cellular activities.

John Gerlach / TOM STACK & ASSOCIATES

Red-spotted toads (*Bufo punctatus*) mating.

CHAPTER 6

Continuity through Reproduction

Introduction

In the last chapter you learned how cells arise from existing cells. When cells reproduce, life continues from one cell generation to the next. In this chapter you will see that cell reproduction is only one aspect of the continuity of life on earth.

Most kinds of cells reproduce fairly directly, such as when one amoeba divides to form two offspring amoebas. In organisms that are larger and consist of many cells, reproduction is more complicated. You are now ready to look at some of the ways that organisms reproduce themselves. We will give special attention to human reproduction.

Reproduction

Guidepost: Why is reproduction essential for all living beings?

6.1 Reproduction Is Essential to Life

All organisms alive today arose from preexisting organisms. A new organism grows and develops. Eventually it becomes large enough and mature enough to reproduce. Some organisms, such as bacteria, reproduce after 20 minutes or so of life. Others require months or years to become mature.

For many small organisms, reproduction is a one-time event. On the other hand, complex organisms may continue to reproduce for days, months, or years. These reproductive periods may form a large part of their **life cycle.** The life cycle of an organism includes all the events that occur between the beginning of one generation and the beginning of the next one. Life cycles are continuous, and in a diagram they often are shown as circles.

Figure 6.1 Reproduction in a variety of organisms. (a) strawberry, (b) planarian, (c) *Bryophyllum*, (d) hydra (e) bacterium ×72,000.

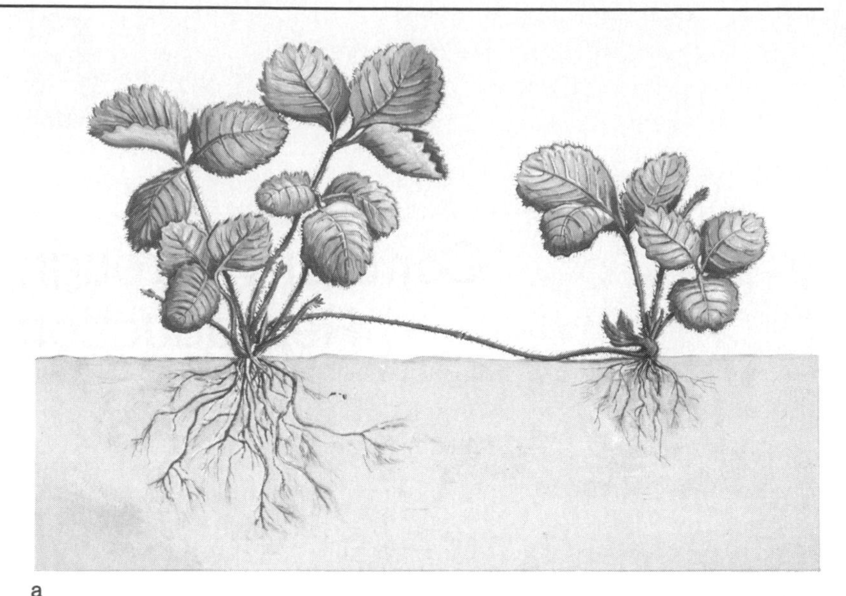

a

b

c

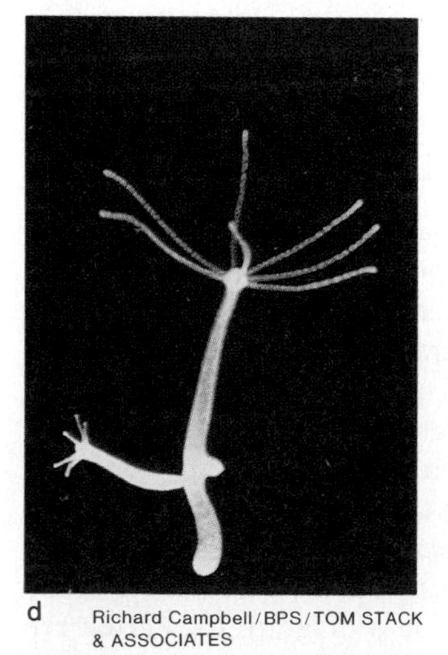

d Richard Campbell/BPS/TOM STACK & ASSOCIATES

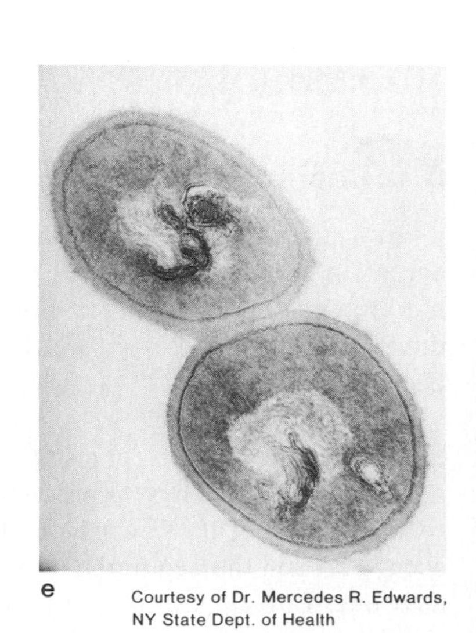

e Courtesy of Dr. Mercedes R. Edwards, NY State Dept. of Health

Some organisms, such as humans, may live longer than their reproductive periods. Other organisms with long lifespans continue to reproduce. The giant tortoises of the Galápagos Islands may live for 125 years. Amazingly, some bristlecone pines living in California are almost 5000 years old; they were alive at the time the great pyramids were built in Egypt.

Even though some organisms live for a long time, no organism lives forever. The lifespan of an organism is part of its genetic program. Not all organisms live out their genetic lifespans, however. Some die because of infections, other diseases, or accidents. The secret of biological success is to reproduce and leave offspring before a fatal illness or accident occurs—such as an animal being eaten by a predator. When organisms do reproduce successfully, their species will continue into future years. A species will become extinct if its members do not produce enough offspring to offset losses by accidents and disease.

6.2 Reproduction May Be Sexual or Asexual

In larger, more complex organisms, reproduction involves two different cells, usually from two parents, and is called **sexual reproduction.** Human beings reproduce sexually.

On the other hand, many organisms are able to produce more of their own kind by nonsexual means. In **asexual** (AY SEK shoo ul) **reproduction** new individuals originate from a single parent. That single parent either divides into two (or more) individuals, or else new individuals arise as buds from the parent's body.

Many kinds of plants reproduce asexually by a process called **vegetative reproduction.** Potato farmers in Maine or Idaho, for example, plant their crops in the spring. They cut potatoes into small pieces, but each piece must contain an "eye." Each little eye, which appears to be a small indentation or bump, is actually a small bud.

You may have noticed that if potatoes are left in a dark, cool, moist place the buds will sprout and begin to grow. In the same way, when potato eyes are planted, they will sprout in the soil and begin to grow. Eventually the bud will produce a shoot and roots, and an entire new potato plant will appear.

Figure 6.2 (a) Sprouting potato. (b) A piece of potato bud containing a bud will produce an entire new plant when planted.

a BSCS by Doug Sokell

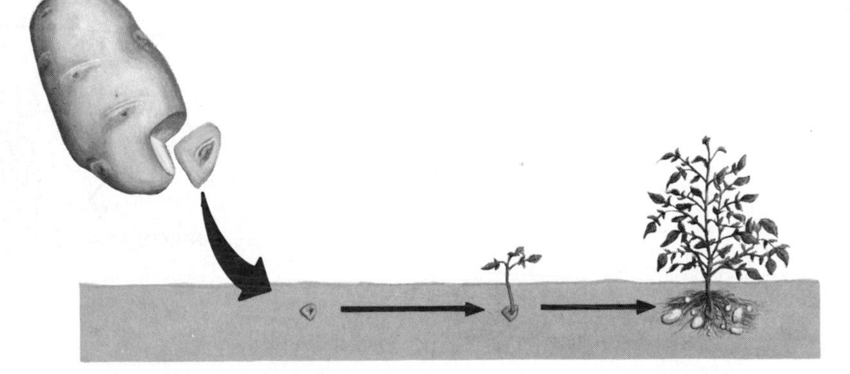

b

Investigation 6.1 VEGETATIVE REPRODUCTION

Introduction

Coleus is a plant that usually does not reproduce vegetatively. However, gardeners often cause it to do so. In this investigation you will explore the conditions in which vegetative reproduction occurs.

Materials (per team)

live coleus plant
shallow flowerpot, 15- to 20-cm diameter
stone or piece of broken pot
enough sand to fill flowerpot
saucer or shallow pan
4 pot labels
scalpel
plastic bag
string

Procedure

1. Place a large stone or a piece of broken pot over the drainage hole in the flowerpot. Pour sand into the pot to within 2 cm of the rim. Place the pot in a saucer or shallow pan.
2. Water the sand thoroughly. Pour excess water from the saucer.
3. Using a pencil, divide the surface of the sand into quarter sections. Mark 4 pot labels A, B, C, and D. Place a label along the outer edge of each section (see figure 6.3).
4. Using a scalpel, take 4 cuttings from the coleus plant. Three of these (A, B, and C) must each have 3 pairs of leaves and a terminal bud. The 4th cutting (D) must be at least 5 cm long. It must be taken from *between* pairs of leaves. If possible, obtain D and 1 of the other cuttings from the same plant.

Figure 6.3

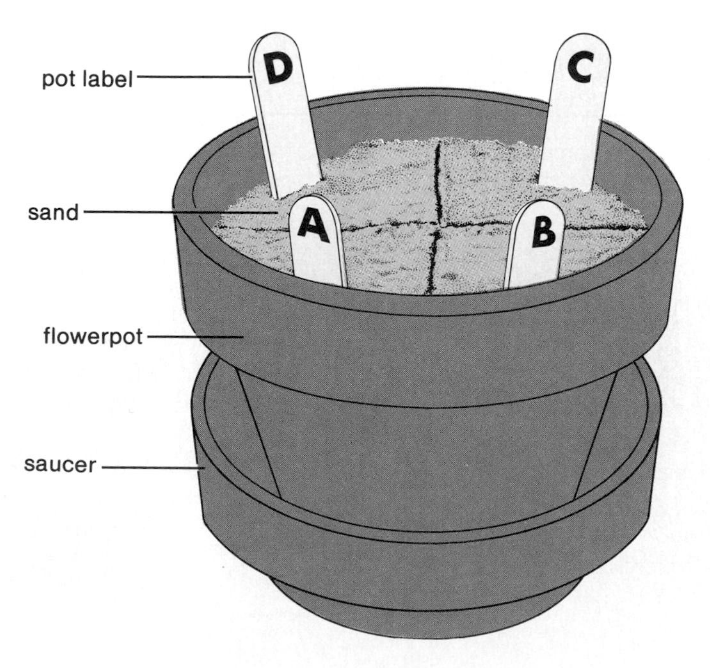

5. Remove the bottom pair of leaves from cutting A. With a pencil, make a hole in the sand in the center of section A. Insert cutting A into the hole so that the lower pair of leaves is just above the sand. Press the sand together around the cutting.
6. From cutting B remove the tip of the branch and all but the uppermost pair of leaves. Make a hole in the center of section B, and plant as you did cutting A.
7. Prepare cutting C just as you did B. Plant it in section C. Then remove its remaining pair of leaves.
8. Place cutting D so that at least 5 mm project above the level of the sand.
9. Cover the cuttings with a plastic bag. Fasten the bag's open end around the rim of the pot with a string.
10. Set the pots containing the coleus plant and the cuttings in a place where they will receive abundant light. Add water to the saucer whenever necessary.
11. After about 3 weeks, examine the plant from which the cuttings were taken. What, if anything, has happened at the points where cuttings were removed?
12. Remove the plastic cover from the pot containing the cuttings and examine them. Which ones seem to be alive? In each case, what is the evidence for your decision?
13. Loosen the sand and remove the cuttings. Examine them carefully. Answer the following questions about each one.
    (a) Have roots developed? If so, at what points on the cutting?
    (b) What, if anything, has happened to the cut surface?
    (c) What, if anything, has happened to the tip of the cutting?

Discussion

1. First consider only the plant from which the cuttings were taken. What evidence do you have that coleus has the ability to regenerate parts lost by injury?
2. Now consider the evidence from the cuttings. To what extent might the accidental breaking up of a coleus plant (by a hailstorm, for example) result in the reproduction of coleus plants?

For Further Investigation

Use this procedure to investigate and compare the abilities of other plant species to reproduce vegetatively. Plants such as tomato, household geranium, begonia, bean, pepper, marigold, and zinnia can be used.

6.3 Some Animals Show Both Kinds of Reproduction

It is interesting that some animals and plants can reproduce in more than one way. For instance, some organisms that usually reproduce sexually also may be able to reproduce asexually and, as a result, increase their chances of survival. Other organisms may have asexual reproduction as their main method.

Starfish, which usually produce sexually, illustrate this feature. To obtain food, starfish may invade oyster beds in coastal water. Starfish can open the oyster shells with their powerful arms and then feast on the oysters inside.

Figure 6.4 This starfish is regenerating an entire new body from the long arm on the right.

Brian Parker/TOM STACK & ASSOCIATES

To protect the oysters, scuba divers at one time collected the starfish in the oyster beds. Then they "destroyed" the starfish by cutting off their arms and throwing the pieces back into the water. What they did not realize at the time was that a starfish arm can regenerate an entire starfish if part of the central body is attached to it. So, in their efforts to eliminate starfish from the oyster beds, the divers actually increased the starfish population.

Self-Review

1. What is the main difference between sexual and asexual reproduction?
2. What do vegetative reproduction and regeneration have in common?
3. How do some organisms use two different kinds of reproduction?

Guidepost: How do gametes differ from other cells?

Sexual Reproduction

6.4 Gametes Are Reproductive Cells

Sexual reproduction is very important in the continuation of life on Earth. It affects the behavior of organisms, their genetic natures, and their evolution. Because it usually combines genetic material from two different organisms, sexual reproduction increases the amount of genetic variation in a population. This variation is very important to the evolution of populations by natural selection, as you will see in chapter 9. We will be studying sexual reproduction in animals. Sexual reproduction in plants is similar in principle.

The main point of sexual reproduction is quite simple. A new individual begins as a union of nuclei from two different parental organisms. Usually each parent of a new organism produces a different kind of specialized reproductive cell. Each reproductive cell contains a nucleus. One parent may produce relatively large, stationary cells. The other parent may produce smaller cells that can move about. In some organisms, the reproductive cells of both parents are similar and motile.

In sexual reproduction only certain kinds of cells can unite to form a new individual. These cells are called **gametes** (GAM eets). They usually differ in appearance from other cells of the body, and they contain fewer genes.

There are two main types of gametes: **sperm cells** and **egg cells.** Sperm cells are produced by males, and they are usually quite small. (The word sperm can be used to refer to one sperm cell or to many sperm cells.) A sperm cell consists of little more than a nucleus, a tail that can move the cell about, and an energy generator in its mitochondria.

The other kind of gamete, produced by females, is an egg cell, or **ovum.** An ovum may be large, sometimes thousands of times larger than a sperm cell. In addition to its nucleus, it often contains a reserve food supply. Ova and sperm of several organisms are compared in figure 6.5.

Figure 6.5 Eggs and sperm of several organisms. Note that the sperm are enlarged much more than the eggs, and direct comparison between the two is not possible. In chicken, snake, frog and fish, the ova are surrounded by other materials (shown in outline).

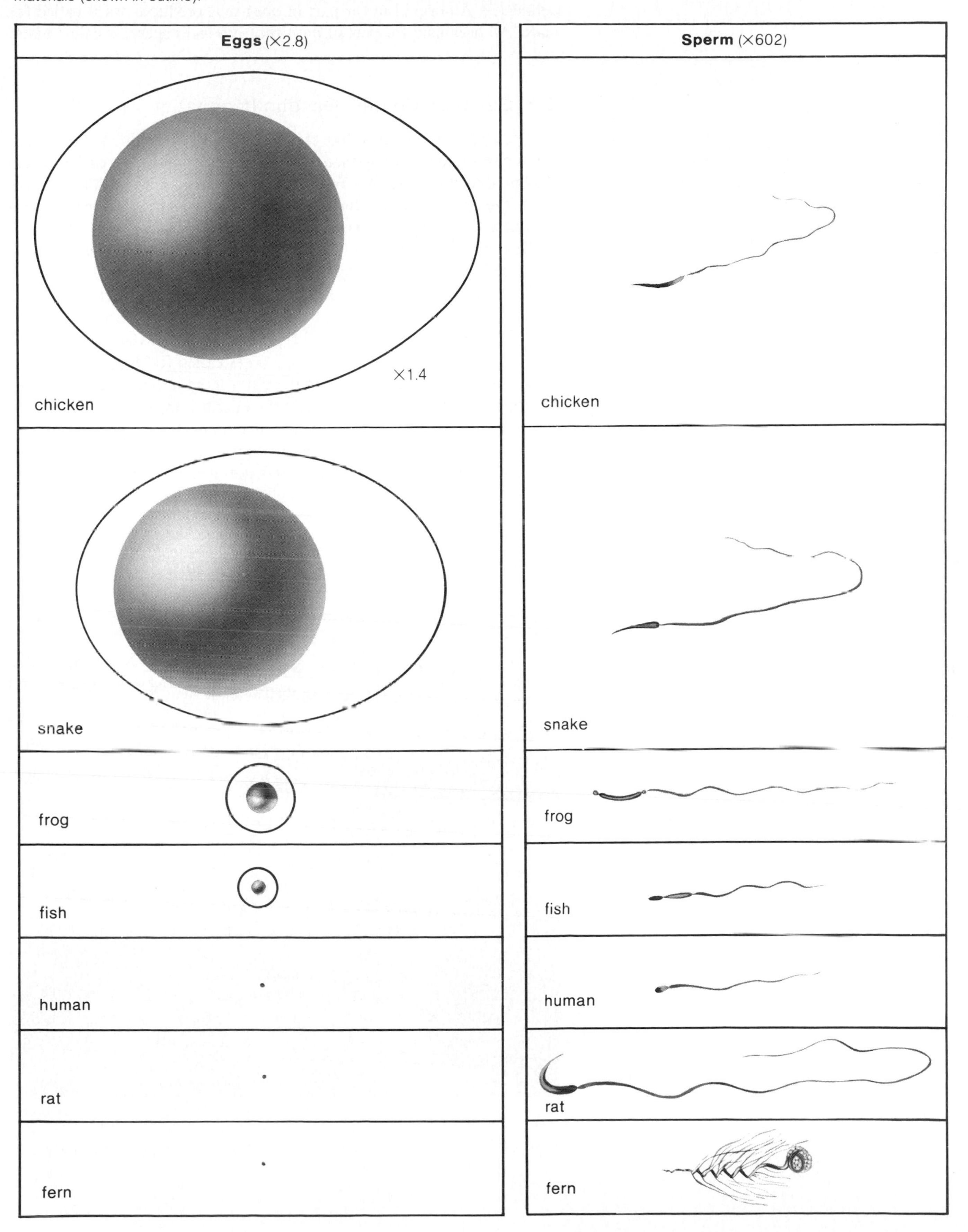

It is mainly these differences in size and function of gametes that define sex. An organism (or part of one) that produces ova is called **female.** An organism (or part of one) that produces sperm is called **male.**

6.5 Gametes Contain Genetic Information

The nuclei of gametes, like those of all cells, contain chromosomes. Each chromosome in a gamete carries genes from the parent organism that produced the gamete. When parents form sperm or ova and reproduce, they pass genetic information to their offspring. The new individuals then develop in response to these genetic instructions.

Gametes do not contain as many chromosomes as are present in the other cells of the parent organism. Instead, each gamete contains only half as many chromosomes as a typical body cell. The particular chromosomes (and genes) a gamete contains is partly a matter of chance. We will soon see how this game of genetic dice is played.

A sperm and an ovum unite in a process called **fertilization.** A sperm fertilizes an ovum by penetrating the outer membranes of the ovum and entering its cytoplasm. In that way the sperm introduces its genes into the ovum. Each new fertilized egg is called a **zygote** (ZY goht). A zygote joins together the two gametes. In this way, genes from both parents also are joined together in the zygote, and the development of a new individual can begin.

Figure 6.6 Sea urchin egg covered with sperm. Scanning electron micrograph, ×1600.

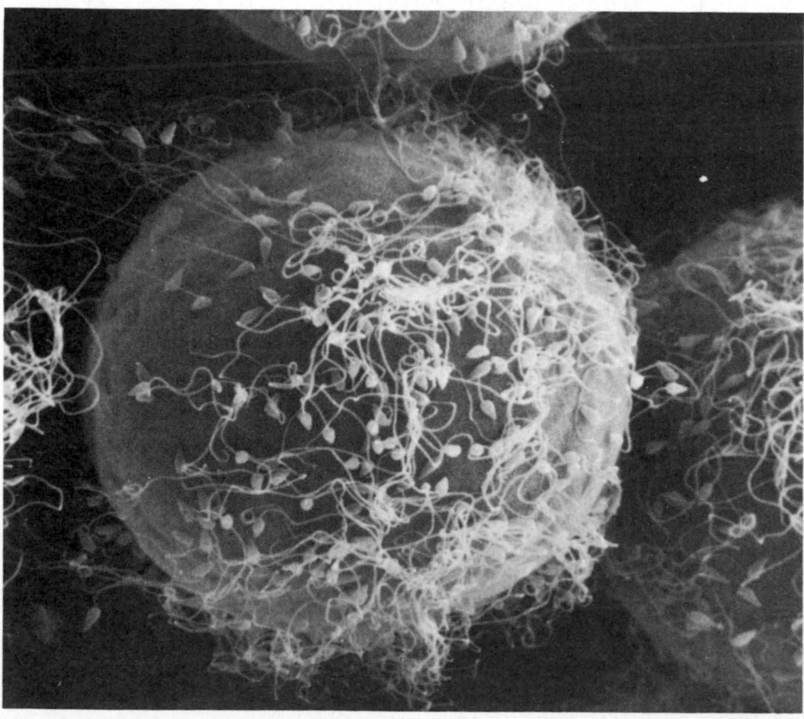

Dr. Mia Tegner, Scripps Institution of Oceanography

6.6 Gametes Are Unusual Kinds of Cells

Late in the 19th century, biologists learned how to stain the long, thin chromosomes in the nucleus. The name chromosome, in fact, means colored body. After chromosomes were stained, cell biologists were able to study and count the chromosomes of many kinds of plants and animals. They also worked out the detailed steps of cell division, which were described in chapter 5.

Cell biologists learned that the body cells of each species contain a definite number of chromosomes. Now we know, for example, that the body cells of corn plants have 20 chromosomes. The common fruit fly, used in genetic research, has 8 chromosomes. Human beings have 46 chromosomes in each body cell.

Another important fact was discovered: each chromosome in a cell has a partner of the same length and appearance. It became clear that chromosomes occur in pairs. Because genes are in the chromosomes, genes also occur in pairs. This information is essential for understanding how characteristics are inherited.

The total genetic content of the chromosomes of a cell is called its **genome** (JEE nohm). In human cells the genome consists of 23 pairs of chromosomes.

Each member of a chromosome pair is called a **homolog** (HOH moh log). In other words, a pair of chromosomes consists of two homologs that are similar in appearance; they also usually contain the same kinds of genes.

Biologists learned that one homolog of each pair comes from the sperm, and the other one from the ovum. In other words, of the 46 chromosomes of a human zygote, 23 came from the sperm and 23 from the ovum. Each parent contributes half the chromosomes of the total number in the genome.

Figure 6.7 Metaphase chromosomes in a root tip cell of the hyacinth, *Hyacinthus orientalis*. The chromatids and centromeres are clearly visible. Root tips are first treated for several hours with a chemical that disrupts the spindle and allows the chromosomes to spread. Then they are fixed in a solution that preserves cell structures, softened in acid so the cells can be spread, and stained.

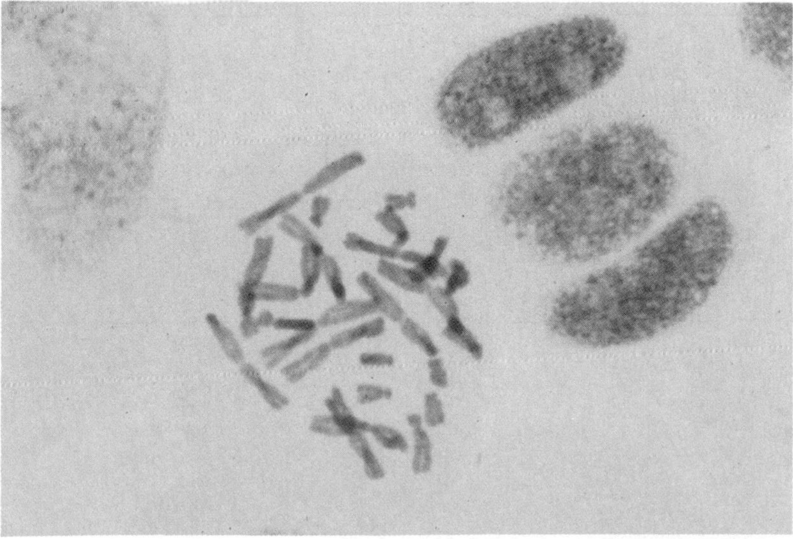

BSCS by Werner Heim

Figure 6.8 Gametes unite in the process of fertilization. The new individual has a combination of chromosomes from the two gametes.

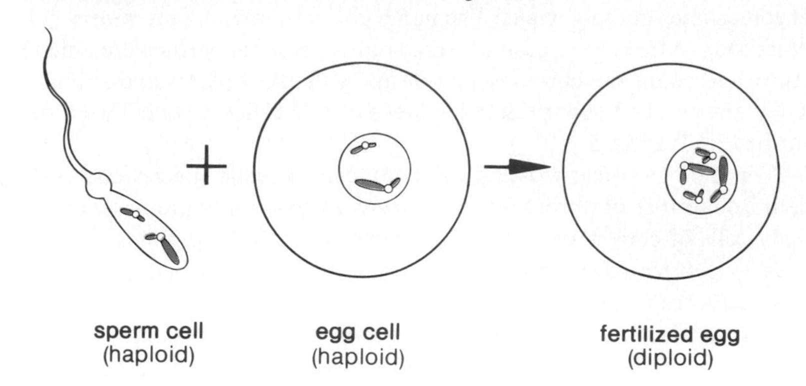

We now can think of zygotes as containing two sets of very similar chromosomes. Each gamete thus contains one set of chromosomes. This set has the **haploid** (HAP loyd) or N number of chromosomes. The gamete is, therefore, a haploid cell; when two gametes unite in fertilization, two haploid cells join together (figure 6.8).

The total number of chromosomes in the zygote, and in all body cells of an individual, is known as the **diploid** (DIP loyd) or 2N number. A human body cell contains a diploid number of 46 chromosomes—23 pairs.

In the life cycle of each sexually reproducing organism, the diploid number of chromosomes in the reproductive cells must be reduced by one-half, to the haploid (N) number, before reproduction. Otherwise the number of chromosomes would double in each generation, and soon they would fill the cell completely.

It is this reduction of chromosome number to one-half the total (2N to N) that permits sexual reproduction to occur. We shall see that it also introduces another element of chance into life, because it permits great numbers of new combinations of genes. This reduction of chromosome number takes place in a special cell division process called **meiosis** (my OH sis).

Self-Review

1. How many pairs of chromosomes does the human genome contain?
2. Name the two main types of gametes.
3. What is the biological distinction between male and female?
4. How do gametes differ from other cells of the body?
5. How many sets of chromosomes does each gamete contain?
6. How many sets of chromosomes does each body cell contain?
7. How is a zygote formed?

Meiosis

Guidepost: What are the main differences between mitosis and meiosis?

6.7 Gametes Are Produced in Special Organs

The number of chromosomes is reduced from diploid to haploid when gametes are formed. This reduction in chromosome number takes place during meiosis. Meiosis requires two cell divisions, one after the other. At the end of the second cell division, a gamete contains the haploid number of chromosomes.

The stages of meiosis are similar to those of mitosis, but there are important differences. Because the phrases have similar names, it is sometimes easy to get confused. Review the stages of mitosis in section 5.11 and figure 5.22 before you study the next sections on meiosis. Then you will be prepared to recognize the differences between meiosis and mitosis.

Meiosis occurs in special reproductive organs. Such an organ, where gametes are produced, is called a **gonad** (GOH nad) in animals. In male animals the gonads are **testes** (singular, **testis**) and in females they are **ovaries** (singular, **ovary**). The organs that produce male and female gametes in plants have various names, depending on the kind of plant.

Ovaries and testes are made of the usual kind of diploid (2N) body cells. At a certain time in the life cycle of an animal, however, some of the cells in a gonad enter meiosis. They begin a series of chromosome and cell changes that lead eventually to the formation of haploid (N) sperm or ova.

If we study these changes under the microscope, we can see how meiosis differs from mitosis. All the steps of meiosis can be viewed in the testis of an animal such as a grasshopper. Grasshopper chromosomes are larger than human chromosomes and, therefore, easier to study.

6.8 Meiosis Requires Two Nuclear Divisions

Before they enter meiosis, the future reproductive cells continue to divide by mitosis. In each cell cycle before meiosis the DNA is replicated during interphase, as usual. This synthesis of new DNA results in twin structures. Each chromosome at this time consists of two threadlike structures, which are still connected at the single centromere (figure 6.10a). We call them twins because they contain identical DNA; they are genetically the same. Each twin is called a **chromatid** (KROH muh tid) at this stage.

After meiosis begins in a cell, no more DNA is made. The DNA already present is distributed by meiosis to the reproductive cells. This happens in two different nuclear divisions, one after the other. The first nuclear division is called Meiosis I, and the second division, which usually follows immediately, is called Meiosis II.

6.9 Chromosome Number Is Reduced by Half in Meiosis I

At the start of meiosis, just as in mitosis, the long, thin chromosomes shorten and thicken. This shortening takes place during prophase of the first division of meiosis—prophase I. As the chromosomes thicken, something very different from mitosis happens. Each homolog finds its

Figure 6.9 Early (a) and late (b) prophase of the first meiotic division in formation of pollen grains in *Lilium* anthers. Note the homologs twisted around each other in (b).

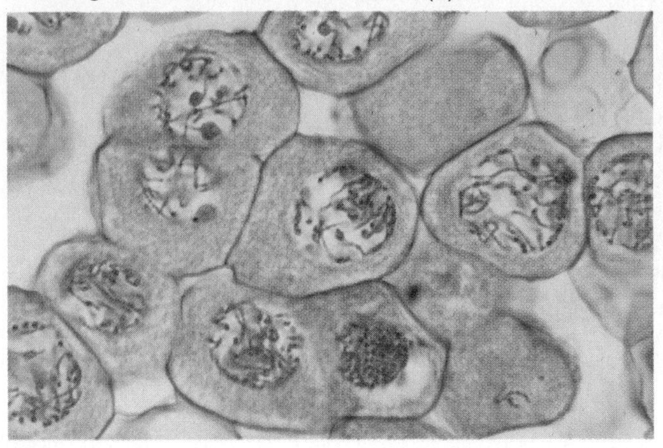

a John D. Cunningham/VISUALS UNLIMITED

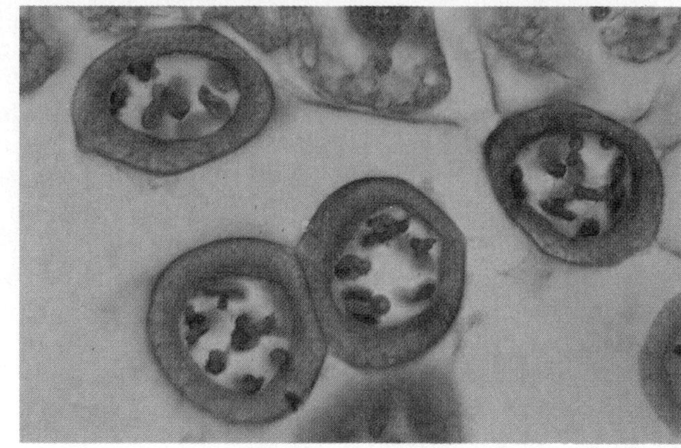

b John D. Cunningham/VISUALS UNLIMITED

Figure 6.10 Events of crossing over in prophase I. (a) Tetrad of homologous chromosomes. (b) Homologs twisted around each other. (c) Recombination has occurred.

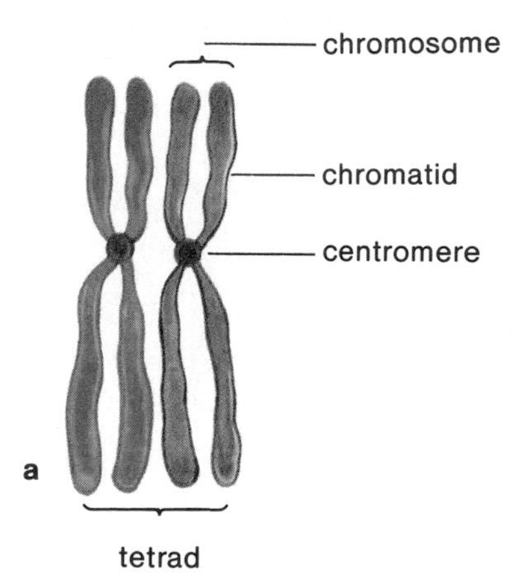

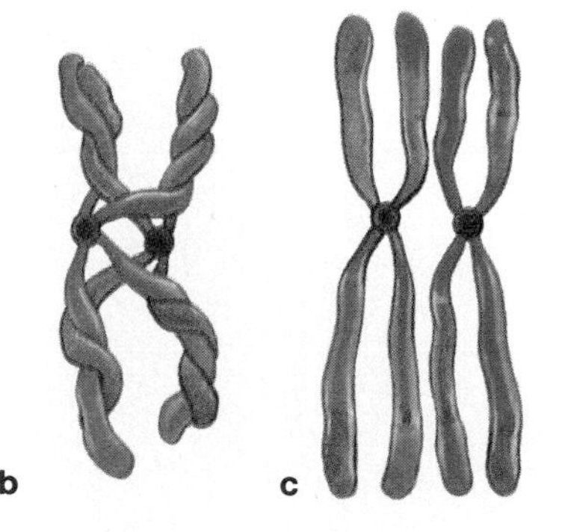

partner, and they pair with one another along their entire lengths. Because of that action, one now sees N pairs of chromosomes instead of 2N separate chromosomes. In a human ovary, for example, one would see 23 pairs of chromosomes, instead of 46 separate chromosomes. The following sections describe meiosis in the formation of sperm cells; the accompanying photographs show meiosis in the formation of pollen grains in the lily.

Because each chromosome is now made up of two chromatids, each pair of chromosomes actually consists of a bundle of four chromatids, as shown in figure 6.10a. This is sometimes called the tetrad stage (*tetra* means "four" in Greek). Knowing about the tetrad stage is the secret to understanding what happens in meiosis.

During this time the two homologs lie very close, and often are twisted around one another (figure 6.10b). Their chromatids actually can break at various places and join with broken chromatids from the other homolog. Breaks first occur at the same place in two chromatids, followed by joining and healing of the breaks (figure 6.10c). Because chromatid segments are exchanged, this process is called **crossing over,** and results in recombination of genes. The genes in the new chromatids are often in new combinations and much new genetic variation results from this process of recombination in prophase I.

Figure 6.11 Metaphase I

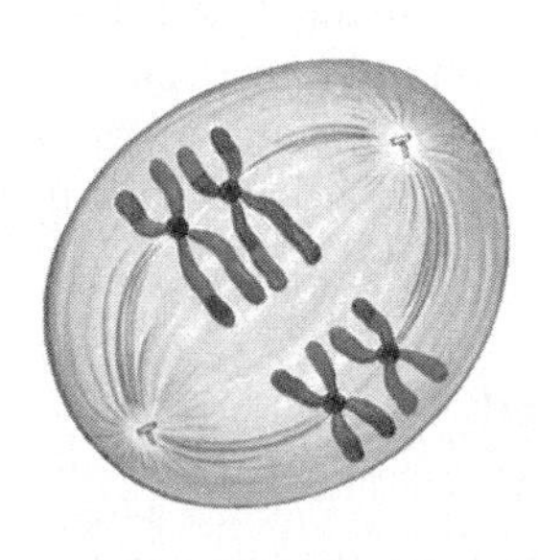

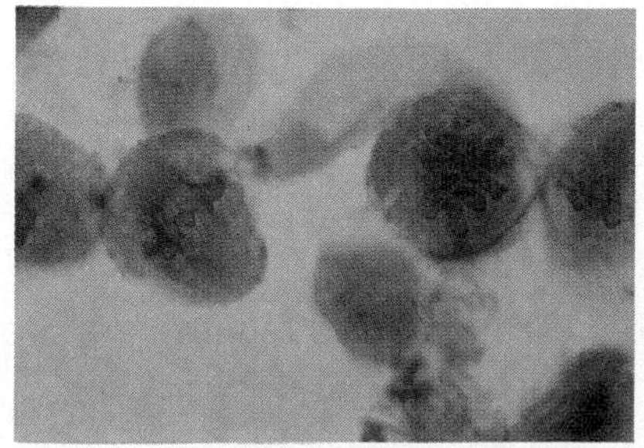

John D. Cunningham/VISUALS UNLIMITED

Toward the end of prophase I the chromosome pairs (still tetrads) move to the equatorial plate, just as in mitosis. Metaphase I (figure 6.11) marks their arrival in the center of the cell.

Figure 6.12 Anaphase I

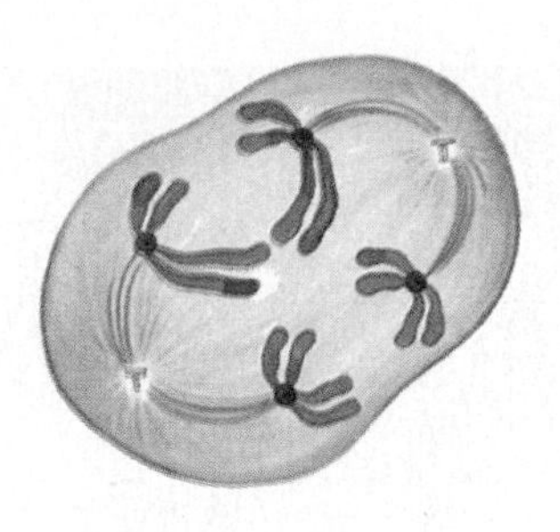

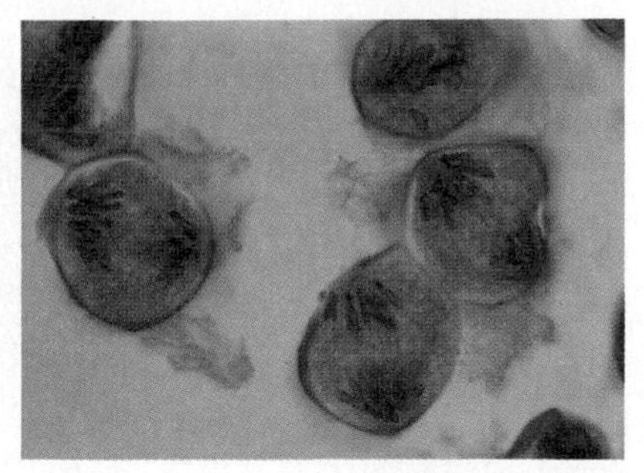

John D. Cunningham / VISUALS UNLIMITED

Now another important event takes place. In anaphase I (figure 6.12) the homologs of each pair separate and begin to move toward opposite poles of the spindle. Remember that each chromosome still consists of two chromatids, attached at the centromere. In human meiosis, 23 chromosomes move toward each pole of the spindle.

Figure 6.13 Telophase I

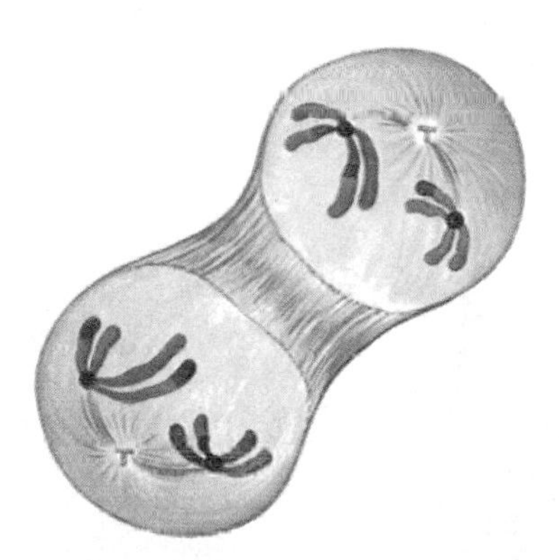

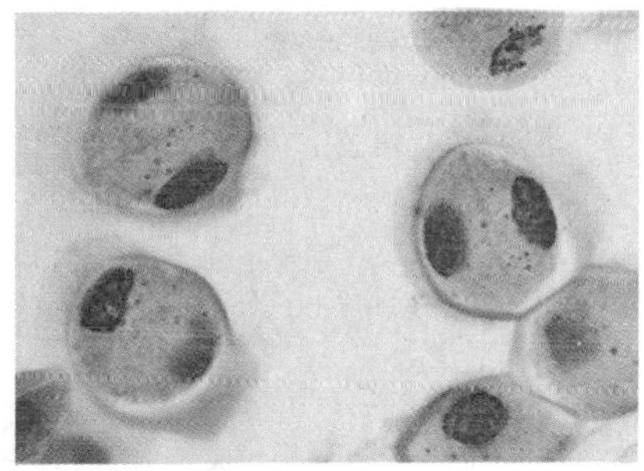

John D. Cunningham / VISUALS UNLIMITED

The homologs, one from each pair, continue to move in opposite directions. As they approach the poles in telophase I, cytokinesis occurs, and two cells are formed (figure 6.13). The homologs are now in different cells for the first time since they were brought together by fertilization in the zygote. Each new cell now has only half as many chromosomes as in a body cell. That means that each cell has only half the parent cell's total genetic information.

This series of events, from the start of meiosis to the formation of two cells, is Meiosis I. Because the amount of genetic information has been reduced by one-half, this division is often called the reduction division. There is still one more nuclear division before meiosis is complete.

6.10 Chromatids Separate in Meiosis II

In each new cell formed at the end of Meiosis I, the second meiotic division usually begins almost immediately. There is no new replication of DNA in the period between Meiosis I and Meiosis II. In its main features, Meiosis II is very much like a mitotic division.

Figure 6.14 Prophase II

Figure 6.15 Metaphase II

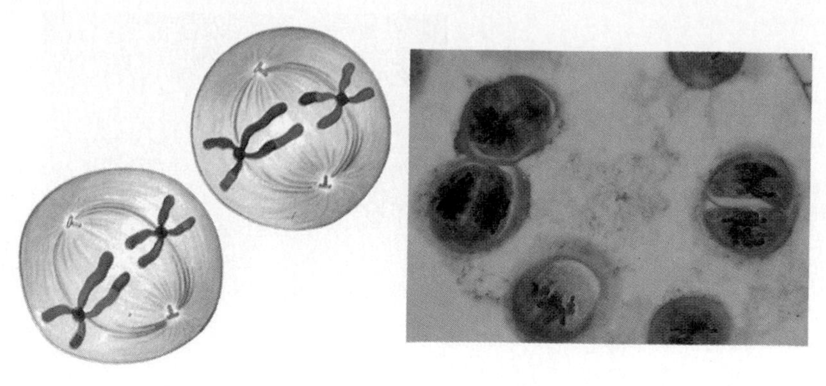

John D. Cunningham/VISUALS UNLIMITED

Figure 6.16 Anaphase II

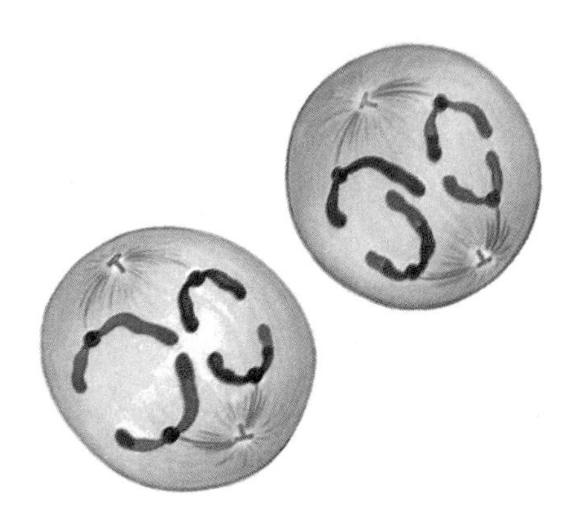

In prophase II (figure 6.14) the remaining chromosomes move toward the equatorial plate on a new spindle. The two chromatids of each chromosome are about to separate at the centromere.

The chromosomes align themselves on the new equatorial plate in metaphase II (figure 6.15).

Figure 6.17 Telophase II

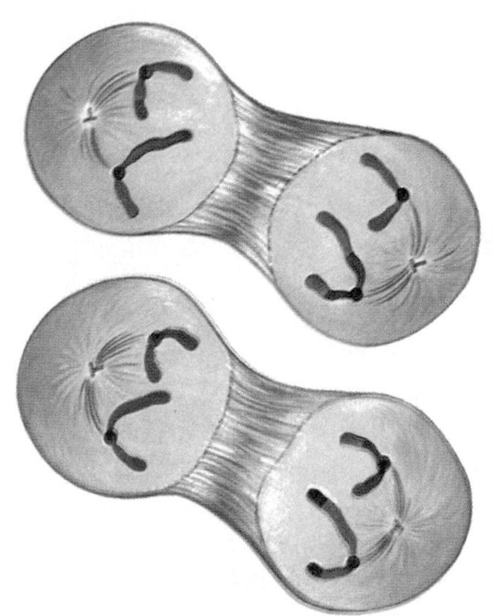

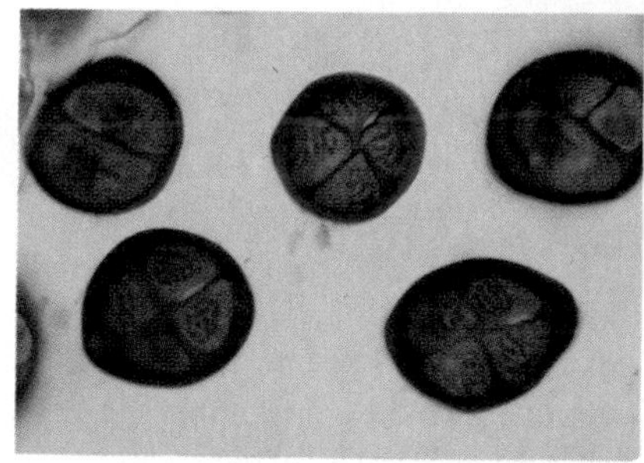

John D. Cunningham/VISUALS UNLIMITED

The centromeres divide and the two chromatids of each chromosome separate and move toward opposite poles. This takes place in anaphase II (figure 6.16). Each chromatid is now an independent chromosome from this time forth.

The chromosomes gather at the poles and are enclosed by a new nuclear envelope. The cytoplasm now divides again. Afterwards the cells undergo further cytoplasmic changes, such as developing a tail. The DNA is concentrated in the head of the sperm cell. Mitochondria are packed into the middle piece of the sperm. The mitochondria provide energy for the tail, which moves the sperm through the female reproductive tract. When those changes are completed, the cells will be fully formed sperm.

Figure 6.18 Comparison of mitosis and meiosis.

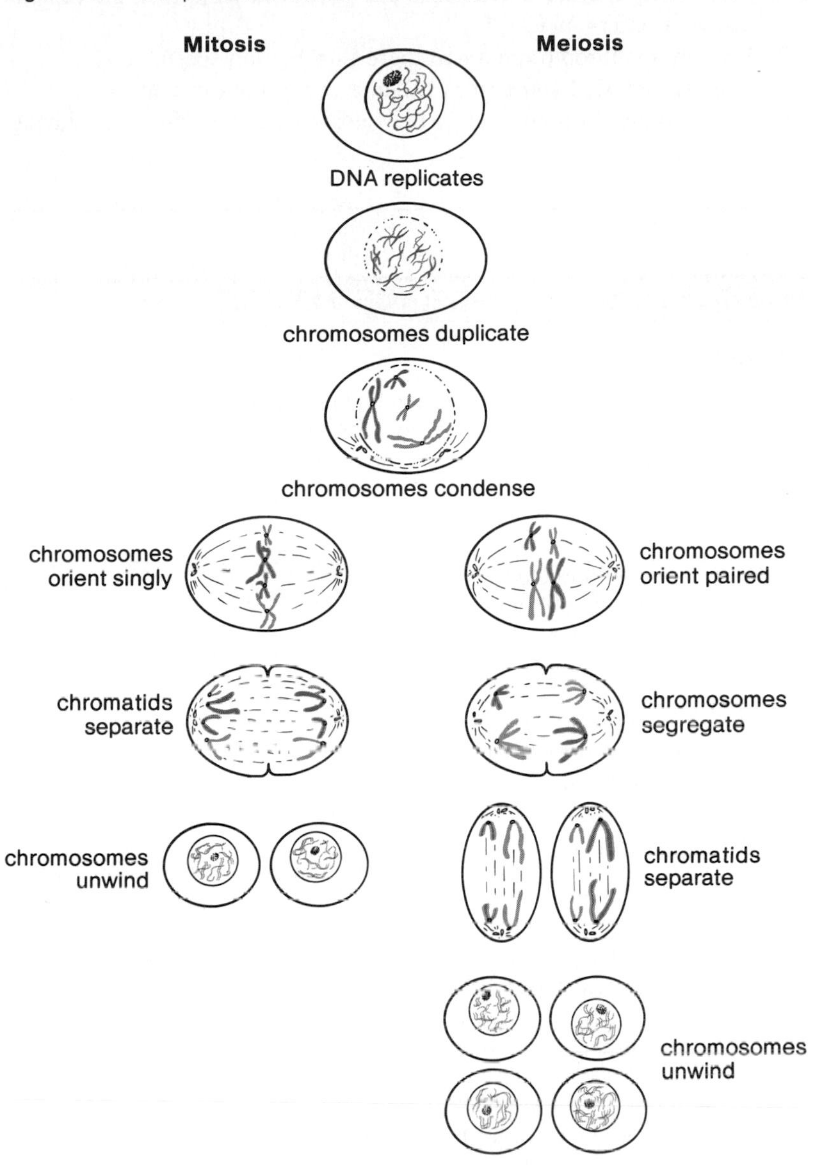

Each cell entering meiosis in the testis has thus become four mature sperm cells. Each one is capable of fertilizing an egg cell, and each has the haploid (N) number of chromosomes.

Figure 6.18 compares the processes of mitosis and meiosis.

Self-Review

1. What is a male gonad called in animals?
2. What kind of gamete is produced by ovaries in animals?
3. How many cell divisions occur in meiosis?
4. In a human cell about to enter meiosis, how many chromatids are present?

5. Name two important events that occur in Meiosis I.
6. How many mature sperm cells are produced from a single diploid cell that enters meiosis?
7. How many chromosomes are there in a human sperm cell?
8. Why is meiosis I sometimes called a reduction division?
9. What do the chromosomes do in Meiosis I that they do not do during mitosis?

Investigation 6.2 A MODEL OF MEIOSIS

Introduction

Many biological events are easier to understand when they are explained by models. In this investigation you will use a model to duplicate the nuclear events of meiosis.

Materials

modeling clay (red and blue)
pipe cleaners (6 cm to 8 cm)
piece of wrapping paper

Procedure

1. Use the clay to form 4 chromatids, 2 of each color. They should be 6 cm long and about as thick as a pencil.
2. Form 4 more chromatids. These should be 10 cm long, 2 of each color.
3. Use the pipe cleaners to represent centromeres. With 1 pipe cleaner fasten 2 similar chromatids together to form 1 chromosome, as shown in figure 6.19. Form 3 other chromosomes in the same manner.
4. Draw a spindle on a large sheet of wrapping paper. Make it large enough to contain the chromosomes you have made. Assume that the early events of the 1st division have already occurred. In other words, the spindle and chromatids have been formed, and the nuclear membrane has disappeared.
5. Pair the 2 short chromosomes. Pair the 2 long ones. Assume that 1 chromosome of each pair (the red one) was derived from this organism's male parent. Its homolog (the blue chromosome) came from the female parent.
6. Arrange the 2 chromosome pairs along the equator of the spindle. Show the overlapping of chromatids by overlapping the strands of clay of each homologous pair.
7. To show the possible exchange of chromatid parts (figure 6.10), exchange a small part of the clay from 1 chromosome with an equal part from its homolog. The colors make the exchange visible throughout the rest of the investigation.
8. Begin to move the chromosomes of each homologous pair toward opposite poles of the spindle. Move them by grasping the centromeres and pulling. (Note that either 2 red or 2 blue chromosomes or 1 red and 1 blue chromosome can move to each pole.)
9. Draw 2 more spindles. Center these spindles on the poles of the 1st division. Their axes should be perpendicular to the axis of the 1st. The model is now ready for the 2nd division of meiosis.

Figure 6.19

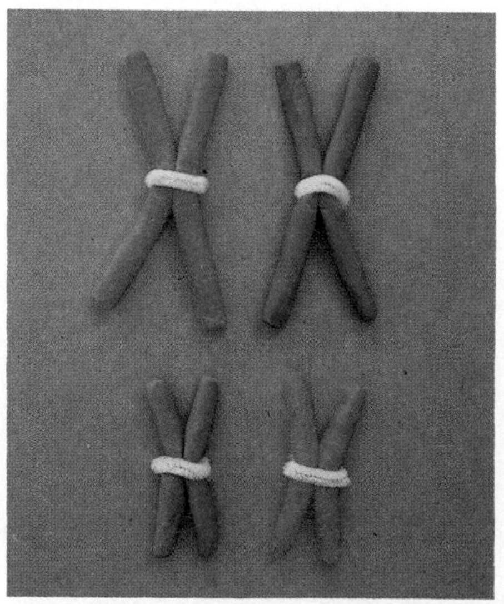

BSCS by Doug Sokell

10. Place the chromosomes along the equators of the 2 new spindles. Unfasten the centromere of each chromosome. Grasp each chromatid at the centromere. Pull the chromatids to opposite poles of their spindles. If there are 4 members on your teams, all the chromatids can be made to move at once, as they do in a living cell.
11. Reassemble the chromosomes as they are shown in figure 6.19. Use the other side of your piece of wrapping paper and repeat the process of meiosis without referring to the directions printed here.

Discussion

1. How would a mitosis model differ from this one?
2. What are some advantages of using a model to visualize a process?
3. What are some disadvantages?

Fertilization

Guidepost: What factors influence fertilization?

6.11 Millions of Sperm Cells Are Produced in Testes

Meiosis and gamete formation take place in the gonads. In humans and other animals, male and female gonads look alike in early development. It is not until the embryo is about eight weeks old that the gonads are clearly different in the two sexes. They then can be called testes and ovaries. You will study more about the development of the embryo in the next chapter.

In section 6.10 you learned that in testes certain diploid cells give rise to four haploid cells in meiosis. Each of these then is transformed into a mature sperm cell.

The testes develop in the abdominal cavity of an embryo, just as the ovaries do. Before birth the two testes move downward and then to the outside of the abdominal cavity. There they are housed in a pouch called the **scrotum.** The scrotum is located just below the external male organ, the **penis** (see figure 6.20).

The penis is used both for reproduction and for discharging urine from the kidneys. Its role in excretion will be discussed in chapter 16.

If a testis is cut into very thin slices, it can be studied under the microscope. Each testis is made up of thousands of tiny tubules. Meiosis occurs in these tubules. Figure 6.20c shows a cross section of one tubule. The diploid cells that will enter meiosis are located around the outer edge of each tubule.

As meiosis proceeds, the new cells are formed toward the center of the tubule. For that reason, the phases of meiosis can be followed in order, from outside to the inside central canal. You can see cells in the various stages of meiosis in figure 6.20c. The last stages are at the inner edge of the canal. Around the edge of the canal you can see the dark heads of mature sperm, with their long tails extending into the center of the canal.

Figure 6.20 The human male reproductive system.

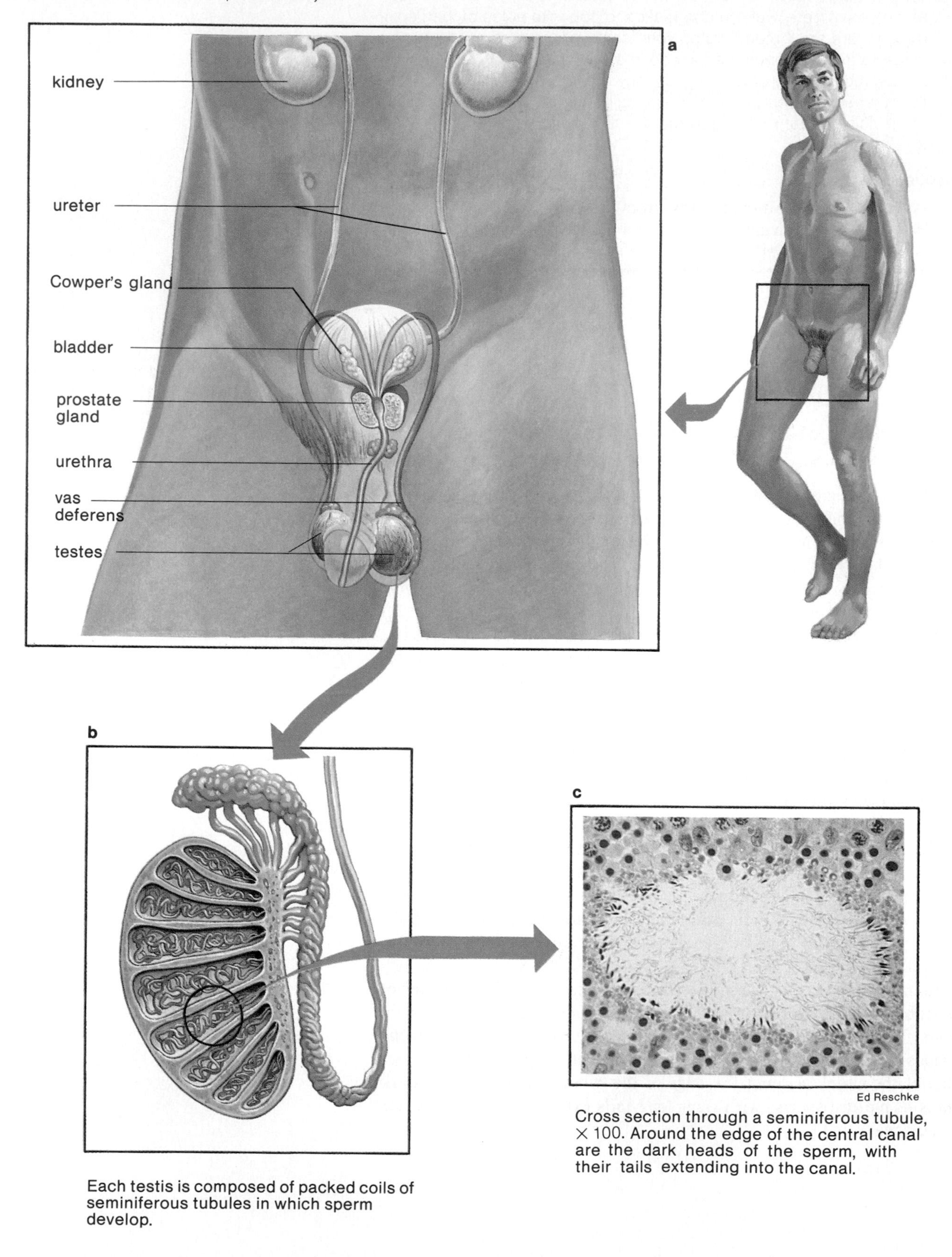

Each testis is composed of packed coils of seminiferous tubules in which sperm develop.

Cross section through a seminiferous tubule, × 100. Around the edge of the central canal are the dark heads of the sperm, with their tails extending into the canal.

The sperm move out of these canals into a special collecting duct near the testis, the **epididymis** (ep ih DID ih mis). This structure, which would be about 50 cm long if uncoiled, can hold billions of sperm. The sperm remain there until they are released in sexual activity, or until they are reabsorbed by the body.

Meiosis and the formation of sperm cells takes about 72 days in humans. Mature human males can produce huge numbers of sperm. A male may release from 200 million to 500 million sperm cells at one time. In human females, on the other hand, only 400 to 500 ova will be produced during an entire lifetime. Clearly there are important differences in gamete formation between males and females.

6.12 Meiosis Is Interrupted in Females

The formation of ova in human females provides a fascinating look into the life history of certain cells. Millions of potential ova form in the ovaries of a female embryo. Most of these soon disappear, but hundreds of thousands still remain at birth.

Gametes are not produced until puberty in males, but in females meiosis begins in the embryo. Certain diploid cells of the newly formed ovary enter meiosis. The first cell division is soon interrupted, however. The potential egg cells actually stop developing in prophase I, right in the midst of a complicated cell division. They remain in suspended animation for a period of years.

Meiosis does not resume until later in life, when a young women enters puberty. The potential ova remain in prophase I all that time. Then, at monthly intervals, one cell will resume meiosis, and the potential ovum continues into Meiosis II, where the process stops once more. Later the cell is released from the surface of the ovary, a process called **ovulation.** In humans one ovum is usually released each month, though sometimes two (or more) may be released. In many other animals it is usual for a number of eggs to be released at the same time, and a litter of offspring may be produced.

The reproductive span of human females may extend from puberty (which usually begins sometime between ages 10 and 14) until age 45 or 50. Therefore, some of the partly mature egg cells may take as long as half a century to complete meiosis.

6.13 Hormones Control Reproductive Cycles

Many organs in the body produce chemical messengers—substances that influence other organs. These substances, called **hormones,** travel in the blood to all parts of the body. A hormone from one organ may affect another organ, which responds in striking ways. The first organ, in turn, can be influenced by other hormones. A complex set of interactions occurs, a network of stimuli and responses. This is one way the various parts of the body communicate.

Hormones are very important for sexual reproduction in both males and females. The hormone interactions often are more complex in females than in males.

Under the influence of hormones produced in the brain, the testes and ovaries are stimulated to produce distinctive sex hormones. These in turn help bring about the secondary indicators of approaching sexual maturity: changes in voice and body proportions, growth of hair, and increased interest in sex. In females, the brain and ovarian hormone initiate a regular monthly cycle, the **menstrual** (MEN stroo ul) **cycle** (after the Latin word *mensis,* meaning "month").

It is clear that the gonads have two major roles: they produce sex hormones, and they form gametes. To understand how hormones affect reproduction, let us look in more detail at the functions of the female reproductive system, which is shown in figure 6.21.

The two ovaries are located low in the abdominal cavity, one on each side. Each ovary is located close to a short tube, the **oviduct** (OH vih dukt). The oviducts serve as passageways, and ova travel through them on their way to the **uterus.** The uterus is a muscular organ that protects and nourishes a new individual while it develops. A tiny embryo becomes attached to the inner lining of the uterus, and there it remains and grows as it is nurtured by the mother during pregnancy (see figure 7.11, page 207).

Each potential ovum is enclosed in a **follicle,** a small oblong sac of cells on the surface of the ovary. Study figure 6.21b. As an egg cell matures, its follicle increases in size. The follicle reacts to hormones from the brain, and produces a hormone, **estrogen** (ES troh jen). During the 10 days before an ovum is released, estrogen from the follicle stimulates the inner layer of the uterus. That layer fills with blood vessels and fluids and becomes much thicker.

An ovulated ovum has not completed meiosis and will not do so unless it is fertilized. After its ovum is released, the follicle cells are converted to another role. They fill the follicle cavity, and appear yellow in color. The structure is now called a **corpus luteum** (KOR pus LOOT ee um), meaning yellow body. It produces still a different hormone. That hormone, **progesterone** (proh JES teh rohn), helps maintain the thick layer of the uterus for two more weeks. That is enough time for an embryo to attach itself to the uterus wall. If an egg has not been fertilized, the thick layer disintegrates. Then the corpus luteum stops producing progesterone. The inner layer of the uterus breaks away and passes through the **vagina,** a muscular passageway that connects the uterus to the outside. These hormonal interactions are shown in figure 6.22.

This loss of blood and tissue from the uterus is called **menstruation** (men stroo AY shun). The flow usually lasts for four to five days. The first menstruation indicates that a young female has become capable of producing ova, and of having them fertilized. Young women who have begun to menstruate are able to become pregnant.

6.14 Only One Sperm Fertilizes an Ovum

How does an embryo begin? You will recall from section 6.5 that it develops from a fertilized egg, or zygote. In order for fertilization to take place, sperm cells must enter the body through the vagina. Usually this takes place by means of sexual intercourse. Under sexual excitement the penis of the male fills with blood and becomes rigid. The sperm cells begin to move from the epididymis into a special duct, the **vas deferens** (VAS DEF eh renz). The vas deferens, after connecting with several male glands, enters the duct of the penis.

Figure 6.21 The human female reproductive system.

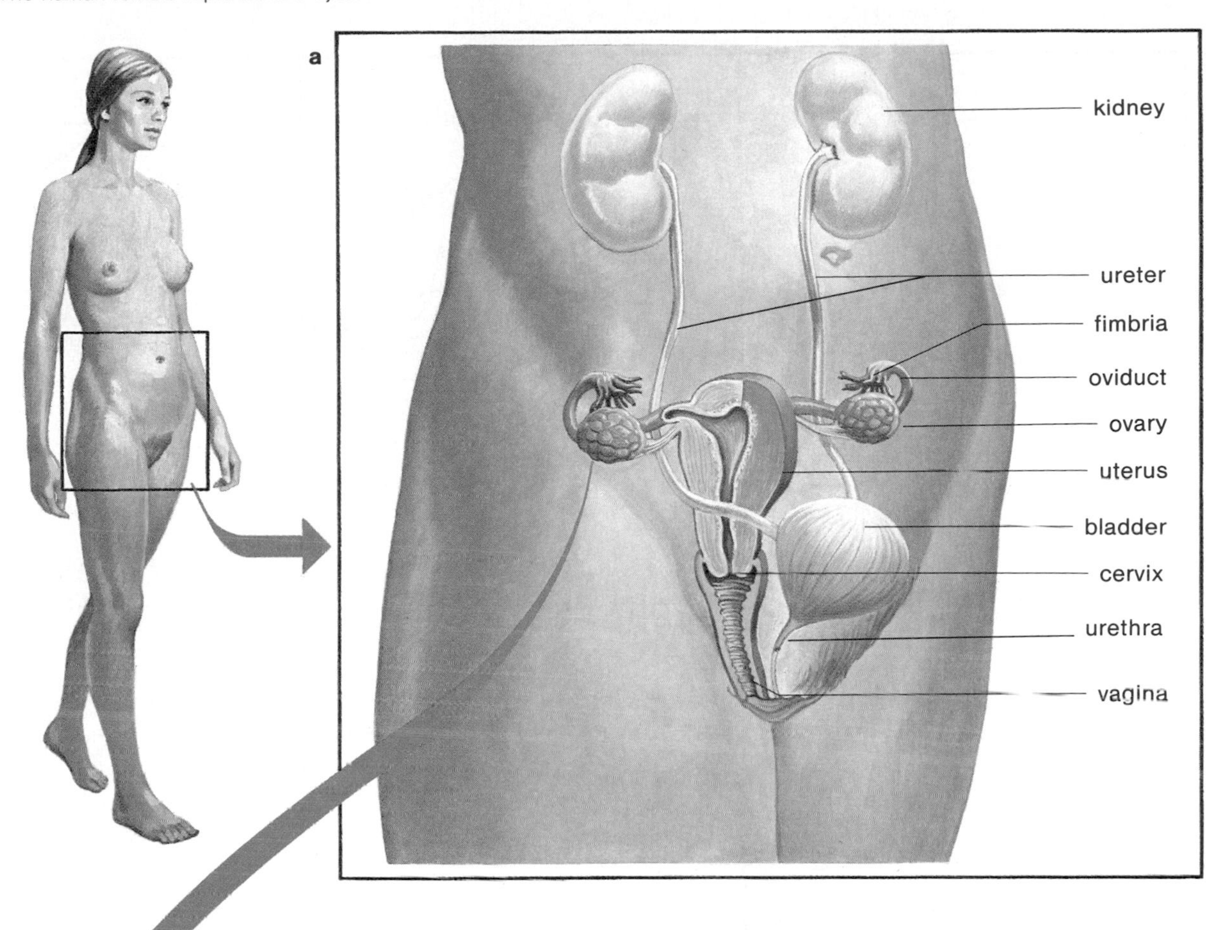

b

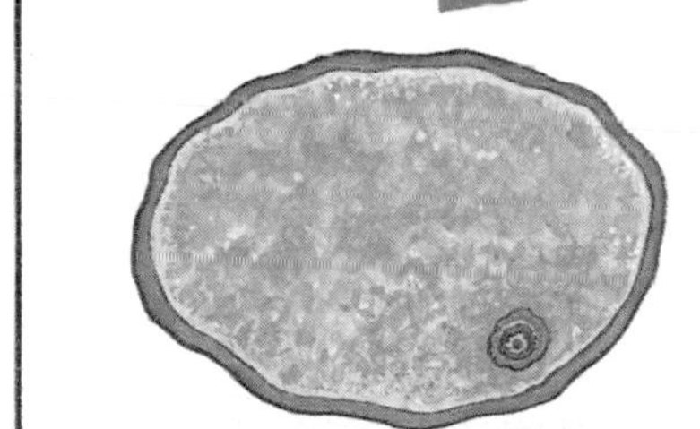

The ovum begins to enlarge and additional tissue layers are formed in the primary follicle.

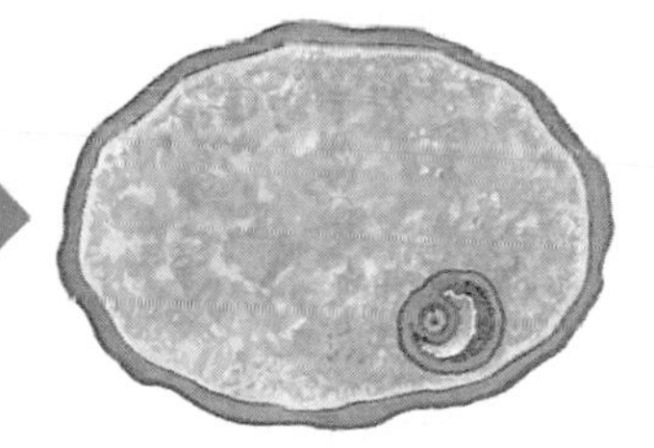

The follicle continues to enlarge.

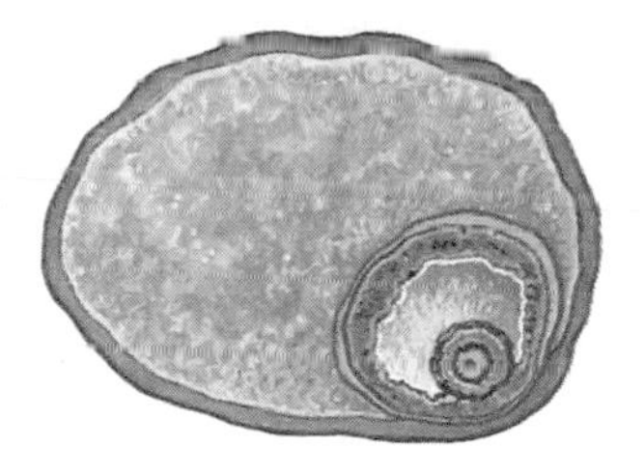

Mature follicle just before ovulation.

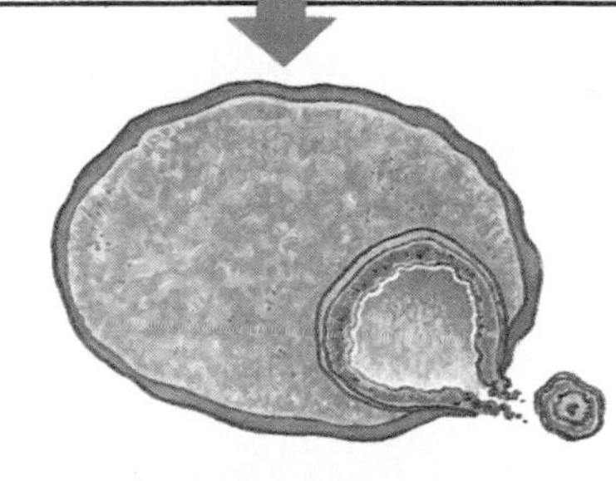

The follicle ruptures and the ovum is expelled in ovulation.

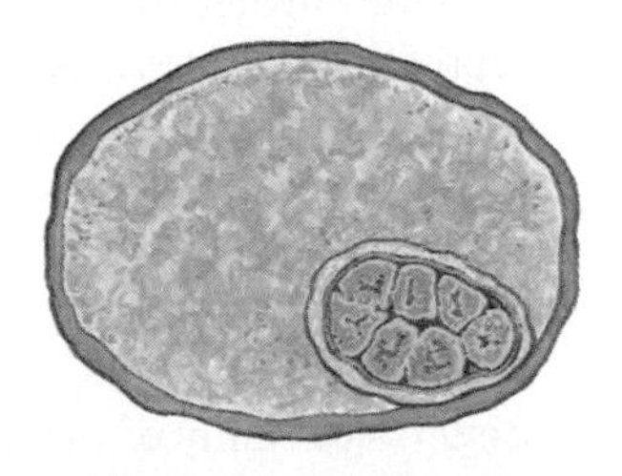

The remaining follicle cells undergo rapid change and become the corpus luteum.

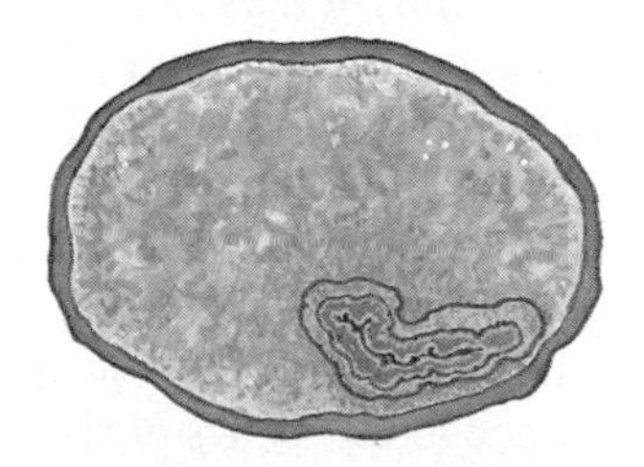

If fertilization does not occur, the corpus luteum shrinks and is reabsorbed.

Figure 6.22 Hormonal changes in the human female reproductive cycle.
FSH = follicle stimulating hormone; LH = luteinizing hormone.

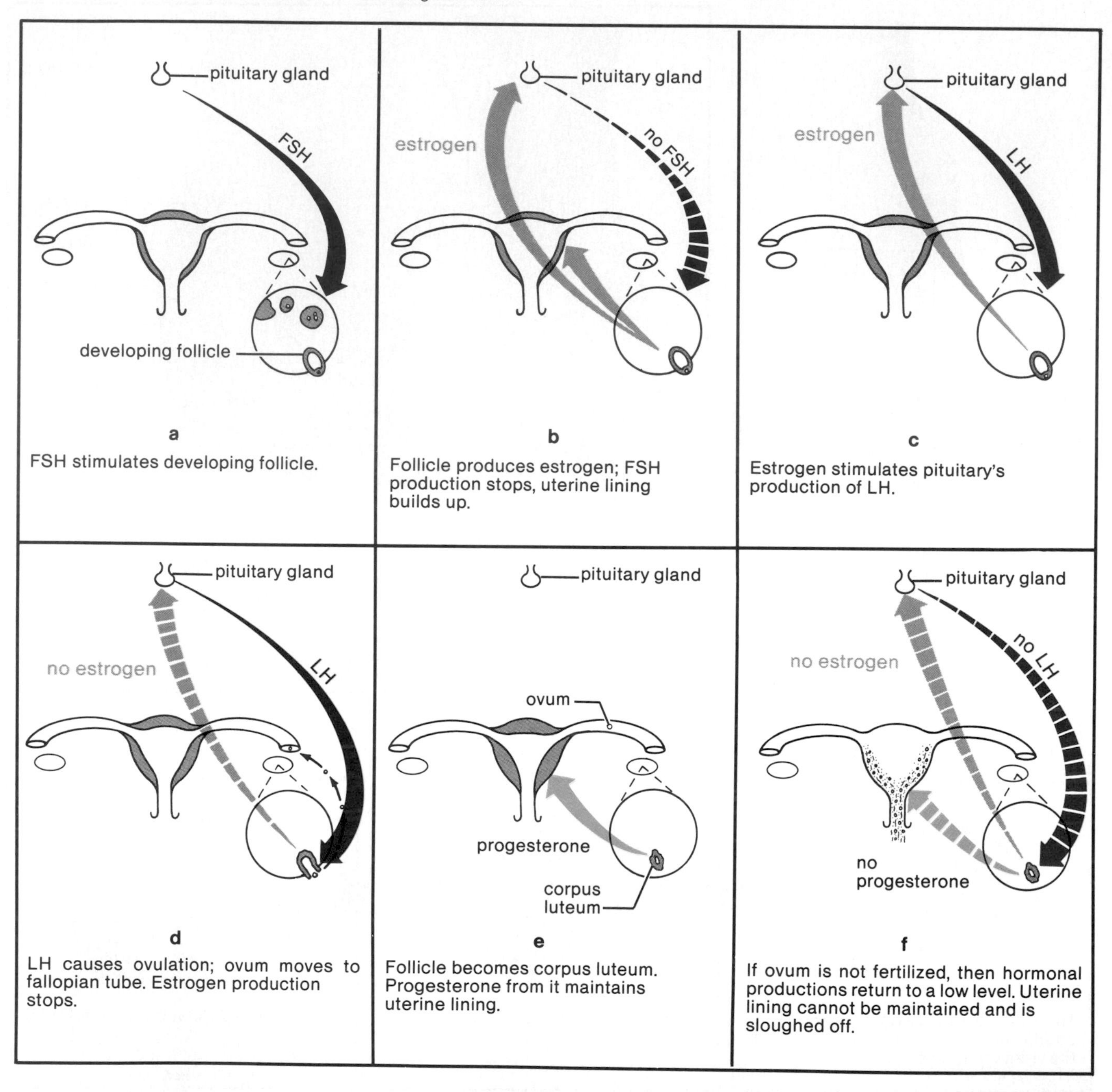

pituitary gland
FSH
developing follicle
a
FSH stimulates developing follicle.
pituitary gland
estrogen
no FSH
b
Follicle produces estrogen; FSH production stops, uterine lining builds up.
pituitary gland
estrogen
LH
c
Estrogen stimulates pituitary's production of LH.
pituitary gland
no estrogen
LH
d
LH causes ovulation; ovum moves to fallopian tube. Estrogen production stops.
pituitary gland
ovum
progesterone
corpus luteum
e
Follicle becomes corpus luteum. Progesterone from it maintains uterine lining.
pituitary gland
no estrogen
no LH
no progesterone
f
If ovum is not fertilized, then hormonal productions return to a low level. Uterine lining cannot be maintained and is sloughed off.

After further stimulation, such as by the walls of the vagina, the male reproductive system responds by expelling 3 to 4 ml of **semen** (SEE men). This whitish fluid contains the secretions of the male glands (prostate gland, seminal vesicle, and Cowper's gland), as well as hundreds of millions of sperm. The relationships of these structures in males are shown in figure 6.20.

After they are released into the vagina, the sperm cells swim in all directions. Many of them swim up along the moist linings of the female reproductive tract. They enter the uterus and swim into the two oviducts.

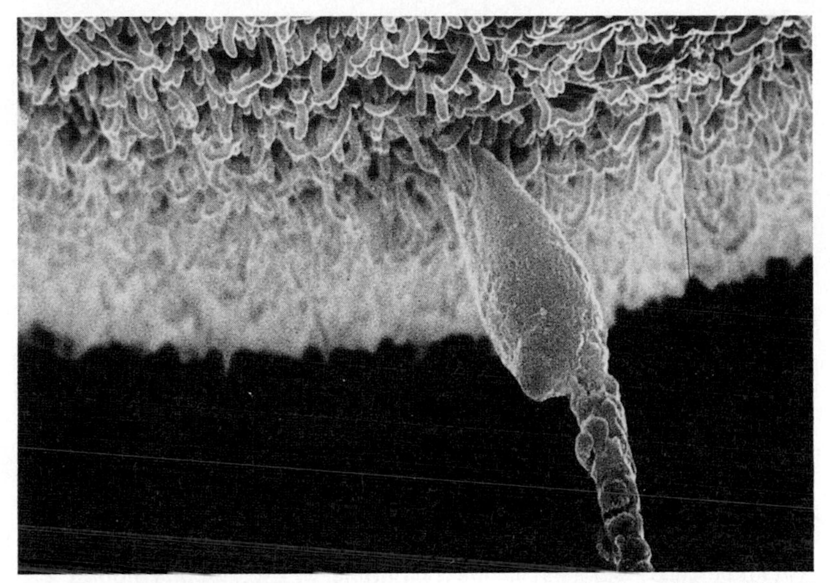

Figure 6.23 Human sperm fertilizing an egg. Scanning electron micrograph, ×17,000.

David M. Phillips/VISUALS UNLIMITED

After an ovum is released, it moves into the nearest oviduct. Once released from the ovary, an ovum will live about three to five days. If sexual intercourse occurs during this period, the ovum may meet many sperm cells there. One sperm may penetrate the outer membranes of the egg cell. The membranes react immediately and become a barrier to other sperm cells. Only one sperm cell fertilizes an ovum (figure 6.23), and only the head of the sperm, which contains the genetic material, enters the egg. If only one sperm actually fertilizes the ovum, why are so many sperm released in the semen? One answer is that sperm secrete an enzyme that helps break down the layer of cells that surrounds an ovum. Apparently, many sperm are required to provide enough enzyme.

You will remember that the ovum has been released without completing meiosis. Fertilization stimulates the ovum to complete Meiosis II. Meiosis in ova differs from that in sperm in a very important way. During meiosis in egg cells, the division of the cytoplasm—cytokinesis—is unequal. During each of the meiotic divisions, most of the cytoplasm goes to only one of the offspring cells, along with one haploid set of chromosomes. The other sets of chromosomes produced in meiosis have been expelled as tiny cells with very little cytoplasm. These **polar bodies** cannot give rise to a new individual. At the end of meiosis the ovum will have one haploid set of chromosomes, just like a sperm cell. These events are diagrammed in figure 6.24. Figure 6.25 shows a polar body on a whitefish egg.

Thus we see that in females each diploid cell that enters meiosis eventually forms only one haploid ovum, not four haploid cells as in males. Virtually all the cytoplasm of the original cell is preserved in the ovum. Additional cytoplasm is produced in the periods between divisions. The cytoplasm provides the material and energy needed for the early cell divisions of development. The supply can last only until the embryo implants into the inner layer of the uterus. From that time on the embryo receives nourishment from its mother.

Figure 6.24 Formation of polar bodies.

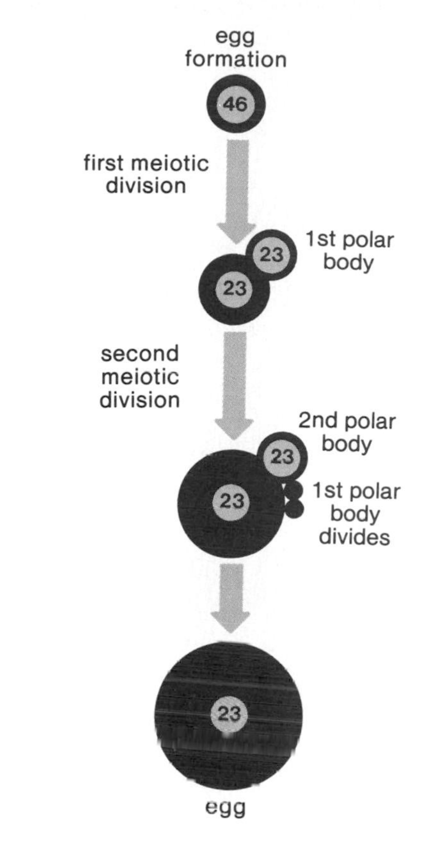

Figure 6.25 Whitefish egg with a polar body formed in the first meiotic division.

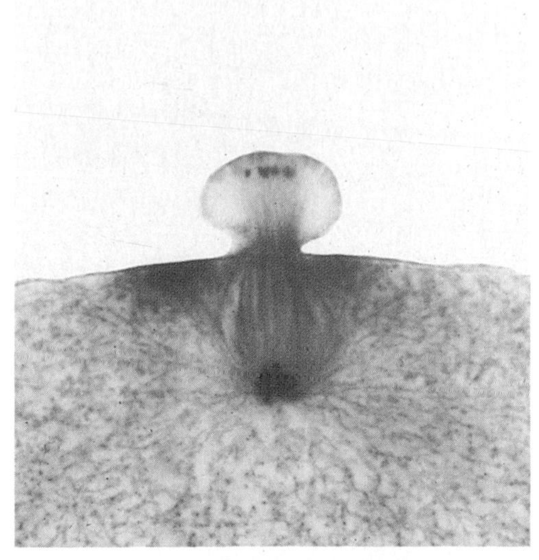

John D. Cunningham/VISUALS UNLIMITED

Development of a new individual usually begins in the oviduct. The zygote divides into two cells following mitosis. From this time on, until gametes are formed in the next generation, all cell divisions are mitotic.

Remember, each new gamete, male or female, contains new combinations of genes. The random combination of gametes further increases genetic variability.

In the next chapter we will follow the zygote as it develops into a new organism and enters the outside world, leaving the dark, warm aquarium within its mother's uterus.

6.15 Sexual Reproduction Is Similar in Plants and Animals

If one merely looks at a higher plant, it is not always easy to understand how it reproduces sexually. Yet plants share many features of sexual reproduction with animals. They form haploid cells by meiosis, fertilization occurs, and new individuals are produced by mitotic cell division and differentiation, as in animals. However, there are important differences in the details, as you might expect.

We already know that plant cells have many of the same structures as animal cells—such as plasma membrane, cytosol, Golgi complex, endoplasmic reticulum, nucleus, and chromosomes—as well as features distinctive to plant cells. They divide in much the same way, and you could study mitosis in plant cells even more easily than in many animal cells.

After intense study of many plants, biologists learned that meiosis also occurs in plants. However, the haploid cells that result are not gametes. Instead they form a generation of haploid cells. You will learn more in chapter 13 about this alternation of haploid and diploid generations in plants.

Even though there are a few extra haploid cell divisions, these cells soon give rise to haploid egg and sperm nuclei. These nuclei are often in cells with other nuclei. However, the egg and sperm nuclei do unite in fertilization to form a zygote. In principle, the events are the same as those that occur in animal fertilization. We will examine when and where these events in plant reproduction take place, and how new plants come about, in chapter 13.

Self-Review

1. Compare the numbers of ova and of sperm produced in humans.
2. How long might a human ovum remain in the midst of Meiosis I?
3. Describe what happens in the menstrual cycle.
4. What are some ways in which meiosis differs in males and females?

Summary

Reproduction is essential for the continuity of life on earth. Organisms reproduce in various ways. Some plants and animals may reproduce either asexually or sexually. Sexual reproduction increases genetic variation in a population. This variation is important in the evolution of populations.

In sexual reproduction two parents are required. Each parent contributes a reproductive cell, or gamete, to the new individual. When the two gametes combine in fertilization, a zygote is formed. Each gamete contains only half the parental genetic information. By fertilization the chromosome number is maintained from one generation to the next.

The reduction of the genetic content of a body cell by half is brought about by meiosis. In meiosis genetic material is exchanged and reduced to one-half in two successive cell divisions. A diploid cell in a testis will give rise to four haploid sperm cells. In females it will produce one haploid egg cell, because all the stored food in the cytoplasm is distributed to only one of the four cells.

In principle, higher plants reproduce sexually in the same general way as animals. Haploid cells are produced by meiosis, and these in turn give rise to gametes after a short generation of haploid cell divisions. As in animals, a zygote is formed by fertilization.

Application Questions

1. Trace the stages of meiosis in a slice through a testis.
2. What are the advantages to humans of propagating plants by rooting portions of an older plant instead of planting seeds? What is the relation of grafting to this propagation by cuttings?
3. Mitochondria have their own, circular DNA. This DNA differs from the DNA found in the nucleus. Studies show that mitochondrial DNA is derived from the female parent, not the male parent. Use your knowledge of fertilization to explain this phenomenon.
4. Explain how the behavior of chromosomes during the first meiotic prophase differs from that during prophase in mitosis.
5. Only one sperm is required for fertilization, yet hundreds of millions are present in the semen. What function do the sperm play that do not fertilize the ovum?
6. Describe the mechanisms by which sexual reproduction increases genetic variability.

Problems

1. Is human reproduction lacking in seasonality? Record by months the birthdays of the members of your biology class and of as many other classes as possible. If you can obtain the data from all the students in your school, you will have a fairly satisfactory sample. Present the data in the form of a bar graph—one bar for each month. What does the graph indicate about the question?
2. There is some indication that the age at which human females reach puberty is declining. Collect data on this phenomenon and on its possible causes.
3. The environment of the female reproductive tract is slightly acidic, which can be harmful to sperm cells. Investigate the components of semen and show the ways in which they help to counteract the acidic environment in the female reproductive tract.
4. There are two kind of twins: fraternal (dizygotic) and identical (monozygotic). Explore the cause of twinning in each case.

Suggested Readings

L. B. Andrews, 1985, *New Conceptions* (New York: Ballantine Books). A "consumer's guide" to the newest infertility treatments and alternatives, including *in vitro* fertilization, artificial insemination, and surrogate motherhood.

C. J. Cole, "Unisexual Lizards" *Scientific American* (January 1984). Populations of whiptail lizards consist only of females and reproduce themselves by virgin birth (parthenogenesis).

T. H. Clutton-Brock, "Reproductive Success in Red Deer" *Scientific American* (February 1985). The reproductive strategies of these deer, studied for 12 years on a Scottish island, can be applied to other mammals as well.

J. E. Lloyd, "Mimicry in the Sexual Signals of Fireflies" *Scientific American* (July 1981). Some of the females responding to male flashes are members of other species looking for a meal.

P. B. Stacey and W. D. Koenig, "Cooperative Breeding in the Acorn Woodpecker" *Scientific American* (August 1984). Discussion of the unusual social system and reproductive methods of these birds of the southwestern U.S.

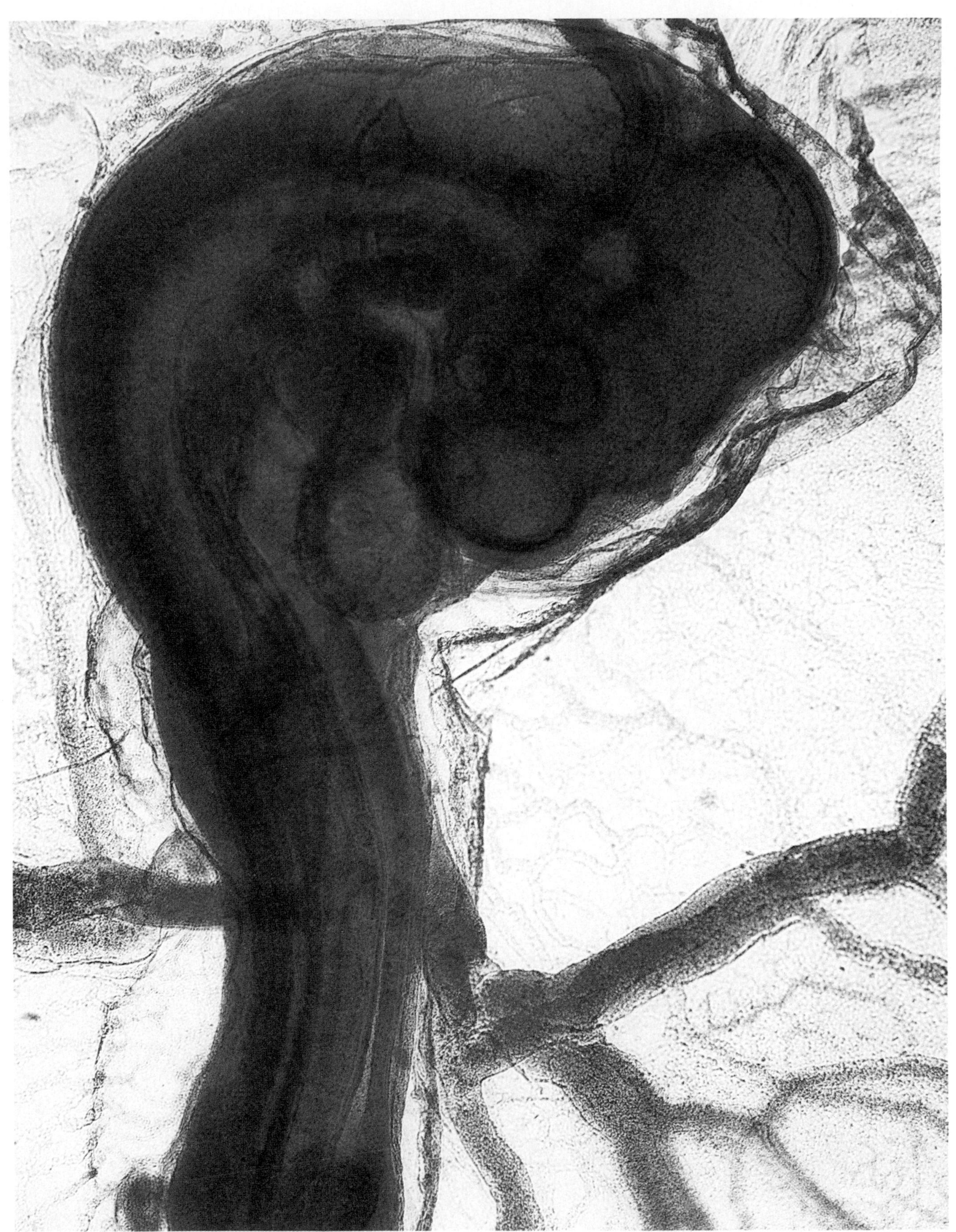

Ripon Microslides, Inc.

Development in many animals is similar. This chick embryo is 72 hours old.

CHAPTER 7

Continuity through Development

Introduction

In most higher organisms the fertilization of an egg cell by a sperm cell initiates a complex series of events. The zygote formed is still a single cell. Yet that one cell contains all the genetic information needed to form a complex organism with millions or billions of cells. Many of these cells are different in both structure and function. How can one set of genetic instructions determine so many different kinds of cell fates? The series of events that lead from the zygote to a complex many-celled organism is called development. Its very nature presents one of the most difficult problems in biology. The answers to its many questions are being sought at this moment.

Development

Guidepost: How does a zygote become a many-celled, complex organism?

7.1 A Zygote Gives Rise to Many Cells

When a sperm nucleus approaches an egg nucleus, it carries one set of chromosomes. Its haploid set (N) joins with the haploid set (N) of chromosomes of the ovum. By fertilization the diploid (2N) of chromosomes is restored. The new zygote is now ready to begin **development,** the process by which the zygote becomes a fully formed new individual.

After fertilization, the zygote divides into two cells—by mitosis and cytokinesis. Each of those two cells divides again (to four cells) and again (to eight cells) and again. Soon the tiny embryo is made of dozens of cells. In animals there is no growth for a while—no new substances are added. The cells just continue to divide, and new cells are smaller than their parent cells. The material stored in the egg is provided to new cells. In some zygotes there is enough stored material to complete a major part of development. A fertilized chicken egg, for example, contains all the instructions and materials needed to form an entire chick. After three weeks of development it hatches, provided with eyes, feathers, and claws. A chick already shows typical behavior in chipping its way out of its egg shell. That behavior was part of the genetic program of the zygote.

A chicken's development is not complete at hatching, however. The chick now begins to eat and grow, and its size and structure continue to change. In time it becomes a mature hen or rooster, with characteristic behavior, and the life cycle is repeated. The bird also ages, and eventually its life comes to an end. Aging is one aspect of development.

Unlike birds and reptiles (which also develop within an egg shell), many kinds of organisms do not have enough yolk in their eggs to develop into an independent organism. They achieve only the earliest of the long series of steps to maturity. In the human egg, for example, there is only enough yolk to sustain the embryo through the first six or seven days. By then it is an embryo of a few hundred cells, and must implant in the wall of the uterus. There it receives further nourishment, delivered to the uterus by the blood of the mother, that permits development to continue.

Figure 7.1 Two-cell stage of a human embryo, still showing one of the polar bodies from meiosis.

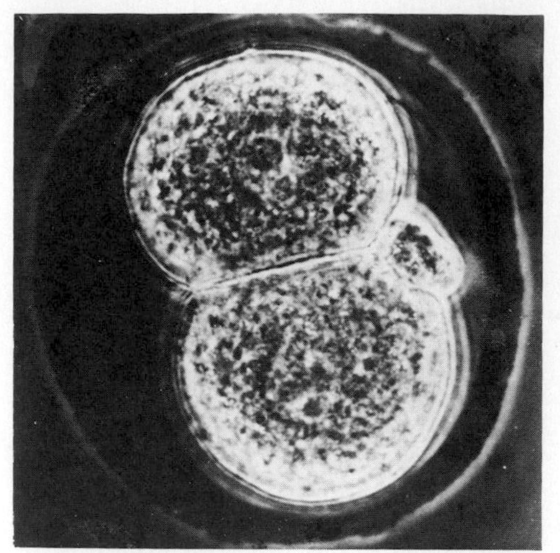

Landrum B. Shettles

7.2 Cell Movements Help Shape an Embryo

After a zygote is formed by fertilization, it undergoes a number of cell divisions. In animal embryos those early divisions are called **cleavage.** As cleavage continues, a ball of cells results. Further divisions and cell movements produce a hollow ball of cells. Now the cells are able to obtain oxygen more easily and to rid themselves of carbon dioxide.

Figure 7.2 Drawings of early starfish development published in 1877 by Louis Agassiz.

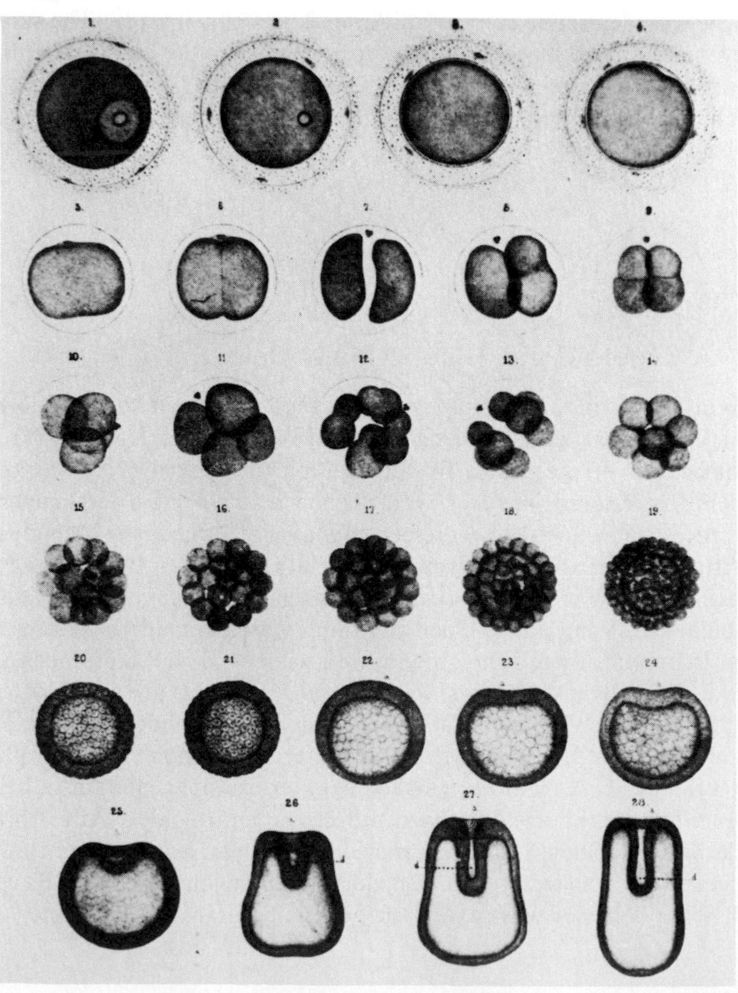

BSCS

The hollow-ball stage of development is called a **blastula** (BLAS chuh luh). Development of the blastula is shown in figure 7.3. At this stage the cells are more or less equal in size and function. In frog eggs, the cells on one side of the embryo are larger, because they contain extra yolk. Bird eggs have so much yolk that cleavage can only occur in the tiny bit of living substance on top of the egg, but the process is the same in principle. If the yolk were removed, cleavage would resemble that of other forms.

Now one side of the blastula begins to push in. This is the beginning of a long series of cell movements and foldings. The outer layer of cells folds inward, and other foldings will soon occur.

After one side of the blastula has pushed in, there is then a second layer of cells. It is inside the embryo and lines the new cavity just formed. The new cavity will become the digestive system. A pore is formed that connects to the outside. The pore marks the future opening of the end of the digestive system. These movements form the **gastrula** (GAS truh luh) stage, shown in figure 7.3d.

Figure 7.3 Development of the blastula and gastrula in a frog. (a) Cells in the vegetal hemisphere of the blastula are larger than those in the animal hemisphere because they contain extra yolk. (b) Cells begin to push to the inside through an opening called the blastopore. (c) As cells continue to push in, a new cavity called the archenteron forms. The archenteron will become the digestive system. (d) The blastula cavity gets smaller as the archenteron enlarges. The embryo is now called a gastrula. (e) The three cell layers, ectoderm, endoderm, and mesoderm begin to appear. (f) The archenteron continues to enlarge and the neural fold starts to develop.

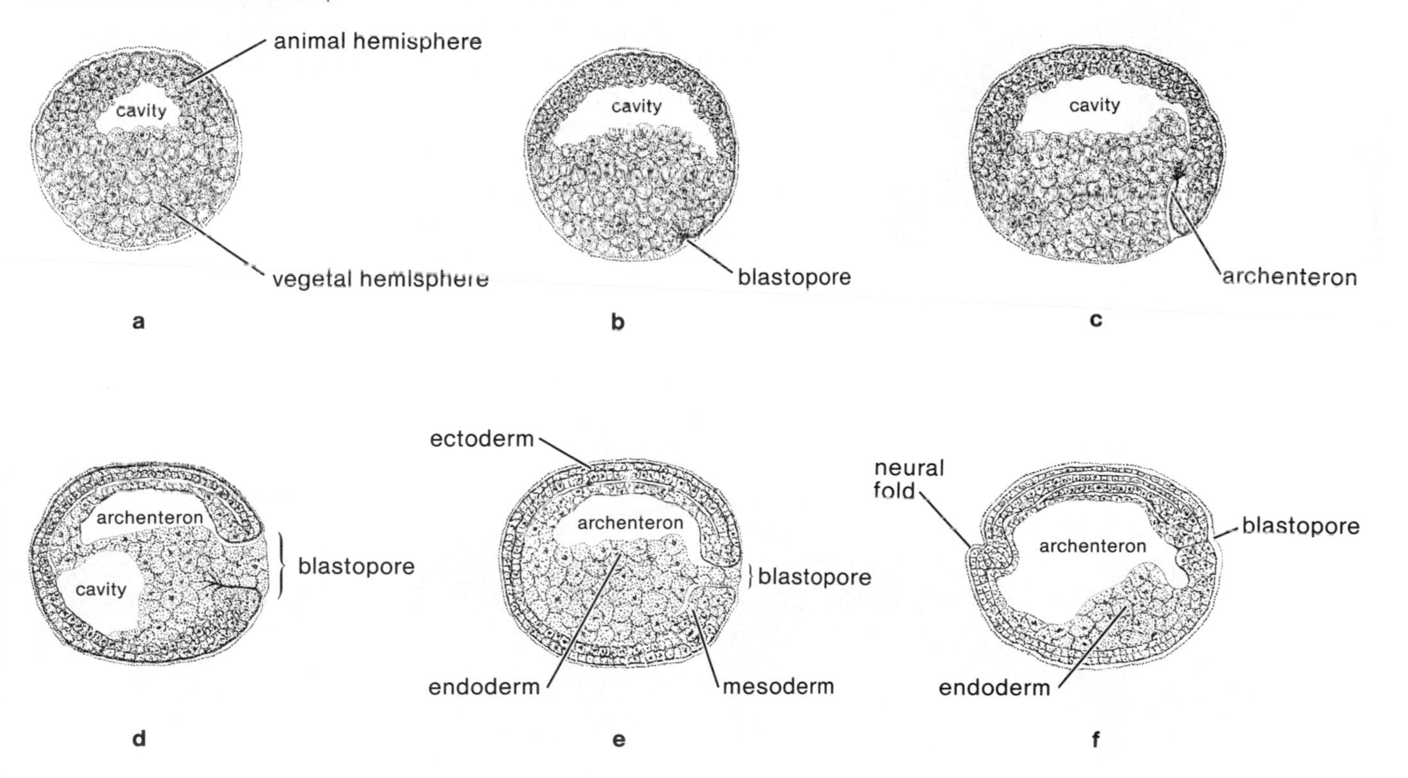

Eventually a third layer of cells also forms, and comes to lie between the outer and the inner layers. These three cell layers, often called the **germ layers,** give rise to all the different tissues of the body. They contain the "germ," or potential, for future development.

The origin of many kinds of cells from the germ layers is the result of differentiation. That term describes the process in development by which new cells may become very different in appearance and function from their parent cells. We will now look at one example of differentiation. The nervous system is the first organ system to form. Similar examples could be found in any system of the body.

Figure 7.4 Three-week human embryo, showing the neural folds and the beginning of segments along the midline.

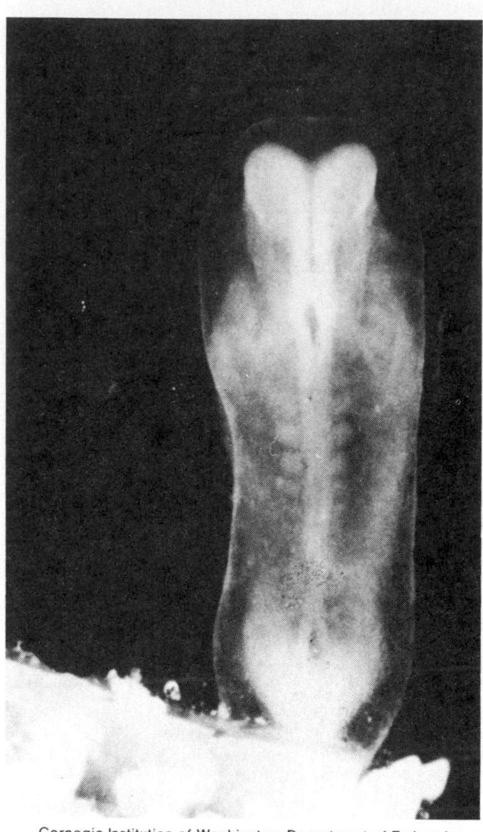

Carnegie Institution of Washington, Department of Embryology, Davis Division

7.3 The Nervous System in Animals Develops from the Outer Germ Layer

In the early gastrula the outer layer of cells is called the **ectoderm** (outer skin). As the embryo gets larger, the ectoderm at the top of the embryo begins to form two long, parallel folds of cells, which show clearly in figure 7.4. At first the folds are small. Soon they become striking ridges of cells, forming a groove between them. Eventually the groove rounds into a tube, and other ectodermal cells close over it, as shown in the diagrams in figure 7.5.

The inner tube thus formed by cell movement and folding is called the neural tube. It stretches from one end of the embryo to the other, and eventually gives rise to the brain and spinal cord, including nerve cells and other cells related to nerve function. By studying development, we learn that the nervous system, which allows communication among all parts of the body, arises from the ectodermal layer.

Sometimes the neural tube does not close completely, and part of the nervous system is exposed to the outside. This condition is called spina bifida (SPY nuh BIH fih duh). In infants born with this condition, the brain or spinal cord remains exposed. Knowing the way the nervous system develops helps us understand this birth defect. Spina bifida is a serious condition, and it often results in abnormalities in the function of the nervous system. Infection also may set in. There are now tests before birth to indicate whether it is likely that the spinal cord is open to the outside.

Figure 7.5 These cross sections through a frog embryo show how the ectodermal layer of cells at the top of the embryo is shaped into a neural tube.

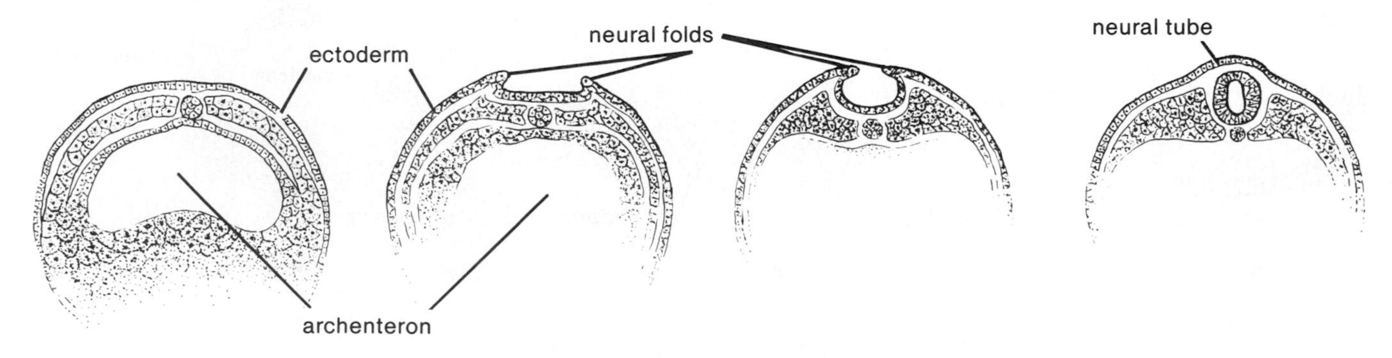

Recent knowledge about human development has led to a whole series of tests that can be done during pregnancy to give information about the condition of the developing embryo. These tests help physicians prepare to treat such conditions. Some of these tests are described in the Biology Today feature on page 212.

7.4 All Tissues Come from One of the Three Germ Layers

We now can begin to view the development of an animal embryo as the result of differentiation from the three primary germ layers, summarized in figure 7.6.

The ectoderm, as we know, gives rise to the nervous system. It also gives rise to many structures on the outside of the body: the outer layers of the skin, the hair, and the nails. The ectoderm is the source of feathers, scales, and other outer structures in animals.

The inner layer of cells, called the **endoderm** (inner skin), gives rise to the very inner structures of the body. The cells that line the internal organs, such as the intestines, the lungs, and various glands, come from the endoderm.

The remaining structures of the body come from the **mesoderm** (middle skin). These organs make up most of the mass of the body. The muscular system, circulatory system, excretory system, reproductive system, and most of the digestive system (all except the lining cells), come from this layer. The mesoderm also gives rise to connective tissues that play many roles in strengthening tissues and organs, as well as the connections between them.

Organs may contain tissues from different germ layers. The digestive organs are mainly of mesodermal origin, but have linings from the endoderm. The nerve cells and lens of the eye come from the ectoderm, but the muscles, blood vessels, and related structures come from the mesoderm.

Figure 7.6 Diagram showing the locations of the three primary germ layers in a typical vertebrate embryo.

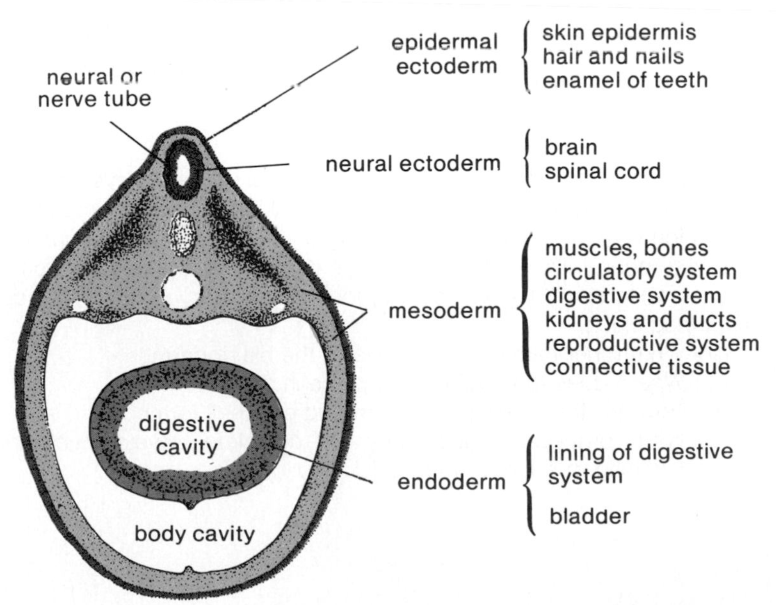

Self-Review

1. How many cells does an embryo contain after the zygote undergoes six mitotic cell divisions?
2. How long is the period of development for a chicken?
3. Why does cleavage appear to be different in a human embryo and a chick embryo?
4. What is the name of the hollow-ball stage of early development?
5. What germ layer gives rise to most of the mass of the body?
6. What germ layers contribute to the formation of the eye?
7. What structures arise from the neural tube?

Investigation 7.1 DEVELOPMENT IN THE CHICK

Introduction

A fertilized hen's egg has all the materials and all the instructions necessary to form a chicken. How does this process operate? Is there a very tiny chicken in the egg, which simply grows larger, or are the events more complex than that? How does the developing chicken obtain necessary food? How does it get oxygen, and how does it get rid of water? What happens to the contents of the egg as the chicken develops? This investigation explores answers to these questions using drawings and photographs of various stages of development. A short description of the process accompanies each figure. Answer the questions in your data book.

Procedure

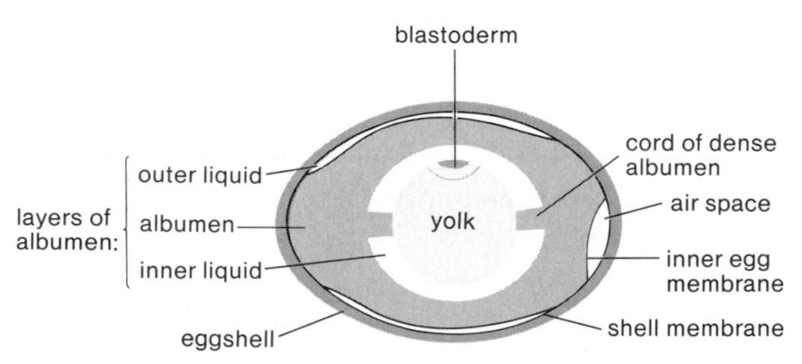

Figure 7.7a

1. A new chick, like all organisms that reproduce sexually, develops from a fertilized egg. After the hen lays the fertilized egg, she incubates it with the warmth of her body by sitting on it most of the time during a 21-day period. During these 21 days development proceeds from a small white spot, the blastoderm, located on the yolk, to a fully developed chick.
   (a) What other name can you give to the blastoderm?
   (b) Where does fertilization take place in a chicken?
   (c) How are the layers of albumen and eggshell formed?
   (d) What process is necessary for complete development and hatching of a fully formed chick?

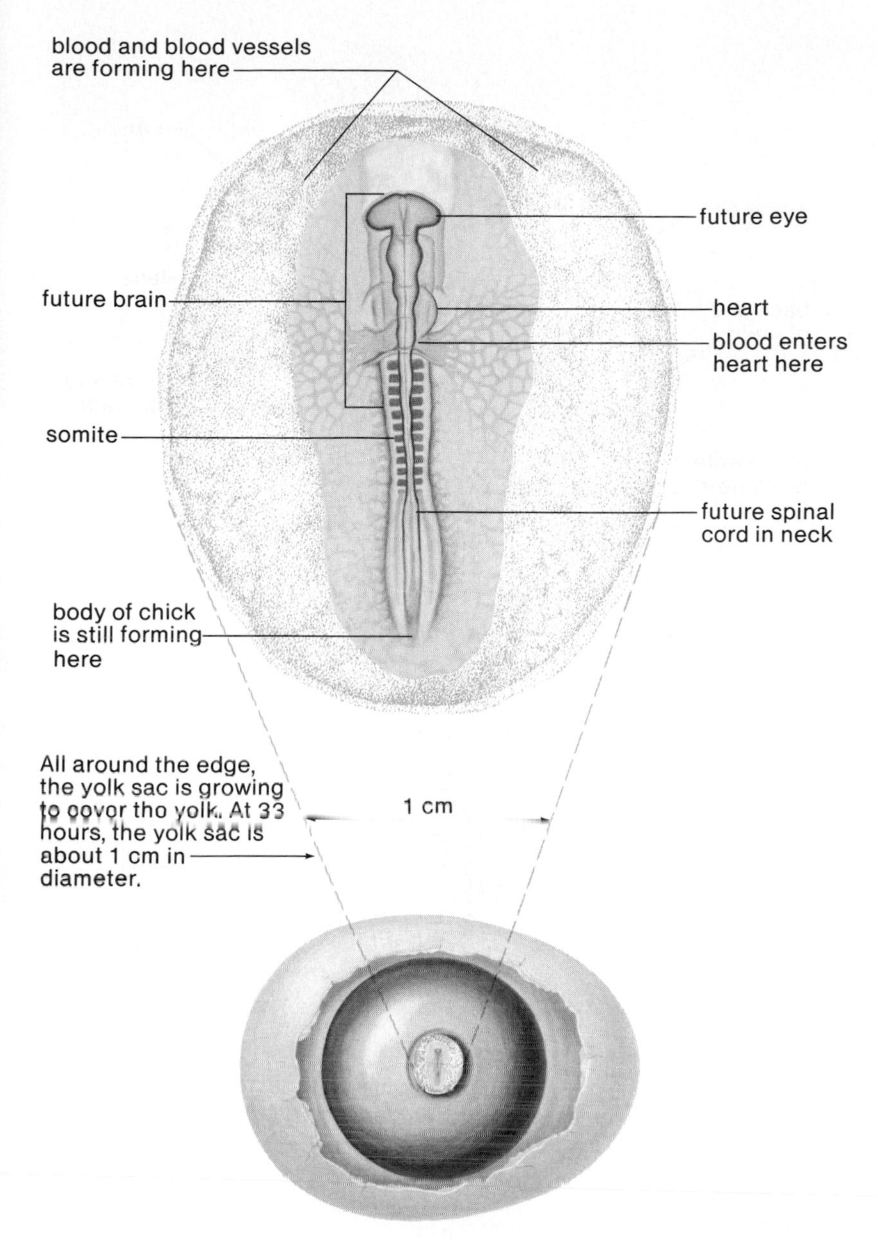

Figure 7.7b

2. After 33 hours of incubation only the head and neck of the embryo have formed. Blood vessels are developing on the yolk sac and are beginning to grow over the yolk. These blood vessels will lead to and from the heart.
   (a) What connection can you make between the blood vessels and the yolk over which they are growing?
   (b) Why should the heart be one of the first organs to function in the developing embryo?

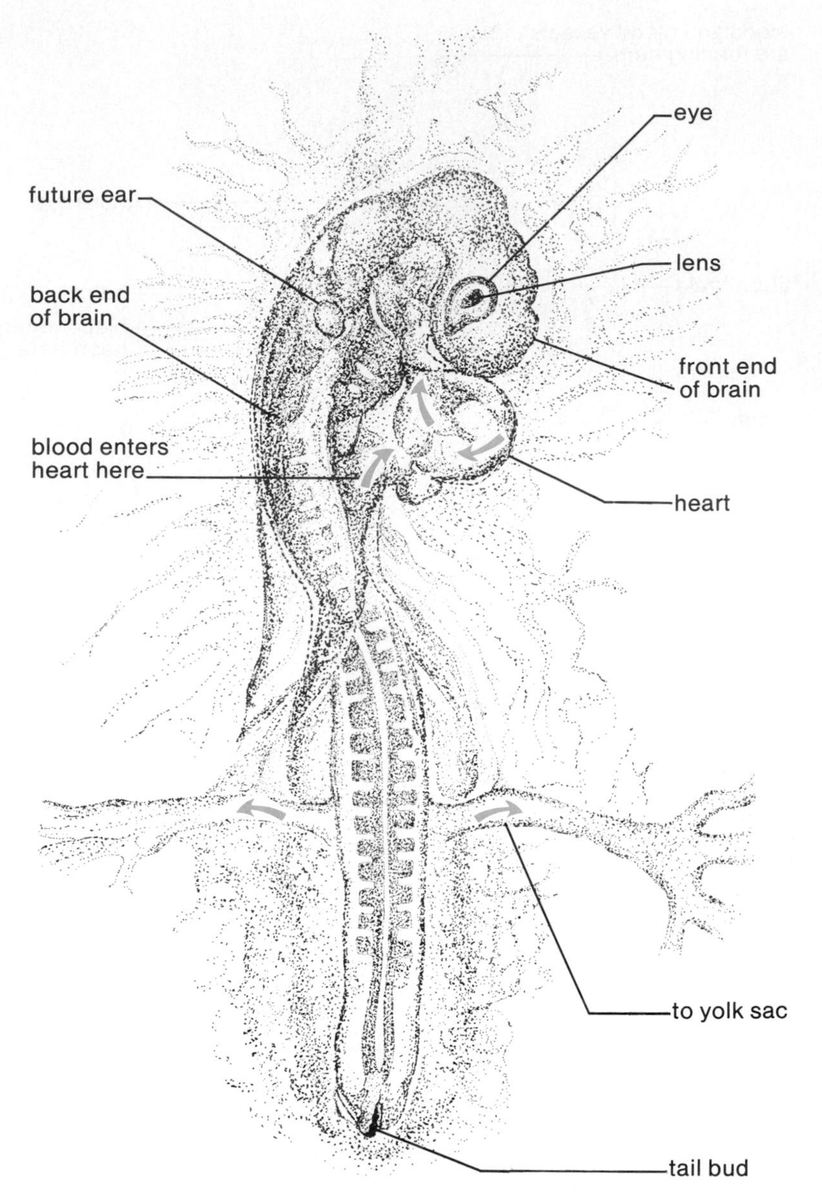

Figure 7.7c

3. The embryo at 56 hours has a tail forming and has turned and is now lying on its left side. The brain is larger, and the heart can be seen beating and moving blood through the blood vessels. Does the 56-hour embryo look like it will develop into a chick?

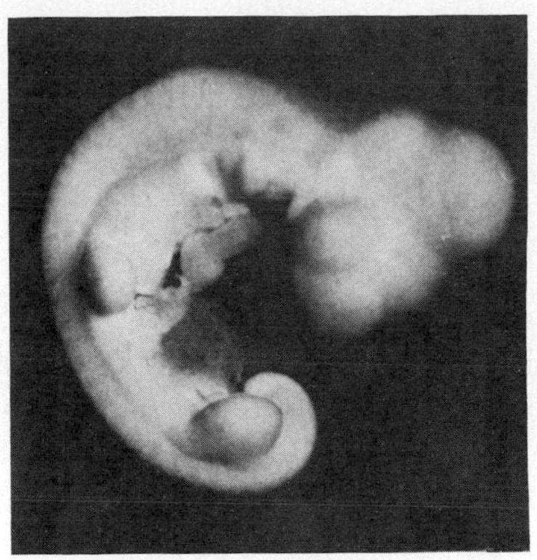

Figure 7.7d BSCS

4. The embryo in figure D is about 3½ days old. It was removed from the shell, and all the membranes were removed before the embryo was photographed. Note the distinct curve of the body bringing the head and tail of the embryo close together. Note the bulges near the end of the tail and near the center of the embryo. These are called buds. What structures in the developed chick will these buds become?

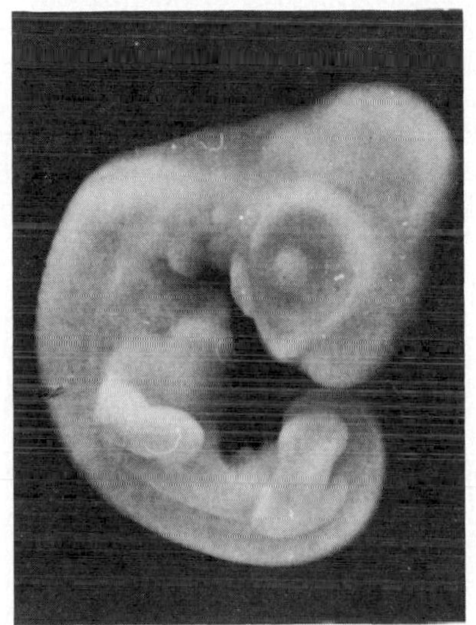

Figure 7.7e BSCS

5. This embryo is about 5 days old. Notice the large size of the head in relation to the rest of the body. However, the length of the entire embryo is only a few centimeters. What structure can be seen in this 5-day embryo?

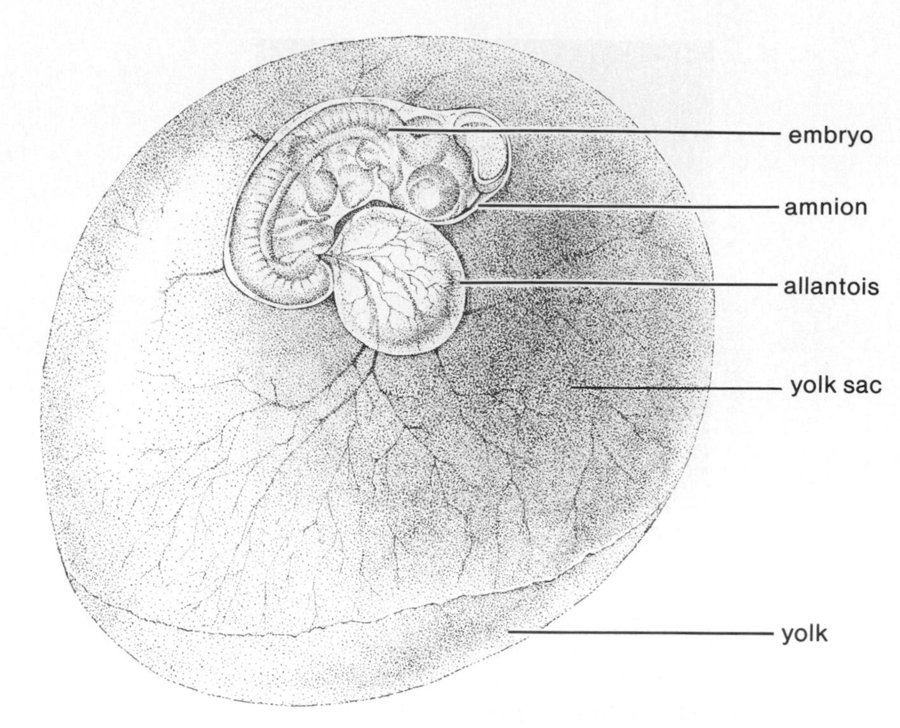

Figure 7.7f

6. Locate the 3 membranes that surround the 5-day-old chick. These are the yolk sac, the allantois, and the amnion. From the following descriptions, identify the functions of the 3 membranes.
   (a) The yolk sac is covered with blood vessels.
   (b) The allantois is a small, balloonlike membrane lying next to the eggshell and connected to the embryo by a thin stalk.
   (c) The amnion completely surrounds the embryo and contains a waterlike fluid.

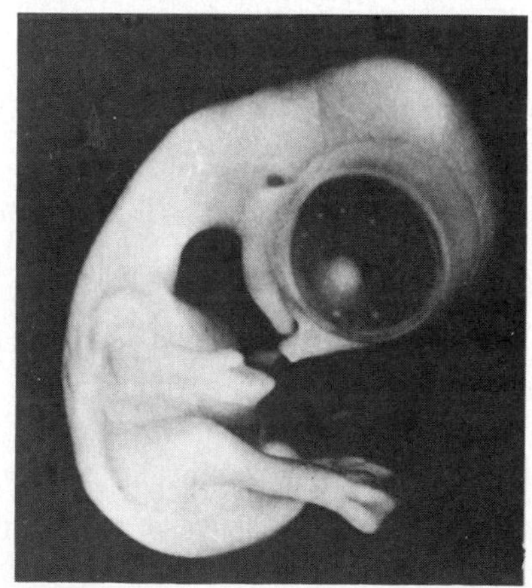

Figure 7.7g BSCS

7. After about 7 days, what new structures are evident?

Figure 7.7h BSCS

8. What 3 new structures can be seen in this 11-day-old chick?

Figure 7.7i BSCS

9. This is an 18-day-old embryo. Compare the development between 11 and 18 days with the development between 3½ and 7 days. What seems to be the biggest difference in development in the 2 time periods?

Figure 7.7j BSCS

10. By 19 or 20 days, the development is almost complete and the chick almost fills the shell. In 1 or 2 days it will hatch. Summarize briefly what happens, not only during chick development, but during the development of any multicellular organism.

Guidepost: Why is water important for development in animal embryos?

Animal Development

7.5 Some Animals Develop Independently of Their Parents

You will remember how important water is to the life of cells. Zygotes and embryos require adequate water in order to develop normally. Most fish and amphibian females deposit their eggs directly into the water. The eggs may have been fertilized already, or they may be fertilized by the male after they have been released.

Fertilization is one aspect of courtship and reproduction. When salamanders or frogs mate, for instance, the male awaits the release of hundreds or thousands of eggs by the female. Then he sheds large numbers of sperm over the eggs or nearby. Some of the sperm encounter eggs and fertilize them. However, the vast majority of sperm are diluted by the pond water and lost. Although this process may seem inefficient, frogs and salamanders have reproduced this way for millions of years. Their survival today is a measure of success of the method.

Young amphibians develop as far as the tadpole stage within the egg. (The photographs in figure 7.8 show development in a frog.) By then

Figure 7.8 Stages of cleavage and later development in the frog: (a) a fertilized egg, (b) 2-cell stage, (c) 8-cell stage, (d) 32+ cell stage, (e) early blastula, (f) neurula, with early neural groove, (g) tailbud embryo.

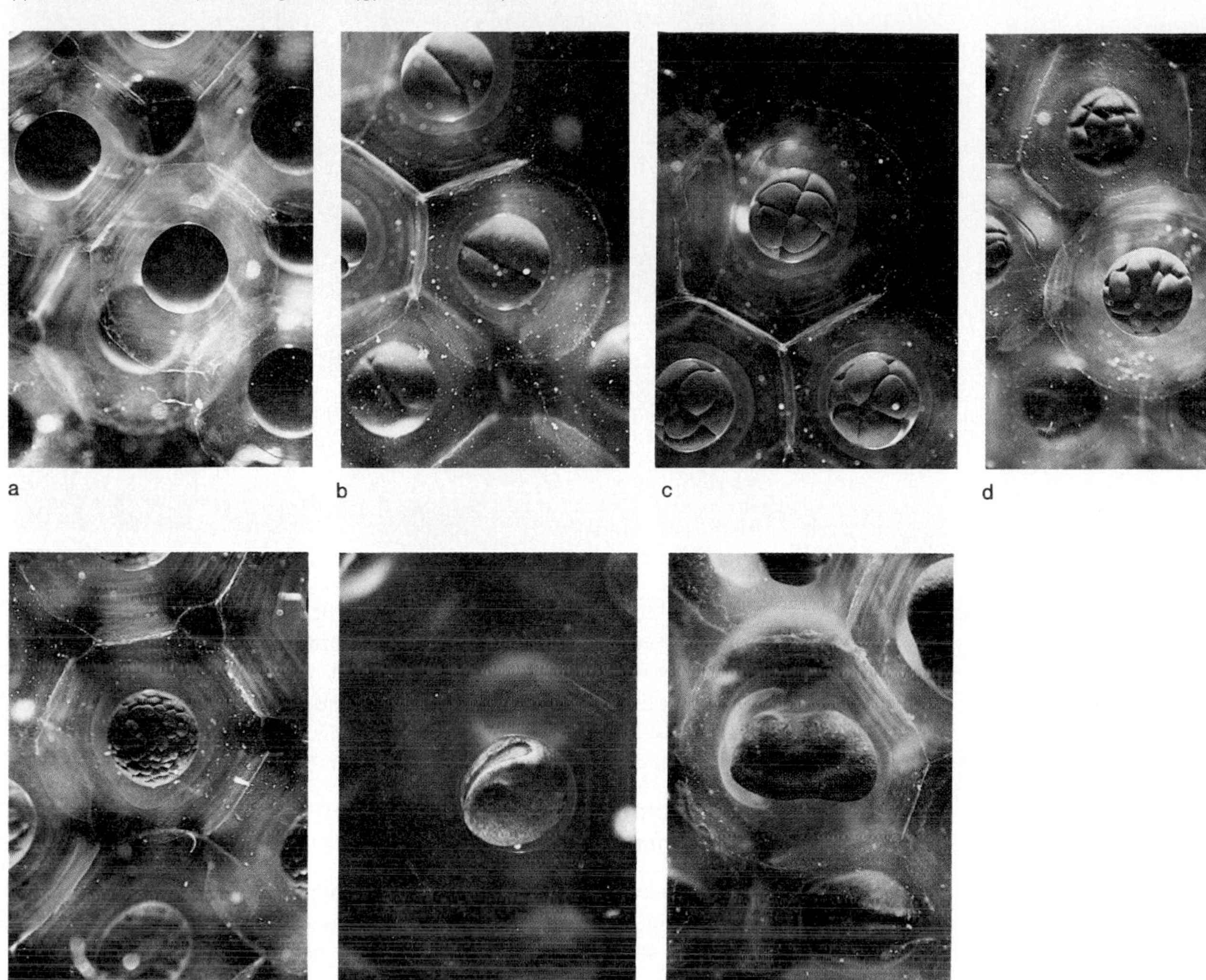

Figures a–g from Carolina Biological Supply Company

they can feed, and they have a tail and can swim. They hatch and become independent, and further development depends on their ability to find food for themselves. They also must escape predators, such as large fish.

Reptiles and birds usually do not lay their eggs in the water. These eggs must retain the water within the leathery or hard shell, which retards evaporation. Reptiles, including those that spend most of their lives in water, often bury their eggs in order to protect them from predators and from the hot sun. Large sea turtles, for instance, come ashore, dig

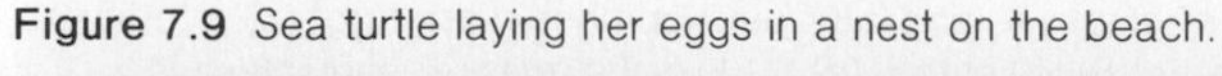

Figure 7.9 Sea turtle laying her eggs in a nest on the beach.

C. Allan Morgan

a nest, lay their eggs, and then cover the nest carefully before returning to the sea (see figure 7.9). When the baby turtles hatch, they are on their own. They waddle down the beach, swim into the sea, and begin an independent life. Many of them soon become the victims of predators, but enough survive to maintain the species.

7.6 Mammalian Embryos Develop within the Mother

As we have already mentioned, a mammalian embryo cannot survive very long on the small amount of raw material stored in the ovum. The embryo is still only a hollow ball of cells when it sinks into the spongy tissue of the uterus. This stage corresponds to the blastula in many other animals and is called a **blastocyst** (BLAS toh sist). After the blastocyst implants, it begins to absorb nutrients provided to the uterus by the mother's blood.

The blastocyst has a thick mass of cells on one side. Part of this inner cell mass continues to develop as the embryo (see figure 7.10). Other cells in the mass develop into important embryonic membranes: the **amnion** (AM nee on), the **allantois** (uh LANT oh wis), and the **yolk sac.** The thin-walled part of the blastocyst becomes the **chorion** (KOR ee on), which will function to nourish the embryo as it develops.

The human embryo becomes three-layered, as in the amphibian embryo. Soon the chorion sends fingers of cells, called **villi** (VIL eye), into the wall of the uterus. The villi are supplied with tiny blood vessels from the developing circulatory system of the embryo, as shown in figure 7.11. This is the embryo's contribution to the **placenta** (pluh SENT uh), its lifeline to the mother's circulatory system.

The placenta is a complex organ. The blood of the mother pools around the tiny villi of the embryo. To visualize this relationship, place your hand, fingers spread, into a large pan of water. The fingers on your hand correspond to the villi extending from the embryonic tissue. The water corresponds to the pool of mother's blood. In the Biology Today feature on page 212 you can read about how analysis of cells from these villi can help diagnose genetic disorders before birth.

A bit later the growing embryo forms a flexible cord between its own body and the placenta. This **umbilical** (um BIL ih kul) **cord** consists of membranes and, especially, blood vessels that run to and from the placenta. Those blood vessels show clearly in figure 7.12b.

About this time one embryonic membrane encloses the entire body of the embryo. This membrane, the amnion, becomes filled with fluid, and is clearly visible in figure 7.12d. The amniotic fluid has a salt concentration similar to that of sea water. Thus an embryo has its own small marine aquarium. It may swallow amniotic fluid, and also give off products into it. It does not drown, of course, because it is receiving oxygen directly into its bloodstream through the umbilical cord.

Gases and other molecules pass by diffusion from the blood of the mother, through the tiny blood vessel walls, into the circulatory system of the embryo. Carbon dioxide and other waste substances diffuse from

Figure 7.10 Human blastocyst. The embryo will develop from the inner cell mass, the thicker part on the left.

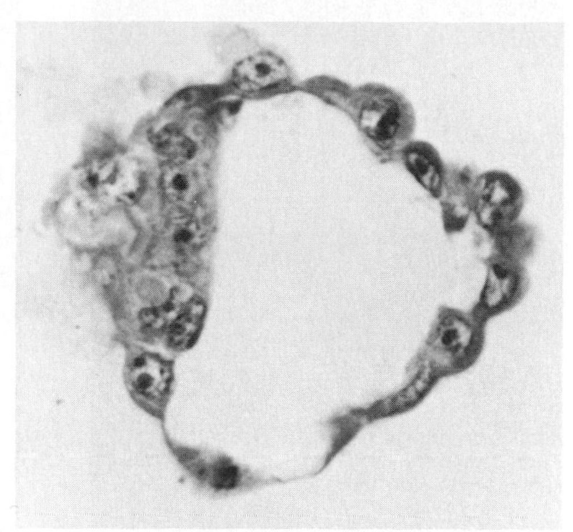

Carnegie Institution of Washington, Department of Embryology, Davis Division

Figure 7.11 Developing human fetus in uterus, showing the placental connection. Part of the placenta is enlarged to show the circulation of the mother and the fetus. The two systems do not mix, and exchange of substances and gases occurs between small pools of maternal blood and capillary walls of the fetus.

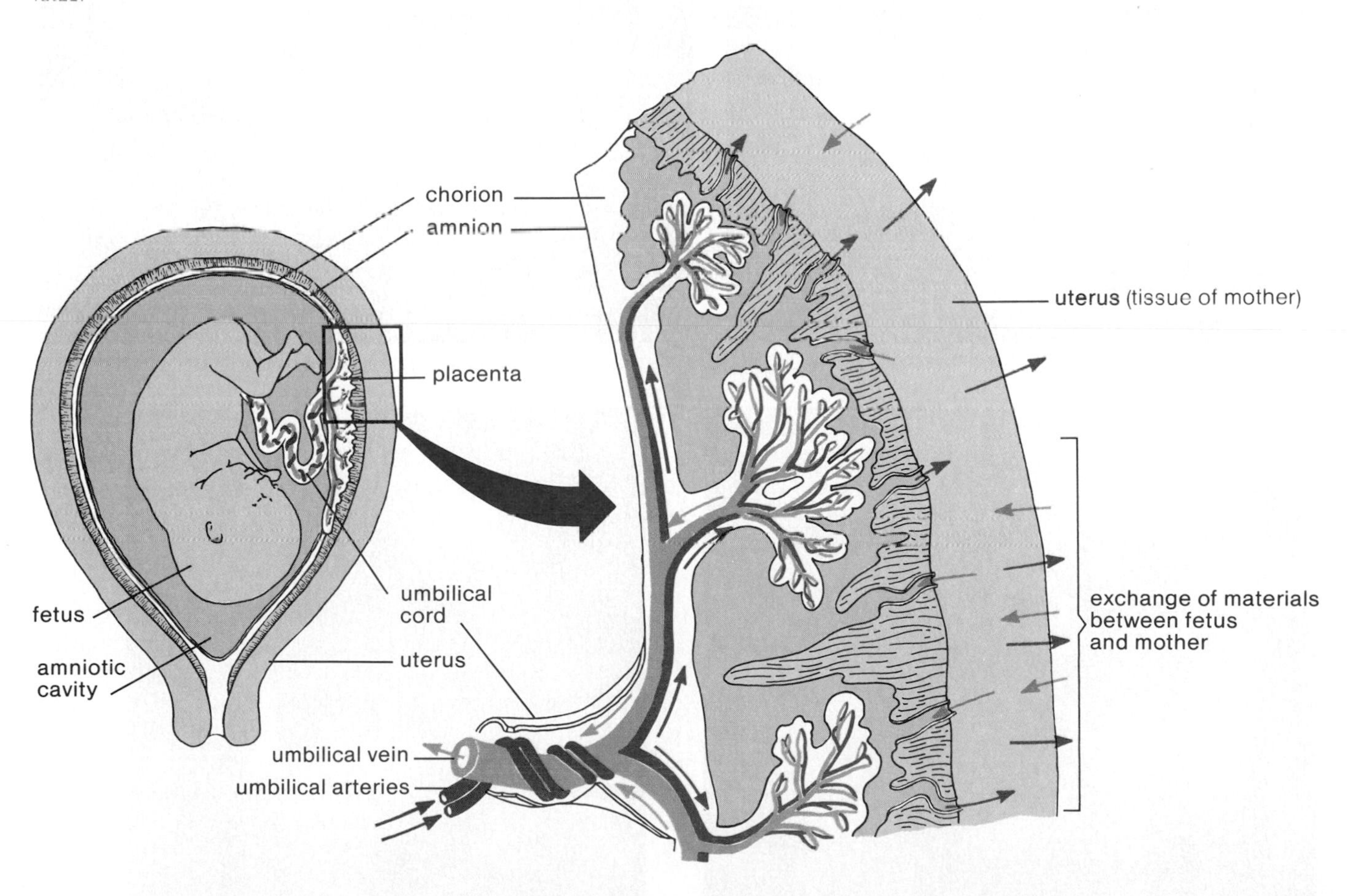

Figure 7.12 Stages in the early development of a human embryo: (a) 4 weeks, (b) 6 weeks, (c) 8 weeks, (d) 12 weeks, (e) 14 weeks, (f) 16 weeks.

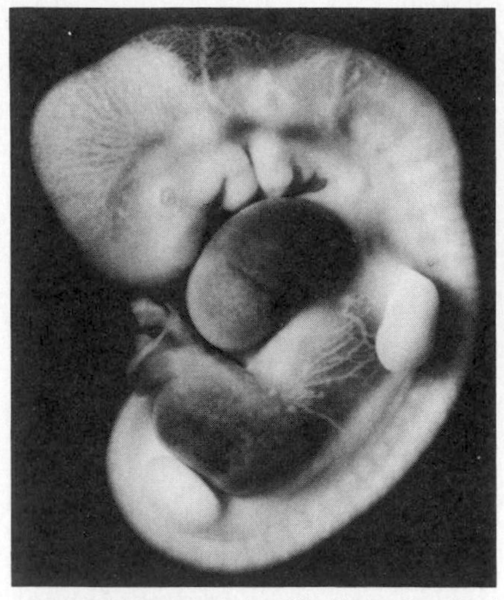

a Carnegie Institution of Washington, Department of Embryology, Davis Division

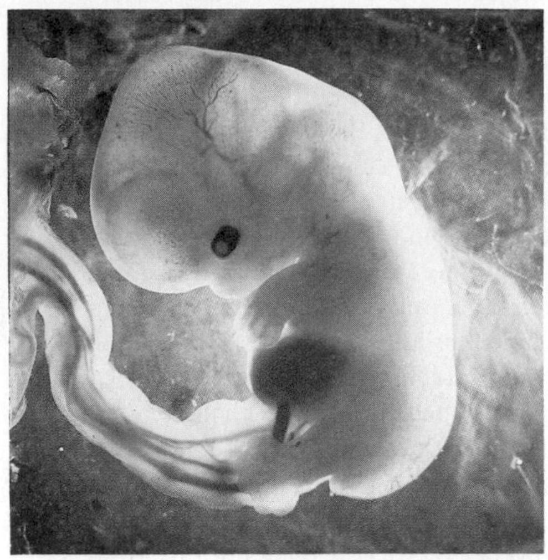

b Lennart Nilsson, A CHILD IS BORN, Dell Publishing Co., Inc. New York 1986

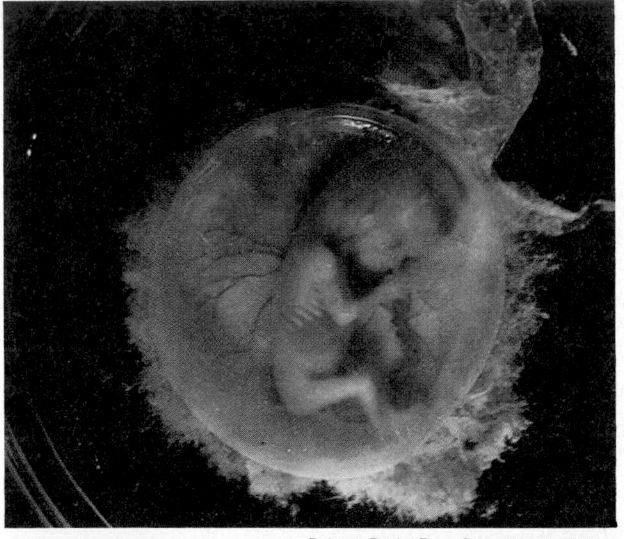

c Roberts Rugh "From Conception to Birth"

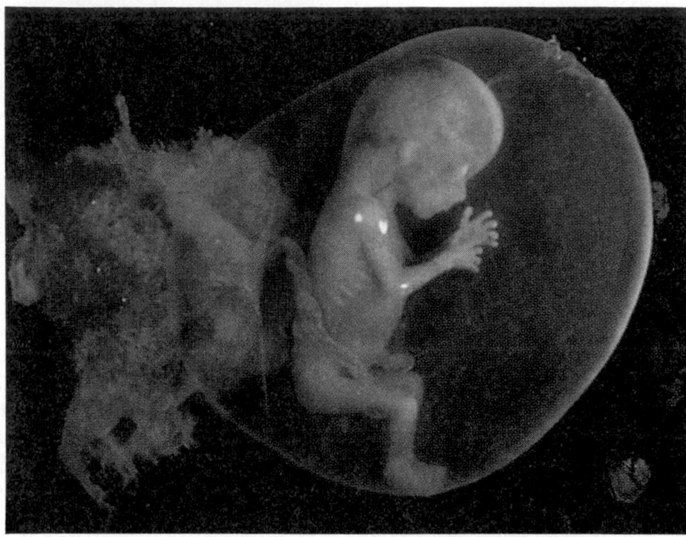

d Roberts Rugh "From Conception to Birth"

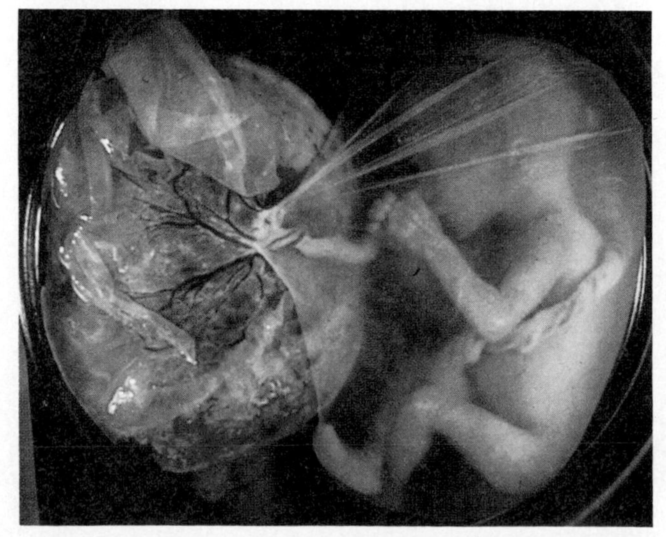

e Roberts Rugh "From Conception to Birth"

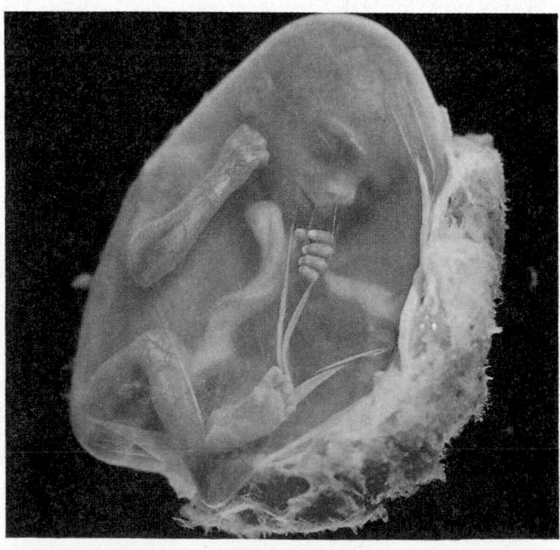

f Lennart Nilsson, A CHILD IS BORN, Dell Publishing Co., Inc. New York 1986

Figure 7.13 Prenatal diagnosis of genetic disorders by amniocentesis. Fetal cells from the amniotic fluid are cultured for later chromosomal and biochemical analyses. Biochemical analysis of the fluid also can reveal certain problems.

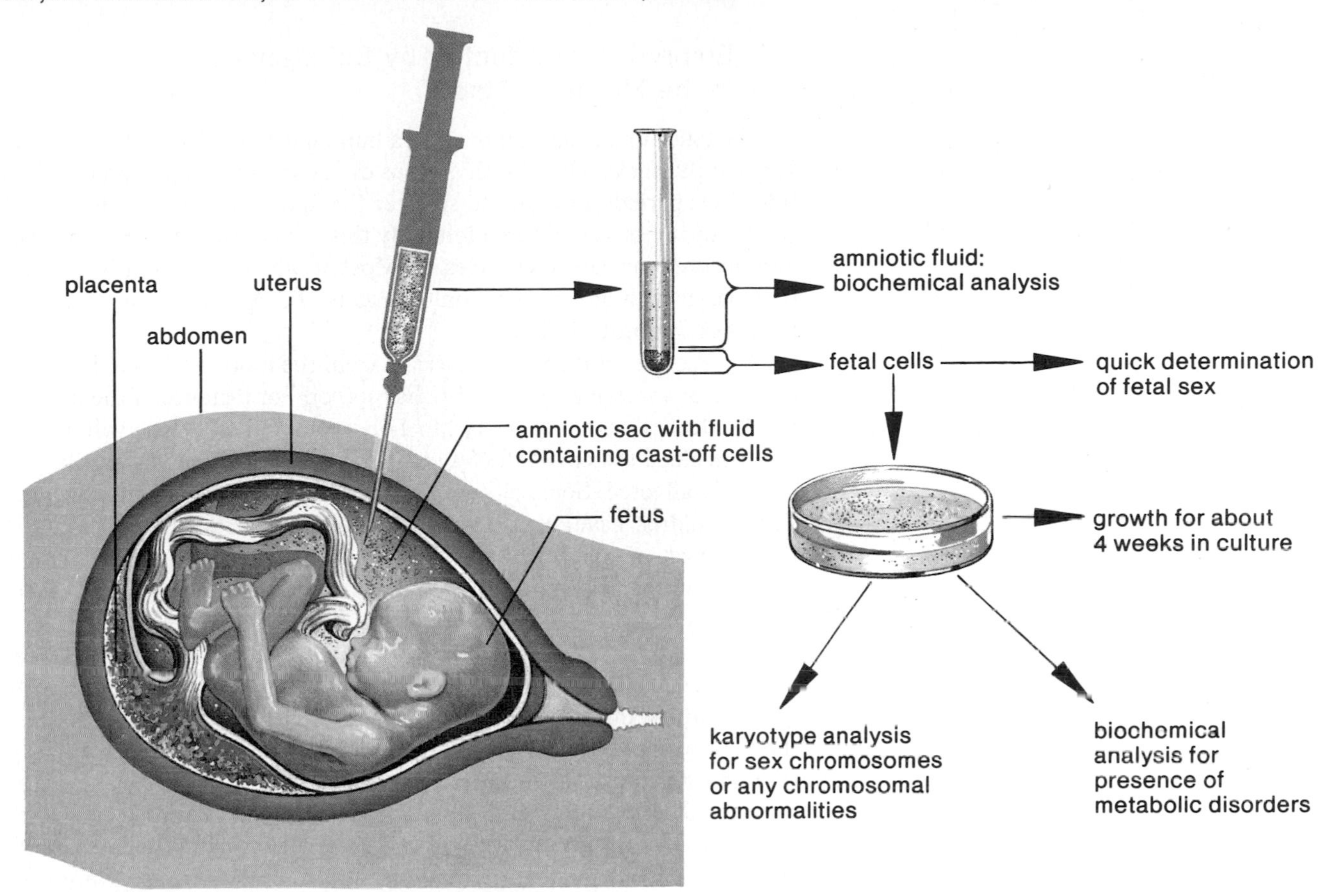

the villi into the blood of the mother. The mother's lungs and kidneys get rid of the waste products. In these exchanges, the blood of the embryo and the blood of the mother do not mix.

If it is properly nourished, the embryo grows and its cells differentiate into distinctive types. Cells of similar kind are found together in **tissues.** Tissues perform a general function for the body; muscle tissue contracts, for instance, and glandular tissue secretes certain substances. When several tissues are grouped together in a special arrangement to do a particular job, an **organ** is formed. A stomach is an organ—the lining cells, which secrete enzymes, are combined with layers of muscular tissue, which causes the stomach to contract. The whole stomach is enclosed in a thin layer of cells on the outside. Finally, several organs are related in a general function to form an **organ system.** The digestive system, for example, consists of a whole series of organs, arranged in single file, that carry food from the mouth, through all the steps of digestion and absorption, and eliminate the undigested remains. All parts of the system must work together if digestion is to be effective.

Often the amniotic fluid contains some cells from the embryo. These cells are useful in testing the embryo for biochemical or chromosome abnormalities. A sample of amniotic fluid is removed, and the cells are grown in the laboratory. This process, called **amniocentesis** (AM nee oh sen TEE sus), is used to test for the absence of chromosomes, for the presence of extra chromosomes, and for some genetic disorders of a biochemical nature. We shall see later in the chapter what these tests sometimes reveal.

7.7 Embryos Are Affected by Substances in the Mother's Blood

The total time of development of a human being in its mother's uterus is about 39 weeks. Usually physicians divide the total development time into three periods, or trimesters. After the first trimester, which lasts 12 weeks, the embryo is called a **fetus.** By this time most organs are formed, and the skeleton can be seen clearly. Most of the last trimester is a period of rapid growth and maturation of organs and systems as the fetus approaches the time of birth.

Because the fetus shares materials from the mother's blood, it can be affected by materials taken in by the mother. For instance, if the mother drinks alcoholic beverages, the alcohol in the mother's blood will diffuse into the blood system of the fetus, and the fetus may be physically and mentally affected. Some children are born with fetal alcohol syndrome. These children have certain abnormal facial features (figure 7.14) and the prospect of mental retardation. Most physicians recommend that pregnant women consume no alcohol whatever during the period of their pregnancy.

Other substances taken in by the mother also have been shown to affect the normal development of the fetus. If the mother smokes cigarettes, for example, the birth weight of the child is significantly less than normal, and the head size is smaller. It is probably accurate to say that any substance taken in by the mother during her pregnancy may be reflected in the fetus. Substances harmful to the mother are likely to be harmful to the fetus as well. Even substances apparently harmless or even beneficial to the mother may turn out to be exceptionally harmful to the embryo.

Figure 7.14 Child with fetal alcohol syndrome at 1 year (left) and 4 years (right). Note the short nose and the smooth, long, narrow upper lip, as well as the narrow eye opening apparent in the 4-year old.

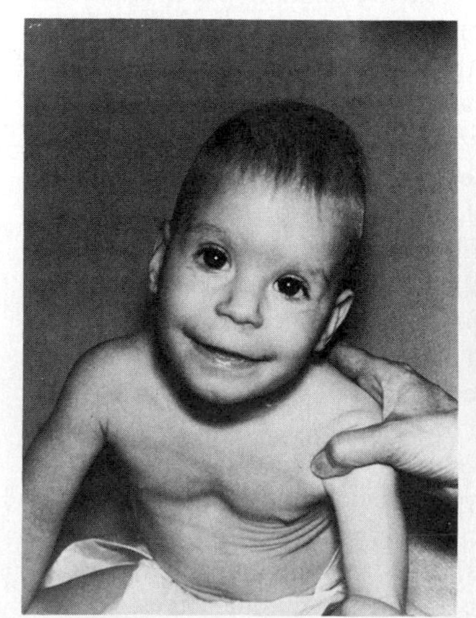

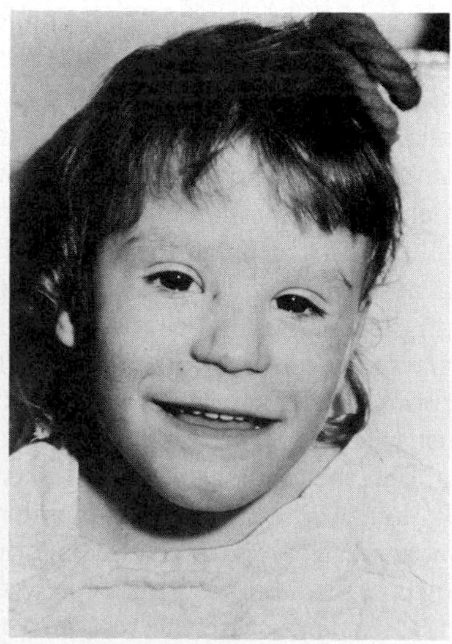

Embryos in the earliest stages of development, during the first trimester, are especially sensitive to harmful agents. Around 1960 a sedative containing the drug thalidomide (thuh LID uh myd) was widely prescribed for women who had nausea during their pregnancy. Unfortunately, thalidomide interfered with early development at a crucial time. More than 5000 children in European countries were born with very short arms or legs, or limbs that were missing entirely. It was several years before the cause of these developmental problems was traced to this drug. Thalidomide acted on the embryo just at the time the arm and leg cells were differentiating. Now a generation has passed, and some of the thalidomide victims have become parents themselves. Their children have had normal limbs, because the absence of limbs was not a genetic problem. It was the result of a substance in the mother's blood that acted during a critical stage of development in the embryo.

7.8 The Fetal Period of Development Ends with Birth

At the completion of fetal development, and sometimes earlier, a complex series of hormone interactions begins. The final result is birth, during which the fetus is propelled from the uterus by muscular contractions. These birth contractions usually cause pain for the mother.

Figure 7.15 Human birth. (a) Labor is beginning. (b) The uterus is contracting; the opening of the uterus is enlarging; the amnion is still intact. (c) The baby is being born, the head and shoulders appear first; the baby turns so it is face up. (d) The doctor's hands receive the baby as it is born. After the baby is born, the placenta and the lining of the uterus are pushed out.

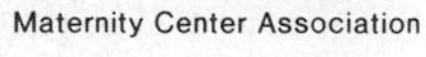

a

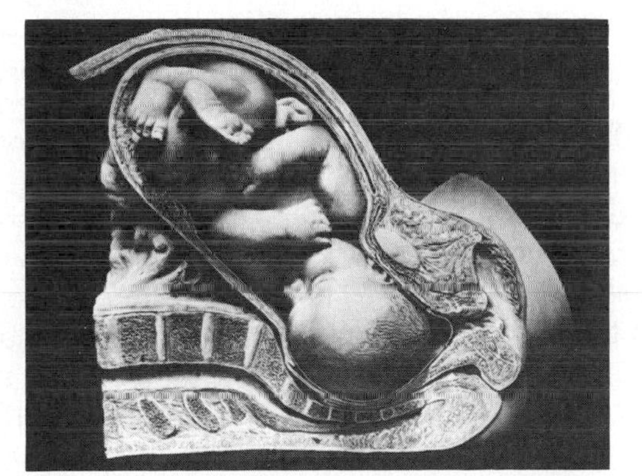

b Maternity Center Association

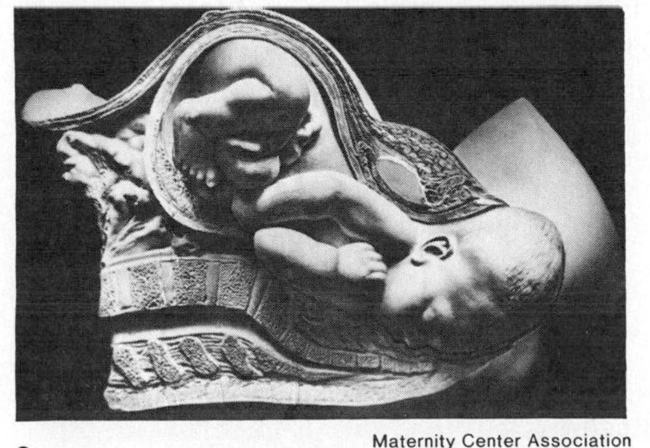

c Maternity Center Association

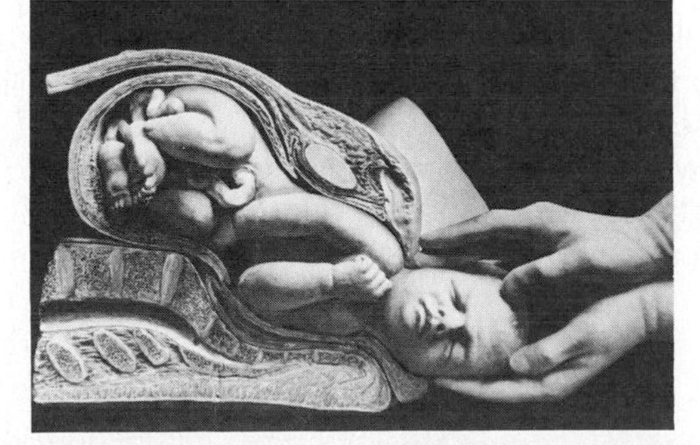

d Maternity Center Association

Biology Today

Progress in Prenatal Diagnosis

Among the most progressive areas of genetics is research on the detection, prevention, and treatment of genetic disorders in the developing fetus. Two techniques are most prominent in prenatal diagnosis.

Amniocentesis: This technique came into prominence in the 1970s and is now widely used throughout the world. The obstetrician first determines the position of the fetus and the location of the placenta with ultrasound. A long thin needle is inserted through the abdominal cavity into the uterus. About 10 ml of amniotic fluid is withdrawn through the needle. The fluid contains cells that have been sloughed off from the fetus. These cells are cultured for three to four weeks. They then can be analyzed for chromosomal abnormalities and for certain enzymatic disorders. The fluid itself is analyzed for increased levels of a substance called alphafetoprotein (AFP). High levels of AFP can mean the presence of disorders such as spina bifida, or open spine. Amniocentesis cannot be performed until about 16 weeks of pregnancy because there is not enough room in the amniotic sac to allow safe withdrawal of fluid before that time. Amniocentesis is quite accurate and safe. The risk of spontaneous abortion after the procedure is less than 0.5 percent (1 in 200).

Chorionic villi sampling (CVS): This procedure was first introduced in the early 1980s in China, the Soviet Union, and Italy. CVS can be performed as early as the 9th week of pregnancy, considerably earlier than amniocentesis. A catheter is inserted through the vagina into the uterus and directed by ultrasound to a region called the chorion frondosum. Small, fingerlike projections called villi begin to grow into the uterine wall at this point. The villi are composed of rapidly dividing fetal cells.

Suction is applied to the catheter, and some villi are withdrawn. Because the cells in the villi are actively growing and dividing, they can be analzyed quickly. Results from chromosome studies are available in a few days, and results from enzyme studies in about a week. Because no amniotic fluid is obtained during CVS, analysis for AFP cannot be performed; otherwise, diagnoses from CVS are as accurate as those from amniocentesis. The procedure carries a higher risk of spontaneous abortion—about 1 to 2 percent—than does amniocentesis, but it provides an earlier diagnosis of defects.

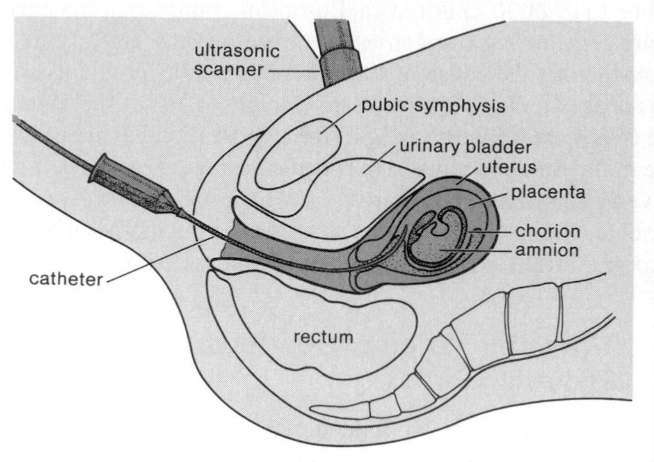

Based on art from Michael Reese Hospital and Medical Center, Division of Medical Genetics, Chicago, IL.

Prenatal diagnosis is routinely recommended for women age 35 or over. The risk of chromosomal disorders increases with advanced maternal age. Prenatal diagnosis is also recommended for women who already have a child with a genetic disorder or who have a history of genetic disorder in the family of either parent. All detectable chromosomal disorders and more than 200 single gene disorders are diagnosable using amniocentesis and CVS.

The application of techniques from genetic engineering has allowed the prenatal diagnosis of sickle cell anemia, thalassemia, muscular dystrophy, and phenylketonuria (PKU). More progress is virtually certain as these techniques are used in conjunction with amniocentesis and CVS.

The fetus is born through the vagina, which becomes the birth canal at this time. The vagina usually is able to expand to allow the head and body of the fetus to pass through. After birth it returns to normal size.

Occasionally, the fetus is not in proper position, or the body of the mother is unable to expel the fetus. In such cases the physician may deliver the fetus by cutting through the body wall. The abdominal muscles of the mother and the wall of the uterus are parted, and the fetus is delivered directly. This major surgery is called a cesarean birth, or C-section.

Modern medicine can stimulate ovulation in females who have difficulty in becoming pregnant. Because of this treatment, several ova may be released at once, and four to seven fetuses may develop. Multiple fetuses also occur naturally, of course. Occasionally the uterus cannot accommodate the full development of the several fetuses. In such cases the physician usually removes the small fetuses by cesarean section. Such delivery is premature. Premature infants are placed in incubators to keep them warm, and are given special care (figure 7.17). They are kept in the hospital until they are able to breathe and feed without special attention. Very small infants, those weighing 1 kg or so, may spend weeks or even months in the hospital before they are large enough and strong enough to go home.

Figure 7.16 A newborn baby.

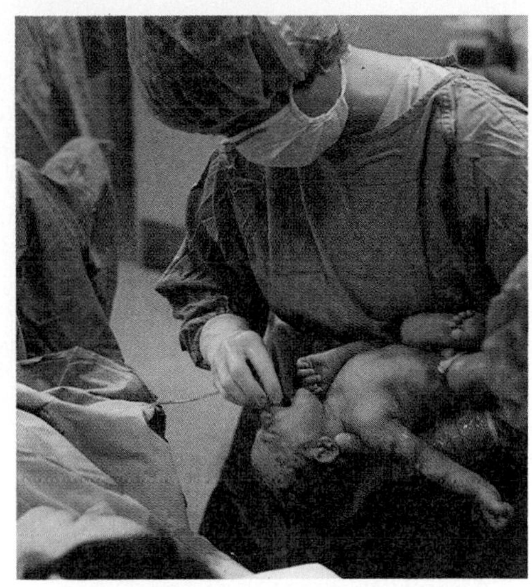

Leonard Kamsler/Medichrome

Figure 7.17 Premature babies are kept in intensive care units so they can receive the special, round-the-clock care they require.

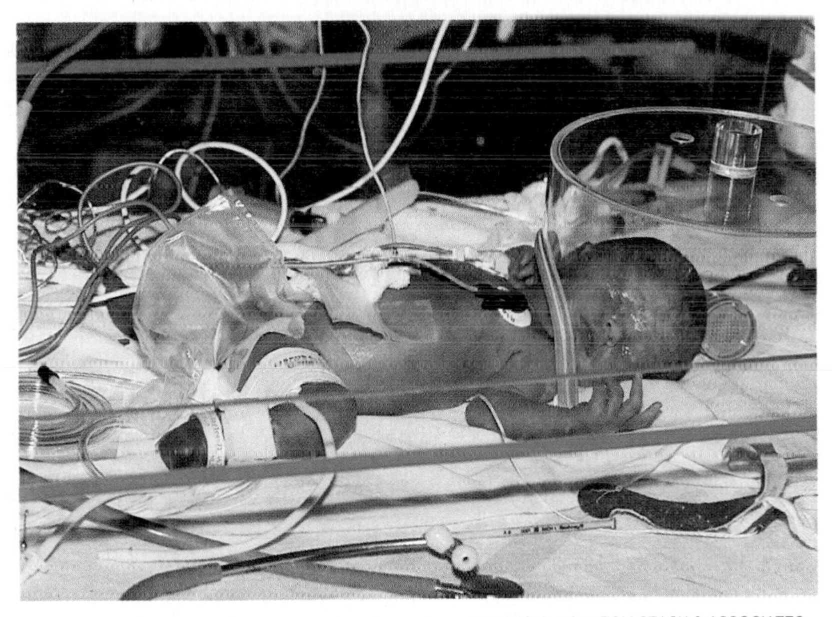

David C. London/TOM STACK & ASSOCIATES

Self-Review

1. What kinds of animals deposit their eggs directly in the water?
2. Explain how substances pass from the mother to the embryo in mammals.
3. What membrane surrounds the fetus during development?
4. How does the fetus get rid of waste products?
5. What is the difference between a cell, a tissue, an organ, and a system?
6. Give two examples of how substances in the mother's blood may affect the fetus.
7. Why do children born to parents without arms or legs, due to thalidomide, have normal limbs?
8. What are some reasons for a cesarean birth?

Guidepost: What are the methods used to prevent or interrupt a pregnancy?

Control of Conception

7.9 Birth Control Depends on Preventing Fertilization

As we saw in earlier chapters, the population of the earth is increasing at a rapid rate. Some countries are already overpopulated, and means are being taken to limit the number of children that can be born. These methods depend on birth control.

When a sperm fertilizes an ovum, a conception occurs. In order for conception to take place, an egg cell and a sperm cell must be in the same place at the same time. Birth control methods depend on preventing this physical contact between the two gametes.

Some methods of birth control, also called contraception, depend on providing barriers between sperm cells and egg cells. Usually an effort is made to interfere with the movement of sperm cells. For example, a membranous sheath, or condom, can be placed over the penis prior to intercourse. The sperm are thus prevented from entering the body of the female.

Another method makes use of a flexible cap, or diaphragm, that can be placed over the entrance to the uterus. Since the uterus is a different size in different women, a diaphragm must be fitted by a physician or other health-care professional if it is to be effective.

Still another method of contraception in women depends on preventing ovulation, the release of the immature ovum from the ovary. This can be accomplished by taking synthetic sex hormones in pill form. These must be prescribed by a physician.

There are also surgical procedures that provide permanent sterilization (figure 7.19). In males the vas deferens, which carries sperm from the epididymis to the penis, may be tied and cut. This simple procedure,

Figure 7.18 These contraceptive devices can help prevent unwanted pregnancies.

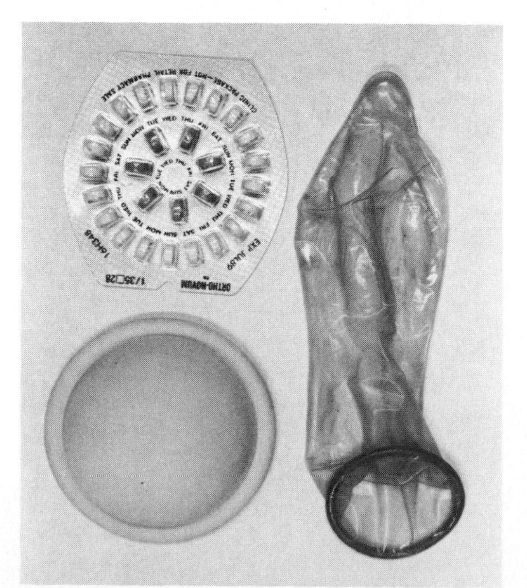

BSCS by Doug Sokell

done on both sides, is called a vasectomy (vuh SEK tuh mee), and is widely used in some countries. In females the oviducts may be tied and cut in a procedure called tubal ligation (ly GAY shun), which requires small openings into the abdominal cavity. Both methods generally are considered irreversible.

Effective contraception requires planning ahead. Once sperm have entered the body of a female, there is little chance of heading them off. That is because the sperm are able to reach the egg in the oviduct in a very short span of time.

In some countries, methods of birth control are not readily available, or their use is forbidden by religious beliefs.

Unwanted pregnancies in teenage girls is a serious problem. In some areas of the United States as many as 50 percent of births are illegitimate—that means that the babies are born to unmarried, and usually teenage, women.

Figure 7.19 Tubal ligation (a) and vasectomy (b) both can be used to prevent pregnancy.

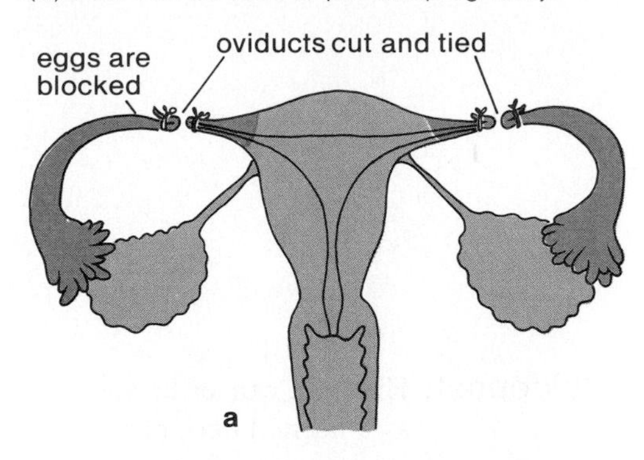

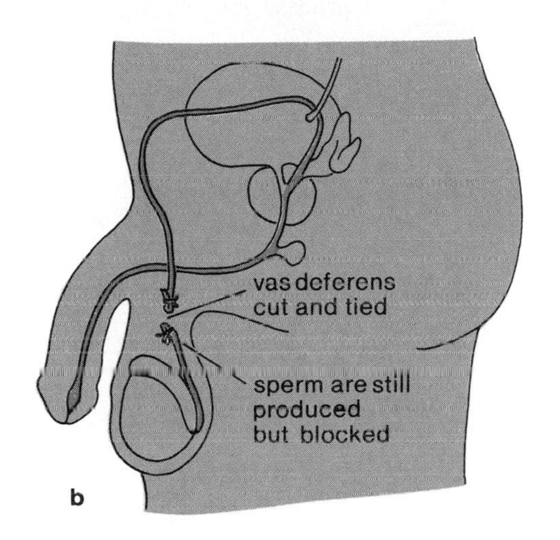

7.10 Pregnancy Can Be Terminated

Pregnancy can be terminated involuntarily or voluntarily. Nature aborts many fetuses before birth. If there is a major chromosomal or genetic abnormality that prevents normal development, for example, the embryo might be aborted within the first few days of development. In other cases the death of the fetus occurs later. These natural events are called spontaneous abortions. They are thought to occur in some 70 percent of all conceptions.

Voluntary termination of pregnancy occurs for several reasons. As we shall see later, parents may feel there are genetic reasons for terminating a pregnancy. If amniocentesis or chorionic villi sampling reveals a chromosome abnormality or a genetic disorder in a developing fetus, the parents may decide to terminate the pregnancy. Certain birth defects can be devastating to the parents, both psychologically and financially.

Unmarried women who find themselves pregnant may feel that having a child at that particular time would have a distressing effect on their lives. Even married women sometimes find that contraceptive methods have not worked with 100 percent effectiveness. (It is often said that *no* contraceptive method is "perfect" except abstention—the complete avoidance of sexual intercourse.) Married women, too, may want to terminate a pregnancy because they are not able to support and properly raise a child.

Some people and groups feel very strongly that human fetuses should not be aborted under any circumstance. Others feel just as strongly that the individual woman should decide whether she wants to continue or terminate her pregnancy.

The debate that surrounds the abortion issue is very complex and emotionally charged. It involves different opinions on such issues as the quality of human life, and of whether an unborn fetus should have the same legal (in this instance, life-saving) rights as someone *after* birth. There are no clear-cut answers to such issues, and the debate is likely to continue for a very long time.

Self-Review

1. Name three methods that could be used by females to prevent conception.
2. What method would be used by males who want to be sterilized completely?
3. What is meant by spontaneous abortion?

Guidepost: How can cancer be viewed as a normal developmental process gone wrong?

Cancer

7.11 Development Is Usually Well Controlled

We have now studied a number of developmental events. They begin with fertilization, which initiates a series of orderly cell divisions. The increase in cell number, accompanied by growth, leads eventually to differentiation of cell types. Each kind of cell has a particular task to perform in the development and life of a new individual.

Cells of the same kind make up tissues, and these in turn work with other kinds of tissues to form organs. An organism consists of a number of organ systems, each consisting of a group of related organs. The mature individual is able to perform all the functions of living, such as food intake, survival against enemies, courtship, and reproduction. The life cycle is completed when an individual attains maturity and gametes are produced that can start another generation. This cycle has repeated itself for untold numbers of generations and in millions of different species. Development thus provides continuity extending from gamete formation in one generation to the gamete formation in the next generation.

This entire drama of development depends on a certain number of cell divisions. When an animal reaches full size, most cell divisions cease. Cells do continue to divide, but only to replace worn-out or lost cells. Cells of the nervous system almost never divide after differentiation is completed. Other cells, however, such as blood cells, have a limited lifespan. They are replaced by new cells on a regular basis. The lining of the digestive system also wears away, and those cells are replaced continuously. Our outer skin cells are lost and are replaced from layers of cells below. Normal life functions mainly require cell replacement activities once maturity is reached.

As we mentioned earlier, aging is a normal part of development. At the end of the aging process, an organism dies. This process is built into the genetic program, and is rather precise for each species. Most cells are able to divide only a certain number of times. This fact seems to be true for organisms from protists to human beings. But in cancer, this control over cell division seems to be lost, and cells begin to divide again.

Figure 7.20 In cancer, abnormal numbers of certain cells are produced. These photomicrographs of stained blood cells show normal human blood (a), and blood from a person with leukemia (b). Note the large number of white blood cells in (b).

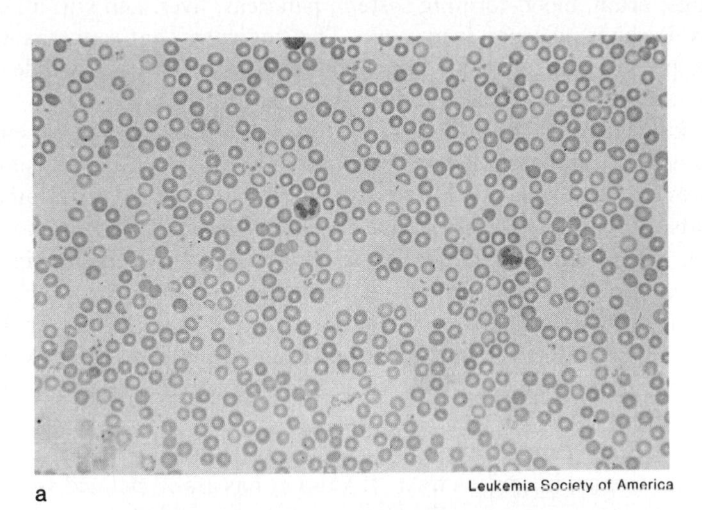

a Leukemia Society of America

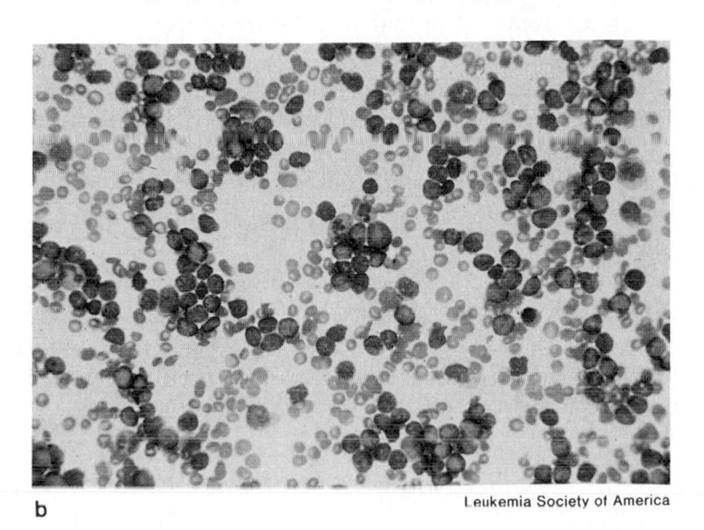

b Leukemia Society of America

7.12 Cancer Cells Divide without Limit

Just as organisms are mortal and have a certain lifespan, so do the cells that make up the organism. Occasionally, however, a cell will begin to divide again. Usually this event happens in a single cell, which then undergoes a burst of cell division. The resulting cells form a growing mass called a tumor. If the tumor remains in one place, near its origin, it is said to be benign. But sometimes the rapidly dividing cells spread to invade other tissues. Small groups of these dividing cancer cells may break off and move to establish themselves in other, more distant parts of the body. Cell masses that continue to divide and spread at the expense of other tissues are said to be malignant.

There are many theories for the origin of cancer. Actually there are many different kinds of uncontrolled cell growth, so there may be many different causes of cancer. Cancers can affect many different organs in the body. In humans, cancers occur in the lung, stomach, reproductive organs, brain, blood-forming system, pancreas, liver, and still other organs. Perhaps no organ is immune. That indicates that cancer is a very widespread and general kind of condition. It may occur in people of all ages, though more often in the late stages of life.

Some cancers may be caused by viruses. In others a genetic change may occur. It appears that various factors are involved in releasing the brakes on cell division. Many cancers are triggered by environmental agents. When sensitive tissues are damaged over and over, a tumor may form. A well-known example is the relationship between smoking and lung cancer. Not everyone who smokes tobacco gets lung cancer, but the majority of lung cancers do occur in smokers. It is also a cancer that is almost impossible to treat after it has been discovered. The risk of developing lung cancer can be lowered significantly by the simple act of not smoking.

Some other cancers are more difficult to prevent. When discovered, they are treated in various ways. If a tumor has a well-defined structure, it may be removed surgically. Cancers that appear first as lumps in the breast often are removed in that way. Other cancers are treated with high-energy radiation. Care is taken to try to kill the cancerous cells without harming healthy cells that lie nearby. Chromosomes are sensitive to radiation. In cancerous tissue, cells are in frequent division. That means the chromosomes are short and thick at each mitosis and, hence, provide a larger target for the radiation. Other treatments include chemical treatments that interfere with cell division. This treatment is called chemotherapy.

In cancer cells, some part of the control of cell division has gone wrong. The cells also may be less differentiated than mature ones. Clearly the solution to the riddle of cancer depends on understanding normal cell division and its role in development. It is only then that we will know what has gone wrong when a cell becomes cancerous.

Self-Review

1. For what main reason do cells divide in mature adults?
2. What is the difference between benign and malignant tumors?
3. Why is radiation used in the treatment of tumors?
4. What is the purpose of the chemical substances used in chemotherapy?
5. Give a very brief definition of cancer.

Summary

Development is the whole series of events that are initiated when a zygote begins to divide and grow. Cells that are similar in early divisions gradually become specialized to perform certain tasks. This process is called differentiation, and it leads to a complex, mature organism. Developing organisms continue to change throughout life. Aging occurs continuously and eventually ends the life of an individual. The lifespan is part of the genetic program set at fertilization.

Development is aided by cell movements and tissue foldings. In animals the blastula stage is transformed into an embryo with three germ layers. Each germ layer gives rise to specific tissues and contributes to various organs. Much development can be understood in terms of germ layer differentiation. In differentiation, like cells are grouped into tissues. Organs consist of several kinds of tissues. A number of related organs make up a system of organs.

Most animal development occurs in an aqueous environment. In mammals the fetus is surrounded by a fluid-filled amnion. Early development may be strongly influenced by substances in the mother's blood, such as alcohol or drugs. Human conception can be controlled by various methods of birth control.

Development is usually under strict control, and in mature organisms most cells seldom divide. When cells resume cell division without limit, cancerous growth results. Cancer cells that invade other tissues are malignant; tumors are treated by surgery, radiation, or chemotherapy.

Application Questions

1. Differentiation leads to organization into specialized cells, tissues, and organs. Initially, in the embryo, it involves formation of specific embryonic cell layers. What are these embryonic layers, and what structures in the mature animal are formed from each of them?
2. A human developmental disorder called phocomelia results in arrested development of arms and legs. How does understanding the way thalidomide affects embryos add to an understanding of developmental disorders?
3. How does a fertilized egg differ from a blastula? from a gastrula?
4. In what ways is the medical problem of cancer related to an understanding of developmental processes?

Problems

1. Generally, the ability to regenerate missing tissues or organs decreases as complexity and specialization in body organization of animals increases. Investigate why this is so.
2. How can biologists hope to learn more about aging and death by studying development earlier in life?

Suggested Readings

P. Beaconsfield, G. Birdwood and R. Beaconsfield, "The Placenta" *Scientific American* (August 1980). Interesting article discusses this remarkable organ, and its usefulness for research after delivery.

G. Corea, 1985, *The Mother Machine* (New York: Harper and Row). Reproductive technologies from artificial insemination to artificial wombs.

G. Hardin, "Some Biological Insights into Abortion" *BioScience* (October 1982). Discusses nonbiological as well as biological aspects of the abortion issue.

G. S. Stent and D. A. Weisblat, "The Development of a Simple Nervous System" *Scientific American* (January 1982). Traces the pedigree of nerve cells in the embryonic growth of dwarf and giant leeches.

A. C. Upton, "The Biological Effects of Low-Level Ionizing Radiation" *Scientific American* (February 1982). What is the hazard to humans of low-level radiation from natural and artificial sources?

Tom E. Meyers/TOM STACK & ASSOCIATES

Offspring are like their parents. Reticulated giraffe, *Giraffa camelopardalis reticulata.*

CHAPTER 8

Continuity through Heredity

Introduction

Development is a very complicated series of events, as you have just seen. It results from a genetic program that is printed out over a period of time. Just what does this mean? In a very general way, it means that certain events in development occur at certain times and in certain places, and that these events are controlled by genes. That must mean that some genes are active at one time or at one place, whereas others function at a different time or in a different place. The importance of the roles of genes in living organisms has been hovering in the background throughout the earlier chapters. Now we want to have a closer look at genes and how they function.

Heredity

Guidepost: How does mathematics help us understand the rules of heredity?

8.1 Genes Are the Information Bank of the Cell

Since the invention of computers and of modern ways of handling data, our understanding of information has increased. When data are put into proper form, computers can handle vast amounts of information in seconds. Genes are the information bank of the cell.

Heredity is the transmission of genetic information from one generation to the next. Genes store the information in a molecular code. This information then is used by cells and organisms at specific times during the life of the individual. The genes thus provide a set of instructions, a genetic program, for the development of an individual. Just as in a data bank, stored genetic information can be used again and again.

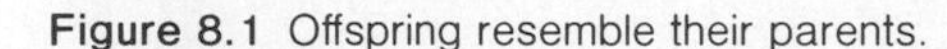

Figure 8.1 Offspring resemble their parents.

BSCS by Carlye Calvin

Reproduction provides the means for the inheritance of genetic information. When reproduction is viewed in this way, sperm cells are seen to be little more than bundles of genetic information, properly packaged for delivery to the egg cell. The egg in turn has its own genetic information, plus a certain amount of raw material stored in the cytoplasm.

Genes thus provide the continuity between generations that is essential for life. They also control to a large extent the structure, function, and development of an organism during each generation. Without such an information system, life would be impossible.

8.2 Genetic Events Are Often Unexpected

A bouncing baby girl was born to a joyous young couple. The beauty and alertness of the infant were striking. By the time the child was six months old, however, the parents were very concerned. The baby was no longer as alert, and she had trouble keeping her balance while sitting. The little girl was easily startled by noises. She was no longer as observant, and gradually she became listless. Soon she could only lie on her back.

For this young couple, hope had turned to despair. The infant was diagnosed as having a serious genetic disorder, Tay-Sachs disease. The problem lay in the child's lack of ability to break down a chemical substance in the brain. When that substance accumulates in brain cells, it causes degeneration. The gradual degeneration of the nervous system continued, and by two years of age the infant was paralyzed, blind, and could be fed only with difficulty. She died before she was three years old.

The parents were crushed by this genetic tragedy. They also were angry and perplexed. This disorder had never been known to occur in either the father's or the mother's family. How then was it possible for them to have a child with Tay-Sachs disease?

Figure 8.2 Each flip of a coin is an independent event.

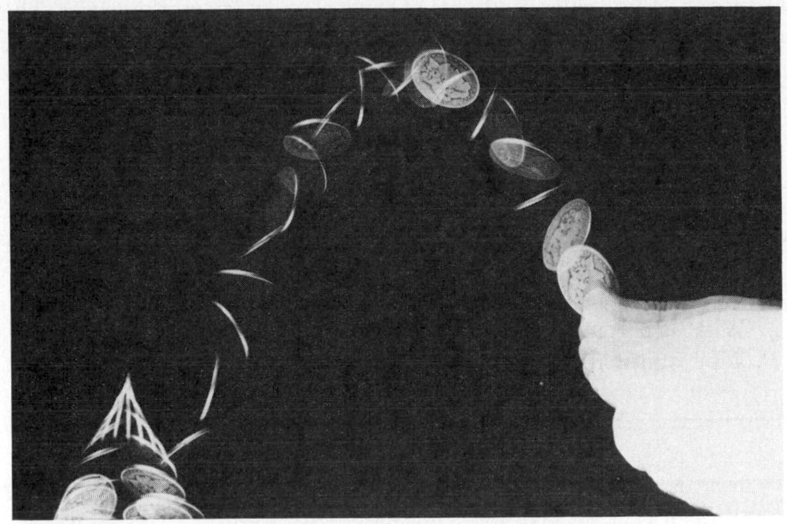

Dr. Harold Edgerton, MIT, Cambridge, MA

The genetic counselor in the hospital was able to explain the reasons. She had to tell them that the gene had been there all the time, and in both families. The fact that the genetic disorder appeared in their child was a matter of chance.

How can we predict whether a particular hereditary trait will appear in an offspring? To predict means to make a statement with a certain amount of confidence. The skill of prediction is used in the study and practice of genetics all the time. Prediction in heredity is expressed in terms of **probability.** It is important to know about probability in order to understand the rules of heredity.

8.3 Probability Measures the Chance of Certain Events

When a weatherman predicts that it could rain tomorrow, he might say, "There is a 50 percent chance of rain tomorrow." He means that, in his best judgment, there is a 50 percent probability—in other words, an even chance—that it will rain tomorrow. Given the same atmospheric conditions on any number of similar days, it is likely to rain on half of those days. With this prediction in mind, we might take our umbrellas just to be on the safe side. In a long series of such predictions, on half the days we would need umbrellas, and on the other half we would not. All this assumes, of course, that the weatherman is accurate. Each prediction about the weather deals with a different, independent event. Independent events are those that are unaffected by one another. For example, one flip of a coin has no effect on other flips. Each flip is an independent event.

The rules of genetics are much the same. Each time a particular mating occurs, we can determine the probability that a specific trait will be present. We subtract that probability from 1, or 100 percent, to determine the chance that the trait would *not* be present. The total of all the chances for a certain outcome must equal 1, or 100 percent. For example, if the probability that an event will happen is .25 (25 percent), then the probability that it will not happen is .75 (75 percent).

For centuries it seemed that hereditary traits could not be predicted with any confidence. Eventually, in the 19th century, a set of rules was discovered. These rules made use of some elementary mathematics. The rules were so simple that no one believed they could be correct. In fact, mathematics was not thought to be important in biology at all. Surely heredity was not just another game of chance.

Self-Review

1. How are genes like an information bank?
2. What is a genetic program?
3. Why is probability important in genetics?

Investigation 8.1 PROBABILITY

Introduction

The probability of a chance event can be calculated mathematically using the following formula:

$$\text{probability} = \frac{\text{number of events of choice}}{\text{number of possible events}}$$

What is the probability that you will draw a spade from a shuffled deck of cards? There are 52 cards in the deck (52 possible events). Of these, 13 cards are spades (13 events of choice). Therefore, the probability of choosing 1 spade from this deck is 13/52 (or 1/4 or 0.25 or 25%). Use the formula to determine the probability that you will draw the ace of diamonds. Again there are 52 possible events, but this time there is only 1 event of choice. The probability is 1/52.

Materials (per pair of students)

2 pennies (1 shiny, 1 dull)
cardboard box

Procedure

1. Student A: Prepare a scoresheet with 2 columns. Label 1 column H (heads). Label the other T (tails).
   Student B: Toss a penny 10 times. Toss it into a cardboard box to prevent the coin from rolling away.
2. Student A: Use a slash mark (/) to indicate the result of each toss. Tally it in the appropriate column on the scoresheet. After the 10th toss, draw a line across the 2 columns and pass the sheet to student B. Take the penny and make 10 tosses.
   Student B: Tally the results of student A's tosses. Draw a line across the scoresheet.
3. Students A and B: Continue reversing the roles until the results of 100 (10 series of 10) tosses have been tallied.

4. Student A: Prepare a scoresheet with 4 columns: Both H, Both T, Dull H/Shiny T, and Dull T/Shiny H. (H = heads; T = tails)
   Student B: Obtain 2 pennies—1 dull and 1 shiny. Toss both pennies together 20 times.
   Student A: Tally each result in the appropriate column of the scoresheet.
5. Students A and B: Reverse roles once (resulting in a total of 40 tosses).
6. (a) How many heads does probability lead you to expect in a series of 10 tosses of the penny?
   (b) How many did you actually observe?

Discussion

Deviation is a measure of the difference between expected and observed results. It is *not* the difference itself. It is the ratio of the difference between expected and observed results to the total number of observations. To calculate deviation, 1st determine the difference between the number of heads you expected and the number of heads you observed. Then determine the difference between the number of tails you expected and the number of tails you observed. Add these 2 numbers together. Divide the sum by the total number of tosses. This will give you the deviation. Thus:

$$\text{deviation} = \frac{\text{difference between heads expected and heads observed} + \text{difference between tails expected and tails observed}}{\text{number of tosses}}$$

1. Calculate the deviation for each of the 10 sets of 10 tosses.
2. Then calculate the deviation for your team's total (100 tosses).
3. Add the data of all teams in your class. Calculate the class deviation.
4. If your school has more than 1 biology class, combine the data of all classes. Calculate the deviation for all classes.
5. How does increasing the number of tosses affect the average size of the deviation? You have just worked out an important principle of probability. What is it?
6. On the chalkboard, record the data on tossing 2 pennies together. Total each column of the chart. In how many columns do data concerning heads of a dull penny appear?
7. In what fraction of the total number of tosses did heads of dull pennies occur?
8. In how many columns do data concerning heads of a shiny penny occur?
9. In what fraction of the total number of tosses did heads of the shiny pennies occur?
10. In how many columns do heads of *both* dull and shiny pennies appear?
11. In what fraction of the total number of tosses did heads of *both* pennies appear at the same time?
12. To which of the following is this fraction closest: to the sum, the difference, or the product of the 2 fractions for heads on 1 penny at a time?
13. You have just worked out a 2nd important principle. It is the relationship between the probabilities of separate events and the probability of a combination of events. What is this relationship?

Guidepost: How did Mendel's experiments lay the foundation for modern genetics?

Mendelian Genetics

8.4 Mendel Did Experiments with Garden Peas

The basic rules of heredity were discovered by Gregor Mendel, a monk who was trained as a mathematician and natural scientist (figure 8.3). Mendel was born in 1822, in what is today Czechoslovakia, and as a young man joined the monastery in Brno. The son of a peasant farmer, Mendel was especially interested in the inheritance of animal and plant features (traits or characteristics). When the parents showed different forms of a trait, their offspring seemed to be **hybrid** (HY brid)—that is, they expressed traits from both parents. How did this happen?

Mendel began a series of experiments to explore this problem. He selected ordinary garden peas for his experiments and collected various strains of peas from seedsmen. Then he tested each strain to make certain it was genetically pure. If all the plants appeared the same generation after generation, that showed the plants were pure breeding, or that they bred true.

Mendel's work, which we now call Mendelian genetics, provides the basis for the modern study of heredity and variation. His experiments differed in four important ways from those of other scientists. First, he concentrated on one trait at a time. Second, he used large numbers of organisms so that his data were statistically sound. Third, he combined the results of many identical experiments. And fourth, he used the rules of probability to analyze his results.

Mendel chose strains that showed two different forms of the same trait. Plants were either tall or short, for example, or produced either green or yellow seed colors. It was important to have distinct and contrasting forms of a given trait, so that he could follow the differences in the offspring. In all, he worked with the seven different traits in pea plants shown in figure 8.4.

Figure 8.3 Gregor Mendel (1822–1884)

The Bettman Archive

Flowers of garden peas contain both male and female reproductive parts, as shown in figure 8.5. Although the pea plant usually self-pollinates under natural conditions, it is possible to interfere with the process. One can collect pollen grains from flowers of one pea plant and transfer them to flowers of another plant. Such cross-pollination results in seeds that are the offspring of two parent plants, not just one.

In his first experiments, Mendel crossed pure-breeding plants that grew from round seeds with pure-breeding plants from wrinkled seeds. Would the offspring of that cross produce round seeds, wrinkled seeds, or something in between?

Mendel found that *all* the plants from that cross produced round seeds. The wrinkled form of the trait had somehow disappeared in the hybrid plants—the first generation. Today we call the parents of such a cross the P_1 (for parental) generation. The offspring are called the first filial generation, or F_1 generation.

Now Mendel allowed the F_1 seeds to grow into plants, and then to self-pollinate. The resulting seeds were planted and gave rise to the F_2 (second filial) generation. In those plants, approximately ¾ of the seeds were round, and ¼ were wrinkled. The form that had disappeared in the F_1 generation (wrinkled seeds) had reappeared in the F_2 generation.

Figure 8.4 The seven traits of garden peas studied by Mendel.

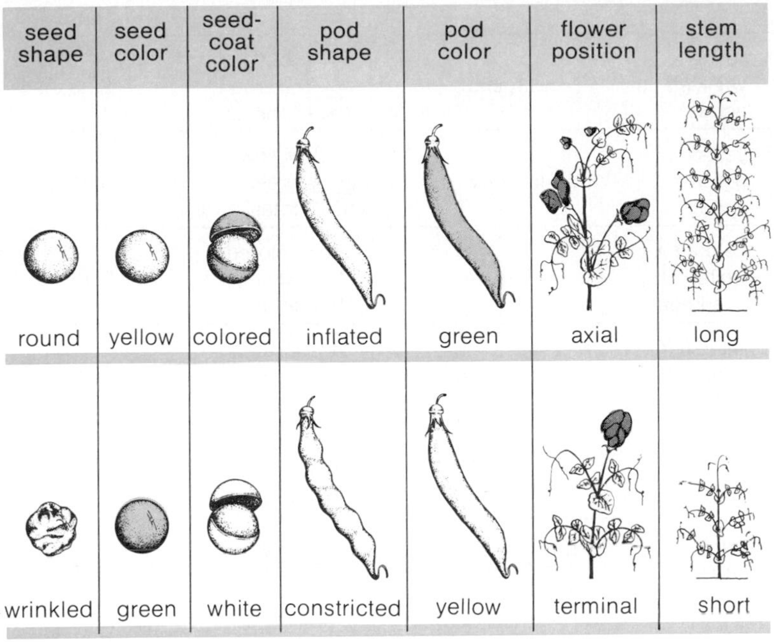

seed shape
seed color
seed-coat color
pod shape
pod color
flower position
stem length
round
yellow
colored
inflated
green
axial
long
wrinkled
green
white
constricted
yellow
terminal
short

Figure 8.5 The flower and fruit of the garden pea. (a) The flower is normally self-pollinating because its stamens and pistil are enclosed by modified petals that prevent cross pollination. (b) The petals are shown opened. (c) An enlarged view of the reproductive structures of the flower.

a
b
stamens
pistil
c
immature seeds
ovary
style
stigma
anthers
pollen

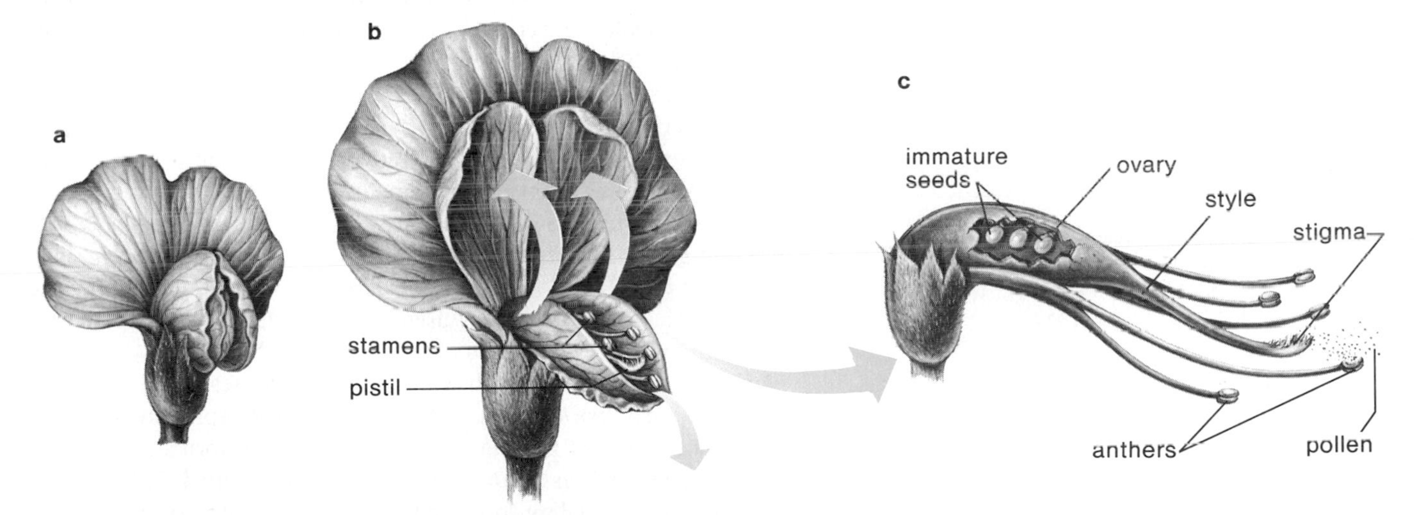

8.5 Mendel Explained His Results

In explaining these results, Mendel introduced two important terms that we still use today. He called the characteristic seen in all the F_1 plants the **dominant** trait. The one that disappeared temporarily in the F_1 but reappeared in the F_2 generation, he called the **recessive** trait.

Mendel repeated this same two-generation cross for six other traits. The data from the F_2 generations, totaled for all his experiments, are shown in table 8.1. He then calculated the ratio of dominant to recessive

Table 8.1 Results from Mendel's experiments

P_1 Cross	F_1 Plants	F_2 Plants	Actual Ratio
1. round X wrinkled seeds	all round	5474 round 1850 wrinkled 7324 total	2.96 : 1
2. yellow X green seeds	all yellow	6022 yellow 2001 green 8023 total	3.01 : 1
3. colored X white seed coats	all colored	705 colored 224 white 929 total	3.15 : 1
4. inflated X constricted pods	all inflated	882 inflated 299 constricted 1181 total	2.95 : 1
5. green X yellow pods	all green	428 green 152 yellow 580 total	2.82 : 1
6. axial X terminal flowers	all axial	651 axial 207 terminal 858 total	3.14 : 1
7. long X short stems	all long	787 long 277 short 1064 total	2.84 : 1

forms for each trait. In each case the dominant form appeared in about ¾ of the plants, and the recessive form appeared in about ¼ of the F_2 plants. All the experiments showed the same simple ratio (3:1), regardless of the trait being tested. What was the meaning of this result?

One of Mendel's insights of genius at this critical time was that the parent plants must transmit, through their gametes, tiny "elements" that control the development of traits. We now know that these elements are genes, and we will use that term from now on.

Another important contribution Mendel made was to assign symbols to different genes. Letters of the alphabet were chosen to represent each trait. In our cross, the symbol ***R*** is used to represent the gene for the dominant trait (round), and ***r*** is used to represent the gene for the recessive trait (wrinkled).

Now study figure 8.6, which will help you understand Mendel's explanation. We can use symbols on the diagram that represent the traits in three generations of pea plants. The two different forms of one gene that are paired, such as ***R*** and ***r***, are called **alleles** (uh LEELZ). In a plant that is pure breeding for round seeds, both alleles are the same in every cell: ***RR***. In the same way, plants that are pure breeding for wrinkled seeds also have two alleles that are the same, in this case ***rr***. The pure breeding round plants produce gametes with one ***R*** allele (plus, of course, all the rest of the genes in their genome as well). Plants that produce only wrinkled seeds form gametes with one ***r*** allele. (Review the discussion of meiosis in chapter 6.)

Such pure-breeding plants, which have both alleles alike, are said to be **homozygous** (hoh moh ZY gus). That simply means that the two members of a pair of alleles present in an individual are the same (***RR***

Figure 8.6 One of Mendel's crosses, using round versus wrinkled peas. Note that the genes of a pair segregate during gamete formation.

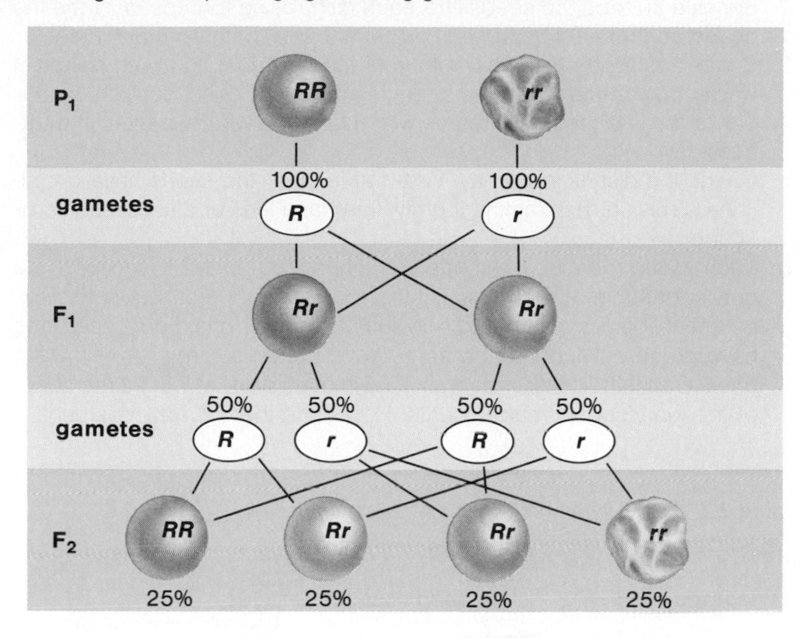

or ***rr***). When the two paired alleles have *different* genetic information, we say that the individual is **heterozygous** (het eh roh ZY gus)—meaning two different alleles (***Rr***).

The genetic makeup of the organism—symbolized in this case by ***RR***, ***Rr***, or ***rr***—is called its **genotype** (JEE noh typ). The genotype does not tell us what the plant will look like, however. In the case of the genotype ***Rr*** the dominant trait (***R***) will be expressed. The recessive trait (***r***) will not. The description of the plant's appearance is its **phenotype** (FEE noh typ). In this case, the phenotype being examined is round seeds. You can study the relationship of genotype to phenotype in investigation 8.2.

Investigation 8.2 SEEDLING PHENOTYPES

Introduction

One variety of pea produces short vines and another produces tall vines. A little observation shows, however, that the size of plants is affected by the kind of soil in which the plants grow. Scientists can control this variable by growing all test plants in the same soil. However, we may still raise these questions: To what extent is the phenotype of an organism the result of its genotype? And, to what extent is the phenotype influenced by its environment?

Materials (per team)

60 tobacco seeds
2 nonnutrient agar petri dishes
2 forceps
hand lens or dissecting microscope
glass-marking crayon
box (1 per class—large enough to cover half the dishes used by the class)

Procedure

1. Label the petri dishes A and B.
2. Sprinkle 30 tobacco seeds into each dish. Using forceps, arrange the seeds so that each is at least twice its own length from any other.
3. Cover the dishes and label with your team symbol. Put both dishes in a warm place that receives strong light but not direct sunlight.
4. Cover the B dishes of all teams with a box that will keep them in darkness.
5. Check the dishes each day. When at least ½ the seeds have germinated (sprouted), examine them with a hand lens or dissecting microscope.
6. Each young tobacco plant has a colorless root and 2 tiny leaves, the cotyledons (figure 8.7). Usually the root appears first, but in this experiment you are concerned only with the cotyledons. Some seedlings have green cotyledons and some have cream-colored, or yellowish, ones. Count the number of each kind in each dish. At least 2 members of the team should make counts. Recount if there is disagreement.

Figure 8.7 Stages in the germination of a tobacco seed.

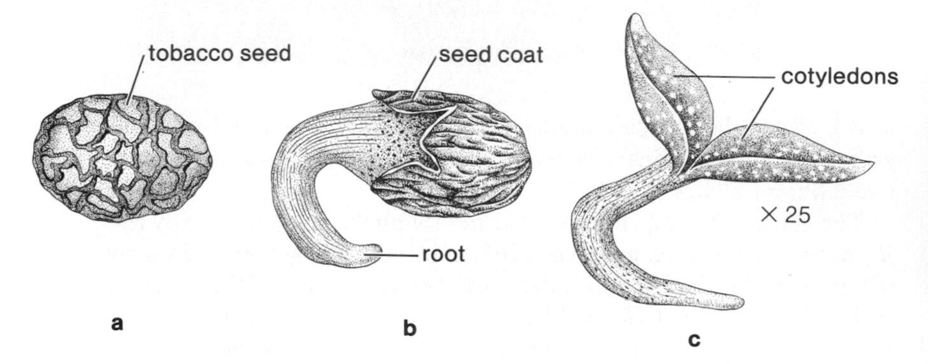

7. Using a form such as the one below, record the counts opposite day 1.

	Dish A			Dish B		
Day	Green	Yellow	% Yellow	Green	Yellow	% Yellow
1			X			X
2						
3			X			X
4						

8. Replace the lids. Return the dishes to the assigned location.
9. On day 2, make another count. Record the counts. Return the dishes to the assigned location. This time do not cover the B dishes. Allow all dishes to remain exposed to light.
10. Calculate the percentage of yellow seedlings. To do this, divide the number of seedlings with yellow cotyledons by the total number of germinated seeds. Make this calculation for each dish.
11. On day 3, count the seedlings again. Record the counts and return the dishes to the light.
12. On day 4, make final counts and calculate the percentage of seedlings with yellow cotyledons in each dish.

Discussion

1. From the data obtained on day 2, compare the percentages of yellow seedlings in dishes A and B. In what ways are they different?
2. What experimental variable may be associated with this difference?
3. Can this variable be considered the cause of yellow color in tobacco seedlings? Why or why not?
4. Compare the percentage of yellow seedlings in dish B on day 2 with the percentage on day 4. What change occurred?
5. What experimental variable is associated with this change?
6. Can this variable be considered the cause of yellow coloration in tobacco seedlings? Why or why not?
7. How can you account for the difference among the seedlings in dish A?
8. Do any data support the statement that the yellow color of tobacco seedlings is caused by environment? If so, which data?
9. Do any data support the statement that the yellow color of tobacco seedlings is caused by heredity? If so, which data?
10. Try to formulate a statement that accounts for all the data.

8.6 The Explanation Depended on Random Fertilization

Mendel realized that the 3:1 ratio he obtained in all his F_2 crosses must result from some common cause. There must be a reason to explain the mathematical regularity in the way genes behaved.

A plant homozygous for a particular kind of gene produces only one kind of gamete. We say the probability is 1—that is, it happens 100 percent of the time—that a plant with the ***RR*** combination of genes will produce gametes containing the ***R*** allele. Likewise, plants with the ***rr*** combination of genes can produce only gametes containing ***r***.

When gametes carrying an ***R*** allele unite with gametes carrying an ***r*** allele, all the offspring will have the combination ***Rr*** (probability = 1). The new organism, represented by the symbols ***Rr*** in this case, is called a heterozygote with respect to the genes for round and wrinkled seeds. Mendel found that all such F_1 plants produce round seeds. Therefore, apparently only one ***R*** allele is needed in a pair of alleles to direct the plant to form round seeds. Round seeds is the dominant trait.

Now the F_1 flowers will self-pollinate to form the next generation of plants. When the ***Rr*** heterozygous plants form gametes, ½ will carry ***R***, and ½ will carry ***r***. That means that both the male and female parts of the plant will form gametes of two kinds, because both are heterozygous, that is, they contain ***R*** and ***r***.

It now becomes clear that the explanation of Mendel's results depends on random fertilization among the gametes. In other words, any sperm nucleus can fertilize any egg nucleus, regardless of genotype. The chance of a union between any particular kind of sperm or egg depends on nothing other than the number of each kind of gamete available.

Now we can apply some well-known rules of probability. If two independent events occur, the probability that both will occur at the same time is the mathematical product of the two separate probabilities. For instance, if the chance of a penny landing heads-up is ½, and the chance of a dime landing heads-up is ½, then the chance of *both* coins landing heads-up, when flipped at the same time, is ½ × ½, or ¼.

In the same way, when an ***Rr*** plant self-pollinates, the chance of an ***R*** gamete (probability of being present = ½) fertilizing an ***R*** gamete is ½ × ½ = ¼. Likewise, ***rr*** individuals would be expected in ¼ of the cases. But the chance that an ***R*** gamete will fertilize an ***r*** gamete is ½, not ¼, because this event can happen in two ways. If the ***R*** gamete comes from a male, and the ***r*** gamete comes from a female, then the probability of that union is ¼. But there is another way an ***Rr*** individual can come about: when the ***R*** gamete comes from a female, and the ***r*** gamete comes from a male. That probability is also ¼. Because the ***Rr*** result can be reached in two different ways, the probabilities of these two separate events must be added together (not multiplied), giving a total probability of ½. In figure 8.6 you can see why these probabilities are correct.

Mendel made his experimental crosses both ways—with ***RR*** plants serving as either the male parent or as the female parent. By combining the ideas of probability and random mating, as Mendel did, we can understand the mathematical regularity in such crosses. If more than one trait is involved in the cross, the explanation becomes more complicated. And yet the same principles apply.

8.7 Mendel Also Crossed Plants that Differed in Two Traits

Later Mendel did make more complicated crosses. For example, he crossed plants that were pure breeding for both round seed shape and yellow seed color with plants that were pure breeding for wrinkled seed shape and green seed color. Such an experiment is called a **dihybrid cross.**

Knowing that the round and yellow traits are dominant to wrinkled and green, you might predict that the F_1 seeds will be all round and yellow. You would be correct. What kinds of seeds would you expect when plants that grow from the F_1 generation are allowed to self-pollinate?

Do the genes for round and yellow always travel together into the same gametes? Or do they separate into different gametes? If they travel together, the result would be ¾ round, yellow seeds and ¼ wrinkled, green seeds. If they do not travel together, more kinds of F_2 offspring would be expected.

The experimental results are shown in figure 8.8. When you count, you will find four different phenotypes. They do not occur with equal frequency, however. The ratio of the four types is 9/16 to 3/16 to 3/16 to 1/16—sometimes called the 9:3:3:1 ratio. Count the different kinds to confirm this ratio.

These results can be explained. Suppose that both the stamens and ovules produced not two, but four kinds of gametes. The ***R*** allele could go into a gamete with the ***Y*** allele. It could, however, equally often go into a gamete together with a ***y*** allele. With which allele for seed color would you expect to find the ***r*** allele for shape in a gamete?

When these gametes come together in random fertilization, 16 combinations are possible. Mendel correctly calculated that there are nine (count them) different genotypes, as shown in table 8.2.

Figure 8.8 A dihybrid cross. R = gene for round seed; r = gene for wrinkled seed; Y = gene for yellow seed; y = gene for green seed.

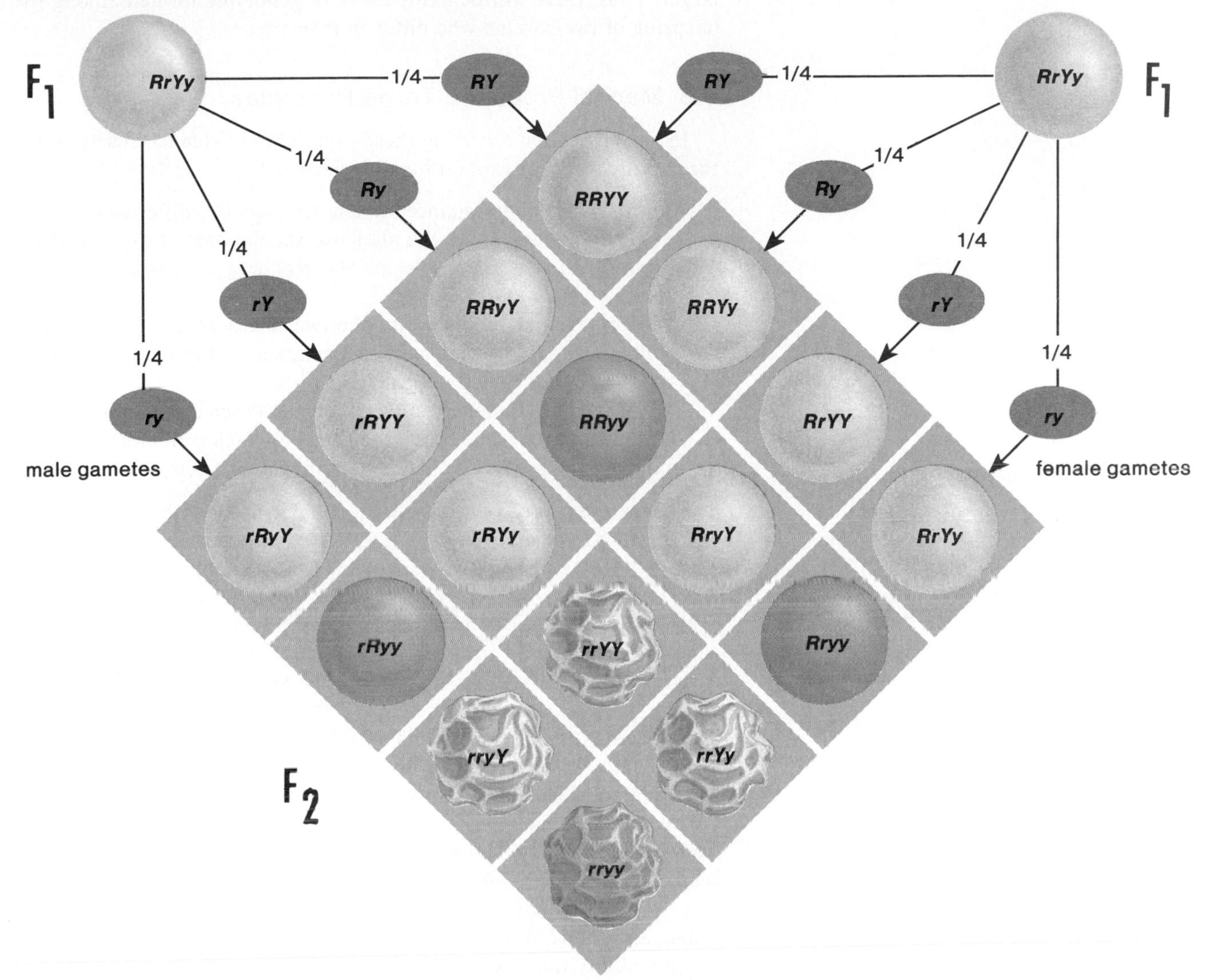

Table 8.2 F_2 results of a dihybrid cross

Fraction	Genotype	Phenotype	Fraction
1/16	*RRYY*	round, yellow	9/16
2/16	*RrYY*	round, yellow	
2/16	*RRYy*	round, yellow	
4/16	*RrYy*	round, yellow	
1/16	*RRyy*	round, green	3/16
2/16	*Rryy*	round, green	
1/16	*rrYY*	wrinkled, yellow	3/16
2/16	*rrYy*	wrinkled, yellow	
1/16	*rryy*	wrinkled, green	1/16

It is not hard to see that as the number of pairs of genes for different traits in a cross increases, the number of possible genotypes becomes larger. Thus, there will be many kinds of genotypes formed among the offspring of two parents who differ in many genes.

8.8 Mendel Proposed Three Principles

In his publication reporting these experiments, Mendel clearly stated three principles that explain his experiments:

1. The principle of dominance: When there are two different alleles of a gene in an individual, the allele for the dominant trait will be expressed, whereas the allele for the recessive trait will not be expressed.
2. The principle of segregation: The two alleles of a gene are segregated (separated) during gamete formation, so a gamete carries only one member of each gene pair.
3. The principle of independent assortment: When more than one trait is studied in the same cross, the genes for each trait assort into the gametes independently of the genes for other traits.

Review the sections on meiosis in chapter 6. Note that principles 2 and 3 can be explained by the way the chromosomes line up during Meiosis I. Research since Mendel's time has shown that principles 1 and 3 are not universally true. In some cases both alleles of a gene may be expressed. Exceptions to principle 3 are obvious in studies that show that genes for two different traits may be **linked,** that is, they are on the same chromosome. For example, in humans the gene for the Rh blood group and the gene for a disease known as PKU are both on chromosome 1. A geneticist studying those traits would find no evidence of independent assortment.

Although Mendel used garden peas in his experiments, his findings are applicable to humans. Recall the young girl with Tay-Sachs disease, from section 8.2. Medical geneticists now know that Tay-Sachs disease is a recessive disorder. Assume that ***T*** represents the normal allele, and that ***t*** represents the abnormal allele. What are the genotypes of mother, father, and child? What can the genetic counselor tell this couple about the probability that their next child will have Tay-Sachs disease?

8.9 Some Traits Are Not Inherited According to Mendel's Rules

In Mendel's experiments, one allele was dominant over the other. A pea plant with a genotype ***YY*** (homozygous yellow-seeded) may look like a ***Yy*** individual (heterozygous yellow-seeded). Geneticists now know of many cases in which neither allele dominates the other: they are **codominant.** Three phenotypes result. Hybrid organisms show an intermediate degree of the trait. Their phenotype is different from that of both the homozygous parents. An example is flower color in morning glories, represented in figure 8.9.

With codominance and just two kinds of alleles, three phenotypes are possible. In some cases, there are more than two kinds of alleles for a trait. They are known as **multiple alleles,** and result in more than three

Figure 8.9 Inheritance of flower color in morning glories, an example of codominance.

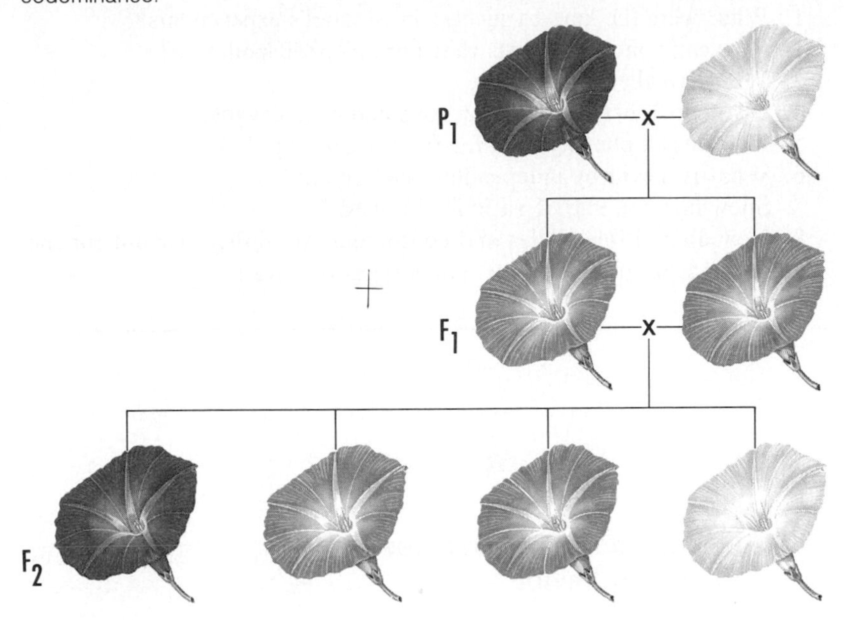

phenotypes. Normally, an individual has only two of these alleles for any trait—one gene from its male parent, the other from its female parent.

A good example of multiple alleles is the inheritance of certain blood characteristics in humans. In some cases, blood from one person can be transfused safely to another person. In other cases, it cannot. A system exists for distinguishing the types of human blood that are important in transfusions. These were designated Type A, Type B, Type AB, and Type O. Together they constitute the ABO system.

ABO types are determined by three alleles: I^A, I^B, i. Allele I^A causes the formation of blood factor A. Allele I^B causes the formation of factor B. Allele i does not cause either factor to form. The table shows the genotypes that are responsible for the various phenotypes.

Genotype	Blood Type (Phenotype)
I^AI^A or I^Ai	A
I^BI^B or I^Bi	B
I^AI^B	AB
ii	O

Many traits do not have only two, or a few, phenotypes. Instead, they vary continuously. Suppose you plotted on a graph the heights of all the tenth graders in your school. Between the shortest and tallest person there would be many other people that cover the whole range of height. This kind of trait is different from one such as Tay-Sachs disease, which is either present or absent. That kind of trait is called discontinuous or discrete. Such traits are generally controlled by a single pair of genes.

Continuous variability is explained by polygenic inheritance. That is the interaction of multiple genes (many gene pairs) with a large number of possible environmental variables. This concept of multiple genes is very different from that of multiple alleles. Geneticists believe that most human traits are determined by polygenic inheritance. Environment plays a major role in such inheritance. Some disorders such as cleft lip and spina bifida are polygenic. They are caused by a number of genes interacting with certain environmental factors in the mother's uterus during pregnancy.

Self-Review

1. What were the keys to success in Mendel's experiments?
2. How can you cross plants that normally self-pollinate?
3. What are alleles?
4. Distinguish between homozygous and heterozygous.
5. How does a phenotype differ from a genotype?
6. What is meant by independent assortment?
7. Show how the 9:3:3:1 ratio is obtained.
8. How do multiple alleles and continuous variability account for the presence of more than two phenotypes of a trait?

Guidepost: What is the relationship between genes and chromosomes?

Genes and Chromosomes

8.10 Genes and Chromosomes Show Similar Behavior

No one seemed to understand Mendel's work when he reported it in 1865. In 1900, three botanists, after performing similar experiments, found Mendel's scientific report. They immediately recognized the importance of his work and gave him credit for being the first to discover the rules of heredity. Mendel's work was 35 years ahead of the rest of biology.

The details of mitosis and meiosis were worked out between the publication of Mendel's work and its rediscovery in 1900. The new field of cell biology grew rapidly. Did cell biology have any relationship to genetics?

Within a few years a young graduate student at Columbia University, Walter S. Sutton, and a well-known European biologist, Theodor Boveri, had an answer. They pointed out similarities between the behavior of Mendel's "elements" and the events of meiosis and fertilization. They proposed that the Mendelian genes were physically located in the chromosomes. These parallel features are summarized in table 8.3.

The brilliant insight of Boveri and Sutton was not proved correct until an important organism had been introduced into genetic research. This was the small, complex fruit fly, *Drosophila melanogaster* (droh SOF il uh MEL an oh GAS ter), shown in figure 8.10. In 1931 the direct relationship of genetic and chromosomal events was demonstrated in both *Drosophila* and the corn plant. The chromosome theory of heredity was firmly established. It stated that genes are small particles located in the chromosomes.

8.11 Chromosomes Help Explain Sex Determination

From 1909 to 1928, T. H. Morgan, the first person to win a Nobel Prize for work in genetics, led a group that studied *Drosophila.* When Morgan began his work, it was already known that *Drosophila* has four pairs of chromosomes. Three pairs are alike in shape and size, but one

Table 8.3 A summary of the Boveri-Sutton theory

Hypothesis of Gene Behavior	Observations of Chromosome Behavior
1. Gametes have half the number of genes that body cells have.	1. Gametes have half the number of chromosomes that body cells have.
2. The gene pairs separate during gamete formation.	2. Chromosome pairs separate during gamete formation.
3. In fertilization gametes unite, restoring the original number of genes.	3. In fertilization chromosomes unite, restoring the original number of chromosomes.
4. The individual genes remain unchanged from one generation to the next.	4. Individual chromosomes retain their structure from one generation to the next.
5. The number of possible gene combinations can be calculated.	5. The number of possible chromosome combinations can be calculated.

pair of chromosomes is different in males and in females (see figure 8.11). Because these chromosomes determine the sex of an organism, they are called **sex chromosomes.** Females have two similar chromosomes, called X chromosomes. Males have one X chromosome just like the female's, and one completely different sex chromosome. It is small and hook shaped, and is called the Y chromosome.

This chromosome difference gave the first clue about sex determination. All eggs produced by the female in meiosis must contain an X chromosome. Males, on the other hand, produce two kinds of sperm. One kind contains an X chromosome, and the other, a Y chromosome. They are produced with equal probability. An X-bearing egg can thus be fertilized by either an X-bearing sperm or a Y-bearing sperm. Half the offspring, therefore, will be XX (female), and half will be XY (male).

8.12 Abnormal Development May Be Due to an Unusual Number or Structure of Chromosomes

It took years of work (until 1956) before scientists knew definitely that the diploid number of chromosomes in human cells is 46. Human chromosomes are very small, and special techniques are used to stain them and make them easier to study.

Good human chromosome preparations can be photographed. Then the pictures of individual chromosomes are cut apart and pasted onto a sheet of paper in order of size. This preparation, called a **karyotype** (KAR ee oh typ), permits us to count and identify chromosomes. Any unusual, missing, or extra chromosomes can be detected. Figure 8.12 shows a karyotype prepared in a hospital laboratory, and you can prepare karyotypes in investigation 8.3.

Figure 8.10 An adult fruit fly, *Drosophila melanogaster.*

Peter J. Bryant/BPS/TOM STACK & ASSOCIATES

Figure 8.11 Chromosomes of *Drosophila* arranged in pairs.

Figure 8.12 The upper portion of the figure contains the 46 chromosomes of a human male. Each appears double because of duplication prior to cell division. The chromosomes have been separated from the rest of the cell. The lower part of the figure, the karyotype, is a display of the chromosomes arranged in their homologous pairs. It was prepared by cutting the individual chromosomes out of the photograph and arranging them in their 23 pairs. Note the X and Y chromosomes.

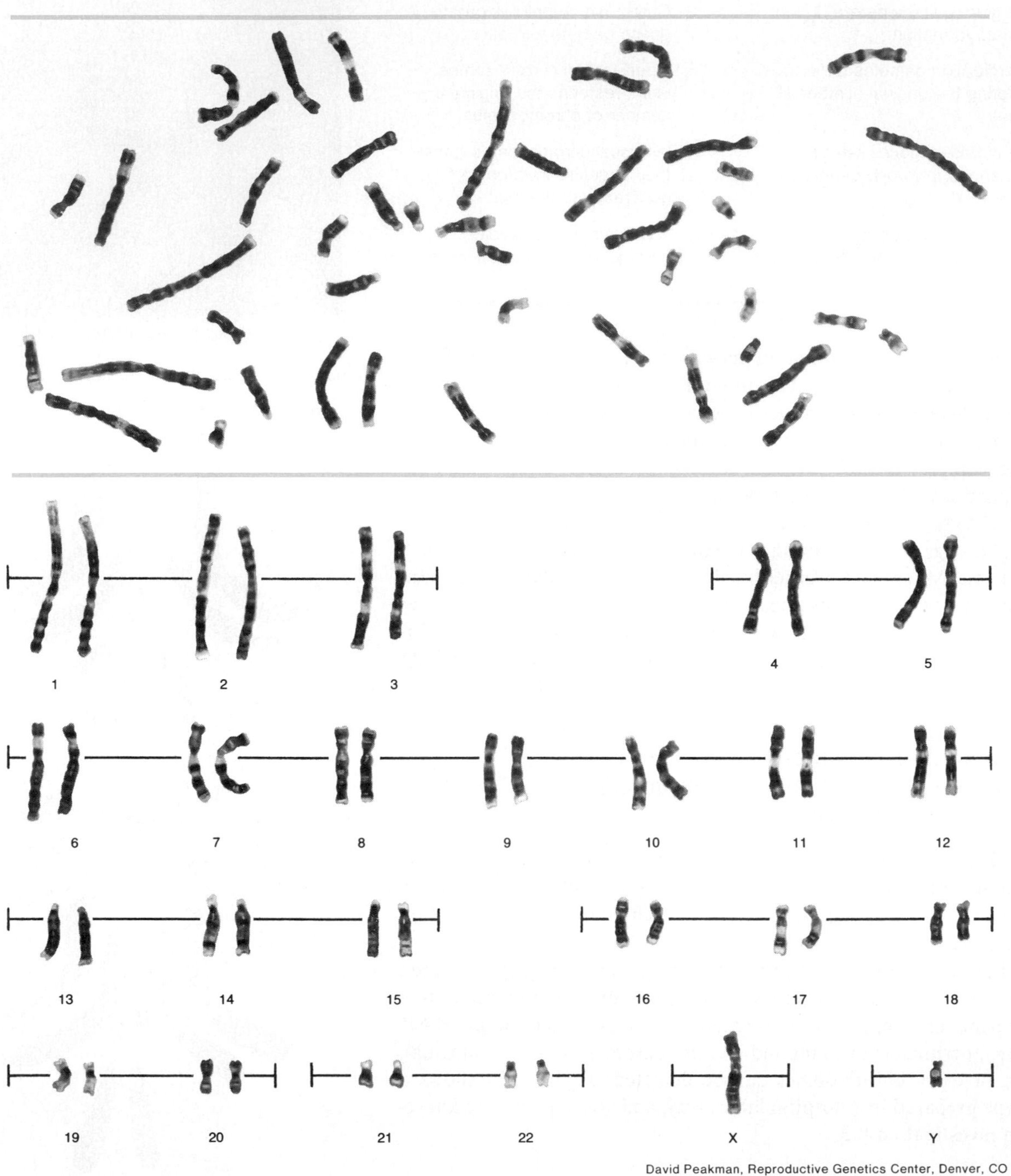

David Peakman, Reproductive Genetics Center, Denver, CO

Biologists confirmed from karyotypes that human beings have the same pattern of sex chromosomes as *Drosophila*. Females are XX and males are XY. When we subtract the sex chromosomes, the remaining 22 pairs of chromosomes are called **autosomes** (AWT oh sohmz).

Geneticists discovered that persons with some kinds of birth defects may have abnormal numbers or kinds of chromosomes. These chromosomal abnormalities are present from birth, and often from the moment of fertilization.

One such condition is Down syndrome. Persons with this condition have distinctive features of the eyes, mouth, hands, and sometimes internal organs, as you can see in figure 8.13. All have retarded mental development, though the degree of retardation is highly variable.

When the cells of such persons are examined, it is found that they contain 47, instead of 46, chromosomes. The extra autosome is the tiny number 21. Down syndrome results from trisomy-21—which simply means three number-21 chromosomes.

In another condition resulting from a chromosome abnormality, females have no functional ovaries. Thus they are unable to produce ova. In addition, they usually have short stature, webs of skin from the neck to the shoulders, and other characteristics as well. These persons have Turner syndrome (figure 8.14). The cells of females with Turner Syndrome have only 45 chromosomes. An X chromosome is missing, and these persons are said to be XO in their karyotypes.

Figure 8.13 (a) Chromosomes in Down syndrome. (b) A child showing characteristic facial features of Down syndrome.

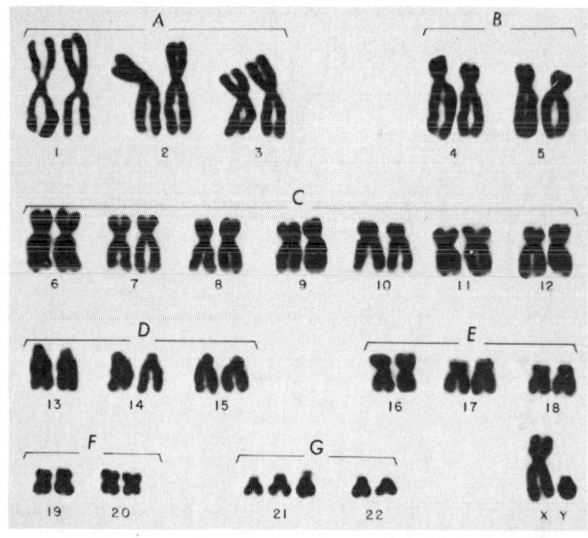

a Margery W. Shaw, M.D., J.D., University of Texas Health Science Center at Houston

b March of Dimes Birth Defects Foundation

In still another example, certain males that are very tall but usually unable to reproduce have Klinefelter syndrome. The cells of these males have an extra X chromosome: they are XXY.

These abnormalities arise when chromosomes do not disjoin (separate) properly in meiosis. This **nondisjunction** of chromosomes results in the formation of abnormal gametes. Some sperm or egg cells get extra chromosomes, and some are missing chromosomes. Such gametes usually result in abnormal development.

Figure 8.14 Chromosomes in Turner syndrome. Note there is only one X chromosome.

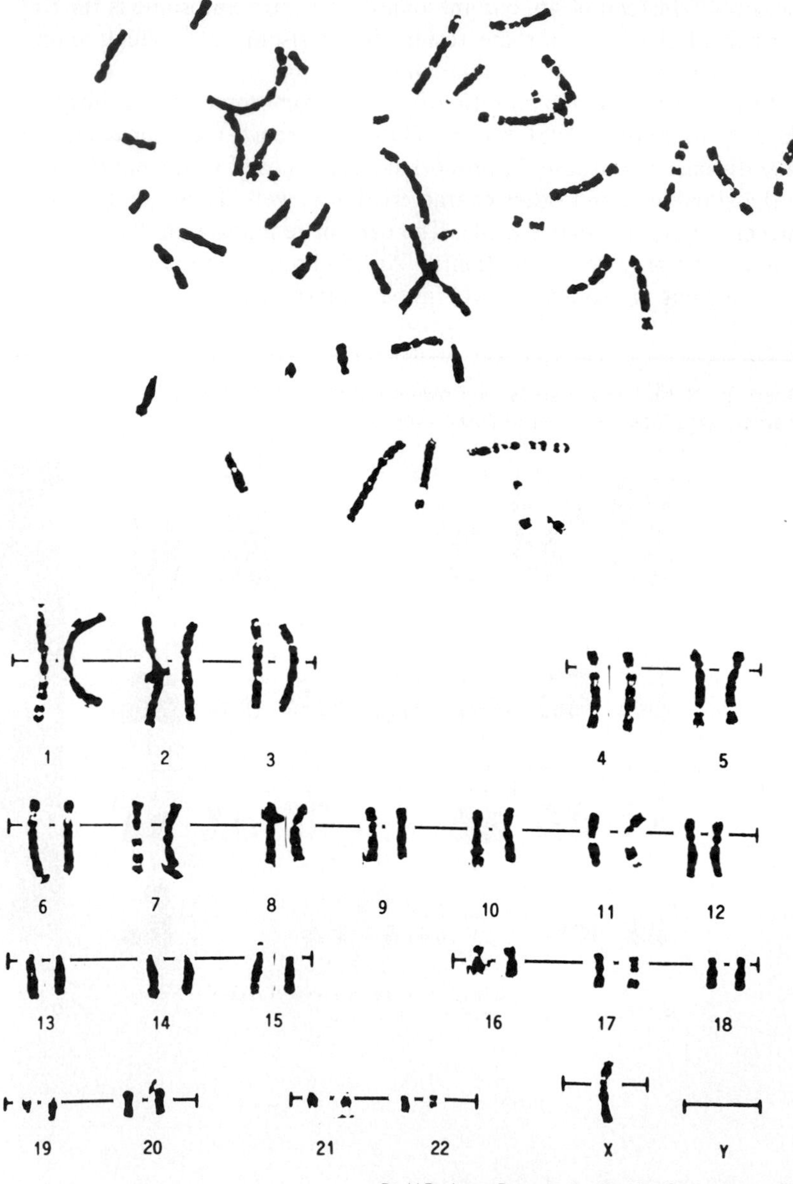

David Peakman, Reproductive Genetics Center, Denver, CO

It appears that there must be at least two of each kind of chromosome in every cell for survival of the embryo. A striking exception is the X chromosome. Only XO persons, with Turner syndrome, can survive missing a chromosome.

Extra sex chromosomes (X or Y) usually permit a fetus to develop, although sometimes development may be abnormal. Extra autosomes, however, except for trisomy-21, rarely permit development to continue. When fetuses are aborted spontaneously, their cells can be examined. Most of them have abnormal chromosome numbers. These did not allow for normal development, and the embryo or fetus died.

Some abnormalities result from altered chromosome structure. For example, a piece of a chromosome may be missing (**deletion**), or a section of a chromosome may be reversed (**inversion**). We can conclude that the proper number and kinds of chromosomes, as well as the proper structure, are essential for normal development.

Advances in medical genetics have allowed the detection of chromosomal abnormalities in the developing fetus. Such diagnoses are now possible as early as 10 weeks after conception (see Biology Today in chapter 7, page 212).

Figure 8.15 Deletion occurs when a piece of chromosome is lost entirely. The deleted segment may become attached to the homologous chromosome, resulting in duplication. In inversion, the position and sequence of genes change, rather than the total number. Translocation occurs when segments break and move from one chromosome to a nonhomologous chromosome.

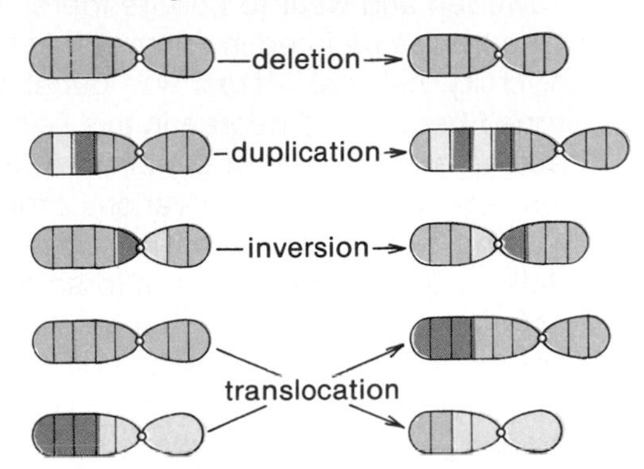

Investigation 8.3 KARYOTYPES

Introduction

The analysis of human chromosomes has led to an understanding of the relationship of chromosome abnormalities to certain genetic disorders. Individual chromosomes are most easily studied during metaphase. At that time, each chromosome is composed of 2 chromatids connected by a centromere. It is possible to stop the process of mitosis in metaphase by chemical means, and to photograph the chromosomes. The resultant photographs are called metaphase smears.

Geneticists have developed a system for identifying each of the 46 chromosomes. The 22 pairs of autosomes are numbered from 1 to 22 according to their length. The sex chromosomes are pair 23. It is very difficult to arrange chromosomes exactly according to number. However, the 23 pairs have been arranged into 7 groups according to size and location of the centromere. The table below gives this information.

Table 8.4 The seven groups of human chromosomes

Group	Chromosomes	Characteristics
A	1, 2, 3	very long; centromeres in center of chromosomes
B	4 and 5	long; centromeres away from center of chromosomes
C	6, 7, 8, 9, 10, 11, 12, X	medium length; centromeres away from center of chromosomes
D	13, 14, 15	medium length; centromeres at or very near end of chromosomes
E	16, 17, 18	somewhat short; centromeres away from center of chromosomes
F	19 and 20	short, centromeres in center of chromosomes
G	21, 22, Y	very short; centromeres at or very near end of chromosomes

Biology Today C

Genetic Counselor

Marie-Louise Lubs is a geneticist, a researcher, and a genetic counselor. She was born and raised in Sweden and went to college there. Though Marie-Louise majored in chemistry at the university, her real interest was genetics. She earned her second degree in this field and became an instructor of genetics. At the same time, she did research on various projects, including the inheritance of heart diseases and the relationship of these diseases to smoking.

Marie-Louise presented the results of some of her research on the inheritance of allergies at an international meeting in Chicago. There she met another geneticist whom she later married. Marie-Louise and her husband decided to stay in the United States. One of her first projects here was a study of the occurrence of birth defects and cancer (such as leukemia) in the children of parents who had been exposed to radiation.

Dr. Lubs has continued her study of inherited disorders. She was surprised to discover how few parents in this country know that many disorders, such as hemophilia and many forms of muscular dystrophy, are inherited.

When a genetic disorder such as Tay-Sachs is known to have occurred in a family, young couples must face the possibility that their children could be affected. A large part of Dr. Lubs's job is counseling such couples about their chances of having a child with a genetic disorder. She explains to potential parents the risks involved with genetic disorders.

Dr. Lubs begins working with a couple who plan to have a child by tracing the history of a genetic disorder in the families of the man and the woman. She then can determine the chances of that couple's having a child affected by the disorder. She gives them information to help them decide whether or not to have children. Babies affected by a genetic disorder may require special care. Dr. Lubs tries to diagnose genetic disorders in newborn babies, so they can receive immediate care.

BSCS by John Thornton

Marie-Louise is pleased that so many families have benefited from her counseling. She plans to continue her research and expand her studies to include some disorders that may have a genetic basis. Her research into the history of families with genetic disorders may help find new means of diagnosis and treatment.

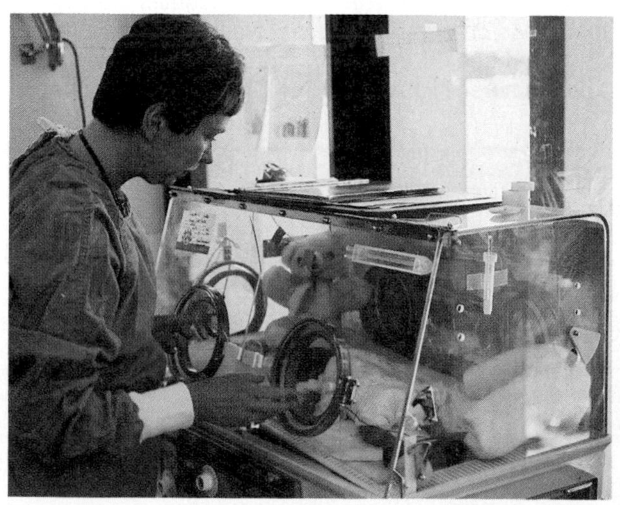

BSCS by John Thornton

Materials

copy of metaphase smear A
copy of metaphase smear B
2 karyotyping forms
scissors
pencil
tape or glue

Procedure

1. Work first with the copy of metaphase smear A and then repeat the procedure with B.
2. Circle each chromosome with a pencil.
3. Cut out the individual chromosomes.
4. Arrange the cutout chromosomes in pairs and decide to which of the 7 groups each pair belongs.
5. Use tape or glue to affix each chromosome to its proper place on the karyotyping form.

Discussion

1. What is the sex of the individual whose chromosomes appear on metaphase smear A? on metaphase smear B?
2. Compare the 2 karyotypes you have made. What specific difference can you find?
3. How important is this difference?

8.13 X-linked Traits Show a Modified Pattern of Inheritance

We have seen how important entire chromosomes are to normal development and to the determination of sex. Each chromosome contains many genes, each able to affect some part of development. Let us return to *Drosophila* to see how individual genes are studied.

Morgan grew pure breeding red-eyed fruit flies on banana food in small bottles. Careful observation of later generations in these cultures revealed some flies with striking differences. Some of these unusual flies had white eyes instead of red, others had short wings instead of long, and still others had yellow or black bodies instead of gray ones. These flies bred true, so the changes were hereditary. Such flies are called mutants, because they are different genetically from wild-type flies.

Lasting changes in the hereditary material are called **mutations** (myoo TAY shunz). Hundreds of mutations were discovered in fruit flies. Each mutation was tested carefully by mating it with nonmutant flies. When the inheritance pattern of each mutation was worked out, the results agreed with Mendel's rules in most cases. However, work with the very first mutation discovered in *Drosophila*—a male with white eyes—was one of the exceptions.

When Morgan crossed the white-eyed male with normal red-eyed females, the F_1 generation contained only red-eyed flies. This was not surprising: red eye color must be dominant to white eye color. Morgan then mated the F_1 flies with one another. In the F_2 generation the ratio was ¾ red-eyed flies to ¼ white-eyed flies. This looked like a Mendelian ratio. However, all the white-eyed flies were males. Clearly the white-eyed trait was somehow related to sex.

Because the Y chromosome differs from the X chromosome in appearance, does it also differ in the genes it carries? If we assume that the gene for eye color is located in the X chromosome, but not in the Y chromosome, what would we expect in a breeding experiment?

Let ***W*** stand for the normal dominant gene producing red eye pigment. Let ***w*** stand for the recessive gene that results in white eyes. If these genes occur only in the X chromosome, three kinds of sex chromosomes are possible: X^W, X^w, and Y. The genotype of the original white-eyed male would have been X^wY. The normal red-eyed females would have been X^WX^W. Using these symbols, figure 8.16 shows the results we would expect, according to our hypothesis. The evidence from the experiment supports the hypothesis that the alleles for white and red eye color are in the X chromosome, and not in the Y chromosome. Traits that are related in this way to the sex chromosomes of an organism are called **X-linked traits.**

Figure 8.16 Inheritance of the white-eye trait in *Drosophila*. Compare this with the results of one of Mendel's crosses shown in figure 8.6.

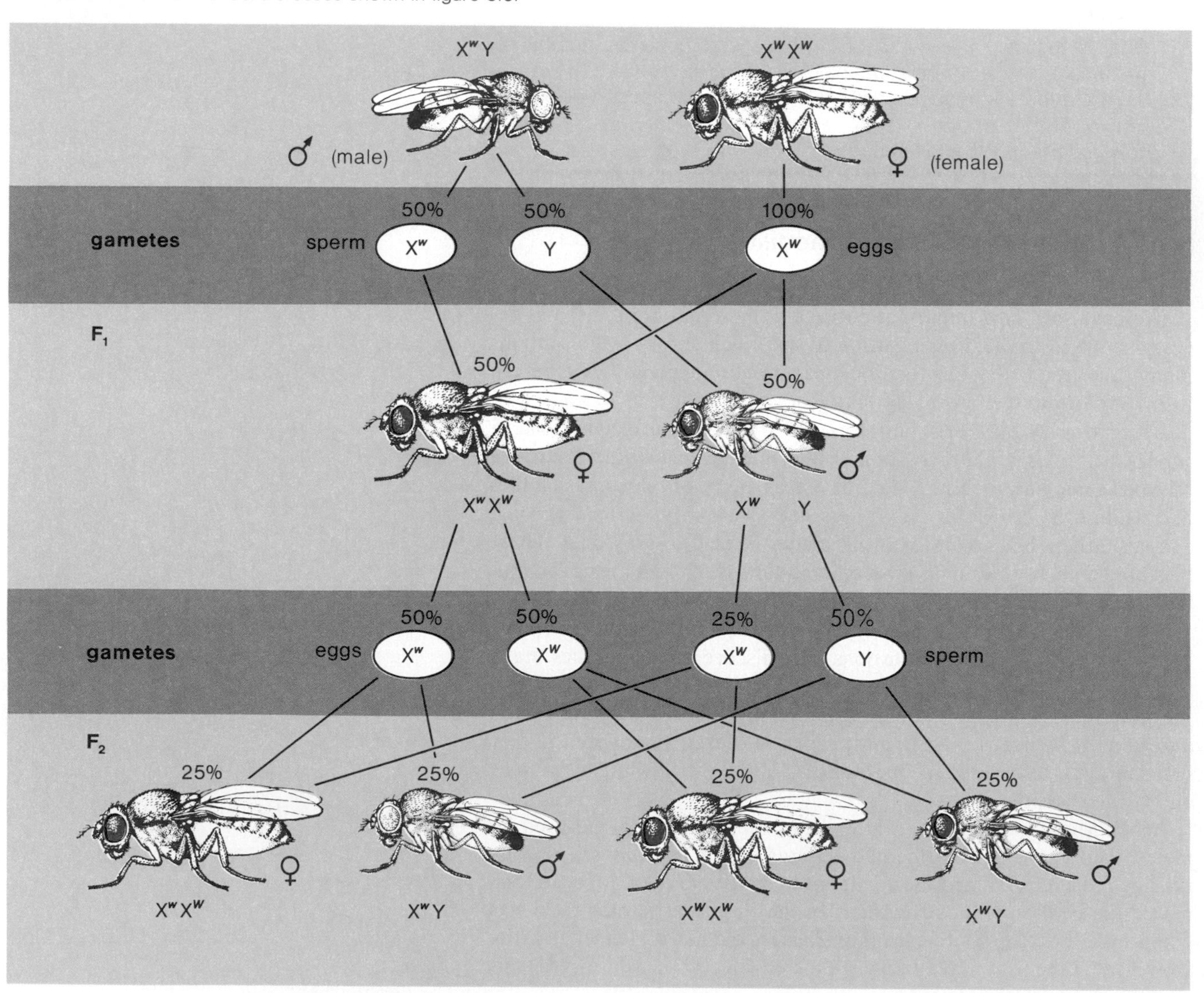

8.14 Genes Are Arranged in Single File

Morgan's work with the white eye-color mutant supported the idea that a gene is located in a certain chromosome. The gene whose action resulted in white eyes was found to be in the X chromosome. Morgan found other genes that were also in the X chromosome. All of them were, therefore, X-linked. Genes not in the X chromosome might be in any other chromosome. One group of genes was shown to be linked to the second chromosome, another group to the third chromosome, and a few to the small fourth chromosome.

But how are genes arranged in a chromosome? The X-chromosome genes provided the answer, because they were easiest to work with. Males have only one X chromosome. Therefore, recessive traits controlled by X-linked genes are expressed in males. There are no alleles for the dominant traits to mask them. In females, on the other hand, a recessive X-linked trait does not appear unless there are two alleles for that trait, one in each of her X chromosomes.

The knowledge that chromatids undergo recombination in Meiosis I was now put to use (review section 6.9). Two different mutant genes such as ***a*** and ***b***, each in a different X chromosome, can recombine. After recombination the two genes will be in the *same* chromosome. Figure 8.17 shows how this can happen: the chromatids break and rejoin *between* ***a*** and ***b***, and thus the two genes end up on the same chromosome. This does not happen in all cells undergoing meiosis. The frequency with which recombination takes place between ***a*** and ***b*** (and their alleles ***A*** and ***B***) depends on their distance apart. The farther apart two genes are, the more often the chromatids are likely to break between the genes and join together again. Recombination frequencies are thus a measure of the distance between two genes.

By recombination experiments, Morgan showed that all known X-linked genes were arranged in a row along the chromosome. It was almost as if the genes were beads on a long string—one behind the other. This early idea, though too simple, turned out to be essentially correct.

Now we know that genes are, in fact, arranged in a single file along a chromosome. Geneticists are able to construct maps of the genes in a chromosome. Each gene has a specific location in the chromosome. Maps of the *Drosophila* X chromosome and the human X chromosome are shown in figure 8.18.

Each gene provides a set of coded instructions for building a specific protein. That protein is essential to the normal life of the fly. If the instructions are changed, as by a mutation, then a different protein, or no protein at all, is made. In the case of the mutation resulting in white eyes, the protein that enabled the normal red eye pigment to be made was changed, resulting in white eyes. Geneticists look for such developmental changes, resulting from mutations, in order to study genes more closely. In the next section we will learn more about what genes do, and how they do it.

Figure 8.17 Genetic effect of crossing-over. Crossing-over during meiosis does not occur with most chromosomes. Note that only the combinations ***Ab*** and ***aB*** occur before meiosis. Crossing-over between ***A*** and ***b*** results in the recombinants ***AB*** and ***ab*** in the gametes.

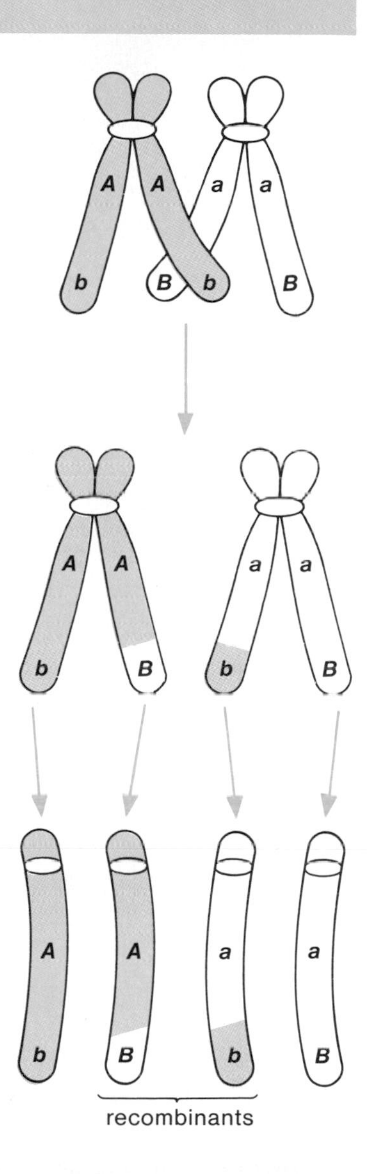

Figure 8.18 Gene maps of (a) *Drosophila* and (b) human X chromosomes, indicating loci of some genes on the chromosomes.

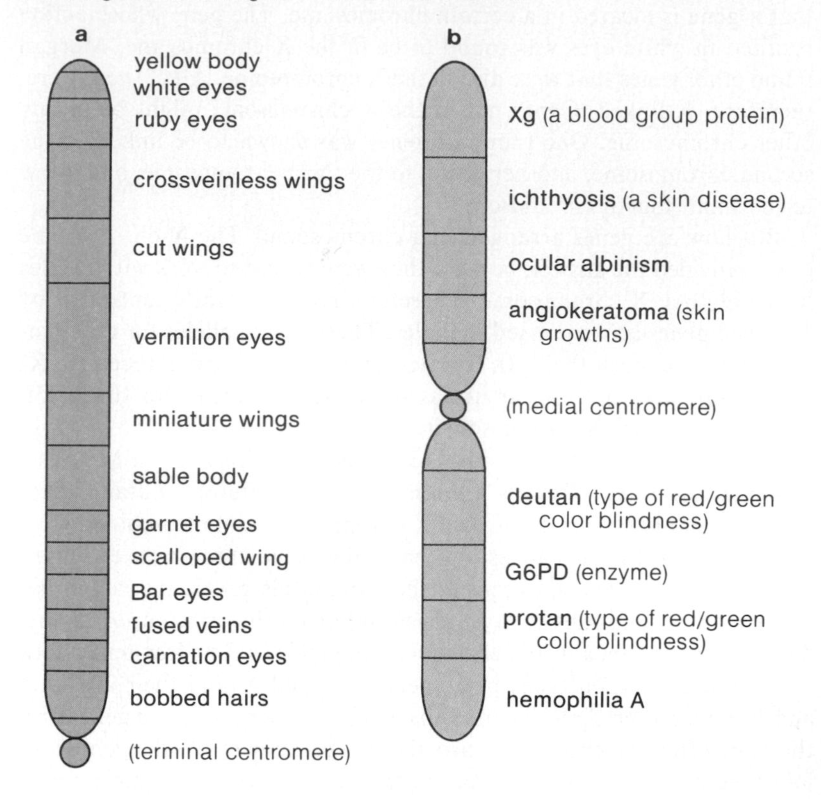

Self-Review

1. What similarities are there between gene behavior and chromosome behavior?
2. What is the chromosome theory of heredity?
3. What are sex chromosomes?
4. Why do most species produce half males and half females?
5. How is a karyotype made?
6. What would the karyotype of a person with Down syndrome show?
7. What is nondisjunction?
8. What is an X-linked trait?
9. What does a genetic map show?

Guidepost: How is genetic information used by cells?

Genes and DNA

8.15 Genes Code for Protein Synthesis

The molecules of life were introduced in chapter 4. You will remember that carbohydrates and lipids are important in the storage and release of energy. They also provide important building materials for cells. Proteins are key molecules in the structure of all cells. They also provide the main part of enzymes, the catalysts that make possible most chemical reactions in cells. Another important group of compounds is the nucleic acids. Genes are composed of nucleic acids. Other nucleic acids are essential in protein synthesis. How do genes coordinate all this molecular activity and synthesis?

We often gain basic biological information from studying less complex organisms. Already we have seen how pea plants and fruit flies have told us much about genetics. A giant step toward understanding what genes do came from studying a pink bread mold, *Neurospora crassa* (noo ROS poh ruh CRAS uh).

In the early 1940s, G. W. Beadle and E. L. Tatum treated *Neurospora* spores with X rays. The treated spores gave rise to defective molds that no longer could grow in a simple medium containing a few salts, some sugar, and one vitamin. However, when vitamins and amino acids were added to the simple medium, most of the deficient molds could grow. The complete medium supplied their needs.

Beadle and Tatum then devised a method for identifying which substance could not be made by a given defective mold. This method is shown in figure 8.20. Radiation apparently had caused a variety of mutations in the mold spores. The mutations could block the synthesis of most substances the mold normally made.

How could the synthesis of a complex substance be blocked? Because enzymes control biological reactions, including syntheses, perhaps defective molds lacked an essential enzyme. The effects of lacking this enzyme could be offset by supplements added to the simple medium.

In time, each missing substance was linked to a missing enzyme. And each missing enzyme was the result of a single gene mutation. Beadle and Tatum presented a hypothesis: a gene functions by providing the information for the synthesis of a specific enzyme. When all genes are normal, all enzymes and essential substances are made, and the mold lives. If a gene has mutated, however, the fact that it is missing an enzyme would prevent the mold from growing on a minimal medium.

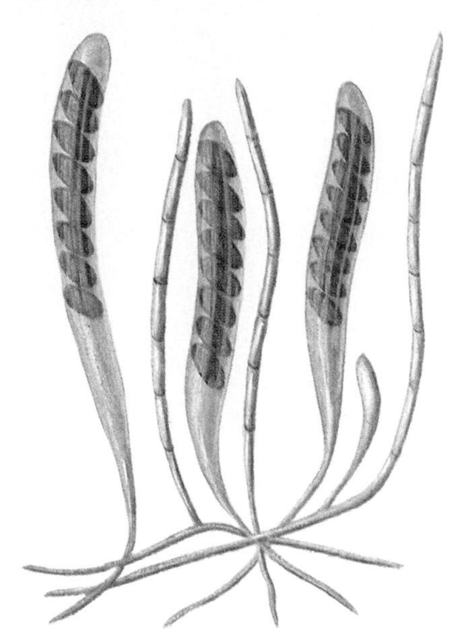

Figure 8.19 *Neurospora crassa*, a sac fungus that has been important in genetic research.

Figure 8.20 Procedure used by Beadle and Tatum. In this case the *Neurospora* spore has lost the ability to synthesize substance c.

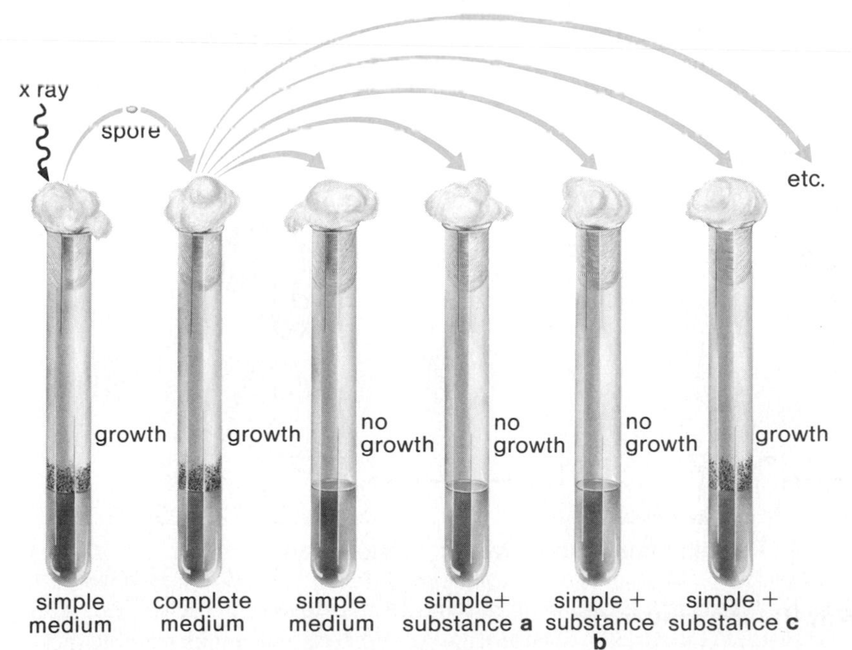

Later work with other organisms extended this idea. Perhaps genes control the synthesis not only of enzymes, but of all other proteins as well. We now know that idea is correct. Somehow a gene dictates the way in which amino acids are attached to form very large protein molecules. How does this happen?

8.16 Genes Consist of DNA

We now can combine several pieces of knowledge: (1) genes are located in chromosomes; (2) genes direct the synthesis of enzymes; and (3) enzymes are proteins. Genes therefore must code for protein synthesis. This conclusion led scientists to look more closely at chromosomes. Could they learn the chemical nature of genes? Chromosomes contained two promising candidates: protein and DNA. How could they discover which one directs protein synthesis?

The first piece of evidence came from experiments with the pneumonia bacterium. Dead cells of one type (called S) can transform living cells of a second type (R) into type S. The change can be inherited by other cells. How could this happen? It was possible to take the dead cells apart and find out which substance caused the transformation. The proteins separated from dead cells were unable to transform living cells.

Figure 8.21 Genetic transformation of pneumonia bacteria. What do these experimental results suggest about heredity?

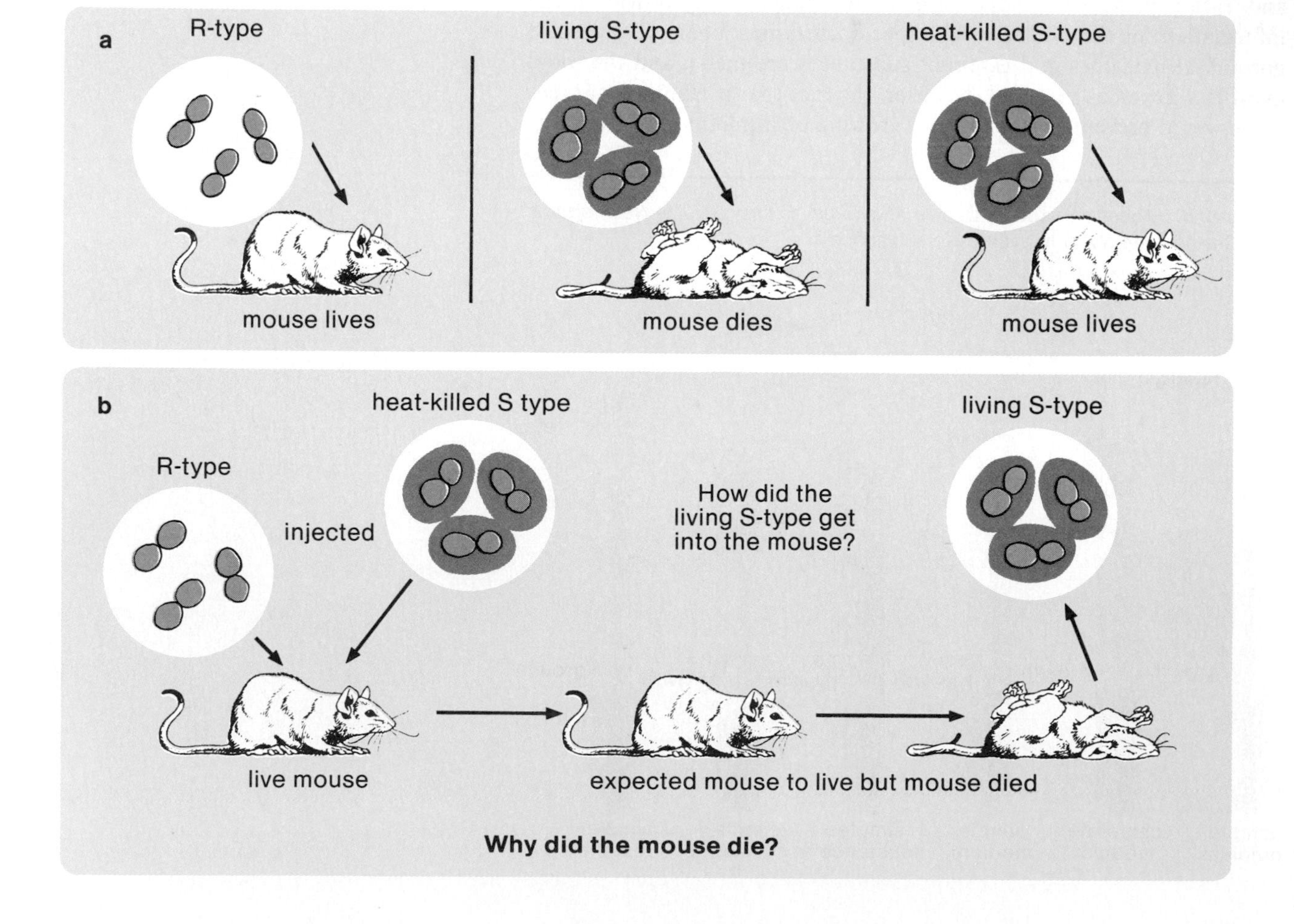

Figure 8.22 The experiments of Alfred Hershey and Martha Chase showed that the hereditary instructions of viruses are carried by DNA. (a) Phages (viruses that attack bacteria) with protein coats labeled with an isotope of sulfur (^{35}S) were allowed to infect bacterial cells. (b) Phages with their DNA cores labeled with an isotope of phosphorous (^{32}P) were allowed to infect bacterial cells. Later, the bacteria and the phage particles that grew in them were tested for radioactivity. The presence of radioactivity inside the bacteria that were infected with ^{32}P-labeled phage showed clearly that *only* the DNA of the phage entered the bacterial cell.

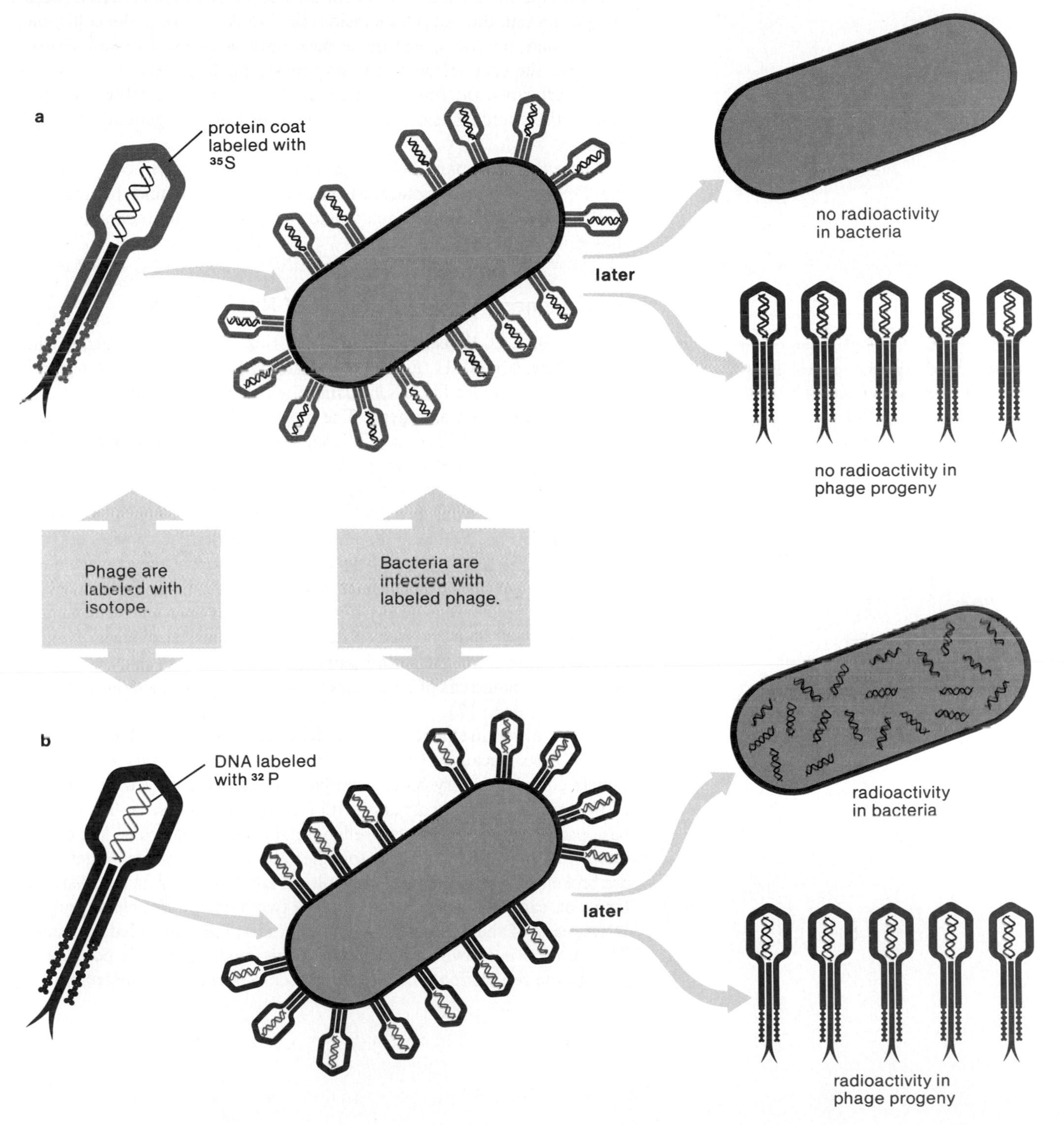

The DNA could do so, however. DNA was shown to be the substance that transformed R cells into S cells. This change was a genetic one. The type S features were transmitted to future generations of pneumonia bacteria.

Another important experiment used viruses that attack bacteria (figure 8.22). These viruses have a core of DNA (or sometimes RNA), surrounded by a protein coat. The protein was labeled with one kind of radioactive marker, and the DNA was labeled with a different marker. Careful experiments showed that the labeled DNA entered bacterial cells, but the protein did not. Once inside, the DNA took over the cell's machinery and materials, and made new viral particles. The new viruses were like the original ones, and had newly made protein coats. Again DNA performed the function of genes. It directed the synthesis of protein. It also could transmit the virus features from one generation to the next.

These two and many other critical experiments convinced scientists that DNA is the genetic material. The next step was to find the structure of DNA molecules. Only then would it be possible to understand how they direct protein synthesis.

8.17 Genes Are Long Chains of Nucleotides

In 1953, J. D. Watson and F. H. C. Crick, working in England with data collected by M. H. F. Wilkins, Rosalind Franklin, and E. Chargaff, proposed a structure for DNA. Using their model, it was possible to see how DNA could act as a gene. The model of DNA structure was such an outstanding contribution to science that Watson, Crick, and Wilkins were awarded a Nobel Prize in 1962.

Watson and Crick proposed that a DNA molecule is a long, twisted, double-stranded structure. Each strand consists of a chain of smaller units, nucleotides. You may remember that a nucleotide consists of three still smaller parts: a sugar, a phosphate group, and a nitrogen-containing base. There are four kinds of nucleotides in DNA. Each of the four has a different base: adenine, thymine, cytosine, or guanine. The sugar-phosphate parts join the nucleotides together and form the sides of a ladder. A base from one strand pairs with a base from the other strand. In this way, thousands of base pairs form the rungs of the ladder. Review figure 4.24, page 121.

A crucial requirement of the model depends on the molecular shape of each base. Because of its shape, each base can pair *only* with a particular complementary base. Adenine (A) can pair only with thymine (T). Cytosine (C) can pair only with guanine (G). These A–T and C–G base pairs occur along the entire length of a DNA molecule. The chemical bonds that hold the bases together are weak, however. When they are broken, two separate strands result. In DNA replication, a new strand forms on each old strand. The result is two identical double strands of DNA, each of them exactly like the original double-stranded molecule. This process is shown in figure 8.23. This model makes it possible to explain the replication—exact duplication—of the DNA molecule.

Figure 8.23 Replication of DNA. The strands come apart at the bonds between the nucleotides. New nucleotides, which temporarily bear extra phosphates, are added one by one. Eventually two new DNA molecules are produced.

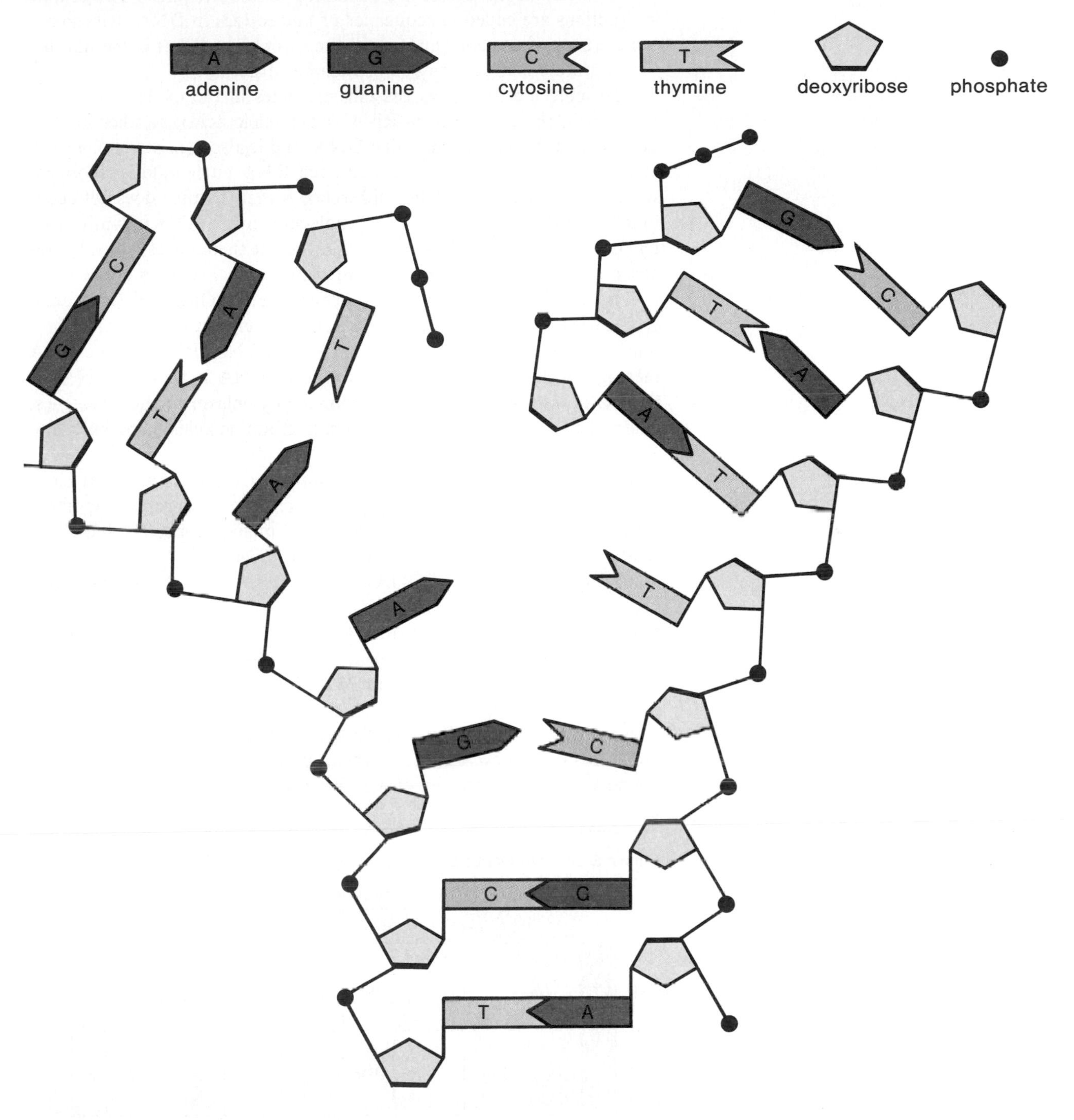

8.18 RNA Carries DNA Instructions to the Ribosomes

The pieces of the puzzle are beginning to fall into place. The genetic instructions are coded in sequences of nucleotides in DNA. Ribosomes are the sites of protein synthesis in the cytoplasm. What is the link between protein instructions and protein construction?

The molecule that links the chromosomes in the nucleus to the ribosomes in the cytoplasm is RNA (ribonucleic acid), another kind of nucleic acid. It is very much like DNA, and it also consists of chains of nucleotides. However, the sugar in each RNA nucleotide is ribose instead of deoxyribose. Another difference is that thymine does not occur in RNA. It is replaced by a similar molecule, uracil. RNA is synthesized by copying a strand of DNA. In eukaryotes it then moves from the nucleus into the cytoplasm, passing through the nuclear membrane.

Three different kinds of RNA occur in cells. One kind (ribosomal RNA, or rRNA), makes up the ribosomes, along with a number of proteins. Another kind is messenger RNA, or mRNA. It carries the DNA message to the ribosomes. A third kind of RNA is transfer RNA, or tRNA. It transfers amino acids from the cytoplasm to the ribosomes, where they are added to a growing chain of amino acids being built into a protein molecule.

Proteins consist of long chains of amino acids. The 20 different kinds of amino acids can be connected in any order. The order is important for protein function, however, so a protein molecule must be built correctly. How do the DNA instructions guarantee this?

Perhaps each base in a DNA strand codes for one amino acid? No, because four bases could code for only four amino acids. A code of two bases together could account for 16 amino acids—still not enough. Biologists reasoned, and later proved, that a sequence of three bases—a **codon**—codes for one amino acid. With four different bases, 64 groups of three are possible.

Scientists have found out which triplet of three bases codes for each amino acid. We now know that most of the 64 triplets code for some amino acid. Some amino acids may be specified by two, four, or even six

Figure 8.24 The genetic code.

first base	second base: U	second base: C	second base: A	second base: G	third base
U	UUU phe	UCU ser	UAU try	UGU cyc	U
U	UUC phe	UCC ser	UAC try	UGC cyc	C
U	UUA leu	UCA ser	UAA STOP	UGA STOP	A
U	UUG leu	UCG ser	UAG STOP	UGG tryp	G
C	CUU leu	CCU pro	CAU his	CGU arg	U
C	CUC leu	CCC pro	CAC his	CGC arg	C
C	CUA leu	CCA pro	CAA glun	CGA arg	A
C	CUG leu	CCG pro	CAG glun	CGG arg	G
A	AUU ileu	ACU thr	AAU aspn	AGU ser	U
A	AUC ileu	ACC thr	AAC aspn	AGC ser	C
A	AUA ileu	ACA thr	AAA lys	AGA arg	A
A	AUG met	ACG thr	AAG lys	AGG arg	G
G	GUU val	GCU ala	GAU asp	GGU gly	U
G	GUC val	GCC ala	GAC asp	GGC gly	C
G	GUA val	GCA ala	GAA glu	GGA gly	A
G	GUG val	GCG ala	GAG glu	GGG gly	G

different codons. Others require a single codon before they will be added to an amino acid chain. The triplets that do not code for an amino acid provide punctuation to the message. They signal when the chain of amino acids is complete. The genetic code is shown in figure 8.24.

All the parts of the story are now in place. DNA codes for protein. The coded instructions are transferred to RNA when it is synthesized on one of the two DNA strands (figure 8.25). In turn, mRNA carries the instructions to the ribosomes. There a triplet of mRNA nucleotides specifies which tRNA will bring in a particular amino acid. At the ribosome, the amino acids are attached, one at a time, to the end of the growing protein chain. At the end of the process, a new protein molecule has been formed. These steps are illustrated in figure 8.26.

Figure 8.25 Formation of part of a strand of mRNA on one strand of a DNA molecule.

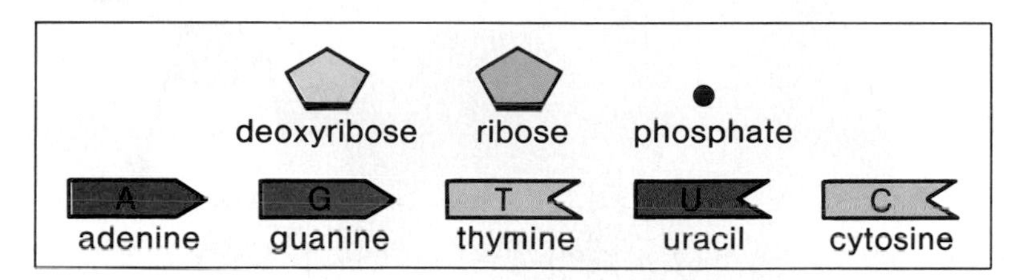

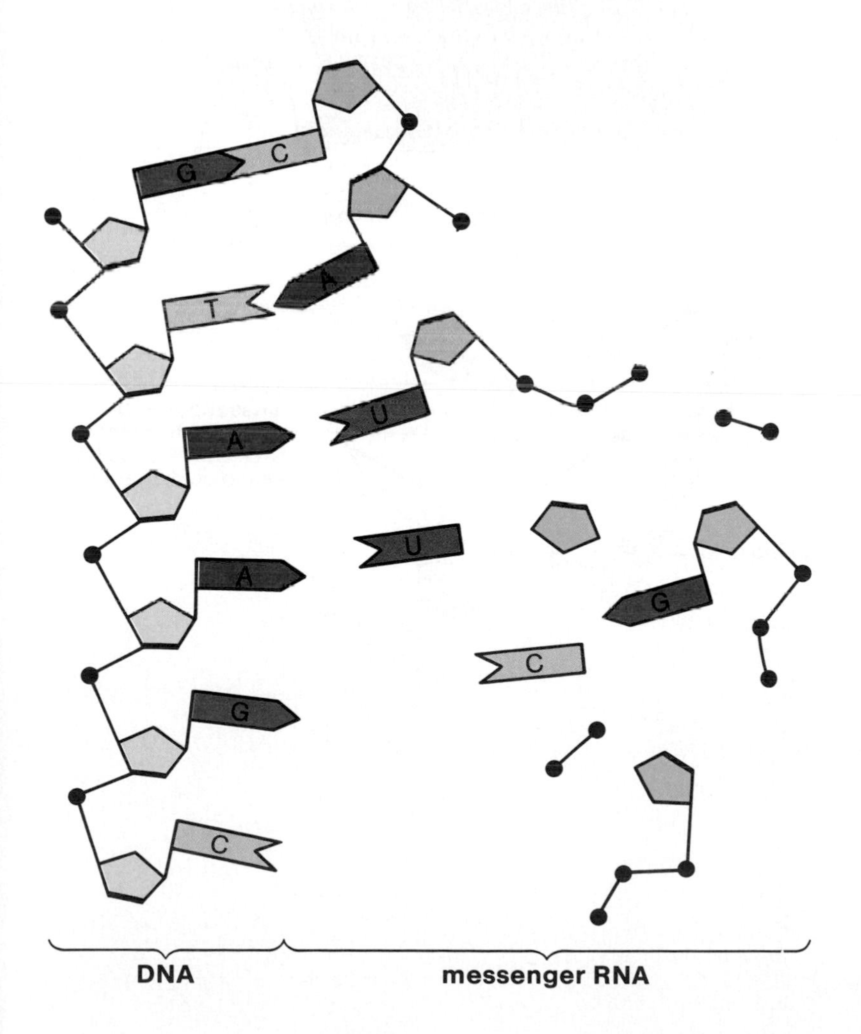

Figure 8.26 How DNA determines the formation of a protein.

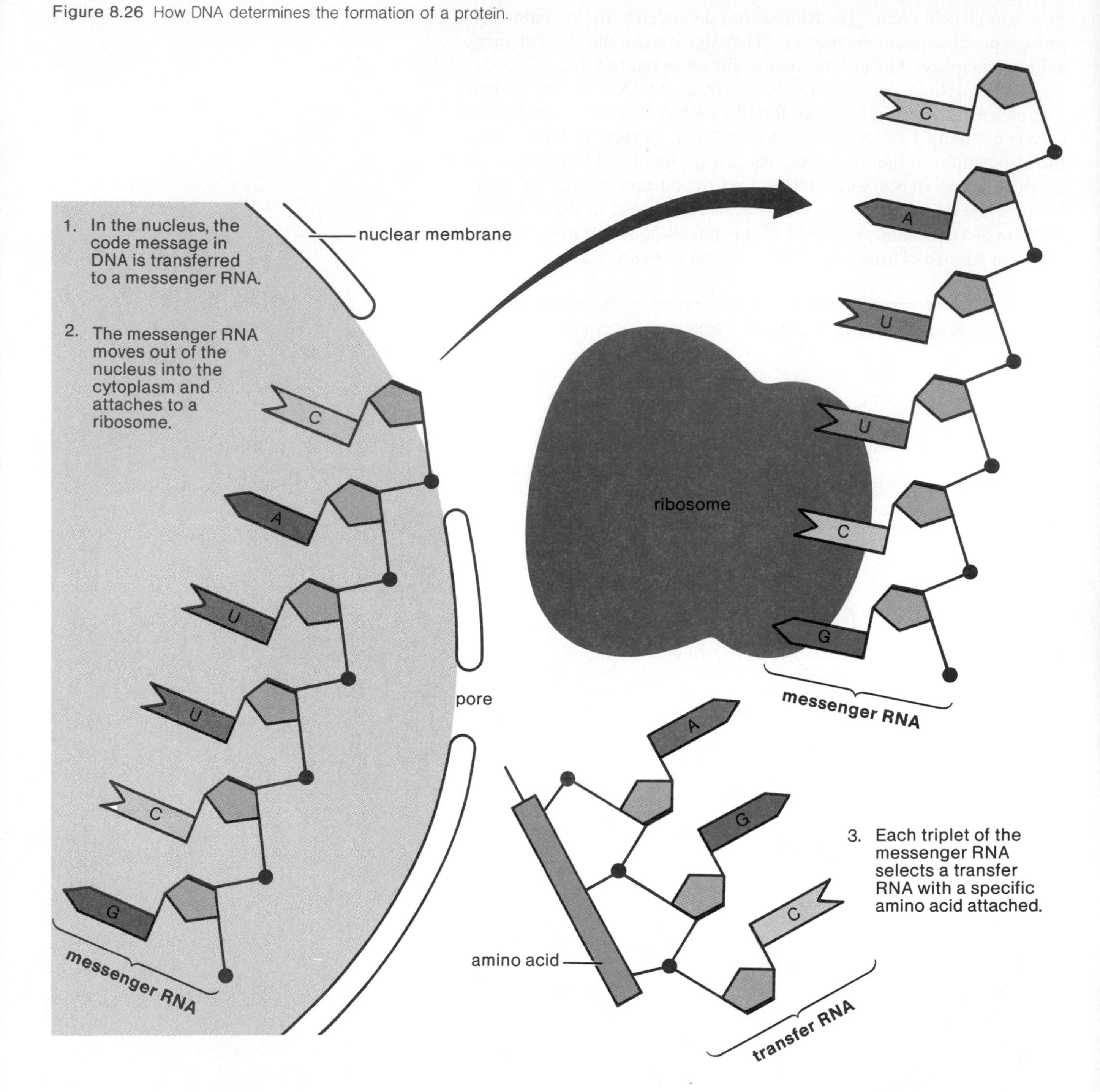
1. In the nucleus, the code message in DNA is transferred to a messenger RNA.
2. The messenger RNA moves out of the nucleus into the cytoplasm and attaches to a ribosome.
nuclear membrane
C
A
U
U
C
G
messenger RNA
pore
ribosome
C
A
U
U
C
G
messenger RNA
A
G
C
amino acid
transfer RNA
3. Each triplet of the messenger RNA selects a transfer RNA with a specific amino acid attached.

4. The ribosome moves along the messenger RNA as it "reads" the code. The amino acids are joined to each other in the order coded. A protein molecule isformed.

5. After delivering its amino acid, transfer RNA can pick up another amino acid molecule.

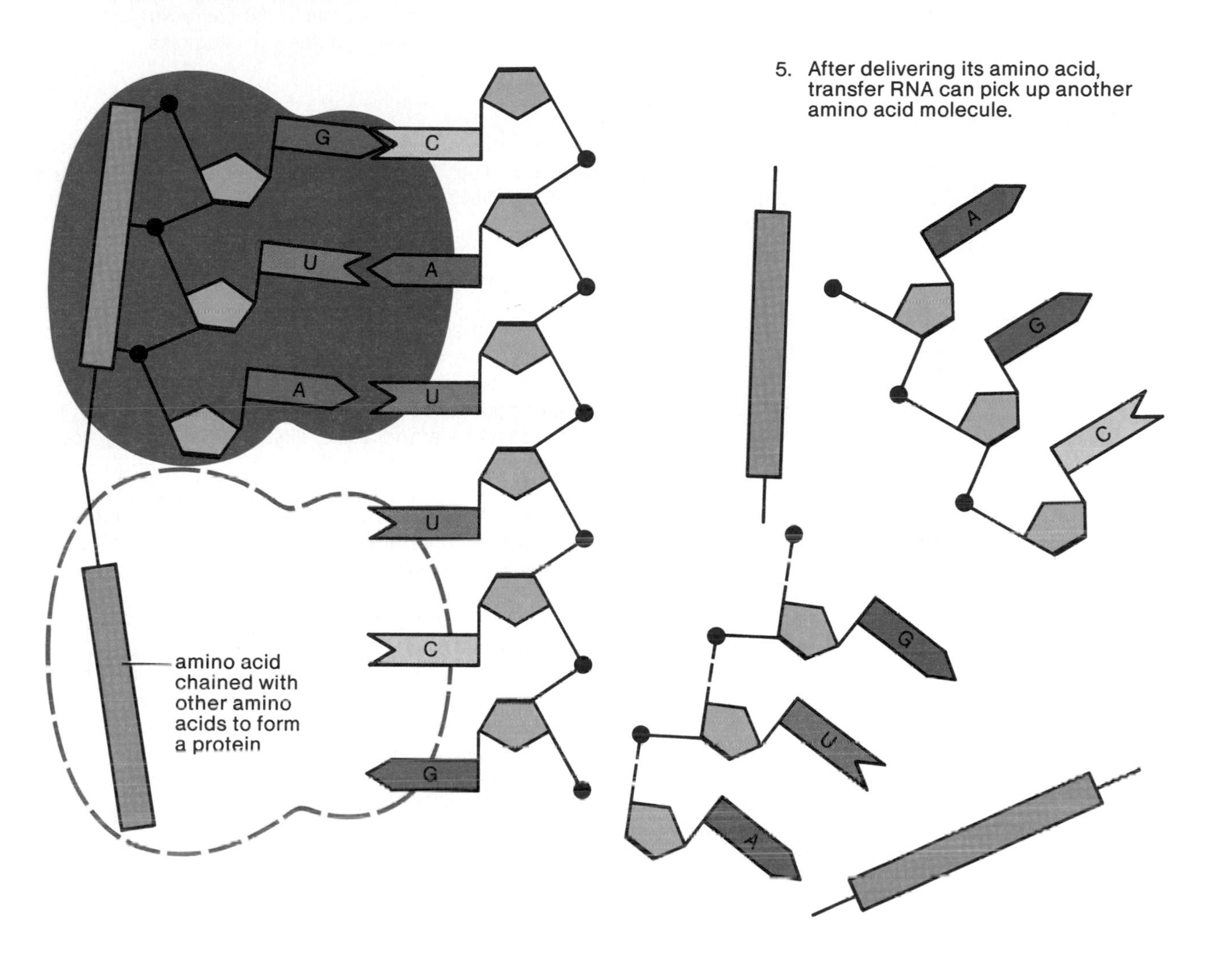

Investigation 8.4 GENE MUTATION

Introduction

We know that the structure of DNA molecules is related to the structure of protein molecules. Now it is possible for you to understand more clearly what is meant by gene mutations. You can most easily arrive at such an understanding by working out some hypothetical examples.

Procedure

1. Assume that figure 8.27 represents a part of a DNA molecule. The whole molecule is much longer, and the strands of deoxyribose and phosphate groups have been omitted. The key to the bases is:
   a = adenine c = cytosine
   t = thymine g = guanine
2. Assume that the lower strand is the one from which a messenger RNA strand will be copied. Using paper and pencil, write the sequence of bases in an mRNA strand that would be formed on the DNA strand. (Remember that in RNA, uracil—symbolized by u—replaces thymine.)
3. Reading from left to right, divide your sequence of mRNA bases into code triplets, or codons. Then, using table 8.5, construct the protein segment—the chain of amino acids—that is specified by your sequence of mRNA codons.
   The dictionary of RNA codons provided here does not include all the amino acids. Even if it did, you would find that there are many more possible codons than there are amino acids. (There is more than 1 codon for some of the amino acids.)
4. Assume that by X-radiation a geneticist destroys and, thus, removes the left-most base pair of the DNA molecule shown in figure 8.27. To discover the effect of this kind of mutation, construct the new mRNA chain indicated by the remaining letters, starting at the new base on the left.
5. (a) Again using the chart, construct the chain of amino acids specified by the complete codons of the new mRNA.
   (b) What has happened to the codon on the right end? The codon that does not appear in the chart specifies arginine. Thus, a single amino acid can be specified by more than 1 codon.
   (c) Does the deletion in the DNA molecule change the resulting protein? If so, in what way? One codon (uga) in the altered mRNA does not specify an amino acid. Codons of this sort specify the ends of protein molecules.
6. Assume that X-radiation deleted the 1st three base pairs on the left instead of just the 1st one. Would this kind of deletion have more or less effect on an amino acid sequence than deletion of a single base pair? Explain.

Table 8.5 A partial list of codons

RNA Codon	Amino Acid
aag	lysine
auc	isoleucine
aug	methionine
cau	histidine
cga	arginine
gaa	glutamic acid
gga	glycine
guc	valine
uac	tyrosine
uca	serine
uga	none
uua	leucine

Figure 8.27

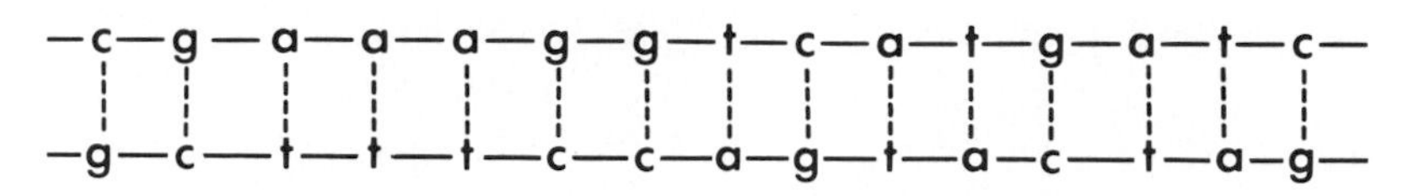

7. Occasionally, errors in DNA replication occur—apparently without environmental causes. For example, at rare intervals adenine pairs with cytosine instead of thymine. The consequence of this error is as follows:
   After 2 replications, 1 of the 4 DNA molecules has the base pair

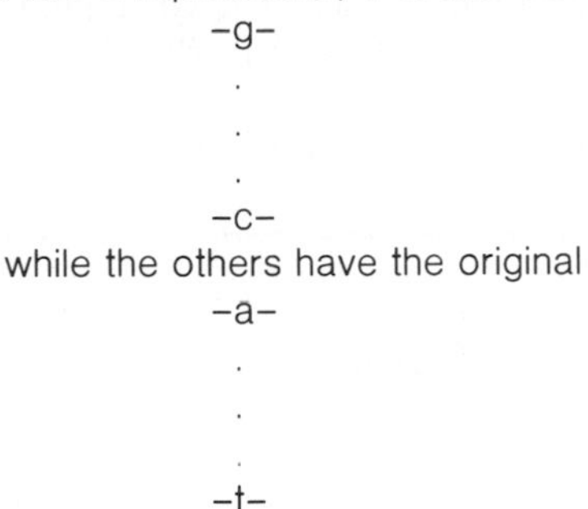

-g-
.
.
.
-c-

while the others have the original

-a-
.
.
.
-t-

as shown in figure 8.28.
   An error of this sort, if it had occurred in the DNA molecule diagrammed at the beginning of this investigation, would substitute c for t at some point in the DNA strand.
8. Assume such a substitution occurs at the 3rd base pair from the right.
   (a) Show how this changes the mRNA.
   (b) Show how it changes the amino acid chain.
9. One of the changes known to occur in this way involves the substitution of glycine for glutamic acid at 1 site within the protein molecule. What error in the normal DNA molecule would account for this mutational change?

Discussion

Studies of amino acid sequences in hemoglobins show that there is only 1 difference between normal hemoglobin and hemoglobin found in persons who have a disorder of the blood known as sickle-cell anemia. This is the substitution of one amino acid (valine) for another (glutamic acid). The substitution occurs in a polypeptide chain 146 amino acids long.

1. According to the codons listed in table 8.5, how many changes in base pairs would be necessary to specify this substitution in amino acids?

Figure 8.28

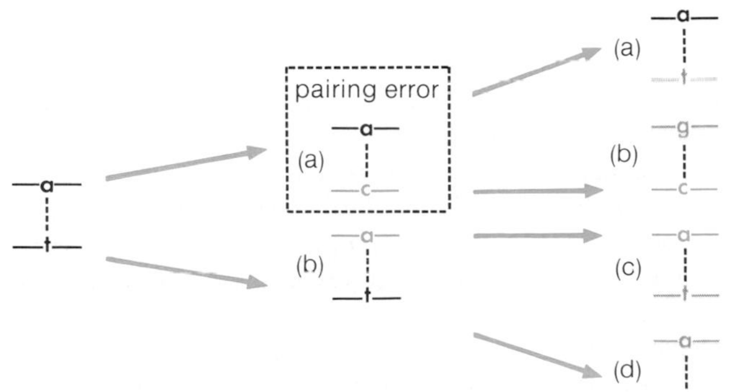

Figure 8.29 Formation of eukaryote mRNA.

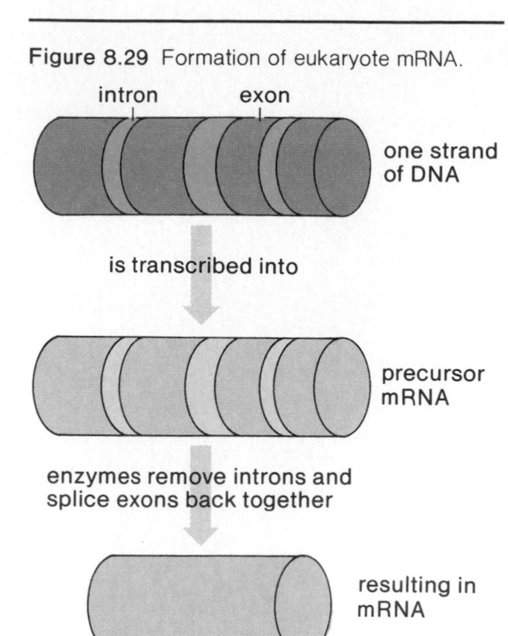
intron
exon
one strand of DNA
is transcribed into
precursor mRNA
enzymes remove introns and splice exons back together
resulting in mRNA

Because there are 4 codons for valine (guu, guc, gua, gug) and 2 for glutamic acid (gaa, gag), the change can be made by a mutation in only 1 base pair.

2. What are the possibilities for such a change?
3. Which possibility is more likely: that the mutation involves changes at 2 base pairs simultaneously or a change at just 1 pair? From such a small difference in genotype arise the great differences in phenotype between persons who have and those who do not have sickle-cell anemia.

8.19 In Eukaryotic Cells, Genes Occur in Pieces

Research in the sciences never stops, and new discoveries often require that previous knowledge be modified. Such is the case with the discovery, in the late 1970s, that eukaryotic genes are actually split. That is, some segments of DNA, in the portion of the molecule normally regarded as a gene, are not translated into protein. These segments are called **introns** (IN tronz). The introns are copied and then cut from a precursor mRNA strand in the nucleus (see figure 8.29). The remaining pieces—called **exons** (EKS onz)—then are spliced together into the mRNA that leaves the nucleus. This mRNA directs the synthesis of protein on the ribosomes.

Therefore, the mRNA strand that leaves the nucleus is shorter than the DNA strand that makes up the genes. This discovery of genes in pieces changed the view that DNA and mRNA are colinear, that is, exactly the same length.

Thus far, only one prokaryote has been shown to have introns. Split genes, therefore, seem to be the rule only in eukaryotes.

8.20 Protein Molecules Can Be Manufactured by Genetic Engineering

The genetic code is almost universal. The same genetic code functions in bacteria and in human beings. Can the genetic instructions from one kind of organism be interpreted by another kind of organism?

The answer is yes. The protein-making machinery of a cell reads DNA instructions even when they come from another kind of organism. By using special kinds of enzymes, DNA can be cut into small pieces and spliced into the DNA of another organism, as shown in figure 8.30. The resulting DNA is called **recombinant DNA,** because DNA from different organisms has been recombined. (Note that this use of the term recombinant differs from that used to explain how chromatids exchange genetic material during Meiosis I.) Recombinant DNA techniques are widely used in genetic engineering procedures.

Hundreds of applications of genetic engineering techniques exist. For example, people who have diabetes sometimes have an insufficient supply of insulin made by their pancreas. For years diabetics have depended on insulin extracted from the pancreases of hogs and cattle. The animal insulin molecules are similar to human insulin, but differ slightly. Those slight differences can cause problems for some diabetics.

Human insulin is now manufactured in large amounts. A fragment of DNA coding for human insulin can be inserted into the DNA of a

Figure 8.30 Techniques of recombinant DNA. To splice a human gene (in this case, the one for insulin) into a plasmid, scientists take the plasmid out of an *Escherichia coli* bacterium, break the plasmid open at a specific site by means of a restriction enzyme, and splice in insulin-making human DNA. The resulting hybrid plasmid can be inserted into another *E. coli* bacterium, where it replicates together with the bacterium. Thus, it is possible to produce large quantities of insulin.

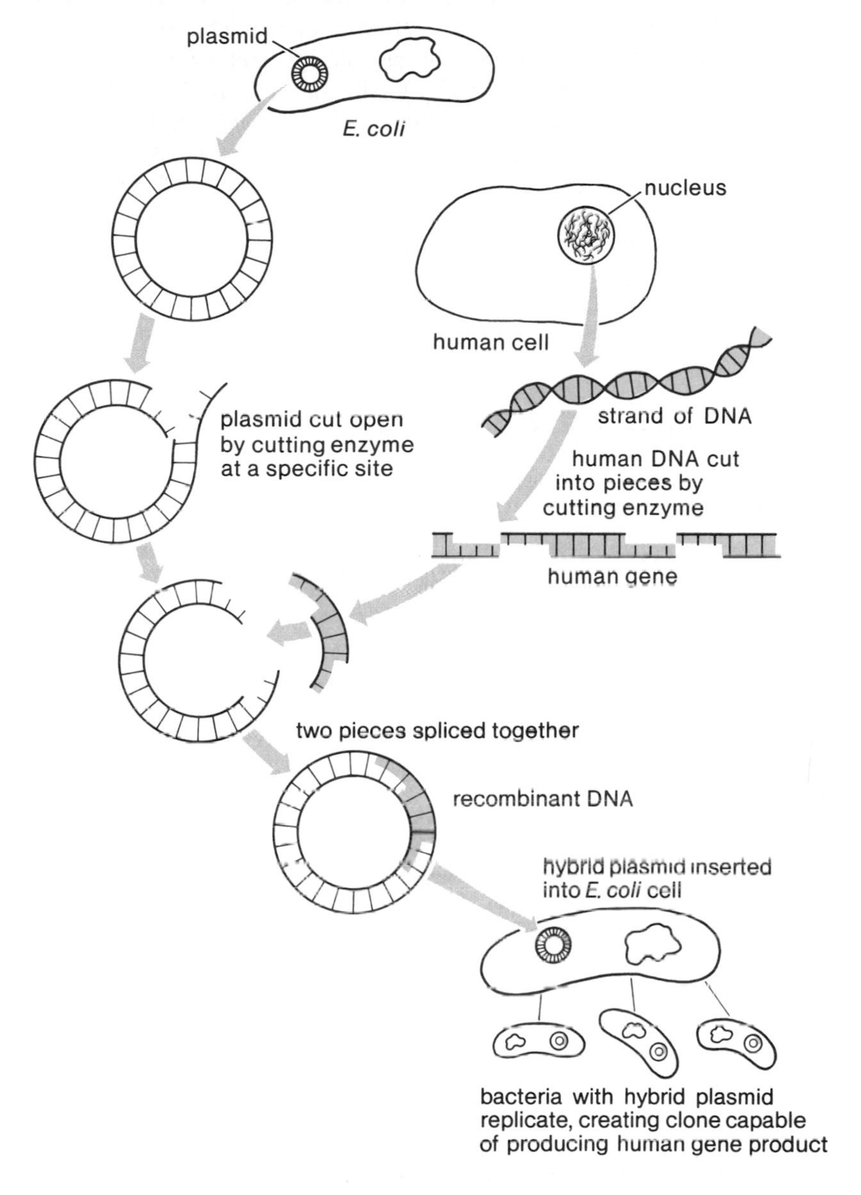

strain of bacteria. The bacteria are grown in large vats. The bacterial cells read the DNA instructions to make human insulin, and they are able to make it in abundance.

Today diabetics can use a molecule that is exactly like the molecule their own pancreas should be making. That achievement of genetic engineering is especially important for people who are unable to use animal insulin. Other proteins produced by genetic engineering techniques are becoming available daily.

The production of valuable biologic products is only one application of genetic engineering. For example, genetic engineers have produced a strain of bacterium that prevents the formation of frost on plants to temperatures as low as −6° C. This could save farmers billions of dollars annually. Some people, however, fear the ecological consequences of releasing such an organism into the environment. This is but one example of the complex scientific, legal, economic, and ethical issues raised by research in genetic engineering. Genetic engineering also has been applied to genetic screening—including prenatal diagnosis—for disorders such as cystic fibrosis, Huntington disease, and muscular dystrophy. Again, these applications involve complex ethical and legal issues.

Genetic engineering has had many intellectual rewards for biologists, as well as practical benefits. The ability to study the exact base sequence of genes has allowed evolutionary biologists to compare DNA from different organisms. That has permitted a better assessment of the degree to which those organisms are related. Techniques derived from genetic engineering also allow molecular biologists to study how genes are turned on and off. That is one of the mysteries in developmental biology.

Self-Review

1. What conclusions were drawn from the experiments with *Neurospora?*
2. What functions of genes are performed by bacteriophage DNA?
3. Describe the Watson-Crick model of DNA.
4. What are the functions of the three kinds of RNA in a cell?
5. What bases are found in the nucleotides of RNA?
6. How many different combinations of three can be made of the four bases in DNA?
7. How does protein synthesis take place in a cell?
8. Describe split genes and tell how they differ from genes in prokaryotic cells.
9. How can bacteria make human insulin molecules?
10. What is genetic engineering, and what are some of its applications?

Summary

Genetic information is passed to the next generation by heredity. The genes provide a set of instructions in molecular form. When a sperm fertilizes an egg, their genes are combined to control the development of the next generation.

Genetic events obey rules. These rules depend on biologic processes, primarily meiosis and fertilization. Probability can be used to calculate the approximate results of the biologic processes. Genes exist in different forms called alleles. Normally, only two alleles for a given trait are present in an individual. In meiosis these alleles segregate into different gametes. Random fertilization brings alleles together in predictable ratios. Mendel's rules describe the behavior of alleles in gamete formation and fertilization. The principles of dominance, segregation, and independent assortment are the basis of Mendelian genetics.

Genes are located physically in chromosomes. Their behavior in patterns of inheritance is explained by chromosome behavior in meiosis. Sex determination in many organisms depends on X and Y chromosomes.

Genes are arranged in single file in a chromosome. Each gene is a segment of DNA. Genetic information is coded in a sequence of DNA bases. A triplet of three bases codes for one amino acid. In eukaryotes, RNA is synthesized on the DNA in the nucleus, and moves into the cytoplasm. mRNA transmits genetic information to the ribosomes, where amino acids are accurately connected in chains to form distinctive proteins. The sequence of DNA bases specifies the sequence of amino acids in a protein. Eukaryotic DNA contains introns, pieces of DNA that are not translated into protein. Most mutations in DNA cause changed proteins to be formed.

DNA from one species can be spliced into the DNA of another species using recombinant DNA techniques. Such genetically modified bacteria can synthesize human proteins such as insulin.

Application Questions

1. How do Mendel's three principles explain his results?
2. Barton Childs, a medical geneticist at Johns Hopkins School of Medicine, has said the following about the relationship between genes and the environments: "Genes propose; environments dispose." What does that statement mean?
3. You learned in this chapter that most human traits are polygenic. Will the distribution of such traits be continuous or discontinuous?
4. Review the material on meiosis (chapter 6, sections 6.7 through 6.10). How does the behavior of chromosomes during Meiosis I explain the ratios that Mendel observed in his experiments?
5. Cystic fibrosis is a common genetic disorder among Caucasians. The disorder is recessive; the gene is not X-linked. A young woman has a brother who has cystic fibrosis. The woman visits a genetic counselor to find out whether she carries the gene for cystic fibrosis. Before performing any tests, what can the counselor tell her about the probability that she carries the gene? (Hint: What are the genotypes of the woman's parents?)
6. Genetic engineering involves the ability to transfer genetic material from one organism to another, even from one species to another. What does this tell you about the importance of DNA in the biosphere? What does it tell you about the continuity of life in the biosphere?

Problems

1. Investigate two discontinuous human traits. Determine what is known about the genetics of those traits. Indicate how the environment influences the expression of those traits.
2. Explore the relationship between advancing maternal age and the occurrence of chromosomal disorders such as Down syndrome.
3. There are many opportunities for employment in the field of genetics. Investigate the educational requirements for a particular job in this field, such as a genetic counselor. Investigate the day-to-day tasks of a person employed in such a position.
4. You learned that human DNA can be inserted into a bacterium and that the bacterium will express the human genes. You also learned that eukaryotic genes have introns; prokaryotic genes do not. Bacteria do not have the enzymes necessary to cut the introns out of human DNA. Investigate how genetic engineers get around this problem. (Hint: The process involves an enzyme called reverse transcriptase.)
5. Many human genes have now been mapped to specific locations on individual chromosomes. Investigate a current human gene map (from a genetics textbook) and locate the genes for the following traits:
   (a) Rh blood group
   (b) ABO blood group
   (c) Hemophilia
   (d) Major histocompatibility complex (MHC) (These genes control the acceptance or rejection of tissues during transplant operations.)
   (e) Huntington disease

Suggested Readings

I. Asimov, "The Union of Genes and Genius" *Science Digest* (March 1983). An interesting discussion of possible future uses of biotechnology and genetic engineering.

G. W. Beadle, "The Ancestry of Corn" *Scientific American* (January 1980). Traces the ancestry of modern corn to a wild grass.

M. Eigen, W. Gardiner, P. Schuster and R. Oswatitsch, "The Origin of Genetic Information" *Scientific American* (April, 1981). In-depth article discussing the possibility of discovering how early RNA genes interacted with proteins and how the genetic code developed.

F. Fuchs, "Genetic Amniocentesis" *Scientific American* (June 1980). Discusses this prenatal procedure used to detect genetic disorders, and when it should be used.

A. G. Motulsky, "Impact of Genetic Manipulation on Society and Medicine" *Science* (14 January 1983).

M. Nomura, "The Control of Ribosome Synthesis" *Scientific American* (January 1984). Excellent article about ribosomes and experimental techniques used to study them.

Carlye Calvin

Fossils such as this ammonite are evidence of past life on earth.

CHAPTER 9

Continuity through Evolution

Introduction

The world is filled with an amazing variety of organisms. Not only is the earth teeming with a great diversity of life today, but evidence shows the existence of at least as great a variety of organisms in the past that are no longer present. Rocks show imprints of organisms that lived many millions of years ago and are now extinct. These evidences from the past are termed **fossils.** Fossil remains enable us to reconstruct organisms from the past such as dinosaurs. The fossil record indicates the earth has continuously supported life for more than 3.5 billion years. When one includes the past with the present, the diversity of life is almost too much to comprehend. How did that diversity come about? In this chapter, we will discuss the theory of evolution, which accounts for the present variety of organisms and explains how changes have occurred in populations over time.

Diversity, Adaptation, and Evolution

Guidepost: What do biologists mean by "unity in diversity?"

9.1 Living Organisms Show a Diversity of Type and a Unity of Pattern

Biologists note the diverse ways in which one group of similar organisms, or species, is distinguished from another. At the same time, however, they are impressed with a unity of pattern among different groups of organisms. For example, organisms are made up of cells or cell products, as noted in chapter 5. Cell functions are similar, even in organisms that are very different. The same cell components can be identified among

Figure 9.1 Diversity of types and unity of pattern. Though species of birds vary greatly, they share characteristics that group them together. Can you determine which feet belong to each bird?

organisms from houseflies to whales 30 m in length. Reproductive mechanisms are similar, and common methods of development and heredity, as noted in chapters 7 and 8, are found throughout many varieties of organisms.

Specific structures further demonstrate unity among groups of organisms. Vertebrates, those animals with backbones, provide a good example. The limb pattern of even the most different types such as whales and bats are consistent, as shown in figure 10.7, page 316. Living organisms share functional features as well. Experiments using tissues of one organism provide results that are found to apply to others. Studying the nerve cells of a squid tells us a great deal about how human nerve cells operate. Medicines tested on rats or guinea pigs produce similar results in humans. This ability to use one organism to understand another further indicates a functional unity of pattern in the living world.

Diversity results in a great variety of species. Unity, however, groups together species and even larger categories of organisms that share basic characteristics regardless of their diversity. In attempting to explain scientifically the problems of diversity and unity, it becomes apparent that organisms are related one to another. That is true no matter how different the organisms are in appearance. The exploration of this relationship led to the formulation of the theory of evolution.

Figure 9.2 People once believed that living organisms could arise from lifeless substances, such as mud or the remains of dead plants or animals. These misconceptions persisted until the end of the 19th century.

Figure 9.3 Each of these honey creepers, found on the Hawaiian Islands, has an adaptation that helps it obtain food in its habitat.

9.2 The Theory of Evolution Has a Long History

Attempts to explain the diversity of type and unity of pattern of living things are probably as old as humankind itself. As early as 600 B.C., a Greek scholar hypothesized a gradual evolution from a formless condition, such as mud, to one of organic coherence, such as a frog (see figure 9.2). He understood what today we would call **adaptation** (ad ap TAY shun). An adaptation is any characteristic that improves an organism's chance for survival in a particular environment. Later Greek scholars developed a crude outline of an evolutionary concept. It hypothesized that the development of life was a gradual process, that plants were present on earth before animals, and that better-adapted forms replaced ill-adapted ones. Those insights can be considered an early form of what we now call the theory of evolution.

Figure 9.4 An example of crossbreeding. The red jungle fowl, a bird of Southeast Asia, is thought to be the species from which the many breeds of domestic chickens have been developed. Which of the breeds shown retains the largest number of the wild bird's traits?

From the time of the Greeks, observations continued on the structure and development of organisms. Naturalists also studied the geographic distribution of organisms, and variation in organisms both in captivity and in the wild. Fossils provided increasing amounts of data about types of organisms that no longer existed.

Experiments in the crossbreeding of organisms resulted in offspring that were different in many respects from both their parents. Furthermore, it was possible to breed animals and plants for specific traits: sheep with longer, thicker wool; faster horses; cows that gave more milk; trees that produced more fruit; and vegetables that reached maturity earlier. For instance, the breeds of domestic chickens shown in figure 9.4 apparently were developed from the red jungle fowl.

Evidence continued to accumulate that organisms had changed through time and were related one to another. Scientists began to understand unity and diversity. By the latter half of the 18th century biologists such as Erasmus Darwin, the grandfather of Charles, recognized a struggle for existence among organisms as they competed for both space and food. A contemporary of Erasmus Darwin, John Baptiste Lamarck, proposed a theory in 1809 to explain changes in species. He felt that environment played a major part in such changes. It was obvious that athletes developed larger muscles by training and that well-fed animals grew larger than poorly fed ones. Lamarck contended that such acquired characteristics could be passed along to offspring by inheritance. However, decades of experimentation provided no evidence to support the inheritance of acquired characteristics. Lamarck would have accounted for the long necks of giraffes by noting that they stretched to reach the leaves on high trees (figure 9.5). The stretched necks would be inherited by the next generation and successive generations would have longer and longer necks. Such inheritance would account for the evolution of long-necked giraffes from shorter-necked ancestors that looked more like antelopes.

By the mid-19th century, there was no question that organisms not only have changed through time, but that they also share great numbers of similar characteristics. The big question, however, was "What causes this natural variation in the first place and how is such variation transmitted to the next generation?" You can measure some of the natural variation in organisms in investigation 9.1.

Figure 9.5 Lamarck's theory stated that the giraffe developed its long neck, and made its front legs longer than its hind ones, by stretching for leaves over countless generations. What makes this theory unacceptable?

Investigation 9.1 VARIATION IN SIZE

Introduction

Within populations of organisms, there are variations that make each individual different from others in the same species. Variations among familiar organisms are more obvious. You are more aware of differences among humans than you are of those among ants. In this investigation, you will study individual variations in size among plant populations, and you will interpret the data by statistical methods.

Materials

metric ruler
graph paper
50 objects of a kind—dried bean seeds, carrots, peanuts in the shell, and so on.

Procedure

1. Divide into teams with 1 person to record the data. With a metric ruler, measure the length of the 50 objects to the nearest millimeter. Record the measurements in your data book.
2. Construct a frequency distribution table as follows:
   (a) Determine the range of the sample. This is the difference between the largest and the smallest objects.
   (b) Divide the sample into 10 intervals, selecting a convenient size. For example, if the range of the sample is 23 (16 mm–39 mm), it could be divided into 8 intervals of 3 mm each as follows: 16–18, 19–21, 22–24, 25–27, 28–30, 31–33, 34–36, and 37–39.

(c) Assemble your data in a frequency distribution table where the intervals are listed in the X column and the number of individuals falling in each interval (frequency) are listed in the f column, as shown in the example below.

X	f
16–18	2
19–21	7
22–24	4
25–27	9
28–30	14
etc.	etc.

3. Construct a histogram from the frequency distribution table. A histogram is simply a bar graph with the intervals on the horizontal axis and the frequency on the vertical axis. Make the range of the intervals on the histogram 0.5 lower than you did on the table. The lowest interval would have a range of 15.5 to 18.5 instead of 16 to 19, as shown in the example below.

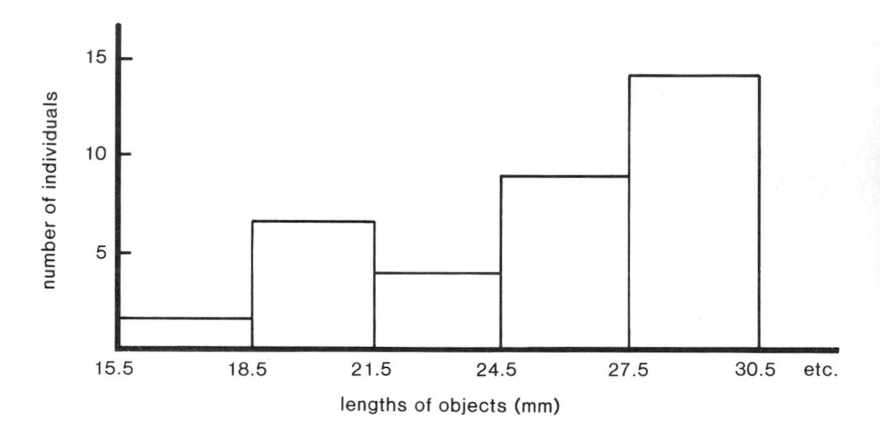

4. Calculate the mean or average of your data. The mean is the sum of all measurements divided by the number of individuals.
5. Find the mode, or high point, on the histogram. The value of the mode is usually given as the midpoint of the interval with the highest frequency.
6. Find the median, which is the value for the middle individual of the sample when the values (lengths) are arranged in order. If a series of measurements is 2, 3, 4, 7, 8, 9, 11, the median would be 7.

Discussion

1. Look at your data and your histogram. Is there variation within your population?
2. What was the difference between the largest and the smallest objects in your sample?
3. Given the overall size of the objects, is this difference significant?
4. Would you notice the difference if you had not measured them?

9.3 Darwin Formulated the Theory of Natural Selection

Charles Robert Darwin (figure 9.6) initially studied medicine at Edinburgh University in Scotland. Darwin did not enjoy the study of medicine and left to enter Cambridge University in England to prepare for the ministry. He continued his interest in science.

In 1831, at the age of 22, he was selected as naturalist to accompany Captain Robert Fitzroy of the Royal Navy on a survey voyage to South America and the Pacific islands. On December 27, 1831, Darwin sailed on the *Beagle*. He spent the next five years observing and collecting organisms and studying the biology of South America and the Pacific islands, especially the Galápagos (figure 9.7). The route of the *Beagle* is shown in figure 9.8.

Darwin saw his first tropical forest in Brazil, found his first fossils in Argentina, and observed the primitive natives of Tierra del Fuego. In Chile he witnessed an earthquake and saw its effect in raising the level of the land and its connection to volcanic eruption. He went on dangerous, demanding, and long expeditions and on more than one occasion saved the lives of his companions. Once he did so by running far and fast enough to alert them of a wave raised by a glacier fall that would have destroyed their boat.

The voyage of the *Beagle* is important because it laid the basis for Darwin's subsequent thoughts about evolution. On his return he wrote a journal concerned with the geology and natural history of the countries visited by the *Beagle*. He also wrote about coral reefs, volcanic islands, and the geology of South America. He remained concerned by questions such as why animals sharing many common characteristics lived so far apart geographically while adjacent areas were populated by similar, though not identical, species. By 1839, Darwin had become convinced that species were not unchangeable. They were not "fixed" as commonly believed, but rather could evolve, over time, into one or more new species.

Figure 9.6 Charles Darwin as a young man.

Down House

Figure 9.7 The Galapagos Islands. These seemingly desolate volcanic islands lying on the equator influenced Darwin more than any of the many places he visited.

A. Nelson/TOM STACK & ASSOCIATES

Figure 9.8 The route of HMS Beagle during her 5-year voyage around the world.

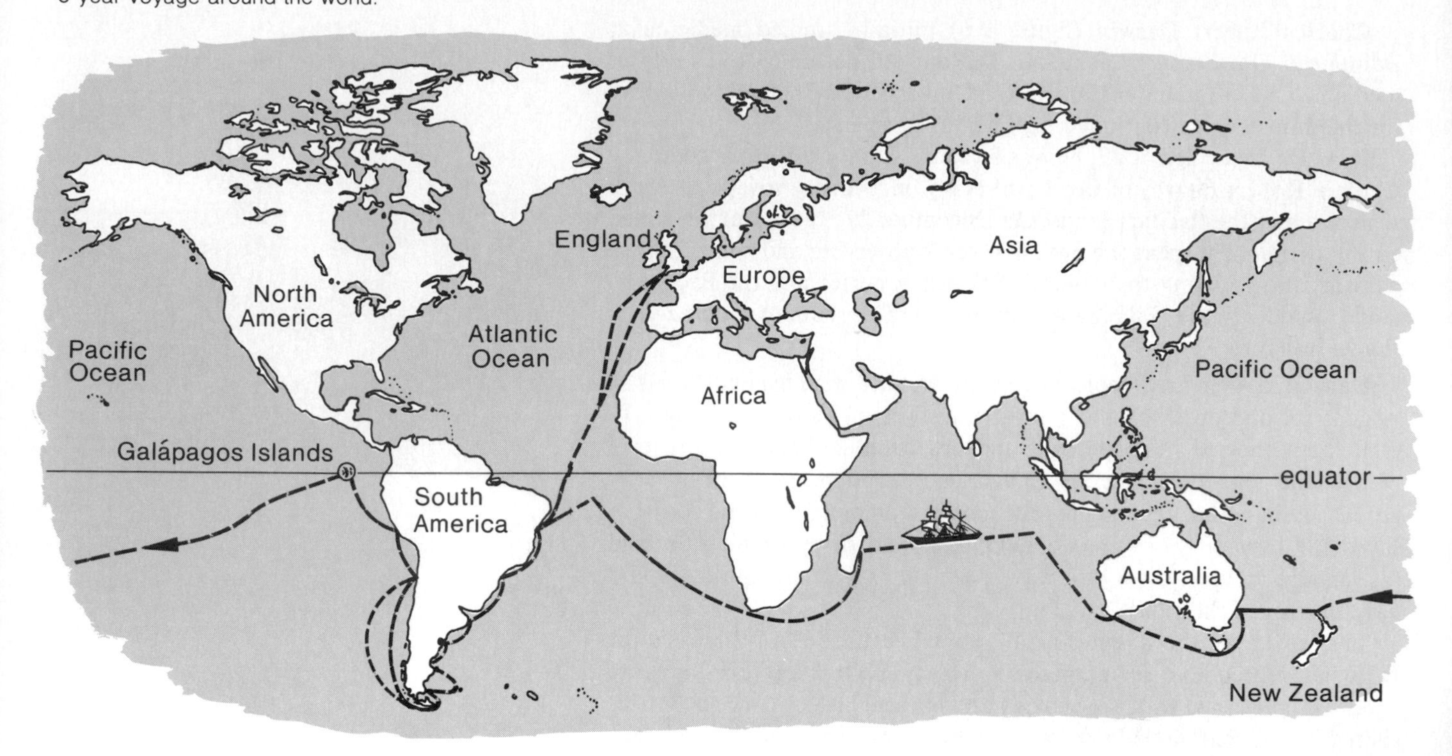

Thus, Darwin, by his extensive observations, came to the conclusion that current species had descended from ancestral ones. However, this conclusion was unlikely to be accepted by the people of his day unless he could explain how change had occurred from ancestral species to current species.

The Galápagos Islands off the coast of Ecuador were especially interesting to Darwin. Organisms such as mockingbirds and finches seemed to be different on each of the islands. Darwin was particularly curious about finches. They generally resembled those he had seen in Ecuador, but there was a greater diversity among those of the Galápagos. Finches normally are seed eaters, as were some of the Galápagos finches. Others, however, fed on the fleshy parts of cacti. One even used a cactus spine as a tool, holding it in its beak to extract insects from under the bark of tree cacti. A woodpecker does this with its own bill instead of a cactus spine.

The finches had adapted to every habitat. There were big and little ones; some lived on the ground and some lived in trees; there were seed eaters, fruit eaters, and insect eaters; and there was even a "woodpecker" finch (figure 9.9). These odd finches displayed a basic unity that identified them as finches. At the same time each had some peculiar characteristics of its own. How did such diversity occur among finches on this small group of tiny islands?

Darwin speculated about the origin of islands in the ocean and began to relate geological and biological problems. If rocks, islands, and continents could change, as Sir Charles Lyell pointed out in his book *Principles of Geology,* might not time also allow for changes in living things?

Figure 9.9 The Galapagos finches, today known as Darwin's finches. Which part of the body varies most? Find the finch that uses cactus spines to dig insects out of tree bark.

Figure 9.10 Brazilian rain forest. It was here that Darwin began recognizing that, for most organisms, life is a constant struggle for survival.

G. Prance/VISUALS UNLIMITED

If Darwin had known only the peaceful English countryside, he might never have answered his questions concerning populations adapted to their environment through the selection of variations. The environment selects those variations that best adapt organisms to it. Such selection of variations creates diversity among organisms—some selected for one environment, some for another. Darwin's most pressing question was "What directs the selection of variations?" He recalled the teeming life of the Brazilian rain forest (figure 9.10). The many plants seemed to struggle upward toward the light. Darwin began to detect in many habitats the struggle among individuals to obtain the necessities of life.

During this period he read a book by the sociologist Thomas Malthus, *An Essay on the Principle of Population.* Malthus (figure 9.11) had concluded that humans tended to produce more offspring than they can support. If this were also true of organisms other than humans, would this not result in a struggle for existence among them? Under such circumstances would not the offspring best fitted for survival be those most likely to grow up to produce offspring like themselves? Darwin looked for more evidence to answer those questions.

Darwin was familiar with the activities of breeders of domestic animals. These breeders selected as parents for their next generations those individuals that had certain desired characteristics, and prevented those with less desirable characteristics from breeding. This process was **artificial selection.** Darwin thought that the struggle for existence in nature might be similar, removing from each generation the individuals poorly fitted to live in their environment. Thus, only the more fit would be left to produce the next generation. In short, just as plant and animal breeders practiced artificial selection, nature was practicing **natural selection,** favoring those organisms best fitted to a given environment. According to Darwin's hypothesis, the long neck of the giraffe would have come about as shown in figure 9.12b. Compare this with the Lamarckian explanation in figure 9.12a.

In investigation 9.2, you can simulate the process of natural selection.

Figure 9.11 Thomas Malthus. His *Essay* influenced Darwin's early ideas about the origin of species.

The Bettman Archive

Figure 9.12 A comparison of Lamarckian (a) and Darwinian (b) hypotheses of the evolution of giraffes.

a. Lamarck's hypothesis

Existing data do not support this hypothesis.

Ancestral giraffes probably had short necks that were subjected to frequent stretching to enable the giraffes to reach the foliage of trees.

The offspring had longer necks that also were stretched frequently in the quest for food.

Eventually the continued stretching of the neck gave rise to modern giraffes.

b. Darwin's hypothesis

Existing data support this hypothesis.

Ancestral giraffes probably had necks that varied in length. The variations were hereditary.

Natural selection led to survival of longer-necked offspring.

Eventually only long-necked giraffes survived.

Investigation 9.2 NATURAL SELECTION— A SIMULATION

Introduction

Natural selection appears to be the chief mechanism of evolutionary change. Biologists regard it as the process that has populated our planet with diverse life forms and that gave rise to humans. It continues today to shape the living world. In this investigation you will experience one way natural selection operates.

Materials (per team of 4 to 6)

piece of fabric 3 feet × 6 feet
containers with 100 paper chips of assorted colors
small bowl

Procedure

1. Spread out the fabric habitat on a table top.
2. Appoint 1 team member as the keeper of your vial of paper chips. With your backs turned, allow the keeper to spread the chips uniformly over the fabric, making sure no chips stick together.
3. Imagine yourselves as predators, the paper chips as your prey, and the fabric background as your habitat. One at a time, turn around and select a paper chip using only your eyes to locate it. Do not use your hands to feel the chips. When you have a paper chip, place it in the bowl. Take turns until only 25% of the paper chips remain on the fabric. Your teacher will help you determine individual quotas to ensure survival of 25% of the chips.
4. Carefully shake the fabric to remove the survivors.
5. Group the survivors according to color. Arrange them in a horizontal row about 1 cm apart. Place chips of the same color together. Record the numbers of each color that survived.
6. Assume each survivor produces 3 offspring. Using your teacher's reserve supply, place 3 chips of the same color underneath each survivor.
7. Mix the survivors and their offspring thoroughly and distribute them as in procedure 3.
8. Repeat the entire process of selection (procedures 3–7) 2 more times.

Discussion

1. Study your survivor populations.
   (a) Was 1 color of paper chip represented more than others in the 1st generation of survivors?
   (b) Were shades of that color also represented?
   (c) What, if any, change occurred between the 1st and 2nd, and between the 2nd and 3rd generation survivors?
2. Compare the original and survivor populations. Is there any color from the original population that is not represented in the survivor population?
3. Examine your survivor chips and the fabric from which you took them. How do you think the colors of the survivors related to their habitat?
4. Assuming no new individuals migrate into the habitat, what do you think the character of the population will be like? Will it change with time?
5. If new individuals with different colors do migrate in, what do you think the effect on the population will be, assuming the habitat and predators remain the same? What will be the effect if the habitat and predators change?

Figure 9.13 Darwin's study, in his home near London. It was here that he organized the data collected during his voyage on the *Beagle*, and formulated his ideas on evolution.

Down House

Figure 9.14 Alfred Russel Wallace. His ideas about evolution supported many of Darwin's beliefs, prompting Darwin to publish his book *On the Origin of Species by Means of Natural Selection* in 1859.

National Library of Medicine

9.4 Darwin's Theory of Natural Selection Provides an Explanation for the Origin of Species

Darwin was convinced that natural selection was the mechanism that allowed certain variations to survive and others to die out. He began nearly 25 years of work, gathering evidence to support his idea of natural selection. As a good scientist, he also examined contrary evidence and reworked the flaws in his reasoning. He formulated other hypotheses to see if they would better account for the facts. In 1842 he wrote a sketch of his results. He expanded this to an essay in 1844, but he showed it only to a botanist friend. From 1846 to 1854 he produced four specialized books on barnacles, which provided him with firsthand experience with the amount of variation found in species and the problems of classification. It was not until 1856 that he started to put on paper his theory of natural selection. He did this as he continued to study the problems of diversity and geographic distribution.

On June 18, 1858, Darwin received a scientific paper from a young man who had been exploring in Malaya. This naturalist was Alfred Russel Wallace (figure 9.14). Imagine Darwin's surprise when he discovered in reading this paper that Wallace had worked out ideas almost identical to his own. Darwin felt that he could not now, in fairness to

Wallace, publish his own ideas. However, a few of his friends persuaded him to summarize his theories and make a joint presentation with Wallace. On July 1, 1858, both papers were presented at a meeting of the Linnaean Society of London. Neither Darwin nor Wallace was present, and the presentation caused little stir among the scientific community. Darwin then prepared what he called an abstract of the full work on which he was engaged. This abstract became the book *On The Origin of Species by Means of Natural Selection.* In it Darwin presented evidence in support of the theory of evolution. His book was not directed solely to scientists, but rather to an intelligent lay population. It presented an enormous body of evidence, much of which was already familiar, to support the theory that evolution occurred through the natural selection of random variations. The weight of evidence was such that, within a decade, significant numbers of biologists around the world were convinced that the theory of evolution was as true as any theory can be. Darwin's theory of natural selection, proposed to account for evolution, also was widely accepted.

Darwin had collected facts on a large scale and used them as the basis for formulating a hypothesis to account for his observations. He deduced from the hypothesis the consequences that should follow. Those deductions could be tested to support or refute the hypothesis. A well-tested hypothesis that accounts for all the facts and that has the ability to predict additional facts is known as a **theory.**

The theory of evolution was supported by a vast quantity of data from a wide variety of fields. Furthermore, Darwin's theory of natural selection provided a mechanism whereby the best adapted variations would be preserved. The next big question was "How are variations transmitted from one generation to the next?" For an answer to this question we must return to the work of Gregor Mendel, which you studied in chapter 8.

Self-Review

1. What do biologists mean when they say there is "unity in diversity" in the living world?
2. How was Charles Darwin influenced by the variety of organisms he observed on the Galápagos Islands?
3. What caused Darwin to question the idea that all species were fixed and unchanging?
4. How was Charles Darwin influenced by the work of Thomas Malthus?
5. Compare the explanations of Lamarck and Darwin to account for evolutionary change. Why was Darwin's explanation the better of the two?
6. How did Darwin test his original hypothesis?

Figure 9.15 Comparative embryology of some vertebrates. Zygotes are shown on the left, adults on the right, and comparable embryological stages between. Drawings are not to the same scale. The similarity between early stages in the development of many different animals helped convince Darwin that all forms of life shared common ancestors.

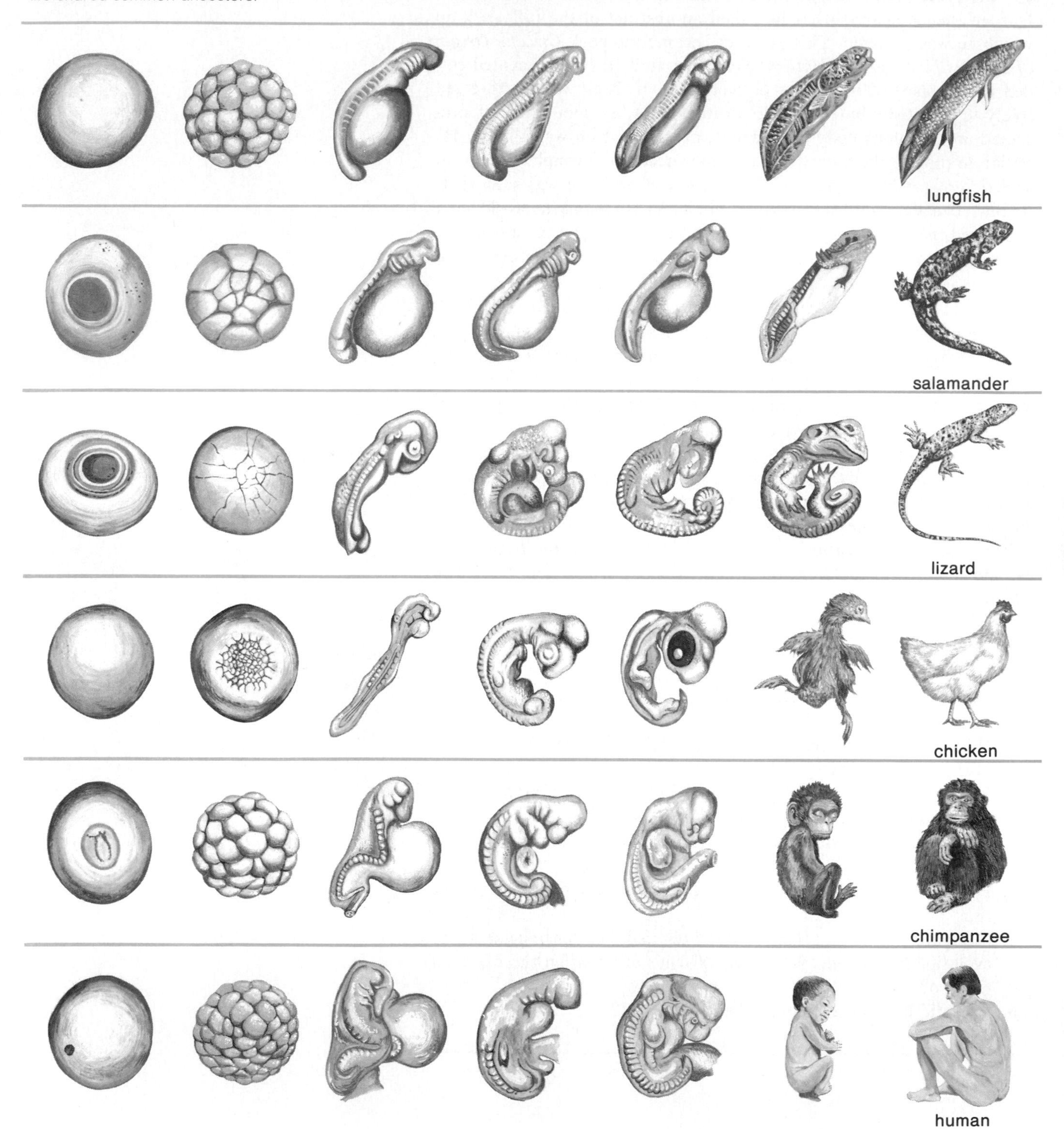

Natural Variation and Natural Selection

Guidepost: What is the raw material for evolutionary change?

9.5 Mendel's Work Helped Explain How Characteristics Are Inherited

Darwin had little knowledge of genetics. He did not know of Mendel's work with garden peas, which was not rediscovered until 1900. That rediscovery led to the development of the science of genetics. In turn, genetics influenced understandings of evolution, development, physiology, biochemistry, medicine, agriculture, and even social science.

Darwin's theory of natural selection acting on natural variations provided a mechanism for evolution. Mendel's discoveries, which led to the chromosome theory of heredity introduced in chapter 8, showed the way in which such variations could be inherited and maintained in a population. Darwin clearly understood that only hereditary variations would have any meaning for the evolutionary process. The hereditary traits of all living organisms are a product of their genes and chromosomes. Obviously, then, when genes and chromosomes mutate or change, they affect the characteristics of a species. How could the characteristics of a species remain the same if its genes and chromosomes changed? That would be possible only if every mutation were to be eliminated. That is not the case in nature, however. Many mutations *are* eliminated, but as time passes the hereditary makeup does change; that change provides the raw material for evolution. That is one of the most important concepts in all of biology.

Biologists can now subject genes and chromosomes to X rays or chemicals and can produce mutations in large numbers. These can be studied to determine their effects on viability and fertility. Mutations can be introduced into populations of organisms and the changes observed. Such experiments provide powerful evidence for evolution. Biologists now have the power to speed up the rate of evolution or to alter its course. Genetic engineering, discussed in section 8.20, makes it possible for biologists to create organisms so different from any existing that the U.S. Patent Office issues a patent on them as unique and proprietary.

Figure 9.16 Hermann J. Müller. In 1927 he discovered that exposure to X rays greatly increases the rate at which mutations occur.

Arthur Shay—Fortune Magazine

9.6 There Are Major Common Characteristics of the Evolutionary Process

Three major principles underlie the evolutionary process.

1. An evolutionary event involves a change in a *population,* not in individual members of that population. Individuals do not undergo evolutionary changes during their lifetimes. However, the makeup of the population changes—over a long period of time. In other words, the frequency of various kinds of individuals in the population changes. That means that the frequency of different genes in that population changes. We can think of evolutionary change as changes in gene frequencies in a population.

2. Only one or a few characteristics change at any one time in an evolutionary event. Organisms are systems of complex interactions. The change in the frequency of one trait may bring about other changes that are related. However, populations tend to be stable systems. When we consider all the characteristics of a population, only a few have changed.
3. An evolutionary event involves a change in a particular direction. Genetic variations provide the raw material on which natural selection acts. Environmental factors guide the selection.

As an example of the application of these three principles, we can consider the case of *Biston betularia* (BIS tun bet yoo LAY ree uh), the peppered moth. It is a common inhabitant of English woodlands. To a casual observer all peppered moths look alike, but if you examine a large population you will find many individual differences. For example, a few have shorter antennae than most; some have longer legs. The most notable difference, however, is in color: some individuals are light and others dark.

Collecting moths has long been a popular hobby in Britain, and many specimens collected over the last two centuries and from all parts of the country are available for study. Biologists find that the variations among moths caught in 1850 are mainly the same as those among moths collected 100 years later. There is one startling difference, however. Among moths collected in 1850 there were more light than dark ones; in 1950 there were many more dark moths than light ones.

If biologists examine only the moths collected from rural, southern England in 1950, they find the same ratio of light to dark as in 1850. However, when they examine collections from the heavily industrialized midlands of England in 1950, they find very few light moths. Why should light moths predominate in one region and dark moths elsewhere? Why should dark moths have been rarer in the past than now?

The biologists who investigated this matter developed a hypothesis and proceeded to test it. In the midlands they placed both light and dark moths on smoke-blackened tree trunks (figure 9.17). The moths were placed in the positions they normally take during their daytime rest. The biologists soon observed that birds ate more light moths than dark ones. Both light and dark moths then were placed on trees common to southern England—soot-free and encrusted with white lichens. Here the birds ate more dark than light moths.

What conclusions can one reach from these observations? In the industrialized midlands the tree trunks became covered with black soot. The soot made dark moths harder to see, so they survived predation better than white moths on these trees. Moth coloration is controlled genetically. During the last century, therefore, natural selection favored the moths whose color protected them best in the new environment. Meanwhile, white moths survived successfully in rural areas, where tree trunks were not sooty. Thus, our first evolutionary principle is supported. The makeup of the moth population changed over a period of time as the frequency of different kinds of individuals in the population changed. Some dark individuals occurred in the 1850 moth population, but they were much more frequent in the 1950 population.

The change in frequency of dark moths may have brought about some less obvious changes in other moth characteristics. This would support

Figure 9.17 The basis for natural selection in the peppered moth (*Biston betularia*). (a) The two forms of the moth on a tree blackened by soot. (b) Dark and light forms on a tree covered with light-colored lichens. Which moth in each photo is most likely to be eaten by predators?

a J. A. Bishop, University of Liverpool b J. A. Bishop, University of Liverpool

our second evolutionary principle. The studies, however, were dealing only with changes in color, not with changes in a large number of characteristics.

The 1850 population included both white and dark moths. This coloring is hereditary. An evolutionary event, such as the increase in the frequency of dark moths, first requires genetic variation as its raw material. The dark color became the foundation for a change in the population that resulted in a greater frequency of dark moths. Environmental factors, such as the soot and the birds, guided this selection, which illustrates the third of our evolutionary principles.

Figure 9.18 In the life cycle of a leopard frog (*Rana pipiens*), the animal changes rapidly (in the course of one to two weeks) from a tailed tadpole, with structure and behavior suited for life in water, to a tailless adult frog, with structure and behavior suited for life on land.

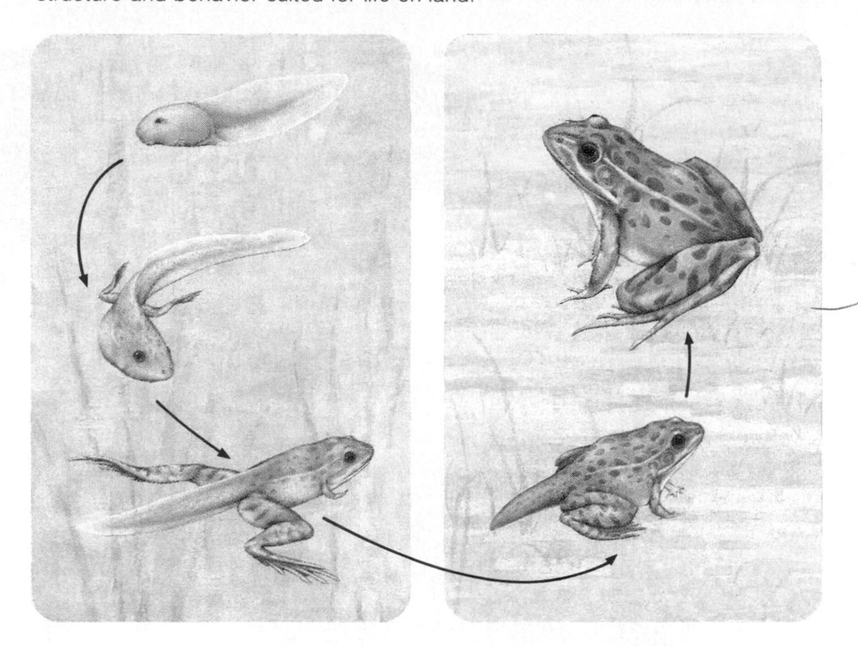

9.7 Living Material Is Able to Change from One Form to Another

Some people find it hard to believe that living material can change from one form to another. For example, how could a fishlike organism become adapted to life on land? Yet one of the characteristics of living material is its capacity for change. Imagine, for example, that the life cycle of a butterfly was unknown. Caterpillars and butterflies would then be considered separate organisms entirely because of the great differences in their appearance and their life-styles. In the life history of a given organism, early stages are frequently so different from the adult that they would be considered different species or even different classes were they not observed to change from one into another.

One can observe a change from an aquatic to a terrestrial life in a single organism. Consider the tadpole of a frog: it is limbless and aquatic, very fishlike in appearance. It breathes by means of gills. It is a herbivore and its intestinal tract and mouth parts are adapted to a plant diet. Raising tadpoles in an aquarium allows you to see in a single species some remarkable changes. As the tadpole develops into a frog it loses its fishlike form and assumes the characteristics of an adult (figure 9.18). Its tail is reabsorbed, it develops limbs, its gills are replaced by lungs, and it becomes a carnivore with intestine and mouth parts adapted to a diet of other animals. If one had seen only tadpoles and frogs and had never observed the changes from one into the other, tadpoles would probably be classified as fish and adult frogs as amphibians. What other examples can you cite that show the great ability of living material to change from one form to another?

Self-Review

1. What is the raw material for evolutionary change?
2. How did the rediscovery of Mendel's work provide support for Darwin's theory?
3. What are the three major characteristics of the evolutionary process?
4. In what ways does the peppered moth illustrate natural selection?

The Forces of Evolutionary Change

Guidepost: What natural forces direct evolutionary change?

9.8 Mutations and Genetic Recombination Increase Variability

In section 9.6 we showed how genetic variation in the peppered moth provided the kinds of raw material necessary for evolutionary change. How is genetic variation brought about? There are at least two major sources of the variability required for evolution: mutations and genetic recombination.

A mutation is a change in a gene. Frequently one hears that mutations are both rare and harmful. The frequency of gene mutation is variable. One of the genes that produces colored grains in an ear of corn may mutate as frequently as once in 2000 germ cells. Other genes are so stable that they fail to mutate during millions of cell divisions. On an average, however, a mutant form of any particular gene occurs about once in 100,000 germ cells. This would seem to support the rarity of gene mutation. Remember, however, that evolution is concerned with populations and with every gene within a population.

There may be thousands of genes in each individual germ cell, and for each species there may be thousands or millions of individuals producing germ cells in each generation. There are many generations over the span of evolutionary time. Therefore, although any paticular gene mutates rarely, there is ample opportunity for mutation. In human beings alone there are probably more than 20,000 genes per gamete. Each person results from a union of two gametes, so the probability that a person carries a new mutation is about 2 in 5.

One would expect that an organism well adapted to a given environment would more likely be hindered rather than helped by further mutations. The probability of becoming better adapted is simply far less than the probability of becoming less well adapted. Even so, the opportunity for beneficial mutations is very large, as shown in table 9.1.

Genetic recombination results from meiosis and sexual reproduction, as we showed in section 6.8. Like mutations, recombination increases the genetic variability in a given population by bringing about different combinations of genes (figure 9.19). This contributes to the variation in the **gene pool.** The gene pool is the total amount of genetic information—all the alleles—in a population. Natural selection sorts out particular

Figure 9.19 How mutation and recombination produce a wide variety of individuals.

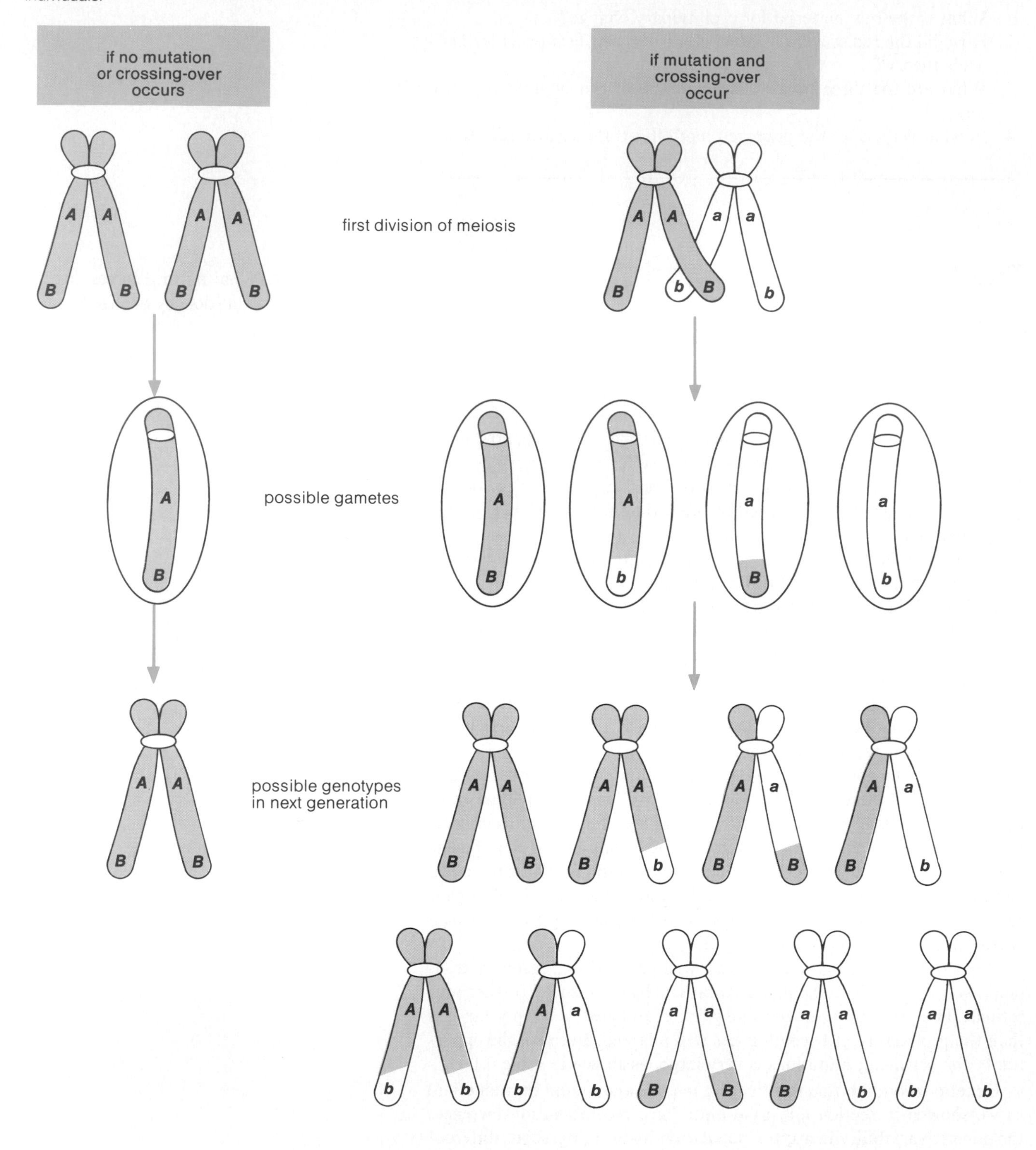

Table 9.1 Calculation of the probable number of beneficial mutations that can occur during the evolutionary lifetime of a species*

Estimates	Calculations
1. Mutation rate per gene 1/100,000	6. Number of beneficial mutations per individual per generation equals no. 1 × no. 2 × no. 3, or 1/100,000 × 1000 × 1/1000 = 1/100,000.
2. Number of genes in the organism capable of mutating 1000	7. Number of beneficial mutations in the species population per generation equals no. 6 × no. 4, or 1/100,000 × 100,000,000 = 1000.
3. Proportion of mutations that are beneficial 1/1000	8. Number of beneficial mutations during the evolutionary life of the species equals no. 7 × no. 5, or 1000 × 10,000 = 10,000,000.
4. Population size of the species 100,000,000	
5. Number of generations in the evolutionary life of the species 10,000	

*Based on conservative estimates of gene number, population size, and number of generations during which the species exists.

gene combinations from this pool. Genetic differences can arise between different subpopulations derived from the same gene pool because each selected subpopulation has a smaller gene pool than the original population. Thus, there is likely to be less variability in the subpopulation.

9.9 The Size of a Population Affects Its Stability

Gene frequencies in a population remain stable unless modified by some directing factors. Several kinds of factors affect gene frequencies. First, mutations may bring about changes in genes and, thus, in gene frequencies. Second, a population may migrate to a new environment, which then will select the genes that best adapt the population to the new situation. Third, one population may migrate into the territory of another of the same species. The result will be a change in the frequencies of alleles in both populations.

Evolutionary change in large populations is guided primarily by natural selection. In small populations, however, chance may play a role and lead to some nonadaptive characteristics. For example, a new and isolated population may be established when a small number of individuals leaves the parent population. It is unlikely that these few individuals carry all the alleles, and in the same frequencies, as the parent population. They form an atypical sample, but this sample may migrate to where it can live well and reproduce effectively. In time, it may form a large population on its own. However, in the new environment the gene pool—already smaller than that of the parent population—may be further modified by both selection and **random genetic drift.** Random genetic drift is variation in gene frequencies that occurs in the absence of natural selection. For example, the small population may lose—just by chance—an allele with a low gene frequency. Unless that allele reoccurs by mutation, or in a new immigrant to the population, it is gone forever.

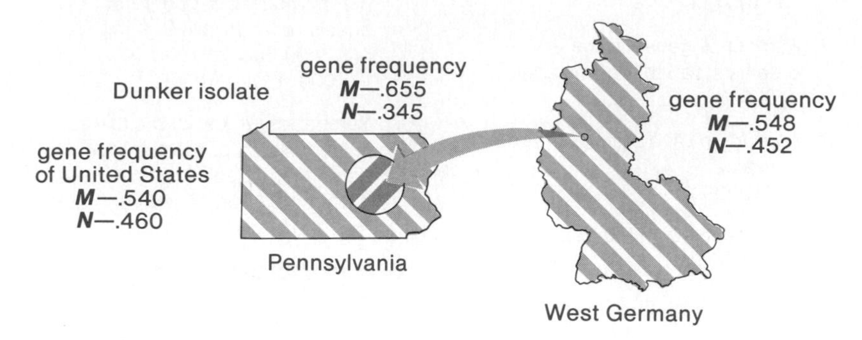

Figure 9.20 Genetic drift in *MN* blood groups. A Dunker group that by chance had a relatively high frequency of the allele for *M* emigrated to Pennsylvania. Because the Dunkers do not marry outside their group, they continue to exhibit a higher frequency of alleles for *M* and a lower frequency of alleles for *N* than in West Germany or the United States.

Its frequency has become zero. This and other forms of genetic drift occur primarily in small populations, and the random changes can accumulate from one generation to the next. Genetic drift can change significantly the gene frequencies in such small populations. As a result, nonadaptive as well as adaptive characteristics can become established, provided that the nonadaptive characteristics are not actually harmful.

There are examples of genetic drift in human populations. The Dunkers are a small religious group whose ancestors migrated from Germany to what is now Pennsylvania in the 18th century. The size of the population is only a few hundred. Outsiders are not accepted into the group, even by marriage. Thus, the gene pool of the group remains separated from the influence of outside genes.

In section 8.9, you studied the ABO blood groups. The MN blood group is another one present in humans. Among the Dunkers, the frequency of blood type M is much higher than its frequency either in Germany or the rest of the United States (see figure 9.20). There is no known advantage to having blood type M as compared to the other types (MN and N) in this particular system. Thus, natural selection appears not to be a factor in maintaining the high frequency of type M. The high frequency is a result of chance—random genetic drift. The Dunker population that emigrated from Germany had a higher frequency of type M by chance. The limitations on the flow of new genes into the population have allowed this frequency to remain high. If many new genes entered the population, the effects of genetic drift would be lost.

9.10 Events in the Natural World Are Not Completely Random

Although many factors introduce random variation into the gene pool of a population, not all events in the natural world take place at random. Chemical elements, for example, do not combine in random patterns, but, rather, in specific and limited ones. For example, carbon can form four chemical bonds with other elements. Because hydrogen can form only one, the expected combination of carbon and hydrogen is CH_4, methane gas. Oxygen can form two bonds and, therefore, oxygen and hydrogen combine as H_2O, water. Thus, the combination process is not random but fixed and predictable. (Review figures 4.3 and 4.4, page 97.)

In a similar way, the genetic patterns of organisms do not allow for random patterns of structure or function. Rather, structure and function develop within limitations imposed by the genotype of the organism. Genetic changes that vary greatly from the established pattern may result in the death of the organism. Even if the variation does not cause death, the organism may be unable to breed with others of its own species, and the genetic change will not continue.

Investigation 9.3 GENETIC STABILITY

Introduction

Natural selection works to change the frequency of characteristics in a population. In this investigation you will study a population existing through time with no selective forces acting on it.

Evidence for genetic stability was found when mitosis and meiosis were linked with the inheritance of characteristics. Because these processes are so precise, it seems that organisms must conserve genetic characteristics through many generations.

Procedure

1. Consider a hypothetical species of squirrel. Assume that among the variations in this hypothetical species are 2 hereditary hair types. One type is straight, and the other is curly. Assume that the trait is determined by a single pair of alleles. Straight (***S***) is dominant over curly (***s***). Finally, assume that the species population consists of 1000 squirrels, with equal numbers of males and females. Among the 500 squirrels of each sex, 250 are homozygous straight haired (***SS***), and 250 are homozygous curly haired (***ss***).
2. Use the symbols ♂ for male and ♀ for female. Identify all the possible phenotype matings in this hypothetical population.
3. List all the possible kinds of matings in terms of genotypes—for example, ***SS*** × ***ss***.
4. Beside each kind of mating, write all the kinds of genotypes that occur among the offspring. Does any cross produce more than one kind of offspring?
5. Assume that the offspring generation also consists of 1000 squirrels, Assume also that each kind of mating you listed for item 2 contributes equally to this population.
   (a) What is the expected ratio of straight-haired squirrels to curly-haired squirrels in the offspring?
   (b) Is this phenotype ratio the same as that in the 1st generation?
6. The frequency of any particular characteristic within a group is expressed as a fraction. Thus, in a group of 100 marbles containing 20 red and 80 blue ones, the frequency of red marbles is 20/100 or 1/5 or 20% or 0.2. The frequency of blue marbles is 80/100 or 4/5 or 80% or 0.8. Regardless of how the fractions are written, their sum must always equal 1:
   $20/100 + 80/100 = 100/100 = 1$
   $1/5 + 4/5 = 5/5 = 1$
   $20\% + 80\% = 100\% = 1$
   $0.2 + 0.8 = 1.0.$

In this example, suppose each marble is a gamete and gametes unite at random. Recall that the probability of two separate events occurring at the same time is the product of their individual probabilities. Thus, the frequency of genotype red-red in the next generation would be $0.2 \times 0.2 = 0.04$. The frequency of blue-blue would be $0.8 \times 0.8 = 0.64$. What would be the frequency of the red-blue genotype? We know that the total of the frequencies of the genotypes must equal 1.0. Therefore, $1.0 - 0.04 - 0.64 = 0.32$. This means that in the next generation of 100 individuals, we expect 32 to be heterozygotes.

7. Now consider the 2 genes ***S*** and ***s***.
   (a) What were their frequencies (expressed as decimal fractions) in the original squirrel population?
   (b) What are their frequencies in the offspring generation?
   (c) How do the gene frequencies in the original population compare with those in the offspring generation?
8. Now make the same calculations for a 3rd generation. You could do this by mating every genotype with every other genotype in proportion to their frequencies. You can obtain the same result, however, by using the gene-pool method. Write the frequencies of all the kinds of gametes in the 2nd generation (in this case, the frequencies of genes in item 7b). Then assume random combination of those gametes. The frequency of ***S*** plus the frequency of ***s*** represents the total sperm population. (Likewise, the frequency of ***S*** plus the frequency of ***s*** represents the total egg population.) By algebraic multiplication of these frequencies, you can obtain the frequencies of the 3rd-generation genotypes just as you did with the red and blue marbles above.
9. Use the gene-pool method to answer the following questions:
   (a) What are the frequencies of the genotypes in the 3rd generation?
   (b) Assuming that the 3rd-generation population is again 1000, what are the frequencies of ***S*** and ***s*** in the 3rd generation?
   (c) Is the phenotype ratio the same as in the 2nd generation?
   (d) Are gene frequencies the same as those in the 2nd generation?
10. Retaining all other assumptions, change the original population to 400 homozygous straight-haired squirrels and 600 homozygous curly-haired squirrels. Each group contains males and females in equal numbers.
   (a) What are the frequencies of the 2 genes among males in the population?
   (b) Among females?
   (c) By algebraic multiplication, determine the frequencies of genotypes among the offspring.
   (d) What are the frequencies of the 2 genes in the offspring population?
   (e) Calculate the frequencies of the genes in a 3rd generation.

Discussion

In a single sentence, try to state a conclusion concerning gene frequencies in populations.

If you have been successful in formulating your sentence, you have stated the basic idea of the **Hardy-Weinberg principle.** G. H. Hardy was an English mathematician, and W. R. Weinberg was a German physician. In 1908 they independently worked out the effects of random mating in successive generations on the frequencies of alleles in a population. You have just done the same thing.

You may have noticed that in many ways the hypothetical population differs from real ones. Nevertheless, the Hardy-Weinberg principle is important for biologists because it is the basis of hypothetical stability from which to measure real change.

9.11 Isolation Is Important for the Formation of a New Species

Mutation, recombination, selection, migration, and random genetic drift bring about changes in a population. If these changes are linked by a large number of individuals that can interbreed, such individuals are normally considered as one species. For example, one might think that a Pekingese and a Great Dane would be different species of dogs because they cannot interbreed. They do contribute to the gene pool of the dog species as a whole, however, and can cross with intermediate breeds, as shown in figure 10.2, page 313.

A new species must be isolated if it is to remain a separate species. Otherwise, interbreeding with any other species to a significant extent could cause its distinctive character to disappear. Reproductive isolation may arise in several ways. The first is separation in time. A species that disappeared a million years ago obviously cannot breed with a species living today. Even a species that becomes reproductively active in the spring cannot interbreed with another that becomes reproductively active in the fall. Thus, isolation by time prevents interbreeding, even if it could otherwise occur.

A second origin of reproductive isolation is geographic isolation caused by naturally occurring barriers such as mountains and rivers. Organisms that cannot come into contact with each other cannot interbreed. Distance, though not impossible to overcome, is itself a geographic barrier. Large populations that spread over a wide geographic range often demonstrate marked variations from one end of the range to the other. The flicker population of North America is a good example (figure 9.21). There are three types of flickers that can interbreed. Their color is due to a codominant trait. The yellow-shafted flicker is most common in the eastern part of the United States. In the western part of the United States, the red-shafted flicker is dominant. In between, heterozygous individuals termed hybrid flickers are most abundant. Hybrid flickers have mingled reddish-yellow feathers that look orange. If one did not know of the intermediate population of hybrid flickers, the red-shafted flicker and the yellow-shafted flicker would appear to be two distinct species on the basis of their appearance.

There have been numerous instances of populations described as distinct species that have later been found to be connected by intermediate populations. Often a large, widespread species is divided into geographic **subspecies** or races on the basis of distinctions of this kind. You may gain a clearer picture by studying the salamanders in California, as presented in investigation 9.4.

A third factor in reproductive isolation can be genetic or behavioral. These are conclusive isolating factors. They can be illustrated by two similar populations that do not cross successfully with each other. A wild coyote looks much like a domestic dog, but mating between the two species is rare. Behavioral differences, particularly in the care and feeding of the young, result in the early death of the offspring. This type of reproductive isolation allows dogs and coyotes to exist side-by-side and remain distinct species.

Many species are reproductively isolated in nature, but in captivity they may be crossed to produce vigorous, fertile hybrids. Mallard and pintail ducks (figure 9.23), for example, are found in the same habitats

Figure 9.21 Distribution of flickers in the U.S. How has the history of the Great Plains affected these flickers?

Figure 9.22 (a) Domestic dogs (*Canis familiaris*) and (b) coyote (*Canis latrans*). Though distantly related, the two species are behaviorally isolated and rarely interbreed.

a BSCS by Doris Strumbel

b Larry Brock/TOM STACK & ASSOCIATES

Figure 9.23 Mallard duck (left) and pintail duck (right). Females of the two species are much more alike than these males.

throughout North America, but individuals intermediate between the two are relatively rare. Their mating instincts and nesting habits are very different. It is most unusual for a mallard and a pintail to be sexually active at the same time in nature. When they are put together in the same pen, however, they will mate with each other and produce fertile hybrids.

Courtship patterns also provide reproductive isolation. The male grouse performs a dance that apparently stimulates the sex hormones in the female, causing release of egg cells prior to mating. Males of other species produce far less stimulation in front of a female grouse, and so there is little chance of fertile mating.

Even ecological isolation can occur when two populations live in different habitats. In Michigan, for example, there are two populations of the deer mouse *Peromyscus maniculatus* (figure 9.24). One inhabits the shoreline of the Great Lakes. The other lives in wooded areas. Between the shore and the woods is a zone of meadowland that both populations avoid. Thus, individuals from the two populations rarely meet, even though there is good reason to suppose that if they did, they could still interbreed.

[payr oh MIS kus man ik yoo LAH tus]

Figure 9.24 Prairie deer mouse.

Larry Master, The Nature Conservancy

Figure 9.25 Spawning Kokanee salmon in a creek. The salmon seek out quiet, smooth, gravel-bottomed streambeds in which to deposit their eggs. Their usual silvery color turns to red as they begin to spawn.

Brian Parker/TOM STACK & ASSOCIATES

Finally, behavioral patterns can contribute to reproductive isolation. Pacific salmon spend most of their lives in the ocean, but they do not breed there. Instead, they enter rivers and swim upstream toward the small streams in which they were hatched (figure 9.25). There they breed and die. Thus, the new generation in each stream obtains its genes from a preceding generation from the same stream. As a result, salmon that have been living together for years in the open ocean do not constitute an interbreeding population. Instead, they are genetically separated by behavioral isolation.

In investigation 9.4 you can consider some of the factors that might lead to speciation, or the development of new species.

Biology Today

The Cheetah—On the Way to Extinction?

Wildlife Safari, Winston Oregon

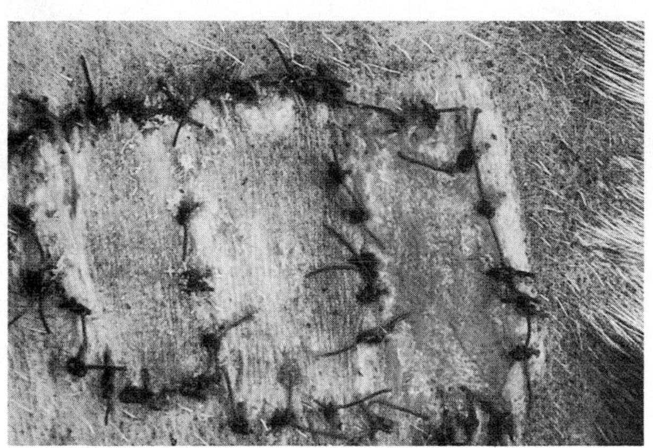
Wildlife Safari, Winston Oregon

Plant and animal extinction has many causes. Humans often cause changes in the environment that modify or even destroy habitats. These changes reduce or eliminate food supplies, living space, and breeding grounds. Other factors may be more important in the case of the cheetah, which has been listed by the Convention of International Trade in Endangered Species as being threatened by extinction. Recent studies have produced evidence that a "population bottleneck" has limited the cheetah population. An infectious disease or a natural catastrophe at some time in the cheetah's recent evolutionary history must have caused its number to become very small. The result was a reduction in the variety of alleles in its gene pool.

Transplants of organs such as the heart, kidney, or liver from one human to another have become fairly common in the past 10 years. An important factor in the success of those transplants has been the development of drugs to prevent rejection, which occurs because the donated organ is recognized as "foreign" by the immune system of the recipient. The greater the genetic variation between donor and recipient, the greater the possibility of rejection. In genetically similar individuals the chances of rejection are greatly reduced.

Researchers used this rejection mechanism to test the hypothesis that a population bottleneck reduced the genetic variation in the cheetah and was an important factor in the decline in the cheetah population. The researchers exchanged skin grafts between six pairs of unrelated cheetahs. They also grafted patches from one part to another of the same cheetah on all 12 as a control. As a second control, the researchers grafted skin patches from another species, the domestic cat, onto each cheetah. The photo on the right above shows one of the grafts after 12 days. The grafts between unrelated cheetahs, on the left, and from one part to another of the same cheetah, in the middle, are healing. There was no rejection of the grafts between unrelated cheetahs or between parts of the same cheetah. The graft from the domestic cat, however, shows acute rejection.

When there is a normal variation of alleles in the gene pool, one would expect rejection of grafts between unrelated cheetahs after 7 to 13 days. The nonrejection of these grafts supported the hypothesis that the population bottleneck reduced the allelic variation in the gene pool of the cheetah. The rejection of the grafts from the domestic cat indicated that the immune system was responsive to genetically different transplanted tissues.

The skin grafts supported the hypothesis that all the cheetahs were closely related. The cheetah population is an example of a genetically uniform species that could be wiped out by a deadly infectious disease. There would be natural selection against the population. Evolution of the cheetah species would stop and it would become one of the many animal species that exist only in books and museums.

Figure 9.26 Specimens of the salamander species *Ensatina eschscholtzii*.

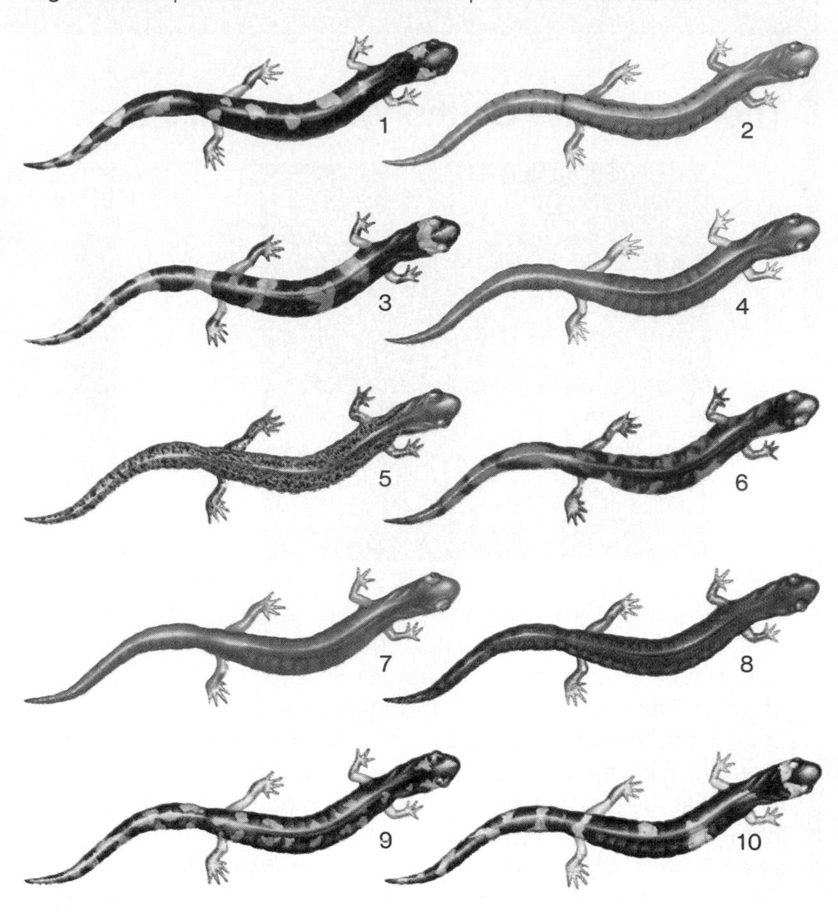

Investigation 9.4 A STEP IN SPECIATION

Introduction

The small salamanders of the genus *Ensatina* are strictly terrestrial. They even lay their eggs on land. Nevertheless, these salamanders need a rather moist environment and do not thrive in arid regions. In California, *Ensatina eschscholtzii* has been studied by R. S. Stebbins of the University of California, Berkeley. This investigation is based on his work.

Materials (per student)

outline map of California
colored pencils

Part A

Procedure

Imagine that you are working with Stebbins's salamander specimens, some of which are pictured in figure 9.26. In the following list, the parentheses after each subspecies name contain a number and a color. The number is the total of individuals that Stebbins had available in his study. The color is for you to use in designating the subspecies. Following this is a list of collection areas. Each is indicated by a number/letter coordinate on the map of California in figure 9.27. For example, 32/R means that 1 or more *E. e. croceator* specimens were collected at the intersection of line 32 and line R.

Figure 9.27 Map of California, with the grid to be used in plotting distributional data.

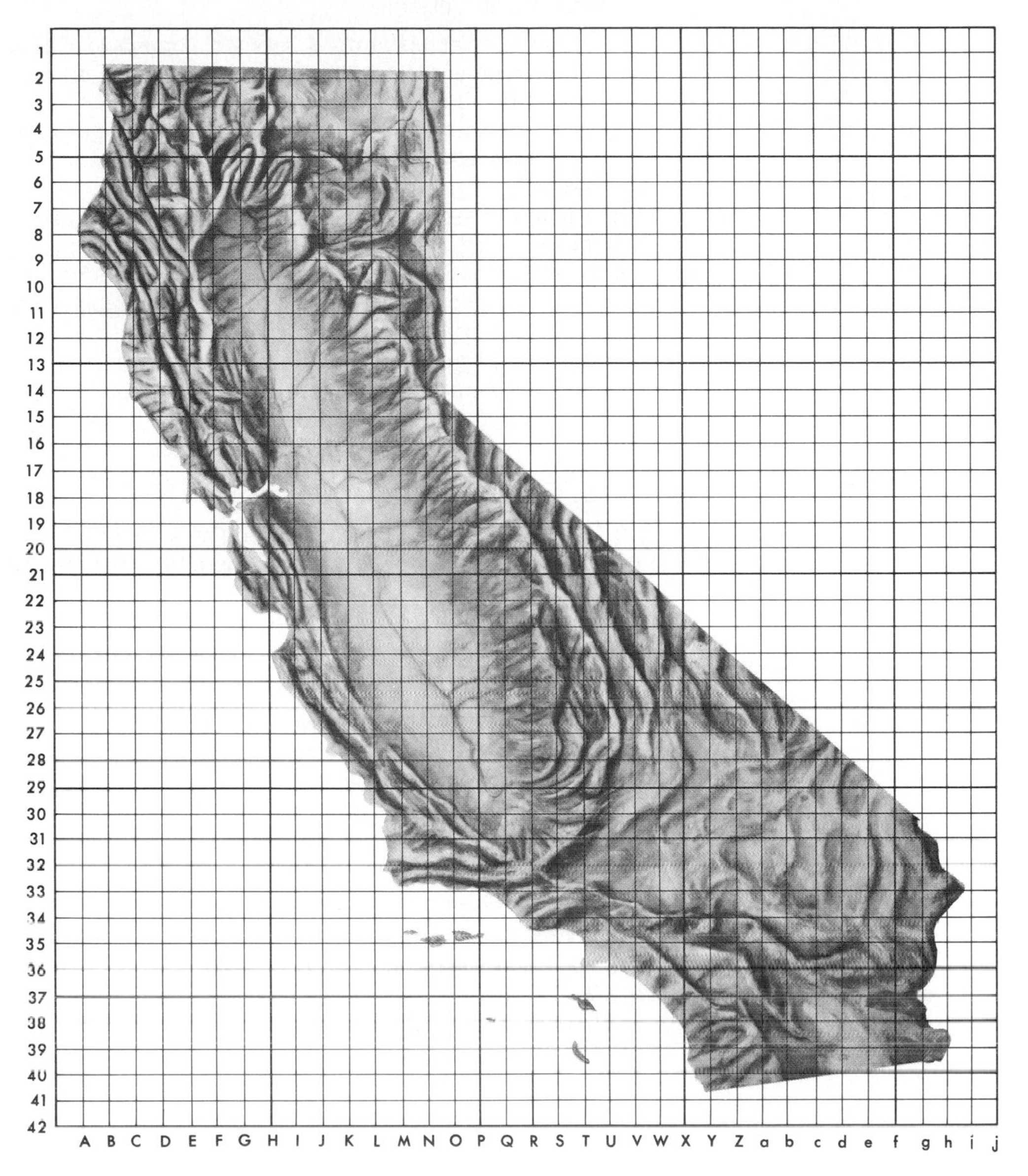

1. *E. e. croceator* (15; brown): 32/R, 32/S, 30/T, 31/T.
2. *E. e. eschscholtzii* (203; red): 30/M, 32/O, 34/S, 35/V, 36/W, 35/Z, 38/Y, 40/Z.
3. *E. e. klauberi* (48; blue): 36/Z, 38/a, 40/a, 39/a.
4. *E. e. oregonensis* (373; pink): 9/B, 7/E, 6/E, 13/C, 10/C, 7/D, 15/D.
5. *E. e. picta* (230; yellow): 2/B, 2/C, 3/C, 4/C.
6. *E. e. platensis* (120; green): 8/J, 10/J, 11/M, 13/M, 15/M, 15/O, 17/M, 15/P, 20/Q, 24/S, 21/R, 25/T, 26/U.
7. *E. e. xanthoptica* (271; orange): 17/G, 17/F, 19/H, 19/O, 20/I, 20/J, 21/I.

Plot each collection area by marking a small X on an outline map that has a grid like the one in the figure. Write with pencils of different colors to indicate the different populations.

Discussion

You now have a distribution map of the subspecies of *Ensatina eschscholtzii* in California.

1. Is the species uniformly distributed throughout California? Use your knowledge of the species' ecological requirements to offer an explanation for its distribution.
2. Now consider the physiography of California (figure 9.27). Does the species seem more characteristic of mountain areas or of large valley areas?
3. Do you expect any order in distribution of subspecies? Why or why not?
4. Examine the salamanders in figure 9.26. Note that some subspecies have yellow or orange spots and bands on a black body. Some have fairly plain, brown-orange bodies. One has small orange spots on a black background. There are other differences as well. For example, some of them have white feet. Now refer to your distribution map. Does there appear to be any order to the way these color patterns occur in California? For example, do the spotted forms occur only along the coast? Do spotted forms occur in the north and unspotted ones in the south?
5. Subspecies *E.e. eschscholtzii* and *E.e. klauberi* are very different from each other. What relationship is there between their distributions?

Part B

Procedure

You may wonder whether there might not be salamanders in some of the areas for which you have no records. You also may wonder whether there might be additional subspecies for which you have no specimens. A biologist faced with these questions would leave the laboratory and go into the field to collect more specimens. Imagine that you do so, too, and return with the following additional data:

- *E. e. eschscholtzii* (16; red): 36/Z, 41/Z, 33/M, 34/W, 34/U
- *E. e. klauberi* (23; blue): 40/b, 40/Z, 36/a
- Unidentified population no. 8 (44; black and green): 4/I, 5/H, 7/H, 7/F, 6/J, 9/F
- Unidentified population no. 9 (13; black and red): 28/T, 27/T, 26/T, 28/S, 29/T
- Unidentified population no. 10 (131; black and blue): 23/J, 24/K, 24/I, 29/M, 25/J, 25/I
- Unidentified population no. 11 (31; black and yellow): 6/C, 7/C, 6/B

Mark with an O the following places that were searched for *Ensatina* without success:

11/I, 14/I, 17/K, 19/K, 22/N, 26/Q, 5/M, 32/U, 32/a, 35/f.

Specimens of nos. 8 and 9 are shown in figure 9.26. There are no illustrations for nos. 11 and 12.

Discussion

According to Stebbins, the unidentified populations are not additional subspecies.

1. What, then, is the probable genetic relationship of populations no. 8, no. 9, and no. 10 to the subspecies already plotted on the map?
2. Why is it unlikely that you would ever find individuals combining characteristics of *E.e. picta* and *E. e. xanthoptica?*
3. Now consider *E. e. eschscholtzii* and *E. e. klauberi.* Look at the distribution of the original collections. What reasons were there for trying to collect additional specimens from extreme southwestern California?
4. How do the results of the additional collections differ from the results in other places where 2 different populations approach each other?
5. Bear in mind the biological definition of a species and also the appearance and distribution of the named populations of *Ensatina.* Which population could best be considered a species separate from *E. eschscholtzii?* This population was, indeed, once considered by biologists to be a separate species.
6. Now imagine that, while examining another museum collection, you find the specimen shown in figure 9.26, no. 10. Compare its characteristics, especially the spotting pattern, with those of the named populations. Also consider the distribution of these populations. Between which 2 is this specimen most likely a hybrid? On your map, draw a line along which you might expect to collect other specimens like this one.
7. In a brief paragraph explain why Stebbins concluded that there is but 1 species of *Ensatina* in California.

For Further Investigation

Problem: What accounts for the 1 record of *E. e. xanthoptica* in the Sierras, whereas the rest of the subspecies occurs along the coast?

9.12 An Alternate Hypothesis Suggests that Speciation May Occur in a Relatively Short Period of Time

A frequent misconception regarding evolution is that it always takes a very long time for a new species to form. That is not necessarily so. Speciation may occur in a relatively short period of time. The geologic record shows that organisms are largely stable for long periods of time. The record also shows, however, that many disappear during a shorter period of time. That disappearance is accompanied by an increase in frequency of fossils of new species.

The longer periods of stability, or equilibrium (millions of years) punctuated by short periods of greater change (thousands of years) gave rise to the hypothesis of **punctuated equilibrium,** proposed in 1972 by S. J. Gould and N. Eldridge. Briefly stated, the hypothesis says that major genetic changes may have caused new species to evolve in relatively few

Figure 9.28 Diagram representing punctuated equilibrium—long periods of relatively little change punctuated by shorter periods of greater change. The letters represent species; A through D, and F, are the oldest species represented in the diagram.

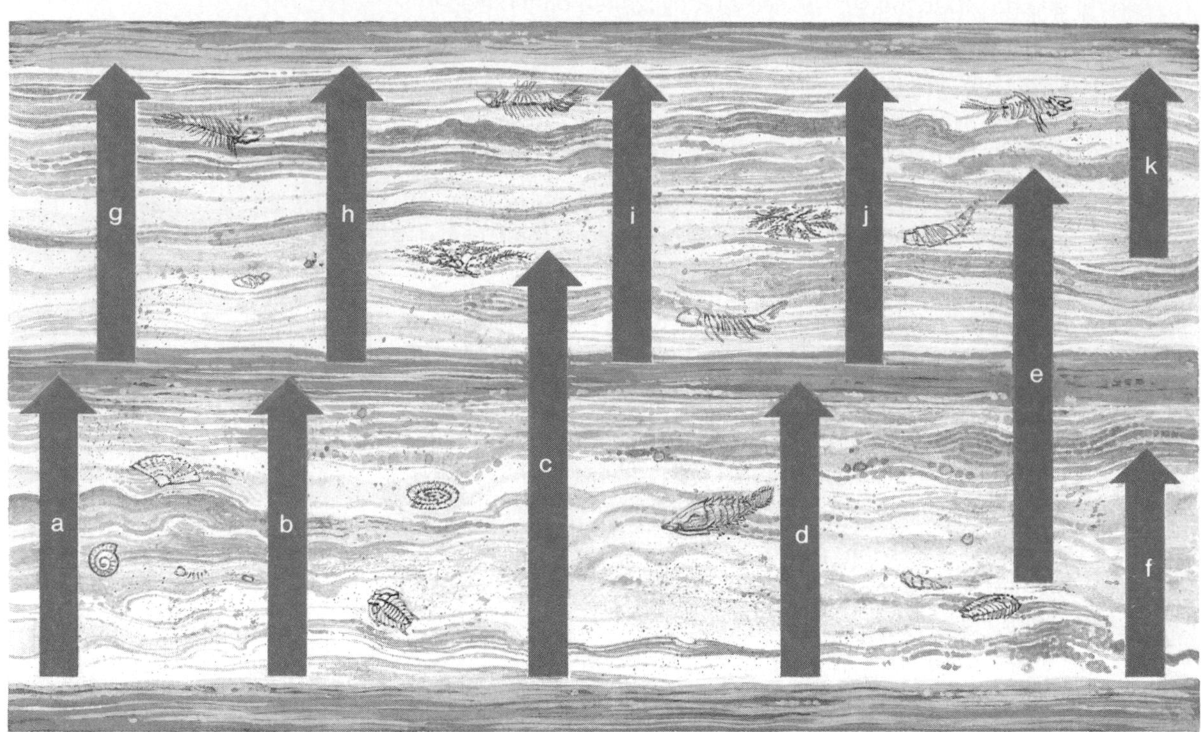

steps. According to the hypothesis these changes occur in small isolated populations. Gould has suggested that punctuated equilibrium resembles a climb up a staircase, whereas the traditional notion of slow gradual change is like a slide up an inclined plane.

Evolutionary biologists are still debating whether the development of new species occurs relatively quickly, or whether slower, more gradual change is the rule. Even the punctuated equilibrium model, however, allows thousands of years for the formation of new species.

Biologists also debate exactly what constitutes a new species. In studying extinct organisms scientists can observe only structures, not behavior. It is difficult to determine whether a new species has developed if one studies only form.

Debates about the mechanisms of evolution are good examples of the continuous refinement of scientific theories. Such debates indicate that a particular discipline is healthy and progressing. New information leads to new questions and hypotheses. The hypotheses then can be tested scientifically to determine their validity.

Self-Review

1. Give an example that shows that events in the natural world are not completely random.
2. What is genetic drift?
3. How is isolation important for evolution? Illustrate with examples of types of isolation.
4. In a well-adapted population, is a mutation more likely to be beneficial or deleterious? Why?
5. How does sexual reproduction increase genetic variation?
6. How does the hypothesis of punctuated equilibrium differ from the traditional view of evolution?

Darwinism Extended

Guidepost: How has the theory of evolution by natural selection been supported by modern research?

9.13 Origin of Higher Categories Occurs by Operation of the Same Principles that Create New Species

Darwin was concerned with the origin of species, but the origin of genera and larger groups of organisms also is important in studying life in the biosphere. Evidence shows that the origin of higher categories is governed by the same forces as those responsible for the origin of species.

A new genus may result from the appearance in a species of a particularly successful combination of characteristics. Populations with this successful combination may spread over a large area. Small groups within the population may become adapted to different habitats in the large area, leading eventually to the formation of several species. Each species may retain the successful combination of characteristics originally in the group.

In addition, new mutations and recombinations will continue to take place. The origin of genera and higher categories makes use of the requirements for new species. Those requirements are combined with (1) the multiplication of populations that have a particular combination of genetic characteristics and (2) the extinction of intermediate populations. Thus, diversity of species and formation of higher categories can be accounted for by similar biological processes. That process is clearly shown in the *Drosophila* in figure 9.29.

Figure 9.29 *Drosophila* mutants. Compare the 8-legged fly (a) with the normal 6-legged one (b), and the 4-winged (c) with the normal 2-winged (d). The extra appendages of the mutants are not functional, and the mutants probably would not survive in nature. Nonetheless, these mutant flies clearly show that the characteristics of organisms are all subject to genetic variation.

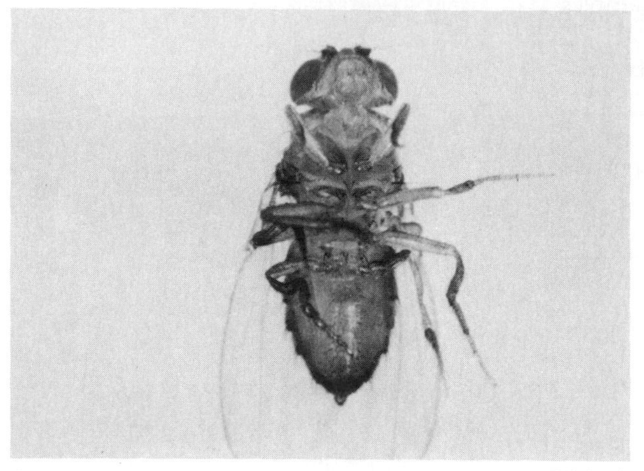

a E. B. Lewis

b E. B. Lewis

c E. B. Lewis

d E. B. Lewis

9.14 Research in Biology and Geology Have Added Support to the Theory of Evolution since Darwin's Time

Darwin's process of natural selection explained how variations are selected in nature. This mechanism became the basic part of the theory of evolution by natural selection. Darwin used the data available to him in the mid-19th century, and his contribution is all the more impressive when one considers that he knew almost nothing of the mechanisms of heredity. Every major biological discovery since Darwin's time has strengthened the theory of evolution. None has called it seriously into question. That is almost unique among scientific theories. Mendel's work explained the inheritance of variation and was as supportive in its way as was natural selection.

Figure 9.30 Phylogenetic trees based on (a) morphology and (b) biochemistry. Note how similar the trees appear. Morphologic trees are based on similarities or differences in physical appearance. In this tree, the short distance between the branches leading to humans and chimps indicates that they are morphologically similar. The great distance between the branches leading to humans and kangaroos indicates they are not very similar. Biochemical trees represent the degree of relatedness of organisms based on analysis of biochemical data such as amino acid sequences in proteins or base sequences in DNA.

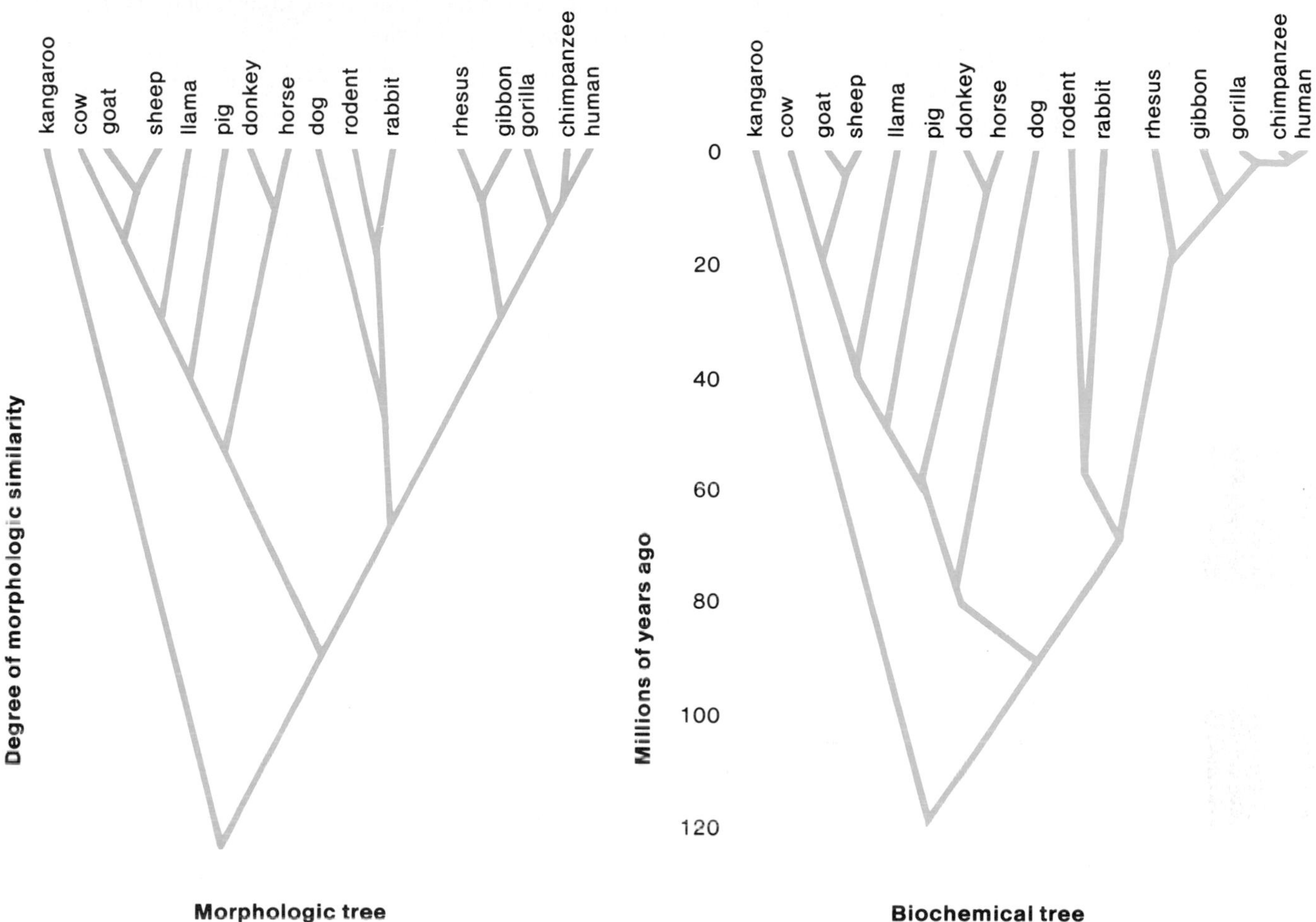

Fitch, W. and Langley, C. *Protein Evolution and the Molecular Clock*, Federation Proceedings Volume 35, pp. 2091–2097 (1976).

Geologic discoveries have continued to strengthen evolutionary theory. The ability to date the age of the earth has improved through the use of techniques such as radiometric dating. Those techniques show that the long periods of time required for Darwinian evolution actually existed. Molecular biology, a field not even anticipated by Darwin, has provided evidence that is generally consistent with evidence based on structure. Using biochemical and structural data, biologists can construct **phylogenetic** (fy loh jeh NET ik) trees—diagrams that show the evolutionary relationships among major groups of organisms. The remarkable similarity of two such trees (figure 9.30), based on entirely different data sources, confirms a pattern of organismic relationships.

The history of science is strewn with discarded theories made obsolete or impractical by new discoveries. The theory of evolution, in contrast, has been strengthened and confirmed by many discoveries since the publication of *On the Origin of Species by Means of Natural Selection* in 1859. Although biologists may not agree completely on the mechanisms of evolution, an overwhelming majority agree that diversity of type and unity of pattern are best explained by the theory of evolution. Evolutionary theory pervades all aspects of biology and provides a cornerstone for understanding the discipline, much in the same fashion as the atomic theory does for chemistry and physics.

Self-Review

1. What types of modern evidence support the theory of evolution?
2. How do the factors that govern the origin of species compare with those that govern the origin of higher categories?
3. Compare a phylogenetic tree constructed on the basis of gross structure (seen by the naked eye) with one based on biochemical evidence. What does this tell you about relationships of organisms?

Summary

Attempts to account for the diversity of living things as well as their similarities led to the statement of the theory of evolution. Since the time of the ancient Greeks, and perhaps even before, attempts had been made to explain differences and similarities among organisms.

It was obvious that there was variation in organisms, even of the same species. It was further obvious that such variations were inherited. It could be shown that organisms underwent change through time. Despite their differences, organisms could be grouped according to similarities among group members. Thus, both change and relationships were evident.

Until the time of Charles Darwin, there was no satisfactory explanation of a mechanism for change and relationship. With the publication of *On the Origin of Species by Means of Natural Selection,* Darwin provided a mechanism for evolution—natural selection. Rapid advances in evolutionary biology followed. Gregor Mendel showed how traits were passed from generation to generation. The discovery of mutations provided an explanation of how genes could change and introduce variability into living systems. Observation demonstrated the capacity for change of living cells and tissues.

Events in the natural world are not random, but follow definite patterns of change. Populations are the units of evolution. They are affected by mutation, migration, recombination, selection and genetic drift. When populations are isolated, changes can accumulate that separate them further from one another. When reproductive barriers develop, such isolated populations may form new species.

Today evolution forms a central unifying theme for biology. Without it, the data of biology have no organizing principle and become only isolated and unrelated facts.

Application Questions

1. Trace the concept of evolution from the Greeks to modern times. How does our present view differ from that of Darwin?
2. How do you explain that the variability in a domesticated species is greater than that in the same species, or a similar one, in the wild? (For example, dogs v. wolves; chickens v. red jungle fowl; pigeons v. rock doves.)
3. *Polydactylyism* (more than the normal number of fingers and toes) is caused by several different genes. One type of polydactyly is dominant, yet the phenotype is rare in humans. Type O blood results from a recessive gene. Yet in some populations of North American Indians, as many as 97 percent of the individuals may have Type O blood. Explain these two situations.
4. In many species of birds, populations living at higher latitudes lay more eggs per clutch than do those living at lower latitudes. Would you expect the former gradually to replace the latter? Why or why not?
5. What effects may modern medicine have on the future of the evolution of humans? The facts needed for investigating this problem are found in biological science, but the interpretation of the facts lies outside the realm of verifiable conclusions. It is necessary, therefore, to distinguish carefully between the facts and your interpretation of them.
6. In Cambrian rocks, fossilized brachiopods have been found that are indistinguishable from the modern *Lingula* (page 761). Modern cockroaches are very similar to those of the Carboniferous period. Turtles of the genus *Caretta* occur in the modern seas and as fossils in Cretaceous rocks. Yet, during these same long years, other organisms have changed greatly. How can you explain such great differences in the rate of evolution among species?

Problems

1. Suppose no data had existed to support the theory of evolution until the 20th century. Using only data compiled since 1900, how would scientists develop the theory of evolution today? In what ways would it resemble Darwin's presentation? How would it differ from Darwin's presentation?
2. Suppose species of organisms were not related to each other and did not change through time. How would our view of biology then change? Would it be harder or easier to study?
3. Using an imaginary population of organisms, detail how it could evolve into two distinct species. Describe the environment of the population and the factors that led to its separation into two species.

Suggested Readings

C. J. Bajema, "Charles Darwin and Selection as a Cause of Adaptive Evolution 1837–1859" *The American Biology Teacher* (April 1985). Interesting article dealing with the processes of scientific discovery and the justification of scientific theories, using Darwin as a model.

S. J. Gould, "Free to Be Extinct" *Natural History* (September 1982). Informal discussion of the causes for extinction of species.

R. L. Hay and M. D. Leakey, "The Fossil Footprints of Laetoli" *Scientific American* (February 1982). A discussion of the Laetoli fossil sites in Tanzania.

R. A. Kerr, "Periodic Extinctions and Impacts Challenged" *Science* (22 March 1985). The author refutes the theory that meteors or comets have been responsible for periodic and large-scale extinctions.

R. Lewin, "Punctuated Equilibrium Is Now Old Hat" *Science* (14 February 1986). Mathematical models are used to support traditional explanations for the rapid changes seen in the fossil record.

T. A. McMahon and J. T. Bonner, 1983, *On Size and Life* (New York: Scientific American Books). Investigates why living things are the size and shape they are.

B. Rensberger, "Bones of Our Ancestors" *Science 84* (April 1984). Illustrated with many fine photographs, this article discusses the rare and extremely important early hominid fossils that are protected in museums throughout the world.

P. Shipman, "Baffling Limb on the Family Tree" *Discover* (September 1986). Discusses characteristics and implications of a recent, very important discovery of an early human fossil skull.

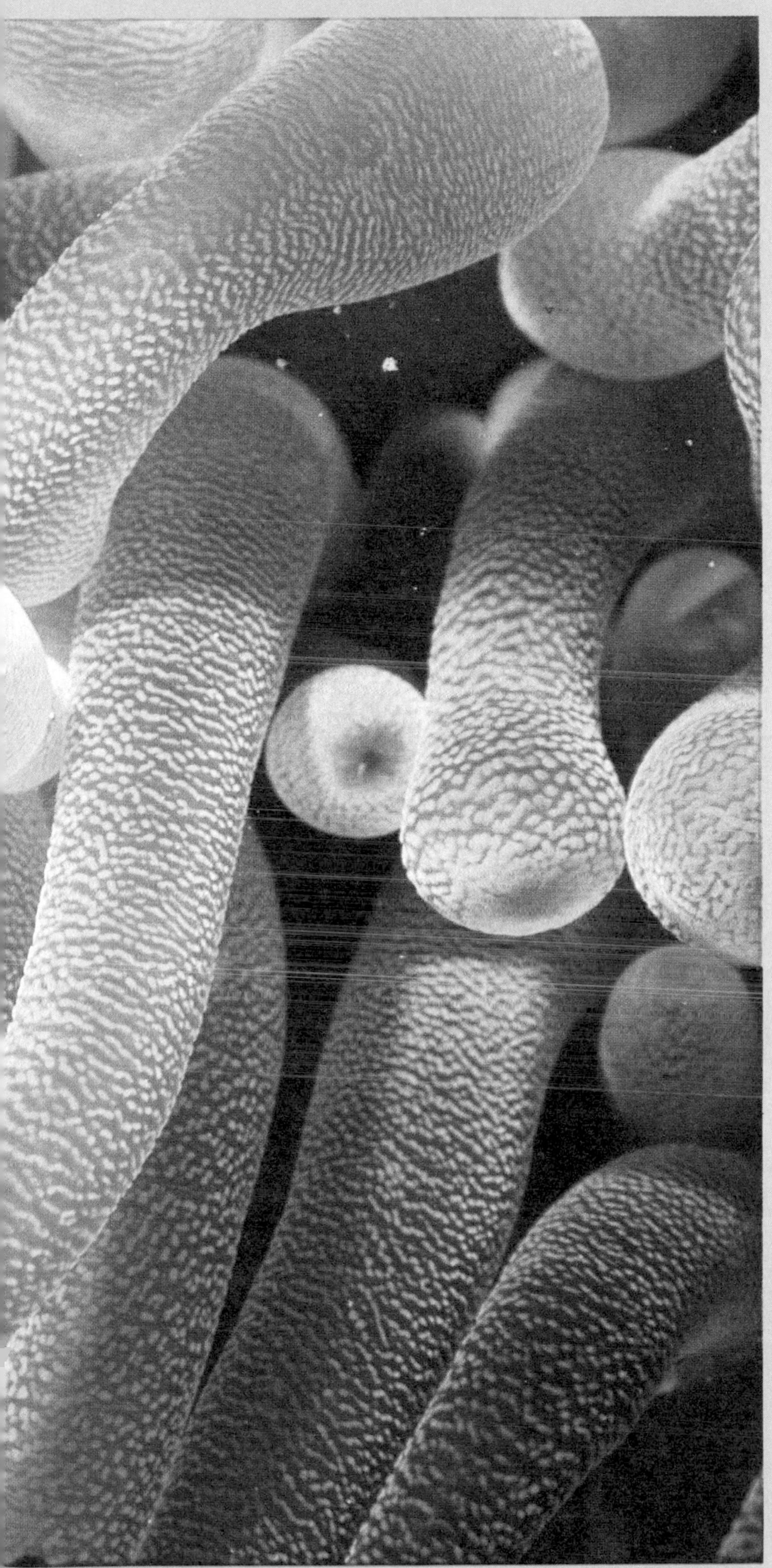

CARIBBEAN COLLECTION/Nancy Sefton

Section Three

Diversity and Adaptation in the Biosphere

Wherever we go to observe living creatures we come away with an impression of incredible diversity. Biologists have described nearly 3 million types of organisms and more are discovered every year. Why are there so many different living things? What adaptations have enabled all these organisms to survive?

These questions provide the framework for Section Three. We cannot describe every type of organism, but we can examine representative forms and see how each is adapted to its environment. We also can learn how biologists name organisms and how they keep track of all life forms and bring order to diversity.

Special adaptations enable the blennie to find shelter in the tentacles of the sea anemone without being stung.

Doug Sokell

A diversity of wildflowers. How many kinds can you count? How would you keep track of them?

CHAPTER 10

Ordering Life in the Biosphere

Introduction

How many different kinds of organisms can you recognize? Tens? Hundreds? A thousand? Biologists have identified more than 3 million different types of organisms, which they call species. Some estimate that we share this planet with as many as 10 million species. And that number does not include organisms that have become extinct. How do biologists keep track of such an overwhelming number of living things? How did all those living things originate? In this chapter we will learn something about how biologists classify organisms. We also will examine current ideas about the origins of this great diversity of life.

Biological Classification

Guidepost: What are the objectives of the modern biological classification system, and on what characteristics is it based?

10.1 Classification Is a Way of Creating Order from Diversity

The diversity of the living world is awesome. It exists at every level of organization, in the many molecules and structures that make up the great variety of living organisms. It extends back in time beyond the fossil record to the earliest forms of life. There is diversity in every aspect of life—in size, from the smallest microorganism to the largest whale; in habitat, from the deepest ocean bottom to the top of the highest mountain; and in life-style, from a parasite to a rooted tree to a free-flying bird.

From earliest times, humans have searched for order in the diversity of nature. They have tried to find ways to group the many kinds of living things that would reflect relationships and help distinguish one from another. From those efforts has grown the science of classifying organisms, or **taxonomy** (tak SAHN uh mee).

Figure 10.1 Appearance may be unreliable as a guide to grouping individuals in species. Above: These dissimilar birds are both indigo buntings. Below: These dissimilar birds are both red-winged blackbirds. Right: These similar birds are from populations that do not interbreed.

10.2 Biological Classification Begins with Species

The basic grouping used in biological classification is the species. Organisms may look very different from each other and still be recognized as the same species. If we look at all dogs, we can easily see that there are many intermediate mongrels between such different breeds as Great Danes and greyhounds. That is so because breeds of dogs can interbreed. That means they can mate with each other and produce offspring that differ in various ways from both parents. Those offspring also can mate, and they may produce offspring even more different. Extremely different dogs, such as the Great Dane and Pekingese, have difficulty interbreeding because of physical differences. They nevertheless are part of one related series, because they can mate with intermediate breeds. All dogs, therefore, are grouped into a single species. On the other hand, two groups of individuals that may look alike are considered separate species if they do not interbreed and produce vigorous, **fertile** (FERT il) offspring. Fertile offspring are those that are capable of reproducing.

The distinctness of a species is maintained in several ways, as we have seen in section 9.11. First, one species may be physically unable to mate with another. Clearly, an elephant and a crab cannot mate and produce offspring. Second, offspring may be formed but die when young. If the

Figure 10.2 Five breeds of dogs. Beginning with the Great Dane, breeds are represented by every other dog. Mongrel offspring are intermediate between the breeds.

Figure 10.3 When a horse (top) and donkey (bottom) are mated, the offspring is a mule (middle) which is sterile and cannot reproduce.

eggs of a bullfrog are fertilized by a leopard frog, they develop for a short time, then die. Third, mating may occur and produce offspring that are **sterile** (STEHR il), that is, unable to reproduce. Mules, which result when horses and donkeys are mated, are almost always sterile.

Finally, individuals from two different species may be able to form fertile offspring in captivity but seldom do so otherwise. In such cases, distinctness of the species is maintained not by lack of ability to interbreed but by geographic isolation. Alaska brown bears and polar bears in a zoo have mated and produced vigorous, fertile offspring. In the wild no such cross has ever been discovered. Because brown bears live in forests and polar bears live on snowfields and ice floes, they rarely, if ever, see each other in nature.

Although we characterize species as reproductively isolated groups, we must take account of occasional exceptions. Plant species, for example, often form fertile hybrids with other species, as shown with the Indian paintbrush in figure 10.5. Bacteria employ unusual means of genetic exchange. Plants utilize various forms of vegetative reproduction. One-celled organisms reproduce by cell division, forming clones of identical cells. Nevertheless, we still can recognize species among those organisms.

Figure 10.4 Polar bear (top) and Alaska brown bear (bottom).

10.3 Classification Is Based on Homologies

Specialists in taxonomy use a variety of characteristics to classify organisms. Those include structure, function, biochemistry, behavior, nutrition, embryonic development, genetic systems, evolutionary histories, and ecological interactions. The more constant a characteristic is, the more valuable it is in determining classification. For example, structures such as skeletal form, internal anatomy, and reproductive parts of flowers are less variable characteristics than size or color. Structure, therefore, generally provides a consistent and useful basis for classifying organisms.

Similarities of structure that indicate *related ancestry* are especially important in classification. Such relationships are called structural **homologies** (hoh MOL uh jeez). For example, the flipper of a whale, the wing of a bat, and the arm of a human have many homologies in their bone and muscle structure, as you can see in figure 10.7. Similarly, fish, amphibians, reptiles, and birds share that same limb pattern with mammals. The limbs have the same relationship to the body, and they develop in the same way in the young.

Biochemical homologies have become increasingly important in determining relationships. They include similarities in body substances, such as blood, and in molecules, such as proteins and DNA and RNA. Comparisons of DNA or RNA sequences have led to important changes in our understanding of relatedness. The greater the similarities in DNA sequences, the more closely related two organisms are thought to be. You will be able to use DNA sequences to determine relatedness in investigation 10.1. Sometimes studies of DNA sequences give results that differ somewhat from more traditional studies of structural characteristics. For example, DNA studies have indicated that chimpanzees are more closely related to humans than are gorillas. Studies of structural homologies did not reveal that information.

Figure 10.6 A taxonomist at work.

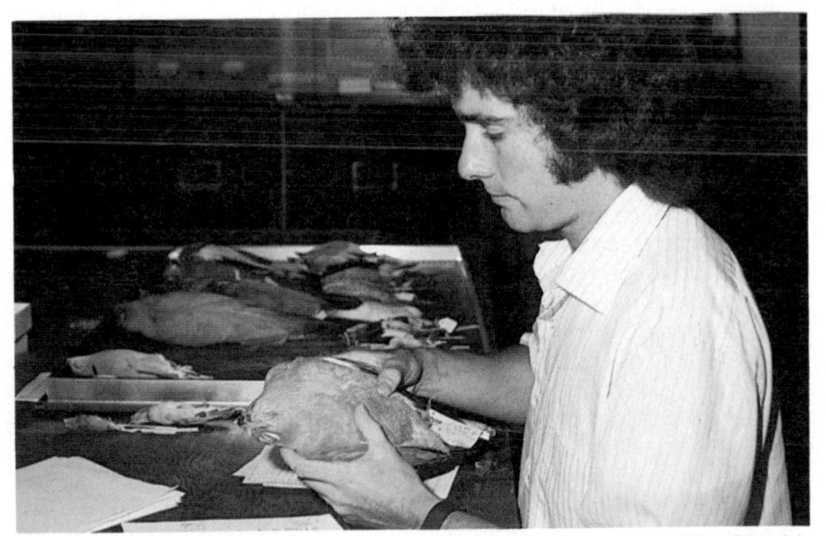

BSCS by Oliver Ash

Figure 10.5 Indian paintbrush: (a) *Castilleja rhexifolia* and (b) *C. sulphurea,* two different species, can form a fertile hybrid (c).

W. D. Bransford and the National Wildflower Research Center

W. D. Bransford and the National Wildflower Research Center

W. D. Bransford and the National Wildflower Research Center

Figure 10.7 Bones of the forelimbs of seven vertebrates. Follow the color key to similarities; they indicate to biologists that these animals once had a common ancestor. Also check the structure of each forelimb for its adaptations to the animal's way of life.

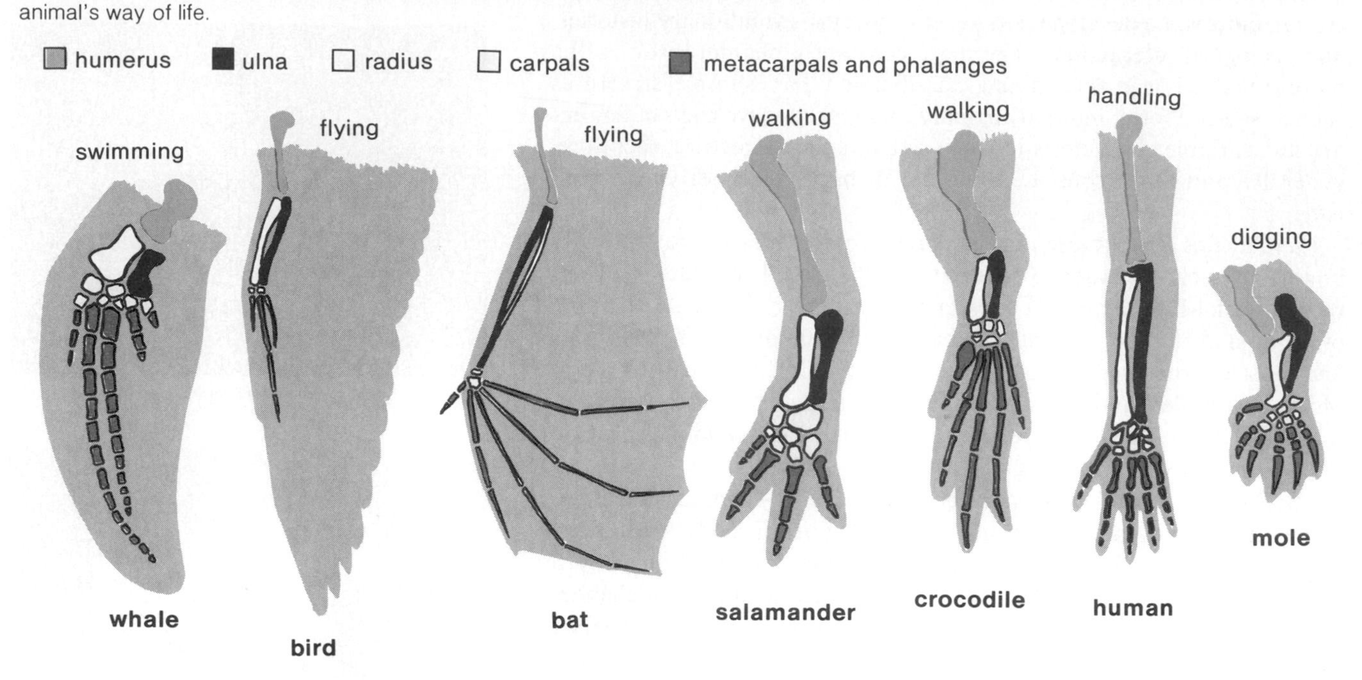

Two factors, however, still make structural characteristics particularly important. The first is that a taxonomist can observe structural characteristics in preserved specimens or geological records, and those observations can be verified easily. The second is that structural evidence is all we are ever likely to have for organisms known to us only from fossils. We can make some good guesses about the behavior of such organisms, but our guesses are based on structure. Organisms of the past may be the ancestors of living organisms. Thus, knowledge of past organisms can help us figure out the relationships of living ones.

Investigation 10.1 DNA SEQUENCES AND CLASSIFICATION

Introduction

Biological classification is the process by which organisms are assigned to specific groups. The group may be as large and encompassing as a kingdom, such as animalia, or as small and limiting as a species, such as *Homo sapiens,* the species to which humans are assigned.

Classification is not merely a method of assigning organisms to groups so that biologists can keep track of them. The groups to which organisms are assigned also imply the degree of relatedness between those organisms. Organisms that share smaller groups of classification are more closely related than are organisms that share only large groups.

Until the mid 1970s, classification was based largely on the comparison of observable structures in a given organism. For example, taxonomists might compare the structure of forelimbs in mammals. In recent years, they also have been able to compare the structure of certain proteins.

Modern research techniques now allow biologists to compare the DNA that codes for certain proteins. The comparison of the DNA sequences then is used to make predictions about the relatedness of the organisms from which the DNA was taken. This investigation shows you a model of that technology. It might be helpful for you to review the relationship between DNA and proteins (chapter 8).

Materials (per team)

plastic paper clips
- 50 black
- 50 white
- 50 green
- 50 red

Part A—Comparing DNA Strands

Procedure

1. Consult table 10.1 below.
   (a) Which organisms share the most groupings?
   (b) On the basis of the data in the table, which organisms are least closely related?

Table 10.1 Examples of classification of animals

	Human	Gorilla	Southern Leopard Frog	Katydid
Phylum	Chordata	Chordata	Chordata	Arthropoda
Subphylum	Vertebrata	Vertebrata	Vertebrata	
Class	Mammalia	Mammalia	Amphibia	Insecta
Subclass	Eutheria	Eutheria		
Order	Primates	Primates	Salientia	Orthoptera
Suborder	Anthropoidea	Anthropoidea		
Family	Hominidae	Pongidae	Ranidae	Tettigoniidae
Subfamily			Ranidae	
Genus	*Homo*	*Gorilla*	*Rana*	*Scudderia*
Species	*Homo sapiens*	*Gorilla gorilla*	*Rana pipiens*	*Scudderia furcata*
Subspecies			*Rana pipiens sphenocephala*	*Scudderia furcata furcata*

From C. P. Hickman, L. S. Roberts, and F. M Hickman, 1984, *Integrated Principles of Zoology,* 7th ed. (St. Louis: Times Mirror/Mosby College Publishing), 148.

2. Working in teams of 4, synthesize the DNA strands indicated below. Allow the paper clips to represent the 4 bases of DNA according to the following key:
   black = adenine (A)
   white = thymine (T)
   green = guanine (G)
   red = cytosine (C)
   Synthesize DNA strands by hooking together paper clips of the appropriate colors. Stretch the string of paper clips out on the lab table with position 1 on the left. Tape a small piece of paper next to the strand and label it as indicated. Each strand will represent a small section (20 bases) of a gene that codes for the protein hemoglobin.

3. Team member 1: Synthesize the following piece of DNA by hooking together paper clips in this sequence.

   pos. 1 pos. 20

   A–G–G–C–A–T–A–A–A–C–C–A–A–C–C–G–A–T–T–A

   Label the strand human DNA. This will represent a small section (20 bases) of the gene that codes for the protein hemoglobin in humans.
4. Team member 2: Synthesize the following strand.

   pos. 1 pos. 20

   T–C–C–G–G–G–G–A–A–G–G–T–T–G–G–C–T–A–A–T

   Label this strand chimpanzee cDNA. cDNA stands for complementary DNA. cDNA is a single strand of DNA that will match up with its partner strand. Remember, the bases in DNA are complementary. That is, adenine (A) will always pair with thymine (T), and cytosine (C) will always pair with guanine (G). This cDNA was made from the gene that codes for chimpanzee hemoglobin.
5. Team member 3: Synthesize the following piece of cDNA.

   pos. 1 pos. 20

   T–C–C–G–G–G–G–A–A–G–G–T–T–G–G–T–C–C–G–G

   Label this strand gorilla cDNA. This cDNA strand was made from the gene that codes for gorilla hemoglobin.
6. Team member 4: Synthesize the following piece of DNA.

   pos. 1 pos. 20

   A–G–G–C–C–G–G–C–T–C–C–A–A–C–C–A–G–G–C–C

   Label this strand hypothetical common ancestor DNA. This strand will be used in the second part of the investigation.
7. Compare the sequences of the human DNA and the chimpanzee cDNA. Match the human DNA and the chimpanzee cDNA base by base (paper clip by paper clip). Remember, black (adenine) must always pair with white (thymine), and green (guanine) must always pair with red (cytosine). If the bases are complementary (that is, if the colors match correctly), allow the clips to remain touching, as shown in figure 10.8. If the bases are not complementary, separate the clips slightly to form a loop, as shown in the figure. Count the number of loops. Also count the total number of bases that do not match. Record the data in the appropriate columns in table 10.2 below.

Table 10.2 Hybridization data

Human DNA Hybridized to:	Chimpanzee cDNA	Gorilla cDNA
Number of loops		
Number of differences		

Figure 10.8

BSCS by Doug Sokell

8. Repeat procedure 7, using the gorilla cDNA and the human DNA. Enter the data in the appropriate columns in table 10.2

Discussion

1. Based on the data you have collected for this one protein, is the gorilla gene or the chimpanzee gene more similar to the human gene?
2. Does the gorilla or the chimpanzee seem more closely related to humans? Do the data you have collected for this one protein prove your answer?

Part B—An Evolutionary Puzzle

Procedure

Scientists have determined that mutations in DNA occur at a regular rate. They can use this rate to make some predictions about how long ago in evolutionary history two organisms began to separate from a common ancestor. In this part of the investigation, you will use your paper-clip model to provide data in support of 1 of 2 hypotheses about a common ancestor for humans, chimpanzees, and gorillas.

1. Read the following information about a current debate among scientists who study human evolution:

   Most scientists agree that humans, gorillas, and chimpanzees shared a common ancestor at one time in evolutionary history. However, one group thinks the fossil record shows that gorillas, chimpanzees, and humans split from one common ancestor at the same time. Their model for this split is shown directly below.

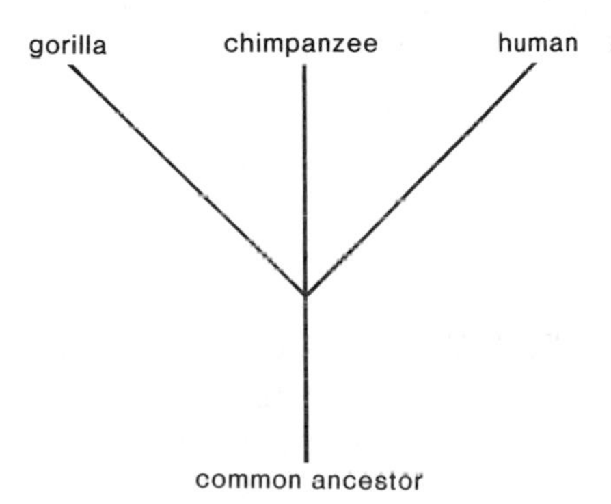

   A 2nd group thinks the fossil record shows that there were 2 splits. In the 1st split, gorillas split from the common ancestor. Humans and chimpanzees then shared another common ancestor for perhaps 2 million years. They then split again and evolved into their present states. The model for this pattern of splitting is shown directly below.

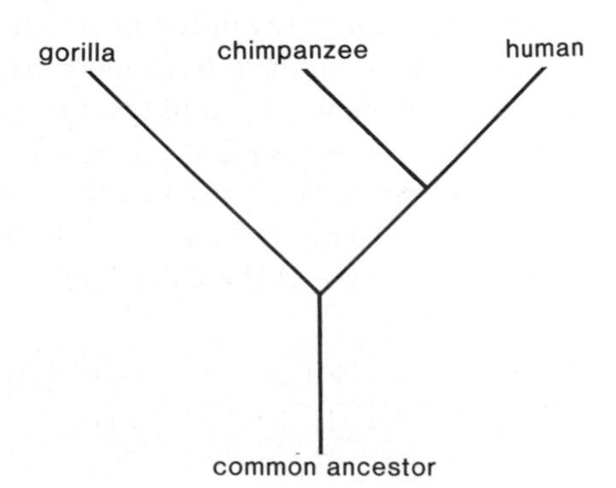

2. Use your DNA model and the DNA sequences from part A to investigate this debate. First, you must use your human DNA as a guide to synthesize a human cDNA. Do that as a team. Make certain that the human cDNA is complementary to the human DNA strand.
3. The hypothetical common ancestor DNA you synthesized in part A is DNA for hemoglobin extracted from a hypothetical common ancestor. Now, match all 3 samples of cDNA (gorilla, human, and chimpanzee) with the common ancestor DNA, 1 sample at a time. Again, allow the paper clips to touch where the bases match correctly. Form loops where the bases do not match. Record your data in table 10.3.

Table 10.3 Hybridization data: Common ancestor

Common Ancestor DNA to:	Human cDNA	Chimpanzee cDNA	Gorilla cDNA
Number of loops			
Number of differences			

Discussion

1. Which cDNA is most similar to the common ancestor DNA?
2. Which cDNAs are most similar to each other in their patterns of matching and looping when matched to the common ancestor DNA?
3. Which model in the evolutionary debate described above does your data support?
4. Do your findings prove that this model is the correct one?

10.4 Species Are Grouped into Larger and More General Categories

Based on homologies, organisms of different species are grouped into larger, more general categories. For example, dogs, coyotes, and wolves are separate species, but they are similar in many ways. Species with many similar characteristics are grouped into the same **genus** (JEE nus). The genus for dogs and doglike animals is *Canis*.

[KAY nus]

Similar genera (plural of genus) are grouped together in a **family.** Taxonomists place *Vulpes,* the foxes, with *Canis* in the family Canidae. In some ways weasels resemble dogs and wolves, but they are less like them than are foxes. Taxonomists express this difference by placing weasels in a separate family, Mustelidae. Bears, which also are furry predators, are structurally different from weasels or foxes in several ways. So, taxonomists place them in still another family, Ursidae. Those three families (Canidae, Mustelidae, Ursidae) are grouped with other similar families into the **order** Carnivora.

[VUL peez]

[KAN un dee]

[muh STEL uh dee]

[UR suh dee]

[kar NIV uh rah]

Wolves, weasels, and bears have many differences, but they still share many likenesses. Certainly those animals have more likenesses among themselves than they have with monkeys. Monkeys, therefore, are placed in a different order, Primates. But monkeys—and rats, cows, horses, and many other organisms—do share some characteristics with wolves, weasels, and bears. Those similarities are the basis for putting them all together in the next larger grouping—at the **class** level—Mammalia.

[muh MAY lee uh]

Figure 10.9 Some animals in the order Carnivora. Which two look most alike?

Continuing with that method of grouping, taxonomists place the classes containing birds, frogs, fish, and snakes with the Mammalia into the **phylum** (FY lum) Chordata. (Botanists group classes of plants into **divisions** instead of phyla.) And finally, chordates, snails, butterflies, and thousands of other organisms are grouped into the **kingdom** Animalia. That kingdom contains all the living things we think of as animals.

As we go from species to kingdom, the organisms that are grouped together share fewer characteristics at each succeeding level. At the species level the individuals are so much alike they can interbreed. At the kingdom level many fewer characteristics are shared among all the individuals.

We can say that all dogs are of one species. Dogs and wolves do not ordinarily interbreed, but it is not impossible. The two species had a common ancestor not so long ago in evolutionary history. That is why taxonomists put them together in one genus, as figure 10.10 shows. By placing foxes in a separate genus, taxonomists indicate that foxes are less closely related to dogs and wolves than these two are to each other.

Figure 10.10 Classification of several animals.

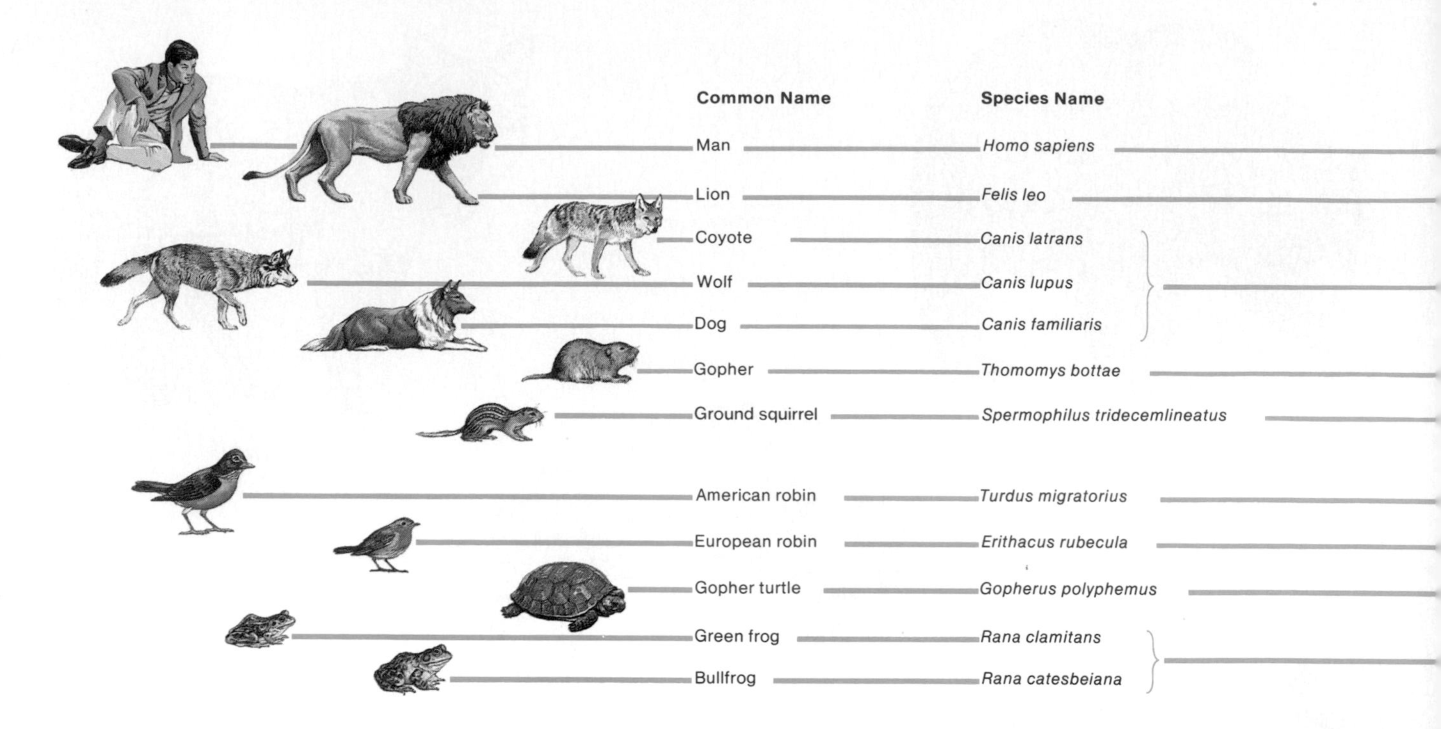

All this is somewhat similar to saying that you are closely related to your sister, but you are less closely related to your first cousin. By placing the dog family, the bear family, and the weasel family together in the same order, taxonomists imply that all of those animals descended from a common ancestral group—but probably long ago. As we continue up the list of levels, the relationships become more distant. Thus, when taxonomists place a dog and a goldfish in the same phylum but in different classes, they imply a very distant relationship indeed.

It is important to recognize that *a taxonomic classification is not a fact.* It results from the interpretation of facts. It shows what the facts mean to the person developing the system of classification. That cats and eagles and alligators have claws is a verifiable fact. But whether those three kinds of organisms should be grouped together is a matter of opinion. There is no total agreement among biologists about the place

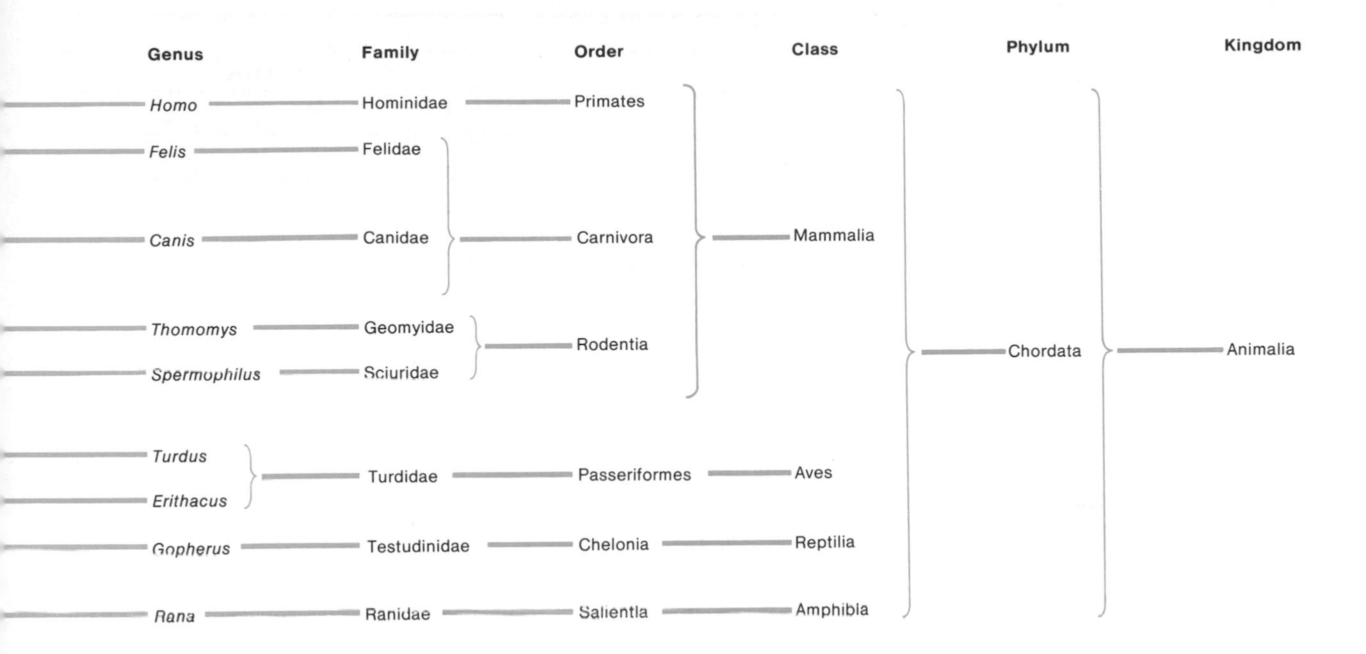

at which organisms fit into the classification scheme. That is true even though all taxonomists base their classifications on a system of levels.

The more evidence taxonomists obtain, the more complex the relationships of organisms appear to be. Taxonomists also differ in how they interpret the evidence. As a result, there are many schemes of classification, all designed within the same framework of levels.

Investigation 10.2 LEVELS OF CLASSIFICATION

Introduction

You will investigate some of the structural characteristics that taxonomists use in separating animal groups at different classification levels. Because you will be using the observations of other persons (recorded as drawings), your conclusions can be no more valid than those drawings.

Procedure

1. Prepare 4 forms like the one below.

Table

Characteristics	Animals		
	1.	2.	3.
a.			
b.			
c.			
d.			
e.			
Classification level ______			

2. Label the 1st form Table 1. In the spaces under the word animals, write human, chimpanzee, and gorilla. In the spaces under the word characteristics, copy the italicized key words in each of the following questions. These words should remind you of the full questions when you review the table.
   (a) How does the *length of the arms* of the animal compare with the length of its legs?
   (b) Are the *canine teeth large or* are they *small* as compared with other teeth of the same organisms?
   (c) How many *incisor teeth* are present in the upper jaw?
   (d) Is the *brain* case of the skull *large or* is it *small* as compared with the brain cases of the other organisms in the table?
   (e) Is there an *opposable first toe on the foot?* (An opposable toe is one that can be pressed against all the others, just as your thumb can press against your other fingers.)
3. Study figure 10.11. For each of the animals, fill in all the spaces in table 1 with your answers. Then, write the word family in the space following "Classification level." Refer to appendix 3 to find the family into which each of these organisms has been placed. Write this information in the spaces at the bottom of the table.
4. Label the 2nd form Table 2. Under the word animals, write human, dog, and cat. Under the word characteristics, copy the italicized words in each of these questions:
   (a) How many paired *appendages* (arms and legs) does the animal have?
   (b) Are *nails or claws* present on the toes of the foot?
   (c) How does the size of the *canine teeth* compare with that of other teeth in the lower jaw?
   (d) How many *incisor teeth* are present in the lower jaw?
   (e) How does the size of the *collarbone* compare with that of the other organisms?

Figure 10.11

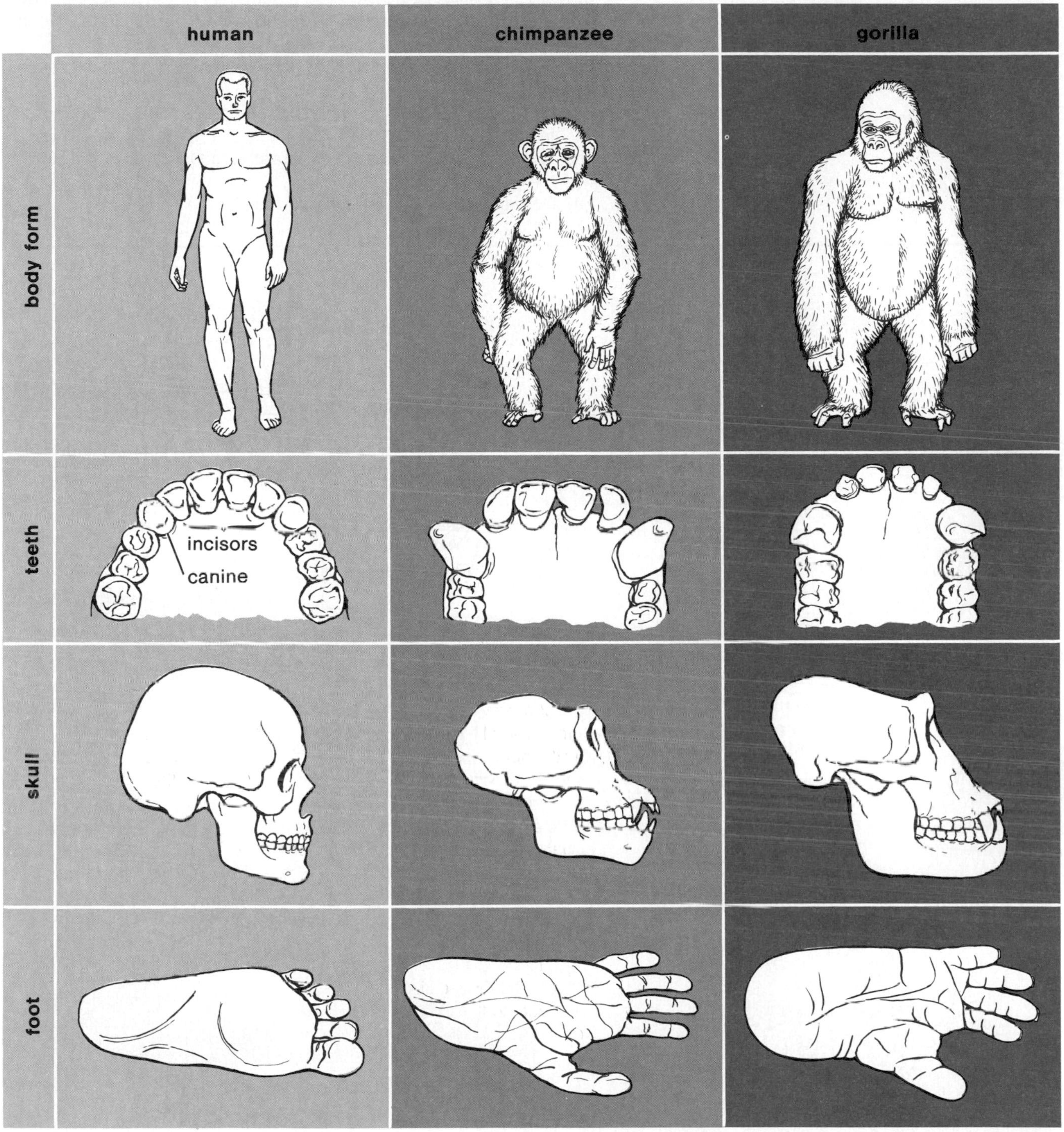

	human	chimpanzee	gorilla
body form			
teeth	incisors canine		
skull			
foot			

5. Study figure 10.12. For each animal, fill in the spaces in table 2 with your answers to the questions. Write the word order in the blank space following "Classification level." From pages 991–994, select the order into which each of these organisms has been placed. Enter this information in the table.
6. For table 3, use the information in figure 10.13 and the following questions:
   (a) What kind of *body covering* (hair, feathers, scales, or none) does the animal have?
   (b) How many paired *appendages* (arms and legs) does the animal have?
   (c) Do the ears *project from* the surface of *the head?*

Figure 10.12

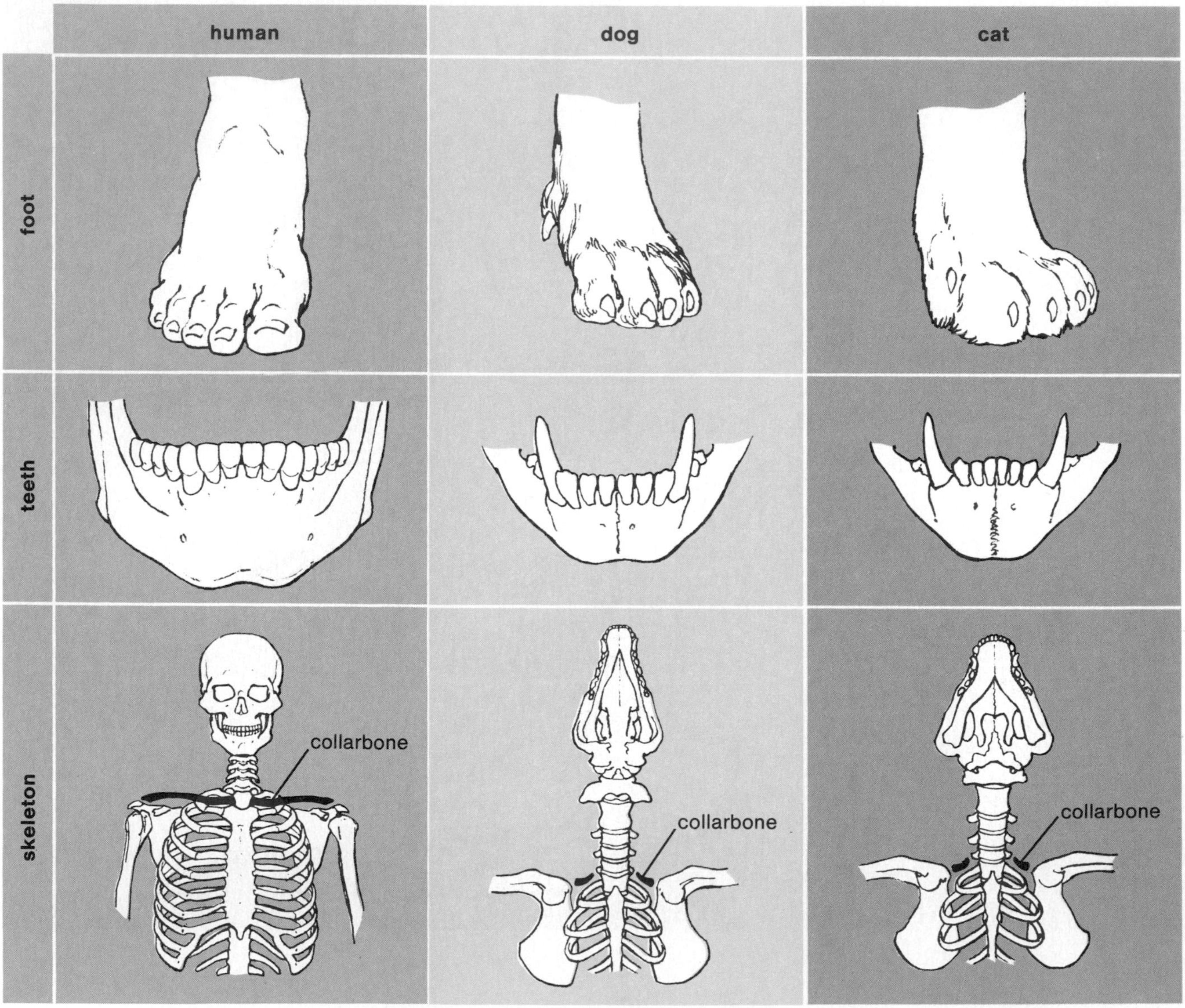

(d) Is the *body temperature* similar to the temperature of the environment, or is it quite different?
(e) How many *ventricles* are *in the heart?*

7. The classification level for this table is the word class. Determine the class for each organism in figure 10.13 and write it in the table.
8. For table 4, use the information in figure 10.14 and the following questions:
   (a) What kind of *skeleton* (internal or external) does the animal have?
   (b) Is the *position of* the *nerve cord* along the back or along the belly?
   (c) Compared with the rest of the nervous system, is the *brain* large or small?
   (d) Are paired *appendages* present or are they absent?
   (e) Are there *grooves behind* the *head region* of the very young organism?
9. Write the word phylum in the space following "Classification level," and add the name of the phylum into which each animal in figure 10.14 is placed.

Figure 10.13

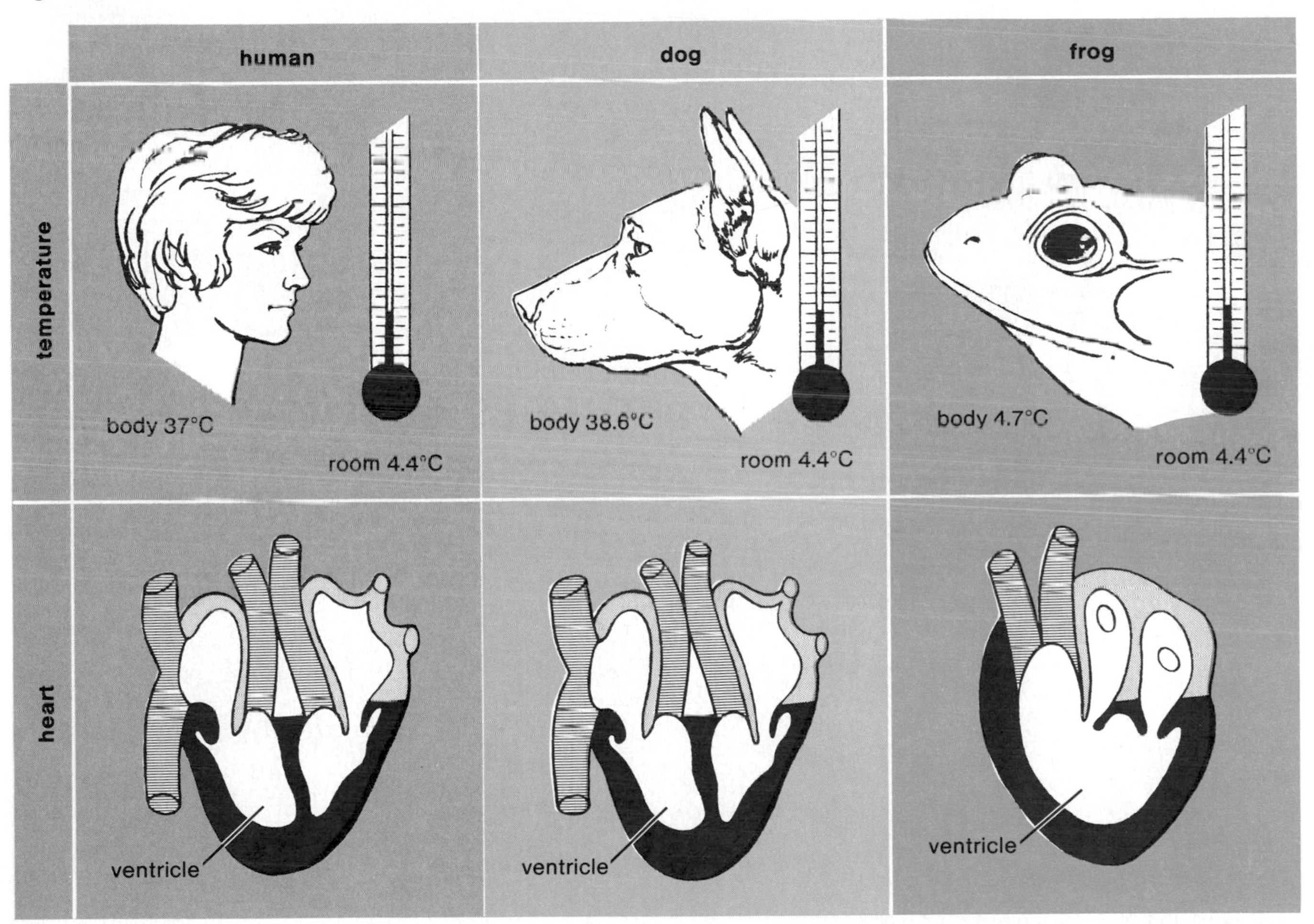

Figure 10.14

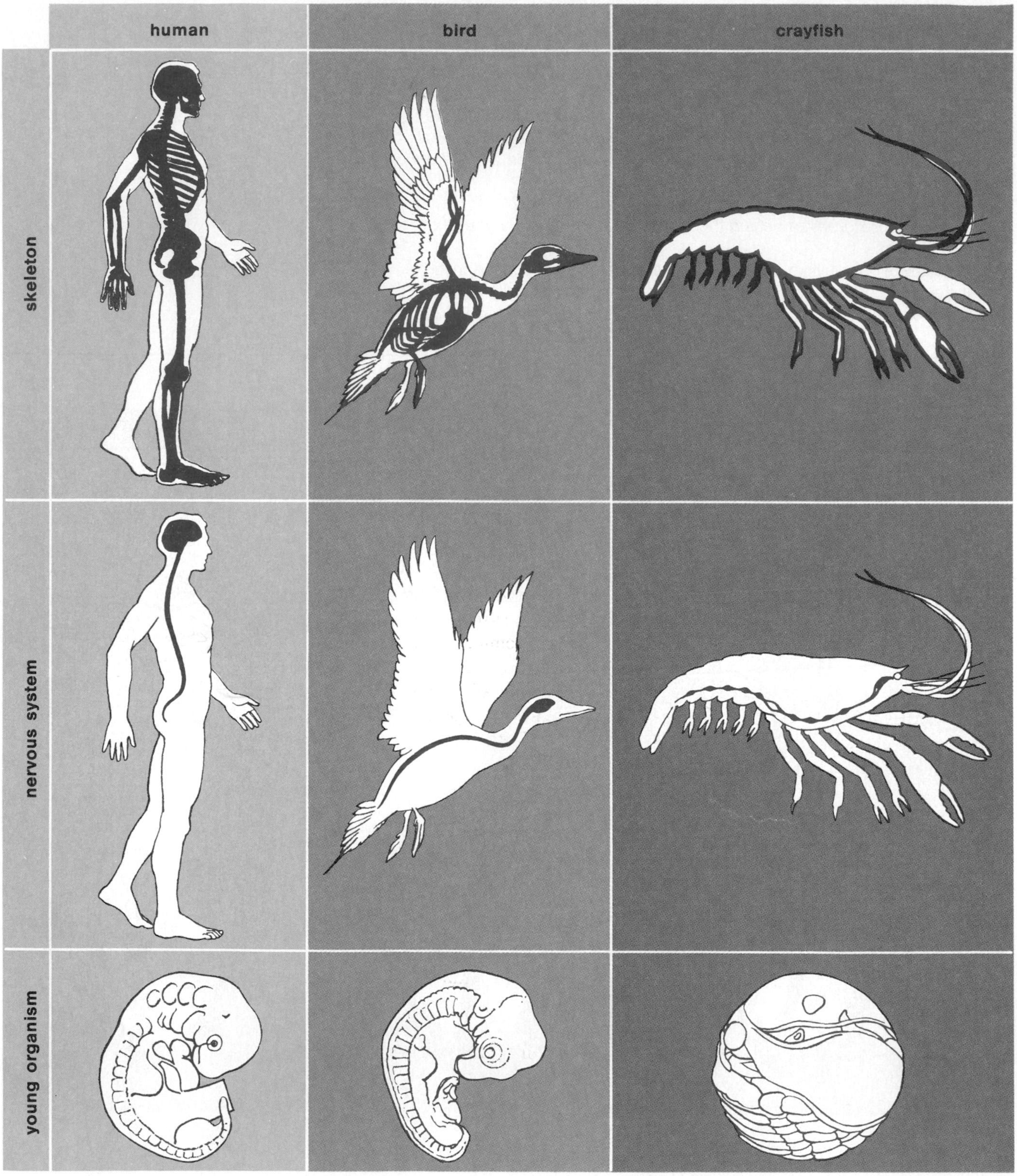

	human	bird	crayfish
skeleton			
nervous system			
young organism			

Discussion

1. There are more structural similarities between chimpanzees and gorillas than between chimpanzees and humans. How does the classification system you used express this fact? Focus on the levels in the classification system into which these organisms are placed together.
2. How does the classification system you used express the following?
   (a) There are more structural similarities between dogs and cats than between dogs and humans.
   (b) There are more structural similarities between humans and dogs than between humans and frogs.
   (c) There are more structural similarities between humans and birds than between humans and crayfish.
   (d) There are more structural similarities between humans and chimpanzees than between humans and dogs.
3. You are told that species A and B are classified in the same kingdom but different phyla. You are also told that species C and D are classified in the same phylum but different classes. What general statement can you make about similarities among species A, B, C, and D?

10.5 Biologists Use a Binomial System to Name Species

As long as there have been languages, humans have had names for the organisms that were important to them. Before the time of written history, probably the only plants named were those useful to humans as spices, medicines, and foods, or for religious purposes. Those so-called common names are still very useful. If you go into a lumberyard and ask for some *Sequoia sempervirens* fence posts, you are not likely to get what you want. A request for redwood posts works much better. Why, then, do biologists need any other names than the ones in common use?

Biological names are necessary for scientific exactness. For one thing, there is no other single, agreed on set of names available for all organisms. Further, different languages have different names for the same organisms—carrot (in English) is zanahoria in Spanish, and Mohrrube in German. Worse still, the *same* word may refer to different organisms: in Florida gopher refers to a turtle; in Kansas, to a rodent.

The first attempts to give names to *all* known organisms, and not just to those of special interest to farmers and hunters, were probably made by the Greeks. At that time Latin was the language used among most educated people—scholars, clergy, and physicians. Because they were the only ones interested in all organisms, they gave the plants and animals Latin names.

During the Middle Ages efforts were made to fit the names used by the Greeks to the plants and animals of the rest of Europe. That did not work, because the plants and animals of England, Germany, and other northern lands were often different from those of Greece. The differences had to be recognized. That was usually done by simply attaching a new adjective to the old name of a similar plant or animal.

Then came the age of exploration. Year after year, explorers sent back to European scientists strange new organisms—from Africa, South America, North America, the East Indies. The scientists kept adding words to names to indicate differences between the newly discovered organisms and those already known. By the 18th century that practice made names very long and difficult to use. The name used at that time for the carnation plant was *dianthus floribus solitariis, squamis calycinis subovatis brevissimis, corollis crenatis*. That means "the pink (a

Figure 10.15 A carnation.

[dy AN thus FLOR uh bus sol uh TAR ee is, SKWAH mis kal ih SIN us sub oh VAY tus breh VIS ih mis, kor OH lis kree NAYT is] general name for the carnation) with solitary flowers, the scales of the calyx somewhat egg-shaped and very short, the petals scalloped."

For many years both botanists and zoologists fumbled for an easier system of nomenclature. The solution to the problem came in 1753 from a young Swedish botanist named Carolus Linnaeus. He used a system of **binomial nomenclature** (by NOH mee ul NOH men klay chur), or two-word naming, to name each species. The first word in each name indicates a group of similar species. Linnaeus called that larger group a genus, which we described in section 10.4. Thus all species of pinks are in a group named *Dianthus*. (The first letter of a genus is always capitalized.) The second word in each name indicates a group of similar individuals. It is the trivial name, and is usually an adjective describing the species. For the common carnation Linnaeus picked the word *caryophyllus*. Neither the word indicating the genus nor the second word is, by itself, the species name. The species name consists of both words—*Dianthus caryophyllus*.

[dy AN thus]

[kar ee oh FIL us]

Linnaeus established two rules that have made his system succeed. The first is that *Dianthus* can never be used for any other genus—only for pinks. The second rule is that *caryophyllus* can never be used for any other *Dianthus* species. It might be used with some other genus but that does not create duplication, because the scientific name of a species always has two words. Thus the carnation plant is *Dianthus caryophyllus*. As long as Linnaeus's rules are followed, no other species can have this name.

Linnaeus was not the first botanist to use a binomial system, but he is largely responsible for the present system of biological nomenclature. That system has been used for more than 200 years to name hundreds of thousands of organisms. Though there have been many refinements, Linnaeus's two basic rules remain unchanged.

Biological names are not a part of the Latin language. They are Latin because Linnaeus and other early scientists wrote in Latin, and because Latin is a suitably precise language. Although Latin and Greek word roots are used frequently, the words may be from any language or may be entirely manufactured. *Tsuga* (the hemlocks) comes from Japanese. *Washingtonia* (a genus of palms) is obviously not Latin. All such names are given Latin endings, however. Furthermore, the names always look the same. Thus, in a Russian or Chinese biology book, biological names are printed in the same form as they appear in this book, though the rest of the printing is different.

Although biological names may seem strange, they are not always long or difficult to pronounce (*Rosa*, roses; *Poa*, bluegrasses). Many words for genera have been absorbed into the English language. As common names, they are correctly spelled without a capital first letter—for example, iris, petunia, aster. The strangeness of words disappears as we use them.

There is nothing wrong with using common names when you do not need to be exact. Up to this point in this biology course, we have managed to get along without biological names. Sometimes, though, it is better to say "*Pinus strobus*" instead of "white pine." There are several species of trees called white pines, and a biologist may need to state exactly which species is being studied.

Figure 10.16 A short section on poisonous mushrooms from a Chinese BSCS biology book. Note the scientific name.

有些蕈菌含有毒性化合物，**稱爲瓢菌素**，若誤食後會引起呼吸及循環的失常，對人類是有害的。蕈類約有70種，其中以**瓢菌** *Amanita verna* 最毒（圖 12—6），它有潔白的子實體，雖僅食用少許的蕈帽，也必在一日之內致死，所 **以俗稱**"死神蕈"，眞是名符其實。通常這類毒蕈，柄的基部有一"杯狀物"（圖 12—6），**這杯狀物**常深藏土中不易發現，毒蕈與可食蕈的區別，普通傳述有如下的幾種謬見："銀匙與 毒蕈共煮則呈黑色"；"可食的蕈帽易於剝落，毒 蕈則不然"；"若昆蟲或其他動物吃過的蕈，人亦 可食之"等等，其實皆不可信。惟一可靠的選擇方 法是由市場購買人工栽培的食蕈。如從野外採來的 ，就應先經專家檢定後方可食用。

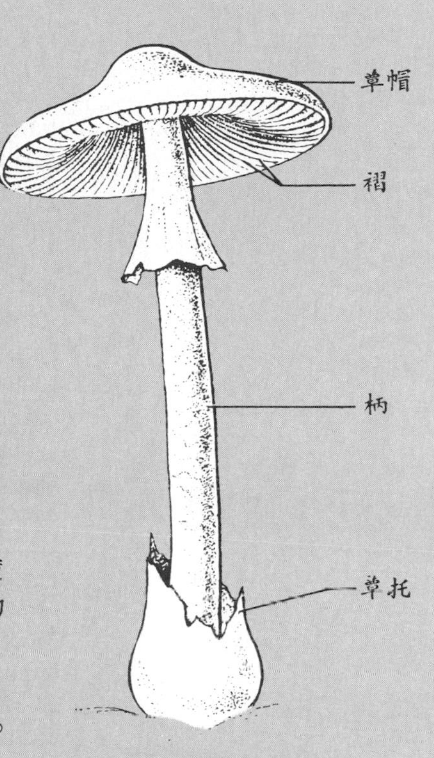

圖 12—6 瓢菌 *Amanita verna* 圖示蕈托杯狀物位在柄的基部（或藏地下）。這是許多種毒蕈的特徵。蕈帽下放射狀蕈褶是蕈的特徵。

Self-Review

1. What is the basis for biological classification? What advantages does it have over other possible bases?
2. What are some of the means by which members of one species are kept from interbreeding with members of other species?
3. How does the number of characteristics shared by all members of a classification level change as you progress from species to kingdom?
4. Why is it possible for equally experienced taxonomists to differ from each other about the classification of a particular species?
5. Why is it necessary for biologists to have a system of nomenclature?
6. What are the basic rules of the binomial system of nomenclature?
7. Why is the use of biological names necessary for scientific exactness?

Guidepost: What characteristics determine how organisms are grouped into kingdoms?

The Kingdoms of Organisms

10.6 Biologists Separate All Organisms into Two Major Groups on the Basis of Their Cell Structures

From species to kingdom, each successively broader category contains more organisms. The more organisms or species, the more difficult it is to find homologies among them. In addition, it is more difficult to find features that set them apart from other groups at the same taxonomic level.

We learned in chapter 5 that all organisms are made up of cells and cell products. Just as the cell is a basic unit of structure and function, it also contains clues about the rleationships among organisms. On the basis of cell structure, biologists can separate organisms into two major groups: **prokaryotes** (pro KAIR ee ohtz) and **eukaryotes** (yoo KAIR ee ohtz).

The differences between those two groups are profound. Cells of prokaryotes are distinguished primarily on the basis of structures they do *not* have. Although they have internal membranes, they do not have nuclear membranes, and thus do not have a distinct nucleus. They also do not have membrane-bounded organelles such as mitochondria or chloroplasts. There does not seem to be any movement of the cytoplasm. Most prokaryotes have rigid cell walls, but the walls are made of proteinlike chains, rather than cellulose as in plants. Their genetic material consists of a single circular thread of DNA. Somctimes they have additional, smaller, circular DNA chains called **plasmids** (PLAZ midz). Mitosis does not occur. They move by gliding, or by means of long, hairlike projections called **flagella.**

Cells of eukaryotes are generally larger than those of prokaryotes, as can be seen in figure 10.17. They are distinguished by a definite nucleus bounded by a membrane. Mitochondria, lysosomes, and other organelles also are found in eukaryotic cells. The cytoplasm often appears to move or stream within the cell. Cell walls, when present, are made of cellulose or chitin, another polysaccharide. The DNA of eukaryotes is associated with special proteins and is organized into distinct chromosomes within the nucleus. There are no plasmids. Cell division follows mitosis.

The major differences between prokaryotes and eukaryotes are summarized in table 10.4. Biologists use those differences in cell structure to group organisms into the two major categories. The many kinds of bacteria and related organisms are all prokaryotes. The organisms with which we are most familiar are all eukaryotes—roses, monkeys, grasshoppers, frogs, ferns, and humans.

Figure 10.17 A prokaryotic cell (upper left) compared with a eukaryotic cell (below). The prokaryotic cell is a bacterium; the eukaryotic cell is an amoeba. Prokaryotic cells are generally much smaller than eukaryotic cells.

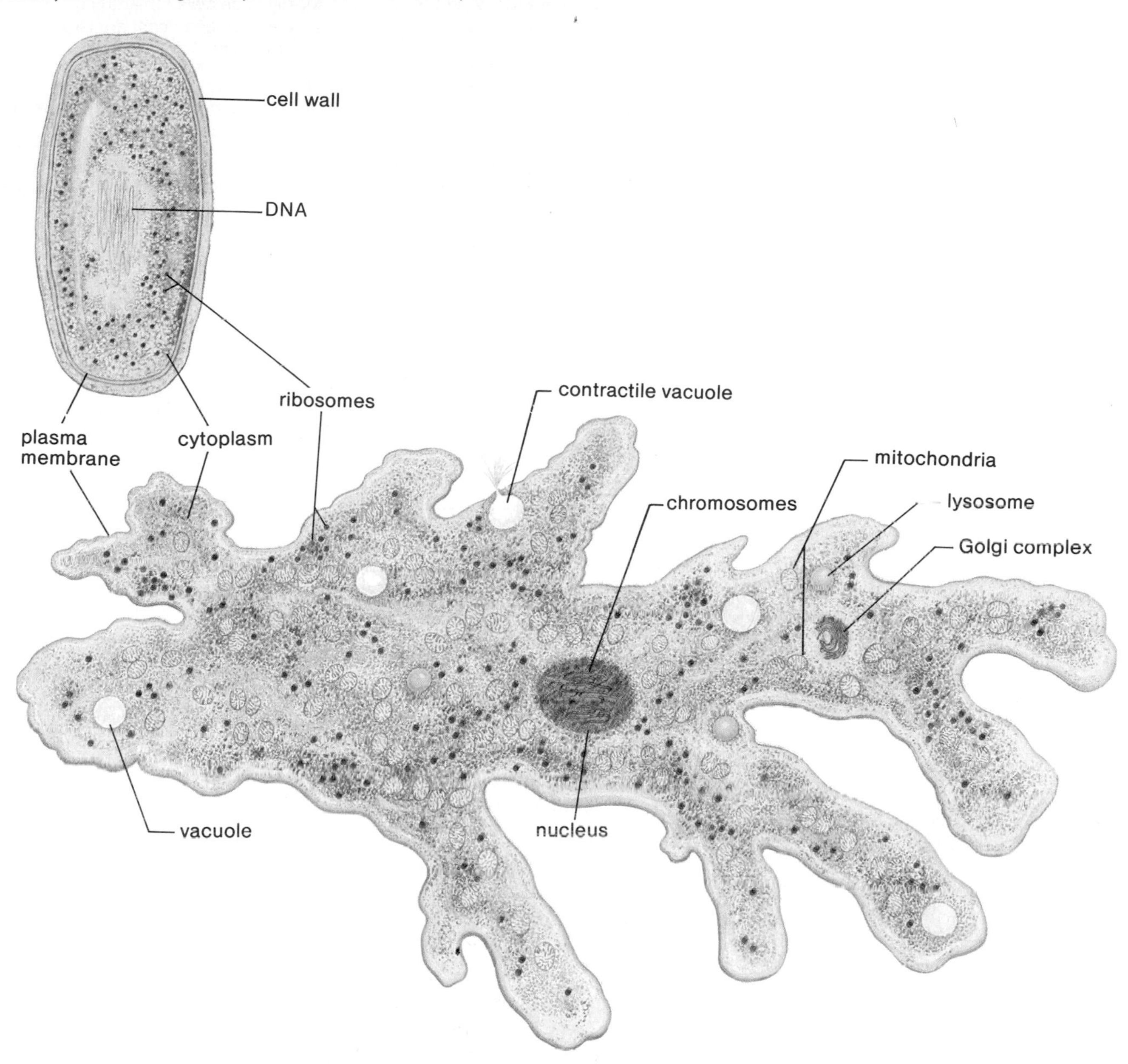

Table 10.4 Major differences between prokaryotes and eukaryotes

Prokaryotes	Eukaryotes
Mostly small cells (1–10 μm). All are microbes.	Mostly large cells (10–100 μm). Some are microbes; most are large organisms.
DNA not membrane-bounded. No chromosomes.	Membrane-bounded nucleus containing chromosomes made of DNA and proteins.
Cell division direct, mostly by simple fission. No centrioles, mitotic spindle, or microtubules. Sexual systems rare; when sex does take place, contributions of genetic material are unequal.	Cell division follows various forms of mitosis; mitotic spindles (or at least some arrangement of microtubules). Sexual systems common; equal participation of both partners (male and female) in fertilization. Alternation of diploid and haploid forms by meiosis and fertilization.
Multicellular forms rare. No tissue development.	Multicellular organisms show extensive development of tissues.
Many are killed by oxygen, others can live with or without oxygen, still others require oxygen to live.	Almost all require oxygen to live.
Enormous variations in the metabolic patterns of the group as a whole.	Same pattern of cellular respiration within the group.
No mitochondria; enzymes for cellular respiration are bound to plasma membranes, not packaged separately.	Enzymes for most reactions of cellular respiration are packaged within mitochondria.
Simple bacterial flagella, composed of the protein flagellin.	Complex flagella composed of the protein tubulin and many others.
In photosynthetic species, enzymes for photosynthesis are bound to plasma membrane, not packaged separately. Various patterns of photosynthesis, including the formation of end products such as sulfur, sulfate and oxygen.	In photosynthetic species, enzymes for photosynthesis are packaged in membrane-bounded plastids. All photosynthetic species have oxygen-releasing photosynthesis.

Adapted from *Five Kingdoms: An Illustrated Guide to the Phyla of Life on Earth,* by Lynn Margulis and Karlene Schwartz.

10.7 Organisms Are Grouped into Five Kingdoms

In section 10.4 we stated that only a few characteristics are shared among all the individuals in a kingdom. What, then, are the characteristics by which we sort all the diverse forms of life into kingdoms?

First, we determine whether the organisms are prokaryotic or eukaryotic. Second, we consider their nutritional pattern. All organisms require a source of energy and a source of food. Some organisms obtain energy and produce food from nonliving substances. They are called producers or **autotrophs** (AWT oh trohfs). Others obtain energy and food from other organisms, either living or dead; they are consumers or **heterotrophs** (HET eh roh trohfs). Third, we consider whether reproduction is sexual or asexual, and whether or not the organisms develop from an embryo, which is a multicellular structure formed by sexual processes. Finally, we consider the general structure and function of the organisms. However, none of those characteristics resolves all the problems of classifying organisms, and classifications change as we gain new knowledge. Today, most biologists favor the five kingdom classification scheme shown in figure 10.18, pages 336–37.

All prokaryotes are presently grouped into one kingdom, the **Monera** (moh NEHR uh). Monerans display a greater variety of chemical and functional patterns than do eukaryotes. Like plants and other eukaryotes, some monerans produce food by photosynthesis. However, photosynthetic monerans use a wider variety of substances as raw materials than do plants. Other monerans use energy obtained from inorganic chemicals to produce food. Many monerans are heterotrophs. Most monerans are unicellular, but multicellular forms exist as well. Reproduction is largely direct, by cell division. When sexual reproduction is present, the parents do not contribute equal amounts of genetic material.

Figure 10.19 Representative monerans include (a) cyanobacteria, *Anabaena circinalis;* (b) purple photosynthetic bacteria, *Rhodospirillum rubrum* (stained); and (c) nitrogen-fixing bacteria.

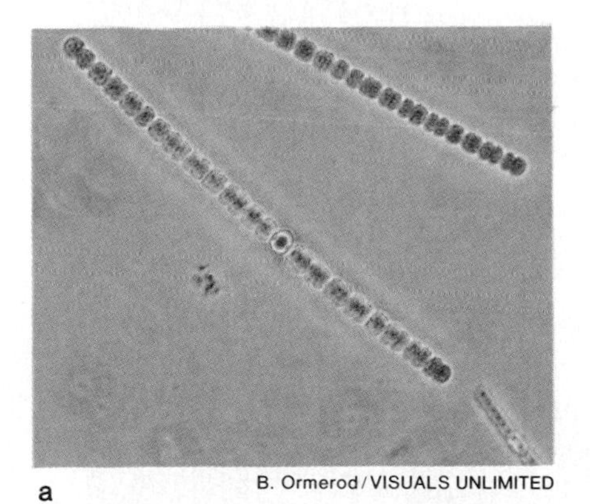

a B. Ormerod/VISUALS UNLIMITED

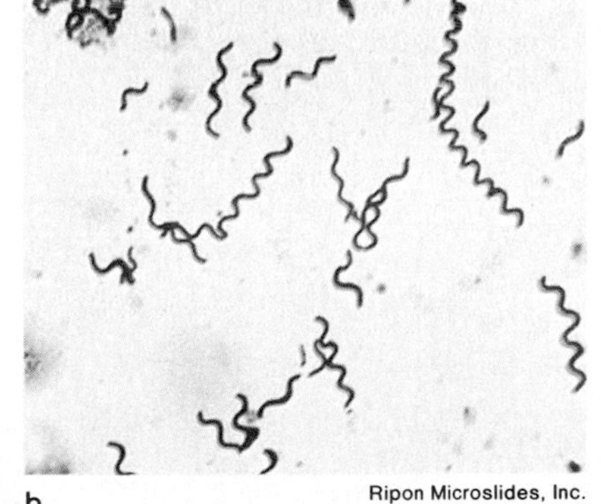

b Ripon Microslides, Inc.

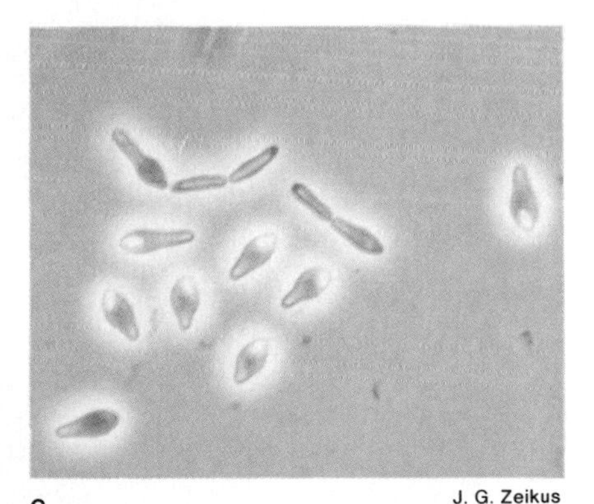

c J. G. Zeikus

Figure 10.18 Currently all organisms can be classified in the five kingdoms shown in this diagram. However, increased understandings of the prokaryotes may lead to creation of more kingdoms for that group.

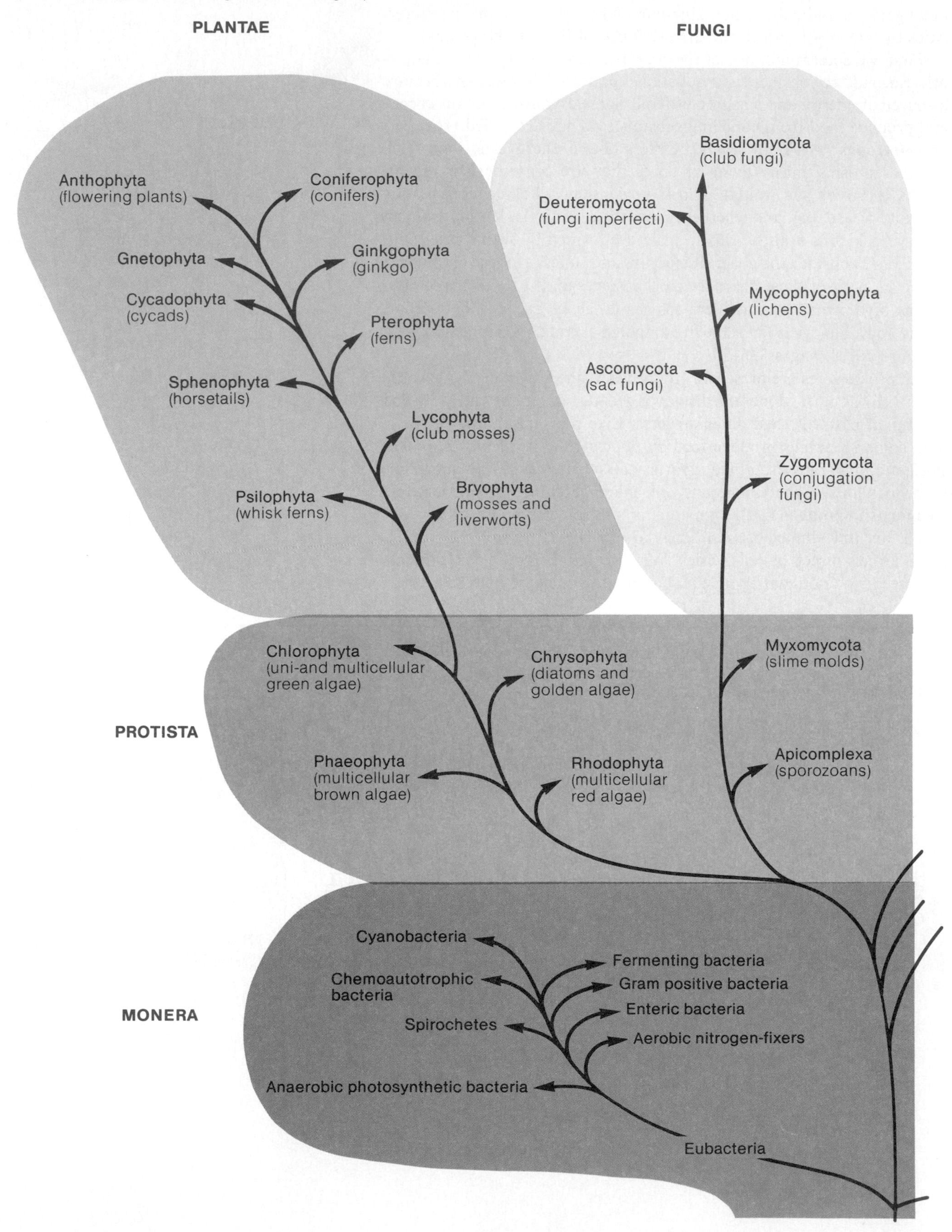

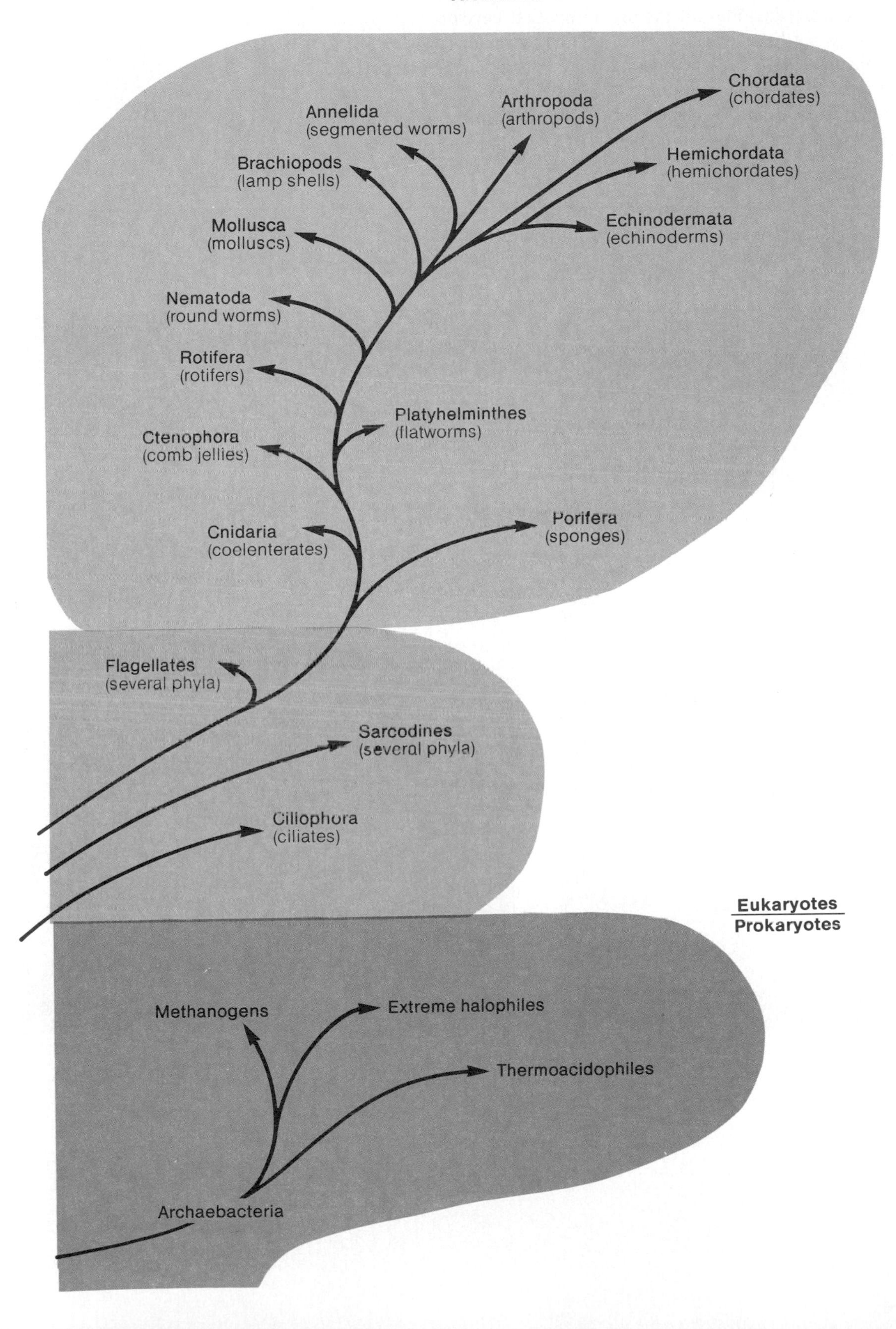
ANIMALIA
Chordata
(chordates)
Arthropoda
(arthropods)
Annelida
(segmented worms)
Hemichordata
(hemichordates)
Brachiopods
(lamp shells)
Echinodermata
(echinoderms)
Mollusca
(molluscs)
Nematoda
(round worms)
Rotifera
(rotifers)
Platyhelminthes
(flatworms)
Ctenophora
(comb jellies)
Porifera
(sponges)
Cnidaria
(coelenterates)
Flagellates
(several phyla)
Sarcodines
(several phyla)
Ciliophora
(ciliates)
Eukaryotes
Prokaryotes
Methanogens
Extreme halophiles
Thermoacidophiles
Archaebacteria

Most eukaryotes can be grouped according to whether they are producers or consumers. Some of the microscopic forms, however, are both; they make their own food at some times and use ready-made food at other times.

Currently eukaryotes are placed in four separate kingdoms. The kingdom **Plantae** (PLAN tee) includes all the organisms that develop from an embryo that does not have a blastula stage. The vast majority of plants are autotrophs that make their own food by oxygen-producing photosynthesis. Plants have cellulose-containing cell walls and reproduce sexually (for some, also asexually). Their cells contain chloroplasts. The bulk of the world's food and much of its oxygen are derived from plants.

Figure 10.20 Plants include the (a) mosses and ferns, (b) conifers, and (c) flowering plants. (b) is the Norway spruce, *Picea abies;* (c) is the waxflower, *Jamesia americana.*

a Doug Sokell

c Doug Sokell

b Karlene V. Schwartz

All of the organisms that develop from an embryo that has a blastula stage are members of the kingdom **Animalia** (an ih MAYL yuh). Animals are all heterotrophic, and they range in size from microscopic forms to giant whales. They are the most diverse in form of all the kingdoms. They generally must search for their food. Thus, most are motile. Reproduction is usually sexual, but some asexual reproduction occurs.

Organisms of the kingdom **Fungi** (FUN jy) develop directly from spores; none form embryos. Fungi are heterotrophs that absorb small molecules from their surroundings through their outer walls. Many are decomposers and play an important role in the biosphere. Reproduction may be sexual or asexual. Most fungi are haploid, rather than diploid like plants and animals. Fungi have cell walls of chitin, and most are multicellular. They range in size from microscopic species to large mushrooms. All are nonmotile. The fungi include yeasts, molds, bracket fungi, and mushrooms.

Figure 10.21 Animals exhibit great diversity of type. Shown here are (a) sea slug, *Hermissendra crassicornis;* (b) dragonfly, *Libullaria;* (c) mallard, *Anas platyrhynchos platyrhynchos;* and (d) blacktailed prairie dog, *Cynomys ludovicianus.*

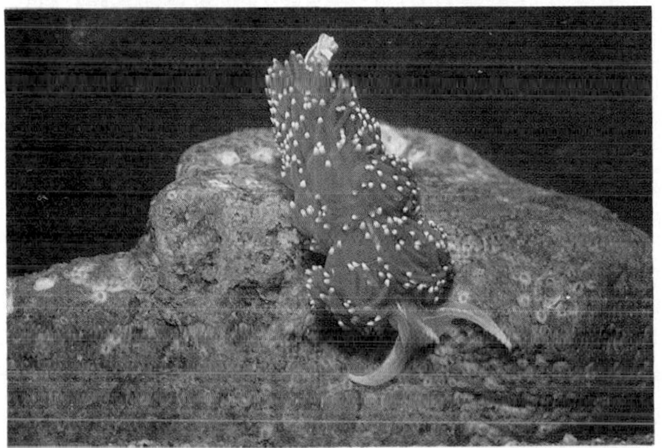

a Stan Elems/VISUALS UNLIMITED

b Werner W. Schulz

c Rod Planck/TOM STACK & ASSOCIATES

d BSCS by Carlye Calvin

Figure 10.22 Typical fungi include (a) mushrooms, *Lactarius fulvissimus;* (b) jelly fungus, *Sacrymyces palmatus;* and (c) hat thrower fungus, *Pilobolus.*

a Athalie Barzee

b Athalie Barzee

c Kenneth D. Whitney/VISUALS UNLIMITED

Figure 10.23 Examples of protists are (a) slime molds, *Physarum;* (b) protozoa, *Amoeba proteus;* and (c) algae, *Tribonema aequale.*

a Karlene V. Schwartz

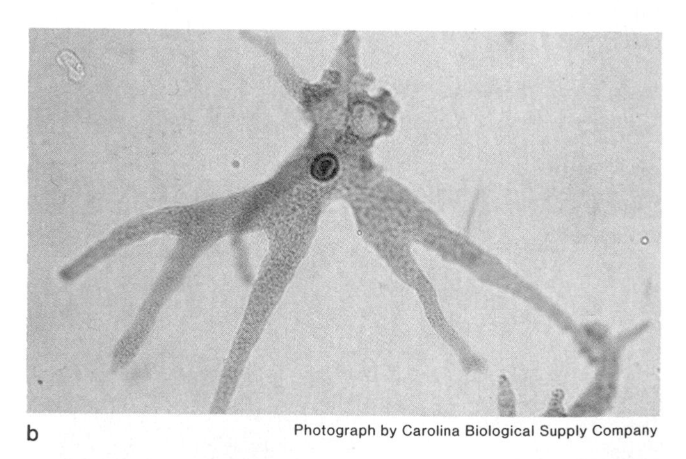

b Photograph by Carolina Biological Supply Company

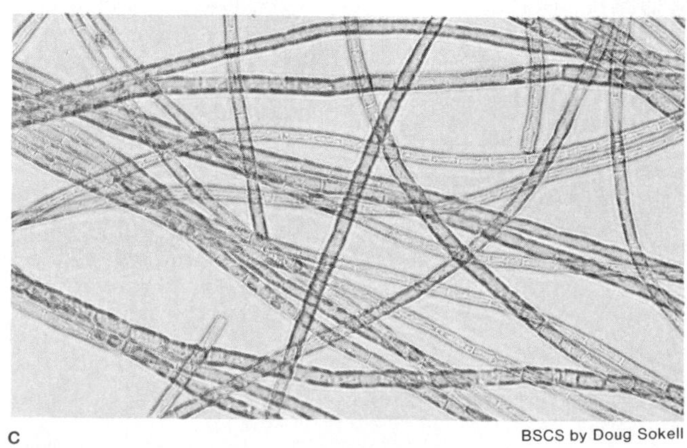

c BSCS by Doug Sokell

All the eukaryotes not included in the three kingdoms described above are grouped in the kingdom **Protista** (pro TIST uh). Many protists are microscopic and unicellular. However, all of the groups in this kingdom have multicellular members, and the giant kelps may reach 100 m in length. Among the protists there is great variability in cell organization, chromosome structure, mitosis, meiosis, and life cycles. Protists may be producers, consumers, or decomposers; some switch from one form of nutrition to another, depending on conditions. Despite their differences, these organisms are probably more closely related to each other than they are to members of the other kingdoms. Protists include all the algae, the protozoa, the slime molds, slime nets, water molds, and many other organisms.

Classification of an organism from each kingdom is shown in figure 10.24.

Figure 10.24 Classification of an organism from each kingdom.

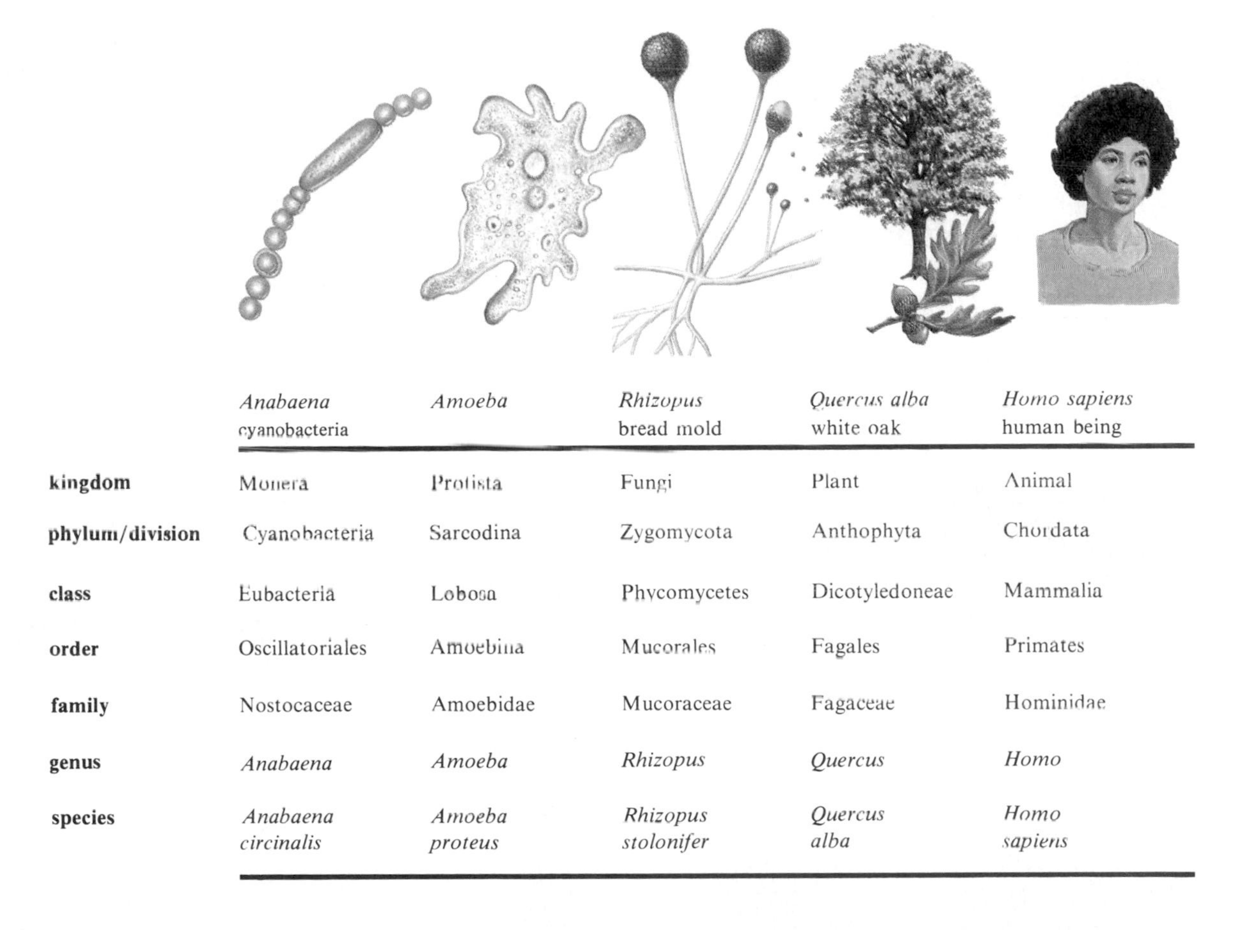

	Anabaena cyanobacteria	*Amoeba*	*Rhizopus* bread mold	*Quercus alba* white oak	*Homo sapiens* human being
kingdom	Monera	Protista	Fungi	Plant	Animal
phylum/division	Cyanobacteria	Sarcodina	Zygomycota	Anthophyta	Chordata
class	Eubacteria	Lobosa	Phycomycetes	Dicotyledoneae	Mammalia
order	Oscillatoriales	Amoebina	Mucorales	Fagales	Primates
family	Nostocaceae	Amoebidae	Mucoraceae	Fagaceae	Hominidae
genus	*Anabaena*	*Amoeba*	*Rhizopus*	*Quercus*	*Homo*
species	*Anabaena circinalis*	*Amoeba proteus*	*Rhizopus stolonifer*	*Quercus alba*	*Homo sapiens*

10.8 Classifications Can Change

We pointed out at the end of section 10.4 that a taxonomic classification is not a fact. As our knowledge of the living world increases, we perceive new relationships among organisms. New knowledge often requires changes in the way we group organisms. That is especially true at the level of kingdoms.

A classification should be exclusive as well as inclusive. That is, the characteristics we select should allow us to form a group of similar organisms that are different from other groups of similar organisms. As we have seen, monerans are prokaryotes; all other organisms are eukaryotes. Plants are autotrophic; animals and fungi are heterotrophic. Animals develop from blastulas; fungi develop from spores. Those characteristics serve to *include* similar organisms into one kingdom and *exclude* them from the other kingdoms.

At one time it seemed that organisms could be classified in two kingdoms—animals and plants. As improved microscopes increased our understanding of microscopic organisms, it became evident that many of those organisms did not fit well into either of the two kingdoms. The kingdom Protista was suggested for some of those and certain nonmicroscopic organisms.

Electron microscopic studies made clear the profound differences in cell structure between the prokaryotes and eukaryotes, as seen in figure 10.25. Taxonomists added the kingdom Monera for the prokaryotes. And because the fungi do not share many characteristics with any of the other groups, a separate kingdom was proposed for them.

Figure 10.25 Electron micrographs of prokaryotic (left) and eukaryotic (right) cells. Notice the membrane-bounded organelles and generally more complex structure in the eukaryotic cell.

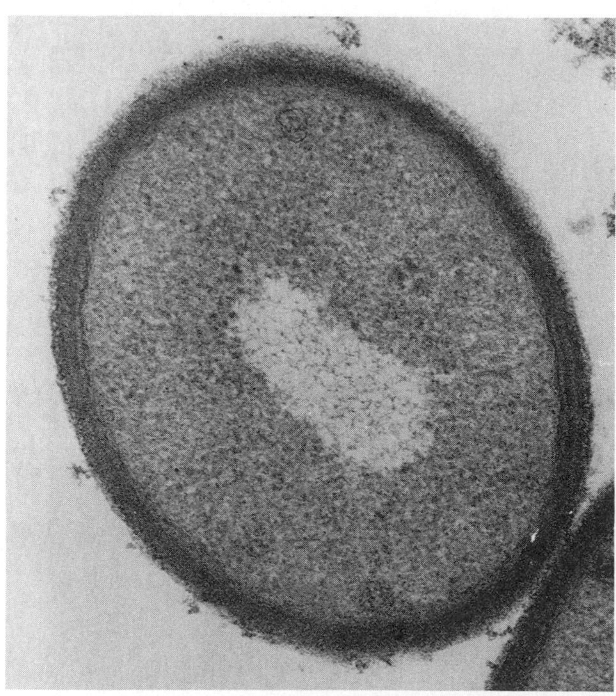

a BPS/TOM STACK & ASSOCIATES

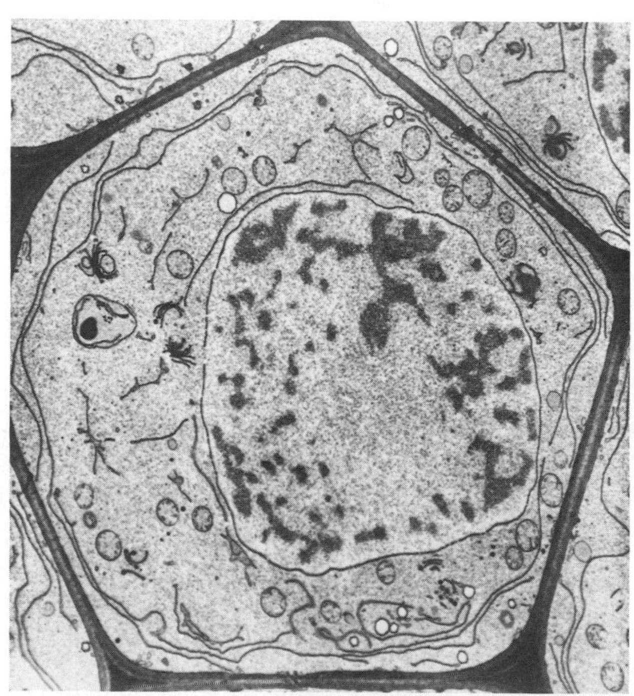

b W. Gordon Whaley and American Journal of Botany

The five-kingdom system of classification described in section 10.7 is not accepted by all biologists. Some place multicellular algae with the plants. Zoologists may include the heterotrophic protists in the animal kingdom. Further studies of the bacteria may require the formation of still other kingdoms.

Classification schemes also depend on the purposes of the person doing the classifying. Grouping organisms as producers, consumers, and decomposers works well for an ecologist but would not work well for a biologist comparing the anatomy of worms, for example. Grouping animals as worms and nonworms would not be useful in studying the evolution of a four-chambered heart.

Classification systems are products of our knowledge of the living world. Species, genera, families, orders, classes, and kingdoms do not exist in nature; only individual organisms exist. Classification systems are simply means that enable us to think more easily about nature. They are human creations. Thus, they will continue to change as research in the biologic sciences continues.

Self-Review

1. What is the most fundamental characteristic that separates organisms?
2. What characteristics do biologists use to sort organisms into kingdoms?
3. Describe the distinguishing characteristics of each kingdom.
4. Why do classification systems change?

The Origin of Diversity

Guidepost: How did life originate and evolve into the many forms found today?

10.9 All Species May Have Come from a Single Ancestral Species

The cell theory states that cells arise from preexisting cells. The theory of evolution demonstrates that organisms arise only from others of their own kind. However, evolution often increases the numbers of species as a result of variety among individuals in preexisting species. For example, all of the Galapagos finches (see figure 9.9 page 275) probably descended from the same ancestors. The pattern that emerges is that of many kinds of organisms evolving from few. If that is true, we could expect fewer and fewer species farther and farther back into the past. Thus, all species could have come from the same ancestral species living at the time when life must have originated.

Fossil studies have supported the hypothesis of one or a few initial forms of life. The oldest fossil records reveal few species. That may be due, at least in part, to the erosion, weathering, and recycling of the oldest fossil-bearing rocks. However, only delicate fossils of microscopic organisms are found in the surviving older rocks.

The fossil record at later times reveals numerous examples of the idea that many forms evolved from a few ancestral forms. One group would flourish, then die out because of changes in the environment or because of competition from other groups. Another group would then increase to its greatest variety in numbers of species. For example, when there were more reptiles, there were fewer mammals and almost no birds. When there were more mammals, reptiles were declining and birds were evolving into more species.

That pattern appears in each age in the fossil record, and in the history of each group. During the age of dinosaurs, there was a greater variety of species than among reptiles today (figure 10.26). The greatest diversity of mammals also appears to be past. Throughout the history of life, new species have evolved and older species have become extinct. Again and again, species have evolved from a smaller number of species before them.

There was a remote time, however, when relatively few species of organisms apparently existed. Were those organisms ancestral to all later ones? Were they themselves far from life's beginning? How did the first organisms arise?

Figure 10.26 The age of reptiles produced tens of thousands of species, from small lizards to flying reptiles and giant dinosaurs. Turtles, alligators and crocodiles, and snakes are the only surviving orders of reptiles today.

10.10 The Origin of Life Must Be Investigated Indirectly

Professor Elso S. Barghoorn of Harvard University discovered the bacteriumlike fossil, more than 3 billion years old, shown in figure 10.27. Other investigators have discovered algalike or bacterialike fossils in ancient rock 3.5 billion years old. Fossil traces of the pond scum that the latter organisms formed led to further evidence of the fossil microorganisms themselves.

The search is not as simple as looking for older and older rocks, with older and older fossils. The oldest rocks formed on the earth have not remained unchanged. If the fossil record once included traces of the first life forms on earth, it no longer does. Other, less direct methods of investigation must be employed.

The evidence derived from life today, as well as from fossil life extending 3.5 billion years into the past, is the most reliable evidence biologists have from which to form hypotheses about the origin of life. That evidence indicates a continuing evolutionary relationship between past and present living things. If evolution is the thread that links life through the ages, then there is reason to investigate the origin of the first life as a part of evolution. That is, life itself may have originated through evolution. That hypothesis presupposes that the chemical substances necessary to form a living thing were present on the earth long ago. Biologists have discovered that *some* investigation of this view is possible in the laboratory.

Evolution is, therefore, being studied as the process by which life not only diversified, but first arose. Taking that hypothetical step also makes it possible to predict what the first life was like—it was very small and relatively unstructured. The reason it would not include large organisms with specialized body parts is that evolution cannot build everything at once, but works in stages. Evolution works like a remodeler, not an architect. Evolution could only have worked at first with whatever small clusters of particles were present on the earth.

Figure 10.27 Electron micrograph of *Eobacterion isolatum* (left) and its imprint (right). This fossil bacterium is 3.2 billion years old, bar = 1 μm

Photograph by Elso S. Barghoorn, Harvard University

Biology Today

RNA as an Enzyme

Biology, like all other sciences, is an incomplete body of knowledge. New information is added to the existing store of knowledge on a continuing basis. This continuous modification of the body of knowledge separates science from other ways of knowing such as religion. A dramatic example of the revision of a long-held assumption in biology occurred in the early and mid 1980s, when a young University of Colorado biochemist began to question the role of RNA.

You learned in chapter 4 that RNA is one of two nucleic acids that store genetic information and that proteins often act as enzymes. For many years, biologists believed that the categories of information molecules and enzymes were mutually exclusive. That is, an enzyme could not serve as an information molecule, and an information molecule could not serve as an enzyme.

In 1981 and 1982, Thomas R. Cech and his colleagues, while working with the protist *Tetrahymena thermophila,* discovered that RNA can indeed act as an enzyme. Like all eukaryotes, *T. thermophila* contains portions of DNA that are not translated into messenger RNA or protein. These segments, the introns, are cut out of the precursor mRNA that is made from the DNA in the nucleus. The remaining segments of mRNA, the exons, then are spliced together to form a shorter piece of mRNA. That mRNA is released from the nucleus into the cytoplasm, where it directs the synthesis of protein on the ribosomes.

The removal of the introns and splicing together of exons requires energy and enzymes. Cech and his colleagues, Paula J. Grabowski and Arthur J. Zaug, conducted splicing experiments in the test tube. They used unspliced RNA with extracts from *Tetrahymena* nuclei, and also unspliced RNA without extracts. (The extracts would supply the necessary enzymes.) They found that a particular *Tetrahymena* intron was removed even in the absence of nuclear extract.

The researchers thought there might be a nuclear protein bound together very tightly to the *Tetrahymena's* RNA. To eliminate that possibility, they synthesized an artificial *Tetrahymena* RNA, using recombinant DNA techniques. As Cech explained in a 1986 *Scientific American* article, "the resulting RNA had never been near a cell and therefore could not be contaminated by splicing enzymes." Yet, when Cech and his team tested the newly-synthesized RNA, the proper intron was still removed. The only conclusion possible was that the RNA itself was acting as an enzyme. That revolutionized completely the assumption that an information molecule cannot act as an enzyme.

Zaug added another startling piece of information in 1985, when he showed that *Tetrahymena's* self-spliced intron could organize short pieces of RNA into longer segments. RNA, therefore, not only can act as a splicing enzyme, but also can organize its own replication in certain situations. That discovery has implications for evolution theory, because a system for the replication of information is required for the origin of life. Cech and his coworkers had uncovered just such a mechanism, all within RNA.

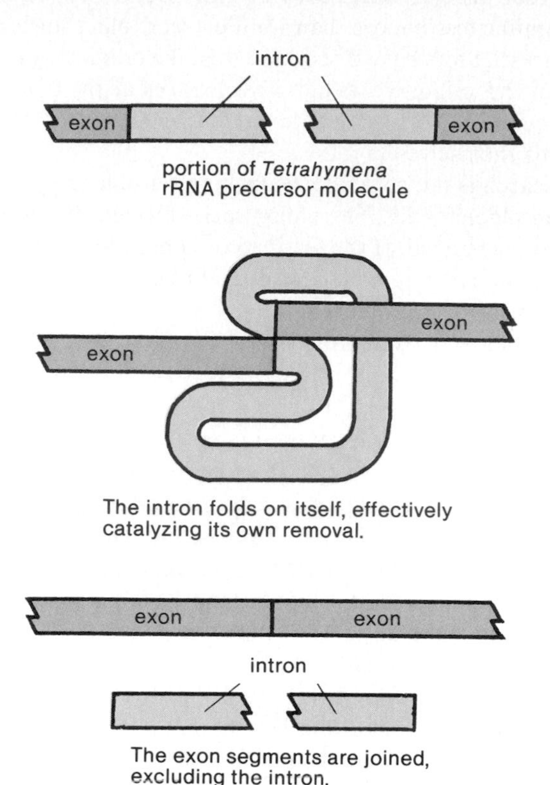

portion of *Tetrahymena* rRNA precursor molecule

The intron folds on itself, effectively catalyzing its own removal.

The exon segments are joined, excluding the intron.

Figure 10.28 These fossils, drawn 1250 times actual size, were found in the Gunflint Iron formation along the shore of Lake Superior in Ontario, Canada. They have been dated at approximately 2 billion years old. The organisms in (k) and (l) have structures that resemble a nucleus, and could be eukaryotes. The other fossils are all prokaryotes.

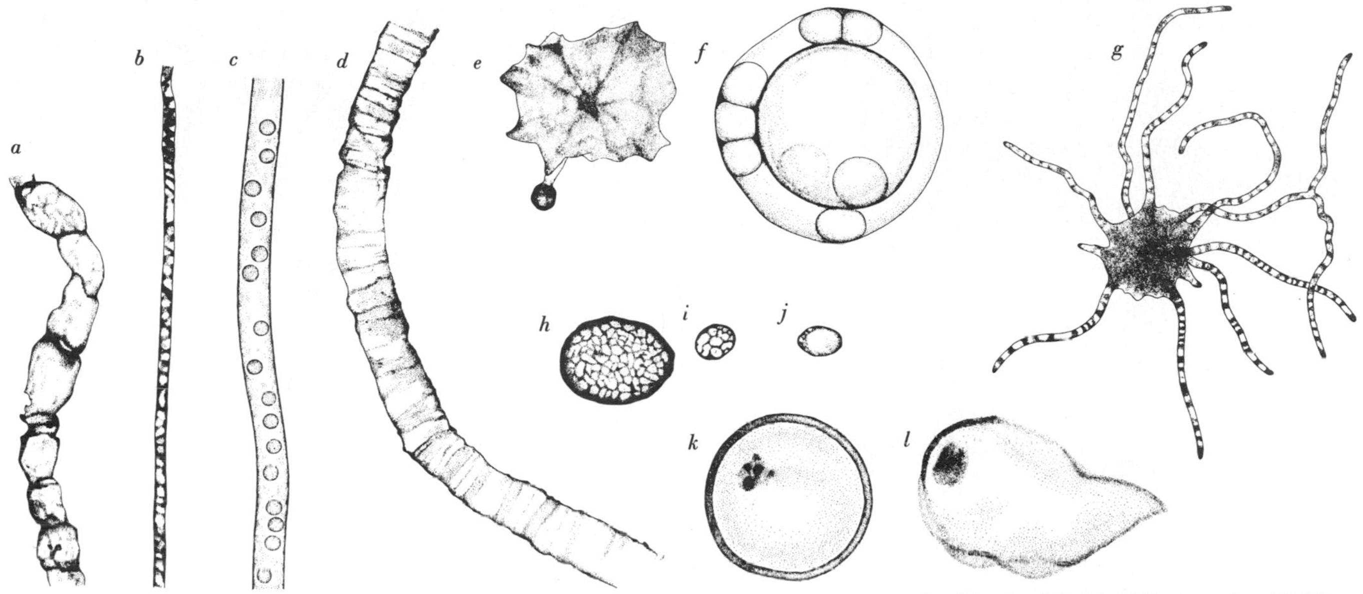

The fossil record supports that reasoning. Fossils of the earliest known life are all microscopic in size. Not a single exception has been found. Figure 10.28 shows composite drawings of fossils about 2 billion years old. Notice the diversity of form as well as the microscopic size.

Biologists and other scientists are studying the evolution of the earth, the other planets, and the sun for many kinds of clues. Space explorations have helped to gather data in probes of the sun's other planets. The data available thus far show that life is not likely on any other planet in our solar system. Even planets around other stars are important to the search, for if life evolved on Earth, it may have evolved elsewhere as well. However, planets around other stars are very difficult to detect. Only indirect evidence that such planets exist has been obtained so far, as in the multiple objects observed circling the star *Vega*. Sending out space probes to the areas around such stars is not likely in the near future.

10.11 Studies of Present-Day Stars Provide Evidence for the Formation and Early History of the Earth

Little about the evolution of the earth or other planets is established beyond question. Studies of the birth of stars provide information about how the sun might have been formed. Other stars develop from a revolving cloud of gas and dust. Hydrogen is always the major element in the gas, as it is in the sun today.

Figure 10.29 A sequence of events that might have led to the first life.

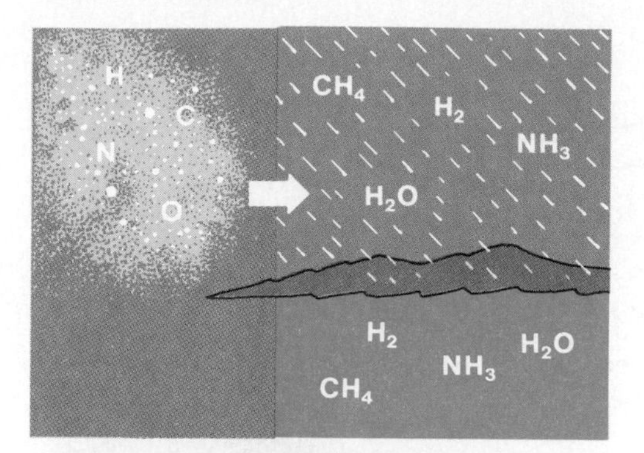

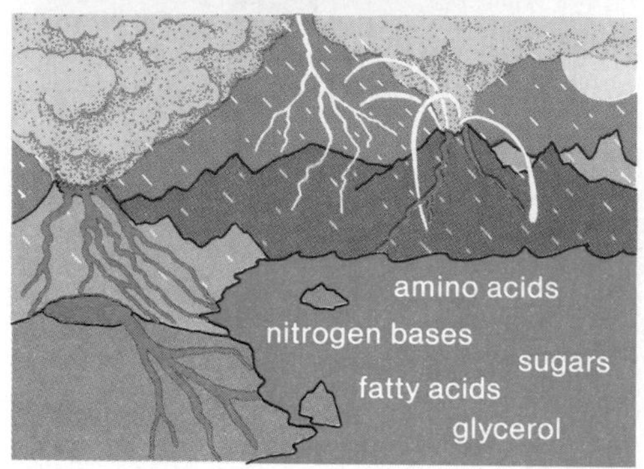

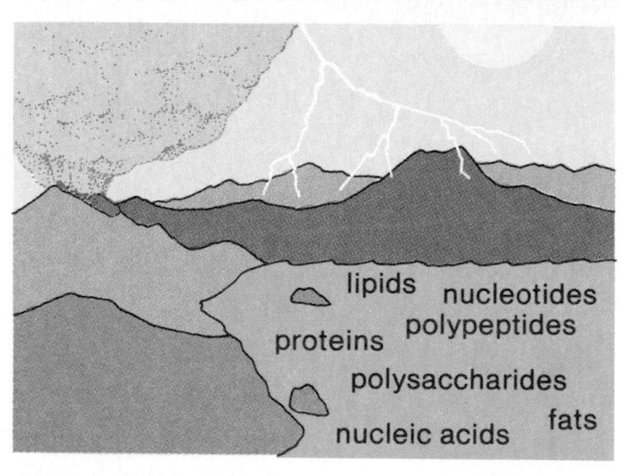

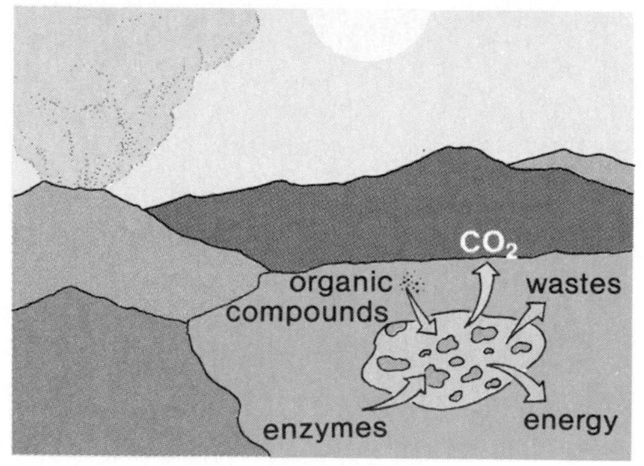

Figure 10.30 A drawing of Miller's apparatus, in which conditions thought to exist in the primitive atmosphere were reproduced in the laboratory. Does this experiment prove how life originated on earth?

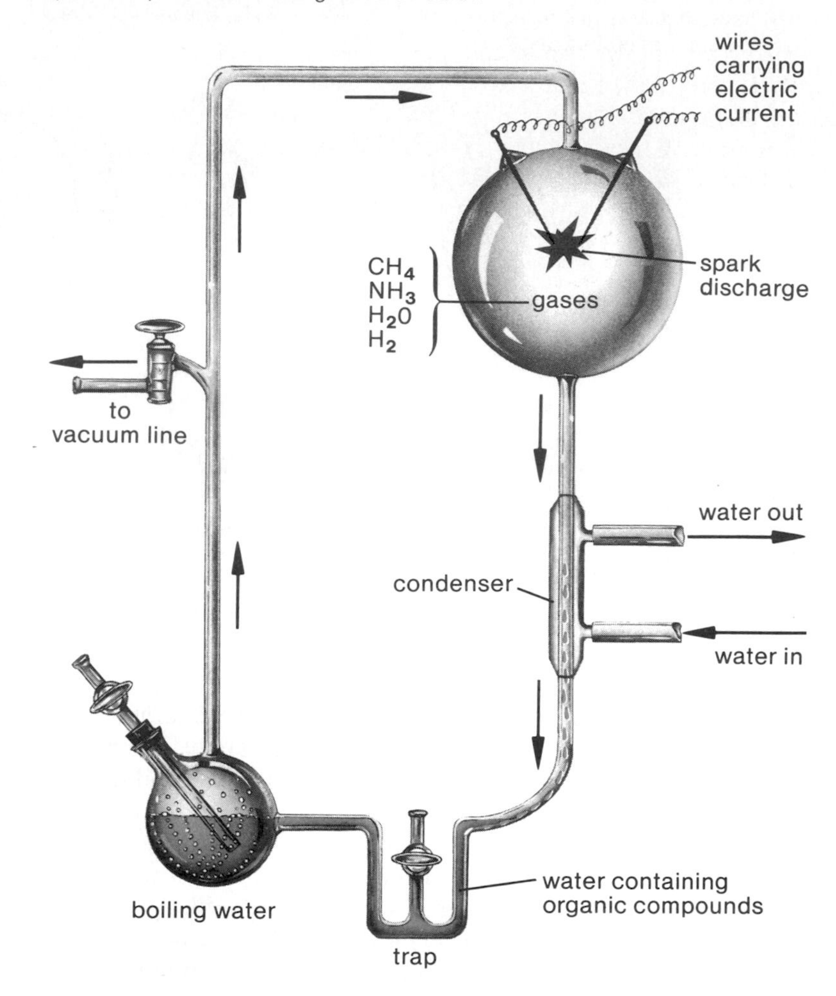

Trailing arms can be seen in giant revolving clouds of gas in space. When the sun condensed from the solar system's early gas cloud, some of those arms probably condensed to form the planets.

Geological evidence suggests that the earth grew very hot after it first formed approximately 4.7 billion years ago. Heat speeds up chemical activity. At that time atoms must have been constantly combining and recombining. They must have been forming many kinds of molecules. Geological evidence also suggests that the early atmosphere of the earth included methane, CH_4, instead of present-day carbon dioxide, CO_2. It probably included ammonia, NH_3, instead of present-day nitrogen, N_2. Most likely some hydrogen, H_2, and much water vapor, H_2O, also were present, but free oxygen, O_2, was absent.

With the energy of heat and lightning, the gases of the early atmosphere might have combined to form substances such as amino acids. Amino acids are found in all organisms today. During millions of years, such organic compounds might have accumulated in the very warm oceans, lakes, and pools, forming an "organic soup." Along the shores, in tide pools, or on particles of clay, those simple compounds might have combined to become more complex molecules. Finally, those more complex molecules might have united somehow to form a very simple kind of reproducing "living thing." The ideas presented above are summarized in figure 10.29.

Are those speculations of origins reasonable? What would happen if a simulated primitive atmosphere were exposed to an energy source? In 1952, Stanley Miller and Harold Urey, at the University of Chicago, decided to find out. Using apparatus like that shown in figure 10.30, they passed electric sparks through ammonia, methane, water, and hydrogen. The electric sparks simulated lightning, and the gases were like those on the earth long ago. Nothing else was added. When the substances were analyzed later, it was found that some simple amino acids had been produced.

That experiment has been verified. Other investigators have used ultraviolet light instead of electric sparks. They have obtained the same kind of results. Since those first experiments, researchers have synthesized many other kinds of organic molecules, including nucleotides and carbohydrates.

Do those experiments suggest a way in which life might have originated in the distant past? Yes, but it is still a long way from complex molecules to even the simplest of known organisms. How, then, might those simple organisms have arisen?

10.12 The First Cells Were Probably Heterotrophs

As time went by, it seems likely that some amino acids in the "organic soup" formed polypeptides and proteins. Other simple organic molecules also might have formed larger, more complex molecules. Eventually, some of the larger molecules might have combined into clusters, and the clusters might have merged to form a primitive cell.

That is a far-reaching assumption. The formation of primitive cells from clusters of organic compounds is more difficult to explain than the formation of the organic compounds themselves under the earth's primitive conditions. The assumption is that at first, large organic compounds in the organic soup were grouped together at random, forming many types of aggregates. Those different types of aggregates might have competed with each other for the organic molecules in the soup that were needed for growth and reproduction. In that competition, some aggregates would have had a composition and an organization that made them more successful than other aggregates. Eventually, natural selection crowded out the less successful ones.

Scientists have proposed different models for a pre-cell. A Russian scientist, A. I. Oparin, suggested that pre-cells might have been like **coacervates** (koh AS er vayts). Coacervates are clusters of proteins or proteinlike substances held together in small droplets within a surrounding liquid, as shown in figure 10.31a. Sidney Fox, of the University of Miami, thinks pre-cells were more like **microspheres,** cooling droplets from a hot water solution of polypeptides. Each microsphere forms its own double-layered boundary as it cools (figure 10.31b).

The ancestors of primitive cells could easily have been of several kinds. Different kinds, with different capabilities, might have come together. In that way some of the features could have developed that are seen today in the simplest heterotrophic bacteria. The cell ancestors formed a membrane that separated them from their external world. They began to grow by using compounds in the surrounding environment for spare parts and energy. They evolved a process of reproduction, producing others like themselves.

Figure 10.31 (a) A complex coacervate can form when a water layer surrounds a cluster of protein molecules. (b) Microspheres are formed when dry mixtures of amino acids are heated and then placed in water. This microsphere is 2 μm in diameter.

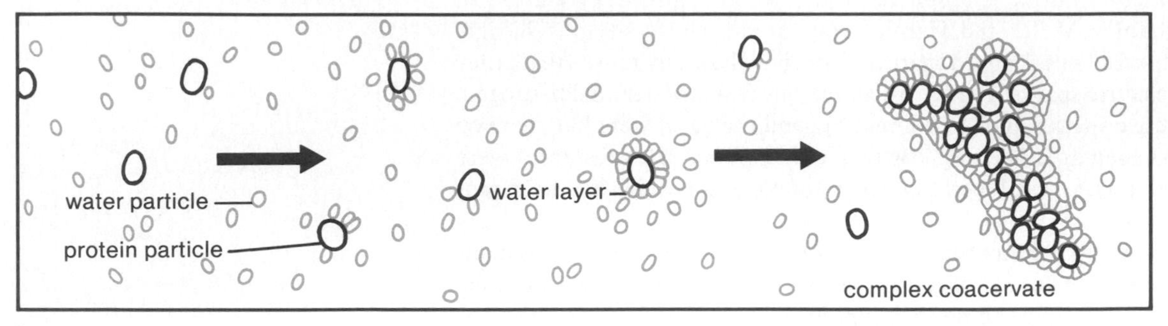

a

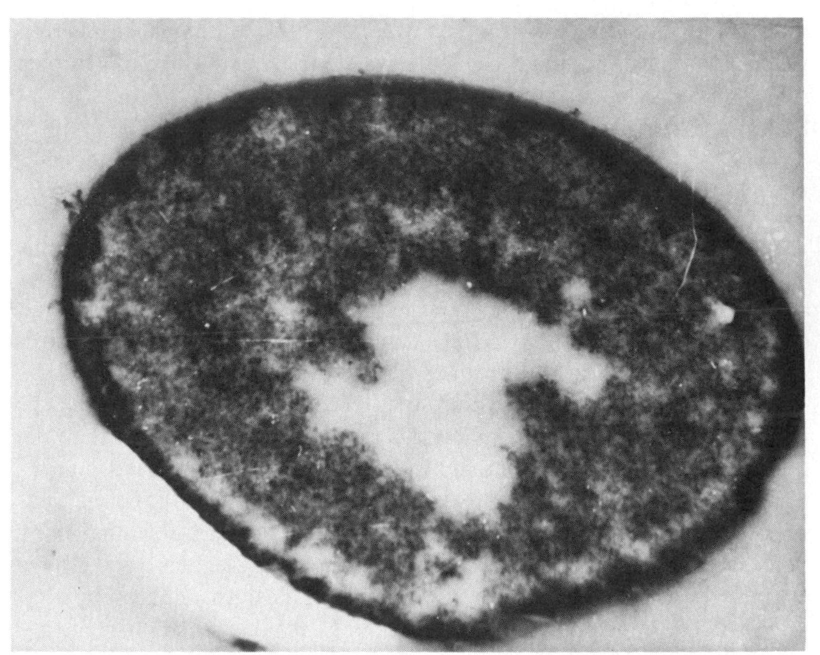

b

Dr. Sidney W. Fox, Institute for Molecular and Cellular Evolution, University of Miami

What did those first living things use for food? Such a question tempts biologists to suggest that the first life made its own food. However, the food-making apparatus is a complex thing to add to all the other complexities of being alive. If evolution took the fewest possible steps, the first living things would have been heterotrophs. For food they could have used the supply of naturally occurring organic compounds.

Many biologists favor the **heterotroph hypothesis.** They propose that the very first life fed on the same organic compounds from which it evolved. That would have made the first organisms consumers. They could not synthesize all the organic compounds they needed as food. Yet those heterotrophs would have required fewer evolutionary steps to develop than would the more complex autotrophs.

An autotroph could have lived in much simpler surroundings than a heterotroph, but it would have required even more complex surroundings to have evolved first. Unless evolution somehow took a great many complex steps almost simultaneously, the heterotroph hypothesis seems the most reasonable explanation of the first cells.

In figure 10.32, notice that the earliest life had appeared and was well established by the time the earth was only one third of its present age.

10.13 Autotrophic Cells Evolved Several Types of Photosynthesis

Eventually the supply of organic compounds would have diminished as they were used for food by the primitive cells. Some of those heterotrophs must have begun to use visible light from the sun as a source of energy. The first organisms able to use sunlight probably acted partly like heterotrophs, taking in organic compounds, and partly like autotrophs, making other organic compounds with energy from sunlight. Certain present-day bacteria have that ability. Other primitive cells evolved the ability to live entirely by means of photosynthesis, though their photosynthesis did not produce free oxygen. Such bacteria are known today; they use light energy to synthesize organic compounds from hydrogen sulfide or other compounds. The bacteria live in environments where oxygen is absent, or present only in low concentrations.

At some point, primitive cells evolved a form of photosynthesis that used water and released oxygen. That is the type of photosynthesis found in all autotrophic eukaryotic cells, as well as in all the cyanobacteria. In fact, some of the oldest known fossils closely resemble modern cyanobacteria.

With the advent of oxygen-producing photosynthesis, a great change took place in the atmosphere of the earth. Free oxygen began to accumulate in significant amounts. Oxygen is a very reactive element, and some of the molecules combined to form ozone (O_3). The layer of ozone that resulted screened out most of the ultraviolet rays from the sun, making synthesis of organic compounds in the seas less likely. Heterotrophic cells became dependent on autotrophic cells for their source of food and energy, as they remain today.

10.14 The Organization of Matter Forms a Continuum

What is life? It is difficult to give a simple definition. Obviously, a cow is living and a stone is nonliving. We can say that an *Amoeba* is living and a coacervate is not. Difficulties arise, however, when biologists try to set up an exact classification system for living versus nonliving things.

Certain characteristics of organisms are shown by nonliving things. If a salt crystal is added to a concentrated salt solution, it will grow and start the formation of other crystals. There is a difference, however, between this kind of growth and that of organisms. The salt crystal can grow only by taking material of the same composition from the environment. Primitive cells proposed by the heterotroph hypothesis may also have grown by first taking materials like their own from the environment. The environment eventually would have become depleted of those materials, however. Modern organisms can take in and use materials from the environment that differ significantly from themselves. They show few superficial resemblances to crystal growths.

Figure 10.32 In this diagram, 4.7 billion years of earth's history are compressed into one calendar year. Each day is equal to almost 13 million years on earth. Notice how recently humans appeared.

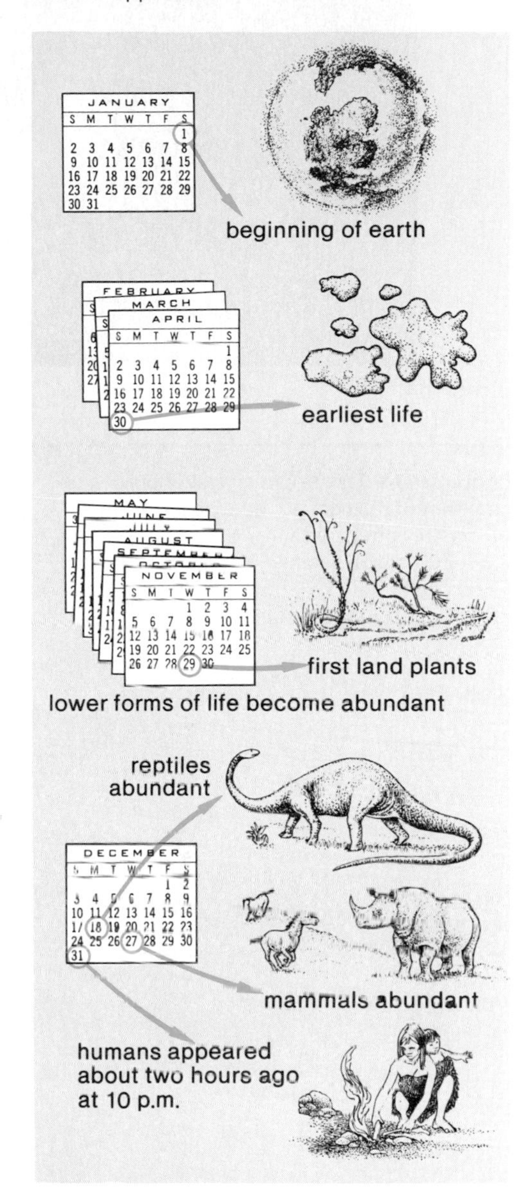

Figure 10.33 A living *Amoeba* (a) is much more complex than a coacervate droplet (b), which is not alive, yet the two look very similar.

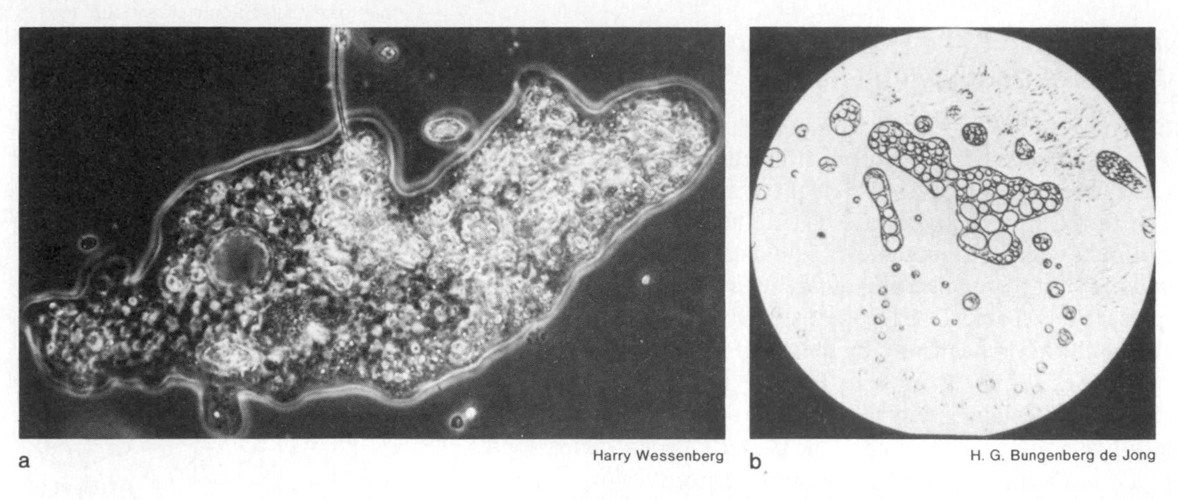

a Harry Wessenberg b H. G. Bungenberg de Jong

Figure 10.34 This single crystal of polio virus, magnified 600 times, appears hollow because the crystal is transparent. The crystal contains about 200 million viruses.

University of California at Berkeley, Virus Laboratory

Viruses provide a biological puzzle in this connection. Like salt, some viruses can be crystallized (figure 10.34) and even stored. Yet when placed inside a living cell, they can take over the cell and cause it to destroy itself, reproducing more viruses. Outside a cell, viruses are inactive: they cannot take in and use materials from the nonliving environment. Are viruses alive?

If we consider the organization of matter, from the smallest subatomic particles to the biosphere, we can see that a continuum is formed (figure 10.35). Where do we draw the line between living and nonliving? At present, there is no way to decide how complex a system must be before one would call it living. The difference between a cow and a stone is obvious. The difference between the simplest living organism and the most complex nonliving system is not so obvious.

Self-Review

1. Which modern organisms do the oldest fossils most closely resemble?
2. What evidence do we have that many species evolved from a few species?
3. Compare environmental conditions on the earth during its early history with conditions today.

Figure 10.35 The organization of matter on earth forms a continuum. The least complex is at the bottom; matter then increases in complexity to the top of the chart.

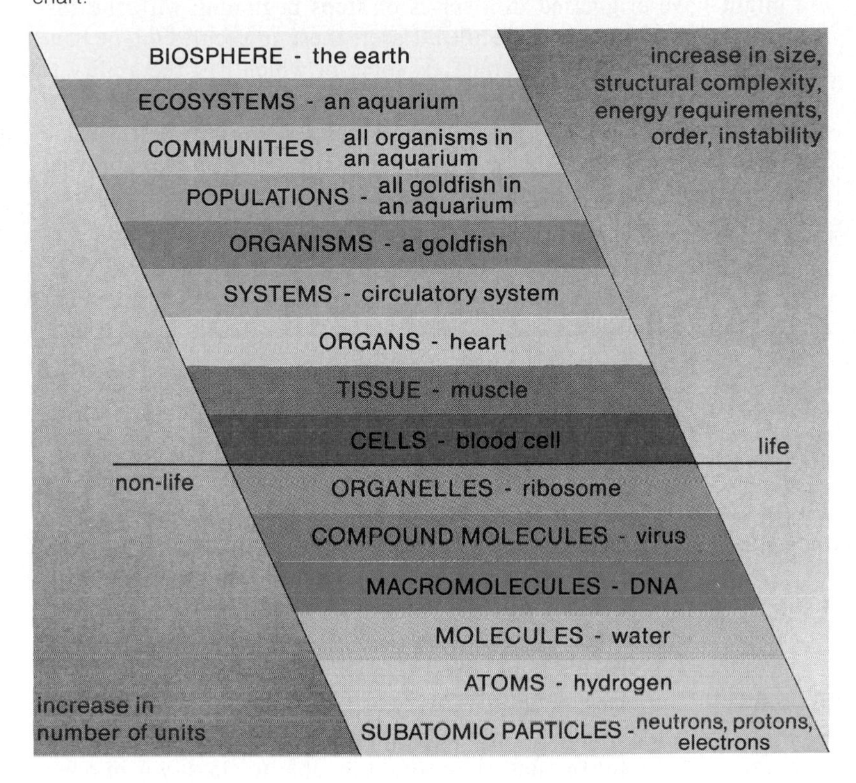

4. How can experiments such as those of Miller and Urey provide evidence for the origin of life?
5. How do scientists think primitive cells might have formed?
6. Why do scientists think it more likely the first cells were heterotrophs rather than autotrophs?
7. What changes did oxygen-producing photosynthesis cause on Earth?
8. Why is it so difficult to draw a line between life and nonlife?

Summary

Classification systems enable biologists to study the great variety of organisms that exist in the biosphere. Taxonomists have developed a system that names organisms and indicates their relationships. That system is accepted throughout the world, and it enables biologists from different places to understand one another when discussing a particular organism. Classification systems may be based on many characteristics, but the most important ones are structural and biochemical homologies. Currently all organisms are classified in five kingdoms—Monera, Protista, Fungi, Plantae, and Animalia. Classification systems will continue to change as biologists learn more about the natural world.

The theory of evolution led to many predictions of what the first life was like. Based on those predictions, scientists have studied the evolution of the earth itself. A variety of experiments has provided evidence that life might have originated in a series of steps beginning with the formation of simple organic molecules. Later, those molecules might have assembled in a variety of aggregates, some of which had the ability to reproduce themselves. Those first "cells" were probably heterotrophs that used the organic molecules around them as sources of energy. Later, some cells developed the ability to use light energy. Fossil evidence supports the view of very simple beginnings; the oldest fossils resemble the monerans of today.

Application Questions

1. What factors cause biologists to change the way they classify organisms?
2. Bats, birds, butterflies, and flying dinosaurs all have or had wings. Why not place them in the same class because of that feature?
3. If many species have evolved from few preexisting ones, why are there fewer species of reptiles today than there were in the age of the dinosaurs?
4. What is meant by the statement that evolution is a remodeler, not an architect?
5. In what ways would an autotroph hypothesis for the first organisms on earth appear to be more suitable than the heterotroph hypothesis? In what ways less suitable?
6. If experiments such as those of Miller and Urey did not prove the heterotroph hypothesis, of what value were they?

Problems

1. Suppose that by the year 2005 every kind of living organism on the earth will have been discovered, described, and classified. Do you think the development of taxonomy would then end? Explain.
2. Suppose that one of the two cell types—prokaryote and eukaryote—could have been ancestral to the other. Present arguments for which might have been the ancestral type.
3. Design an imaginary organism that has characteristics such that a taxonomist observing it for the first time would be able to classify it in one of the kingdoms.

Suggested Readings

G. Blonston, "Mountain of the Mists" *Science 85* (July/August 1985). An isolated Venezuelan mountain becomes a taxonomist's workshop as rare and unknown species are investigated in this unique ecosystem.

M. Eigen and W. Gardner, "The Origin of Genetic Information" *Scientific American* (April 1981). It is now known how early RNA genes interacted with proteins and how the genetic code developed.

L. Garmon, "As It Was in the Beginning" *Science News* (31 January 1981). Chemists testing origin-of-life theories report laboratory success.

S. Kaveski, L. Margulis and D. C. Mehos, "There's No Such Thing as a One-Celled Plant or Animal" *The Science Teacher* (December 1983). Excellent article explaining why organisms are classified into five kingdoms, not four. Also in this issue is an article by C. R. Granger, "The Classification Conundrum," that further addresses the topic.

N. J. Palleroni, "The Taxonomy of Bacteria" *BioScience* (June 1983). Bacterial classification is discussed in historical perspective.

C. Ponnamperuma, "Cosmochemistry—The Earliest Evolution" *The Science Teacher* (October 1983). Scientists are recreating the conditions of the primitive earth to determine how the chemical building blocks of life were formed.

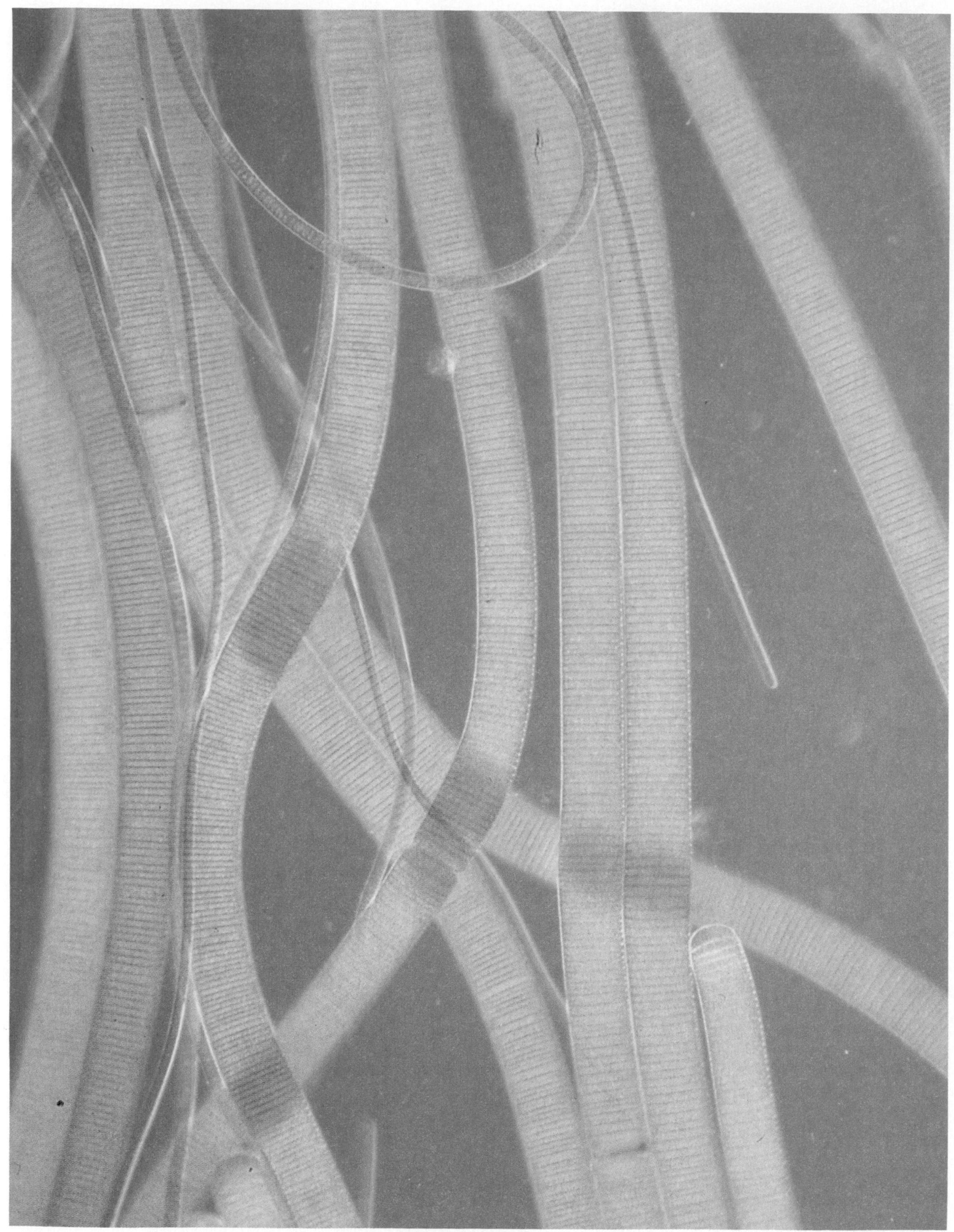

T. E. Adams/VISUALS UNLIMITED

The cyanobacterium *Oscillatoria* is abundant in ponds and streams.

CHAPTER 11

Prokaryotes and Viruses

Introduction

Prokaryotes are microscopic organisms that lack a nucleus and other membrane bounded organelles. They are the most ancient organisms on Earth, and are found in every available habitat. Prokaryotes can be divided into two major groups. The two groups differ in many ways, but both are presently placed in the kingdom Monera. Without prokaryotes, life on earth would be extremely different, and humans, as well as other organisms, would be unable to live. Prokaryotes may be producers, consumers, or decomposers, and they play essential roles in nutrient cycles such as the nitrogen cycle. Although the overwhelming majority of prokaryotes are harmless, some can cause disease, and those are probably the most familiar to you. Other microscopic agents of disease such as viruses, viroids, and prions are not truly living, but they dramatically affect the lives of many different organisms.

Prokaryotes

Guidepost: Where are prokaryotes found, and what are their roles in the biosphere?

11.1 Prokaryotes Are Found Wherever There Is Water

For better or worse, prokaryotes are all around us, on us, and in us. They are found in almost every habitat that contains water or moisture. All prokaryotes are microscopic in size, averaging about 1 μm in diameter. However, they make up for their small size by their enormous numbers. A spoonful of garden soil may contain 10 billion bacteria, and the total number in your mouth is greater than the number of humans who have ever lived. Bacteria cover the skin, line the nose and mouth, live in the gums and between the teeth (figure 11.2), and inhabit the digestive tract in large numbers.

Figure 11.1 Bacteria are extremely small. The scanning electron micrograph in (a) shows the point of a pin magnified 35 times. Bacteria cannot be distinguished. Many bacteria are visible, however, at the greater magnification (175 times) in (b).

© Tony Brain/SPL Science Source

a

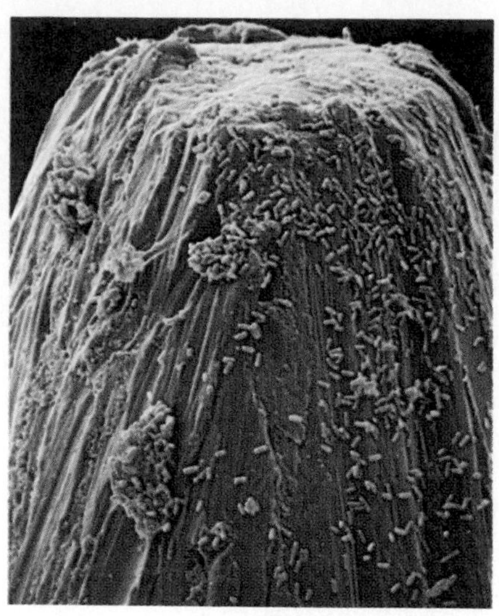

© Tony Brain/SPL Science Source

b

Figure 11.2 Bacteria in the human mouth. This is dental plaque on teeth that had not been brushed for three days. Scanning electron micrograph, $\times 1798$.

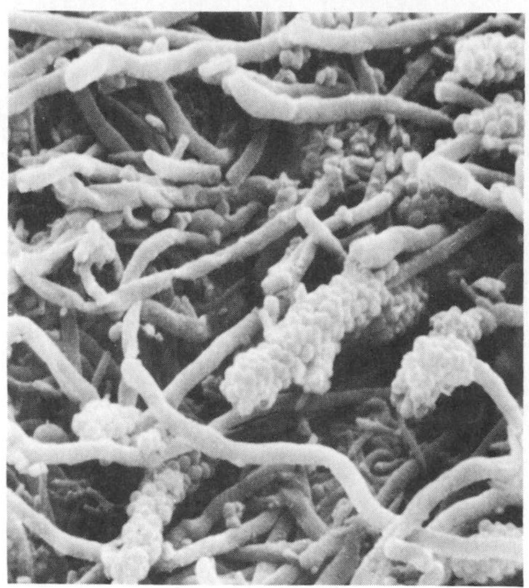

BPS/TOM STACK & ASSOCIATES

Figure 11.3 Bacteria in the human gut break down materials humans cannot digest and release vitamins in the process. Scanning electron micrograph, $\times$ 4225.

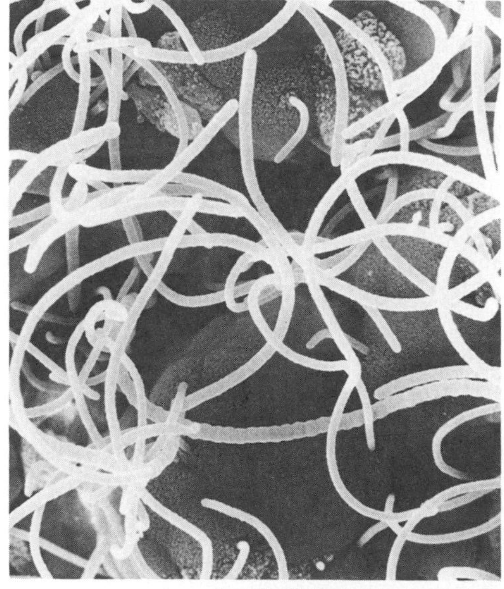

David M. Phillips/VISUALS UNLIMITED

Prokaryotes affect the living world dramatically. Without them, life on earth would be totally different. Without prokaryotes, there would be few decomposers to break down the bodies of dead plants and animals. Without prokaryotes, our oxygen supply would be greatly decreased. Large oxygen-using animals such as humans would find life very difficult without photosynthetic prokaryotes. On the other hand, without prokaryotes, many of the diseases that affect plants, humans, and other animals would be eliminated. Nonetheless, we could not live without prokaryotes. The vast majority are beneficial. For example, bacteria living in our intestines produce essential vitamins that we absorb and use (figure 11.3). Regardless of how they affect other organisms, prokaryotes are found everywhere.

Bacteria are rather simple in structure. In their metabolism, however, they are complex and diverse. Studies of bacteria have concentrated primarily on their role in health and disease, but their role in the environment is of far greater importance. Bacteria play important roles in the cycling of the biologically active gases. Those include nitrogen, oxygen, carbon dioxide, carbon monoxide, sulfur-containing gases, hydrogen, methane, and ammonia. Bacterial photosynthesis and chemosynthesis are essential for cycling the elements and compounds on which the biosphere depends.

Bacteria are essential to all food webs, because they break down complex organic compounds into inorganic materials used by plants. They also transform inorganic materials into complex organic compounds and serve as food for protists and other microorganisms.

Bacteria were probably the first living organisms. Their fossil record goes back 3.5 billion years. By comparison, records of animals date back about 700 million years, and of land plants, 470 million years. Biologists believe that some 2 billion years ago the cyanobacteria started a metabolic revolution that increased the concentration of oxygen in the atmosphere of the earth from less than 1 percent to the present 20 percent.

Figure 11.4 Decomposer bacteria in the soil break down complex organic compounds into inorganic materials used by plants. Some, such as the ones shown here, also produce antibiotics.

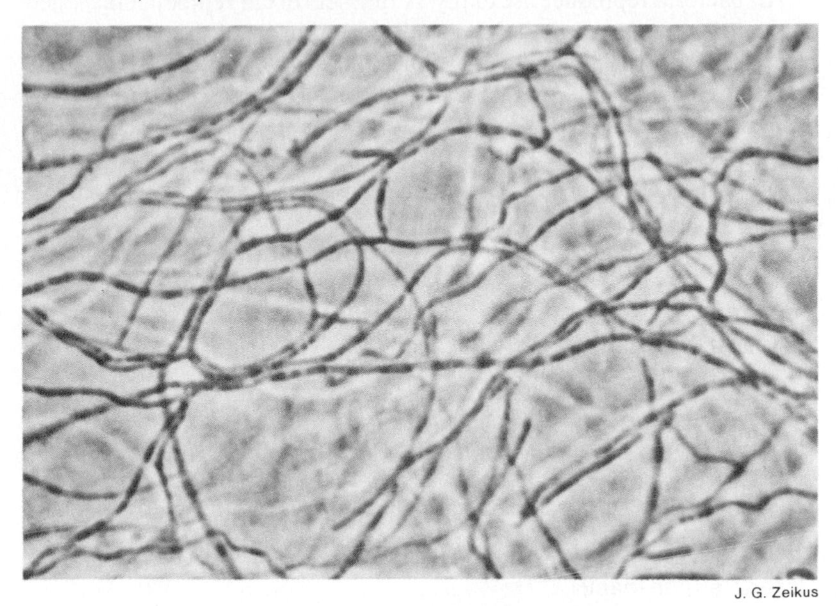

J. G. Zeikus

Figure 11.5 (a) Fossil bacteria *Eoastrion,* thin section through Gunflint chert. These fossils are about 2 billion years old. (b) Modern bacteria very similar to *Eoastrion,* from a microbial mat. (c) Bacteria in (b), magnified 100 times.

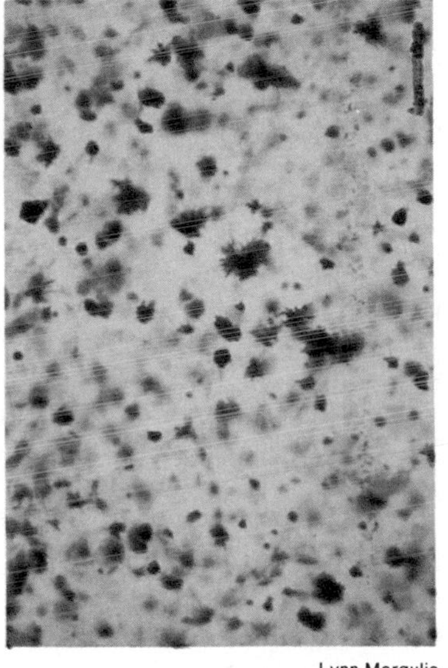

Lynn Margulis

a

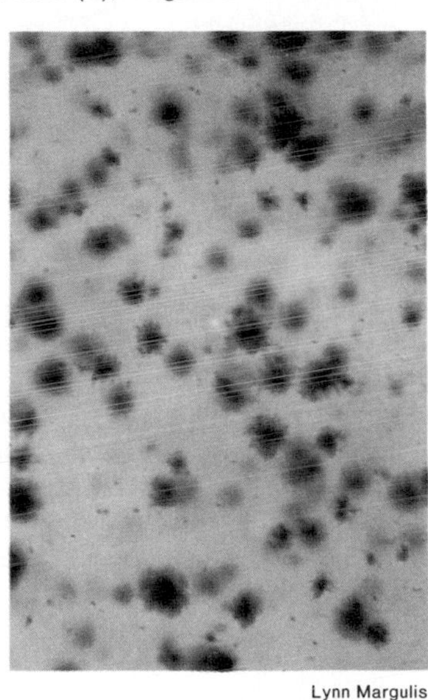

Lynn Margulis

b

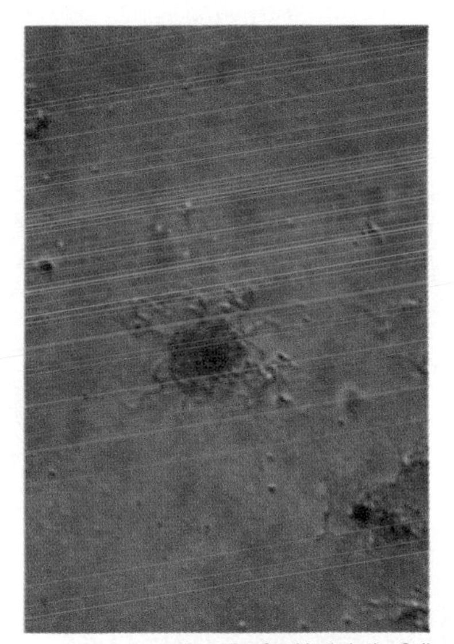

c

Lynn Margulis, *Symbiosis in the Cell Evolution.* Copyright © 1981 W. H. Freeman and Company. Used by permission.

Humans and other animals could not have evolved without that concentration of oxygen.

Bacteria are the most hardy organisms known. They can survive extremely low temperatures, even freezing, for many years. Some species live in boiling hot springs and others in hot acids. They can survive at high pressure in great oceanic depths and at low pressure high in the atmosphere. They can tolerate total drying by forming **spores** (SPORZ),

Figure 11.6 Many bacteria can survive harsh conditions by producing thick-walled spores. Transmission electron micrograph, ×27,540.

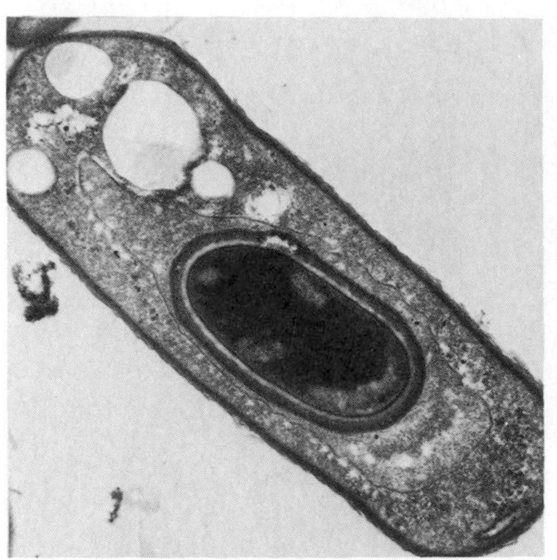

H. S. Pankratz, T. C. Beaman, P. Gerhard/BPS/ TOM STACK & ASSOCIATES

thick-walled structures that contain DNA (figure 11.6). They are among the first organisms to inhabit new environments such as burned or volcanic areas.

All bacteria reproduce asexually. A form of sexual reproduction called conjugation may occur, but the genetic contribution of the parents is not equal. In conjugation, one bacterium injects a portion of its DNA into another. Genetic material also can be transferred between bacteria by viruses. That capability is important to genetic technology, as we saw in chapter 8.

More than 5000 species of bacteria have been described, but the vast majority have not been identified. In the next sections, we will examine a few of the major groups of prokaryotes and their roles in the biosphere.

Investigation 11.1 DISTRIBUTION OF MICROORGANISMS

Introduction

Just where and in what abundance are bacteria and other microorganisms found? In this investigation you will have an opportunity to find out.

Materials (per team)

4 sterile petri dishes with nutrient agar
sterile cotton swabs
glass-marking pencil
transparent tape
dissecting microscope

Procedure

1. Do not yet open any of the petri dishes containing nutrient agar. On the bottom of all 4, write your team's name and the date. Number the dishes from 1 to 4.
2. Do nothing to dish 1.
3. Uncover dish 2 and expose it to the air for 15 to 20 minutes. Teams should select different areas of the laboratory—some in quiet corners, others in traffic areas. Note the exact location in your data book. Cover the dish after exposure.
4. a. Draw a line across the middle of the bottom of dish 2. Mark one side "clean" and the other "dirty." Wipe a sterile cotton swab over part of your lab table. Carefully lift the cover of the dish without completely removing it, as in figure 11.7. Slip in the swab and *gently* rub it over the agar on the side marked "dirty." Be sure the swab does not cut into the agar surface.

Figure 11.7 Innoculating a petri dish.

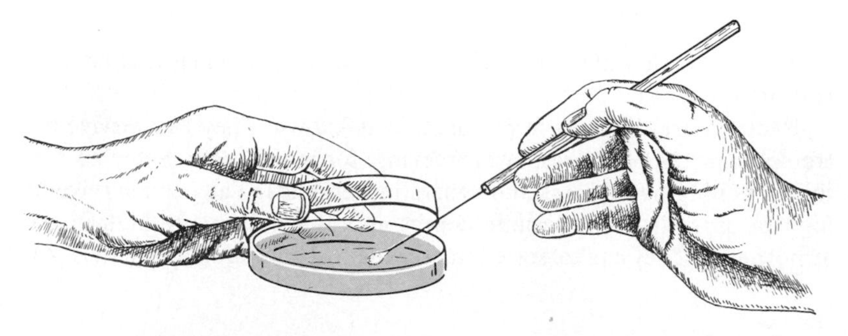

   b. Now carefully wash with soap or detergent and water a small area of your lab table. Use a second swab to wipe that area, and rub it over the agar surface on the side marked "clean."
   c. Instead of wiping the swab over your lab table, you can compare freshly washed laboratory glassware with glassware that has been on the shelf several days.
5. Collect leaves, bark, pebbles, soil, or other materials. Divide dish 4 into 2 to 4 sections. Rub fresh swabs over the materials you have collected and then over the agar surface. Mark the sections with the material used. (It is best to mix the soil with a little water and dip a swab into it.)
6. Tape all petri dishes closed. Incubate all the plates at room temperature for 3 or 4 days. Keep all the plates upside down. This will prevent water droplets that may condense inside the cover from dripping onto the agar.
7. Observe all plates daily, and record your observations. (**CAUTION:** *At no time should you remove the cover of any petri dish.* This is because harmful microorganisms can be picked up and cultivated even on this simple nutrient agar.) Observe all your colonies through the cover. You may want to use a dissecting microscope to help in your observations.
8. Make sketches of the different kinds of colonies and write a description of each. You may have mold colonies present; they are fuzzy and larger than bacterial colonies. Count the number of each kind of colony per plate. On the 4th day, answer the following questions.

Discussion

1. What are the results in plate 1? What was the purpose of plate 1?
2. What are the results in plates 2 through 4?
3. How do you account for the presence or absence of microorganisms on the examined surfaces?
4. Coughing or sneezing may spread droplets from mouth and nose to a distance of 3 m or more. The water in these droplets evaporates rapidly, leaving microscopic bits of dry matter that contain bacteria. Microorganisms from many other sources also may be carried on dust particles. How can you use this information to help interpret the class data?
5. Are microorganisms transmitted by touch alone?
6. In your daily living, how can you protect yourself and others from contamination by microorganisms?

For Further Investigation

Does the kind of medium used in the petri dishes affect the count obtained at any one location? Does the temperature at which the plates are incubated affect the count? Design and carry out experiments that test hypotheses based on these questions.

11.2 Archaebacteria Are Different from All Other Organisms

Archaebacteria (ar kee bak TIR ee uh) have gained attention only recently in the history of microbiology, although the organisms have been on Earth for an extremely long time. Their biochemistry suggests that they were among the earliest organisms on Earth. The first archaebacteria may have lived 3.5 billion years ago.

Figure 11.8 Thermoacidophilic archaebacteria. (a) *Pyrodictium occultum* can grow at temperatures up to 110° C. (b) *Pyrococcus furiosus* grows at temperatures up to 103° C. (c) *Acidianus infernus* grows at temperatures up to 95° C and at pH 1.0 (the pH of concentrated hydrochloric acid). In all three transmission micrographs, the bar = 1 μm.

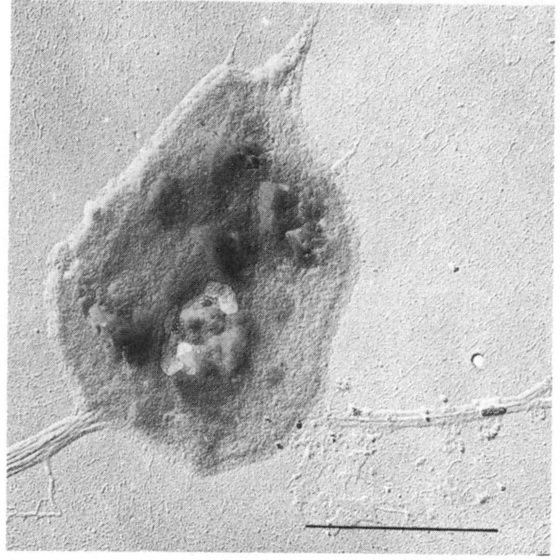

a Prof. K. O. Stetter

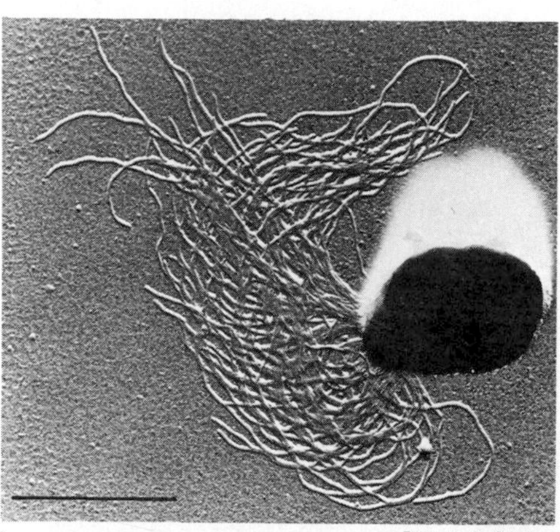

b Prof. K. O. Stetter

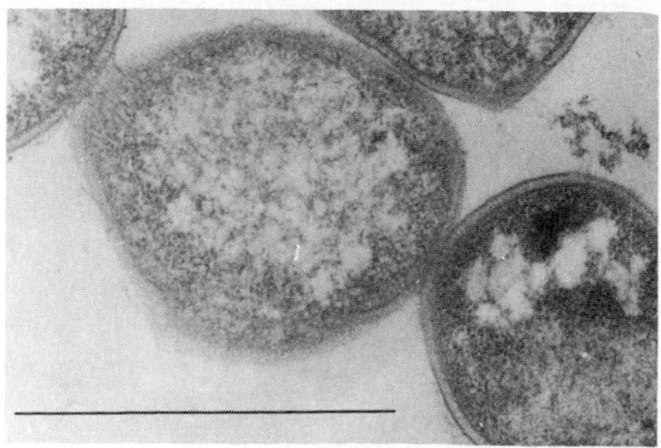

c Prof. K. O. Stetter

Archaebacteria are fundamentally different from all other kinds of life. Although they share some characteristics with the **eubacteria** (yoo bak TIR ee uh), or true bacteria, they have many significant differences. In fact, they are as different from eubacteria as eubacteria are from eukaryotes.

The cell walls of eubacteria contain a carbohydrate called muramic acid, which is never present in the cell walls of archaebacteria. Plasma membranes of archaebacteria contain lipids that are unlike those in membranes of either eubacteria or eukaryotes. Their transfer RNA is different from that of both eubacteria and eukaryotes. Most significant, however, the nucleotide sequence of ribosomal RNA in archaebacteria is different from that of eubacteria.

The study of an organism's RNA can reveal its evolutionary history. All organisms have ribosomal RNA. The sequence of the nucleic acid bases within ribosomal RNA is very stable: it changes little over time. By comparing the RNA of two different organisms, a scientist can estimate relationships of the organisms to each other. If the sequence of the RNA bases is very similar in two organisms, they are thought to be closely related to each other. Conversely, the greater the differences in base sequence, the less closely related are the organisms. Using that analysis, scientists conclude that archaebacteria are distinctly different from all other organisms. Some scientists, therefore, suggest that archaebacteria should be placed in a new kingdom, separate from all other organisms.

11.3 Methanogens Produce Methane Gas

Three distinct groups of organisms have been grouped in the archaebacteria. They are the thermoacidophiles, the extreme halophiles, and the methanogens. The thermoacidophiles live in hot, acidic environments where temperatures average from 80° to 90° C and the water may measure pH 2 or less. Such environments include hot sulfur springs and smoldering piles of coal tailings. In spite of the extremely low external pH, these organisms maintain an internal pH close to neutral (pH 7).

The extreme halophiles require a high concentration of salt to survive, as can be seen in figure 11.9. They can grow in salt brine and often cause discoloration and spoilage of salted fish. The extreme halophiles are found in salty habitats along ocean borders and in salty inland waters such as the Great Salt Lake and the Dead Sea. Some are photosynthetic. Instead of chlorophyll, however, they use bacterial rhodopsin, a pigment very similar to a visual pigment found in our eyes.

The methanogens (figure 11.10) are the best studied and most widely distributed of the archaebacteria. Methanogens are killed by oxygen, so they can live only in **anaerobic** (an eh ROH bik) conditions, where oxygen is excluded. They produce methane (CH_4) gas from hydrogen and carbon dioxide, and they are often found in close association with bacteria that decompose organic matter and release hydrogen gas. Methanogens are common inhabitants of stagnant water, sewage treatment plants, the ocean bottom, hot springs, and the guts of animals, including those of cattle and of humans.

[THER moh a SID uh fylz], [HAL uh fylz] [meh THAN uh jenz] [roh DOP sin]

Figure 11.10 Two methanogens. (a) *Methanobacterium ruminatum,* from cow rumen. The bacterium has nearly finished dividing. (b) *Methanospirillum hungatii.* Transmission electron micrographs; bar = 1 μm.

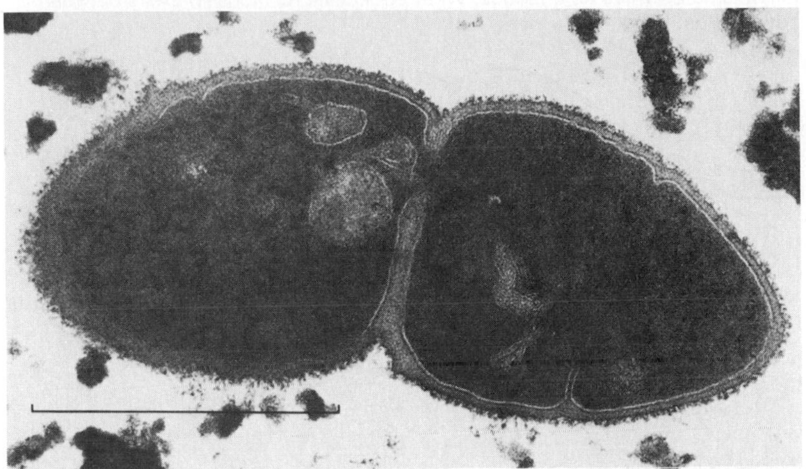

a

J. G. Zeikus; Canadian Journal of Microbiology

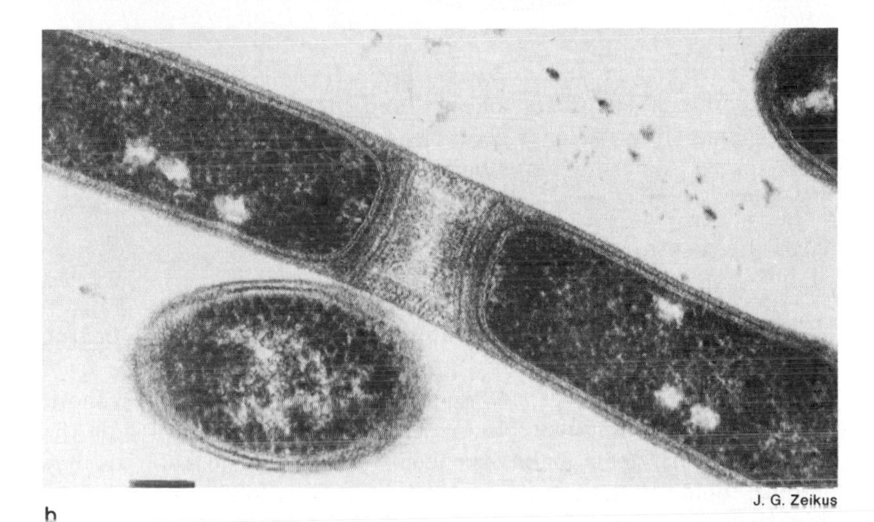

b

J. G. Zeikus

Figure 11.9 Halobacteria require a high concentration of salt to survive. This organism is growing beside a salt crystal (the large rectangle).

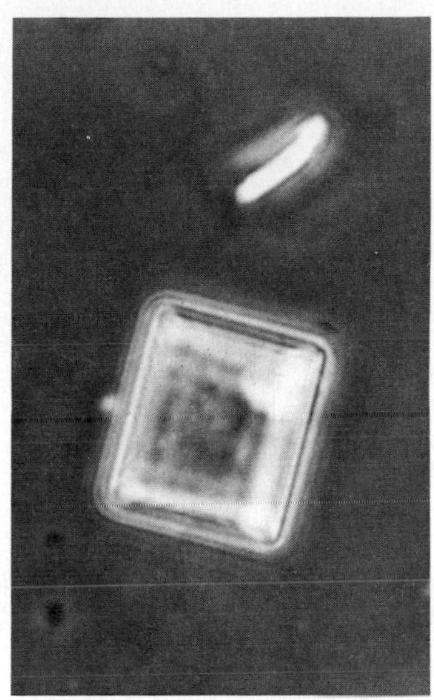

Lynn Margulis, *Five Kingdoms,* 2nd ed., by L. Margulis and K. V. Schwartz, copyright © 1982, 1987, W. H. Freeman and Company.

Cows, goats, deer, sheep, and antelope differ from other herbivores in having a **rumen** (ROO men), a special enlargement of the digestive tract (figure 11.11). Protozoans, eubacteria, and archaebacteria live within the rumen in an unusual ecosystem. The protozoa and bacteria contain enzymes that break down the cellulose in grass and other plant material that the cow eats. The methanogens use the carbon dioxide and hydrogen released by some of those organisms as their source of food, producing methane gas.

Methane gas will burn; hence, it can be used as a fuel if enough is produced and captured. A suggested solution to the growing amount of garbage, sewage, agricultural waste, and manure is to use methanogens to convert those waste materials into methane gas. Around the world people are building methane generators, airtight, anaerobic containers into which organic waste material is placed. Methanogens and various eubacteria are added to the generators, where they grow and reproduce.

Figure 11.11 The complex stomach of a cow. Food is swallowed without being chewed and is stored in the rumen. Later it is brought back into the mouth for chewing. Bacteria in the other parts of the stomach carry on cellulose digestion, for which a cow has no enzymes. What ecological relationship exists between cow and bacteria?

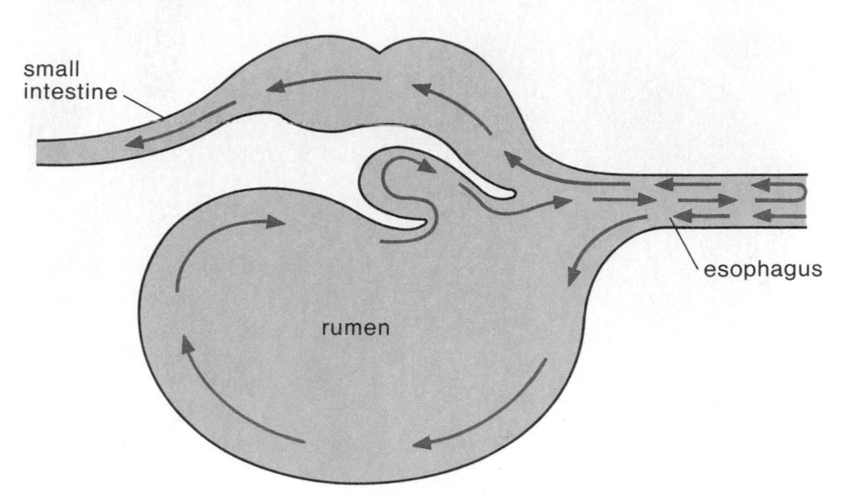

The methanogens produce relatively large amounts of methane gas in such generators. The gas is collected and can be used to heat houses. Such containers could offer solutions to two different environmental problems—waste and garbage buildup, and the energy crisis.

11.4 Eubacteria Include Major Producers in the World

There are many thousands of different species of eubacteria, or true bacteria, and several characteristics are used to distinguish one from another. Most cells are shaped like a rod, a sphere, a spiral, or a short, curved rod, as seen in figure 11.12. They also can be identified on the basis of how they get or make their food and by the waste materials they produce. Some bacteria cluster together or form long chains of individual cells. Bacteria differ in their reactions to certain stains, and in the size, shape, and color of their colonies. While many bacteria move by means of flagella, some glide over surfaces, and spiral shaped bacteria move by using a corkscrew motion that probably involves flagella. Although all eubacteria are microscopic, some are smaller than others. Rickettsia are the smallest known cells, ranging from 0.3 to 0.7 micrometers in diameter. Those tiny organisms, however, have been responsible for many human deaths from diseases such as Rocky Mountain spotted fever, which is transmitted by ticks.

Figure 11.12 The three basic forms of bacteria. Some bacteria occur as single cells; others form colonies in pairs, chains, or irregular clusters.

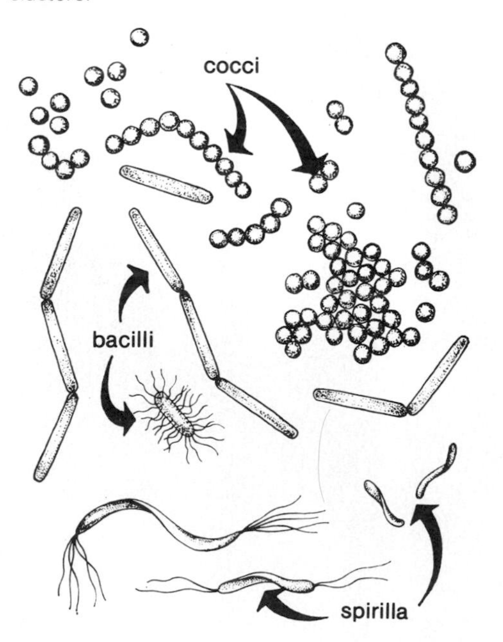

Eubacteria can be considered in two large groups, those bacteria that are producers and those that are consumers. Best known among the producer group are the **cyanobacteria** (SY uh noh bak TIR ee uh), which used to be considered part of the plant kingdom and were called blue-green algae. In their physiology, cyanobacteria are very similar to algae and plants. Like other eubacteria, however, they lack a nucleus and other

Figure 11.13 Cyanobacteria are abundant in all aquatic ecosystems. (a) *Nostoc,* ×600; (b) *Gleocapsa,* ×250, (c) *Calothrix,* ×150.

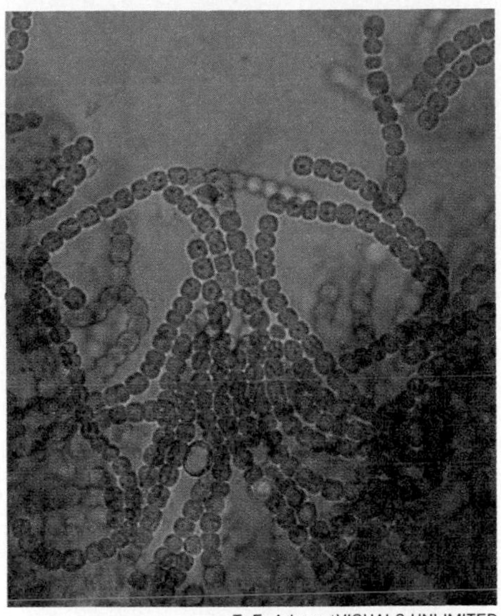

a T. E. Adams/VISUALS UNLIMITED

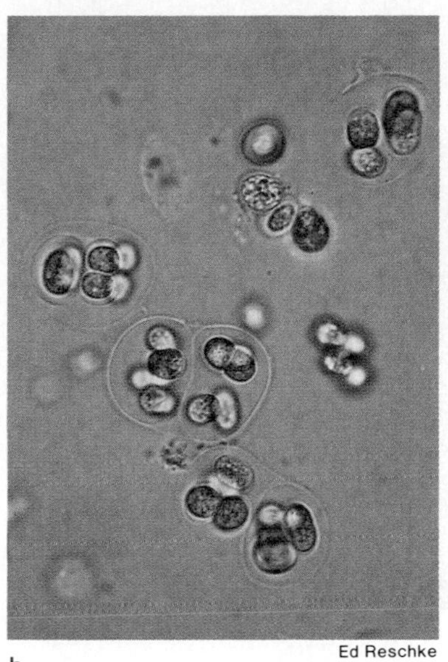

b Ed Reschke

c T. E. Adams/VISUALS UNLIMITED

membrane-bounded organelles. They contain chlorophyll associated with membranes, but the membranes are not organized into chloroplasts as they are in eukaryote cells. Their photosynthesis, however, is like that of plants and algae, and it results in the release of oxygen gas. In fact, cyanobacteria are thought to be primarily responsible for the start of the oxygen revolution that changed the earth's atmosphere and made life possible for large oxygen-using organisms.

Cyanobacteria are among the most hardy of organisms. Some grow in hot springs with water temperatures greater than 70° C, and others grow in dim light under the deep ice of Antarctic lakes. Still others can survive in lakes that are saturated with salt. After aboveground atomic bomb tests in Nevada, a species of cyanobacteria was among the first organisms found within the area of greatest impact. Cyanobacteria grow in fresh and marine water, moist soil, on tree bark, and on snowbanks. They are responsible for algal blooms on freshwater streams and lakes that have been polluted with phosphates. Some of the cyanobacteria grow in colonies that can be seen with the naked eye, although individual cells are microscopic.

A small group of photosynthesizing bacteria known only since the late 1960s is the genus *Prochloron* (figure 11.15). These bacteria look much like a single chloroplast found in eukaryotic algae and plant cells. They contain the same kinds of pigments, and they produce oxygen in photosynthesis. They have been found only in association with a few species of marine organisms.

[proh KLOR on]

Figure 11.14 Many bacteria grow in hot springs such as this one at Yellowstone National Park.

National Park Service

Figure 11.15 *Prochloron* (a) seen through the light microscope, and (b) transmission electron micrograph; bar = 2 μm. Note the photosynthetic membranes around the outer portion of the cell.

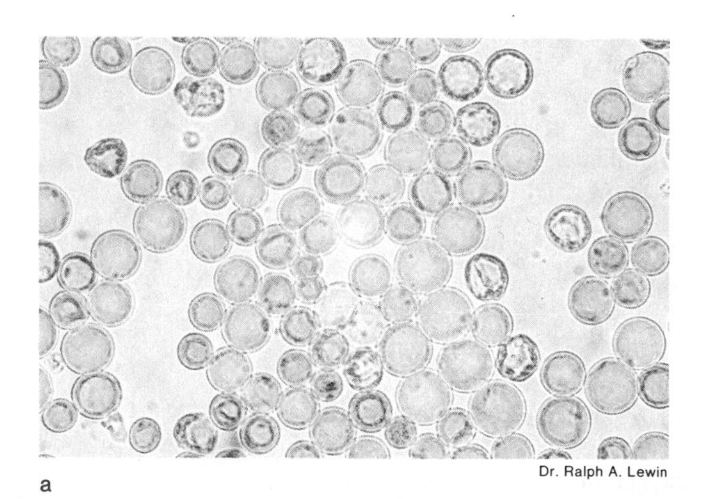

a Dr. Ralph A. Lewin

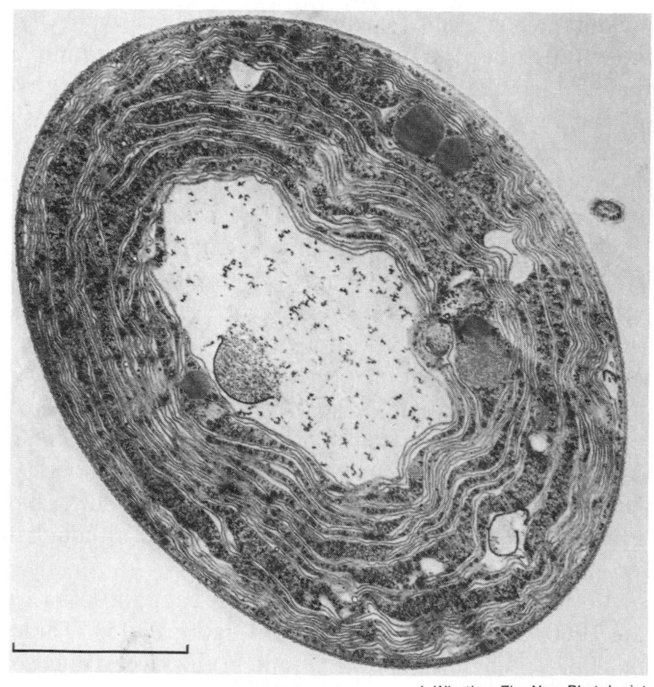

b J. Whatley, The New Phytologist

The other photosynthetic bacteria are anaerobic and, as a result, do not produce oxygen gas in photosynthesis. Based on the pigments present in their cells, these producers are called green bacteria and purple bacteria. Many of them use hydrogen sulfide (H_2S) and release sulfur in the process of photosynthesis. Like plants, however, they synthesize organic compounds from carbon dioxide, and they convert light energy to chemical energy by the same pathway.

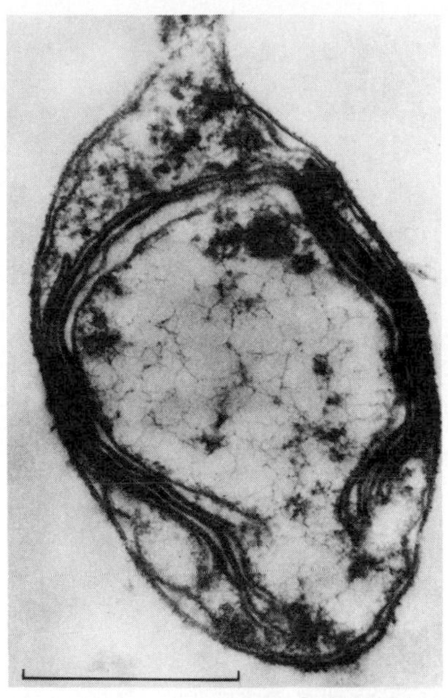
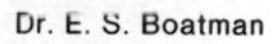

a Dr. E. S. Boatman

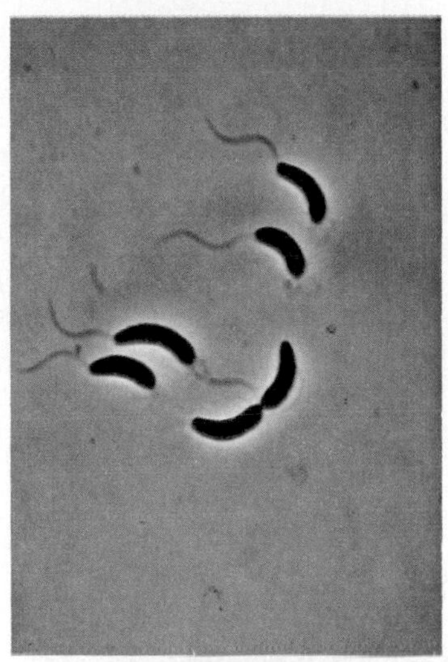

b BSCS/J. G. Zeikus, Dept. of Bacteriology, Univ. of Wisconsin

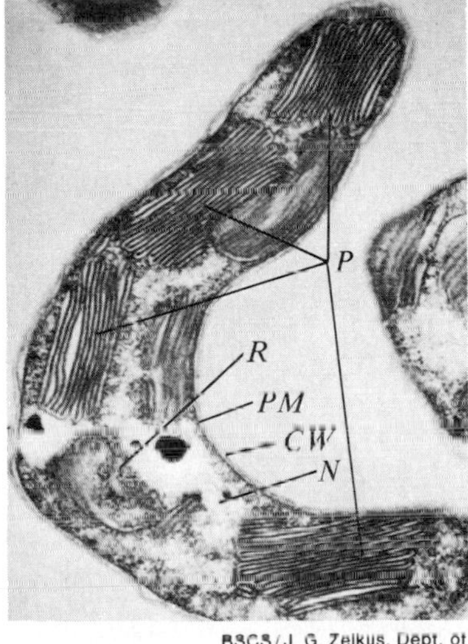

c BSCS/J. G. Zeikus, Dept. of Bacteriology, Univ. of Wisconsin

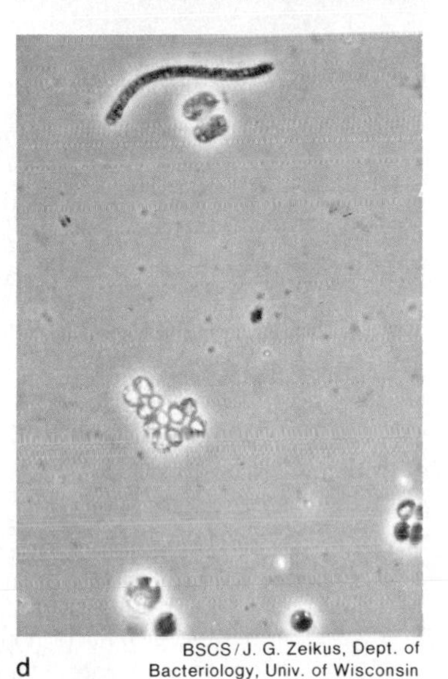

d BSCS/J. G. Zeikus, Dept. of Bacteriology, Univ. of Wisconsin

Figure 11.16 Anaerobic photosynthetic bacteria. (a) Transmission electron micrograph of *Rhodomicrobium vanielli,* a purple nonsulfur bacterium. Note the photosynthetic membranes around the periphery of the cell; bar = 0.5 μm. (b) *Rhodospirillum,* another purple nonsulfur bacterium, can live also as a heterotroph. (c) Transmission electron micrograph of *Ectothiorhodospira mobilis.* P is the photosynthetic membrane system, R indicates ribosomes, PM is the plasma membrane, CW is the cell wall, and N is the nuclear material, not membrane-bounded. (d) Three species of purple sulfur bacteria: *Thiopedia, Thiospirillum,* and *Chromatium.*

11.5 Soil Bacteria Make Possible the Cycling of Nitrogen

Cyanobacteria make their own food using energy from the sun and carbon from carbon dioxide. Most bacteria must get their energy from foods produced by other organisms, either living or dead. If the food source is living, the bacteria are called parasites. If the food source is dead, the bacteria are called decomposers. Still other bacteria neither photosynthesize nor use organic molecules as their source of energy. Instead, they obtain energy from inorganic molecules in the environment. Such bacteria are called **chemoautotrophic** (kee moh awt oh TROH fik). Both chemoautotrophic and decomposer bacteria play important roles in the nitrogen cycle.

Nitrogen is essential to all living things. It is found in two of the four kinds of biological molecules needed for life, proteins and nucleic acids. Most of the world's nitrogen is actually found in the atmosphere as a

Figure 11.17 The nitrogen cycle.

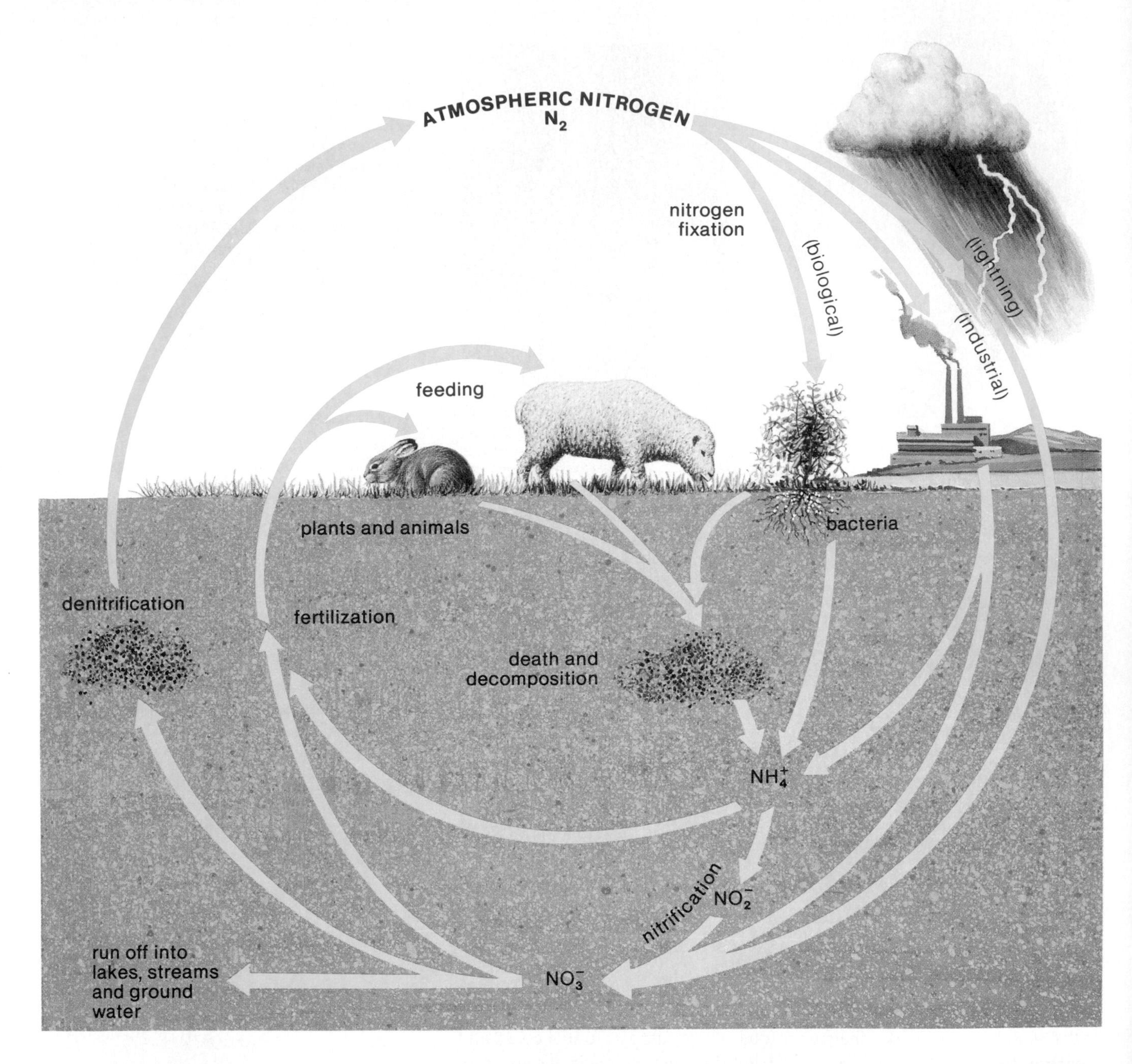

gas. Although nitrogen gas (N_2) makes up about 78 percent of the atmosphere, neither plants nor animals can use the nitrogen in that form. You inhale nitrogen with every breath you take, but exhale it unused. Recall from chapter 4 how the element carbon cycles through a community and back into the physical environment from which it came. Nitrogen also cycles back and forth from the abiotic to the biotic parts of the ecosystem. Study the nitrogen cycle shown in figure 11.17 as you read the remainder of this section.

Figure 11.18 (a) Soybean roots bearing abundant nodules formed by a species of *Rhizobium*. (b) Alfalfa nodule cells packed with actively nitrogen-fixing *Rhizobium*. Scanning electron micrograph ×270; bar = 10 μm.

a The Nitragin Company

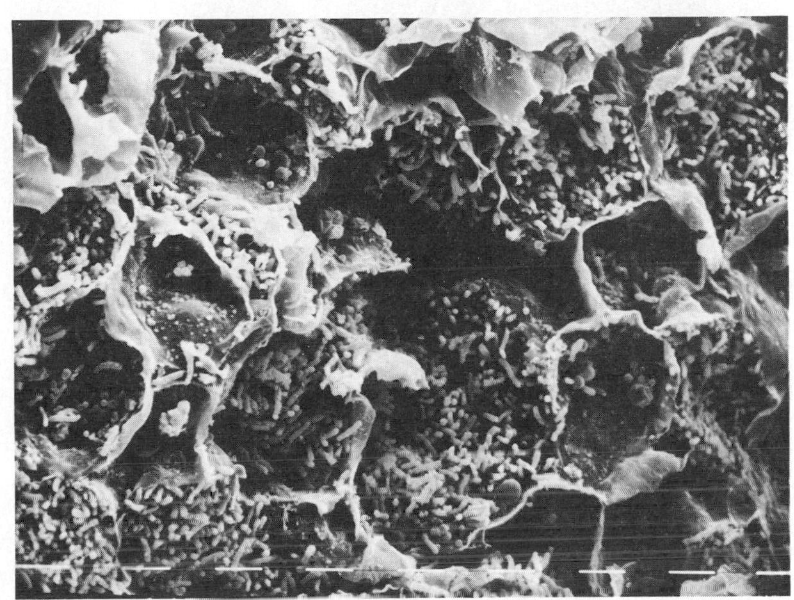

b C. P. Vance/VISUALS UNLIMITED

All consumers get nitrogen-containing compounds in the things they eat. All food, of course, can be traced to producers. Producers get their nitrogen-bearing compounds from the soil (or the water) in which they grow. Nitrogen gas is present in the soil, dissolved in water. Living in the soil or in the roots of certain plants are **nitrogen-fixing bacteria.** They can "fix" nitrogen, converting it to a form they or other organisms can use. Nitrogen fixers convert nitrogen gas to ammonia (NH_3), which can be used to synthesize proteins and other nitrogen-containing compounds.

Centuries ago, farmers discovered that soils in which clover had been grown produced better crops than did other soils. In addition to clover, other members of the legume family, such as peas, beans, and alfalfa, have the same effect on the soil. We know today the crops grow better because of an increase in the nitrates in the soil. The increased nitrate level in the soil is the result of nitrogen fixation and chemical reactions following fixation. However, it is not the plants that fix the nitrogen, but bacteria. Bacteria of the genus *Rhizobium* live in the roots of many legumes. The bacteria induce the plant to form swellings called **nodules** (NOD yoolz) on its roots (figure 11.18). Under favorable conditions,

[ry ZOH bee um]

Figure 11.19 Nitrifying bacteria. (a) *Nitrosomonas* converts amonia (NH_3) to nitrite (NO_2^-). (b) *Nitrobacter winogradskyi* converts nitrite to nitrate (NO_3^-). Transmission electron micrographs, (a) ×47,307; (b) ×83,226.

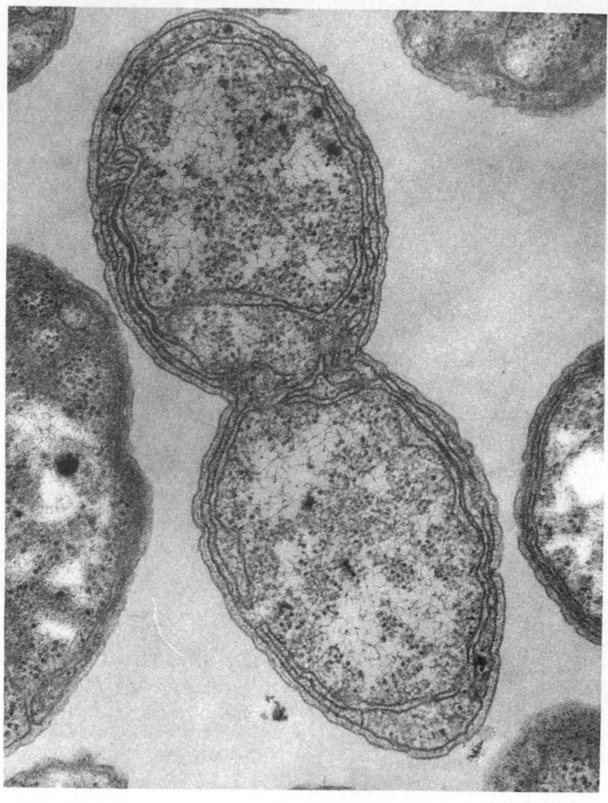

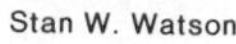

Stan W. Watson

a

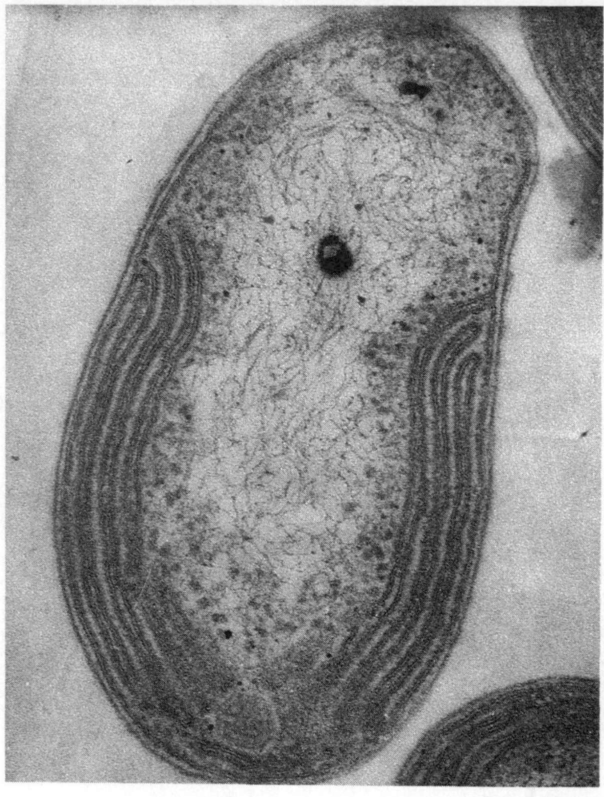

b

Stan W. Watson
American Society for Microbiology

root-nodule bacteria can fix as much as 225 kg of nitrogen per hectare per year. Some free-living bacteria and many cyanobacteria also have the ability to fix nitrogen. The ammonia produced by nitrogen-fixing bacteria can be used by the legume plants or can spill into the ground and be used by bacteria or other plants.

Decomposers in the soil break down the complex organic compounds in dead plant and animal bodies. They use the energy in those compounds and convert them to simpler substances. The chief nitrogen-containing substance is ammonia. Ammonia is a gas, and some of it escapes into the atmosphere. However, it also dissolves readily in water. In soil water, ammonia reacts chemically with hydrogen ions to form ammonium ions (NH_4^+) In the form of ammonium ions, nitrogen may be absorbed by the roots of plants. It is then built into living material again by the plants.

Other chemical reactions also may occur in the soil. Two groups of bacteria called **nitrifying** (NY trih fy ing) **bacteria** continue the nitrogen cycle. One group changes ammonium ions (NH_4^+) to nitrite ions (NO_2^-). The other group changes the nitrite ions to nitrate ions (NO_3^-). Plants can absorb the nitrates from the soil and use them to build proteins.

Both groups of nitrifying bacteria are chemoautotrophic. They are producers because they make their own food, but instead of using energy from the sun as plants do, they use energy from chemical compounds.

Nitrifying bacteria operate only under **aerobic** (eh ROH bik) environmental conditions, when oxygen is available in the soil. Oxygen dissolves into soil water from the air spaces found between soil particles.

Sometimes, all the spaces fill up with water, leaving no room for air. When that happens, the soil environment becomes anaerobic. Under anaerobic conditions, nitrifying bacteria cannot carry on their activities. **Denitrifying** (dee NY trih fy ing) **bacteria** however, thrive in such anaerobic environments. They change any remaining nitrates to nitrogen gas. The nitrogen gas gradually escapes back into the atmosphere, and the cycle of nitrogen is complete.

Self-Review

1. In what ways are prokaryotes important in the biosphere?
2. In what ways do archaebacteria differ from other bacteria?
3. How can methanogens help with the energy crisis?
4. What characteristics do microbiologists use to distinguish eubacteria?
5. What important atmospheric change was caused by cyanobacteria?
6. What are the principal nitrogen-bearing nutrients used by producers?
7. What is nitrogen fixation and where do nitrogen-fixers live?
8. How is nitrogen returned from organisms to the atmosphere?

Microorganisms and Disease

Guidepost: What is the relationship between a pathogen and a disease?

11.6 All Organisms Can Suffer from Disease

Disease is a condition of an organism that interferes to some degree with its ability to perform a vital function. Every living organism can suffer from a disease of one kind or another. **Pathology** is the study of diseases, especially of the changes they cause in the organism.

Pathologists now know that many diseases are caused by microorganisms such as the bacteria discussed in this chapter. Some of the protists and fungi, as well as some animals, about which you will learn in the next two chapters, also can cause disease. Humans have not always known that diseases can be caused by infectious agents. Primitive people thought that disease came from an evil spirit that entered the body. The cure for the illness was to frighten or coax the spirit out of the body. That became the function of a medicine man, or shaman, who may have used mask, rattles, and charms. Even early humans, however, did not rely entirely on magic. If a "patient" had a toothache, the medicine man might have shaken his rattle, but at the same time he might have applied coca leaves to ease the pain. Coca leaves contain cocaine, a very strong pain reliever. Today, your dentist might say your toothache was caused by a buildup in the population of tooth-decaying bacteria. Your dentist would not give you coca leaves for your pain, but he or she might inject cocaine to numb your mouth. You also would be instructed to brush your teeth more often so the bacteria do not build up again.

The first evidence that diseases might be caused by microorganisms came from the study of a plant disease. Late in the summer of 1845, potato plants throughout northern Europe were struck by a disease called a blight. Almost overnight, whole fields of potatoes became black masses

Figure 11.20 Navaho medicine man, administering chant to mother and baby for better health.

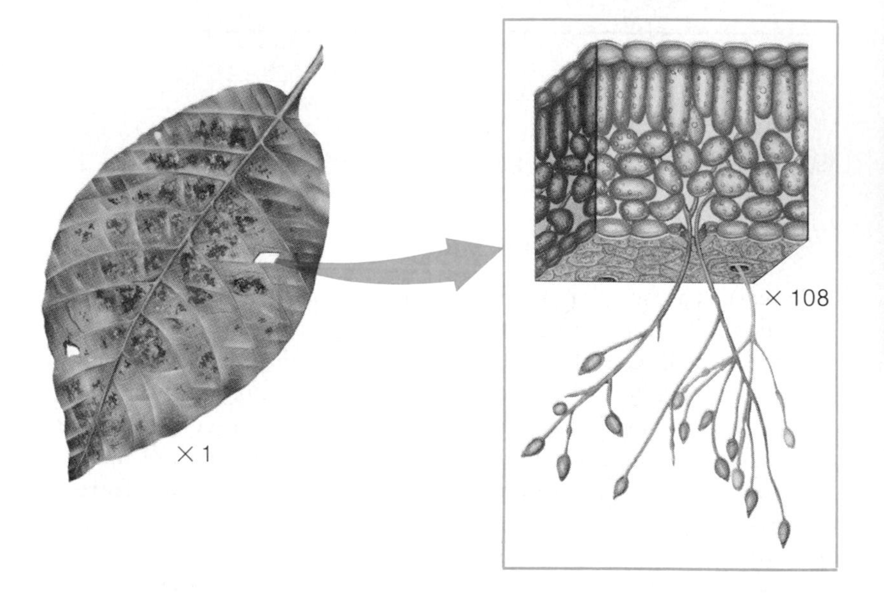

Figure 11.21 Late blight of potato. Infected leaflet (left). Section through the leaflet with hyphae of the fungus growing from it (right). The hyphae bear spore cases. (Note that the cube on the right is a very small piece lifted from the leaf on the left.)

of rotting plants. In Ireland the consequences of the blight were disastrous because most of the people depended on potatoes as their main food. During the next two years nearly half a million Irish died in the famine, and 2 million emigrated to America.

Scientists investigated the crop failure and famine and found that a fungus was present in the dead potato plants. Did the fungus kill the plants or did it appear because the plants were already dead? It took many years of investigation, but by 1861, scientists had gathered convincing evidence that the blight was caused by the fungus in the potato plants. By the end of the nineteenth century most scientists agreed that microorganisms could cause disease. In fact, it seemed that all diseases might be caused by microorganisms such as bacteria and fungi. Diseases are not so simple, however. Today, pathologists recognize many diseases in which microorganisms play little or no part.

Figure 11.22 Rickets is caused by a deficiency of vitamin D. Without adequate vitamin D, calcium cannot be absorbed from the gut and bones do not develop properly, resulting in the bending seen here in this x-ray of a 10-month-old child.

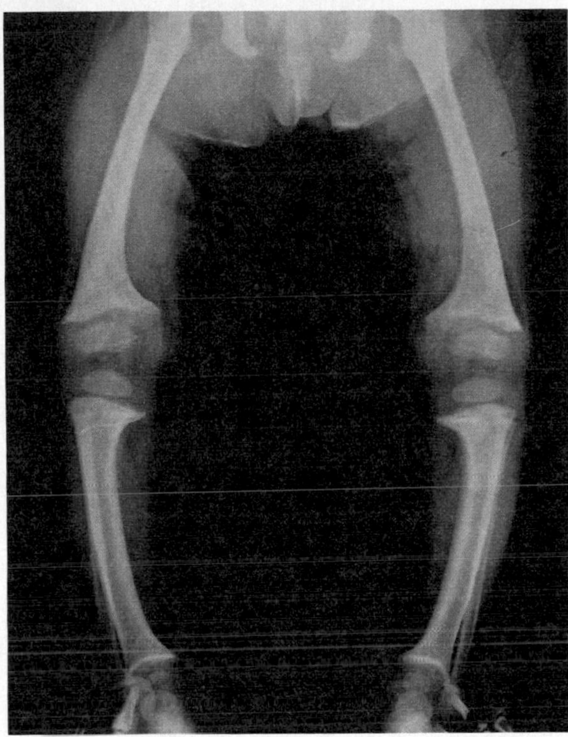

George P. Bogumill, M.D.

11.7 Disease May Be Caused by a Variety of Factors

Diseases may be classified into five broad groups. First, we have diseases that are caused by microorganisms. They are called infectious diseases, and we sometimes call the microorganism a germ. Colds, influenza, and the potato blight are all infectious diseases. The other four groups of diseases are noninfectious.

Deficiency diseases are one group of noninfectious diseases. They develop when some necessary substance is lacking in an organism's diet. Scurvy, for example, is a human disease caused by a deficiency of vitamin C. Sailors learned to take limes and oranges on their long voyages to ensure a constant source of vitamin C and, as a result, sailors became known as limeys. Without the vitamin C source, the sailors were likely to develop scurvy, which causes bleeding gums and loss of teeth.

A second group of noninfectious diseases is environmental diseases. These diseases are on the rise in the United States and other industrialized nations today. Such disorders result from reaction to substances that invade the body of an organism but do not reproduce there. Asthma is such a disease. It often results when people inhale plant pollens. Other environmental diseases occur when people are exposed to pollutants. Coal miners may develop black lung, an environmental disease caused by breathing coal dust. Asbestos workers may develop lung and other diseases caused by intake of asbestos particles. Offices and school buildings have been stripped of the asbestos in their walls and ceilings to prevent lung diseases in workers and students. Some disease-causing pollutants

Figure 11.23 Automobile exhaust contains many harmful substances.

John Pawloski/TOM STACK & ASSOCIATES

Figure 11.24 Cancer in lungs from a heavy smoker. Arrow indicates cancerous area.

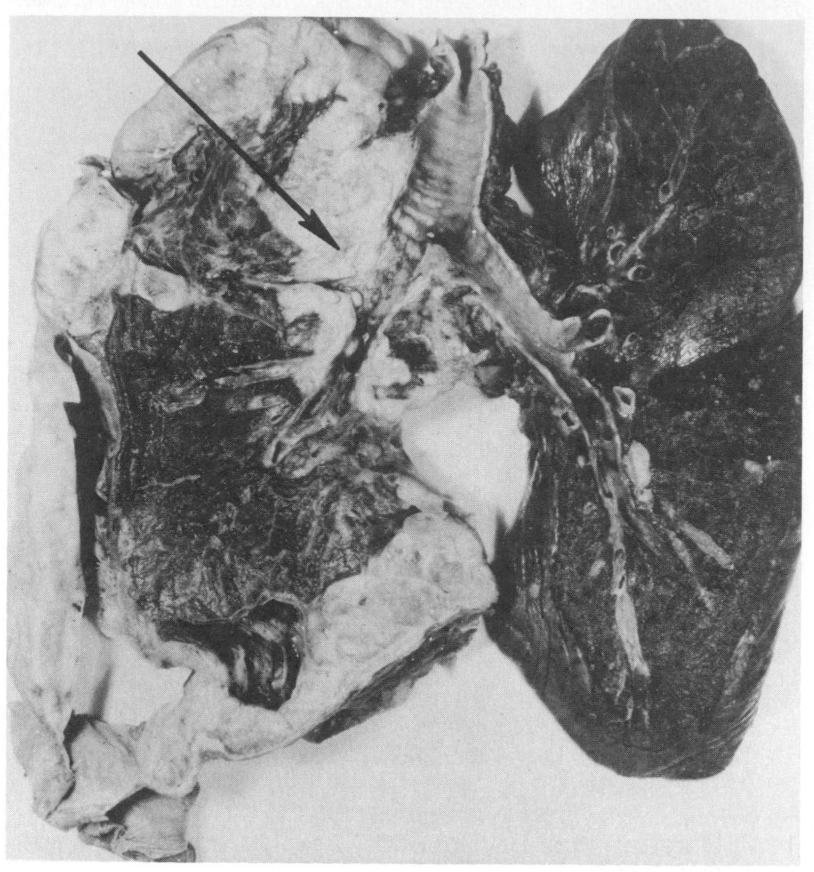

American Cancer Society

affect everyone in the community. The waste gases from automobiles have become a general threat to human health (figure 11.23). Among other poisonous substances in automobile waste gas is lead, which affects the nervous system. In some cities the amount of lead in the air has become great enough to damage the health of people who live there.

Hereditary diseases make up the third group of noninfectious diseases. Hereditary diseases are disorders passed on by inheritance from one generation to the next. Tay-Sachs disease, which was described in section 8.2, is one example. Cystic fibrosis, a genetic disorder that results in production of abnormally thick mucus secretions, is another.

The fourth group of noninfectious diseases is the degenerative diseases, which are disorders in the functioning of an organism's body—usually as it becomes old. Heart disease and some forms of arthritis are examples. You will learn more about some of those diseases in the remaining chapters.

Cancer is difficult to classify. Cancer is the second greatest cause of death in the United States, but there is still much to learn about it. A cancer is a rapidly spreading group of abnormal cells. Although viruses may be involved in certain human cancers, such as leukemia, hereditary factors appear to be necessary for cancers to develop. Many cancers are started by chemicals that a person takes in from the environment. Those may be tars in tobacco smoke, chemicals used in manufacturing plastics, or nuclear wastes. Thus, cancer may be an environmental, an infectious, and a hereditary disease.

Figure 11.25 Incidence of gonorrhea in the United States between 1956 and 1981.

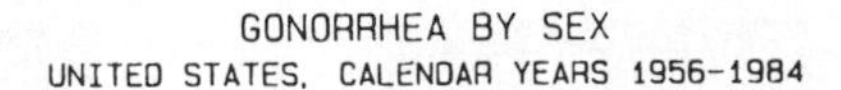

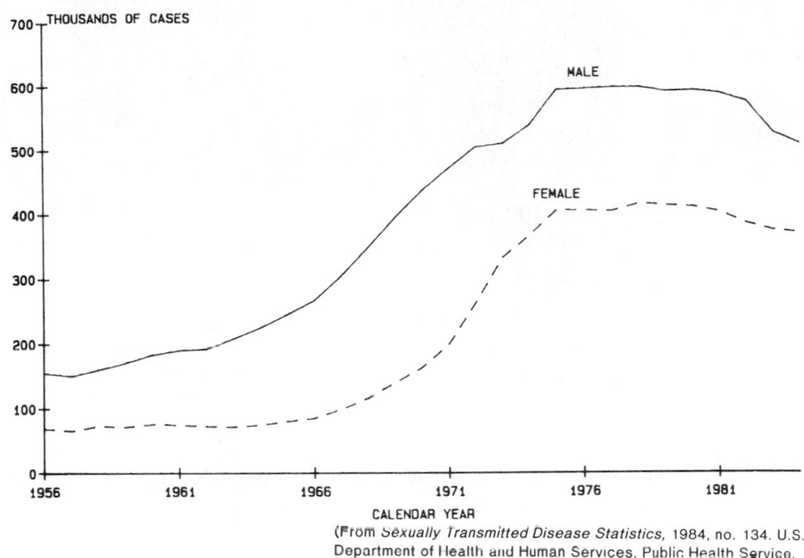

(From *Sexually Transmitted Disease Statistics,* 1984, no. 134. U.S. Department of Health and Human Services, Public Health Service, Centers for Disease Control, Atlanta, GA.)

11.8 Hosts Spread Pathogens Directly or Through Vectors to Other Hosts

An infectious disease results from an interaction between two organisms. One is the **pathogen** (PATH uh jen) that causes the disease. The second is the host, or infected organism. Their relationship is parasitic: the pathogen is parasitic on the host. Not all parasites in the world are pathogens. For instance, a parasite may live at the expense of another organism without producing symptoms (signs of illness) in the host. On the other hand, an organism that is not a parasite may still be involved in a disease. An example is the fungus associated with athlete's foot. The fungus is not a parasite, but a decomposer living on the dead layers of your skin. Yet, if you suffer from athlete's foot, you certainly have a disease.

How do infectious diseases spread? Actually, the disease itself cannot be transmitted, or carried. Rather, it is the pathogen that is transmitted from host to host. The pathogen infects a new host, and then that host may develop the disease. To control the spread of an infectious disease, it is necessary to control the transmission of the pathogen.

Some pathogens are transmitted directly from host to host. Sexually transmitted diseases, such as syphilis, herpes, gonorrhea, and acquired immune deficiency syndrome (AIDS) are examples of diseases spread by direct transmission. Gonorrhea is one of the most widespread human diseases, even though excellent drugs are available to treat it. The disease is caused by a bacterium (figure 11.26) that is killed rapidly by drying, sunlight, or ultraviolet light, but survives inside the human body. Gonorrhea pathogens are transmitted from an infected person to another person by way of moist membranes of the sex organs. In females, infection usually causes mild irritation of the vagina, and often goes unnoticed. In males, however, the organism causes a painful infection of the urethra. It also can cause eye infections in newborns and adults.

Figure 11.26 The bacterium that causes gonorrhea, *Neisseria gonorrhoeae,* ×21,000.

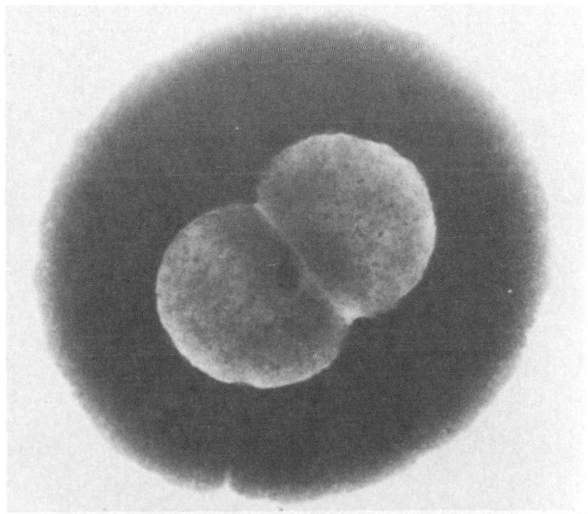

Center for Disease Control/BPS/TOM STACK & ASSOCIATES

Figure 11.27 Transmission of malaria. What would be the best way to stop the spread of this disease?

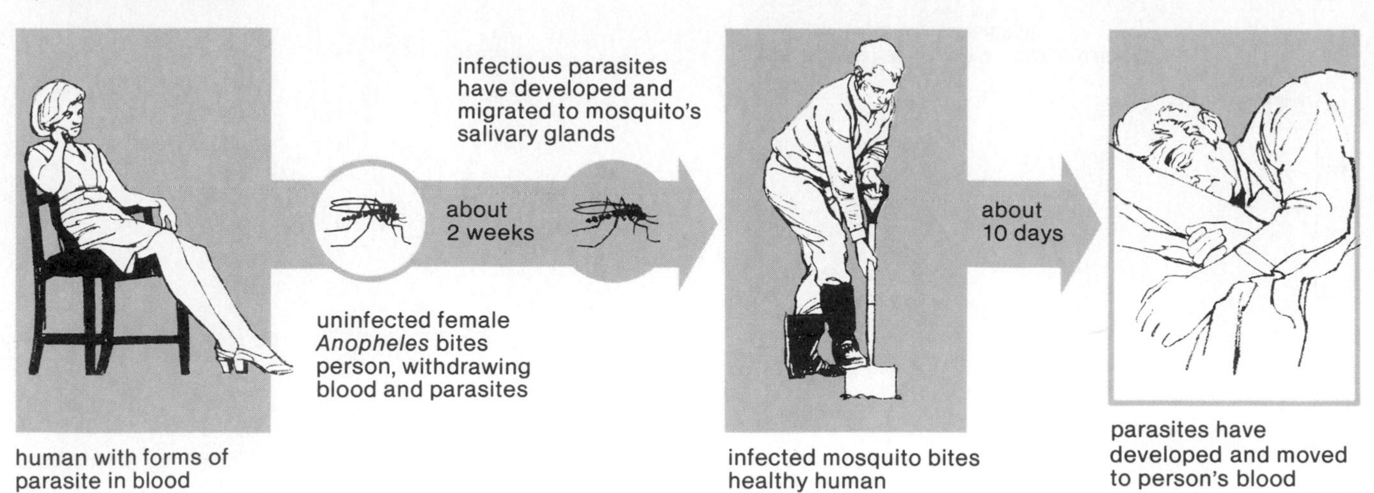
infectious parasites have developed and migrated to mosquito's salivary glands
about 2 weeks
about 10 days
uninfected female *Anopheles* bites person, withdrawing blood and parasites
human with forms of parasite in blood
infected mosquito bites healthy human
parasites have developed and moved to person's blood

Gonorrhea can be cured with **antibiotics,** chemicals that kill or slow the growth of microorganisms. Nonetheless, the incidence of gonorrhea infections remains high for three reasons. One is the mildness of symptoms in females, so that an infected female can unknowingly infect many males. Another is the widespread use of oral contraceptives, which bring about a change in the pH of the vagina that allows the bacteria to grow more readily. Finally, for reasons not yet understood, acquired immunity does not develop, so repeated infections are possible.

Some diseases such as malaria are transmitted indirectly from one host to another by a third organism that carries the pathogen. The pathogen-carrier is called a **vector.** In the case of malaria, the pathogen is a protist of the genus *Plasmodium,* and the vector is a mosquito. If an infected person happens to be bitten by a female mosquito of the genus *Anopheles,* the pathogens may be picked up by the insect. In the mosquito's body the *Plasmodium* undergo many changes. The microorganisms migrate through the mosquito's body to its salivary glands. When the female mosquito bites another human, it injects saliva into the blood of its victim. The malarial parasites are injected along with the saliva. In that way the disease is transmitted to a new host. The pathogens travel through the bloodstream to the human's liver, where they multiply. Their offspring move back into the blood and enter the host's red blood cells. The parasites continue to multiply, and as they do, they destroy blood cells. The destruction of blood cells takes place at definite intervals. At those times the host experiences alternating violent chills and high fever, the principal symptoms of the disease.

Thus, malaria can get from one human host to another only when a mosquito carries it. The pathogen, *Plasmodium,* lives in two different organisms at different times of its life—a human and a mosquito. In other words, the pathogen requires **alternate hosts** in order to complete its life cycle. A pathogen that requires alternate hosts can occur only in places where both hosts live. Rocky Mountain spotted fever is caused by a ricksettsia. The alternate hosts of the pathogen are ticks and humans or rodents. African sleeping sickness is caused by a protist carried by tsetse flies and humans or cattle. In the United States today, diseases involving alternate hosts are not common. That is because we have been

Figure 11.28 Distribution of tsetse flies in Africa. Into what parts of the world would African sleeping sickness most likely spread?

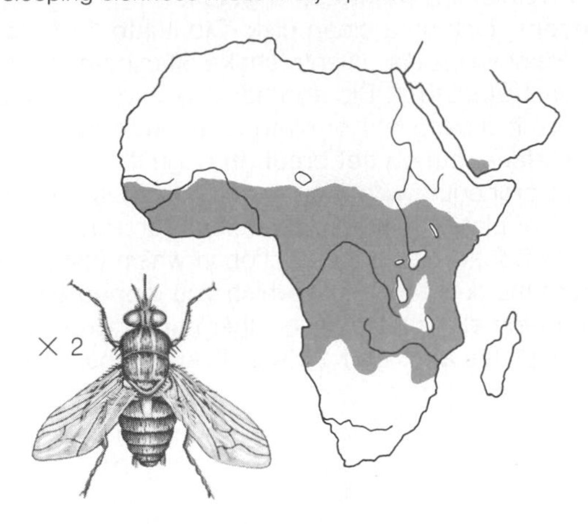

able to control the alternate hosts through sanitary measures. Malaria, for example, has almost disappeared wherever *Anopheles* mosquito populations have been destroyed. In addition, constant checking by public health specialists helps prevent transportation of disease organisms around the world.

Investigation 11.2 CONTROL OF BACTERIA

Introduction

In this investigation you will observe some relationships of bacteria and substances used to control them.

Materials (per team)

4 antiseptic disks
4 antibiotic disks
8 disks with no chemicals
broth cultures of *Micrococcus luteus* and *Escherichia coli*
4 sterile nutrient agar plates
glass-marking pencil
forceps
sterile cotton swabs
transparent tape

Procedure

1. With a glass-marking crayon, mark the bottoms of the plates as follows: Label your 4 plates A, B, C, and D. Divide each plate into 4 sections. Number the sections 1, 2, 3, and 4. On plates B and D, print "control."
2. **CAUTION:** *In this investigation you should follow the same sterile procedures and cautions as in investigation 11.1.* Using a sterile cotton swab, streak the entire surface of plates A and B with *Micrococcus luteus* as shown in figure 11.29.
3. Streak the entire surface of plates C and D with *Escherichia coli*.
4. Use forceps to place 1 disk with no chemical in each section of plates B and D.

Figure 11.29 Two patterns for streaking culture plates.

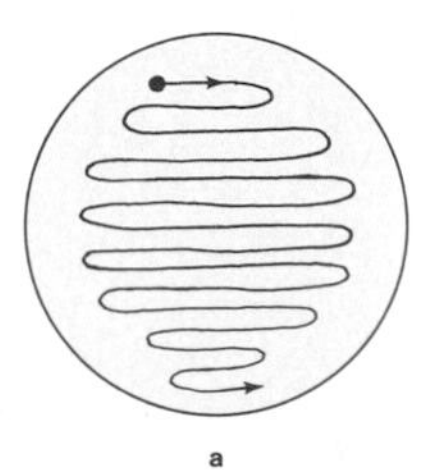

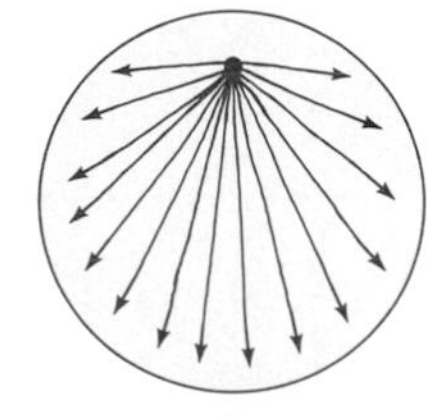

5. Your teacher will have a variety of antiseptic, disinfectant, and antibiotic solutions. Choose any 4 of these. Make certain, however, that at least 1 disk is dipped into an antibiotic.
6. Using forceps, pick up a clean disk. Dip it into 1 of the solutions you selected. Remove the disk. Gently shake off excess liquid. Quickly place it in section 1 of plate A. Dip another disk into the same solution. Dry it, and place it in section 1 of plate C. Be sure the disks are stuck to the agar surface, but do not break through it.
7. Repeat this procedure with 3 other solutions, placing them in sections 2, 3, and 4 of plates A and C. Use clean forceps for each solution.
8. In your data book, record the section in which you placed each disk. Also record the substance into which you dipped each disk.
9. Cover and tape all 4 plates. Invert them and incubate at 37° C.
10. Observe all plates after 1 or 2 days. Record your observations.

Discussion

1. What do the clear areas indicate?
2. What evidence do you have that the inhibition of microorganisms is due to the chemicals on the disk and not the disks themselves?
3. Which of the 2 species of bacteria is more sensitive to all the chemicals?
4. Which product would you use to control *Micrococcus luteus?* To control *Escherichia coli?*
5. *E. coli* are normally harmless bacteria that live in the human intestines. Does the reaction of *E. coli* to antibiotics suggest that antibiotics should be used only when necessary? Explain.
6. How does an antibiotic differ from a disinfectant?

For Further Investigation

Test different concentrations of the same antibiotic. Be sure to have at least 1 antibiotic disk and 1 antiseptic disk in each plate to compare their effects.

11.9 Not Everyone Is Affected in the Same Way by the Same Pathogen

Some people never seem to get sick. How serious an infectious illness becomes depends on the characteristics of both the host and pathogen. The ability of a pathogen to cause disease is called its **virulence** (VIR yuh lents). The ability of a host to cope with a pathogen is called its **resistance.** A pathogen with high virulence may cause death in a host with low resistance. A host with high resistance may show only mild symptoms of the disease. During a famine, more people die from disease than from starvation. At such times a moderately virulent pathogen may produce serious illness because many hosts have lowered resistance. A host that is poorly nourished has much less resistance than a well-fed host. The improved diet of the United States population in the past half century probably has been an important factor in reducing cases of tuberculosis and other infectious diseases.

What determines the virulence of a pathogen? That is a complex problem. Most pathogens are harmful because of the poisonous substances, or **toxins,** they produce. As the pathogens multiply, more toxins are produced and released into your body. Those toxins may kill your cells and cause other symptoms of disease. Some pathogens are extremely virulent because they produce potent toxins. Consider the organism that produces tetanus. If a person steps on a rusty nail, this pathogen may enter the body. Although the pathogen rarely leaves the wound, it produces a deadly toxin that affects the central nervous system, causing muscle spasms that can lead to death of the host.

In addition, a pathogen can be very virulent if it has the ability to spread rapidly through the body of the host. The pathogen that causes pneumonia is such an organism. Although it does not produce a potent toxin, it grows and reproduces in tremendous numbers after it invades the host's lungs. Because there are so many pathogens, they can cause extensive lung damage, and even death of the host.

In winter you can sit in your classroom and listen to your classmates sneeze, sniffle, and cough. Not everyone in the class is sick, and of those who are sick, some are more sick than others. Why do different individuals of the same host species have different degrees of resistance to a pathogen? That is another complex problem. We can develop varieties of domestic plants and animals that are more resistant to particular diseases than are other varieties. It seems, therefore, that some resistance involves inherited characteristics.

On the other hand, much resistance is not inherited. It may be acquired during the lifetime of the individual. Resistance, either inherited or acquired, is called **immunity** (im MYOO nih tee). When a human host is invaded by a pathogen, or any other foreign protein, the host produces **antibodies** (AN tih bod eez). An antibody is a protein produced by a host to destroy the pathogen. The antibodies combat the pathogen or the poisons produced by it. In addition, the immune system has a memory. If the host survives the initial infection, its body may retain the ability to produce these antibodies quickly. Then, if a new infection by the same kind of pathogen occurs, the host's body can act against it more rapidly. In that way, the disease may be prevented, or its severity reduced. That is why the risk of catching measles twice is very low.

The number of infectious organisms present affects the severity of the infection. An extremely large dose of bacteria, for example, can overwhelm the immune system even when the body has been exposed to that particular bacterium previously.

Each kind of antibody is effective against only the particular pathogen that brought about its production, or sometimes against very similar pathogens. For example, once you have measles, you will not get measles again because the antibodies you develop during the first exposure to the virus will prevent reinfection. Those antibodies are not effective against the chickenpox virus, however. You get many colds because there are many different viruses that cause the common cold. You may be immune to one type after you have been infected with it, but that does not make you immune to the other cold viruses. In addition, a cold virus that once caused you to be ill can mutate. That is, it can change its structure slightly, so that the antibodies you produced during the first infection are no longer effective.

Figure 11.31 Drawing blood containing antibodies that will be used in treating human disease. What advantage do horses have for this purpose?

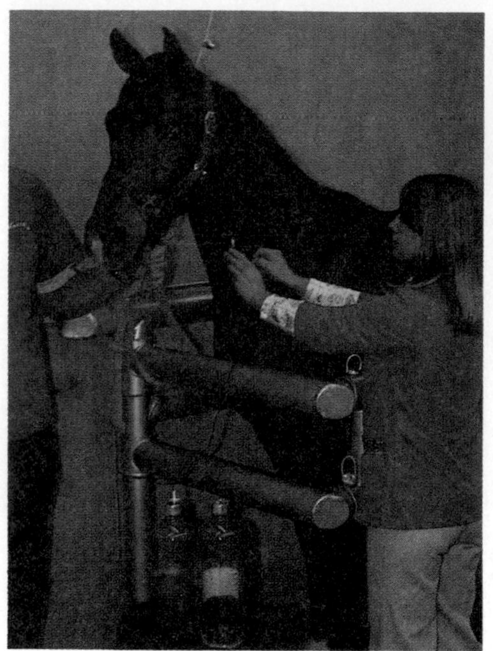

BSCS by Bob Wilson

Figure 11.30 A cartoonist of Jenner's day shows the fears that vaccination aroused.

BBC-Hulton Picture Library / The Bettman Archive

Antibodies may be produced even though the pathogen does not produce symptoms of disease. A person might, therefore, become immune without knowing it. By the time you reach adulthood, you may have had some contact with the poliomyelitis pathogen. Thus, you might have acquired some immunity to that disease, even if you never had any symptoms of the disease. However, it is best to be immunized.

With immunizations, we do not have to depend entirely on inherited resistance, or natural immunity. We can produce immunity in an artificial way. In the late eighteenth century, smallpox was a common and often fatal disease. Edward Jenner observed that people who worked with cows seldom had smallpox, although they usually had been affected by a mild disease of cattle called cowpox. Jenner concluded that a person might become immune to smallpox by being deliberately exposed to cowpox. He developed this idea into a successful medical procedure—vaccination, now generally called immunization.

Today, we have several ways of bringing about artificial immunity. The kind of antibody formed in a host depends on the type of pathogen rather than on the host. It is possible, then, to inject a pathogen into a nonhuman host, such as a horse, in which antibodies are produced. Those antibodies can be removed from the blood of the horse and injected into a person (figure 11.31). The person is then immune to the disease for a short period of time, until the antibodies break down. Sometimes the pathogens themselves, weakened or killed, can be injected into a human. The human host then produces antibodies on its own, but usually without producing symptoms of disease. That method is used in immunizing against the poliomyelitis virus.

11.10 Pathogens Can Be Spread by Nonliving Agents

Pathogens also can be transmitted between hosts indirectly by nonliving agents, such as air, water, food, or hypodermic needles. Indoors, the main source of air-carried microbes is the human respiratory tract. These organisms do not survive for long in the air, but a sneeze can transmit pathogens very quickly over a short distance. Whenever you open your mouth and exhale, you are releasing small droplets of moisture. Each droplet may contain one or two bacteria. With a sneeze, you release many thousands of droplets at great speed. Droplets from a sneeze (figure 11.32) have been clocked at 200 miles per hour, and at about half that speed for a cough. Each time you sneeze, you expel from 10,000 to 100,000 bacteria. The bacteria travel through the air without being killed, and may infect another person standing close to you.

Bacteria, viruses, and protozoa that cause human diseases can be transmitted by water. Many pathogens multiply in the human intestinal tract and then leave the body in the feces. If untreated feces get into the drinking water, the pathogens might enter a new host when he or she drinks the water. Typhoid fever is transmitted in such a fashion, although you also could get it by eating contaminated food or by having direct contact with an infected person. Typhoid fever has been eliminated in many parts of the world because of effective water treatment methods. However, an epidemic of typhoid fever may occur after a natural disaster that damages the treatment operations. Such was the case following the devastating earthquake in Mexico City in September 1985.

Figure 11.32 Droplets from a sneeze.

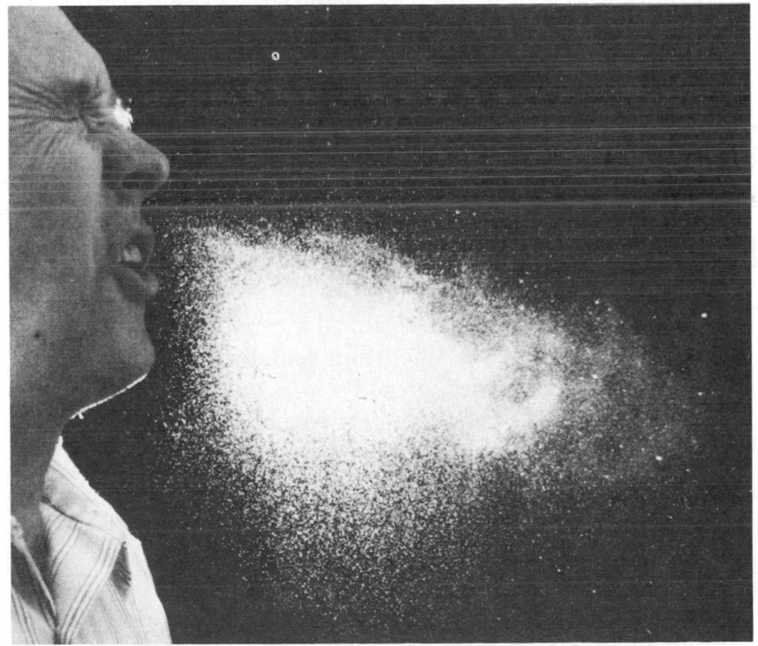

Science Tech Publishers

Figure 11.33 Bacterial population growth beginning with one bacterium. What other population graph does this remind you of?

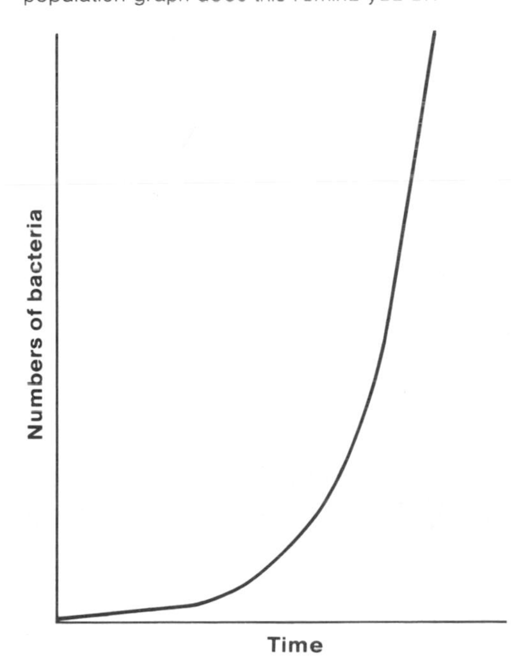

Pathogens also can be carried in food, where they grow and reproduce. That occurs if you do not store your food properly. You can get food poisoning, a bacterial infection, or traveler's diarrhea from spoiled food. How does the food change when it spoils? The biggest change is in the size of the bacterial population within the food you eat. Under the best conditions for growth, a bacterial population can double in size every 20 to 30 minutes. Starting with one bacterium that divides every 20 minutes, how many bacteria will there be if this rate continues for 24 hours? This rapid rate of reproduction may explain why food spoils so quickly. As the bacteria grow, they may change the quality of the food, or they may produce a toxin that gets into the food. Such toxins are one cause of food poisoning.

Botulism is one kind of food poisoning that is usually fatal. It occurs after someone has eaten food containing the toxin produced by an anaerobic bacterium (figure 11.34). This bacterium produces thick-walled reproductive cells called **endospores** (EN doh sporz). Endospores are very resistant to unfavorable conditions such as heat and lack of water. In conditions suitable for growth, an endospore can germinate and grow into a bacterial cell. That one cell then can divide into a population of cells that causes disease. When preserving fruits and vegetables in the home, it is important to heat the food to a temperature sufficiently high and for a long enough time to kill any bacteria or endospores. Otherwise, the bacteria can multiply in the jar and produce a toxin. Botulism may result from eating the contaminated food. Botulism is just one kind of food poisoning. Others are not as severe, but still may cause headache, nausea and vomiting, or diarrhea.

Figure 11.34 A toxin produced by *Clostridium botulinum* is the cause of botulism. Note the round endospore. Transmission electron micrograph of a freeze-etch preparation, ×36,700.

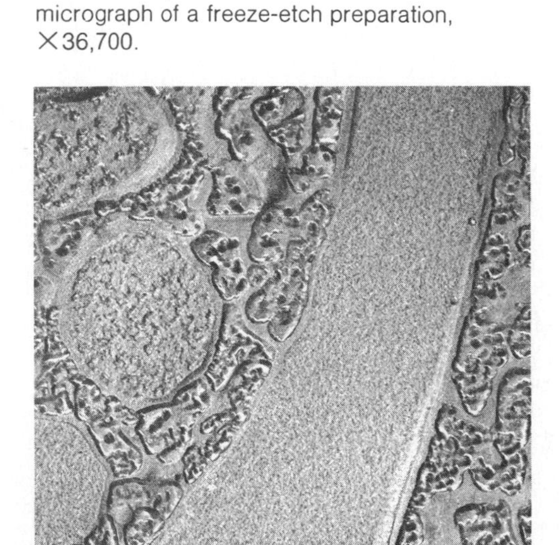

BPS/TOM STACK & ASSOCIATES

There are a variety of methods to prevent food from spoiling. Because living organisms require water, drying foods prevents spoilage. Cold or freezing temperatures slow down the growth of bacteria and fungi. Addition of salt, sugar, or chemicals that inhibit growth are other means to prevent spoilage. Milk is generally **pasteurized** (PAS tyoor ized)—heated very quickly to kill most of the unwanted microorganisms in the milk—to maintain its freshness until you drink it. All methods of food preservation attempt to prevent bacterial and fungal growth on the food.

Self-Review

1. How did biologists come to associate microorganisms with disease?
2. How do infectious diseases differ from noninfectious diseases?
3. How are infectious diseases spread?
4. What is the difference between infection and disease?
5. How are alternate hosts involved in the spread of disease?
6. What is an antibiotic?
7. What causes food to spoil, and how can spoilage be prevented?

Viruses, Viroids, and Prions

Guidepost: How are these agents of disease different from other pathogens?

11.11 Viruses Are Protein-Covered Nucleic Acids

What do rabies, measles, mumps, influenza, colds, and polio have in common? They are all caused by viruses. A virus is an infectious agent that contains a nucleic acid (either DNA or RNA) and a protein coat. Viruses are so small they can pass through most bacteriological filters and can be seen only with an electron microscope. Some viruses enter host cells, disrupt their normal functioning, and kill the cells. Other viruses enter cells and cause permanent, inheritable changes. Sometimes those changes are not harmful; they might even benefit the host.

Figure 11.35 All viruses are pathogenic. (a) Tobacco mosaic virus, ×109,150, causes a disease of plants; (b) adenovirus, ×110,000, causes respiratory illnesses in humans; (c) T4 bacteriophage, ×240,000.

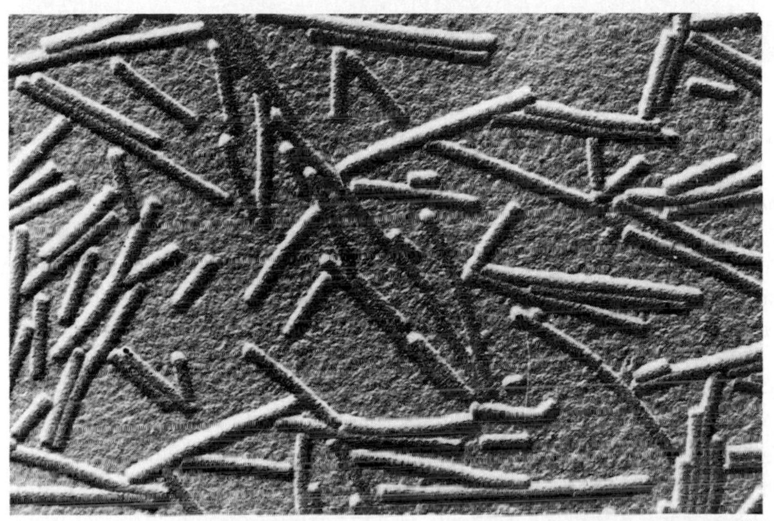

a Courtesy Carl Zeiss, Inc., Thornwood, NY

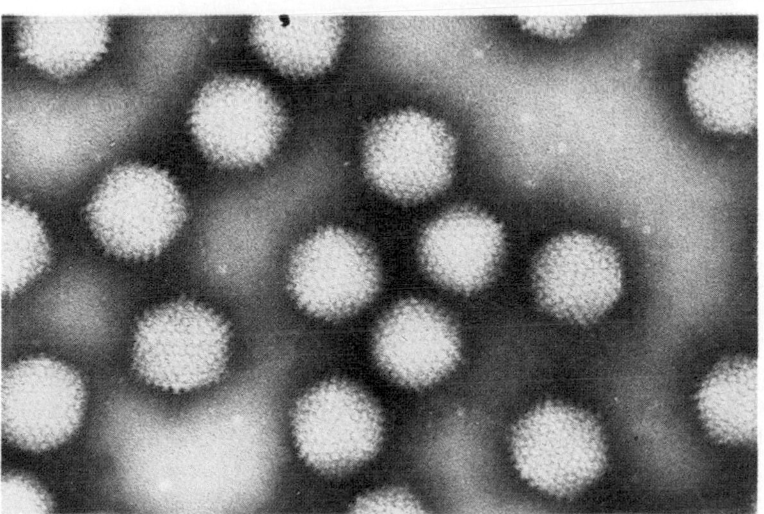

b © Science Source/Photo Researchers

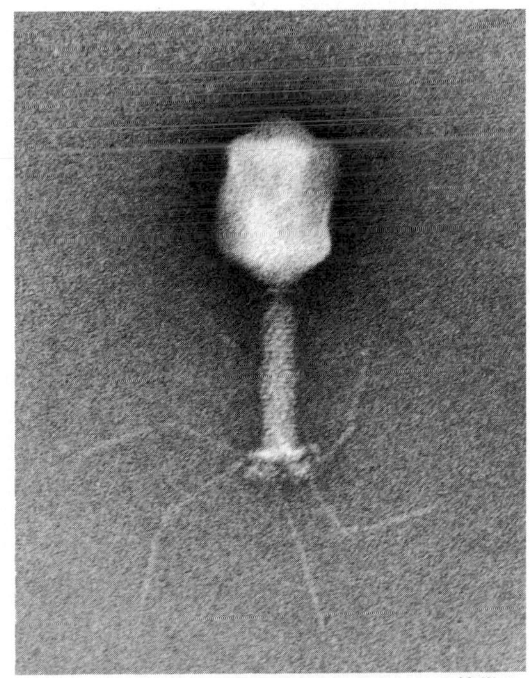

c M. Wurtz

Figure 11.37 A bacterial virus, or bacteriophage, attacking a single bacterium.

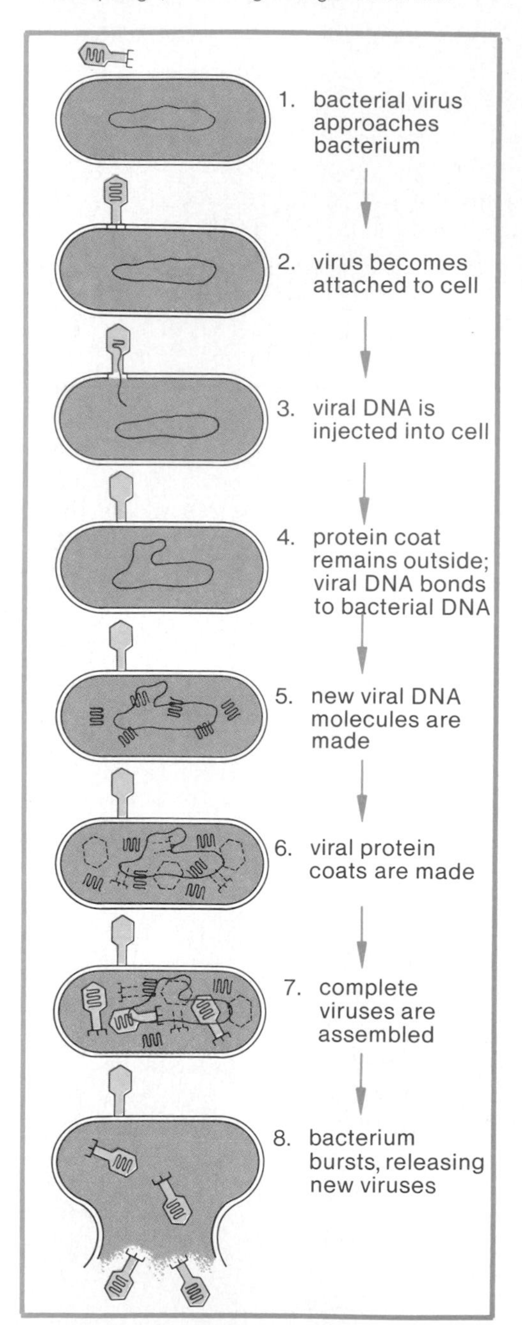
1. bacterial virus approaches bacterium
2. virus becomes attached to cell
3. viral DNA is injected into cell
4. protein coat remains outside; viral DNA bonds to bacterial DNA
5. new viral DNA molecules are made
6. viral protein coats are made
7. complete viruses are assembled
8. bacterium bursts, releasing new viruses

Figure 11.36 TYMV (turnip yellow mosaic virus) in cabbage.

BSCS by Richard Tolman

Are viruses alive? Some people would say yes and some would say no. Certainly, viruses are different from all living things we have discussed before. Although viruses can reproduce, they cannot produce copies of themselves without the aid of another living organism. Outside the host cell, viruses do not reproduce, feed, or grow. They have no metabolism of their own, that is, they do not take in and use energy. They do not have cell parts. Some can even be crystallized and can survive for years in that state. Only when they enter the appropriate host cells can they can resume reproduction.

Viruses infect plants, animals, fungi, and even bacteria. Viruses that infect bacteria are called **bacteriophages** (bak TIR ee oh fayj ez). A virus attaches itself to its host by means of its protein coat. It then injects its DNA or RNA into the host cell. When a bacteriophage attaches itself to a bacterium, the nucleic acid of the virus moves inside. The viral nucleic acid takes over the machinery of the host cell, commanding it to make more viral protein and viral nucleic acid. After the host cell has done that, the pieces are assembled into new virus particles. In about 20 minutes the infected bacterium splits open, releasing 200 or more newly made bacteriophages. These events are shown in figures 11.37 and 11.38. Each new virus has the ability to infect a single new bacterium, yet the virus could not make copies of itself on its own.

Viruses that have RNA as their genetic material must go through an additional step before they can reproduce. To take over the host cell machinery, their RNA must be transcribed into DNA. That process is the reverse of what generally takes place in cells, and is accomplished by means of a specific enzyme known as reverse transcriptase (see Biology Today, page 385). The virus that causes Acquired Immune Deficiency Syndrome (AIDS) is an RNA virus. The AIDS virus attacks and kills certain cells of the immune system, so that system is unable to perform its normal function of defending the organism against disease.

Biology Today

The AIDS Virus: Reversing the Flow of Information in Biological Systems

Genetic information is organized in a nucleic acid called DNA. That information is transcribed into RNA, and then translated into protein. That information system has been observed in the vast majority of organisms in the web of life. One group whose information patterns violate the rule is called retroviruses—"retro" meaning reverse or backward. Among the most important of these to humans is the virus that causes acquired immune deficiency syndrome, or AIDS.

Retroviruses, first isolated in the early 1900s, have RNA rather than DNA, as their genetic material. In order to multiply, RNA viruses must make copies of DNA from their RNA. That is the reverse of the normal flow of stored information in biological systems.

The AIDS virus, like all retroviruses, is a cellular parasite. It must replicate itself in a host cell. The virus first binds to the surface of the cell. The RNA then enters the cell (see figure). A special enzyme called reverse transcriptase allows the virus to make a complementary DNA copy of the viral RNA. That DNA is incorporated into the DNA of the host cell. When the cell produces RNA from its own DNA, it also produces viral RNA. That becomes the source of new viral particles, and the infection continues.

Molecular biologists have used their knowledge of the life cycle of retroviruses to develop potential cures for AIDS. AZT, a drug developed in mid-1986, was shown to interfere with reverse transcriptase in the AIDS virus in culture. Scientists are not certain that the drug works the same way in infected cells in the host. AZT did, however, reduce the number of infections in AIDS patients during its clinical trial. In fact, AZT was so effective that the trial was stopped early to allow the drug to be used with more patients. Studies of AZT were continuing at the time this book was published.

The AIDS virus is but one example of viruses that contradict the general pattern of the flow of genetic information. The origin of retroviruses is still a biological mystery, although scientists believe they have been around for millions of years. Some biologists think that retroviruses evolved from normal cellular genes.

Retroviruses are known to cause cancer in some animals. A few human genes have similarities to genes in those retroviruses. These human genes are thought to result in cancerous growth when they are somehow disturbed. The disturbance may result in the production of a different gene product, or in the production of abnormally large amounts of the original gene product. In either case, the result is uncontrolled growth of the cell: cancer.

Improved techniques in molecular biology are allowing scientists to learn a great deal about the structure and function of retroviruses. Increased knowledge will, in turn, lead to improved understanding of diseases such as AIDS and certain types of cancer.

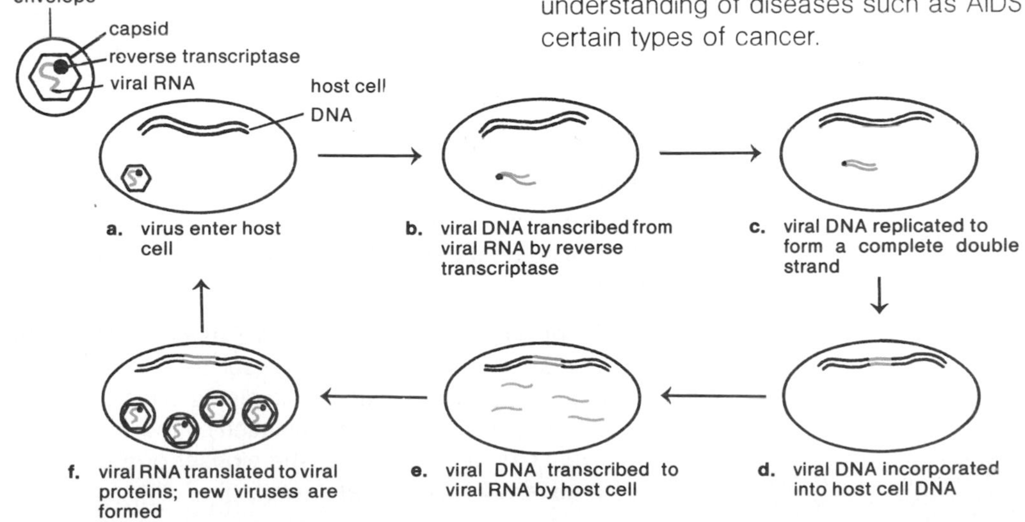
envelope
capsid
reverse transcriptase
viral RNA
host cell
DNA
a. virus enter host cell
b. viral DNA transcribed from viral RNA by reverse transcriptase
c. viral DNA replicated to form a complete double strand
d. viral DNA incorporated into host cell DNA
e. viral DNA transcribed to viral RNA by host cell
f. viral RNA translated to viral proteins; new viruses are formed

Figure 11.38 (a) The fermenting bacterium, *Escherichia coli,* with T4 phage viruses attached to the surface and inside, ×30,000. (b) T4 phage attached to the bacterium after it has injected its DNA, ×120,000.

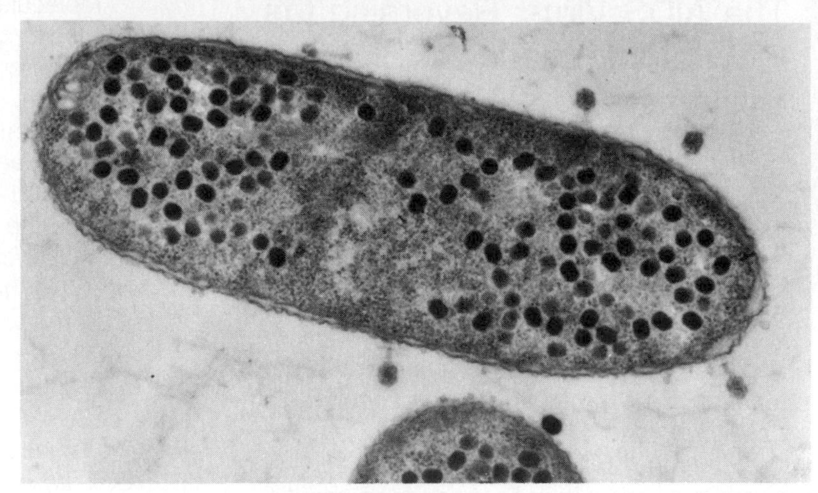

a E. Couture-Tosi

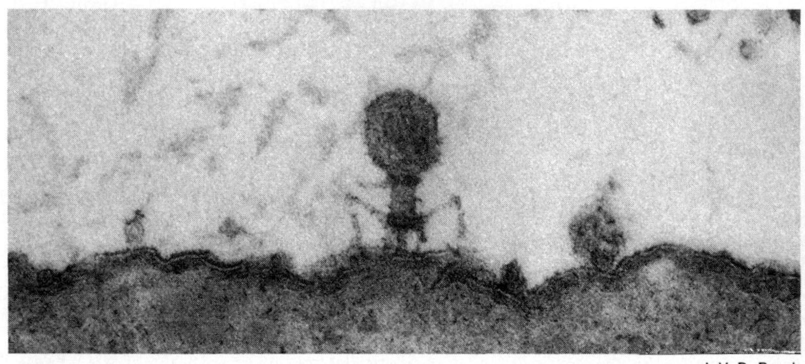

b J. V. D. Broek

Investigation 11.3 SCREENING FOR AIDS

Introduction

The public policy issues surrounding the detection, control, and treatment of AIDS are quite complex and open to debate. This investigation looks at only one such issue, the screening of donor blood for HIV antibody.

Procedure

For this investigation, you will be working in small discussion groups of 3 or 4 students. Read the following article before forming your small groups.

Screening Donated Blood and Plasma for HIV Antibody

AIDS infection has been associated with several well-defined high-risk groups, including recipients of blood and blood products. Screening blood for contamination by the causative agent, the HIV virus, has become one of the highest public health priorities and is currently in place nationwide.

When your body is infected by a virus, it produces antibodies that help destroy the virus. The blood-screening test currently used detects HIV antibody, not the virus that causes AIDS. Having the antibody means a person has been exposed to the HIV virus. It does not necessarily mean that the person has AIDS or even that he or she will develop AIDS at a later date. It does mean, however, that those possibilities exist, and that the donated blood from that person should not be transfused into other individuals.

One of the problems with the current test is that it sometimes produces *false positive* results. False positive results indicates that a person *has* the HIV antibody when in fact the person *does not* have the antibody in his or her blood. Adverse publicity and personal trauma may result for a donor who receives a false positive report from a blood donation. Fear of AIDS and concern with the screening process could decrease the pool of volunteer blood donors.

For the person who is truly positive for HIV antibody, notification and elimination from the donor pool is, indeed, appropriate. However, for donors falsely labeled as antibody positive, these results may do needless harm to their social and personal relationships.

If your small group is designated to group A, your task is to provide arguments *for* the nationwide screening program for HIV antibody in blood banks. If you are group B, your task is to provide arguments *against* the nationwide screening program for HIV antibody in blood banks.

Discussion

1. Group A. During your discussion to develop arguments *for* the nationwide screening program, you might wish to consider the following questions:
   (a) Of what value is the screening program for the general public?
   (b) How do hemophiliacs, who may require frequent blood cell products, benefit from the screening program?
   (c) Of what value is the screening to blood recipients in general?
   (d) Of what value is screening to a healthy donor infected with HIV?
   (e) What rights do blood donors have?
2. Group B. During your discussion to develop arguments *against* the nationwide screening program, you might wish to consider the following questions:
   (a) What problems might arise from screening for HIV and getting a false negative test, results that indicate that a person *does not* have the HIV antibody when in fact the person *does* have the antibody?
   (b) What problems might arise from a false positive result? Consider employment or medical insurance.
   (c) How might a positive test for HIV antibody affect the life of that individual?
   (d) In the use of screening tests, there is concern both for the public at large and for the individual. What kinds of conflicts might arise as a result of those concerns? How might society reach some compromise?

11.12 Prions Cause Slow-Infection Diseases

Two other agents of infectious diseases, like viruses, are considered by many biologists not to be living organisms. Both are simpler in structure than viruses. A **viroid** (VY roid) is a piece of naked RNA; the RNA is not covered by a protein coat as it is in viruses. Viroids cause certain plant diseases, but their role in human and other animal illnesses is less well known.

Prions (PREE ahnz) are made up of protein, and perhaps nothing else. Thus far, no nucleic acids have been found to be associated with a prion. These mysterious agents are thought to cause several diseases of animals. One such disease, scrapie, affects the central nervous system of sheep and goats. Animals infected with scrapie lose their coordination and become unable to walk. A prion also has been linked to the disease of the human central nervous system called Kuru. Victims suffering from Kuru first lose their coordination and their ability to walk and then become demented. Kuru was known to affect only certain tribespeople of New Guinea who ate the brains of their dead relatives as a tribute to them. It is believed the prion causing Kuru was passed from person to person in that manner. Since that ritual has ended, the number of victims suffering from Kuru has decreased. Both Kuru and scrapie are called "slow infection" diseases. The incubation period for the disease is very long—from the time of infection to the time symptoms of the disease appear may be several months or years.

Self-Review

1. Compare the structure of a virus, a viroid, and a prion.
2. How does a virus direct the formation of other virus particles?
3. In what ways are Kuru and scrapie similar?

Summary

Wherever you find water, you will find some kind of prokaryote, either archaebacteria or eubacteria, the true bacteria. Among the different kinds of archaebacteria are methanogens, microorganisms that can produce methane gas from leftover organic material such as sewage, garbage, and waste materials. Eubacteria play many important ecological roles in the biosphere. For instance, cyanobacteria are important oxygen-producers, and bacteria are major decomposers. Several kinds of bacteria are involved in the nitrogen cycle. Diseases can be caused by microorganisms, but noninfectious diseases have other causes and cannot be transmitted from one person to another. Disease-causing organisms can be transmitted either by another living organism or by a nonliving agent such as contaminated food, water, or air. Whenever food, water, or air becomes populated with many bacteria, the incidence of disease increases. Viruses and prions have been linked to a number of different human diseases, including the common cold, influenza, and AIDS. Whether or not viruses and prions are living is still a controversial issue.

Application Questions

1. How does cancer fit into the classification of diseases?
2. What is the difference between a pathogen and a parasite?
3. How does the nitrogen cycle illustrate the interdependence of organisms in the biosphere?
4. Contrast the ways in which the pathogens of gonorrhea and malaria are transmitted.
5. Why have recent epidemics of malaria occurred?
6. Are viruses living? Support your answer.

Problems

1. Investigate an infectious disease of a plant or animal using the following topics: history, symptoms, pathogen, vector (where applicable), treatment, and epidemiology. Suggested diseases: anthrax, bacterial meningitis, Dutch elm disease, filariasis, tsutsugamushi fever, hoof-and-mouth disease, black stem rust of wheat, brucellosis, fire blight of pears, or schistosomiasis.
2. Using the same method as in problem 1, study a noninfectious disease.
3. In recent years epidemics of virus-caused influenza have occurred and spread over many parts of the world. Yet vaccination against influenza viruses is common. Why are the vaccines ineffective against a new epidemic that is given a new name? (Examples: Asian flu, Hong Kong flu, and so on.) Use your understanding of pathogens, resistance on the part of both host and pathogen, and acquired immunity to answer the question.
4. Scientists are aware that some infectious diseases have not been identified. First cases or infrequent cases may go unrecognized. The first epidemic draws attention to the disease. This was the case with the human disease now called Legionnaire's disease. It is named after the American Legion convention at which an epidemic occurred. A number of people died. Consider such an epidemic, its victims, and their autopsies (studies of blood and other body parts after death). How would you employ people in each of the following careers in attempting to identify the cause of the disease? (Do library research on the careers.)
   biochemists
   food inspectors
   medical doctors
   metallurgists
   microbiologists (virologists and bacteriologists)
   pathologist
   toxicologists
5. Infectious diseases are no longer the leading causes of death in developed countries, as they are in many parts of the Third World. Choose one of the most common infectious diseases in the Third World and report on the causative agent, the frequency of the disease, and attempts to control it.
6. In the early 1980s, the World Health Organization reported that smallpox had been eliminated worldwide. Report on the campaign to eradicate this viral disease.

Suggested Readings

M. M. Kaplan and H. Koprowski, "Rabies" *Scientific American* (January 1980). Traces the search for ways to control this deadly disease.

P. A. Mackowiak, "Our Microbial Associates" *Natural History* (April 1983). Investigates the human body's normal flora—is it a liability or an asset?

L. Margulis, D. Chase, and R. Guerrero, "Microbial Communities" *BioScience* (March 1986). Sections through a termite intestine, a mudflat, and colored lake water reveal well-structured microbial communities.

H. J. Morowitz, "Do Bacteria Think?" *Psychology Today* (February 1981). Addresses the basic question: If the simplest forms of life are capable of purposive activity, can they be said to engage in a form of thinking?

E. Rubenstein, "Diseases Caused by Impaired Communication among Cells" *Scientific American* (March 1980). Introduces a new concept of a disease-causing mechanism.

K. Simons, H. Garoff, and A. Helenius, "How an Animal Virus Gets into and out of Its Host Cell" *Scientific American* (February 1982). Experiments with the Semliki Forest virus have helped biologists understand this process.

C. Wallis, "AIDS: A Growing Threat" *Time* (12 August 1985). Offers a good perspective on the status of this disease in mid-1985.

Robert C. Simpson/TOM STACK & ASSOCIATES

The kingdom Fungi includes many colorful mushrooms such as this *Hygrophorus coccineus*.

CHAPTER 12

Eukaryotes: Protists and Fungi

Introduction

All the organisms discussed in this and the next two chapters are eukaryotes, which possess an organized nucleus and membrane-bounded organelles. Evidence suggests that some of these organelles might have originated from free-living prokaryotic ancestors. The kingdom Protista includes a diverse group of organisms that are classified together because they are *not* animals, plants, or fungi. Some protists are heterotrophic and depend on other organisms for their source of energy, while others are autotrophic and can make their own food. All organisms in the kingdom Fungi are consumers and many of them are decomposers. In this chapter we will examine representative protists and fungi, and some of the many roles they play in a community.

The Origin of Mitochondria and Chloroplasts

Guidepost: What is the evidence that some organelles originated as free-living prokaryotes?

12.1 Organelles Are Efficient Packages in which Chemical Reactions Take Place

Although protists and fungi are distinctly different kinds of organisms, both are eukaryotic. That is, their cells contain organized nuclei and many organelles that are surrounded by membranes. Eukaryotes are generally considered to be more advanced than prokaryotes.

What makes eukaryotes more advanced? Although there are many unicellular organisms in both groups, eukaryotes are generally larger and more complex than prokaryotes. In eukaryotes, many cell reactions are packaged in specialized structures called organelles. For example, all the enzymes that eukaryotic producers need to synthesize sugars are found in chloroplasts; in prokaryotes the machinery of photosynthesis is

Figure 12.1 Eukaryotes are generally larger and more complex than prokaryotes. (a) The humpback whale is one of the largest animals that ever lived. (b) Even this unicellular protozoan, *Stentor,* is highly complex, and contains many membrane-bounded organelles.

a Ed Robinson/TOM STACK & ASSOCIATES

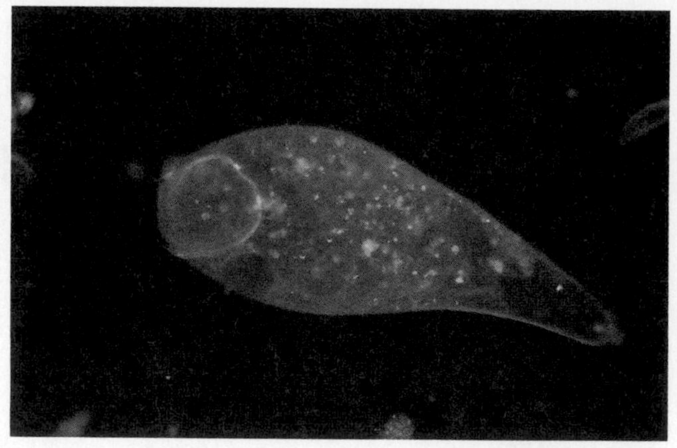

b T. E. Adams/VISUALS UNLIMITED

not packaged separately. All organisms obtain energy for their daily activities by means of cellular respiration. However, in eukaryotes most of the respiratory enzymes are packaged in mitochondria. That packaging in organelles is important for the efficient functioning of a eukaryotic cell.

12.2 Mitochondria and Chloroplasts May Have Originated as Free-living Prokaryotes

How did mitochondria and chloroplasts originate? The oldest fossils resemble modern prokaryotes, which lack membrane-bounded organelles. As we explained in section 10.12, many biologists think the first forms of life were anaerobic heterotrophs. They could have used organic molecules from their surrounding environment as a source of food and energy. As the early heterotrophs increased in numbers, competition likely developed for food sources. Some organisms might have evolved methods of making their own food, thereby increasing their chances of survival.

Photosynthesis probably evolved in anaerobic bacteria very early in the history of life. Oxygen-releasing photosynthesis apparently appeared later, but it brought about a dramatic change in the environment. Oxygen, which reacts readily with organic molecules, was probably toxic to most of the early organisms. As oxygen accumulated in the atmosphere, many organisms probably became extinct. Others remained in niches from which oxygen was largely absent, where they are still found. However, some bacteria evolved ways to use oxygen to produce additional ATP from their food sources. Those oxygen-respiring bacteria may have been the forerunners of mitochondria.

Figure 12.2 The giant amoeba *Pelomyxa palustrus* contains many nuclei but no mitochondria. Mutualistic bacteria apparently perform the role of mitochondria. (a) stained specimen, ×30; (b) scanning electron micrograph (bar = 100 μm); (c) cutaway drawing of (b) showing location of bacteria.

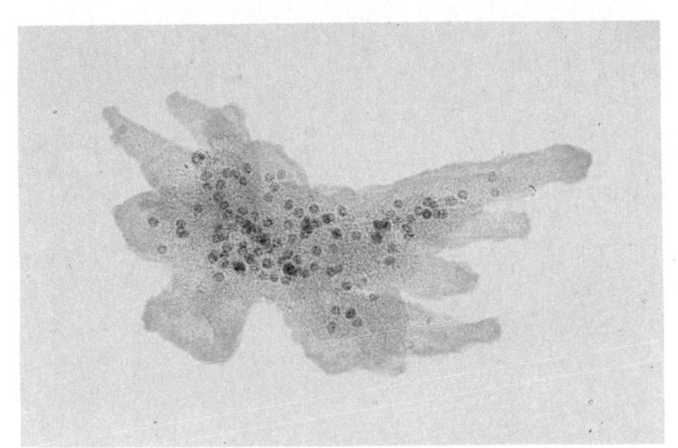

a Ripon Microslides, Inc.

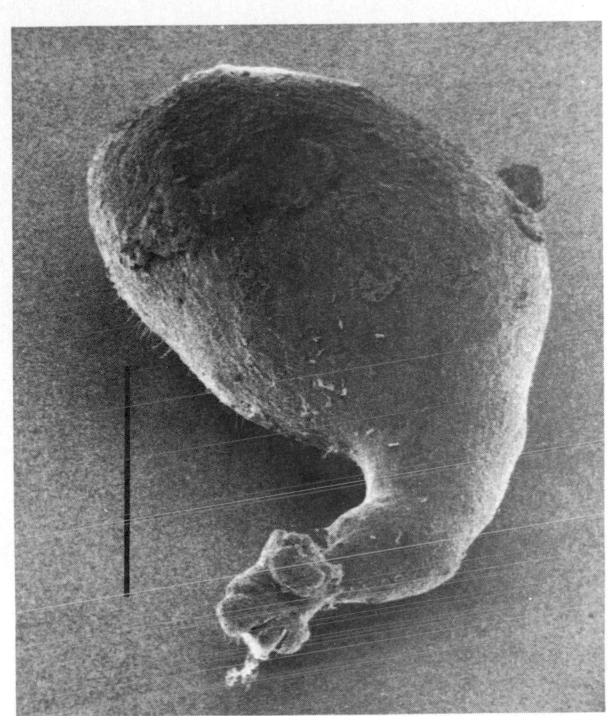

b From THE BIOLOGY OF AMOEBA, edited by K. W. Jeon. New York, Academic Press, 1973.

Small, oxygen-respiring bacteria may have invaded larger, anaerobic prokaryotes. The invaders could have utilized the products of anaerobic respiration in their hosts, while the hosts gained additional ATP from the activities of the invaders. The invaders also would have enjoyed a protected environment, while the hosts were no longer confined to diminishing anaerobic environments. The mutual advantages of the relationship might have led to increasing interdependence, and the invaders might have evolved into mitochondria. Even today there is a giant amoeba (figure 12.2) living in pond-bottom mud that lacks mitochondria. It does contain hundreds of bacteria, and studies have shown that the bacteria perform the role of mitochondria.

Some biologists think chloroplasts might have originated in much the same manner. Photosynthetic prokaryotes could have been ingested but not digested—chloroplasts engulfed with food can remain active for weeks inside animal tissue. The ability to photosynthesize would have been of great advantage in an environment where the nutrient supply was diminishing. Eventually the photosynthetic organism might have evolved into a photosynthetic organelle, the chloroplast. Figure 12.3 summarizes how those events might have resulted in the formation of a eukaryotic cell.

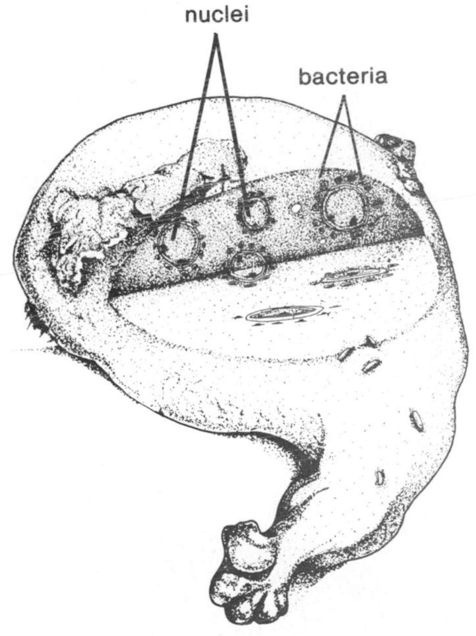

c Robert Golder

Figure 12.3 Possible evolution of eukaryotic cells.

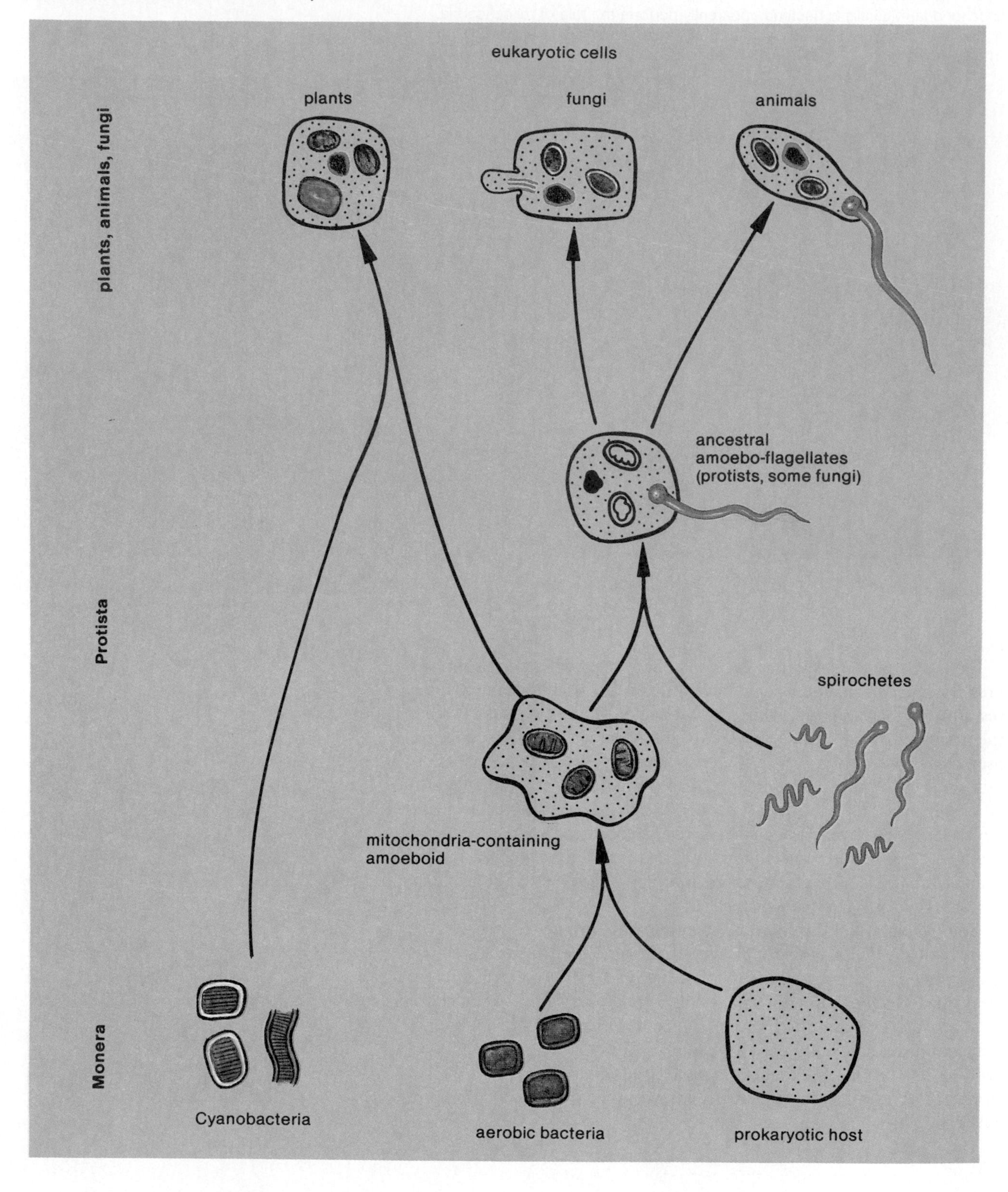

Figure 12.4 (a) Green freshwater hydra, *Hydra viridis,* (b) Digestive cell from *H. viridis* showing concentration of algal cells of the genus *Chlorella.* The digestive cells recognize the appropriate algae and eject those that are not appropriate. Accepted algae are moved to the base of the digestive cell and reproduce by mitosis until the normal algal population is reached. Thereafter the algae reproduce when the host cell reproduces.

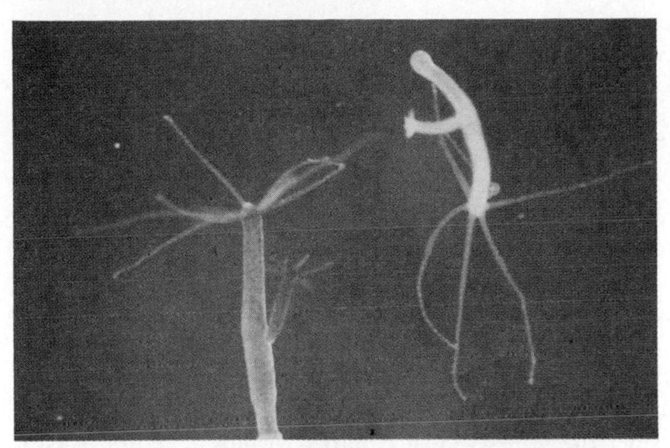

a

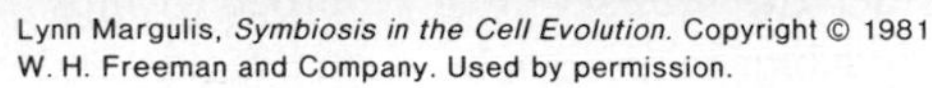

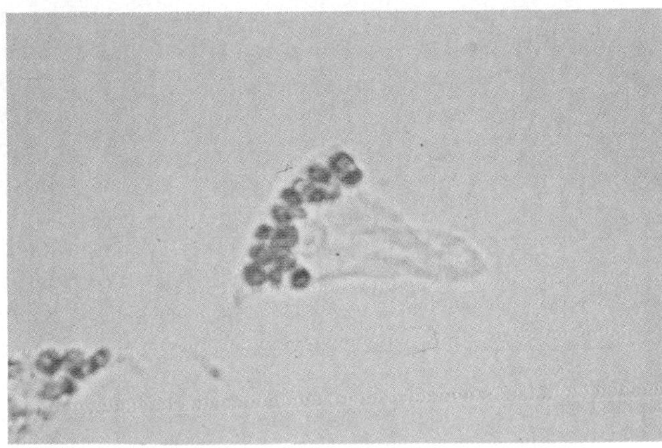

b

There is substantial evidence that mitochondria and chloroplasts had ancestors that once were free-living prokaryotes. Both have their own DNA and ribosomes. In both, the ribosomes resemble those of prokaryotes today. The DNA of mitochondria is a single, circular strand like the DNA of present-day prokaryotes. Mitochondria are produced in cells only by other mitochondria. Chloroplasts are produced only by other chloroplasts. The reproduction of both organelles resembles that of free-living prokaryotic organisms. In addition, mutualistic relationships existing today indicate that such associations are not difficult to establish or to maintain. Many modern organisms have bacteria, cyanobacteria, or algae living inside their cells. For example, the digestive cells lining the gut of the hydra shown in figure 12.4 contain algae the hydra has eaten but not digested. The presence of the algae enables the hydra to survive when food is scarce.

Self-Review

1. Why are eukaryotes considered to be more advanced than prokaryotes?
2. What did the first organisms on earth use as their energy source?
3. How did the environment of the earth change after oxygen-releasing photosynthesis appeared?
4. What is the evidence that both mitochondria and chloroplasts evolved from free-living prokaryotes?

Guidepost: How are the heterotrophic protists distinguished?

Heterotrophic Protists

12.3 Protists Are a Diverse Group

The kingdom Protista includes a diverse group of organisms that have little in common with each other. The kingdom is defined largely by exclusion: its members are eukaryotes, but not plants, animals, or fungi. All protists carry out aerobic cellular respiration in mitochondria. Producer protists carry out photosynthesis in chloroplasts. Most have flagella at some stage of the life cycle .

All protists are aquatic. They live in salt or fresh water or in the watery tissues of other organisms. Many species of protists are parasitic, and most plants, animals, and fungi can have protist parasites. Both malaria and African sleeping sickness, mentioned in the last chapter, are caused by protists.

Protists show great variation in organization—they may be unicellular, colonial, or multicellular. They may be consumers or producers, and some species switch from one method of nutrition to the other, depending on conditions.

We can consider the protists in three broad groups. The first group includes the funguslike heterotrophs: slime molds and certain aquatic fungi. The second is the animal-like heterotrophs or protozoa, which are generally one-celled. The third protist group is the plantlike autotrophs or algae. In the next sections we will describe characteristics of a few organisms from each group.

[proh toh ZOH uh]

12.4 Slime Molds Have Characteristics of Both Fungi and Protozoa

[mik soh MY koh tuh]

Slime molds (Myxomycota) usually grow among damp, decaying leaves and other dead plant material. If you search through such material soon after a heavy rain, you may find a slime-mold plasmodium. The **plasmodium** (plaz MOHD ee um) shown in figure 12.5a is a glistening sheet or net with no definite form, and which may be larger than a meter across. Some are brightly colored. As it moves slowly from one place to another, the plasmodium engulfs bacteria, spores, and small bits of dead organic matter. Some plasmodia contain many nuclei that are not separated from each other by plasma membranes.

As long as there is food and water, the plasmodium continues to grow. When food becomes depleted, the plasmodium may clump into mounds and form **sporangia** (spoh RAN jee uh), stalked structures that produce reproductive cells or spores. When a sporangium breaks open, large numbers of spores are released into the air and carried or scattered by wind, insects, or rain drops. The spores can survive unfavorable environmental conditions, but if they land in suitable spots with moisture, they can germinate. Each spore gives rise to a tiny organism with one or two flagella. After swimming about for a short time, these organisms

Figure 12.5 The slime mold *Physarum:* (a) plasmodium stage, under damp poplar bark; (b) a single sporangium just opening and about to release its spores, ×60.

a E. S. Ross

b Perry Mulleavy

lose their flagella and fuse in pairs. By feeding and growing, each pair develops into a new plasmodium. Figure 12.6 shows the life cycle of a slime mold.

12.5 Flagellates May Be Consumers or Producers

[FLAJ uh luhts]

Flagellates are generally unicellular organisms that move by means of flagella. Some have only one flagellum; others have thousands. There are several phyla of flagellates, some of which contain chlorophyll and synthesize their own food when light is present. Others are heterotrophic, capturing smaller microorganisms, which they digest internally. Some flagellates switch between being a consumer and a producer, depending on the conditions. Flagellates are abundant in damp soil, in fresh water, and in the ocean. They generally reproduce asexually, by dividing in two. Some forms reproduce sexually, by fusion of identical-appearing gametes.

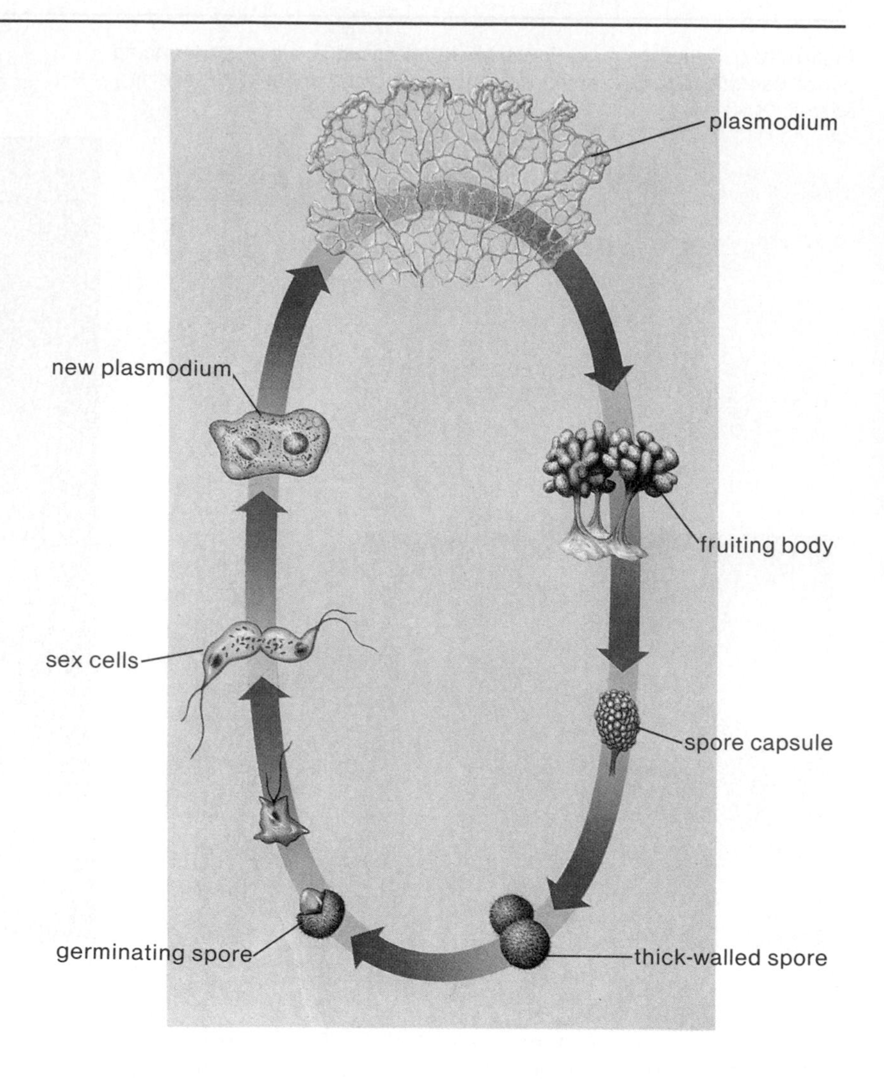

Figure 12.6 Life cycle of a slime mold. Which part of the cycle is best adapted to a dry environment? Which parts of the cycle would require abundant moisture?

[yoo GLEE noids]

Euglenoids are a small group of flagellates named for the genus *Euglena,* a common inhabitant of fresh water (figure 12.7a). Many of the species contain chloroplasts. The nonphotosynthetic forms absorb dissolved organic substances or ingest living prey. *Euglena* lacks a rigid cell wall but has supporting strips of protein inside the plasma membrane. Most species orient to light by means of a light-sensitive eyespot.

Dinoflagellates are marine flagellates, many of which have a stiff cellulose wall resembling a coat of armor. Two flagella beat in grooves, causing the cells to spin like tops as they move through the water (figure 12.7b). Many dinoflagellates are red in color, and some of them produce powerful nerve toxins. Sometimes those dinoflagellates reproduce in great numbers, causing what are known as "red tides." The toxins also may be concentrated in food chains, and clams and other organisms that eat dinoflagellates may become poisonous to humans.

Many flagellates live in close relationships with other organisms. Those relationships may be parasitic, mutualistic, or commensalistic. Several flagellates cause serious human diseases, such as African sleeping sickness (figure 12.7c). Many species of flagellates live mutualistically in the digestive tract of termites, where they break down the wood eaten by the insects (see figure 1.11a on page 15). Without the flagellates, the termites would starve to death, just as you would on a wood diet. That is because neither you nor the termites can digest cellulose.

Figure 12.7 Flagellates: (a) two euglenoids, *Euglena* (green) and *Trachelomonas* (brown); (b) a dinoflagellate, *Noctiluca scintillans*, scanning electron micrograph, ×2030; (c) *Trypanosoma gambiense*, one of the parasites that causes African sleeping sickness.

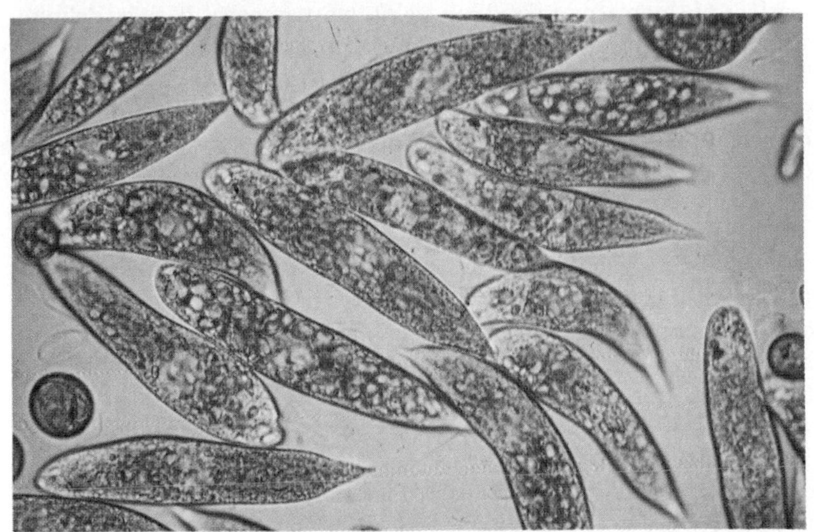

a I. E. Adams/VISUALS UNLIMITED

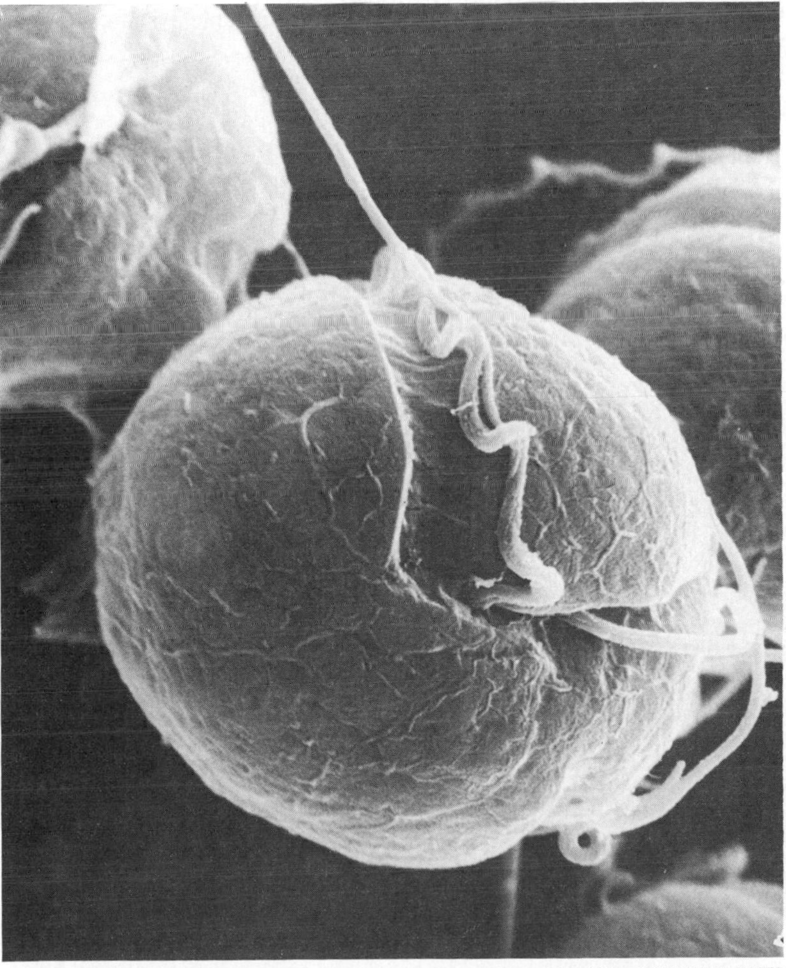

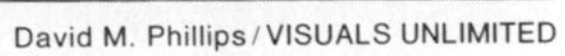

b David M. Phillips/VISUALS UNLIMITED

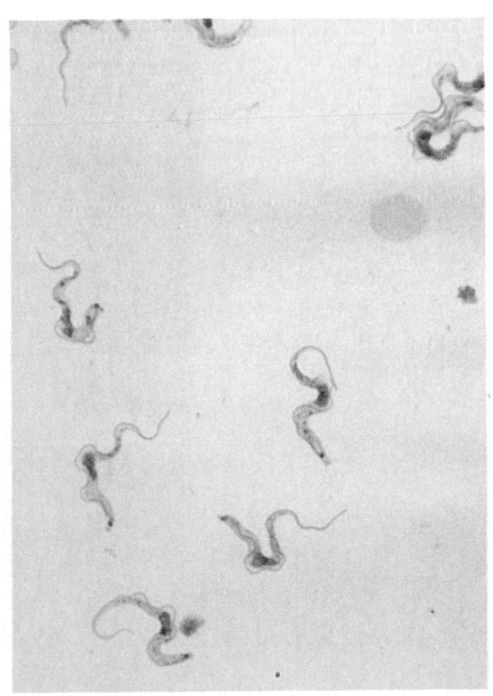

c Ron Hathaway

Figure 12.8 Amoebae surround their prey with pseudopods and engulf them. The prey here is a *Paramecium*.

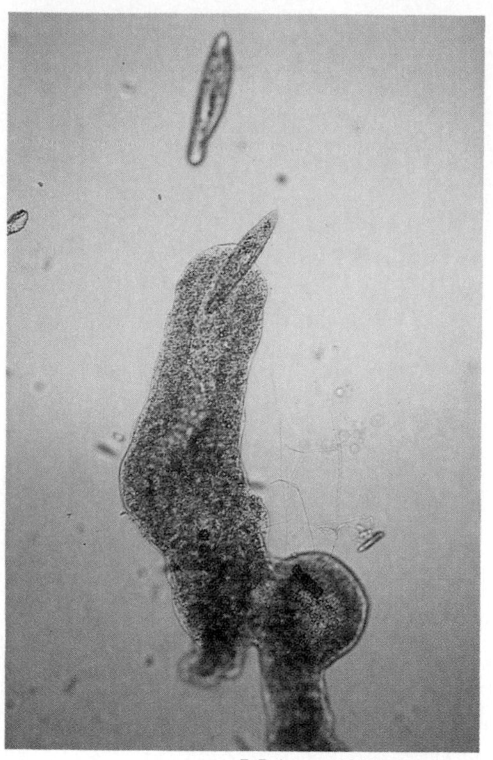

T. E. Adams/VISUALS UNLIMITED

12.6 Many Sarcodines Use Pseudopods to Move and To Obtain Food

The sarcodines include amoebas and their relatives. They generally move and feed by means of **pseudopods** (SOO doh podz), fingerlike extensions of cytoplasm. Like slime molds, most amoebas have no definite shape. Their body substance is a granular, grayish, or transparent mass. The cytoplasm continuously flows into one or several pseudopods. One pseudopod may outgrow the others, and the organism flows in the direction of that pseudopod. Amoebas engulf bacteria, protozoa, algae, or other small aquatic organisms by first surrounding them by pseudopods, as shown in figure 12.8.

One group of sarcodines has outer shells of silica, a substance similar to sand. Many long, stiff pseudopods radiate from the shells (figure 12.9a). Another group, the Foraminifera seen in figure 12.9b, builds shells of calcium carbonate—chemically the same as clam shells. During past ages great numbers of foraminiferan shells have accumulated at the bottoms of seas and have solidified into rock. Chalky deposits such as the white cliffs of Dover in England are the result of such accumulations.

Sarcodines are thought to have evolved from flagellates, and many develop flagella during some stage of the life cycle. They reproduce asexually by cell division. Amoebalike sarcodines may live in ponds, puddles, and damp soil. Most of the shell-bearing forms live in the seas. Other species live with larger organisms in commensal or parasitic relationships. An example is the organism that causes amoebic dysentery in humans.

[SAR koh dynz]

[FOR am ih NIF er uh]

Figure 12.9 Sarcodines: (a) radiolarian, (b) foraminiferan, (c) scanning electron micrograph of amoebae that have just divided.

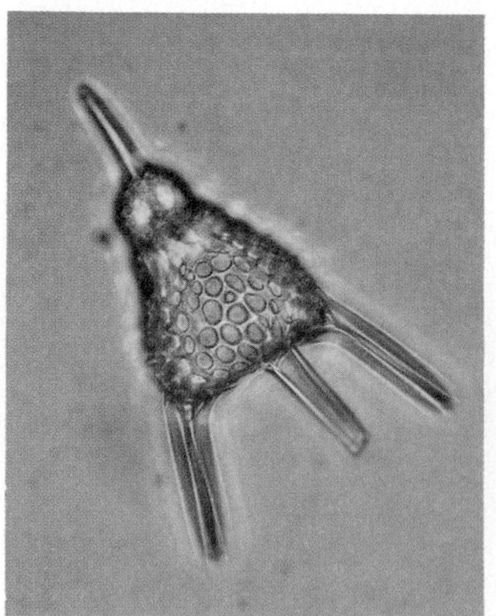

a Ed Reschke

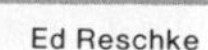

b T. E. Adams/VISUALS UNLIMITED

c BSCS

12.7 Sporozoans Are All Parasites of Animals

[spor oh ZOH unz], [ap ih kum PLEK suh]

Sporozoans (Phylum Apicomplexa) are all spore-forming parasites of animals. They lack any means of locomotion and have complex life cycles involving more than one host. Sporozoans reproduce sexually, and the zygotes form thick-walled cysts that serve to transmit the parasites to new hosts. Inside the cysts, the zygotes divide rapidly to form large numbers of tiny spores, each of which can infect a cell within the host.

Many sporozoans are parasites of the bloodstream and cause serious and even fatal diseases in their hosts. Malaria is one of the human diseases caused by a sporozoan. Malaria has been controlled in two ways. One way has been by using drugs to control the parasitic pathogen, the sporozoan, and the second way has been by using pesticides to kill the mosquito vectors. Unfortunately, some pathogens and vectors have developed resistance to the chemicals used to control them. Today, malaria remains a principal cause of human death in the world.

12.8 Ciliates Have Two Kinds of Nuclei

[SIL ee uhts], [sil ee OFF er uh]

Ciliates (Phylum Ciliophora) are the most specialized and complex of the protozoans. Most are unicellular, free-living organisms of saltwater or freshwater habitats. All move by means of **cilia** (SIL ee uh), short, whiplike extensions that beat in rhythm, driving the organisms through the water (figure 12.11a). In some species, the beating of cilia causes a current that sweeps food particles into the organism. Cilia are sometimes grouped into bundles or sheets, modifications that adapt them to function as mouths, paddles, teeth, or feet.

Figure 12.10 Sporozoans: (a) the organism that causes malaria, *Plasmodium vivax,* showing several different stages of the life cycle in a blood smear; (b) *Gregarina,* a gregarine.

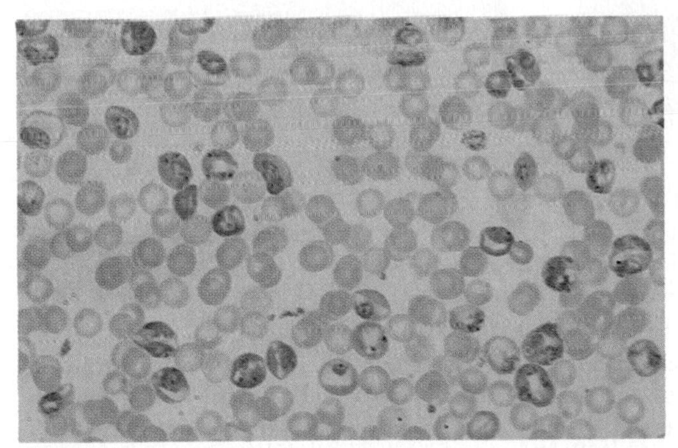

a Ron Hathaway

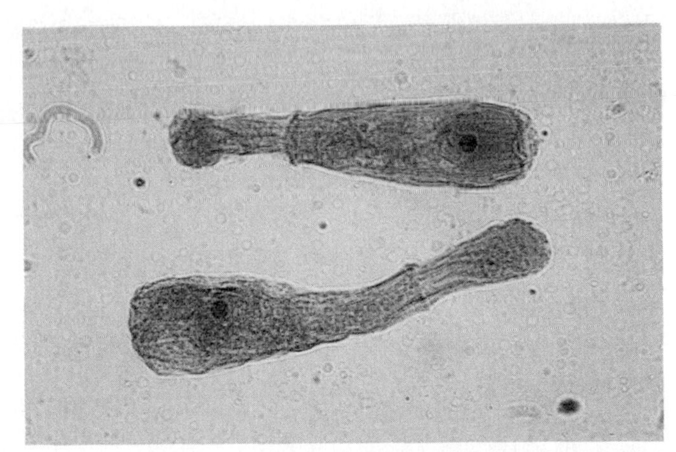

b Stan W. Elems/Visuals Unlimited

Figure 12.11 Ciliates: (a) *Tetrahymena pyriformis,* scanning electron micrograph, ×3350; (b) *Vorticella campanula.*

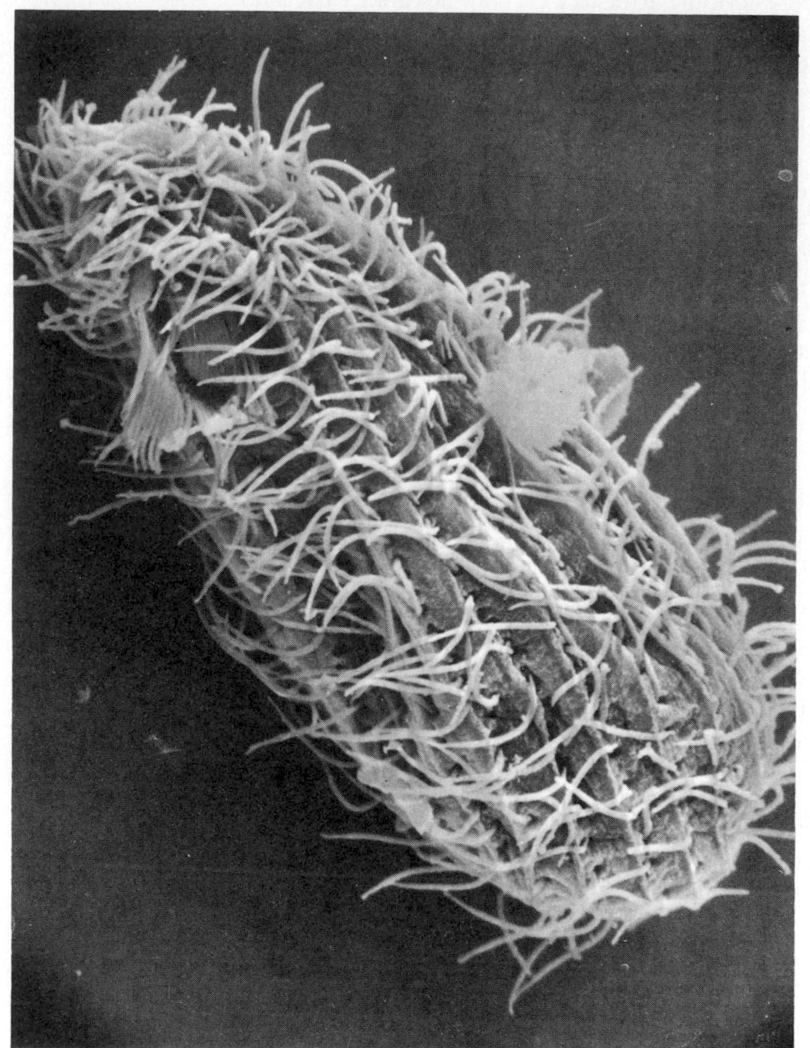

a K. G. Murti/VISUALS UNLIMITED

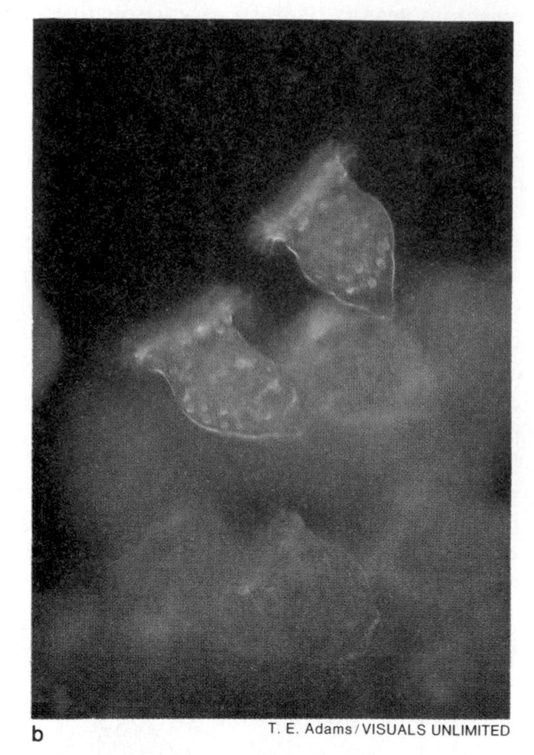

b T. E. Adams/VISUALS UNLIMITED

Ciliates have definite, semirigid shapes. Active swimmers such as *Paramecium* (figure 12.12a), which you can study in investigation 12.1, generally have distinct anterior and posterior ends. All ciliates have two types of nuclei and may contain one or more of each kind. The huge **macronuclei** are required for growth and reproduction, and they take part in routine cellular functions. Macronuclei do not divide by mitosis, but are apportioned approximately equally between dividing cells. **Micronuclei** are essential for **conjugation,** the sexual reproduction of ciliates (see figure 12.12b). In that process, two ciliates remain attached for up to several hours and exchange some of their micronuclei.

Figure 12.12 Phase contrast photomicrograph of vegetative *Paramecium caudatum*. Compare this with the drawing in figure 12.13. Which organelles can you identify in the photo? (b) Conjugating *Paramecium multimicronucleatum* showing the macronuclei.

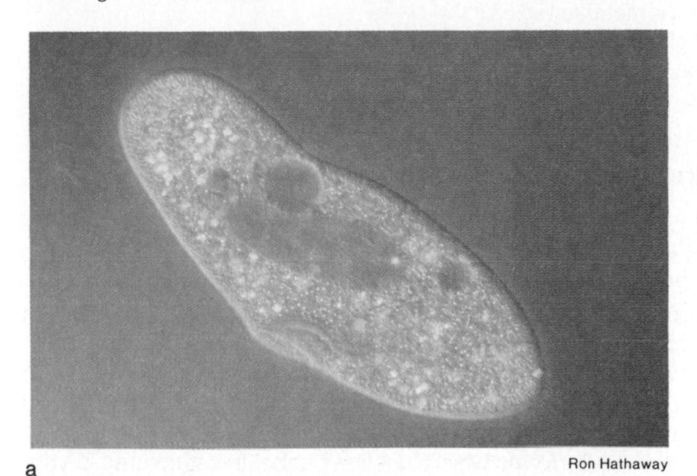

a Ron Hathaway

b Ed Reschke

Self-Review

1. Which characteristics of slime molds are animal-like and which are funguslike?
2. What important roles do flagellates play in the biosphere?
3. How do spores of slime molds and sporozoans differ?
4. In what ways does an amoeba use its pseudopods?
5. In what way are ciliates considered complex?

Investigation 12.1 LIFE IN A SINGLE CELL

Introduction

The relationship between structure and function in complex plants and animals is always significant, but not always obvious. Careful and detailed observations of living organisms, sometimes over a long period of time, are necessary to see which structures are performing which functions. The process of discovering these relationships can be simplified by observing a single-celled organism, *Paramecium*. One of the primary goals of this investigation is for you to observe structures and form hypotheses about their possible functions.

Materials

Parts A–D

Paramecium culture
protozoa slowing agent
alizarin red stain
yeast suspension containing Congo red powder
microscope slide
coverslip
compound microscope
dropping pipets
colored pencil

Part E

2 long vials or test tubes
stopper for one of the test tubes
test tube rack
black paper or metal foil
dilute hydrochloric acid
cotton thread
light source

Part A—Structure and Function

Procedure

1. Place a drop of protozoa slowing agent in the center of a clean slide.
2. With a 2nd pipet add 1 drop of the *Paramecium* culture.
3. Add a coverslip and examine the culture drop under the low power of your microscope. Locate at least 1 *Paramecium*.
4. In your data book make a simple drawing of *Paramecium* as you see it under the microscope. Include all the parts of the organism that you observe.
5. Which structure performs which function? Label the structures in your drawing according to the following scheme. Do not worry if you are unable at this time to associate a structure with every function listed below.
   A. Structure(s) associated with how the animal moves.
   B. Structure(s) associated with food intake.
   C. Structure(s) associated with food digestion.
   D. Structure(s) associated with elimination of the remains of undigested food.
   E. Structure(s) associated with oxygen and carbon dioxide exchange.
   F. Structure(s) associated with excretion of fluid wastes.
   G. Structure(s) associated with removal of excess water.

   Do not worry at this time about the names of the parts you have labeled.
6. After you have hypothesized the function of as many of the structures as you can, add a drop of alizarin red stain.
7. Can you see structures in stained *Paramecium* that you did not see before? Add these structures to your diagram, using a colored pencil to distinguish them from your 1st observation.
8. Follow the same scheme listed above and hypothesize the function of any newly visible structures.

Discussion

1. What is the basic difference between a *Paramecium* before staining and a *Paramecium* after staining?
2. What structures that you observed in the living organism were no longer visible in the stained organism?
3. What functions of a living organism are not represented in your hypotheses?
4. Now look at figure 12.13. What clues to functions do you find in the names of the structures?
5. With this new information, change any of the structure/function relationships that you think need changing.
6. What should you do to determine if your hypotheses are good ones?

Figure 12.13

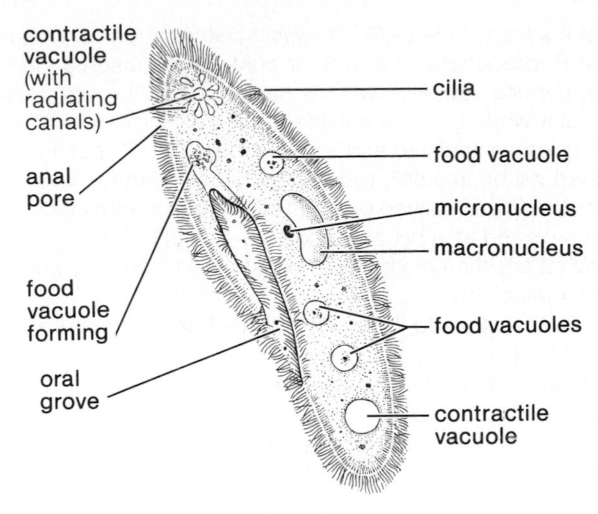

Part B—Movement in *Paramecium*

Procedure

1. Place a drop of protozoa slowing agent on a clean slide as before. Add a drop of *Paramecium* culture. Cover with a coverslip and observe with low power.
2. Before the slowing agent has diffused into the water, the organisms will move very rapidly. When they begin to slow down, switch to high power to observe movement in detail. Which end of *Paramecium* is usually in front as the animal moves?
3. The front end of an organism is referred to as anterior. The back end is referred to as posterior. Label the diagram you made in part A according to what you believe to be its anterior and posterior ends. Can you identify a top (or dorsal) and a bottom (or ventral) side?
4. Diagram the motion of *Paramecium* as it moves in 1 direction. Use arrows to show the directions of the motions of the body.
5. Gently raise the coverslip on your slide. Add a drop of the yeast suspension. Replace the coverslip and observe immediately with high power.
6. Observe the surface of 1 of the organisms. The hairlike structures you see are cilia. Notice carefully what happens to yeast cells that touch the *Paramecium*. Adjust the light until you can see individual cells.

Discussion

1. What do you believe is the function of the cilia?
2. What does the pattern of movement of the yeast cells tell you about the activities of the cilia?
3. On the basis of your observations in this inquiry, review and revise (if necessary) the hypothesis you formed in part A of this investigation of how *Paramecium* moves from one place to another.

Part C—Ingestion, Digestion, and Elimination in *Paramecium*

Procedure

1. Prepare a fresh slide of *Paramecium* culture and yeast suspension as in part B, procedures 1 and 5, or continue to observe the same slide if time permits. Observe what is happening to the yeast cells. Notice their color when they are outside the *Paramecium* and then find some that have been ingested and observe their color. Those that have been ingested will be in small, round structures called food vacuoles.
   The yeast was stained by your teacher just before class. The Congo red stain is red at a pH of 5 and blue at a pH of 3.
   (a) What are the colors of the yeast cells when they are outside the *Paramecium?*
   (b) What happens to the yeast cells that are encountered by the *Paramecium?*
   (c) What parts of the *Paramecium* are first involved in the ingestion of the yeast cells?
   (d) Where do the food vacuoles form in the *Paramecium?*
2. Carefully watch a newly formed food vacuole and note any changes in it. Within 2 or 3 minutes you should begin to notice a color change in the food vacuoles. Describe the change in color. How do you account for the change?
3. Continue to observe the food vacuoles. By means of circles representing food vacuoles and arrows representing their movement, diagram the path a food vacuole takes from its formation to its disappearance. How do the food vacuoles move through the organism?
4. Watch carefully to see how undigested food in a food vacuole is eliminated from *Paramecium.* Where in the body does this happen?

Discussion

1. Refer to the hypotheses you formed in part A regarding the structures in *Paramecium* that you thought responsible for food intake, for food digestion, and for the discharge of undigested food. Were you correct?
2. On the basis of the observations in this investigation, summarize how you now believe food is ingested, digested and eliminated by *Paramecium.*

Part D—Exchange of Materials in *Paramecium*

Procedure

1. *Paramecium,* like all living things, needs a constant supply of oxygen and must eliminate carbon dioxide, liquid wastes, and excess water. To discover the structures associated with these functions place a drop of protozoa slowing agent on a clean slide as before. Add a drop of *Paramecium* culture and a coverslip and observe with high power.
2. Considering the environment of the *Paramecium,* how and through what structure would you expect oxygen and carbon dioxide to move?
3. Concentrate your observation at either end of the *Paramecium.* Locate a structure that fills up with fluid, contracts (expelling its contents) and seems to disappear, then becomes visible again, filling with fluid, and repeats this process. The canals leading into the vacuole give it a star-shaped appearance. This structure is called a contractile vacuole.
   (a) How many contractile vacuoles are there in *Paramecium?*
   (b) Where are they located? If you did not include them in your earlier drawing, add them now.

(c) Do the contractile vacuoles move through the cell as food vacuoles do, or do they stay in one place?
(d) Is the fluid within the enlarged vacuole clear, or granular?
(e) How many contractions does the vacuole make in 1 minute?

4. If you identified any contractile vacuoles in part A, what hypothesis did you form about their function?

Discussion

Students who have investigated the question, "What is the function of a contractile vacuole?" have made the following observations:

Obs. 1. Urea (an end product of nitrogen metabolism) is not found in any great amount in the fluid of a contractile vacuole.

Obs. 2. If vacuoles of freshwater *Paramecium* do not function, the body swells.

Obs. 3. Injection of distilled water into the organism increases the rate of contraction of the vacuole (more contractions per minute).

Obs. 4. Water taken in with food in food vacuoles is equal to only a fraction of the amount of water expelled by the contractile vacuole.

1. What effect does obs. 1 have on the hypothesis that the contractile vacuole is an excretory organ used for eliminating nitrogenous wastes?
2. Considering obs. 2 and 3, what probably is the function of a contractile vacuole in *Paramecium?*
3. List the ways in which water might enter the *Paramecium.*
4. From obs. 4, what would you suggest is the major method of water entry?
5. Develop a hypothesis that will account for the actions of a contractile vacuole.

Part E—Behavior of *Paramecium*

Procedure

Behavior is the response organisms make to their environment. Animals usually have a well-defined brain or nervous system which facilitates the function of behavior. *Paramecium* does not have a brain or nervous system. Will it be influenced by environmental factors?

1. Fill 2 test tubes or vials ¼ full with a *Paramecium* culture. Place 1 test tube upright in a rack so that it receives uniform light from all directions.
2. Stopper the 2nd test tube. Cover the top half with black paper or metal foil. Lay the tube on its side. Illuminate the bottom half evenly.
3. Now observe the upright tube. In a rich culture of *Paramecium,* a concentration of the organism looks like a white cloud. Examine the tube for any concentration of the organisms.
   (a) What evidence do you find that the *Paramecium* are or are not moving toward 1 part of the tube?
   (b) In this controlled situation, the tendency of organisms to concentrate in 1 part of the tube suggests a response to gravity. Is this response to gravity positive, negative, or neither?
   (c) What other factors might account for a concentration in this test tube?
   (d) What additional investigations would you devise to check all variables, including gravity?

4. Observe the partially covered test tube placed on its side.
   (a) Has the *Paramecium* culture concentrated at 1 end of the tube?
   (b) Is the response to light positive, negative, or not definitely either?
   (c) Why could this investigation not have been done with the tube in an upright position?
   (d) How might this response to light be an advantage to *Paramecium?*
5. Place a drop of *Paramecium* culture on a slide. Drop a small piece of thread into the dilute hydrochloric acid solution. Place the thread across the middle of the drop. Add a coverslip. Focus on the piece of thread under low power. Does the *Paramecium* respond positively or negatively to the acid, or neither?

Discussion

Summarize your observations of the behavior of *Paramecium* in response to gravity, light, and acid.

Guidepost: What characteristics distinguish the various groups of algae?

Autotrophic Protists

12.9 Algae Are Photosynthetic Protists

Algae are photosynthetic protists with relatively simple structure. They may be unicellular, colonial, or multicellular. Multicellular species may form long filaments of cells, or thin plates of cells, or solid bodies that develop division of labor. Some of those forms are shown in figure 12.14. Algae can be found just about everywhere—floating in air or water, or attached to trunks or branches of trees, the bottoms of streams, particles of soil, or rocks at the seashore.

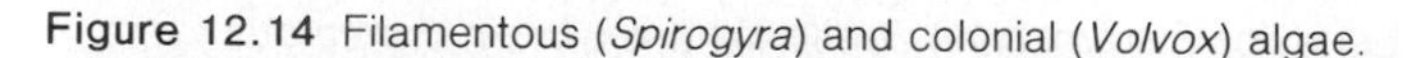

Figure 12.14 Filamentous (*Spirogyra*) and colonial (*Volvox*) algae.

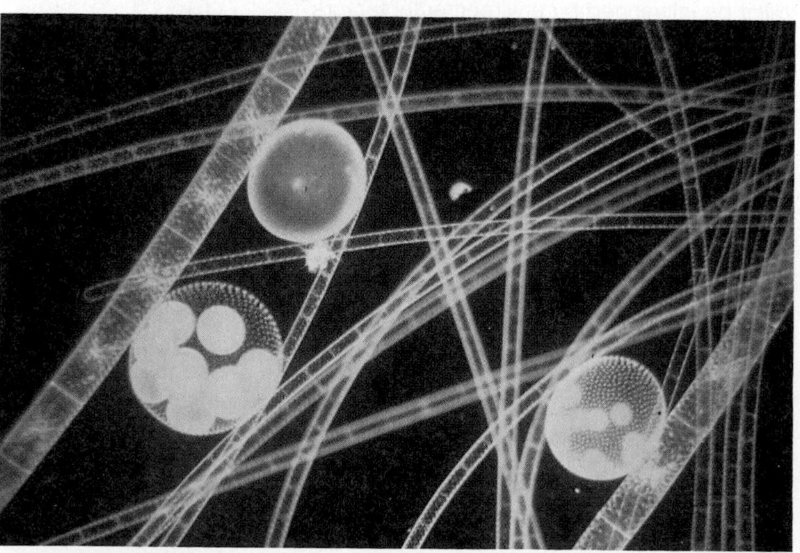

T. E. Adams/VISUALS UNLIMITED

Most unicellular and colonial algae float near the surface of bodies of water, using light energy and carbon dioxide and minerals from the water to carry out photosynthesis. Multicellular algae, on the other hand, are adapted to living along shores and in shallow water, where nutrients are generally abundant, but living conditions are difficult. Such algae are subject to periodic drying and to variations in temperature, light, and other factors. As a result, different groups of algae have become adapted to particular niches.

The term algae is one of convenience that is no longer used in formal classification. Biologists have become convinced that the various groups of what we call algae have little relationship to each other. Algae vary greatly in their biochemical characteristics, especially in the compounds that make up their cell walls, their food storage compounds, and the pigments present in their cells. Cell walls of most algae contain cellulose, as do those of plants, but a variety of other compounds also may be present. Some algae store food as starch, but other, unique carbohydrates are common, often combined with lipids.

In addition to chlorophyll, various other pigments may be present in algae. Often those pigments mask the bright green of the chlorophyll, and some of the groups are named for their characteristic color. The wide variety of pigments suggests that the various groups of algae may have evolved from mutualistic relationships with different photosynthetic prokaryotes.

12.10 Diatoms Are Important Golden Algae

Golden algae (Phylum Chrysophyta) are mostly microscopic aquatic organisms. Some grow in damp places on land. They have chlorophyll, but it is usually masked by yellow pigments. Some are threadlike and grow in masses along the edges of ponds or streams or on moist flowerpots in greenhouses. Within this phylum is a large group of organisms commonly called **diatoms** (DY uh tomz). Diatoms include some of the most intricately patterned creatures on earth, as shown in figure 12.15. They are enclosed in a double shell, the two halves of which fit together like a box. The shells contain silicon, and electron microscope studies have shown that the patterns are intricately shaped pores that connect the inside of the cell with the outside environment. Diatoms are abundant in both fresh and marine waters, where they are the main producers in many food webs and provide much of the world's oxygen. Diatoms store food in the form of oils. They reproduce asexually by cell division, or sexually by producing gametes. The zygote resulting from fertilization grows to the full size for the species and undergoes cell division. The offspring cells then produce new silicon shells.

[krih SOF it uh]

Because of their silicon shells, diatoms remain intact for many years, even after the organisms inside have died. Great masses of intact shells that slowly accumulated many years ago are now mined as diatomaceous earth. The material is used many ways—as a filter (both for beer and for swimming pools), as an abrasive in silver polish, and as a brightener for the paint used to mark highways.

Figure 12.15 Diatoms: (a) Stained mixture photographed through a light microscope; (b) living *Synedra;* (c) and (d) scanning electron micrographs showing the double silicon shell and the pattern of pores. (c) ×342; (d) ×2090.

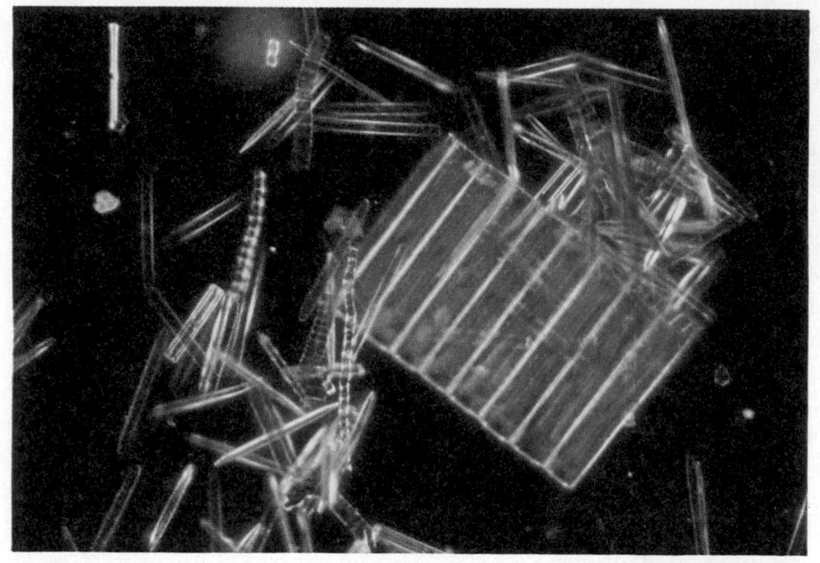

a BSCS by Richard Tolman

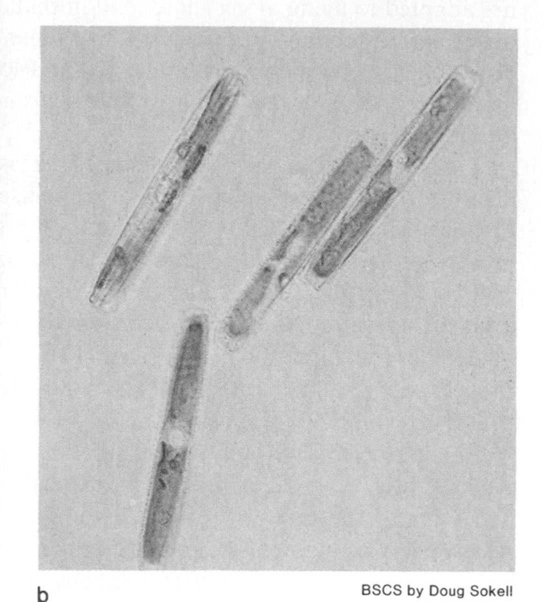

b BSCS by Doug Sokell

c Ken J. Andrews

d Thomas K. Shimotake

12.11 Certain Green Algae May Be the Ancestors of Plants

[kloh ROF it uh]

Most green algae (Phylum Chlorophyta) are aquatic organisms, and the majority are found in fresh water. You can find them in your aquarium at home or on the shady side of trees. Many of the green algae are unicellular and microscopic in size, but they may be so abundant that they color the water of ponds and lakes green. Some of the marine species form large, multicellular seaweeds. A few members of this large group are shown in figure 12.16.

Green algae reproduce both asexually and sexually. In sexual reproduction, some species produce flagellated gametes that look identical (see figure 12.17). Other species produce flagellated sperm and larger, nonmotile ova that are retained in the parent algae. Many of the multicellular green algae produce both gametes and spores in complex life cycles like those found in plants.

Figure 12.16 Green algae: (a) *Acetabularia*, a large, one-celled alga; (b) water net, *Hydrodictyon reticulatum*, a filamentous form; (c) sea lettuce, *Ulva*, a multicellular alga.

a L. L. Sims/VISUALS UNLIMITED

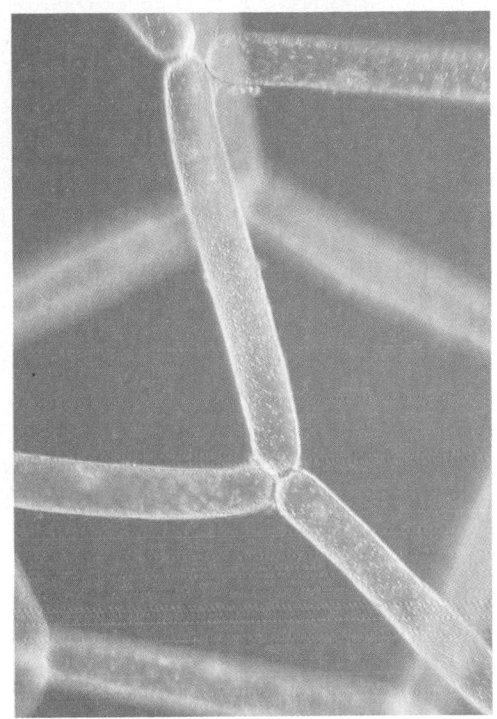

b T. E. Adams/VISUALS UNLIMITED

c John D. Cunningham/VISUALS UNLIMITED

Plants are believed to have evolved from some of the green algae. There are several kinds of evidence that support that theory. First, plants and green algae contain the same photosynthetic pigments. No other group of algae contains the same combination of pigments. Second, both groups store reserve foods as starch. Third, most members of both groups have cellulose-containing cell walls. Fourth, several groups of green algae have developed true multicellularity with some division of labor, and other groups show intermediate steps between unicellularity and multicellularity. And finally, many of the green algae show the patterns of reproduction and life cycles common to all plants. We will examine these patterns in the next chapter.

Figure 12.17 Life cycle of *Chlamydomonas*, a unicellular green alga, showing both sexual and asexual reproduction. Notice that the zygote is the only diploid stage in the life cycle.

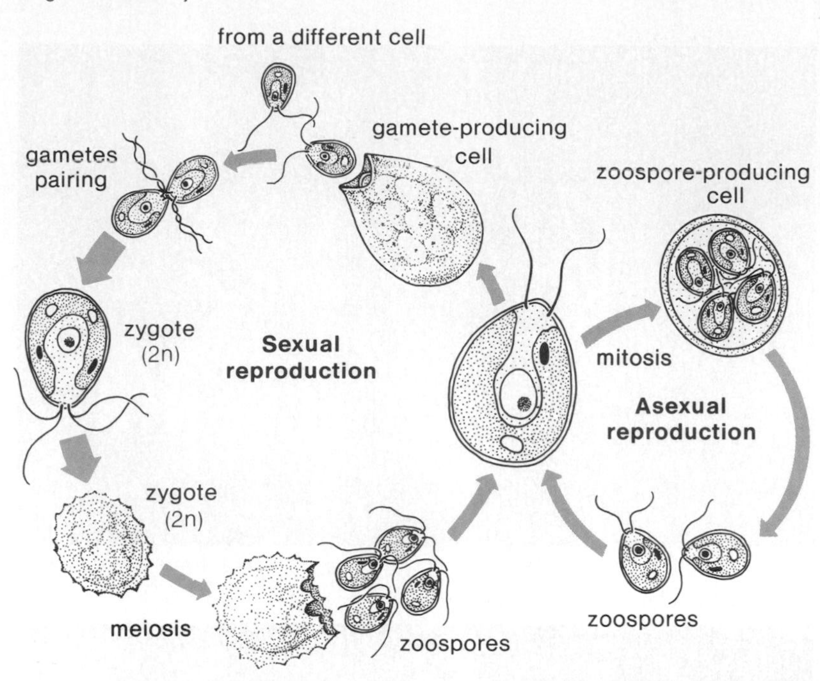

12.12 Brown and Red Algae Are Multicellular

[fee OFF it uh]

The brown algae (Phylum Phaeophyta) are the major seaweeds of rocky shores in the cooler regions of the world. Some, such as the kelps (see figure 23.26, page 875), form extensive beds offshore, where they are the primary producers for many communities of animals and microorganisms. Brown algae have cellulose cell walls and store their foods as an unusual polysaccharide or as oil, but never as starch. The chlorophyll in the brown algae is usually masked by other pigments.

Brown algae may be very large, sometimes reaching 100 m in length. Some of the brown algae are relatively unspecialized, but others are differentiated into areas for anchorage (holdfast), support (stipe), and photosynthesis (blade), as seen in figure 12.18b. Some kelps even have conducting cells in the center of the stipe that resemble the sugar conducting cells of plant stems.

[roh DOF it uh]

Most of the seaweeds of warm oceans of the world are red algae (Phylum Rhodophyta). They generally grow attached to rocks or other algae (figure 12.18c). Because they absorb blue light, which penetrates farther in the water than other light wavelengths, red algae can grow deeper in the ocean than any other algae. Biologists think the chloroplasts of red algae may have evolved from ancestral cyanobacteria, because the two groups contain similar pigments. Cell walls of red algae contain an inner layer of cellulose and an outer layer composed of other carbohydrates such as agar, which is used to culture bacteria in the laboratory.

Figure 12.18 Brown and red algae: (a) a brown alga showing air bladders that help keep it afloat; (b) kelp, *Laminaria,* showing holdfast, stipe, and blade; (c) coralline red alga, *Bossiella.*

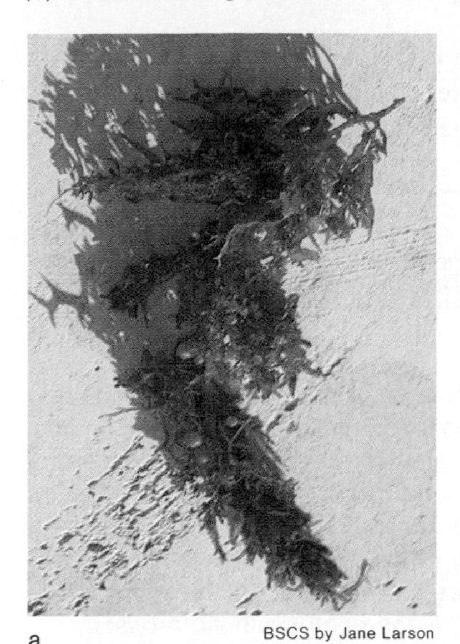

a BSCS by Jane Larson

b John D. Cunningham / VISUALS UNLIMITED

c Gary R. Robinson / VISUALS UNLIMITED

In many parts of the world, both red and brown algae are eaten by humans as part of their regular diet. Although algae do not provide many kcals, they do contain valuable vitamins and trace elements necessary to human health. Certain kinds of red and brown algae produce compounds that are extremely important in the manufacturing of food and goods that require a smooth texture. Each time you use hand lotion, lipstick, or paint, or eat marshmallows, ice cream, or certain cheeses, you are probably using products derived from algae.

Self-Review

1. What characteristics of green algae make them candidates for the ancestors of all plants?
2. What makes diatomaceous earth useful, and how is it used?
3. How do humans use brown and red algae?
4. Which group of algae can live the deepest, and why?

Investigation 12.2 VARIETY AMONG ALGAE

Introduction

Algae are photosynthetic protists. They are found in nearly every aquatic environment. Algae are the foundations of many of the food chains throughout the world. Most of the algae are microscopic, but some of them grow larger than the shrubs that commonly grow around school yards. In this investigation, you will have an opportunity to use a dichotomous key to identify various kinds of algae. Many of the non-photosynthetic protists are found in environments with the algae. For this reason, the key you will use in this investigation also includes the non-photosynthetic protists.

Materials

compound microscope
microscope slides
coverslips
dropping pipet
algae cultures
macroscopic algae
teasing needle
A Catalog of Living Things (appendix 3)

Procedure

1. Examine the algae cultures and specimens. Use the dichotomous key in table 12.1 and A Catalog of Living Things to identify the phylum to which each individual belongs. You will need to use the eyedroppers to prepare microscope slides to observe some specimens.
2. Some cultures may contain non-photosynthetic protists. The key and A Catalog of Living Things will help you identify the group to which these organisms belong.

Discussion

1. Why are most microscopic green algae floating near the surface of the water?
2. Why are the large brown algae (kelp) not classified as plants?
3. Choose 1 of the specimens you observed. Write a short paragraph describing the environment in which you think the organism lives. Describe other organisms that would be found in that same environment. Describe the interactions between the protist you observed and the other organisms in that environment.

Table 12.1 Dichotomous key to some protists

1A. Unicellular organisms	go to 2
1B. Organisms not unicellular	go to 7
2A. Cilia used for locomotion and/or feeding	**Ciliates (Ciliophora)**
2B. Lack cilia	go to 3
3A. Flagella usd for locomotion	**Flagellates**
3B. Lack flagella	go to 4
4A. Locomotion by pseudopods	**Sarcodines**
4B. Lack pseudopods	go to 5
5A. Nonmotile, lack chlorophyll	Sporozoans **(Apicomplexa)**
5B. Contain chlorophyll	go to 6
6A. Green color	Single-cell green algae **(Chlorophyta)**
6B. Yellow color, overlapping double shell	Diatoms **(Chrysophyta)**
7A. Red color, mainly marine	Red Algae **(Rhodophyta)**
7B. Not red in color	go to 8
8A. Brown color, mainly marine	Brown algae **(Phaeophyta)**
8B. Not brown	go to 9
9A. Green color, marine and fresh water	Green algae **(Chlorophyta)**
9B. Yellow color, filamentous	Golden algae **(Chrysophyta)**

For Further Investigation

Write a Haiku poem about one of the organisms that you observed and identified. A Haiku poem consists of 3 lines. The first line has 5 syllables, the second line has 7 syllables, and the third line has 5 syllables. There is no requirement for rhyming in Haiku. Your poem should convey your impressions of the organism.

Fungi

Guidepost: What are the characteristics of the fungi?

12.13 Fungi Are Important Decomposers

Fungi are nonmotile, heterotrophic, eukaryotes. They include mushrooms, molds, mildews, rusts, smuts, and many other, less familiar organisms. Most fungi reproduce by means of spores that germinate and grow into slender tubes called **hyphae** (HY fee). The body of a fungus is made up of a large mass of hyphae, the **mycelium** (my SEE lee um). The mycelium grows in moist soil that contains large amounts of dead plant and animal matter, as shown in figure 12.19. In fact, a mycelium will grow on virtually anything from which the fungus can obtain food. Sometimes growth can be very rapid: a single fungus can produce a kilometer of hyphae in just 24 hours.

Figure 12.19 Fungal mycelium growing on the inner surface of the bark of a log.

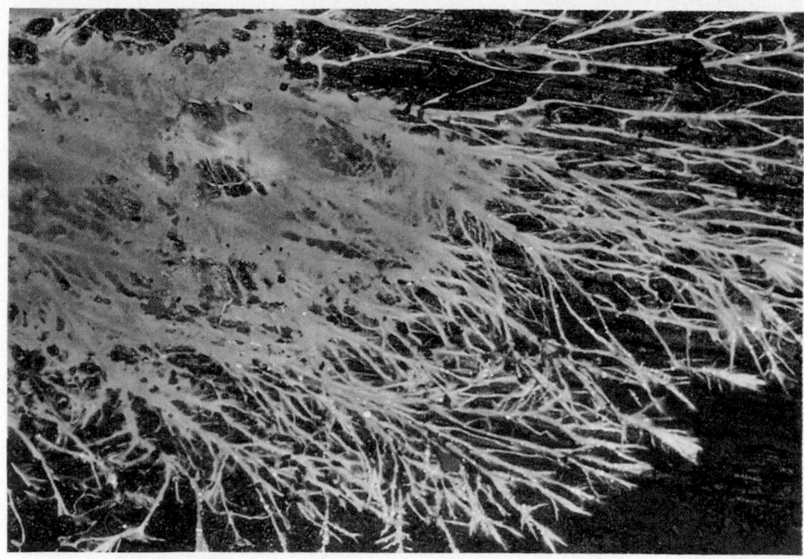

John Richardson, Southern Illinois Univ.

Cell walls of fungi are made up of a carbohydrate known as **chitin** (KYT in). Sometimes the chitin is combined with cellulose, the main component of plant cell walls. The chitinous walls are hard and resistant to water loss, enabling fungi to live in some very extreme environments.

Fungi feed by absorbing small organic molecules. They secrete digestive enzymes that break down the food into small molecules outside the fungus. The small molecules are then transported in through the membrane. In that way, fungi help decompose dead organisms.

Fungi, along with bacteria, are the most important decomposers in the biosphere. Many fungi cause diseases, especially of plants. Many more, however, form essential mutualistic relationships with plants. Others are used for baking breads, making alcoholic beverages, and producing drugs.

Fungi reproduce primarily by means of spores, which may be produced sexually or asexually. Each spore is capable of producing an entire mycelium. The reproductive part of the fungus may appear above ground, as, for example, a mushroom. The spore-producing structures are formed of tightly packed hyphae and may produce a million spores. Generally, fungus spores are surrounded by a tough, resistant wall that enables them to survive drying and extreme temperatures. The spores are usually dispersed by wind and air currents. Their small size keeps them suspended in air for long periods, assuring wide distribution. Fungi also may reproduce sexually by conjugation, in which hyphae of different mating types come together and fuse.

Because the hyphae of many fungi look very much alike, classification of fungi is based mainly on differences in sexual reproductive structures. In the next sections, we will describe some of those differences among the fungi.

Investigation 12.3 GROWTH OF FUNGI

Introduction

Mushrooms and molds are common types of fungi with which you are familiar. Perhaps some of your cultures from previous investigations were contaminated with mold. This might have given you the idea that molds are everywhere, simply waiting to grow when they encounter a suitable environment. Under what conditions will mold grow at the fastest rate? That question is the focus of this investigation.

Materials

Part A (per person)

suitable medium (your choice)
container for medium
ruler
growth chamber (your choice)
dissecting microscope (1 per group)
microscope slide
anything else you want to use

Part B (per group)

fresh mushrooms
glass tumbler
sheet of white paper
small brush
microscope slide
coverslip
compound microscope
glycerine-water solution (1:1)
knife

Part A—Mold Growing Race

Procedure

1. You and your classmates are going to have a mold growing contest to see who can grow the largest amount of mold in the shortest period of time. Think about the conditions that might contribute to the rapid growth of mold.
2. Select a medium on which the mold can grow. Record the reasons for your selection.
3. Decide what you will do to inoculate your medium with mold spores. Record why you selected your particular method of getting the mold started.
4. Decide on where you will keep the medium while the mold grows. Record why you selected the particular environment for growing your mold.
5. The race is on. Get started today. Keep track of the size and quantity of the mold growths you obtain by making daily observations and recording your observations.
6. Your teacher will announce the last day of the race. Be prepared to bring your mold to class on that day. Prepare a short presentation for the class to communicate your procedures and results.

Discussion

1. Now that you have listened to the reports of other class members, what do you think you could have done to increase the amount of mold that grew on your medium?
2. Explain how you can use your results to prevent the growth of mold on food or in other locations in your home.

Part B—Observing Mushrooms

Procedure

1. Examine a fresh mushroom. The mushroom itself is the fruiting body of this particular fungus. It consists of a stalk and umbrellalike cap.
2. Cut the cap from the stalk.
3. Look at the underside of the cap and find the gills. Put the cap, gill side down, on a piece of white paper.
4. Cover the cap with a tumbler or some other object that will protect it from air currents.
5. Set the cap, paper, and tumbler in a place where it will not be disturbed. The next day, uncover and remove the cap by lifting it straight up from the paper.
   (a) What do you observe on the paper?
   (b) What is the relationship between what you observe on the paper and the structure of the mushroom cap?
6. With a small, damp brush, remove some of the material on the paper. Place the material on a microscope slide.
7. Add a drop of the glycerine and water solution. Gently place a coverslip over the liquid.
8. Examine the material under both low and high power.
   (a) Approximately how many particles are there in the sample you are observing?
   (b) Using this number, estimate the total number of such particles coming from the mushroom.

Discussion

1. If we assume that these particles are reproductive spores, how could you account for the fact that the world is not covered with mushrooms?
2. How numerous would mushrooms be if they only produced a small fraction of the number of spores seen here?

For Further Investigation

You may want to conduct an investigation on the specificity of various fungicides toward different species of fungi. Your teacher can obtain spore suspensions of a variety of fungi from a biological supply house. Fungicides that can be obtained easily are copper sulfate and captan (use 3% solutions). You will need petri dishes with potato dextrose agar or oatmeal agar, small sterilized brushes, and sterile distilled water. Some suggestions for fungi include *Pilobolus crystallinus, Aspergillus niger, Penicillium notatum,* or many others.

To prepare a control dish, dip the brush in a spore solution for about 30 seconds. Then place the brush in sterile distilled water for about 30 seconds. Last, touch the surface of the agar, being careful not to expose the plates to airborne spores.

To prepare experimental dishes, repeat the step above for each of the fungicides, using the fungicide instead of the distilled water.

Place the petri dishes in paper bags and store them in a cool room for one week. Compare the percentage of germination between the experimental dishes and the control dish.

12.14 Conjugating Fungi May be Destructive to Foods and Crops

The common black bread mold, ***Rhizopus stolonifer,*** is probably the most familiar example of conjugating fungi (Phylum Zygomycota). Before preservatives were used, bread left in the pantry for several days would develop a black fuzzy growth like that in figure 12.20. Such growth is caused by a spore that germinates on the surface of the bread, producing hyphae. Some of the hyphae push up into the air and form sporangia. Mature sporangia are black, giving the fungus its characteristic color. The sporangia eventually break open, releasing many spores, each of which can germinate to produce a new mycelium.

[ry ZOH pus stoh LON ih fer]
[ZY goh my KOHT uh]

Sexual reproduction in *Rhizopus* occurs when hyphae of two different mating types fuse (figure 12.21). Nuclei from the two hyphae fuse and form zygotes that develop into thick-walled **zygospores** (ZY goh

Figure 12.20 Bread covered with mycelium of *Rhizopus.*

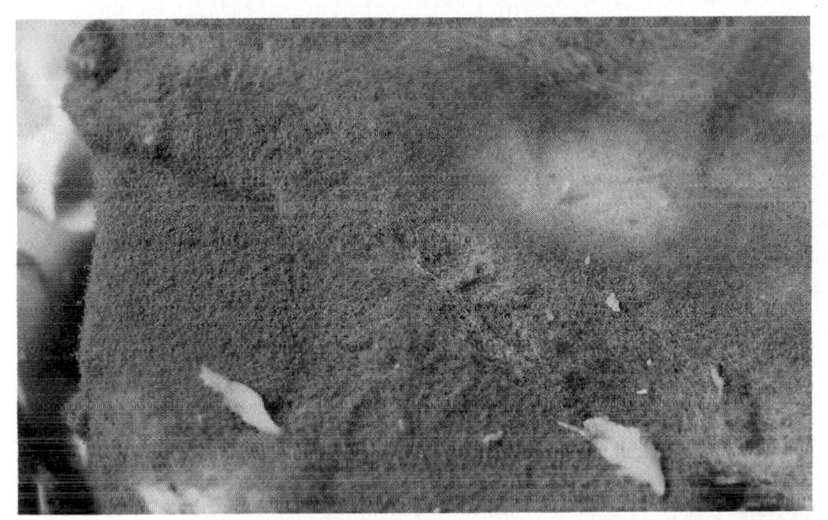

John D. Cunningham/VISUALS UNLIMITED

Figure 12.21 Asexual and sexual reproduction in *Rhizopus.*

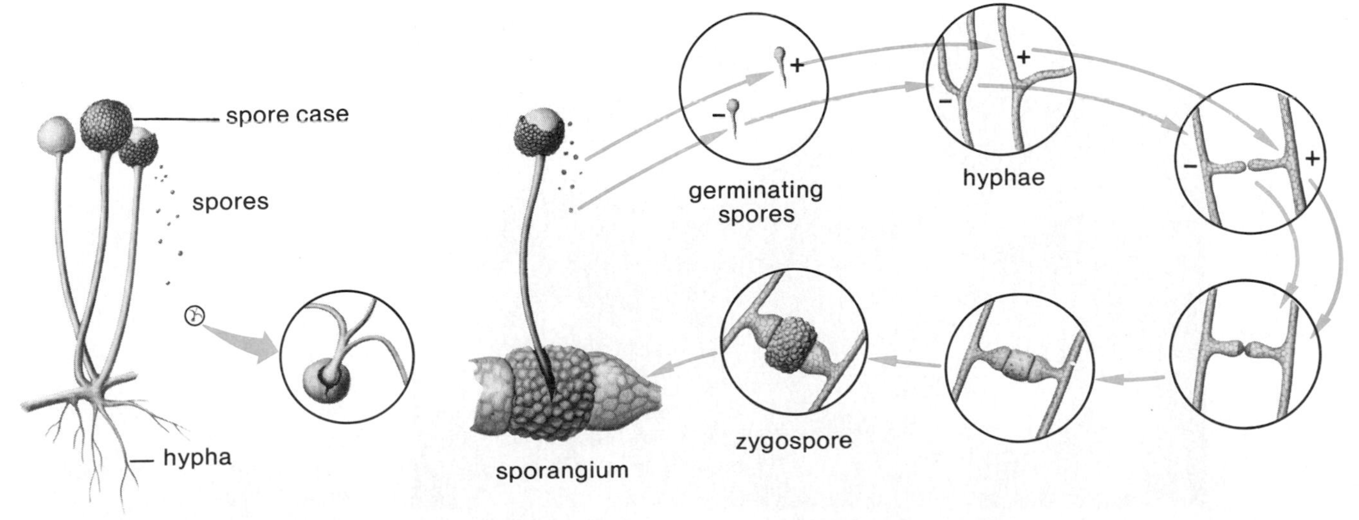

sporz). It is these structures that give the phylum its name. Zygospores can survive periods of extreme temperature or dryness, and when they eventually germinate, they give rise to sporangia that release spores.

Black bread mold is a decomposer that can be destructive to many foods, including fruits such as grapes, plums, and strawberries. Other species in this phylum are parasitic, and some attack crop plants. Most, however, live in the soil and decompose dead plant and animal material.

12.15 Humans Use Sac Fungi in a Variety of Ways

[AS koh my KOHT uh]

The sac fungi (Phylum Ascomycota) include yeasts, powdery mildews, and many common blue-green molds, as well as morels and truffles (figure 12.22). Some sac fungi cause diseases such as chestnut blight and dutch elm disease, which have destroyed many trees in the United

Figure 12.22 Sac fungi: (a) leaves covered with powdery mildew; (b) a morel, *Morchella augusticeps;* (c) red cup fungus, *Peziza.*

a

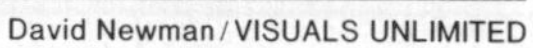

David Newman / VISUALS UNLIMITED

b Athalie Barzee

c David Newman / VISUALS UNLIMITED

States. These fungi are distinguished from other fungi by a microscopic sexual reproductive structure called an **ascus** (AS kus), which gives them their name.

An ascus is formed when two hyphae conjugate. Inside the ascus, nuclei from the hyphae fuse and develop into ascospores. The ascospores eventually are released from the ascus and may travel long distances on the wind. Each ascospore can germinate and produce hyphae. Ascomycetes also reproduce asexually. An individual hypha segments into huge numbers of spores that are dispersed by wind, water, or animals.

[AS koh sporz]

[AS koh my SEETS]

Figure 12.23 Sexual reproduction in a sac fungus.

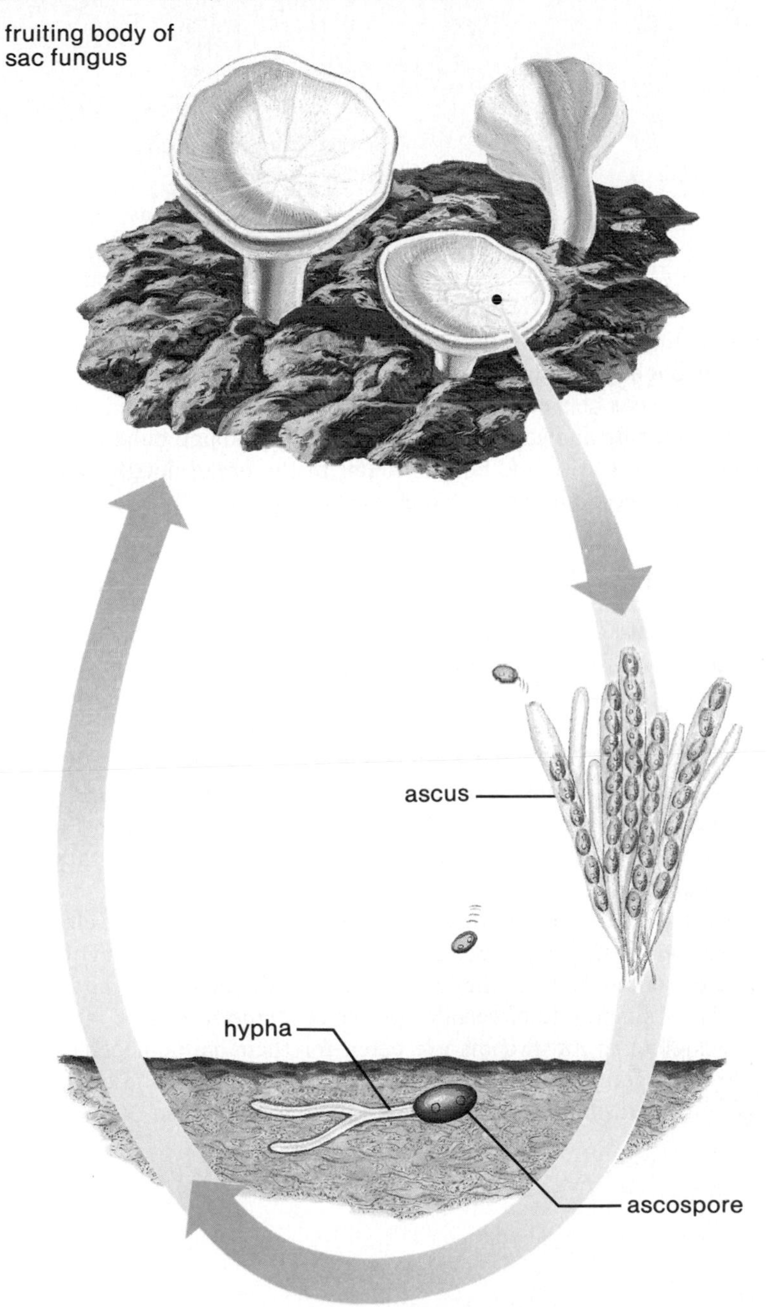

Figure 12.24 Yeast. Notice the budding individual near the center of the photo.

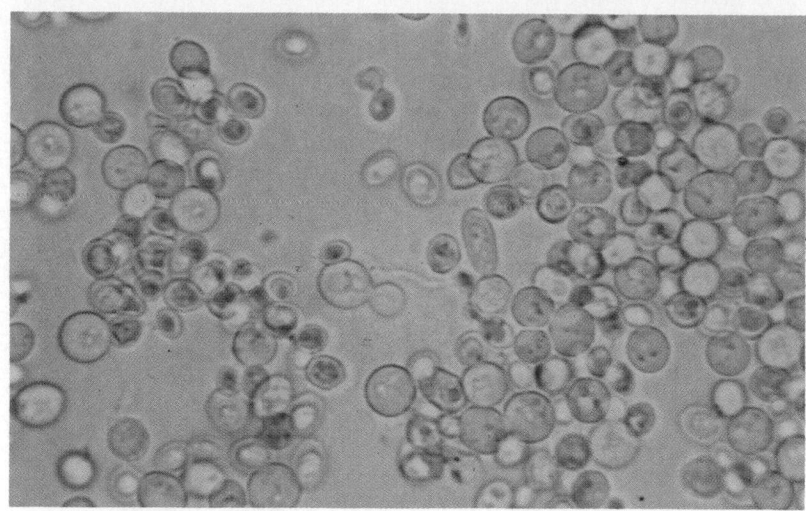

BSCS by Richard Tolman

Yeasts are single-celled ascomycetes. They are small, oval cells that reproduce asexually by budding, as seen in figure 12.24, and sexually by production of ascospores. Yeasts are essential to production of breads and alcoholic beverages such as beer and wine. Under anaerobic conditions, yeasts convert sugars found in bread dough or fruit juices into carbon dioxide and ethyl alcohol. The carbon dioxide bubbles cause the bread dough to rise and beer to foam. In the bread dough, the alcohol evaporates as the bread is baked.

12.16 Many Club Fungi Are Edible

[buh SID ee oh my KOHT uh]

Club fungi (Phylum Basidiomycota) are probably the most familiar fungi. The mushrooms you buy in a grocery store are the sexual reproductive structures of a club fungus. The phylum also includes smuts, rusts, jelly fungi, puffballs, and stinkhorns (figure 12.25). The mushroom is a spore-producing body composed of masses of tightly packed hyphae. Under a mushroom cap you can see what are called gills radiating out from the center. Between these gills many spores are produced on tiny clubs, or **basidia** (buh SID ee uh), that give these fungi their name.

[am uh NY tuh]

Most species of mushrooms, both edible and poisonous, are club fungi. A toadstool is nothing more than a poisonous mushroom, and one of the most poisonous of all is the "death cap" of the genus *Amanita* (figure 12.27). A single bite of certain species of *Amanita* can be fatal. Some species of toxic mushrooms are eaten for their hallucinogenic effects. Other club fungi are parasites of plants such as wheat and corn. Wheat rust and corn smut cause great damage to those crops.

Figure 12.25 Club fungi: (a) mushrooms, *Clitocybe;* (b) rust, Uredinales, on the undersurface of leaves; (c) puffballs, *Lycoperdon perlatum;* (d) bracket fungus from Australian rain forest.

a Athalie Barzee

b Athalie Barzee

c Athalie Barzee

d J. Alcock/VISUALS UNLIMITED

Figure 12.26 Reproductive structures of a field mushroom.

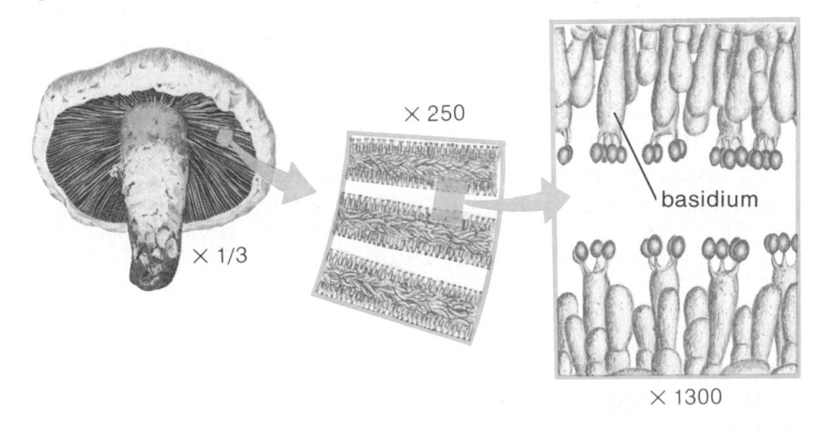

Figure 12.27 *Amanita muscaria.*

Robert C. Simpson/TOM STACK & ASSOCIATES

12.17 Fungi with No Known Sexual Reproductive Structures Are Called Imperfect Fungi

Fungi are identified and classified principally on characteristics of their sexual reproductive structures. Many fungi seldom, if ever, produce such structures. **Mycologists** (my KOL uh jists), scientists who study fungi, have studied certain ones for years without discovering sexually produced spores. Some of these fungi, however, resemble species whose sexual reproductive structures are known. Many of these fungi produce large numbers of asexual spores and can be classified on the basis of similarities in asexual reproductive form. When sexual states of such fungi are discovered, the fungi are reclassified according to their newly discovered sexual reproductive structures. For many fungi, however, no sexual reproductive structures have ever been discovered. So, for convenience only, taxonomists place these "imperfect" fungi together in a separate group. Some of these are important in the manufacture of cheese and antibiotics. For example, *Penicillium roquefortii* is responsible for the distinctive flavor and appearance of Roquefort cheese. *P. camembertii* is used to manufacture camembert cheese, and *P. notatum* produces the drug penicillin. Others are parasites that grow on crop plants and our skin. For example, athlete's foot is caused by an organism that, for years, was thought to be an imperfect fungus. Recently, sexual spores have been discovered, showing the athlete's foot fungus (and a number of related skin disease fungi) to be a sac fungus.

[pen ih SIL ee um rohk FOR tee]

[kam um BER tee]
[noh TAY tum]

Self-Review

1. How are hyphae related to a mycelium?
2. Why are fungi restricted to moist conditions?
3. What characteristics are used to distinguish fungi from each other?

Figure 12.28 Imperfect fungi: (a) a species of *Penicillium* growing on an orange; (b) asexual reproductive structures (conidiophores) of *Aspergillus*.

a John A. Moore

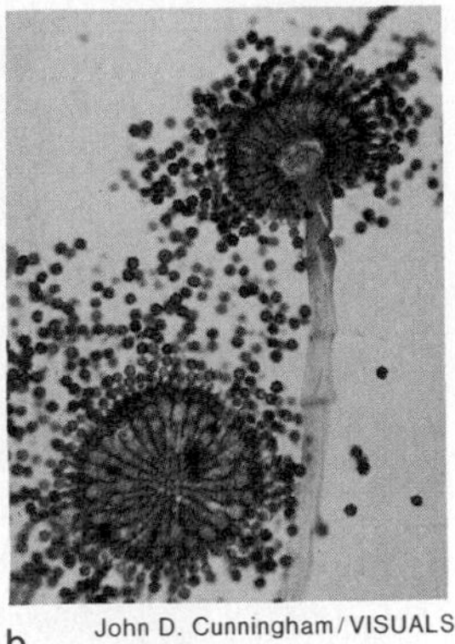

b John D. Cunningham/VISUALS UNLIMITED

4. What human foods are produced using fungi, and what foods are damaged by fungi?
5. What do mycologists mean by the phrase imperfect fungi?

Fungi in a Community

Guidepost: What roles do fungi play in a community?

12.18 Many Fungi in the Soil Are Decomposers

Most soil organisms are consumers. Algae, which are light-requiring producers, can live only at the surface of the soil. Most soil organisms, however, live below the surface. A soil ecosystem is like a city. Its food supply comes from the outside. In soil, some food comes into the roots of plants from their green parts, which are in the sunlight. Most of the food supply comes from the remains of organisms. Therefore, decomposers such as fungi and bacteria are important organisms in soil communities.

In a dead root in the soil, there are still large amounts of complex organic substances such as starch. Likewise, in a dead animal there are complex organic substances such as fats and proteins. These are used as food by beetles and other small animals living in the upper soil layers or on its surface. Other substances, such as cellulose in plant bodies and chitin in insect bodies, can be used only by microorganisms. Certain decomposers break down cellulose and chitin; animals cannot. Decomposers that use cellulose and chitin leave simpler organic substances as waste products. Those wastes still contain energy, which can be used by other decomposers. Even those decomposers may not extract all the energy, but they leave very simple substances in the soil. Still other decomposers make use of those simple substances. Thus, one decomposer

Figure 12.29 A decomposer food chain. Identify each organism and the role it plays in the process of decomposition.

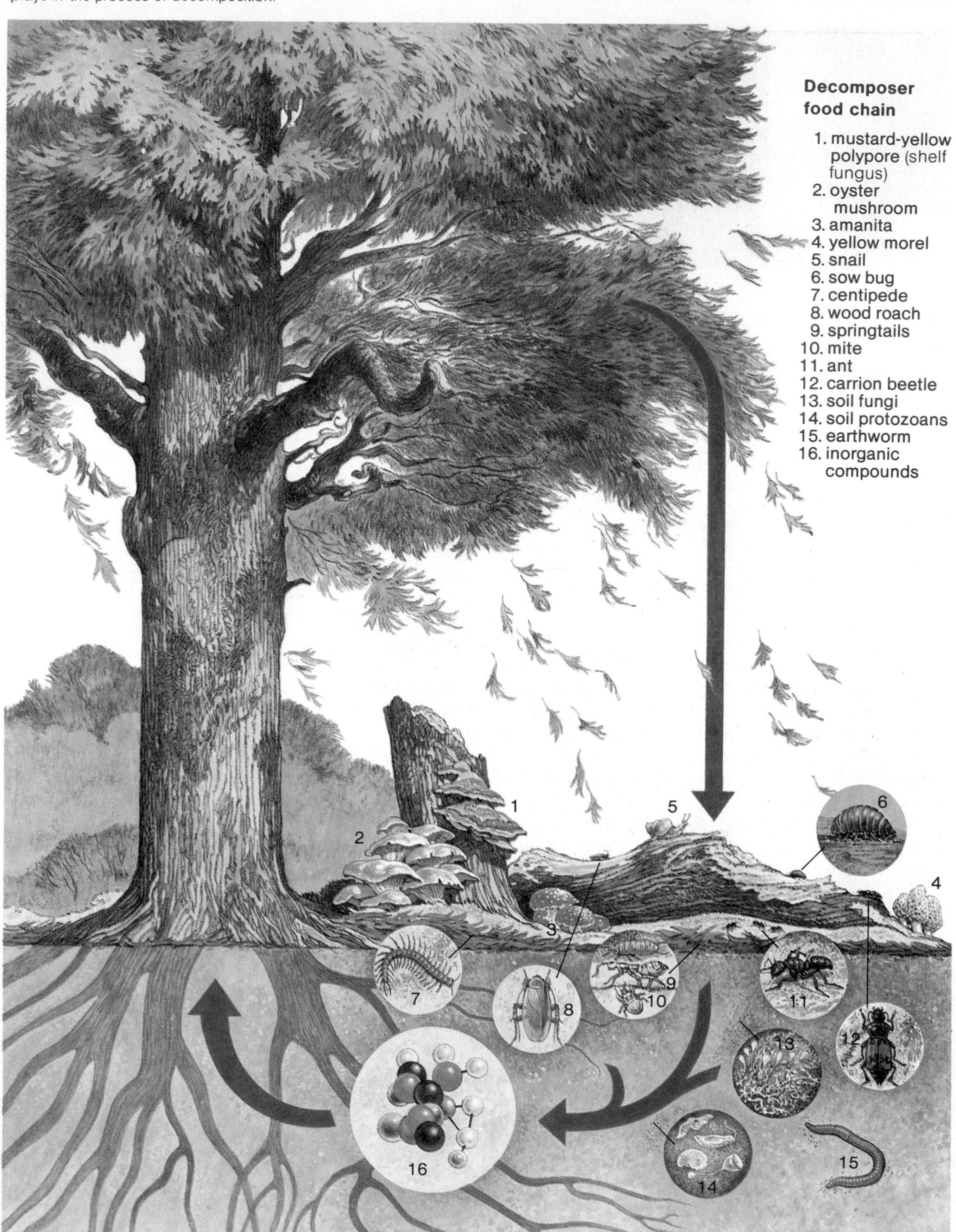

Figure 12.30 Predaceous fungi capture small roundworms present in the soil.
(a) *Dactylella drechsleri* traps the worms with small adhesive knobs.
(b) *Arthrobotrys dactyloides* forms rings that strangle the worm.

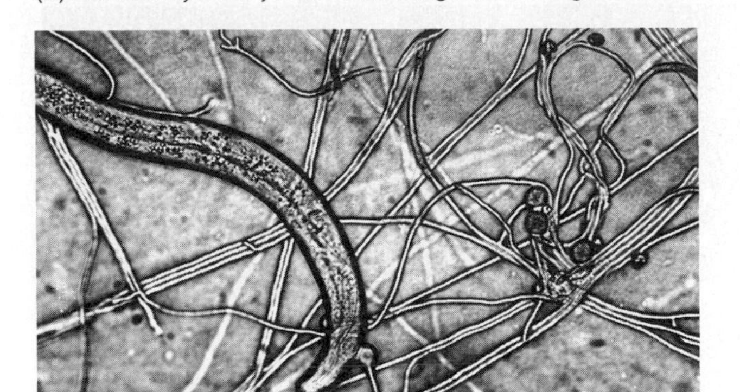

a Dr. David Pramer

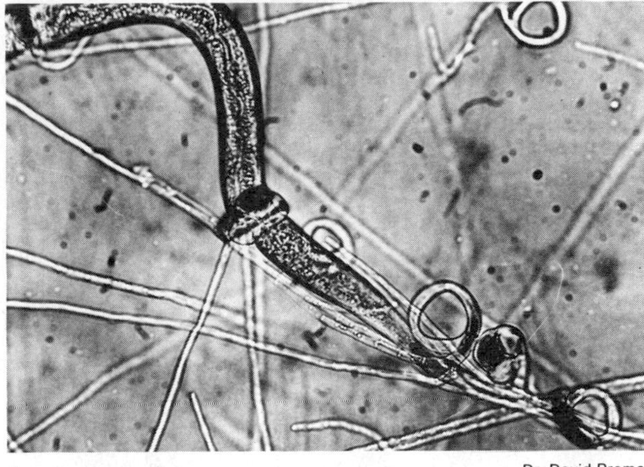

b Dr. David Pramer

depends on another for its food supply. Such a food chain is like an assembly line in reverse. Instead of building a body step by step from simpler to more complex compounds, the decomposer food chain breaks down complex organic substances. At the end of the chain, only inorganic substances such as carbon dioxide, water, and mineral compounds remain. At that point, plants can begin a different food chain by taking those inorganic materials and assembling them into organic compounds.

Some soil organisms produce substances that harm other organisms. Such antibiotic substances accumulate in the soil around the organisms that form them. Antibiotics reduce the growth of competing organisms. Some of those antibiotic substances are used for combating bacterial infections in humans. The drugs aureomycin, derived from a bacterium, and penicillin, from a fungus, are examples.

Fungi can even act as predators. Several species of soil fungi form hyphae with tough branches that curl into loops. The tips of the loops from adjacent hyphae intermesh, forming a network that produces a sticky fluid. Nematodes, small worms living in the soil, are caught in such loops and held fast despite violent struggles. Other fungal hyphae then grow into the bodies of the captive nematodes and digest them.

[NEM um tohdz]

12.19 Mycorrhizal Fungi Help Many Plants to Grow

If you trace fungal hyphae in loose soil, you often find that many lead to plant roots. There the fungi form feltlike covers around branches of the roots (figure 12.31b). Some of the fungal hyphae grow into the other parts of the roots and form masses of tissue there. These associations between fungi and roots are called **mycorrhizae** (my koh RY zee). Mycorrhizae enhance the growth of many plants. Experiments have indicated that the fungus absorbs phosphorus and other minerals from a greater area in the soil than the plant could by itself. The phosphorus

Figure 12.31 Pine roots (a) without micorrhizae and (b) with micorrhizae. (c). Microscopic view of micorrhizae growing into a root cell.

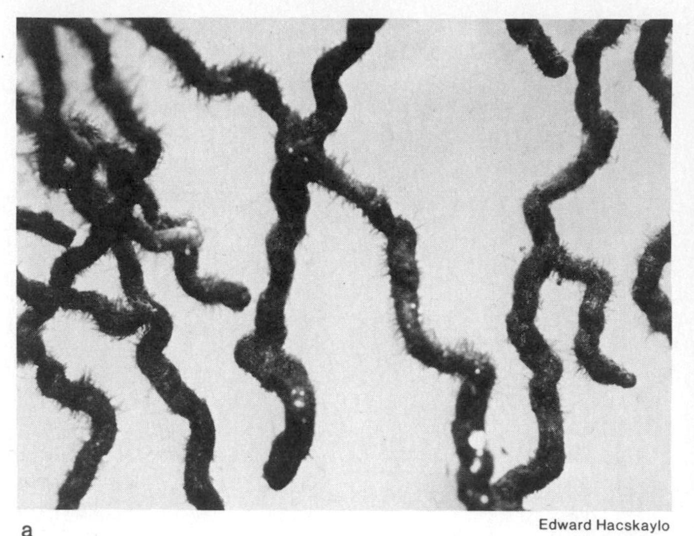

a Edward Hacskaylo

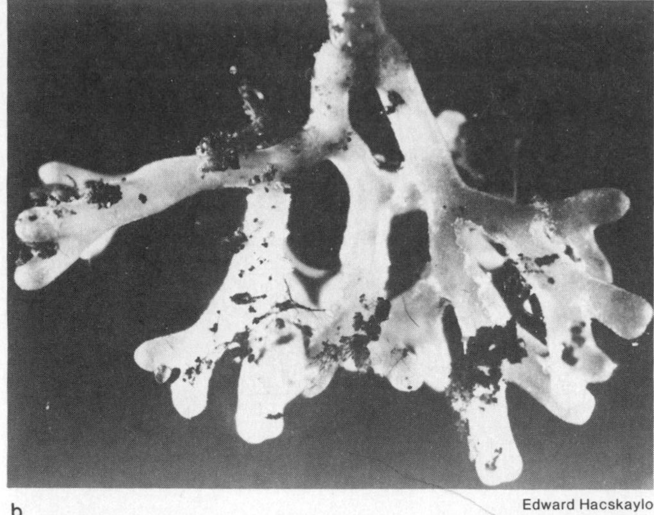

b Edward Hacskaylo

c Mark Brundrett

and minerals are passed on to the plant, which requires the elements to grow. Water also may be transported from the soil to the plant through the fungus. Micorrhizae are thought to occur in more than 90 percent of all plant families, and they are found in some of the oldest plant fossils.

The mycorrhizal fungi also benefit from their relationship with the plant. They absorb sugars and other organic materials from the roots of their plant partners. Thus this relationship is mutualistic. Some plants, such as orchids and pines, either do not grow or grow poorly if their mycorrhizal fungi are not present.

Figure 12.32 Leaflike lichens growing on a tree trunk.

Doug Sokell

Figure 12.33 Crustlike lichens colonizing rock.

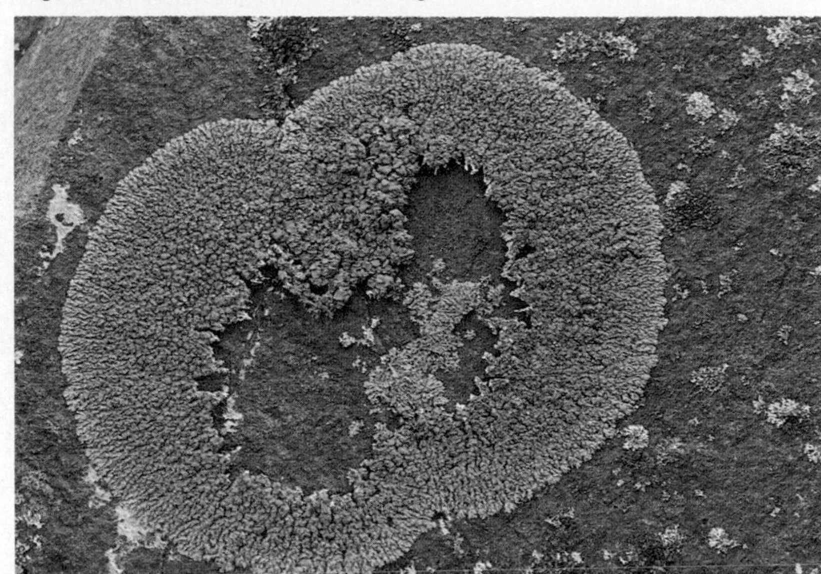

Gary Milburn/TOM STACK & ASSOCIATES

The oldest fossil fungi, dating from the Devonian period, are micorrhizae associated with fossil plant tissue. Micorrhizae may have made it possible for plants to adapt to a terrestrial existence. The fungi may have transported nutrients to plants and prevented them from drying out.

12.20 Lichens Are Mutualistic Relationships between Fungi and Algae

You can find lichens on the bark of a pine tree, on a tombstone in New Hampshire, buried under arctic snow, or on a rock in Arizona. In chapter 3 we discussed the mutualistic relationship between an alga and a fungus that make up a lichen. The shape and color of lichens are so definite that for several hundred years biologists described them as if they were single organisms.

The body of a lichen has a framework of fungal hyphae. In its upper layers are many small producers, usually green algae or cyanobacteria. The producers can grow independently, and many can be recognized as species that also are known to live alone. The lichen fungi, on the other hand, do not grow well when separated from their partners. Many of these fungi are placed in the sac fungi group, but they are unlike any of the species that live alone. More than 25,000 "species" of lichen have been described. Their names have been based on the fungus part of the lichen.

Lichens secrete acidic compounds that break down rocks. Thus, they often are the first organisms to colonize bare rock and other uninhabited places (figure 12.33). Such bare areas are extremely dry, but lichens

Figure 12.34 Reindeer moss, a type of shrubby lichen.

John D. Cunningham/VISUALS UNLIMITED

have the ability to dry out completely and become dormant until they are wet again. When they are dry, lichens can tolerate extreme heat and freezing cold that would kill other organisms, even hardy ones. However, when they are dormant, there is no growth. After rain, fog, or dew, a lichen may absorb up to 30 times its own weight in water. The algal cells in the lichen quickly begin to photosynthesize and growth continues until the lichen dries out again. Because growth occurs in spurts, when water is available, a normal lichen grows extremely slowly—sometimes just 0.1 mm per year. Thus, some small lichens may be several hundred years old.

Reindeer mosses (figure 12.34) cover great areas of the Arctic. These "mosses" are actually lichens that serve as food for reindeer and caribou. Reindeer mosses, like all lichens, absorb some minerals from the soil or rock on which they grow, but they also take in minerals from rainfall. Lichens absorb these nutrients and concentrate them in their cells. In some cases toxic compounds also are absorbed and concentrated in the lichen bodies. Lichens die when the air is extremely polluted, and can be used as indicators of polluted air. In the Arctic, reindeer mosses accumulated radioactive materials that drifted there from aboveground atomic bomb testing. The reindeer and caribou that ate the lichens took in the radioactive materials and passed them on to the Eskimos who ate those animals. That is another example of how unexpected materials are passed along a food chain to a consumer at the top of the chain.

Self-Review

1. How is a food chain involving only decomposers different from one including plants and animals?
2. When can fungi be called predators?

3. What makes the mycorrhizal fungus-plant relationship mutualistic?
4. What characteristics make lichens good pioneer organisms?
5. Why do lichens make good indicators of air quality?

Summary

The first organisms on earth probably were prokaryotes that lacked organelles of any kind. The more advanced eukaryotes possess organelles such as chloroplasts and mitochondria, which may have been derived from free-living prokaryotes. Protists and fungi are eukaryotes. Protists include organisms such as slime molds and amoeba that pick up food as they move along. Some protists are parasites that cause diseases of humans and other animals. Most groups of protists can be distinguished by their method of movement. Some do not move at all, while the others move by using their cilia, pseudopods, or flagella. Algae are autotrophic protists and may be distinguished from each other, in part, by their dominant pigments—red, brown, yellow, or green. Fungi are placed in a kingdom separate from all other organisms. They are all heterotrophic, and are distinguished from each other by their sexual reproductive structures. While some fungi are edible or produce human foods, others destroy foods as parasites of crops. In a community, fungi play a major role as decomposers. Fungi also may be part of relationships with other living organisms, such as mycorrhizal fungi or those found in a lichen.

Application Questions

1. What characteristics of algae make them more advanced than cyanobacteria?
2. How do the characteristics of lichens cause a taxonomic problem?
3. Mycorrhizal fungi use sugars from the plants to which they are attached. Why are these fungi not considered to be parasites of the plants?

Problems

1. How many of the groups of organisms discussed in this chapter can be found in your locality? Consider wild and cultivated, indoor and outdoor, and aquatic and terrestrial organisms.
2. Investigate how fungi and bacteria are used to help fight disease—especially in the production of antibiotics.
3. Mitochondria have their own circular DNA that is different from the DNA found in the nucleus of the cell. Studies in humans have shown that mitochondrial DNA is of maternal origin, that is, it is inherited from the mother only. How might you explain this? (Hint: refer to the discussion of fertilization in chapter 6.)

Suggested Readings

J. C. Ayres, J. O. Mundt, and W. E. Sandine, 1980, *Microbiology of Foods* (San Francisco: W. H. Freeman). Covers the beneficial and harmful relationships of microorganisms to foods.

G. Blonston, "The Biochemistry of Bacchus" *Science 85* (October 1985). Interesting discussion of the biological aspects of winemaking.

"Microbes for Hire" *Science 85* (July/August 1985). Series of three articles discussing how yeasts, bacteria, molds, and other microbes are currently being utilized.

J. A. Miller, "Clinical Opportunities for Plant and Soil Fungi" *BioScience* (November 1986). An increasing number of fungal species are creating medical problems for humans.

G. Vidal, "The Oldest Eukaryotic Cells" *Scientific American* (February 1984). A review of the fossil record indicates that the eukaryotes originally evolved in the form of plankton some 1.4 billion years ago.

Kevin Schafer/TOM STACK & ASSOCIATES

Equisetum is one of the oldest vascular plants. What adaptations have enabled it to survive?

CHAPTER 13

Eukaryotes: Plants

Introduction

Plants are multicellular, photosynthetic organisms mainly adapted for life on land. Evidence suggests they evolved from multicellular green algae that had some division of labor among their cells. That evolution occurred through millions of years and involved many adaptations that allowed plants to live on land. The oldest plant fossils are simple, branched structures with several important adaptations to land. They contain specialized water-conducting, or **vascular** (VAS kyoo ler), tissue. They also have pores through which gases can be exchanged with the environment, and they have thick-walled spores that can be dispersed by wind. Vascular tissue is particularly important for land plants. By contrast, nonvascular plants such as mosses are restricted to moist habitats.

Vascular plants are found in most habitats on land, from prairies to tundra, and in the forests and deserts of the world. Seed plants have colonized many habitats and are extremely successful. Their success is due not only to their having vascular tissue, but also to a method of reproduction that protects the reproductive cells. In this chapter, we will examine those characteristics that enabled plants to invade the land, and describe a few examples of modern plants.

The Evolution of Land Plants

Guidepost: What adaptations allowed plants to colonize land?

13.1 Multicellular Green Algae Probably Were the Ancestors of Plants

Several hundred million years ago the surface of the earth was very different from what it is today. The land was barren. It had no plants or animals as we know them. Life existed only in the water. One-celled algae such as those in figure 13.1 colored the surface waters of the oceans

Figure 13.1 *Chlorella pyrenoidosa,* a one-celled alga that is abundant all over the world.

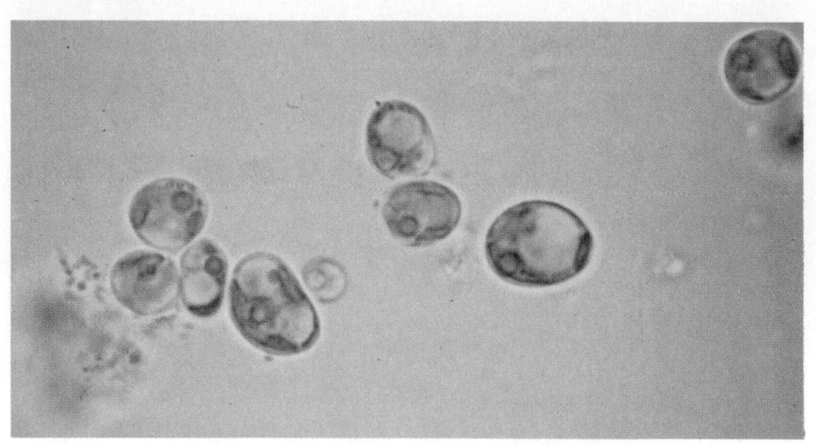

J. Robert Waaland/BPS/TOM STACK & ASSOCIATES

Figure 13.2 The giant redwoods, *Sequoia sempervirans,* are the largest organisms in the world.

Gordon E. Uno

shades of green. Some algae became multicellular organisms and evolved a degree of cell specialization. Such organisms were the likely ancestors of modern plants.

Today, plants are found in almost all places on earth, and they come in a wide range of sizes. The largest organisms in the world are the giant redwoods in California (figure 13.2). Some of those trees are more than 100 m tall and 7 m in diameter. The difference between a simple multicellular green alga in the ancient sea and a giant California redwood tree with billions of cells is tremendous. The evolution of such a complex land organism from a relatively unspecialized multicellular ancestor did not occur overnight. In fact, it took millions of years.

Let us consider the environment in which the ancestors of modern land plants lived 600 million years ago. Water is one of the necessities of life, but in an aquatic environment water is not a limiting factor to growth. Plants also require sunlight to produce their own food through photosynthesis. Near the surface of the water, light is generally adequate for photosynthesis. In addition, plants require carbon dioxide and oxygen, both of which are dissolved in water. Finally, plants require mineral nutrients to produce additional cells, tissues, and organs. Nutrients can be a limiting factor in the middle of the ocean. Along coastlines, however, the currents, wave action, and runoff water from the shore provide an ample supply of nutrients for plant growth. Conditions in the water, then, are generally ideal for plant growth.

The land, on the other hand, may be extremely varied, from hot to freezing and from wet to dry. Water is the major limiting factor for any organism on land. The only reliable source of water on land is underground, where it is too dark for photosynthesis. In the air, organisms lose water through evaporation from their surfaces. Without water, organisms die. What possible advantages of life on land could overcome such a major disadvantage?

There were a number of important advantages for plants to life on land. First, there was the lack of competition. Because no other organisms were present on the land, plants that could tolerate the dry conditions would have little competition for the other necessities of life. Second, carbon dioxide and oxygen are more abundant in the air than

Figure 13.3 Brown and green algae along the ocean shore at low tide.

John D. Cunningham/VISUALS UNLIMITED

in water. Third, there is more light on land—much of the light that reaches water is absorbed. Finally, there is plentiful space, and minerals are readily available in the soil.

13.2 Two Major Groups of Land Plants Evolved

One-celled algae that were tossed up on the beach by the tides probably soon dried out in the sunlight and died. That must have happened countless times. However, a multicellular alga tossed onto the shore might have a much better chance of surviving than would an individual cell on its own. The outer cells of the organism could protect the inner ones from drying out rapidly. The inner cells might be efficient at photosynthesis. Other cells might specialize at collecting water or nutrients from the environment. The resulting division of labor would enable the organism to exploit the resources in its environment efficiently. Such a specialized organism might be able to live, grow, and reproduce on land if occasionally covered by tides or kept moist with ocean spray. The diverse group of multicellular plants that covers the earth today could have evolved, during 600 million years, from some such simple multicellular alga with specialized cells. The known evolutionary history of plants is summarized in figure 13.4.

The first land plants were probably relatively complex multicellular green algae that already had evolved some of the adaptations found in all modern plants. Such algae (figure 13.5) exist today, as we have seen in section 12.11. Two plant lines apparently evolved from those ancestral forms. The more primitive group, with few adaptations to a terrestrial existence, includes the mosses and liverworts. The other group, which includes fossils of the oldest land plants, has many more adaptations to land and is, thus, considered more advanced.

Several adaptations are especially important for survival on land. They include structures that protect the plant against water loss, structures that enable the plant to obtain water and carbon dioxide, and structures that protect the reproductive cells. In the next sections, we will examine some of those adaptations in nonvascular and vascular plants.

Figure 13.4 The evolutionary history of plants. What evidence was used to construct this history?

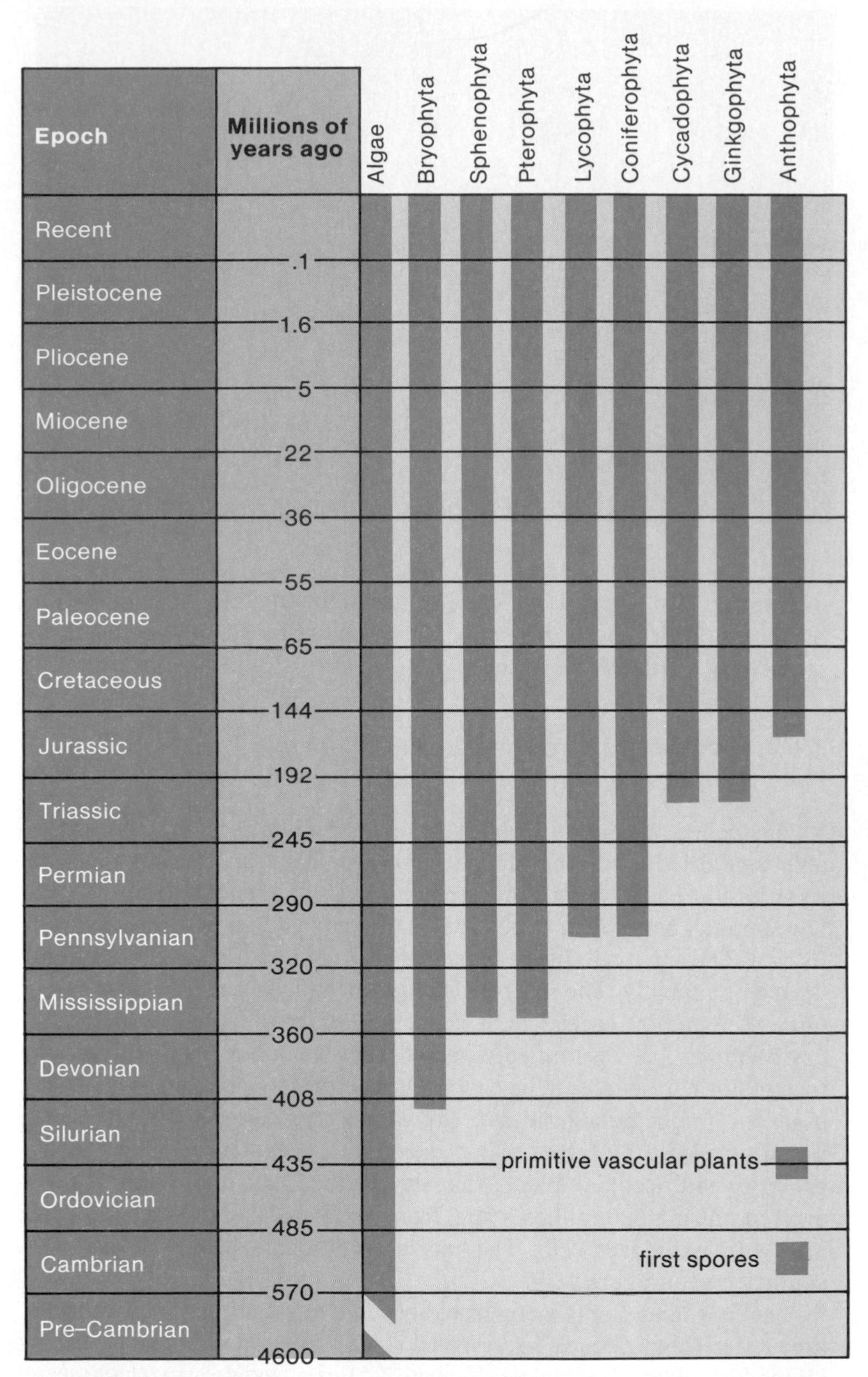

13.3 Land Plants Have Adaptations that Conserve Water and Permit Gas Exchange

The success of plants on land depends on their ability to absorb and hold water. Structures that enable them to do so include roots, vascular tissue, and a waxy covering, or **cuticle.** Mosses, the most primitive land plants, lack those structures and, thus, are restricted to moist or wet habitats.

Mosses live in shady, cool, moist conditions such as the banks of a stream (figure 13.6a). They absorb water through most parts of their

Figure 13.5 The multicellular green alga *Chara*. The fossil record of *Chara*-like algae extends back about 400 million years. Because of their structure and reproductive patterns, algae such as *Chara* can serve as models of the ancestors of land plants.

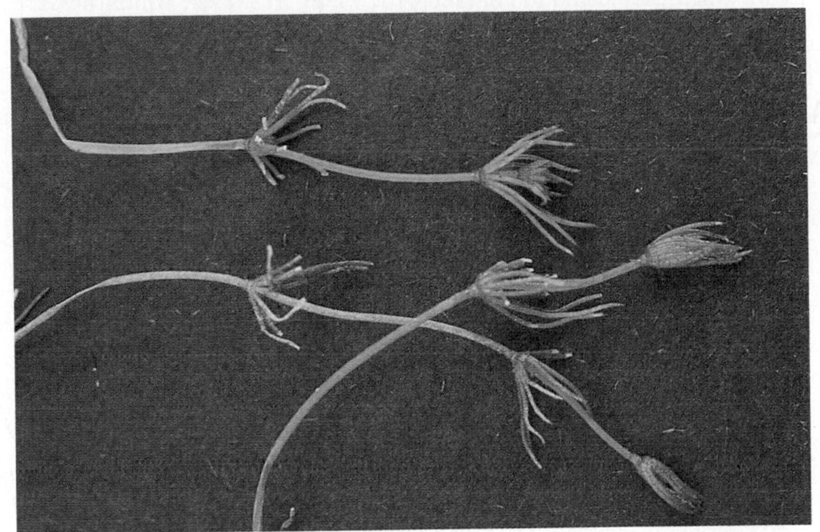

BSCS by Doug Sokell

Figure 13.6 Mosses thrive in moist conditions such as streambanks (a), but become dormant under dry conditions (b).

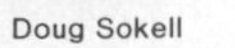

Doug Sokell

a

Doug Sokell

b

bodies. However, like the algal cells that were first tossed on shore, mosses also can lose water through their entire body surface. That means they can dry out quickly if there is no source of water. Mosses have the ability to become dormant under such dry conditions and then to start growing again when they come in contact with water. However, while they are dry, as in figure 13.6b, little growth occurs.

More advanced plants such as ferns, conifers (cone-bearing plants), and flowering plants have a well-developed root system (figure 13.7) that penetrates into many parts of the soil. Such an extensive system can efficiently collect water and minerals from the soil and bring them to the main body of the plant. Thus, rooted plants can grow in places too dry for mosses. Rooted plants demonstrate a good example of division of labor—the cells in the root collect water and minerals and the aboveground cells absorb sunlight and produce food through photosynthesis.

Figure 13.7 A well-developed root system enables a plant to collect water and minerals from the soil.

BSCS by Doug Sokell

Mosses never grow very tall. They lack an efficient water transport system. Tall plants require cells that can transport water from the roots to the leaves, and also cells that can support an upright body. All vascular plants have the specialized tissues shown in figure 13.8. Those tissues conduct water, minerals, and sugars throughout the plant. **Xylem** (ZY lem) transports water and minerals from the roots to the rest of the plant. Xylem cells also provide support. **Phloem** (FLOH em) conducts sugars produced during photosynthesis to all parts of the plant. Xylem and phloem permit vascular plants to grow taller than nonvascular plants and, thus, to capture more sunlight. Taller plants generally produce more sugars and, eventually, more offspring.

In mosses, water can evaporate from the entire body surface. More advanced land plants produce a waxy layer called cuticle that covers the plant body (figure 13.9). That greatly reduces the amount of water that can evaporate from the surface of the plant. The cuticle is often very thick on the leaves of plants that live in dry places—so thick that you can scrape it off with your fingernail. Such a waterproof covering would prevent gas exchange with the environment. Vascular plants, however,

Figure 13.8 Stained, longitudinal section of xylem tissue. How does xylem help a plant survive on land?

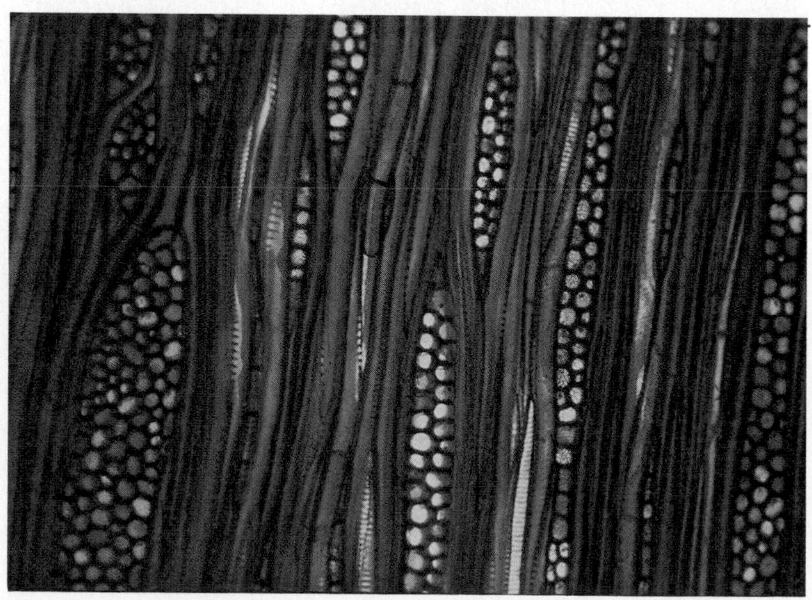

Randy Moore/Visuals Unlimited

have slitlike openings in the surface of their leaves that permit carbon dioxide and oxygen to enter or leave the plant. These **stomates** (figure 13.10) are present in the oldest fossil plants. The combination of roots to absorb water, vascular tissue to support the plant and to conduct water, a cuticle to prevent evaporation, and stomates to permit gas exchange are characteristics that enable plants to live on land.

Figure 13.9 Plants such as this *Aloe vera* have very thick cuticles, an adaptation that enables them to survive in dry climates.

BSCS by Faith Hickman

13.4 Primitive Plants Have Swimming Sperm

Reproductive adaptations also were important in enabling plants to survive on land. Those include the evolution of pollen grains that are transported by wind and animals, protected spores, and protected embryos. Mosses are restricted to moist habitats because their sperm are flagellated, as are those of animals and algae. For sexual reproduction to occur in mosses, the plants must be bathed in water so the sperm can swim to the egg. Mosses can reproduce sexually only if the plants are located where water sprays them, or after they are wet with dew or rain. That greatly restricts sexual reproduction. A more efficient means of transporting the sperm to the egg would enable plants to produce more offspring and, thus, increase their chances of surviving on land.

Special structures called **pollen grains** are found in seed plants. Sperm develop in the pollen grains, which may be blown by wind or carried by animals from one flower directly to another. This very efficient means of transferring sperm to the egg under dry conditions is most highly developed in the flowering plants. Brightly colored flowers with odors attract insects and contain nectar the insect visitors drink. An insect picks up pollen from one flower and carries it to another while it searches for nectar. Thus, flowering plants do not require free water for sexual reproduction to take place. They are, therefore, not restricted to moist conditions, and sexual reproduction can occur whenever the sperm and egg are fully developed.

Figure 13.10 A single stomate in the surface of a leaf.

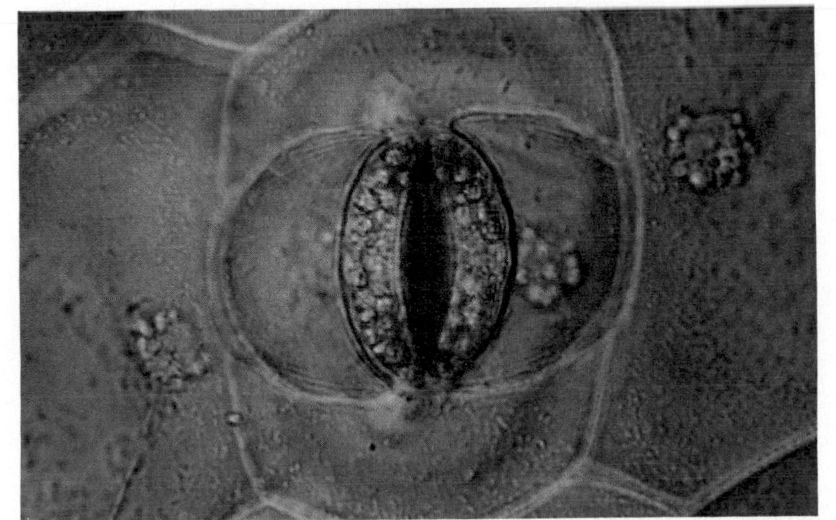

Terry Ashley/TOM STACK & ASSOCIATES

Figure 13.11 Scanning electron micrograph of a pollen grain from the cactus *Opuntia polyacantha*, ×525.

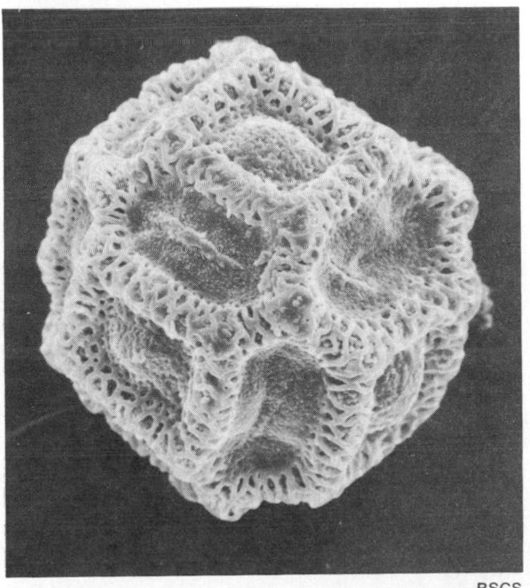

BSCS

Figure 13.12 Moss sporophytes (*Polytrichium*) growing from the female gametophyte plants.

Wm. S. Ormerod/VISUALS UNLIMITED

13.5 The Life Cycle of Plants Alternates between Two Generations

Protection of spores and embryos is another adaptation of plants to life on land. That protection is best developed in the seed plants. To understand the importance of those characteristics we need to compare the life cycle of a primitive plant such as a moss with that of an advanced flowering plant.

Sexually reproducing plants have two genetic phases known as generations. One generation is diploid and the other is haploid. Because these diploid and haploid phases alternate, the life cycle of a plant is called **alternation of generations.**

We can illustrate the life cycle of a primitive plant with the familiar mosses you may see along a stream (look again at figure 13.6). The smooth green carpet of moss is actually many individual plants crowded together. Each plant has tiny leaflike structures and rootlike threads that help hold the plant to the ground. These small plants are all haploid, and each is called a **gametophyte** (guh MEET oh fyt). In time it will produce gametes, usually in special structures at the tips of the plants. In wet conditions, sperm are produced in male gametophytes. The sperm swim in a film of water to the egg cell in the female gametophyte, and a zygote is produced.

The zygote divides and develops into an embryo. Eventually, the embryo grows out of the female gametophyte into a stalklike structure, the **sporophyte** (SPOR oh fyt), easily visible above the small haploid individuals (figure 13.12). Meiosis occurs within the capsule at the end of the sporophyte, and haploid spores are formed. The spores are somewhat protected in the capsule, but not nearly as protected as the spores of flowering plants. Moss spores are released from the capsule and are carried to wherever the wind or water transports them. Most spores fall onto unfavorable habitats and die. If a spore reaches a favorable environment—usually a moist soil surface—its wall bursts open. The cell within

Figure 13.13 Life cycle of a moss.

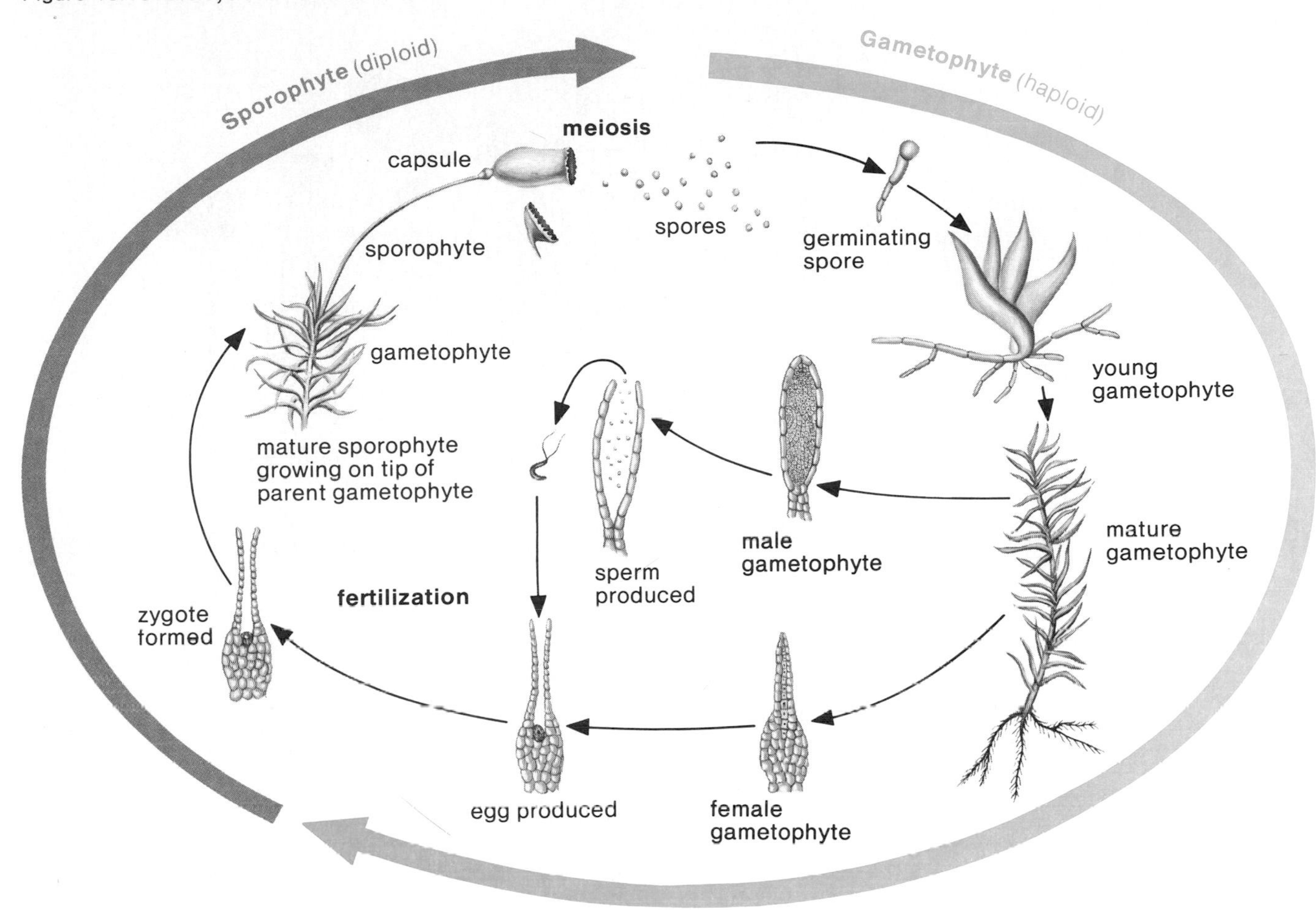

undergoes mitosis and divides, producing long green threads that resemble the filaments of many aquatic algae. The familiar gametophyte moss plant develops from those threads. The life cycle of the moss is complete when a spore germinates in this way and grows into another gametophyte plant. The life cycle of a moss is diagrammed in figure 13.13, and you can compare it with that of a flowering plant in investigation 13.1.

13.6 Flowering Plants Protect Their Spores and the Egg-Producing Gametophyte

Advanced plants also have a life cycle with alternation of generations. However, the gametophyte generation is much reduced in size and remains attached to and protected by the sporophyte. Let us first examine the reproductive structures of flowering plants.

The reproductive organs in higher plants are found in flowers. A flower is actually a short branch bearing groups of specialized leaves. Some of these may resemble ordinary leaves in many ways. Others are so different in structure that it is hard to think of them as leaves at all. If you examine a flower such as a buttercup, you see on the underside a number

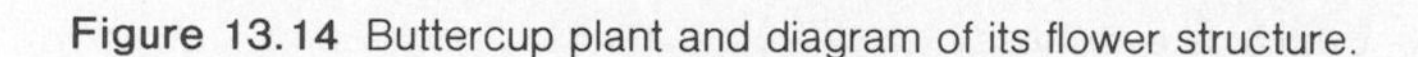

Figure 13.14 Buttercup plant and diagram of its flower structure.

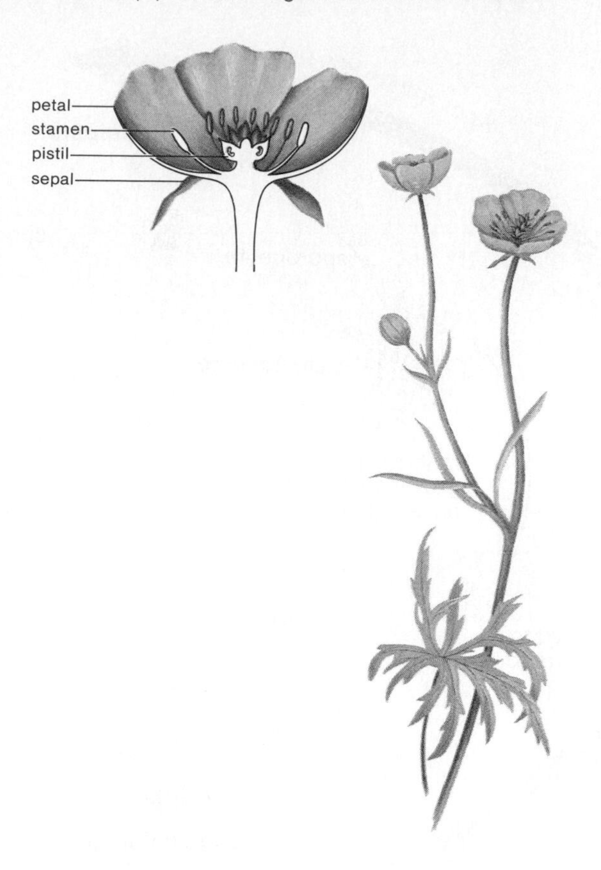

of green, leaflike structures called **sepals** (SEE pulz). Before the bud opens, the sepals cover and protect the other parts of the flower. The most conspicuous flower parts in a buttercup, and most other flowers, are the colorful **petals.** Petals are often leaflike in shape, but they are usually not green.

Just inside the circle of petals of typical flowers is a ring of male reproductive structures, the **stamens** (STAY menz). In the center of the flower are one or more **pistils** (PIS tilz), the female reproductive structures. Although most plants have both male and female organs within the same flower, a few produce flowers with only female parts, or only male parts. Stamens usually have an enlarged tip, the **anther,** while pistils usually have a pointed tip, the **stigma.** Despite their shapes, however, both stamens and pistils are thought to be modified leaves that have been adapted for reproductive roles.

Let us now relate the reproductive structures to the life cycle, shown in figure 13.15. At the base of the pistil is an enlarged portion, the ovary, that contains one to many small structures called **ovules** (OHV yoolz). Meiosis occurs in a special cell in each ovule, resulting in the formation of four haploid cells, the female spores. These spores do not separate from the sporophyte as they do in mosses. Instead, three of the spores disintegrate. The fourth spore divides three times mitotically, forming eight nuclei. The nuclei, with their surrounding cytoplasm, form cells. This is the female gametophyte, and one of the cells is the egg cell.

Figure 13.15 Life cycle of a flowering plant. The parts are drawn to different scales.

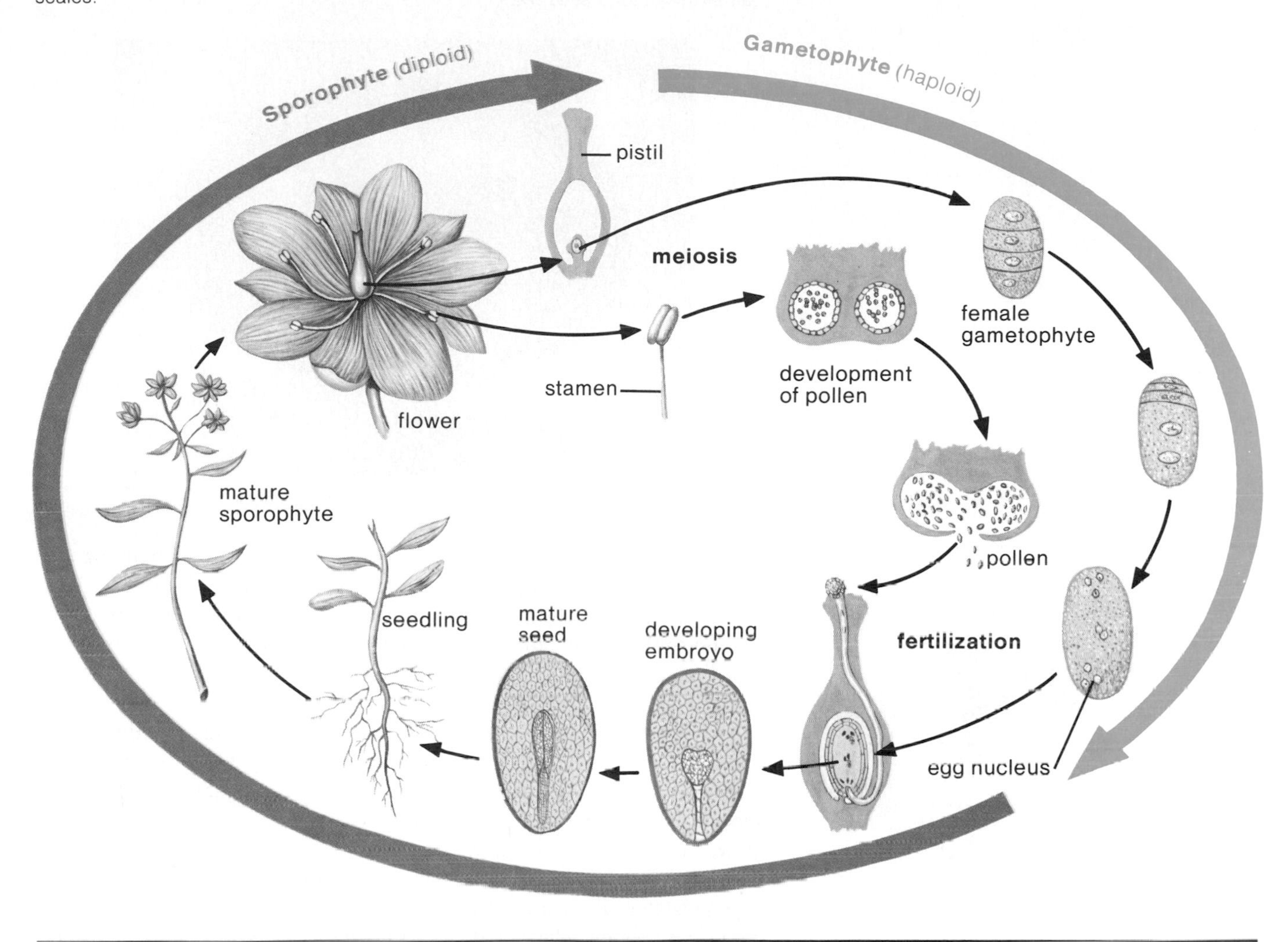

Figure 13.16 Female gametophyte of a lily. (a) Meiosis in the developing ovule. (b) Mature ovule ready to be fertilized; the egg nucleus is one of those on the right.

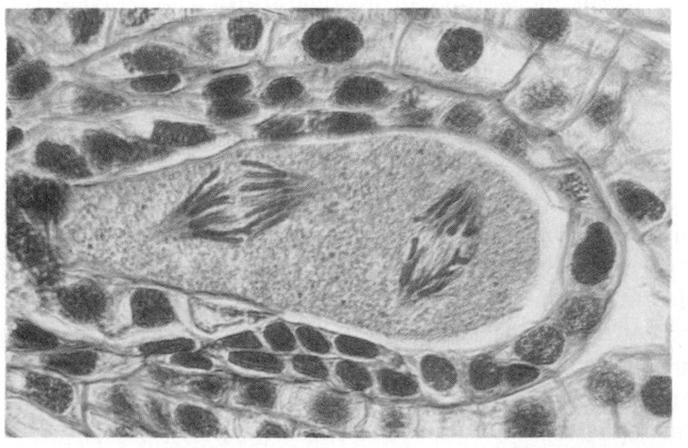

a

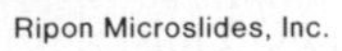
Ripon Microslides, Inc.

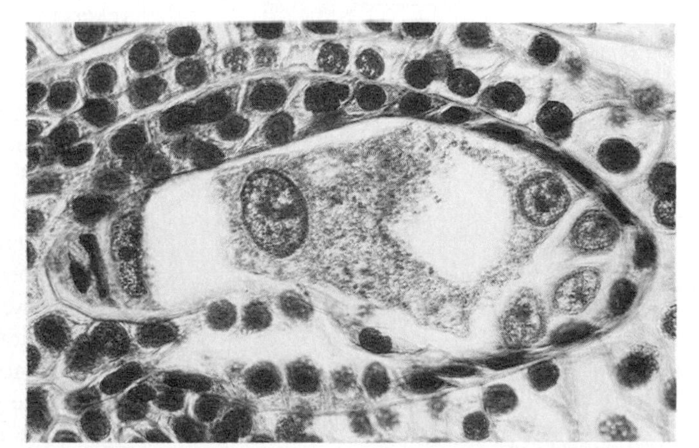

b Ripon Microslides, Inc.

Figure 13.17 Mature pollen grain with two nuclei. A pollen grain is the male gametophyte of a seed plant.

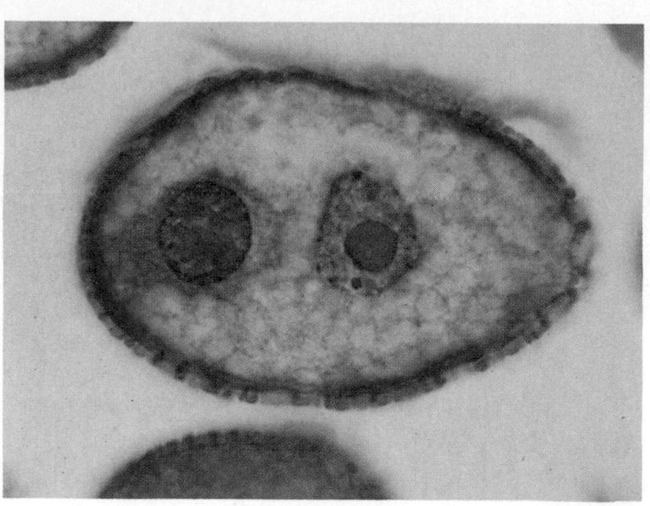

John D. Cunningham / VISUALS UNLIMITED

Figure 13.18 A germinated pollen grain with its pollen tube.

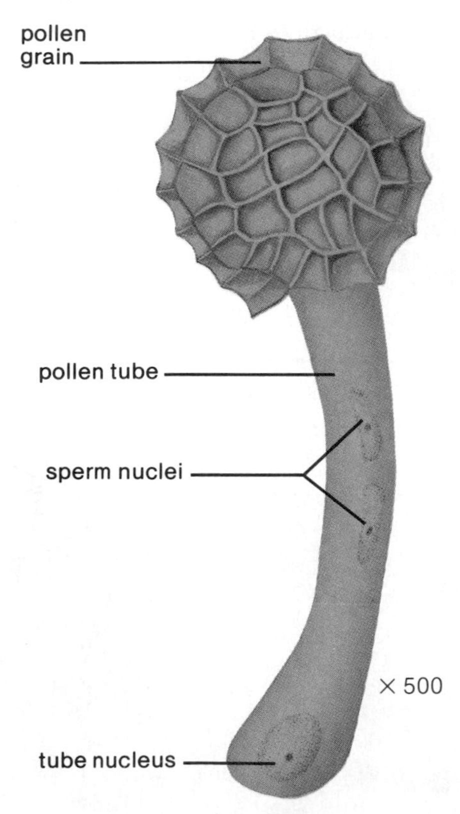

In the stamens, cells in the anthers undergo meiosis, each giving rise to four haploid cells, the male spores. Each spore contains one haploid nucleus that divides by mitosis, forming two nuclei. A spore wall thickens around each nucleus, forming a pollen grain. A single stamen may contain thousands of pollen grains. Each mature pollen grain is a male gametophyte.

Now the stage is set for pollination and fertilization. **Pollination** is the transfer of pollen from the stamens to the pistil, either between flowers of the same plant, or between flowers of different plants of the same species. The stigma at the top of the pistil is sticky, and can trap pollen grains. Pollen grains reach the stigma by chance. They may be brought there be wind, by water, or by a visiting animal.

The hard walls of the pollen grains protect the haploid cells until they land on a stigma. Once there, a thin finger of tissue, the **pollen tube,** grows from the pollen grain into the pistil. Within the pollen tube one nucleus, the tube nucleus, leads the way. The other nucleus divides to form two sperm nuclei. The pollen tube continues to grow down the pistil, transporting the sperm nuclei to the ovule. One sperm nucleus fertilizes the egg, forming a zygote. This new diploid cell will give rise to the embryo of the plant. The other sperm nucleus unites with two other female nuclei known as **polar nuclei.** That fusion leads to the formation of the **endosperm** (EN doh sperm), a mass of food-storing cells. The endosperm is triploid—it has three sets of chromosomes.

The life cycle of a flowering plant is similar to that of a moss in two ways. First, meiosis occurs just before spore formation. Second, there is alternation of generations between the sporophyte and gametophyte portions of the life cycle. There are, however, several differences. First, free water is not necessary for fertilization, as it is in mosses. Second, in flowering plants the gametophytes are much smaller than the sporophytes. Third, the gametophyte that produces an egg, and the spore that produced the gametophyte, do not separate from the sporophyte plant as they do in mosses. Thus, those structures are much better protected from the environment than their counterparts in a moss. Finally, the embryo of a flowering plant grows for a short time, then stops growing or be-

Figure 13.19 Stages in fertilization and embryo development of a flowering plant.

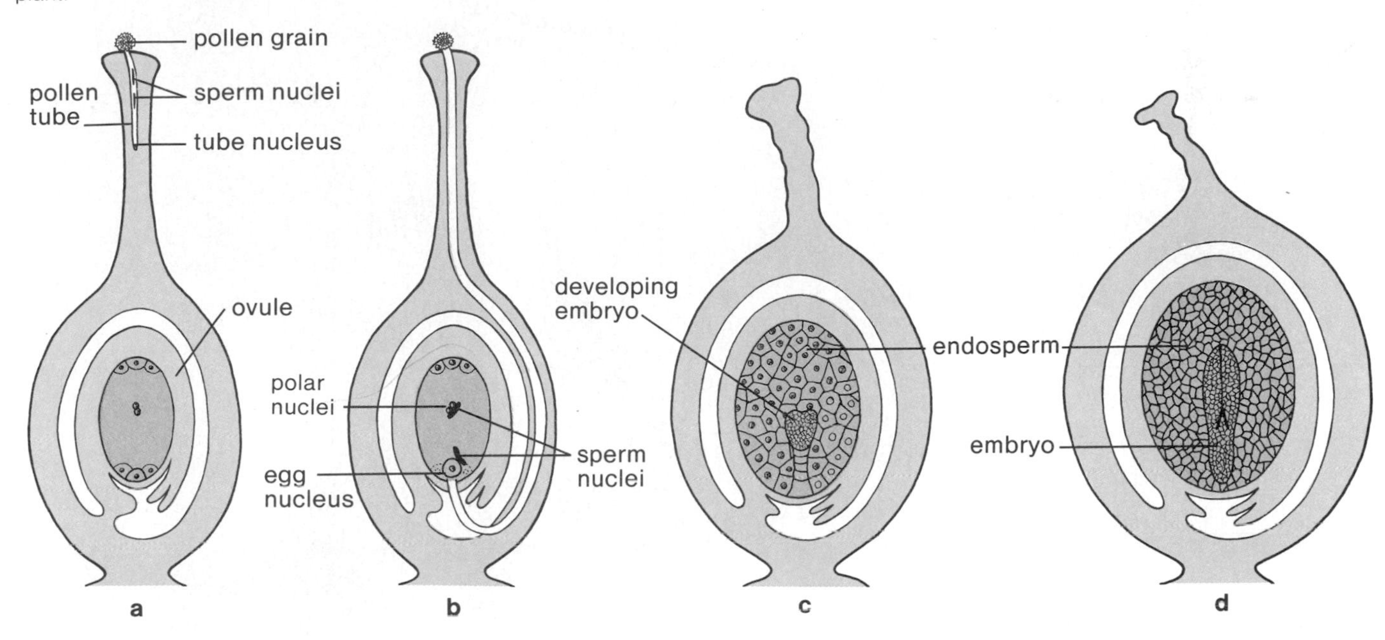

comes **dormant.** The embryo, along with its endosperm, becomes surrounded by sturdy, protective coats formed from ovule tissues. This package is the **seed** (figure 13.20). The seed protects the young sporophyte, which remains dormant until environmental conditions are suitable for it to germinate and to continue its growth. Moss embryos, on the other hand, cannot tolerate extreme or prolonged dry conditions.

In general, land plants show a trend toward increasing specialization of the sporophyte and decreasing specialization of the gametophyte, as summarized in figure 13.21.

Seed plants have been extremely successful because of their adaptations to the harsh and changing environment on land. The combination of the cuticle, vascular tissue, a root system, sperm that develop inside pollen, spores protected on sporophytes, and an embryo protected in a seed make flowering plants extremely well suited to life on land. In the remaining sections of this chapter, we will examine a few examples from the major groups of land plants.

Figure 13.20 Diagram showing the internal structures of a seed.

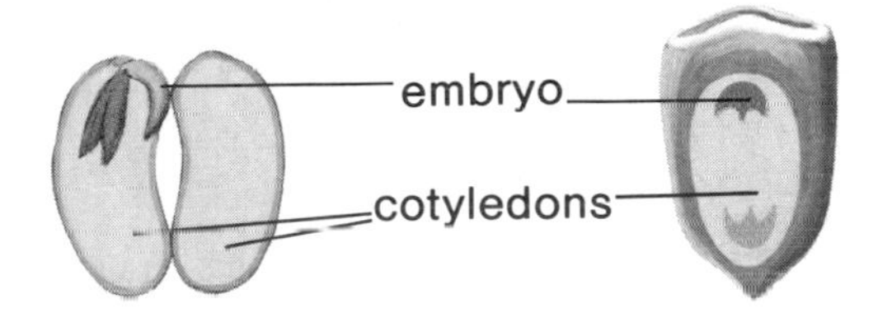

Self-Review

1. What are the disadvantages of life on land compared to life in the water?
2. Why is a clump of cells with some division of labor more likely than a single cell to survive on land?
3. What adaptations do plants have to obtain and conserve water?
4. What is the advantage of pollen-carried sperm compared to swimming sperm?
5. How do the two generations differ in the life cycle of a plant?
6. What is the role of the pollen tube?
7. What happens to the two sperm from a single pollen grain?
8. What part of a flowering plant gives rise to the seed?

Figure 13.21 Evolution and specialization in sporophytes and gametophytes.

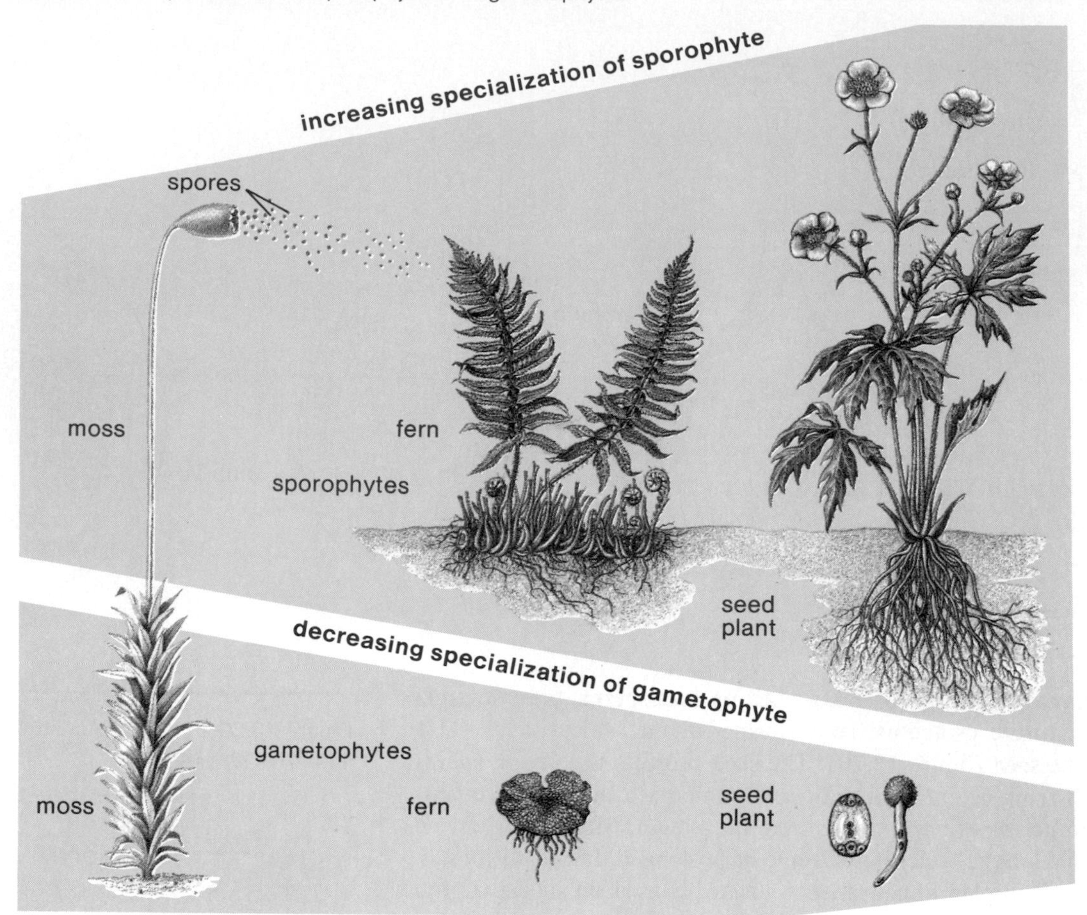

Investigation 13.1 REPRODUCTIVE STRUCTURES AND LIFE CYCLES

Introduction

The basic principles of sexual reproduction in a moss, a flower, a bee, and a human are the same. Their reproductive organs differ, however, as does the environment in which each lives and reproduces.

Mosses form mats on logs and on the forest floor. They grow best in damp, shaded environments. A clump of moss is composed of many gametophytes all growing close together. Sporophytes grow out of the tops of the gametophytes and often look like hairs growing out of the mat of moss. Mosses cannot reproduce without ample moisture.

Flowering plants are found in many different environments and climates. They need moisture to sustain life, but moisture is not required for reproduction. Flowers have evolved in many different colors, shapes, and sizes. In this investigation you will learn how the structures of a moss and a flower serve reproductive functions in their respective environments.

Materials (per team)

For moss

moss plants with sporophytes
moss plants with male sex organs
moss plants with female sex organs
4 fresh moss plants
dissecting needle
microscope slides
coverslips
compound microscope
demonstration slide of filamentous stage of moss (whole mount)

For flowers

gladiolus flower
some other simple flowers for comparison
single-edge razor blade
stereoscopic dissecting microscope
fresh bean or pea pods

Procedure

Part A—Moss Plants

1. Take a moss plant with a sporophyte attached. Separate the 2 generations by pulling the filamentous stalk of the sporophyte out of the leafy shoot of the gametophyte.
2. The sporophyte part of the moss has a smooth, leafless stem terminating in a little capsule. With a dissecting needle, break open the capsule of the sporophyte into a drop of water on a slide. Cover the slide with a cover slip and examine under the low power of your microscope.
   (a) What are the structures you observe?
   (b) How are these structures distributed in nature?
   (c) How are they adapted for life on land?
3. The spores of most mosses germinate readily on damp soil and produce a filamentous stage that looks like a branching green alga. Examine the demonstration slide of this stage.
4. The filamentous stage gives rise to the leafy shoot of the gametophyte. How does this leafy shoot obtain water and minerals for growth?
5. The reproductive organs of the gametophyte are produced at the upper end of the leafy shoot. Obtain a male or a female plant and hold it so that the tip is between your thumb and forefinger. Squeeze the tip and at the same time roll it between your thumb and forefinger. Now submerge the tip of the leafy shoot in a drop of water on a microscope slide. Tease out the fragments from the tip of the shoot with a needle. Some of the fragments will be the moss sex organs.
6. Follow the same procedure for both male and female mosses. Put a cover slip over the fragments from each plant. Observe the preparations under the low power of your microscope. The male sex organs are simple saclike structures that produce large numbers of sperm cells. The female sex organs are flask-shaped and have long, twisted necks. An egg is formed within the swollen base of the female organ.
   (a) How does a sperm reach the egg for fertilization?
   (b) Would you expect to find moss plants growing where there was little or no water present? Explain why or why not.
   (c) The union of the egg and sperm results in a cell called the zygote. Where is the zygote formed?
   (d) What does the zygote grow into?

Part B—Flowers

1. Examine the outside parts of a gladiolus flower. The outermost whorl of floral parts are green, leaflike parts. These green sepals protected the flower bud when it was young. Some flowers, lilies for example, seem to be lacking sepals. Actually they are present and look like an outer whorl of petals. Petals are usually large and colored, and lie just inside the sepals. Both sepals and petals are attached to the enlarged end of a branch. These parts of the flower are not directly involved in sexual reproduction. What functions might petals have?
2. Strip away the sepals and petals to examine the essential parts of the flower. You will find a central stalklike body surrounded by 5 to 10 delicate stalks. Each of these stalks ends in a little sac. The small sacs are anthers in which thousands of tiny pollen grains are produced. Each anther together with its slender stalk is a stamen. The stamens make up the male parts of a flower. The number of stamens varies according to the kind of flower.
   (a) How many stamens are present in the flower you are using?
   (b) How is pollen carried from the anthers to the female part of the flower?
3. The central stalk surrounded by the stamens is the female part of the flower. This female part is called the pistil. It is composed of an enlarged basal part, the ovary, above which is an elongated style. The style ends in the stigma. How is the stigma adapted to trap the pollen grains and to provide a place for them to grow?
4. With a sharp razor blade, cut the ovary lengthwise. Using a hand lens or dissecting microscope, look at the cut surface.
   (a) How many ovules can you see inside the ovary?
   (b) How close to the egg can the pollen grain get?
   (c) If the pollen grain cannot get to the egg directly, how do the sperm cells produced by the pollen reach the egg?
5. The union of egg and sperm causes extensive changes in the female reproductive parts. Fertilization of the egg stimulates the growth of the ovary and the enclosed ovules. Carefully examine a fresh bean or pea pod. Open the pod to find the seeds.
   (a) What part of the female reproductive apparatus is the pod of a bean or pea?
   (b) What is the origin of the seeds?
   (c) If we plant ripe bean or pea seeds and water the seeds, what will they give rise to?
   (d) What can you conclude develops within a seed as a result of fertilization?

Discussion

1. In alternation of generations in a moss, which is the predominant, independent generation?
2. Which is the less conspicuous generation?
3. Compare the life cycle of a moss (with alternation of generations) with your life cycle (with no alternation of generations).
4. In what kind of plants would you expect the most variation, flowering plants or those reproducing by asexual means? Explain your answer.
5. Compare the life cycle of a moss with that of a flowering plant.
6. Do flowering plants represent more or less adaptation to a land environment than the mosses? Explain your answer.

Biology Today C

Biological Illustrator

BSCS by Doug Sokell

Marjorie Leggitt is a freelance biological illustrator. She has been interested in art since she was very young. Her family is composed of writers, sculptors, painters and woodcarvers, so this interest comes very naturally to her. From her family and friends she learned to experiment with materials and colors. Her interest in science, on the other hand, is something Marj says she does not clearly understand. She thinks it might be because she could do so much drawing in science classes.

In college, a biological illustration course sparked her interest, but she continued to study Fine Arts. After studying for a year in Europe, Marj realized she missed science and the technical art that goes with it. She returned to college and designed her own program of independent studies leading to a degree in scientific art. Included in that program was an internship at The Denver Museum of Natural History. After graduation, Marj illustrated a professor's botanical field guide while searching for a full-time job in her field. Her persistence was rewarded by a position at The Field Museum in Chicago.

Marj later returned to Denver to be married and had to reestablish her career there. That proved to be difficult, because opportunities for scientific illustration were far fewer than in larger cities where more research was being conducted. For seven years she worked in art-related jobs, including geological drafting and computer-aided graphics. Marj learned a whole new field of art, but she was not satisfied with her direction.

To keep in touch with the field of scientific illustration, Marj contacted the Guild of Natural Science Illustrators (GNSI), based in Washington, D.C. Knowing Colorado has nothing similar, she founded the Colorado Chapter of GNSI, and made friends with a group of local illustrators.

In February 1986, Marj went into business for herself as a scientific illustrator and graphic artist. She contacted old and new local clients and publishers throughout the country, and spent many hours doing research and marketing.

Artists such as Marj illustrate reports and journal articles prepared by researchers in universities across the country. Many also work in natural history museums. They paint and construct the background scenery for many kinds of displays. These artists may recreate the Alaskan tundra to show off a group of polar bears or a South American hillside for a display of llamas.

In her work, Marj does a great deal of research and uses many references and photos to ensure accuracy. She consults extensively with authors in planning an illustration. It is essential that she understand the author's intent, what the illustration is meant to portray, and how it relates to the text and to other illustrations. Proper interpretation depends on good communication between author and artist.

Marj strongly believes that hard work does pay off. At times the hours are long, the deadlines close to impossible, and the challenges seemingly insurmountable. However, she is doing exactly what she wants to be doing—full-time scientific illustration.

BSCS by Doug Sokell

Figure 13.22 Bryophytes: (a) moss, *Polytrichium;* (b) liverwort, *Marchantia polymorpha.*

a BSCS by Carlye Calvin

b John Shaw/TOM STACK & ASSOCIATES

Guidepost: Why are bryophytes mostly restricted to moist habitats?

Nonvascular Plants

13.7 Bryophytes Have No Roots, Stems or Leaves

[bry OFF ih tuh]

Plants in the division Bryophyta are relatively small, very few exceeding 20 cm in height. Most bryophytes bear structures resembling stems and leaves, but they lack vascular tissue. The largest class of bryophytes is the true mosses. Other bryophytes are liverworts and hornworts (figure 13.22).

Mosses often grow in clumps or small clusters in rock crevices and at the base of trees. An individual moss plant from such a clump is simply an upright green, stemlike stalk with threadlike structures called **rhizoids** (RY zoidz) that function in absorption. The rhizoids also help to hold the plant in place. Many flat, green, leaflike structures are attached spirally along the stalk. Because true roots, stems, and leaves contain vascular tissue, those terms are not used in describing mosses. Water and nutrients are absorbed throughout the body of the moss, so most mosses grow in fairly damp places, and a few grow in water. Some become dormant during droughts, but are rejuvenated after rain. Many mosses can photosynthesize in limited light, so they often are found on the ground in forest ecosystems where other plants cannot grow.

[SFAG num]

An important group of mosses is found in boggy places in the cold and temperate parts of the world. Those mosses, from the genus *Sphagnum,* form peat bogs—small lakes and ponds completely filled with living and dead moss plants. Peat bogs are formed when a lake slowly fills up with peat moss plants that die but are not decomposed. The mosses produce a very acidic condition in the water that keeps decomposers such as bacteria and fungi from growing. The moss plants build up through time, stacking layer on layer. People in Ireland and other countries cut

Figure 13.23 A sphagnum bog.

William J. Weber/VISUALS UNLIMITED

blocks of the peat moss, dry it, and use it for fuel or to build small enclosures. Dry peat moss absorbs water very quickly and holds the water well. Those characteristics make peat moss attractive to gardeners, who add it to their soil to lower the pH and to increase the water-holding capacity.

Self-Review

1. What is a rhizoid?
2. How do mosses absorb?
3. Why do decomposers not grow well in peat bogs?

Primitive Vascular Plants

Guidepost: How do groups of vascular plants differ in structure and habitat?

13.8 Club Mosses and Horsetails Are Primitive, Seedless, Vascular Plants

Probably most of the plants you can name are vascular plants. Vascular plants have a continuous system of tubes (a vascular system) through their roots, stems, and leaves. By means of this system, water, sugar, and dissolved minerals move from one place in the plant to another. For land plants, movement of water upward from the soil is very important. All of the plants described in the remainder of this chapter are characterized by vascular tissue.

Figure 13.24 A reconstruction of the extinct plant *Rhynia*. It had no leaves or roots, and stood about 30 cm high. Sporangia were produced at the tips of upper branches. The branches had a core of xylem with phloem around it. The presence of stomates in the epidermis indicates that photosynthesis occurred in the branches. The cells of vascular tissue (upper right) were oblong and, in the case of xylem, hollow. Thick-walled spores were produced in fours in the sporangia, an indication that the spores were produced by meiosis.

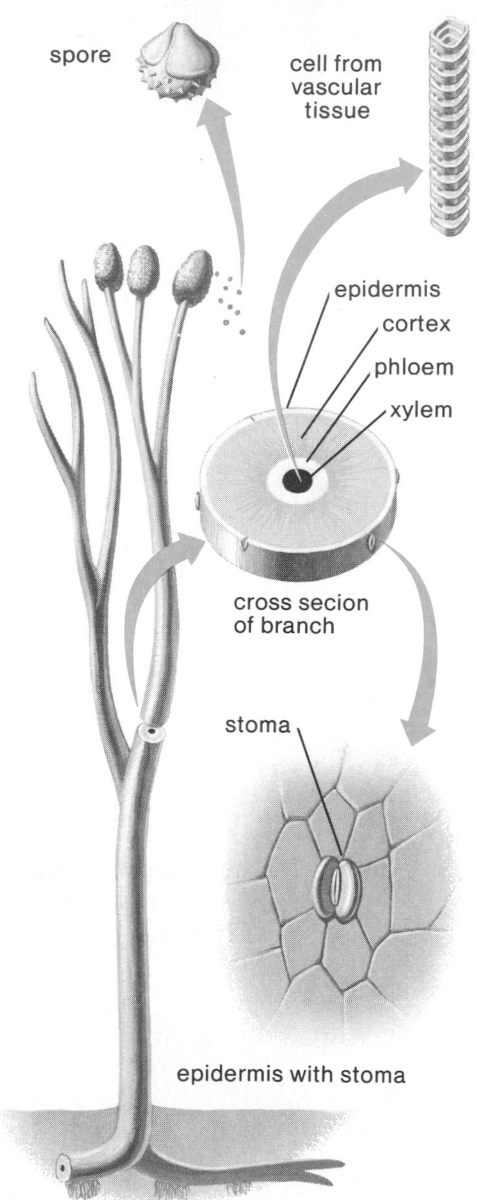

Figure 13.25 The whisk fern, *Psilotum*. Note the sporangia along the stems.

W. Ormerod/VISUALS UNLIMITED

The oldest fossil plants were vascular. They are best represented by *Rhynia major*, a plant formed of a stemlike structure which you can see in figure 13.24. *Rhynia* had an underground stem called a **rhizome** (RY zohm), that probably served to anchor the plant and to absorb water. From the rhizome grew upright branched stems that were covered with cuticle and that contained stomates. At the tips of the stems were sporangia that split open to release thick-walled spores. The closest living relative of *Rhynia* is the whisk fern, *Psilotum*, shown in figure 13.25.

The club mosses (Division Lycophyta) are low-growing evergreen plants that seldom become more than 40 cm tall. Their branching, horizontal stems grow on the surface of the soil or just below it. The most noticeable part of a club moss plant is an upright branch growing from one of these stems. Club mosses reproduce by spores, which are produced on modified, specialized leaves. In many species those leaves form club-shaped cones at the tips of short, upright stems. The name club moss is derived from that feature. Club mosses are rather common plants in much of the eastern and northwestern United States and often are used to make Christmas wreaths. They rarely occur in the dry states of the southwest.

Horsetails (Division Sphenophyta) are plants with hollow, jointed, upright branches that grow from horizontal underground stems. Their small, scalelike leaves are arranged in a circle around each stem joint, as you can see clearly in the chapter opener photo. Spores are produced in conelike structures at the tips of some of the upright branches. The cones can be seen in figure 13.27. In middle latitudes horsetails rarely reach a height of 2 m, but in the American tropics one species may grow several meters tall. They are found in moist places, such as along streams. Horsetails are harsh to the touch; their tissues contain silica, a compound present in sand. American Indians and the pioneers scrubbed pots and pans with them, thus their common name of scouring rushes.

[RY nyuh MAY jer]

[sy LOH tum]

[ly KOF ih tuh]

[sfen OFF ih tuh]

Figure 13.26 A club moss, *Lycopodium*, with cones that will produce spores.

David S. Addison/VISUALS UNLIMITED

Figure 13.27 Spores of *Equisetum* are produced in these conelike structures.

Forest W. Buchanan/VISUALS UNLIMITED

Relatives of the club mosses and horsetails can be traced back to 400 million years ago. During the Coal Age, about 300 million years ago, great parts of North America were covered by shallow swamps and seas. The warm and wet environment allowed plants to grow year-round. Under those conditions giant relatives of today's club mosses, horsetails, and ferns, as well as primitive seed-producing plants, covered the land. Some of those plants were more than 20 m tall (figure 13.29). As they died, their large stems were covered with mud and soil before they completely decayed. A tremendous number of plants from the Coal Age was compressed over long periods of time and under high temperature and great pressure. Eventually, they became what we call fossil fuels, mainly coal and some natural gas.

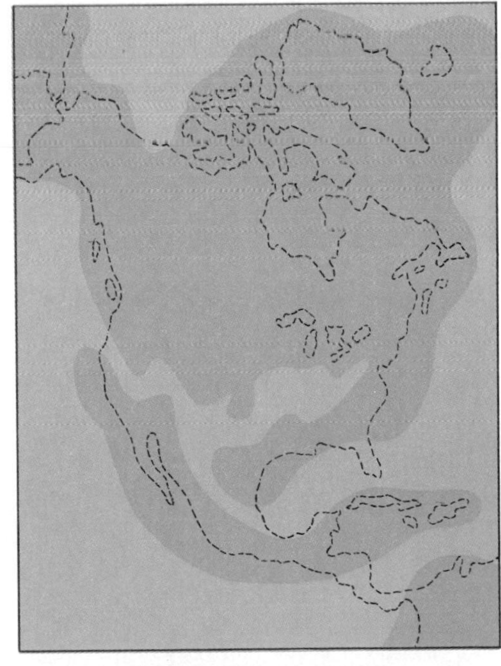

Figure 13.28 North America in the Carboniferous period (about 300 million years ago).

13.9 Fern Leaves Grow from Underground Stems

Ferns (Division Pterophyta), like the club mosses and horsetails, reproduce by spores. At certain times of the year, small brown spots develop on the undersides of fern leaves (figure 13.30). Each spot consists of a cluster of sporangia. Each sporangium produces a large number of spores, which are almost microscopic in size. Spores are far simpler than seeds. A spore contains no embryo and only a small amount of food.

[ter OFF ih tuh]

Figure 13.29 Some trees of the coal-age forests: *Lepidodendron* and *Sigillaria* were club mosses. *Cordaites* were primitive gymnosperms. The seed ferns have no living species. *Calamites* were horsetails.

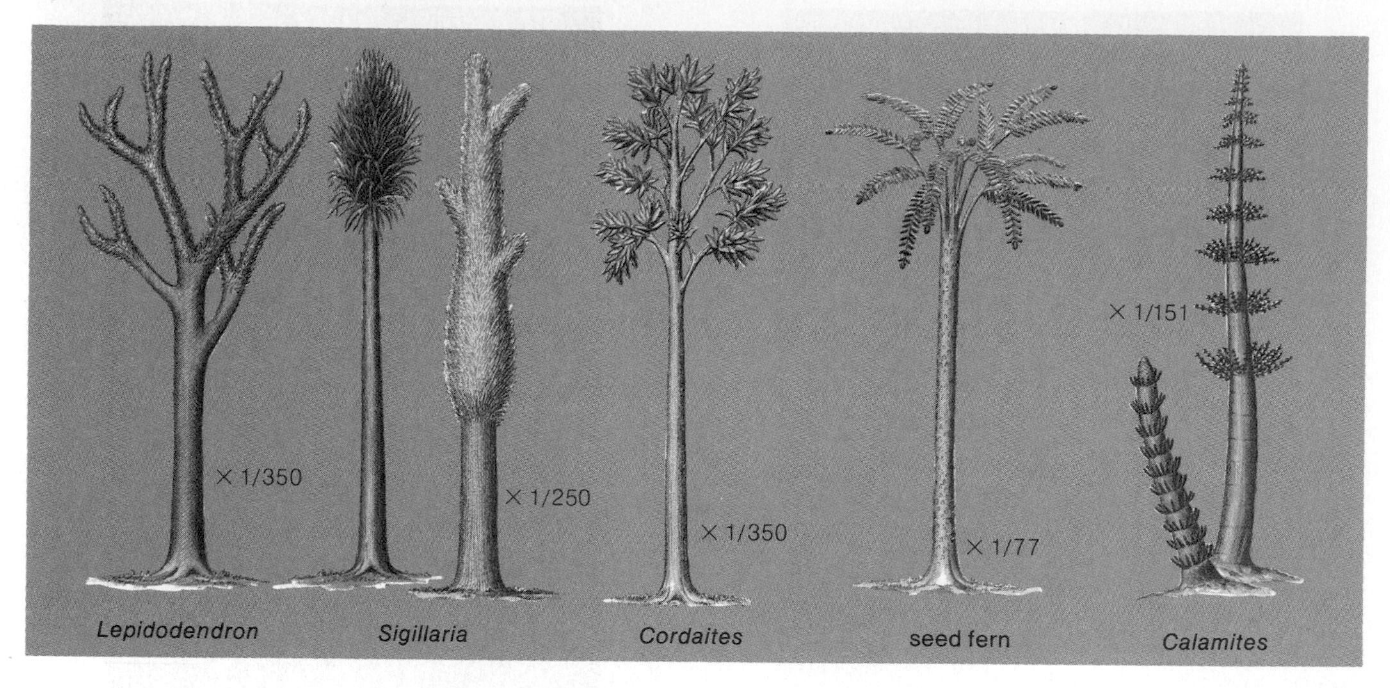

Figure 13.30 Sporangia on the underside of a fern leaf.

BSCS by Carlye Calvin

Figure 13.31 Fern gametophyte (a), and sporophyte (b).

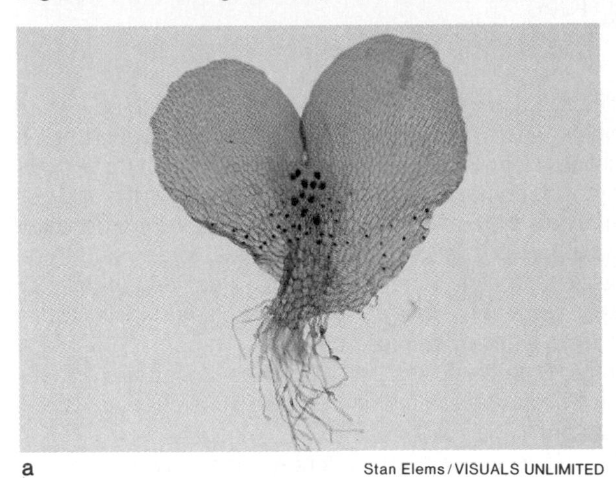

a Stan Elems/VISUALS UNLIMITED

b Pat Armstrong/VISUALS UNLIMITED

When a spore case is mature, it opens and the spores are thrown out into the air. Spores are very light and can be carried for incredible distances by wind. If a spore falls in a suitably moist place, it germinates and develops rapidly into a thin, green, heart-shaped plant that is rarely over 1 cm in diameter (figure 13.31a). The small gametophyte plant is seldom noticed in the woods and is completely different from the familiar fern with its large leaves. The gametophyte produces the sperm or eggs, or in some cases, both. As in mosses, the fern sperm must swim in a film of water to fertilize the egg. The zygote produced by that fertilization eventually grows into the conspicuous spore-bearing fern plant that most people would recognize. That large plant is the sporophyte generation of the fern seen in figure 13.31b.

The ferns native to most of the United States are shade-dwelling plants with underground roots and stems. From those stems, roots grow downward and new sets of upright leaves appear above ground each spring. In Hawaii and elsewhere in the tropics many species of ferns have stems that grow upright. Those tree ferns may reach a height of 20 m with leaves 5 m in length. Most fern species are found in the tropics, but many can be found in forest ecosystems around the world.

Figure 13.32 Tree fern on the island of Sumatra.

E. S. Ross

Self-Review

1. What materials do vascular tissues carry?
2. How did horsetails get the common name of scouring rushes?
3. How was coal formed?
4. What events must occur for a fern sporophyte to be produced from a gametophyte?
5. What is a compound leaf?

Investigation 13.2 INCREASINGLY COMPLEX CHARACTERISTICS

Introduction

Biologists sometimes use pairs of terms such as primitive and advanced or simple and complex when discussing diversity among organisms. In chapter 9 we saw that species living today are related to each other through their ancestors. From that comes a further idea that some of the species living today retain more of their ancestors' characteristics than do other species. A species that has changed little from its ancestors is said to be simple or less complex than organisms that vary a great deal from their ancestors. Conversely, a species that has few of the characteristics of its ancestors is said to be advanced or more complex. There may be many degrees of advancement, so the terms simple and advanced are not absolute terms. They are useful only in making comparisons such as we will make in this investigation.

Scientists have studied many kinds of evidence in the fossil record and in living organisms. They have reached fairly general agreement about which characteristics have been in existence for a long time and which have appeared more recently. Table 13.1 is based on such studies.

Materials (per class)

10 labeled specimens of organisms of various divisions, arranged at stations
monocular microscopes
hand lenses
stereomicroscopes
microscope slides
coverslips

Procedure

1. In your data book, prepare a data table like the one below, with enough lines for all 10 specimens.

Name of Organism	Numerical Values of Choices Made	Total Advancement Score	Rank
1.			
2.			
etc.			

2. Determine the Advancement Score for each of the labeled specimens. Start at the left of table 13.1. Arrows from the starting point lead to 2 descriptions. Choose the one that fits the organism you are scoring. Advanced organisms such as plants are represented at each station as well as some simple organisms from kingdoms other than the plant kingdom.
3. Proceed across the table by following the arrows and choosing in each column the description that best fits each organism.
4. At each description there is a number. Record the numbers of your descriptions in the 2nd column of your data table. Continue as far as the arrows go. The Advancement Score for the organism is the sum of all the numbers appearing after the descriptions you used in working through table 13.1. The more alike 2 organisms are, the more alike

their scores will be. The greater the difference between 2 organisms, the greater will be the difference in their scores. Advanced organisms, such as plants, will have high scores (maximum 26), and simple organisms, such as monerans, will have low scores (minimum 3).

5. When you have the Advancement Score for each of the organisms, give the organism with the lowest score a rank of 1 and the organism with the highest score a rank of 10. Then rank all of the other organisms according to their scores. Record the rankings in the column at the right side of your data table.

Discussion

1. Assuming that today's organisms have developed from simpler, fewer, and older species, would you expect to find less diversity or greater diversity as time goes on? Explain.
2. Basing your conclusions on the way the advancement score key was designed, list some of the most important differences among the organisms that you observed.
3. What are some of the less important differences?
4. On what basis do you distinguish between the important differences and those that are less important?
5. Using the information included in the table, list the characteristics you would expect to find in one of the more simple organisms.
6. Do the same for one of the advanced plants.
7. In what ways does table 13.1 resemble the dichotomous key constructed in investigation 12.2?
8. In what ways does it differ from the key?

Seed Plants

Guidepost: What accounts for the great diversity of flowers and fruits?

13.10 Many Conifers Are Evergreens

Humans have evolved with plants, for food, clothing, shelter, and medicines. The conifers (Division Coniferophyta) are woody plants with seeds borne in cones that provide all of the paper pulp and most of the lumber used in home construction and furniture. Conifers include pines, firs, spruces, and junipers, among others.

[KON ih ferz] [koh NIF er OFF ih tuh]

Almost all conifers are trees or shrubs, and all are at least somewhat woody. Many have leaves that are like needles or scales (figure 13.34), and most of those plants are evergreen. An evergreen tree appears green throughout the year because it always maintains most of its leaves. However, a few leaves die at different times of the year and drop to the ground. Though the number of species is small, the number of individual conifers is enormous.

Many common conifers are well adapted to life in dry habitats. For example, although pine trees may grow where there is much snow, the snow is really frozen water and is not available for growth. In the spring, much of the snow evaporates, and snowmelt may run off into streams before it soaks into the soil. Thus, pines do grow in dry places, and their leaves are well adapted to that. Pine needles are long and narrow. That narrowness reduces the amount of water that can be lost from the leaves, a normal evaporation process that occurs from all leaves. In addition to its shape, a pine needle is often covered by a thick, waxy cuticle that further reduces water loss from the leaves.

Table 13.1 Key for determining the advancement score for an organism

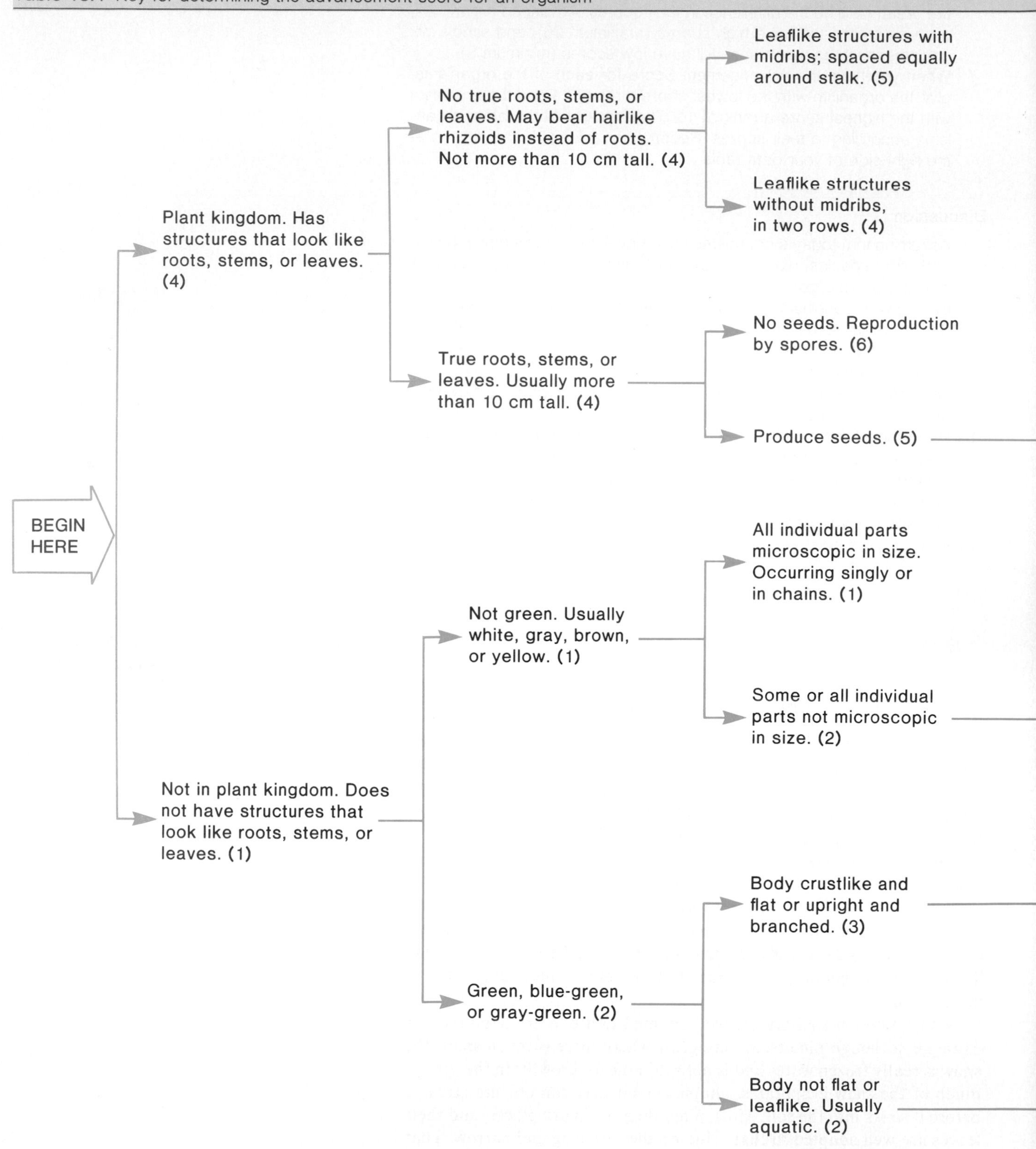

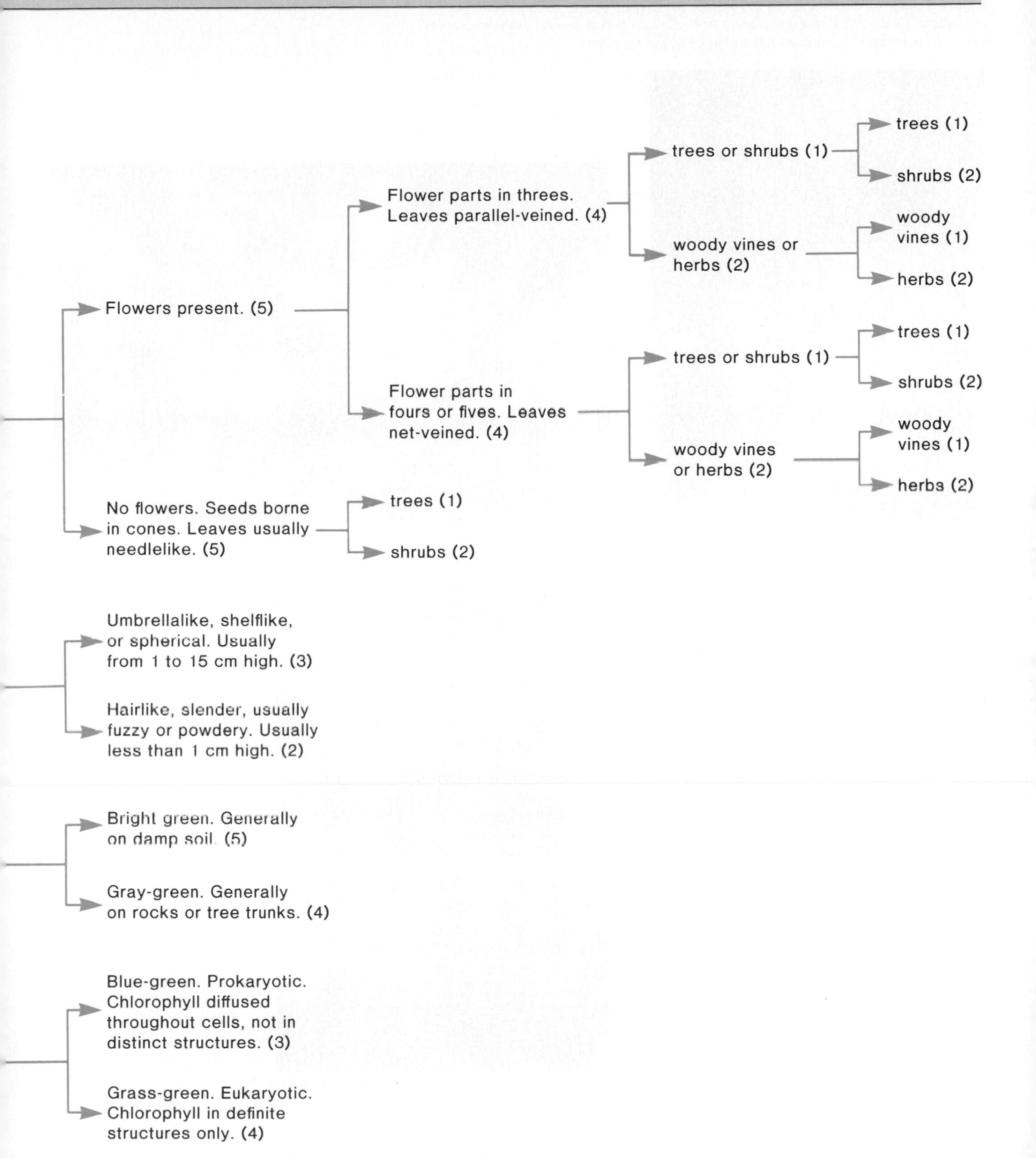
Flowers present. (5)
Flower parts in threes. Leaves parallel-veined. (4)
trees or shrubs (1)
trees (1)
shrubs (2)
woody vines or herbs (2)
woody vines (1)
herbs (2)
Flower parts in fours or fives. Leaves net-veined. (4)
trees or shrubs (1)
trees (1)
shrubs (2)
woody vines or herbs (2)
woody vines (1)
herbs (2)
No flowers. Seeds borne in cones. Leaves usually needlelike. (5)
trees (1)
shrubs (2)
Umbrellalike, shelflike, or spherical. Usually from 1 to 15 cm high. (3)
Hairlike, slender, usually fuzzy or powdery. Usually less than 1 cm high. (2)
Bright green. Generally on damp soil. (5)
Gray-green. Generally on rocks or tree trunks. (4)
Blue-green. Prokaryotic. Chlorophyll diffused throughout cells, not in distinct structures. (3)
Grass-green. Eukaryotic. Chlorophyll in definite structures only. (4)

Figure 13.33 Conifers and related plants: (a) juniper, *Juniperus monosperma;* (b) cycad, *Dioon edule;* (c) maidenhair tree, *Ginkgo biloba.* Seeds of these plants are not enclosed in tissues as are those of flowering plants.

a BSCS by Doug Sokell

b Karlene V. Schwartz

c John D. Cunningham/VISUALS UNLIMITED

Figure 13.34 Many conifer leaves are needlelike or scalelike. (a) Single needles of Douglas fir, *Pseudotsuga menziesii;* (b) clustered needles of Ponderosa pine, *Pinus ponderosa;* (c) scalelike leaves of juniper, *Juniperus chinensis "pfitzerii."*

a BSCS by Doug Sokell

b BSCS by Doug Sokell

c BSCS by Doug Sokell

Figure 13.35 Pine cone and seed.

Figure 13.36 Male (a) and female (b) pine cones.

a Karlene V. Schwartz

b Karlene V. Schwartz

Conifers reproduce by seeds that are attached to the upper surface of scales grouped together in cones. A seed developing in a cone may be protected by the scales, somewhat as a small coin may be concealed between the pages of a book. However, if two scales are separated slightly, you can see the seed between them (figure 13.35). Thus the seeds in cones are not completely covered as they are in the fruits of flowering plants.

Conifer spores are of two kinds, and they are produced in different cones (figure 13.36). Pollen develops from spores in the small male cone, and pollination occurs in the spring when the pollen is blown onto a female cone. The larger, more familiar female cones contain the ovules. Pollen grains, the male gametophytes, lodge in a sticky substance secreted by the ovule and develop pollen tubes. Sperm are formed within the pollen tubes. Within the ovule, the female gametophytes develop and produce eggs. Fertilization occurs approximately a year after pollination, and the seed requires an additional year to mature. Those events are summarized in table 13.2.

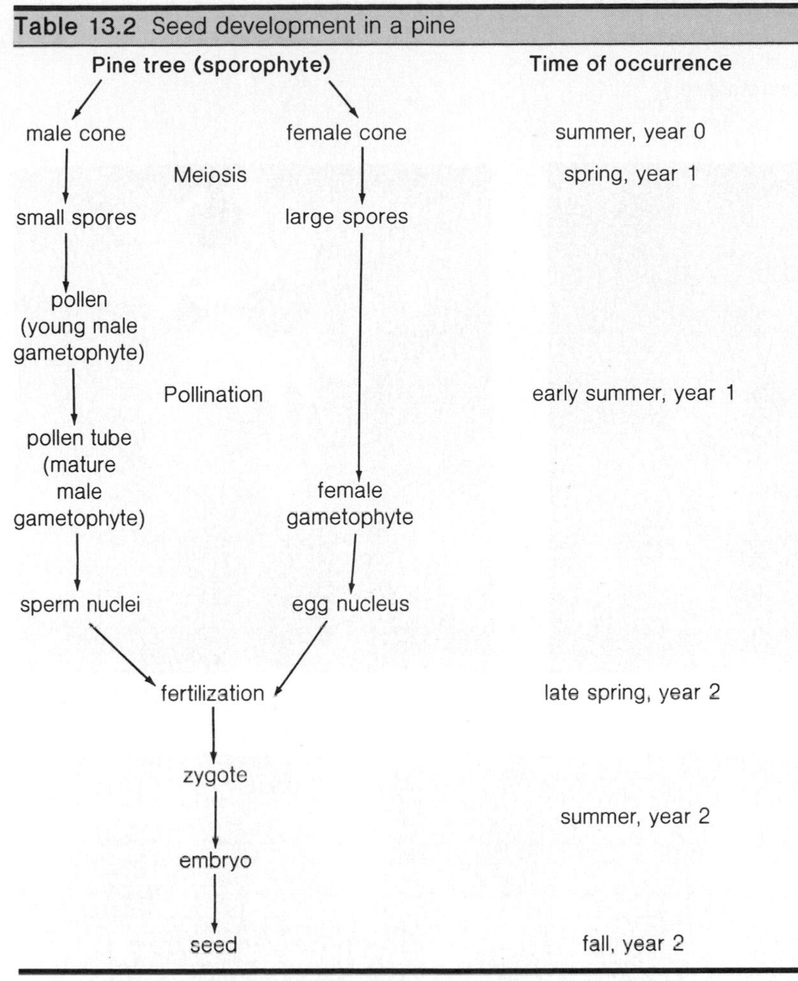

Table 13.2 Seed development in a pine

13.11 Flowering Plants Have Coevolved with Their Pollinators

Flowers are the distinguishing feature of the most successful division in the plant kingdom, the Anthophyta. Although we commonly appreciate flowers for their beauty, their major role is in reproduction, as we have seen in section 13.6. When a flower opens, it reveals the reproductive structures, the stamens and pistils. Insects, birds, or bats that visit the flower may pick up pollen from the anther and carry it to the next flower they visit. When pollen is transferred from a flower of one plant to a flower of another, the process is called cross-pollination. The main pollinators of flowers are insects. Pollen also may be transported from flower to flower by wind.

[an THOF ih tuh]

Figure 13.37 A few examples of the diversity of flowers. (a) fairy slipper, an orchid, *Calypso bulbosa;* (b) brown-eyed susan, a composite, *Rudbeckia triloba;* (c) Dutchman's breeches, *Dicentra rubellus;* (d) beardtongue, *Penstemon.*

a Doug Sokell

b Katherine A. Winternitz

c Doug Sokell

d BSCS by Carlye Calvin

Some flowers, however, seldom or never open. In that case, the pollen falls on the stigma of the same flower. Such flowers are self-pollinating. Flower and vegetable gardeners say that they "self." Most plants, however, have devices that prevent self-pollination.

The sepals and petals are not directly involved in seed formation, so a flower can function without them. In fact, in a few plants a flower may consist of only a single stamen or a single pistil. Petals and their adaptations, however, usually play a major role in flower pollination. Much of the diversity among flowering plant species lies in their flowers. There

Figure 13.38 Insect-pollinated flowers such as the prickly poppy, *Argemone,* in (a) generally have large, colored petals. Wind-pollinated flowers often lack petals and sepals, and produce an abundance of pollen. Shown here (b) is the male catkin of a willow, *Salix.* Note the many stamens.

a BSCS

b Doug Sokell

is no better way to appreciate that than to examine different flowers you can find in a field, a greenhouse, or a vacant lot. That diversity is usually related to the way the pollen is transferred from one flower to another. If pollen is transferred from stamen to pistil by insects, the petals of the flower are often large and brightly colored, as in figure 13.38a. The petals, moreover, often have small glands that produce a sugar solution called **nectar.** Those adaptations attract pollinating insects. On the other hand, flowers in which pollen is transferred by wind usually have small sepals and petals or none at all. They often are located high on the plant and produce an abundance of pollen (figure 13.38b). Their pistils commonly have large, long, or feathery structures at the tips, which are covered with a sticky fluid. Those adaptations increase the likelihood that some pollen will stick to the pistils.

The great variety of flowers has come about by the coevolution of a flower and its pollination agent. As we have seen, brightly colored flowers attract certain kinds of animals. Once at the flower the animal may be able to drink nectar and at the same time may pick up pollen from the flower. As the animal seeks nectar, it pollinates other flowers. The word **coevolution** is often used to describe such an interaction in which both organisms become uniquely adapted to each other. Consider this example. Hummingbirds need lots of nectar to supply their energy needs. They do not have a good sense of smell, but they can see the color red very well. Flowers pollinated by hummingbirds are well adapted to their pollinators, as you can see in figure 13.39. The flowers are red, have little or no scent, and produce copious amounts of nectar. In addition to those characteristics, the nectar is found at the bottom of a long tube formed by the red petals. That shape makes it difficult for other organisms to

Figure 13.39 The hummingbird's head is brushed with pollen from the anthers of the red columbine as it obtains nectar from the base of the flower.

W. A. Calder

Figure 13.40 Stages in the development of tomato fruit from flowers.

rob the flower of nectar. Hummingbirds, on the other hand, have long beaks that can probe the deep flower to reach the nectar. The stamens stick out in such a position that the head of the hummingbird is dusted with pollen when it visits these flowers. When the hummingbird flies to another flower of the same species, the tip of the pistil is in a perfect position to have pollen from the hummingbird's head scraped onto it. Thus, the flower gets pollinated while the hummingbird drinks nectar. Other animals are not shaped correctly to fit these flowers—neither to drink the nectar nor to pollinate the flower.

13.12 Seeds Develop within the Ovaries of Flowering Plants

After pollination and fertilization, seeds begin to develop. The pistil, often with other parts of the flower, develops into a protective fruit around the seed. There may be many seeds in a fruit. Each seed began its development when an egg cell in one ovule was fertilized by a sperm from one pollen grain. In flowering plants, then, an embryo is protected within a seed, and seeds are protected within a fruit.

Part of the embryo in the seed consists of one or two modified leaves, called **cotyledons** (kot ih LEE dunz). Another part is a beginning of a root. Each seed also contains a supply of food that is used when the embryo starts to grow. The food may be stored in the endosperm, or it may be stored in the embryo itself, usually in the cotyledon.

Figure 13.41 Diversity among fruits. (a) A fleshy fruit. (b) A variety of other fruits. How does each of the structural adaptations shown here provide for seed scattering?

a BSCS by Carlye Calvin

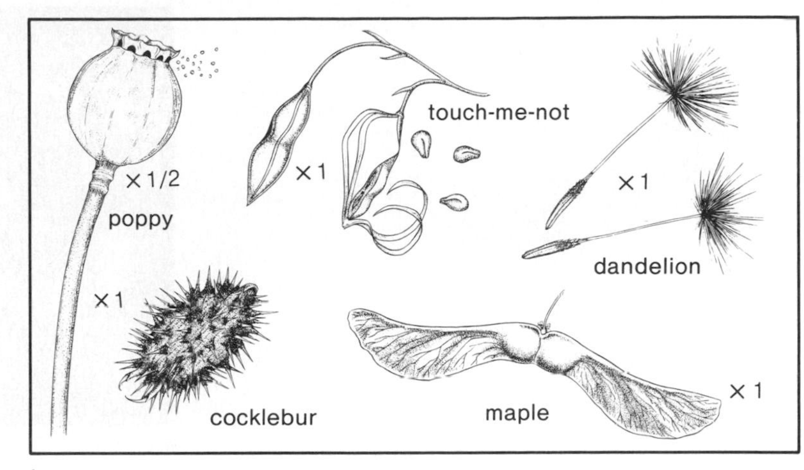

b

Beans and peas are examples of seeds. They are enclosed in protective pods, which are just one of many kinds of fruits. Each bean or pea contains a small embryo and a supply of stored food for its early development. As you know, this stored food is useful to humans as well. Peas and beans can be germinated easily, and each embryo gives rise to a plant, which, in turn, gives rise to new flowers and fruits. This aspect of plant growth and development is explored further in chapter 18.

Apples and oranges are examples of fruits that contain a number of seeds. Under natural conditions, such fruits eventually decay, leaving their seeds behind to germinate and give rise to the next generation. Fleshy fruits, often red in color, may be eaten by birds or mammals. Their seeds can be dispersed far and wide after passing through an animal's digestive system.

Seeds and fruits show as much diversity as flowers. That diversity is related to the method of **dispersal** of the seeds and fruits—that is, how they are scattered from the parent plant. In investigation 13.3 you can observe some of the structures that aid in seed dispersal. In many cases, part of the pistil becomes thick and fleshy, as in the fruits of peach, plum, and tomato. Fleshy fruits often are eaten by animals. The seeds in many such fruits have thick coats that permit them to pass through an animal's digestive system unharmed. They are dropped later at some distance from the parent plant. Many fruits are not fleshy but have other adaptations that aid in scattering their seeds. Those fruits may have spines that catch on the fur of an animal that brushes up against the plant. The fruit is carried from the plant and later falls off or is brushed off by the animal. Many fruits and seeds are lightweight and have special winglike projections that help them to be carried away from the plant by wind. An entire plant, such as the tumbleweed, can be broken off near the ground and blown about by the wind. As the tumbleweed bounces about, it drops its fruits and the seeds within them all along its path.

Figure 13.42 Perennial (a) and annual (b) herbaceous plants. (a) Yellow skunk cabbage, *Lysichitum americanum;* (b) marigold, *Tagetes.*

a Doug Sokell

b Courtesy of W. Atlee, Burpee Company

There is also great diversity in the size of the flowering plants and in the lifespan of their shoots—the parts that appear above ground. Many flowering plants are trees. A tree bears its leaves well above the ground where they are likely to receive more light than do those of shorter plants. Because of their size, trees can store large reserves of food in trunks and roots and can survive through bad years. Trees have relatively long lifespans. A tree species probably will survive even if the entire seed crop of any one year is destroyed. Most species of flowering plants are not trees, however. Some, such as roses and raspberries, are woody shrubs. Others, such as ivy, grapes, and hundreds of tropical species, are woody vines, which grow on rocks, on walls, or on other plants. Most, however, are neither trees, shrubs, nor vines, but nonwoody, or **herbaceous** (her BAY shus), plants like those in figure 13.42.

Many herbaceous plants have roots that remain alive in the soil during winter, when their shoots die. At the beginning of each growing season the roots send up new shoots. These are **perennials** (peh REN ee ulz),

Figure 13.43 Monocot and dicot leaves: (a) pampas grass, *Cortideria selloana*; (b) strawberry, *Fragaria virginiana chiloensis*.

a John D. Cunningham/VISUALS UNLIMITED

b Karlene V. Schwartz

plants, such as goldenrod, iris, and asparagus. Others are **annuals.** These (for example, garden beans, sunflowers, and corn) complete their life cycle, produce seeds, and die after growing for only one season.

Flowering plants are divided into two large classes. The basic characteristic of the monocotyledons, called **monocots** (MON oh kotz), is that the embryo contains a single cotyledon. A cotyledon is a seed leaf, a leaflike structure found associated with the seed or young seedling (review figure 13.20). The monocots include grasses and grain-producing plants such as wheat, rice, and corn, which are the chief food plants of the world. Their fruits, the familiar grains, are a major source of chemical energy for humans. The pasture grasses that feed cattle, another source of human food, are also monocots. Without monocots, the human population never could have reached its present state. Our lawn grasses are monocots as well, so these plants affect our lives in ways other than as food.

The seeds of the other class of flowering plants, the dicotyledons, or **dicots** (DY kotz), have two seed leaves. This class is much larger than the monocot class. Most of the familiar fruits and vegetables, such as carrots, lettuce, apples, and grapes, are dicots. In addition, the so-called hardwoods used in furniture, flooring, hockey sticks, and baseball bats come from dicot trees. Almost all shade trees are dicots, also. Figure 13.44 illustrates the most important differences between monocots and dicots.

Figure 13.44 Comparison of monocot and dicot characteristics.

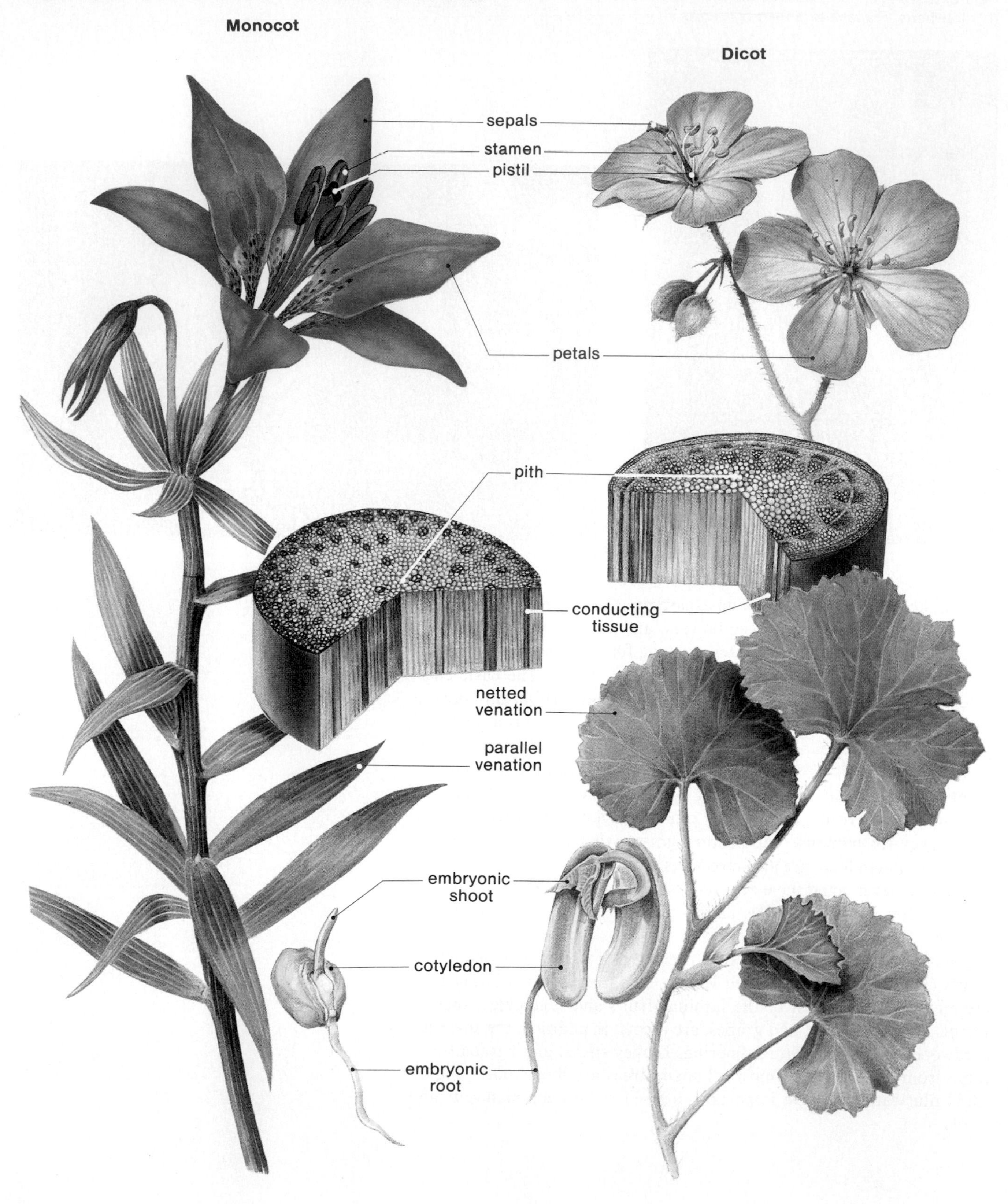

Self-Review

1. What products do humans get from conifers?
2. What adaptations do pines possess for living in dry conditions?
3. Describe an example of coevolution.
4. What part of a flowering plant gives rise to the fruit?
5. What structural characteristics of fruits seem to be adaptations that are related to seed dispersal?
6. In what ways do monocots and dicots differ?

Investigation 13.3 SEEDS AND SEED DISPERSAL

Introduction

Seed producers are the most highly developed group of plants. In flowering plants, seeds are protected by the surrounding tissues of the ovary. The mature ovary usually is called a fruit. Gymnosperms lack an ovary, and produce naked seeds on cone scales.

The survival of plants depends on their ability to reproduce. That, in turn, depends on mechanisms to disperse the seeds and fruits so the seeds can grow without having to compete with the parent plants for nutrients and water.

In investigation 13.1 you examined the structure of flowers and the reproductive parts of flowering plants. In this investigation, you will compare seed production in the tomato with that in a pine, and examine some of the ways by which seeds are dispersed.

Materials (per team)

tomato branch with flowers
tomato
bean or pea seed
pine branch with cones
pollen cones
young seed cones
old seed cones
pine seeds
dandelion seeds
poplar seeds
cockleburs
mistletoe fruits
pyracantha fruits
maple fruits
ash fruits
hand lens
stereoscopic dissecting microscope
compound microscope
microscope slide
coverslip
single-edge razor blade

Procedure

Part A—Seeds

1. Compare the tomato branch and the pine branch.
   (a) In what ways are they similar?
   (b) In what ways are they different?
   (c) The tomato plant and the pine tree are the mature sporophytes. Compare the two whole plants.
2. Use a hand lens to observe the male and female reproductive structures enclosed in the flower of the tomato. Most tomato plants are self-pollinating, which means that pollen is transferred from the anthers to the pistil of the same flower. What are the advantages of self-pollination in the tomato?
3. Male and female reproductive parts of pines are located in different structures. Seed cones are produced singly or in groups of 2 to 5 on the branches. Pollen cones usually occur in closely packed clusters of 10 or more near the tip of a branch. What is the advantage to the pine of producing more pollen cones than seed cones?
4. Observe one of the pollen cones. The small, spirally arranged cone scales that make up most of the pollen cone are modified leaves. Examine a cone scale under the dissecting microscope. Find the 2 elongated spore cases on the lower side.
5. Crush a spore case on a clean glass slide. Add a coverslip and examine the slide under high power. Note the pollen grains with the little bladders. What is the role of pollen grains in the life cycle of the pine?
6. Examine one of the young seed cones. The spirally arranged cone scales are fleshy and may be a little difficult to pry apart. Carefully separate the scales and observe the ovules, a pair of white or cream-colored bumps on the upper side near the base of each scale. The ovules will grow into seeds, as do the ovules in flowering plants.
   (a) How are the ovules of a pine protected?
   (b) How does a sperm cell reach an egg in the ovule of a pine?
   (c) Ovules develop into pine seeds. How are the seeds shed from cones? You may want to look at an old seed cone that has shed most of its seeds to help you answer this question.
7. Cut a tomato in half lengthwise (from the stem end to the bottom). Locate and remove some of the tomato seeds. Tomato seeds are very small and difficult to dissect. Bean and pea seeds are similar to tomato seeds, but they are much larger and easier to observe. Cut a bean or pea seed in half lengthwise. Describe the bean or pea seed.
8. Examine a pine seed, keeping in mind the environment in which it must survive if it is to grow into a pine tree. Break the seed open and remove the contents. What could be the function of the seed coat in the bean, pea, or pine seed?
9. Make a lengthwise cut through the pine seed and observe the cut face. If you made the cut properly, you will see the embryo surrounded by the endosperm.
   (a) Compare the internal structure of the bean or pea seed and the pine seed.
   (b) What might be the function of the endosperm in the seeds?

Part B—Seed Dispersal

1. Assemble the different types of seeds and fruits at your work area.
2. Blow gently at the seeds and fruits.
   (a) What happened?
   (b) Why did it happen?
   (c) What advantage to a plant is illustrated by this demonstration?

3. Some fruits or seeds attract birds.
   (a) What characteristics do you observe that might serve to attract birds?
   (b) Which plants have physical attractants that might function in seed dispersal?
4. Some fruits contain a chemical that acts as a laxative.
   (a) How would this function in plant dispersal?
   (b) How might the contents of bird droppings assist in survival of the new seedlings?
5. Rest the sleeve of your blouse or shirt on the seeds and fruits.
   (a) What type of dispersal is illustrated by the result?
   (b) What kinds of organisms must be present in the environment to disperse this kind of seed?
6. Some types of seeds have tough seed coats to protect the seeds. Some even require exposure to fire to break the seed coat open so the seed can germinate.
   (a) What type of seed do you have that might function like this?
   (b) How much force is required to break open the seed coat? Add weight until the seed breaks open.

Discussion

1. How do the tomato and pine sporophytes compare with the sporophyte of a moss in terms of size and method of nutrition?
2. Which would have a better chance of survival, the spore of a moss or the seed of a pine? Explain.
3. Which would have a better chance of survival, the spore of a moss or the seed of a bean or pea? Explain.
4. What are some of the ways seeds are dispersed?
5. How might some plants develop a dispersal mechanism that relies on the presence of other organisms?
6. What would happen to the distribution of plants that produce cockleburs if they lived on an island where there were no animals?
7. Explain how some poplar trees might inhabit an island in the middle of a large lake.

Summary

The ancestors of plants were probably simple multicellular algae. A multicellular organism has many advantages over a single cell, including its size, a division of labor, and ability to conserve water. Other adaptations that permit plants to absorb and hold water are roots, vascular tissue, and the cuticle. All plants have a life cycle that alternates between two different generations, a gametophyte and a sporophyte. In flowering plants, however, the egg cell, the gametophyte that produced the egg, and the spore that produced the gametophyte all remain protected in the flower. Mosses are nonvascular plants that lack roots, stems, and leaves, and that have other primitive characteristics, such as swimming sperm cells. Club mosses, horsetails, and ferns are all seedless vascular plants, and many of their ancestors produced today's fossil fuels. Gymnosperms and flowering plants are both seed-producing vascular plants, but flowering plants have a fruit that covers their seeds. The great diversity of flowers and fruits is the result of coevolution of the plants and their agents of pollination or dispersal.

Application Questions

1. Which organisms in this chapter would you consider to be primitive organisms? Which would you consider to be advanced? Explain your answer.
2. What advantages and disadvantages does a seed-producing plant have compared with one that produces only spores? How do you interpret the words advantage and disadvantage here?
3. Explain the following statement: the plant parts that furnish the greatest amount of human food are either seeds, roots, or underground stems.

Problems

1. In what ways do plants that live entirely in water differ in structure, reproduction, and limiting factors from plants that live entirely on land?
2. Observe the plants that grow without human help in a city. Try to discover the characteristics that enable them to live successfully in an urban environment.
3. How many of the different kinds of plants discussed in this chapter can be found in your locality? Consider wild and cultivated plants, indoor and outdoor plants, and aquatic and terrestrial plants.
4. Choose some cultivated plants. Investigate the history of their domestication. Examples: wheat, apple, potato, cotton, corn, cabbage, sugarcane.

Suggested Readings

A. W. Galston, P. J. Davies, R. L. Satter, 1980, *The Life of the Green Plant* 3rd Ed. (Englewood Cliffs, N.J.: Prentice-Hall). Covers the basic structure and function of higher-level green plants.

C. W. Hinman, "Potential New Crops" *Scientific American* (July 1986). Buffalo gourd, crambe, jojoba, kenaf, and other plants may soon provide novel foods and materials.

D. F. Mandoli and W. R. Briggs, "Fiber Optics in Plants" *Scientific American* (August 1984). Columns of cells in seedlings may act as "light pipes" to channel light to key pigment molecules.

P. C. Mangelsdorf, "The Origin of Corn" *Scientific American* (August 1986). Breeding experiments are cited to support the author's theory that corn had not one ancestor, but two.

D. H. Morse, "Milkweeds and Their Visitors" *Scientific American* (July 1985). The insects and other animals that frequent milkweed form a model community for the study of interactions among species.

G. A. Rosenthal, "The Chemical Defenses of Higher Plants" *Scientific American* (January 1986). Some compounds poison or repel herbivores; others mimic insect hormones, interfering with their growth.

G. A. Strobel and G. N. Lanier, "Dutch Elm Disease" *Scientific American* (August 1981). Biological controls are aimed at the fungus that causes the disease and the beetles that spread it.

Kenneth A. Pals

This caterpillar soon will enter a resting stage from which it will emerge as a black swallowtail butterfly. What is its function in the life cycle of the butterfly, and how is it adapted for that function?

CHAPTER 14

Eukaryotes: Animals

Introduction

The animal kingdom presents an enormous diversity of organisms, adapted to a wide variety of habitats and life-styles. Although they display an endless variety of structural and functional modifications, all animals share certain basic characteristics. All are essentially multicellular in organization. All are heterotrophic. Most are motile for some part of their lives and are able to react to their environments rather quickly.

Most animals share a common evolutionary origin. Thus, in spite of their great diversity, animals share basic features that developed in ancestral forms. Even unrelated groups, if they occupy similar habitats, may develop similar solutions to common problems.

Animals have been grouped into approximately 30 phyla. In this chapter, we will explore the problems of animal life and some of the adaptations that animals have evolved to solve those problems. We also will examine briefly how some animals carry out the major functions of life. A more detailed discussion of functions in the human animal is the subject of the first three chapters in Section 4.

The Animal Way of Life

Guidepost: What are the major problems of animal life, and what are some of the solutions?

14.1 Bilateral Symmetry Adapts Animals for Movement

Animals are heterotrophic and generally must seek food. As a result, evolution through natural selection has favored a motile life-style. Motility is easier if the organism is elongated in the direction of movement. It also is helpful if sensory organs that can detect food, light, and other stimuli are concentrated in the end that meets the environment first.

Figure 14.1 Body symmetry.

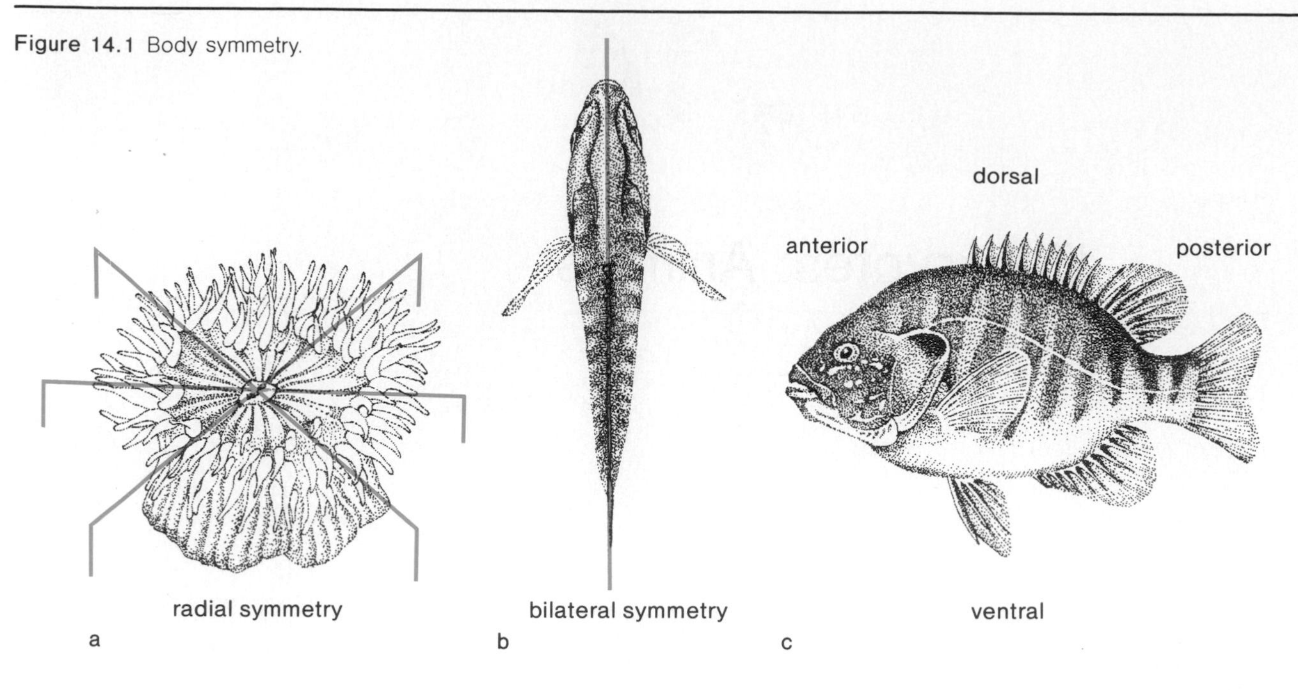

Finally, motility is promoted if the organism has a balanced body, with neither side heavier or larger than the other. The evolution of a body plan with **bilateral symmetry** (by LAT er ul SIM eh tree) adapted animals for a motile life-style. In that body plan, there is an **anterior** (an TIR ee er) or head end that goes first, and a **posterior** (pah STIR ee er) or tail end that follows. The right and left sides are approximately mirror images of each other. Most animals also have a top and a bottom, or a **dorsal** (DOR sul) and a **ventral** (VEN trul) surface.

Active movement, in turn, requires coordination. Thus, evolution has favored development of a head where sensory organs and nerve cells are gathered. Those are the forerunner of a brain. Structures that help an animal capture prey tend to be located at the head end, and digestive, excretory, and reproductive structures toward the tail end.

Organisms that are **sessile** (SES il), or nonmotile, generally have a body plan of **radial** (RAYD ee ul) **symmetry.** The body parts radiate from a center, much as spokes radiate from the hub of a wheel. Radial symmetry is adaptive for a sessile or drifting life-style because the animal meets the environment equally from all sides. However, sessile organisms are very limited. They depend on food that floats by, or they must create water currents to bring food to them. They cannot actively seek mates and must rely on chance meeting of eggs and sperm. In general, sessile animals are much less complex than motile ones.

14.2 An Animal's Environment Imposes Specific Demands

Animals may live in the sea, in fresh water, or on land. Each of those environments imposes special demands on the organism. The ancestral environment was probably the sea, and it remains the most uniform and least stressful place for animal life. Oxygen is usually adequate, temperatures and salt content are fairly constant, and there is no danger of drying up.

Figure 14.2 Animals vary greatly in size. The microscopic *Daphnia* (a) contains perhaps a few hundred cells; the elephant (b) millions.

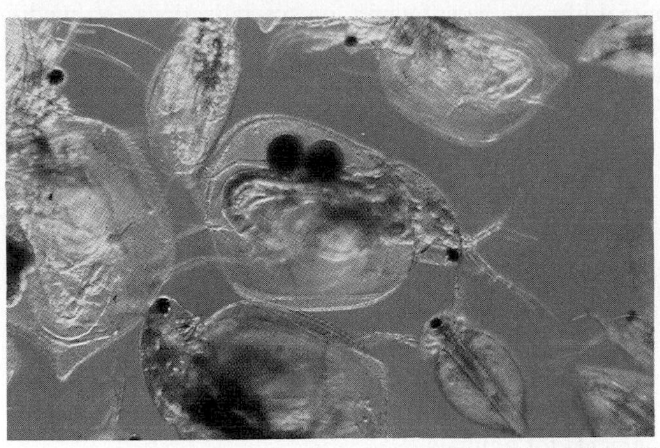

a T. E. Adams/VISUALS UNLIMITED

b BSCS by J. B. Thornton

In fresh water, the salt and oxygen contents vary greatly. On land, oxygen is plentiful, but there is constant danger that the organism will dry up. Temperatures fluctuate daily and seasonally. Air does not provide the buoyancy of water, so large, **terrestrial,** or land, animals require good supporting structures. On the other hand, there is less resistance to movement in air than in water. **Appendages** (uh PEN dij ez)—structures attached to the body—do not hinder movement on land as they do in water. Thus appendages specialized for locomotion could evolve in terrestrial animals.

14.3 Increase in Size Leads to Increased Complexity

Organisms exhibit an enormous range in size, as can be seen in table 14.1. During the course of evolution, most animal groups have shown a trend toward increasing size, an adaptation made possible by their multicellularity. Increased size imposes restrictions that require increased division of labor among the parts. The resulting specialization leads to greater complexity in the organism.

Individual cells, however, remain remarkably constant in size in all organisms. Large animals have *more* cells than small animals, not larger cells. The presence of more cells makes possible more specialization, but requires more coordination.

For example, small animals can easily exchange materials with the environment by diffusion. Diffusion is too slow to move materials within a large animal, however. As size increases, animals require special systems to obtain oxygen, remove wastes, and transport substances. Gas exchange, waste removal, and transport systems must be coordinated. In general, the larger the animal, the more complex are the controls necessary to coordinate its activities.

Table 14.1 Logarithmic scale showing the spectrum of size in living things

Organism	Size
Blue whale	10^8
Human	10^5
Hamster	10^2
Bee	10^{-1}
Large amoeba	10^{-4}
Tetrahymena (flagellate)	10^{-7}
Plasmodium (malaria parasite)	10^{-10}
Mycoplasma (PPLO) (bacterium)	10^{-13}

Adapted from *On Size and Life* by Thomas A. McMahon and John Tyler Bonner. Copyright © 1983 by Thomas A. McMahon and John Tyler Bonner. Scientific American Books, Inc., distributed by W. H. Freeman and Company, New York.

Those, then, are some of the problems of animal life. In the next section, we will examine briefly a few of the animal phyla. Each of the examples we have selected demonstrates a new solution to one of the problems of animal life. We have focused on specializations and modifications that have improved adaptation of the organisms to the environment. You will find descriptions of additional animal phyla in appendix 3, A Catalog of Living Things, pages 969–994. You can become acquainted with animal structure in investigation 14.1.

Self-Review

1. What are the advantages of bilateral symmetry? Of radial symmetry?
2. Compare the advantages and disadvantages of aquatic and terrestrial environments for animals.
3. Describe how increased size leads to increased complexity.

Investigation 14.1 ANIMAL STRUCTURE: THE FETAL PIG

Introduction

No species can fully illustrate animal structure. Fetal pigs have some advantages. They are mammals—enough like ourselves to throw some light on our own structure. Yet they are sufficiently unlike us to provide some important contrast. A false notion about dissection is that all you do is cut and slice. An animal specimen is a marvelously assembled and intricate set of structures held together by connective tissue. Dissection involves making careful incisions to expose parts, then using a probe to separate organs and other structures from their coverings. In a sense, one's intent is to carefully unwrap the animal's structures without damage.

The pig you will dissect is a fetal pig. Fetal pigs have not been born. They were removed from their mother's reproductive tract before birth. Evidence of their fetal condition can be seen by examining the stomach area for the attached umbilical cord.

Materials (per team of 2)

fetal pig
dissecting pan
pair of scissors
scalpel
dull probe
length of string
metric ruler
dissecting needle

Part A—External Anatomy

Procedure

1. The period of gestation for the pig is 112–115 days. The age of your fetal pig can be estimated by measuring the body length from the tip of the snout to the attachment of the tail. Compare this length to the data given on relative sizes of a fetal pig at different times during gestation.
   21 days, 11 mm
   35 days, 17 mm
   49 days, 28 mm
   56 days, 40 mm
   100 days, 220 mm
   115 days, 300 mm
   Record the age of your specimen in your data book.
2. Determine the sex of your specimen. Males can be identified by the presence of small sacs containing the testes, located at the posterior end of the trunk between the upper ends of the hind legs. The opening for the penis, the urogenital opening, is located just posterior to the umbilical cord. In the female, the urogenital opening is situated immediately ventral to the anus. A small fleshy structure, the genital papilla, projects from the urogenital opening. Both sexes have two rows of nipples.
3. Examine the umbilical cord. This structure is present only during fetal life (pregnancy) and is lost shortly after birth. It is located on the ventral abdominal surface. Through it pass the vessels (2 umbilical arteries, 1 umbilical vein, and an allantoic duct, which is difficult to see) that carry nutrients and waste products between the fetus and mother, through the placenta on the mother's uterus wall.
4. Cut a very small piece off the end of the umbilical cord and note the location of the vessels mentioned above on the freshly cut end.

Discussion

1. What was the gestation age of your fetal pig? What is the basis of this determination?
2. What is the sex of your fetal pig? What is the basis of htis determination?
3. The fetus-mother relationship is considered to be similar to a parasite-host relationship by some biologists. How would you support this position?

Part B—The Dissection

Procedure

1. Tie your specimen on its back in the dissecting pan. Tie the left foreleg to right foreleg with a piece of string passed under the pan. Do the same with the hind legs. As you proceed, you may have to tighten the strings.
2. For the following work, use the outline drawing, figure 14.3, which shows where incisions (numbered in sequence), are to be made. Numbered incisions with symbols apply to the sex of the animal.

Figure 14.3 Fetal pig.

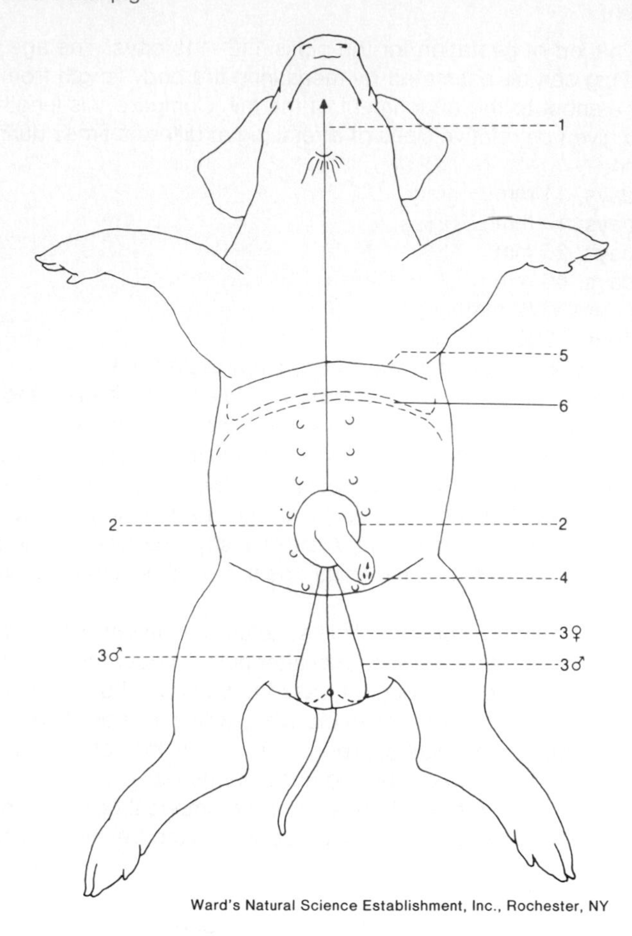

3. Using forceps, lift the skin to be cut, beginning with #1 at the belly, anterior to the umbilical cord, and make a small slit with a scalpel. Then, using scissors, insert and cut to the chin. Pull upward on the umbilical cord slightly while you make these cuts, to avoid cutting the abdominal organs.
4. After you have made incision #2, you will notice that the umbilical cord and flesh immediately around it cannot be laid back freely on the body. Look for a dark tubular structure extending from the umbilical cord forward to the liver (the large brownish organ at the anterior end of the abdominal cavity); this is the umbilical vein. Tie a small piece of string around the vein in two places and then sever the vein between the cords. The umbilical cord can now be pulled down between the hind legs of your specimen.
5. Continue with incisions 3, 4, and 5, always being aware not to cut into the abdominal organs.
6. Notice that the diaphragm (#6) must be freed by cutting its edge where it is in contact with the body wall.

Discussion

What two structures had to be cut during dissection to expose internal organs?

Part C—The Digestive System

Procedure

1. Examine the liver and notice it is divided into three lobes.
2. Use your probe to raise the right lobe of the liver. (Note that right and left refer to your specimen's right and left.) Observe the gall bladder, a small, greenish sac embedded in the underside of the liver.
3. Trace the thin duct leading from the gall bladder. This is the common bile duct, which empties into the intestine.
4. Immediately under the left lobes of the liver lies the stomach. Follow the intestine from the stomach toward the posterior, until it joins the colon, or large intestine. Notice that the intestine is held in place by a thin membrane, the mesentery.
5. Where the intestine and colon join, there is a pouch, called the caecum. In humans, the tip of this pouch is the appendix.
6. Trace the colon toward the posterior. Just before it reaches the anus, there is a slight enlargement, the rectum.
7. Where the stomach and intestine join, there is a tight ring of muscle in the wall of the digestive tract. This is the pyloric valve. At the anterior end of the stomach, there is another muscular ring, the cardiac valve.
8. After the animal is born, food is carried from the mouth to the stomach by way of the esophagus. Trace the esophagus toward the mouth as far as possible without disturbing other organs.
9. The sheet of muscle through which the esophagus passes is the diaphragm. The diaphragm separates the chest and abdominal cavities.
10. The pancreas, a small, pinkish, grainy organ, is also part of the digestive system. It lies just under the stomach, inside the bend made by the first section of the intestine.

Discussion

1. If you were to open the stomach of your specimen, what kind of food would you expect to find?
2. What is the source of food for the fetal pig?
3. List in order the organs through which food actually passes starting with the mouth and ending with the anus.
4. You may have observed a dark organ that partly hides the stomach on the left side of your specimen. If not, locate it now. This organ is the spleen. Why was it not mentioned as part of the digestive system?

Part D—The Circulatory and Respiratory Systems

Procedure

1. Open the chest cavity, using scissors to cut through the sternum, or breast bone. Be careful not to cut too deeply, or you may damage the heart and lungs which are just below the sternum.
2. Notice that the chest cavity is triangular in shape. It is enclosed on the sides by the rib cage and on the bottom by the diaphragm.
3. Tucked between the lungs, which fill each side of the chest cavity, is the heart. The heart is enclosed in a membrane called the pericardium.
4. Spread the heart and lungs with your probe, and trace the esophagus from the abdominal cavity up through the chest cavity.
5. Locate the trachea, or windpipe, which is ventral to the upper part of the esophagus. The trachea continues down into the chest cavity, where it branches into each lung.

6. Continue the dissection in the neck region. Expose the upper part of the trachea, where there is an enlarged organ made of cartilage. This is the larynx, or voice box.
7. Posterior to the larynx and wrapped around the ventral side of the trachea is a rather large gland, the thyroid.
8. Return to the heart and carefully peel off the pericardium. Use your dissecting needle to pick away the connective tissue surrounding the blood vessels that leave and enter the heart.
9. The blood vessels are mostly on the anterior and dorsal surfaces of the heart. These surfaces make up the atria of the heart. These chambers receive blood returning to the heart through the veins.
10. Locate the right and left ventricles of the heart and the coronary artery that runs across the ventral surface, separating the 2 ventricles. This blood vessel supplies the heart muscle with blood.
11. Entering the dorsal surface of the heart are 2 large veins. These are the superior and inferior vena cava. You will need to lift the heart and rotate it to your right to see where these enter the right atrium. The veins bring blood back to the heart from the anterior and posterior parts of the body.
12. The pulmonary veins carry blood back to the heart from the lungs. They empty blood into the left atrium, also on the dorsal surface. Locate these veins.
13. Blood is carried to the lungs via the pulmonary artery. It appears on the ventral surface of the heart near the top where it leaves the right ventricle. Locate this artery.
14. Beneath the pulmonary artery where it arches over the top of the heart lies the aorta. This large artery leaves the left ventricle and carries blood to all parts of the body except the lungs.
15. If you dissect carefully, you may be able to locate a short connecting blood vessel between the pulmonary artery and the aorta. This is called the ductus arteriosus. At the time of birth, this vessel closes off and ceases to carry blood.

Discussion

1. What is the function of the diaphragm?
2. To what organ system does the thyroid gland belong?
3. How can you distinguish between the atria and ventricles of the heart?
4. What is the function of the ductus arteriosus in the fetal heart?
5. What adaptive advantage is gained by its closure at birth?

Part E—The Urogenital System

Procedure

1. Carefully remove the organs of the digestive system from the abdominal cavity. This will expose the organs of the excretory and reproductive systems. Use your dissecting needle to remove any fat deposits there may be around these organs.
2. Locate the kidneys, a pair of dark, bean-shaped organs lying on the dorsal wall of your specimen.
3. Remove the peritoneum (the membrane lining the abdominal cavity and covering the kidneys) and observe the branches of the aorta that bring blood to the kidneys. These are the renal arteries.
4. Lying just below the renal arteries are the renal veins. These drain blood from the kidneys into the inferior vena cava for return to the heart.

5. The third tube leading out of the kidney is the ureter. Follow this duct toward the posterior, until it enters the urinary bladder. The ureter drains urine from the kidneys for temporary storage in the urinary bladder.
6. Spread the hind legs as far as possible. Use scissors to cut through the cartilage of the pelvic girdle (the set of bones to which the legs are connected).
7. Spread the pelvic girdle and expose the urethra. This duct leads from the urinary bladder to the urogenital opening through which urine is eliminated from the body.
8. Male reproductive system: Observe the pair of small sacs near the posterior end of your specimen. Inside these sacs are the testes. Carefully open one sac and locate the sperm duct as it runs forward to join the urethra. The penis is a muscular tube immediately beneath the bladder.
9. Female reproductive system: Just posterior to the kidneys are the two ovaries. Leading from each ovary is a short duct, the oviduct, or Fallopian tube. These are embedded in fairly heavy connective tissue. Trace them to the uterus. Near the base of the uterus is a slight constriction marking the cervix. Posterior to the cervix is the vagina.

Discussion

1. The uterus in the pig is divided into a Y-shaped structure. The arms of the Y are called the horns of the uterus. Human females do not have a divided uterus. What is the function of the uterus?
2. What is the adaptive advantage to the pig to have the divided uterus that you observed?

Diversity and Adaptation in Animals

Guidepost: What major adaptations have evolved in the animal groups, and how are animals complementary to their environment?

14.4 Sponges and Coelenterates Are Adapted to a Sessile Life-style

Sponges (Phylum Porifera) are an ancient group with an extensive fossil record dating back to the early Precambrian period, more than 600 million years ago (figure 14.4). They are all aquatic, and the several thousand living species occupy a variety of marine and freshwater habitats. They show considerable diversity of form, and many are brightly colored, as seen in figure 14.5.

[poh RIF er uh]

Sponges are sessile animals without any apparent symmetry. Their cells are loosely organized and do not form true tissues. The name Porifera, pore-bearer, aptly describes the body of a sponge. The body is adapted to function as a water-filtering system, and consists of a bag pierced by many pores and canals, as shown in figure 14.6. Water containing oxygen and microscopic food is pulled in through the pores by the beating flagella of specialized cells that line the inner body. Water

Figure 14.4 Evolution of animals throughout the earth's history.

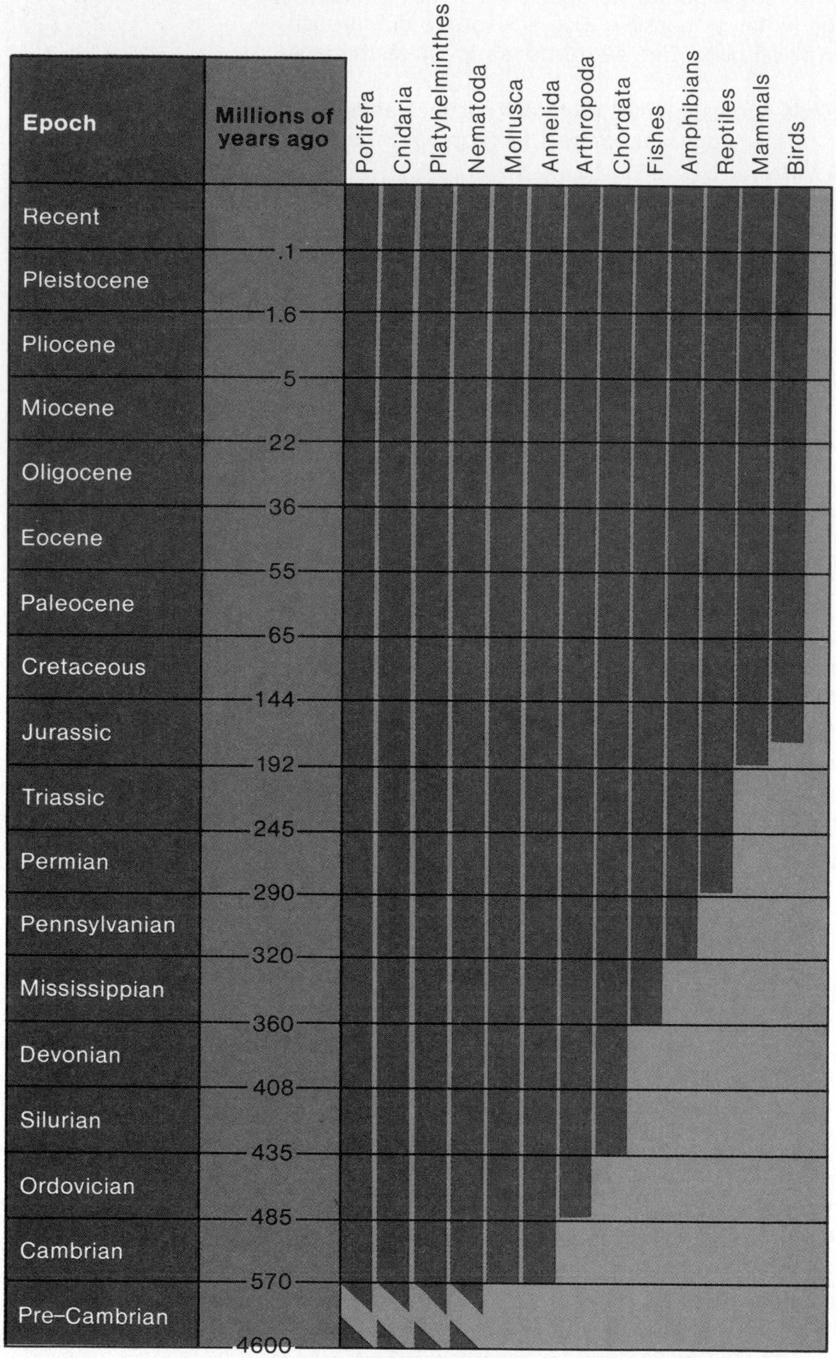

Epoch

Millions of years ago

Porifera
Cnidaria
Platyhelminthes
Nematoda
Mollusca
Annelida
Arthropoda
Chordata
Fishes
Amphibians
Reptiles
Mammals
Birds

Recent
.1
Pleistocene
1.6
Pliocene
5
Miocene
22
Oligocene
36
Eocene
55
Paleocene
65
Cretaceous
144
Jurassic
192
Triassic
245
Permian
290
Pennsylvanian
320
Mississippian
360
Devonian
408
Silurian
435
Ordovician
485
Cambrian
570
Pre-Cambrian
4600

Figure 14.5 Sponges: (a) barrel sponge, *Xestospongia mura;* (b) a red sponge from the family Demospongiae.

a Jeff Gutekunst

b Jeff Gutekunst

Figure 14.6 Body plan of a sponge.

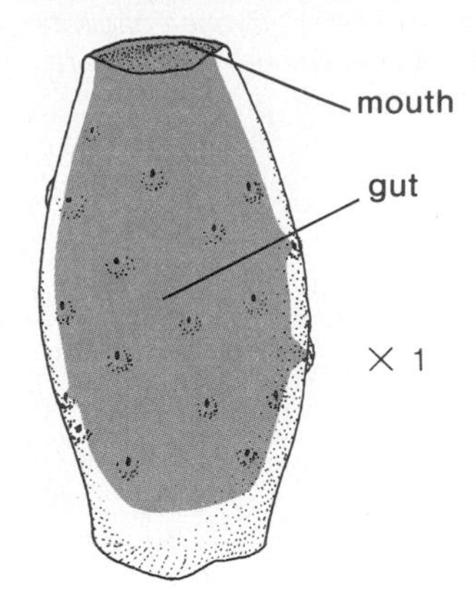

containing carbon dioxide and other cellular wastes flows back out of the body cavity through an opening called a mouth. The body wall is supported by interlocking particles of hard or tough material that form a kind of skeleton.

Coelenterates (Phylum Cnidaria) are aquatic animals usually found in shallow, warm marine habitats. They include the freshwater hydras (figure 12.4), corals, jellyfish, and sea anemones. Many harbor mutualistic algae within their cells, enabling them to thrive in nutrient-poor waters. Coral reefs, limestone ridges just under the surface of the sea, are formed by secretions of several species of coelenterates. These formations are home to the greatest diversity of animal life in the water. Corals have produced islands such as the Bahamas and Bermuda. Coral skeletons have been used to make jewelry since before Roman times. The fossil record of the coelenterates, like that of the sponges, goes back more than 600 million years. (Refer to figure 14.4, page 490.)

[sih LEN teh raytz]

[ny DAR ee uh]

Figure 14.7 Coelenterates: (a) coral, *Astrangia;* (b) jellyfish, *Cyanea capillata;* (c) great green anemone, *Anthopleura xanthogrammica.*

a Carl Roessler/TOM STACK & ASSOCIATES

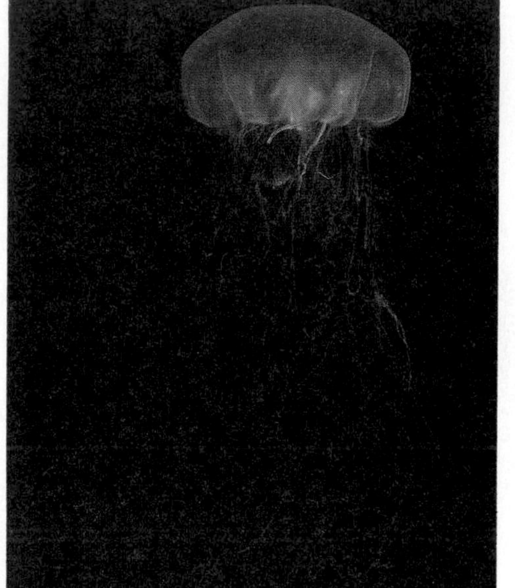

b Neil G. McDaniel/TOM STACK & ASSOCIATES

c Stan Elems/VISUALS UNLIMITED

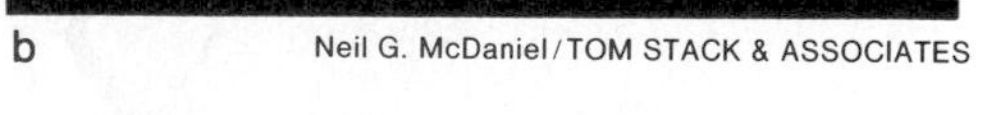

Figure 14.8 Coelenterate body plan.

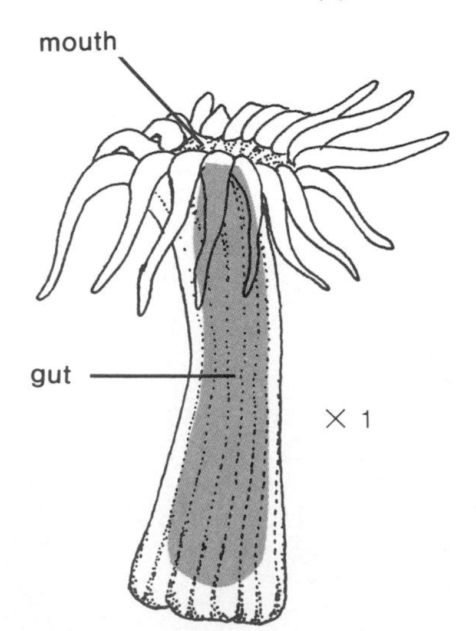

Coelenterates are radially symmetrical and, thus, are adapted to a sessile or drifting life-style. They have two basic body forms. Both the reef-building corals and the freshwater hydra have a tubular body that is usually attached to a surface. The free-swimming or drifting jellyfish forms are like an inverted bowl with dangling tentacles. The body of a coelenterate is little more than a thin-walled bag with an outer and inner tissue layer, as shown in figure 14.8. Sandwiched between the layers is a jellylike material that contains a network of nerve cells and contractile fibers. Digestion occurs in the central cavity of the bag, hence the name coelenterate—hole or cavity plus gut. Food is taken in and undigested particles are released through the same opening. The opening is surrounded by tentacles containing specialized cells that sting prey on contact and give the phylum its name, Cnidaria.

Figure 14.9 Flatworms: (a) free-living planarian, *Dugesia;* (b) parasitic liver fluke, *Clonorchis sinensis;* (c) tapeworm, *Anaplocephala.*

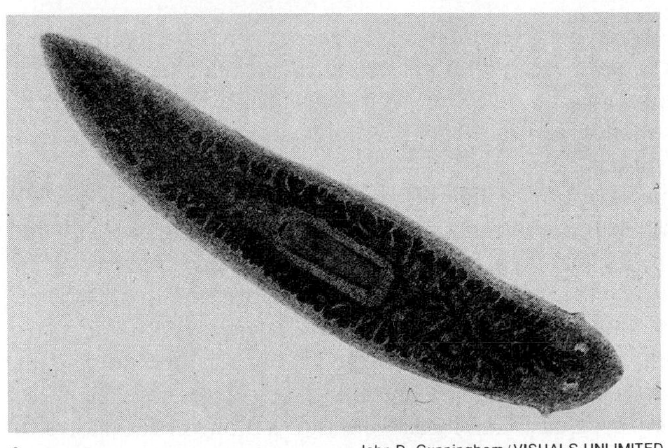

a John D. Cunningham/VISUALS UNLIMITED

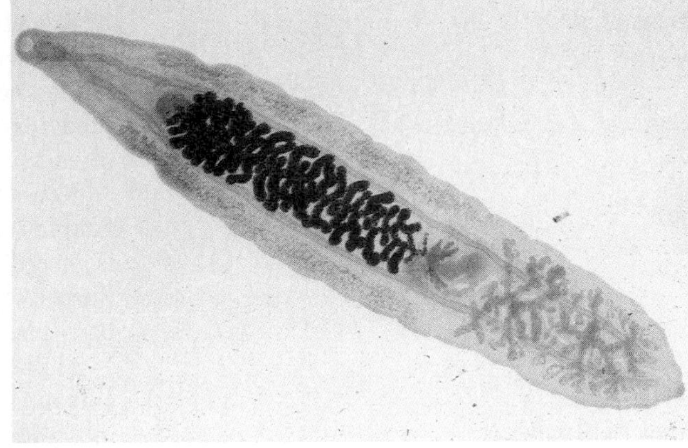

b E. J. Cable/TOM STACK & ASSOCIATES

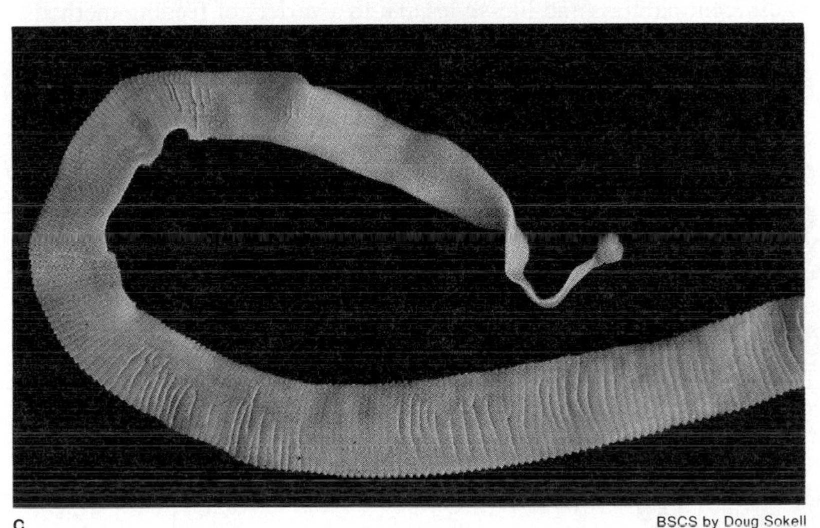

c BSCS by Doug Sokell

14.5 Flatworms Are Bilaterally Symmetrical and Have Three Tissue Layers

Flatworms (Phylum Platyhelminthes) are the simplest animals to have bilateral symmetry and three tissue layers organized into organs and organ systems. As a result, they show greater specialization and division of labor than either sponges or coelenterates. Flatworms are a very successful phylum adapted to a great variety of habitats. Many are parasitic and infect members of almost all other phyla. Parasitic forms include tapeworms and flukes. Free-living forms such as planarians may be marine or live in moist soil or fresh water. Little is known of flatworm origins, because their soft bodies do not form fossils.

[plat ih hel MINTH eez]

The flatworm digestive system, or gut, is diagrammed in figure 14.10. It is a much-branched sac with one opening that serves both to take in food and to eliminate wastes. The branches are an adaptation that brings food directly to the cells or within diffusible distance. Parasitic forms often have no gut, an adaptation to an environment in which they can absorb digested food directly from the host organism. Because of the flat body plan, oxygen and carbon dioxide can diffuse readily in and out of all cells. An excretory system regulates water content.

Figure 14.10 Flatworm body plan. Note the much branched gut.

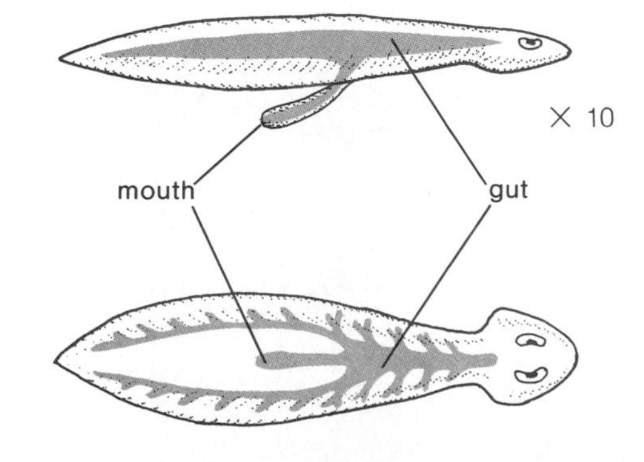

14.6 Roundworms and Mollusks Have a One-way Gut Suspended in a Body Cavity

[nem uh TOHD uh]

Roundworms (Phylum Nematoda) are slender cylindrical animals that are present in almost every kind of ecological niche. There may be a million nematodes in a shovelful of good garden soil. They are efficient predators or parasites, and they can infect almost all plants and animals, often causing serious disease.

Roundworms have a complete digestive tract with two openings, an adaptation that permits continuous processing of food. The one-way gut is generally tubelike and is suspended in a fluid-filled body cavity within the body wall. The resulting tube-within-a-tube (figure 14.12) is the basic body plan of animals in the remaining phyla.

[MOL lusks]

[mol LUS kuh]

Mollusks (Phylum Mollusca) are a large phylum that includes snails and slugs, clams, oysters, scallops, and squid and octopuses. They live in a great variety of aquatic habitats, from the shallows of the shores to the greatest ocean depths. Their great diversity is due to their adaptation to different habitats and life-styles and to a variety of feeding methods. Mollusks are a major source of food for humans and other animals, and many are noted for their intricate shells.

Figure 14.11 Nematodes: (a) in garden soil; (b) *Trichinella spiralis,* a parasite.

a USDA, Office of Communication

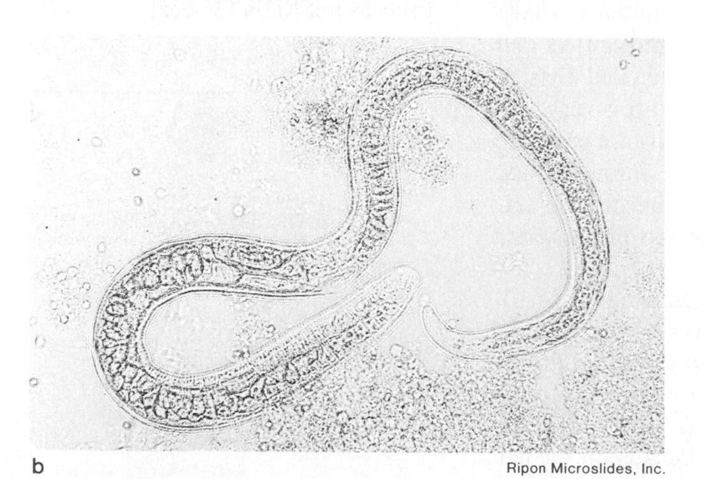

b Ripon Microslides, Inc.

Figure 14.12 Roundworm body plan, a tube within a tube.

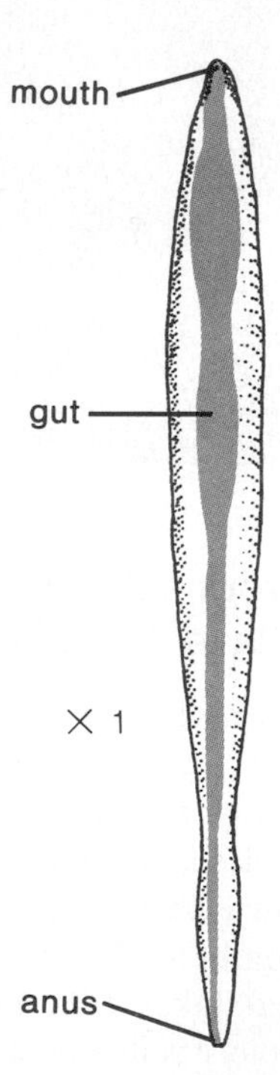

a Werner W. Schulz

b Bill Tronca/TOM STACK & ASSOCIATES

c The Miami Seaquarium, Miami, Florida

Figure 14.13 Mollusks: (a) garden snail, *Helix pomata;* (b) rock scallop, *Hinnites giganteus;* (c) octopus, *Octopus vulgaris.*

Mollusks have a soft body in which the ventral wall is modified into a head-foot region adapted for feeding, sensory reception, and locomotion (figure 14.14). They have a circulatory system and structures specialized for gas exchange. Their most distinctive characteristic, however, is the **mantle** (MANT ul), a modified body wall that forms a cavity and encloses the internal organs. The mantle and mantle cavity play many roles in the life of a mollusk. The mantle secretes the shell and forms its lining. It may be modified into gills or other structures. Muscular pumping of the mantle maintains a current of water that brings in food and oxygen and carries out wastes. The jet propulsion of squids and octopuses is created by the mantle and its cavity. Many mollusks protect themselves by withdrawing the head or foot into the cavity, which is surrounded by the shell.

Figure 14.14 Molluscan body plan.

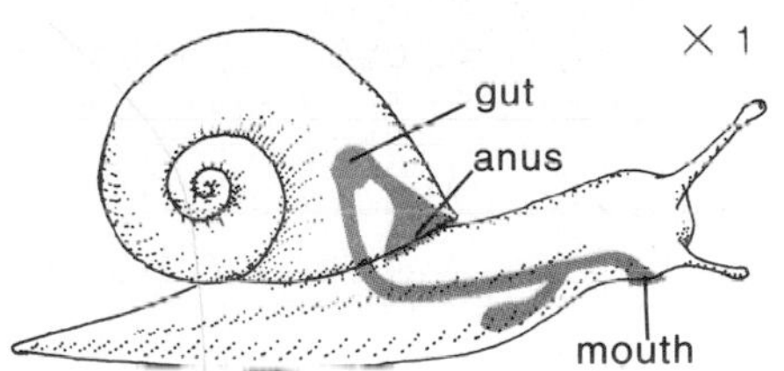

14.7 Annelids and Arthropods Have Segmented Bodies

[AN eh lidz] [uh NEL in duh]

The basic adaptive feature of annelids (Phylum Annelida) is their segmentation. The annelid body is a series of ringlike compartments, each similar to the next. Many internal body organs are repeated in one compartment after another. The fluid-filled body cavity also is segmented. That provides a powerful aid to burrowing and swimming, as muscles contract against the fluid pressure in each segment.

Figure 14.15 Annelids: (a) night crawler, *Lumbricus;* (b) marine annelid, *Sabellastarte;* (c) leech, *Placobdella.*

a BSCS by Carlye Calvin

b Brian Parker/TOM STACK & ASSOCIATES

c John D. Cunningham/VISUALS UNLIMITED

Although earthworms are more familiar, most annelids are aquatic. Marine annelids are an abundant and diverse group and are very important in food chains. They live under rocks or in coral crevices, burrow in sand or mud, or secrete tubes from which they extend feathery tentacles for feeding. Worm burrows are known from the Precambrian period. Leeches have several adaptations related to predation and bloodsucking. Those include suckers, cutting jaws, and the production of anticoagulants.

Arthropods (Phylum Arthropoda) are the most numerous animals on earth, comprising more than three-quarters of all species. They are abundant in every kind of habitat, have a wide variety of feeding habits, and are uniquely able to adapt to changing conditions. Those characteristics have contributed to their great evolutionary success.

Arthropods have segmented bodies usually made of two or three distinct parts: a head, thorax (chest), and abdomen. Many of the segments have a pair of jointed appendages, an adaptation that ensures efficient locomotion. Appendages often are modified for specialized functions such as food getting, sensory reception, or swimming. The basic arthropod body plan is shown in figure 14.16.

[AR throh podz] [ar THROH puh duh]

Figure 14.16 Arthropod body plan. Note the appendages.

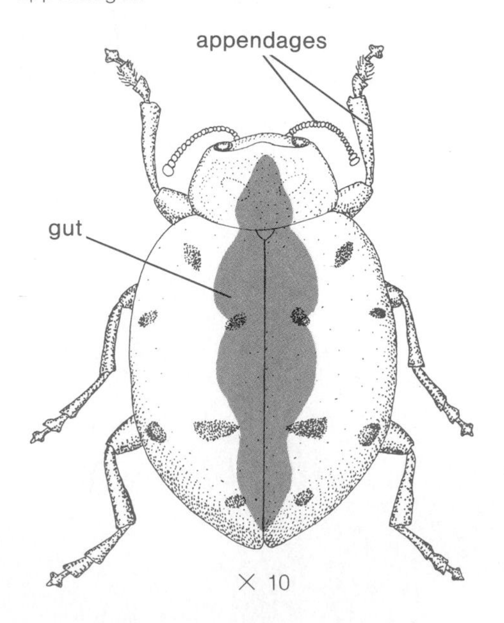

Figure 14.17 Chelicerates: (a) horseshoe crab, *Limulus polyphemus;* (b) crab spider, *Xysitcus;* (c) harvestman; (d) scorpion, *Hadrurus arizonensis;* (e) water mite, *Hydracarina.*

a Milton H. Tierney, Jr / VISUALS UNLIMITED

b Rod Planck / TOM STACK & ASSOCIATES

c BSCS by Carlye Calvin

d C. Allan Morgan

e John Shaw / TOM STACK & ASSOCIATES

There are two major groups of living arthropods. (An extinct group, the trilobites (figure 21.8, page 761), form an important part of the fossil record.)

Chelicerates include horseshoe crabs, spiders, harvestmen, scorpions, and ticks and mites. Their first two body parts are joined to form a head-thorax. They have four pairs of legs and two pairs of chelicerae, appendages adapted for feeding. Spiders are the most familiar chelicerates. Most spiders make webs, and all have poison glands, which they use to kill their prey. Only a few, however, are dangerous to humans. Many ticks and mites transmit parasites that cause serious diseases such as Rocky Mountain spotted fever.

[cheh LIH seh rayts]

Mandibulates include the crustaceans, millipedes and centipedes, and the insects. Most have three distinct body parts, and jawlike appendages, mandibulae, adapted for food-getting. The crustaceans are mostly aquatic, and many of their appendages have been adapted for swimming. They breathe by means of gills and have two pairs of antennae or "feelers." Lobsters, crabs, and shrimp are probably familiar, but most

[man DIB yoo layts]

[krus TAY shuns]

Figure 14.18 Crustaceans: (a) spiny lobster, *Panulirus argus;* (b) cyclops (with egg sacs), *Cyclops varicans;* (c) sow bug, *Oniscus*.

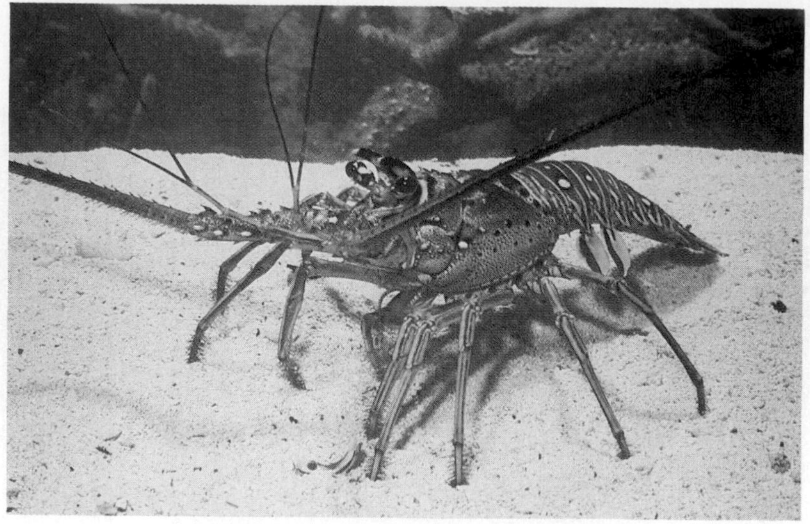

a The Miami Seaquarium, Miami, Florida

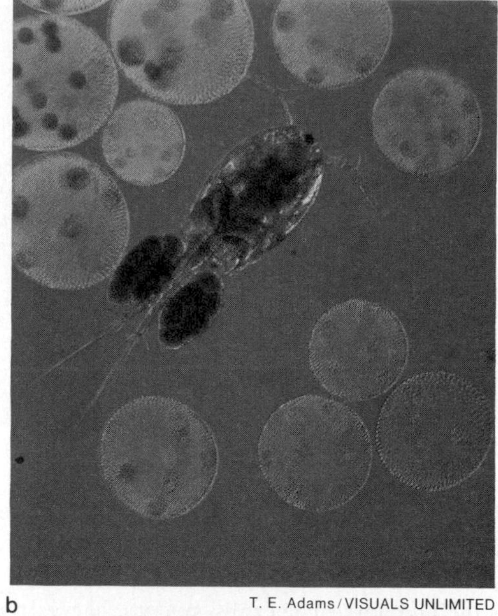

b T. E. Adams / VISUALS UNLIMITED

c C. Allan Morgan

Figure 14.19 Insects: (a) crane fly, Tipulidae; (b) giant hunting ant, *Dinoponera grandis;* (c) buckeye butterfly, *Precis lavinia coenia;* (d) leafhopper, *Graphocephala coccinea,* (e) stag beetle, Lucanidae.

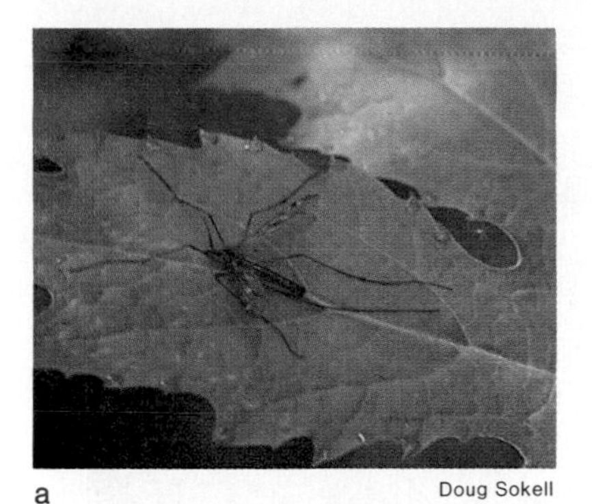
a Doug Sokell

b George D. Dodge/TOM STACK & ASSOCIATES

c Werner W. Schulz

d Rod Planck/TOM STACK & ASSOCIATES

e George D. Dodge & Dale R. Thompson/TOM STACK & ASSOCIATES

crustaceans are small or microscopic animals that exist in huge numbers in all bodies of water. In the ocean those crustaceans are the basic food supply for many animals, from tiny fishes to giant whales. Although they are primarily an aquatic group, a number of crustaceans have adapted to a life on land. Sow bugs and pill bugs are common in moist places and under rocks.

Insects are the most numerous and diverse arthropods. There are perhaps a million species, and about a billion individual insects for every human on earth. Insects have three body parts, one pair of antennae on the head, and three pairs of legs on the thorax. The abdomen usually is clearly segmented. Most adult insects have one or two pairs of wings attached to the thorax. Many insects undergo **metamorphosis** (met uh MOR phuh sis), a change in body form and in the function of many body parts that occurs during development (figure 14.21). The immature, or **larva** (LAR vuh), stage is generally a "feeding machine" such as a caterpillar that may do great damage to crops and ornamental plants. Adults often live only long enough to mate and lay eggs. Insects have adapted to all major terrestrial habitats.

Figure 14.20 The immensity of the class insecta might even be a topic of discussion at some cocktail parties.

THE FAR SIDE By GARY LARSON

7-4 © 1986 Universal Press Syndicate

"Think about it, Ed. ... The class Insecta contains 26 orders, almost 1,000 families, and over 750,000 described species — but I can't shake the feeling we're all just a bunch of bugs."

Figure 14.21 The life cycle of the Cecropia moth, or American silkworm. An egg develops into a small caterpillar in 10 days. The caterpillar, or larva, eats leaves, molts four times and grows up to 10 cm in length in several weeks. It then spins a cocoon around itself, and the pupa develops within the cocoon. The adult moth emerges in the spring.

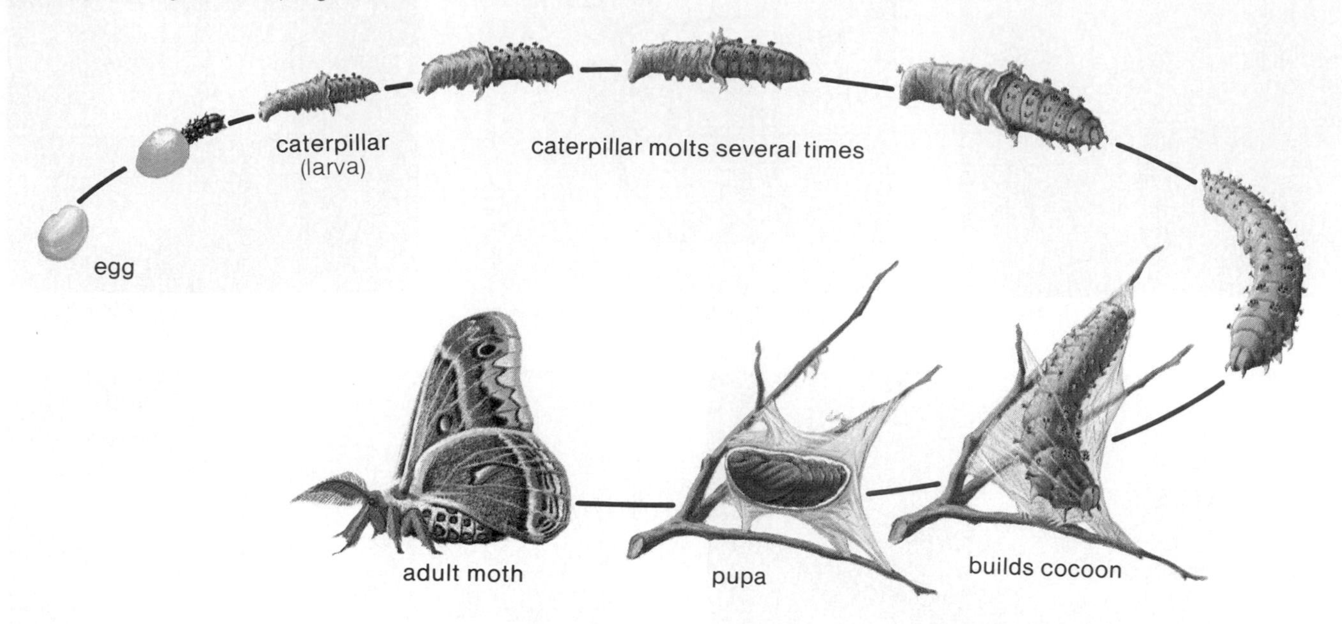

14.8 Chordates Have Internal Skeletons and Well-Developed Brains

At some time in their lives, all chordates (Phylum Chordata) possess paired gill slits, a dorsal, tubular, nerve cord, and a **notochord** (NOH toh kord)—a flexible, rodlike structure that extends the length of the body. In vertebrates, the notochord is replaced by a backbone made up of pieces called **vertebrae** (VER teh bray) that surround the nerve cord. Vertebrates also have paired appendages such as legs, wings, and fins. Their well-developed brain is adapted to provide good coordination. The organs and systems of chordates share a basic unity of plan. Ecologically, they are highly adaptable and are able to occupy most kinds of habitat.

Cartilaginous fishes have an internal skeleton made up entirely of **cartilage** rather than of bone. Cartilage is the substance that gives shape to your ears and nose. It is stiff enough to give support but more flexible than bone. Most cartilaginous fishes lack a flap over the gill slits. The class includes sharks and rays. The rays have oddly flattened bodies adapted to feeding on the sea bottom.

Bony fishes have skeletons made of the hard substance we call bone, and they have an outer covering of scales. Almost all fishes obtain their oxygen through covered gills, although air-breathing lungfishes have evolved lungs for gas exchange. Among bony fishes there is great diversity that involves structural adaptation to many aquatic ecosystems. In fact, of all the vertebrate classes, this one has the most species, and the bony fishes occupy almost all the waters of the earth.

Figure 14.22 Cartilaginous fishes: (a) nurse shark, *Ginglymostoma cirratum*, (b) sting ray, *Dasyatis americana*.

a Dave Woodward

b Dave Woodward

Figure 14.23 Bony fishes: (a) queen angelfish, *Pomacanthus;* (b) muskellunge, *Esox*.

a 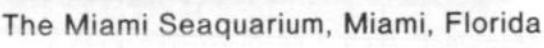

The Miami Seaquarium, Miami, Florida

b P. Ceisel/VISUALS UNLIMITED

Amphibians generally live on land as adults, but return to water to reproduce. They include frogs, toads, and salamanders. Their eggs are laid in water, where the young develop. Biologists think that amphibians evolved from air-breathing lungfishes. Amphibian limbs, which are not very efficient, evolved from the lobed fins of the lungfishes.

Reptiles are completely terrestrial animals. Their embryos develop in eggs with leathery shells that are laid on land. An outer covering of scales prevents excessive water loss in a land environment. They breathe by means of lungs all their lives. Reptiles are thought to be the ancestors of birds and mammals.

All birds have feathers, and all animals with feathers are birds. No other class of animals is so easy to characterize. All birds have wings, too, though not all can fly. Flight gives birds the greatest motility of any animal. In addition, all birds hatch from eggs that have hard shells. Birds differ from most other chordates in having a nearly constant body temperature, an adaptation that enables them to maintain a high rate of metabolism at all times.

Figure 14.24 Amphibians: (a) leopard frog, *Rana pipiens;* (b) newt, *Pseudotriton ruber.*

a John Shaw/TOM STACK & ASSOCIATES

b David M. Dennis/TOM STACK & ASSOCIATES

Figure 14.25 Reptiles: (a) Western long-nosed snake, *Rhinocheitus lecontei lecontei;* (b) iguana lizard, Iguanidae.

a C. Allan Morgan

b BSCS by Carlye Calvin

There are many structural adaptations in both the feathers and the wings of birds. Feathers form the soft down of ducks, the long beautiful plumes of ostriches, and the waterproof coat of penguins. Penguins never fly, but they use their short, broad wings for swimming. Albatrosses, which have long, slim wings, spend almost all their lives gliding on air currents. Modification of structures such as feet and beaks has been important in the adaptation of birds to many kinds of ecosystems.

From a tiny shrew, which measures about 15 cm, to a giant blue whale 30 m long (the largest animal that has ever lived), all mammals share two characteristics. First, all have hair. It is sometimes not very evident, and in some whales it is completely absent after birth. Second, all species of mammals feed their young with milk, a fluid secreted from mammary glands in the skin. That adaptation allows a long period of development under parental care and increases the chances of survival of the young. Further, mammals maintain constant temperature regardless of the environmental temperature, a characteristic they share with birds.

Figure 14.26 Birds: (a) downy woodpecker, *Dendrocopus pubescens;* (b) red-shouldered hawk, *Buteo lineatus;* (c) Canada warbler, *Wilsonia canadensis;* (d) pelican, *Pelecanus occidentalis carolinensis.*

a Tom J. Ulrich/VISUALS UNLIMITED

b Doug Sokell

c Robert C. Simpson/TOM STACK & ASSOCIATES

d Doug Sokell

Although they have many characteristics in common, mammals show great diversity in size, structure, and color. Much of that diversity comes from modifications for motility and for eating different prey. Those modifications have adapted mammals to function in a variety of specific ecological niches. Mammals today belong to three major groups. Monotremes lay eggs. Marsupials have pouches in which the young develop. Placentals have special internal structures that nourish the young until birth.

Figure 14.27 Mammals: (a) lion, *Felis, leo;* (b) buffalo, *Bison bison;* (c) northern sea lion, *Eumetopias jubata;* (d) porpoise, *Tursiops;* (e) red kangaroo, *Megaleia rufa;* (f) raccoon, *Procyon lotor.*

Self-Review

1. What characteristics do sponges and coelenterates share, and how are they different?
2. What adaptations of evolutionary significance are shown by flatworms? By roundworms? By annelids?
3. What is the distinctive structure of mollusks and what functions does it perform?
4. Describe characteristics that distinguish a spider, a crustacean, and an insect.
5. What characteristics distinguish chordates from other phyla?
6. What structural adaptations distinguish the vertebrate classes?

Investigation 14.2 DIVERSITY IN ANIMALS: A COMPARATIVE STUDY

Introduction

This investigation will provide you with an opportunity to sharpen your skills of observation.

Materials (per class)

pencils
paper
materials supplied by your teacher

Procedure

Make an enlarged copy of the table below. It should extend across 2 facing pages in your data book. Each of the 13 spaces should allow for several lines of writing.

Characteristics	Hydra	Planaria	Earthworm	Crayfish	Frog
1					
2					
3					
13					

In the Characteristics column, copy the italicized key words for each of the following questions. (If more than 1 question follows a number, copy only the first.) The 13th space is for any additional observations you may make.

1. What do you think is the *habitat* of the animal? Does it live in water, on land, or in both places?
2. Is *body symmetry* radial or bilateral?

3. Does the animal have a *skeleton?* If it has, is it an *endoskeleton* or an *exoskeleton?*
4. Is the animal's body *segmented* or is it *unsegmented?*
5. Which kind of *gut* does the animal have, an alimentary canal or a digestive sac?
6. Does it have *paired appendages?*
7. How does the animal *obtain oxygen?* (Through lungs, gills, skin, or a combination of these?)
8. Are there any *sense organs* visible? If so, what kinds are they, and where are they located?
9. How does the animal *move* from one place to another?
10. Does it make any kind of *movement* while it remains more or less in one spot?
11. How does the animal *capture* and take in *food?*
12. How does it *react* when touched lightly with a dissecting needle or a small watercolor-type brush?

All the specimens for 1 species of animal and the materials and equipment needed for observing them are arranged at 1 station. Each team will have a turn at each station.

Following are directions for observing each species. Some will help you make the observations needed to answer the questions. Some will direct your attention to additional observations that you should record in the 13th space of your table. You may find some observations impossible to make. Therefore, you may have blank spaces on your table. Do the best you can. Remember that you are recording *your observations,* not what you have read or heard about the organism.

Station 1. Observing Hydras

(a) Observe food capture and feeding in hydras under a stereomicroscope or hand lens. Place a single hydra in a small watch glass with some of the same water in which it has been living. Wait until the animal attaches itself to the dish and expands its tentacles. Then slowly add a few drops of a *Daphnia* culture.
(b) Observe the hydra's reactions when it is gently touched with the watercolor brush.
(c) Examine a prepared slide of a longitudinal section of hydra under a monocular microscope. Try to determine the presence or absence of a skeleton and of an alimentary canal.

Station 2. Observing Planarians

(a) Use a stereomicroscope or hand lens. Place 1 or 2 planarians in a small watch glass that contains pond or aquarium water. Add a small piece of freshly cut raw liver. Record your observations.
(b) Use a monocular microscope to examine cross sections of planarian. Examine whole mounts with a stereomicroscope. Determine the presence or absence of skeleton and alimentary canal.

Station 3. Observing Earthworms

(a) Pick up a live earthworm and hold it gently between your thumb and forefinger. Observe its movements. Are there any regions on the body surface that feel rough? If so, examine them with a hand lens and record your observations.
(b) Watch a worm crawl about on the slightly moistened tabletop until you determine which is its anterior end. Use a hand lens to examine both ends of the animal. How do its anterior and posterior ends differ in structure?
(c) Place an earthworm on some loose soil and observe its movements as it burrows.
(d) Using a monocular microscope, examine cross sections of the body under low power and high power. Try to determine whether it has a skeleton.

Station 4. Observing Crayfish

(a) Observe the movements of the appendages and the pattern of locomotion of a live crayfish in an aquarium. Observe the antennae. Touch them gently with the watercolor brush. Note the animal's reaction.
(b) Put a small piece of liver in a dish with the crayfish. Observe how the crayfish eats.

Station 5. Observing Frogs

(a) Examine the prepared skeleton of a frog. Compare it with a dissected preserved specimen. Determine the position of muscles and other soft tissues in relation to the bones.
(b) Study the breathing movements of a live frog that is not moving about. To do this, observe from the side with your eyes at the level of the animal.
(c) Observe the movements of a frog swimming in an aquarium. How do these movements compare with those of a frog hopping and moving about on a laboratory table? Your teacher will show you how to catch and hold a frog without injuring it.
(d) If a hungry frog is available, your teacher may be able to show you how it captures food.

Discussion

When you have completed your observations and recorded the data, review what you have learned about each of the items in the table. By reading across the table, you should be able to compare and contrast the characteristics of the 5 animals you have studied.

For each animal, select 5 functions that it performs as part of its way of life. Describe how, in each case, its structure enables it to perform these functions.

Guidepost: What adaptations enable animals to perform the basic functions of life?

Life Functions in Animals

14.9 Digestion May Be Intracellular or Extracellular

Animals have evolved a variety of mechanisms for food-getting. Sponges demonstrate a rather primitive method. Individual cells with a single flagellum keep a current of water moving through the sponge. When a food particle comes by, a cell may engulf it and draw it into a vacuole, just as a *Paramecium* does. The process of taking food particles into a body cavity is called **ingestion** (in JES chun).

Most aquatic and land animals, however, actively pursue their food and have means to capture it. Some predators poison their prey. For example, the tentacles of a coelenterate have stinging capsules. Each capsule contains a long, coiled, hollow thread with barbs near its base. When a food organism brushes one of the tentacles, the thread is shot out with such force that it pierces the body of the victim. A paralyzing poison is injected into the prey, which is then drawn into the coelenterate's body cavity by the tentacles.

A leech has another way of obtaining food. It attaches itself to its victim by means of a posterior sucker. It makes a wound with its three-toothed jaw and sucks the victim's blood. Many arthropods also use liquid nutrients as a food source.

Among vertebrates, jaws, beaks, and teeth are structures that aid food-getting. There are many adaptations of those structures. For example, a snake can unhook its lower jaw from its upper jaw and move the two independently. Those adaptations permit a snake to swallow prey that is larger than its own head.

Ingested food enters a digestive cavity inside an animal's body. There are three types of digestive cavities: vacuoles within individual cells; sacs; and tubular alimentary canals. These are diagrammed in figure 14.28.

Figure 14.28 Kinds of digestive cavities: (a) intracellular (vacuole) in a cell of a sponge; (b) extracellular with one opening (sac) in a hydra; (c) extracellular with two openings (alimentary canal) in a roundworm.

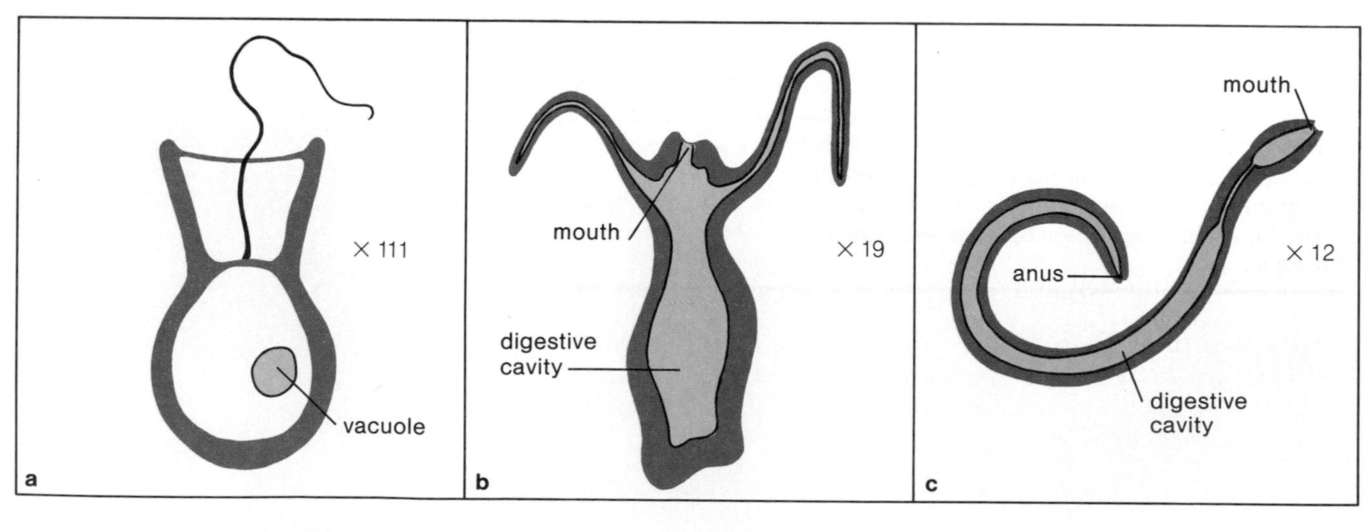

Only relatively small molecules can pass through plasma membranes. However, most nutrient particles that animals ingest are not molecular size. Even the microscopic particles that sponges take in are much too large to pass directly into cells. Food that is ingested by animals must be broken down into small molecules. The processes of that breakdown are known collectively as **digestion.**

The breakdown of large pieces of food into smaller ones is the physical part of digestion. Most mammals have teeth that cut or grind food into smaller pieces. In many animals, however, movements of the digestive cavity break down food. The gizzard of a bird, for example, is a specialized part of the stomach that grinds up food (figure 14.29). Some birds swallow sand and small pebbles, which aid the grinding.

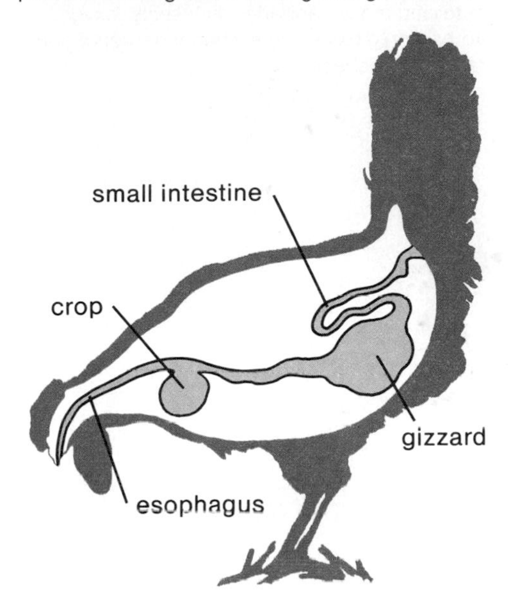

Figure 14.29 Alimentary canal of a bird. Food is swallowed without being chewed and is stored temporarily in the crop. Sand and small pebbles in the gizzard aid in grinding the food.

Physical digestion, such as chewing, increases the surface area of the food. Increased surface area means that the chemical part of digestion can take place more quickly. Here enzymes take over the breakdown of food. The chemical part of digestion is similar in all animals, and we will examine the process in the human animal in chapter 15.

In sponges and to some extent in coelenterates and flatworms, chemical digestion takes place in a vacuole inside a cell. That is **intracellular** (in truh SEL yoo ler) digestion. The vacuole is formed when a food particle is surrounded by a section of plasma membrane. A plasma membrane, however, is made up of lipids and proteins, the same substances that make up foods. Why is the cell itself not digested? Saclike bodies called lysosomes contain the digestive enzymes but are not digested by them. A lysosome fuses with a vacuole, and chemical digestion occurs within that new structure. Small molecules produced by chemical digestion pass out of the vacuole into the cell's cytoplasm. Only then can the nutrients be used by the cell.

In most animals digestion takes place in an **extracellular** (ek struh SEL yoo ler) space. Enzymes are secreted from cells into a digestive cavity. There is great variation in the form and complexity of digestive systems. In the digestive sac of a coelenterate, some of the cells lining the cavity secrete enzymes. In the simple gut of a roundworm, all digestive enzymes are produced by cells in the lining. In most animals, however, digestive enzymes are secreted by tissues specialized as glands. Some herbivorous vertebrates, such as cows, have special chambers (rumens) that contain cellulose-digesting microorganisms and, thus, are able to utilize fibers.

Small food molecules are absorbed from the gut into an animal's cells. The rate of absorption depends on the surface area of the gut lining. The greater the surface area, the faster is the rate. The lining of the gut has many folds, an adaptation that increases surface area.

14.10 Animals Use a Variety of Methods for Gas Exchange and Transport

Animal cells depend on cellular respiration to release energy for living. Therefore, they must be able to obtain oxygen and transport it to all their cells. They also must be able to rid themselves of carbon dioxide, the waste product of respiration.

Figure 14.30 (a) Gas exchange in hydra. (b) Gas exchange in fishes and insects. Gills are made of thin filaments richly supplied with blood vessels. Each filament is made of delicate plates containing many capillaries. In insects, oxygen and carbon dioxide are exchanged through the branching tracheae.

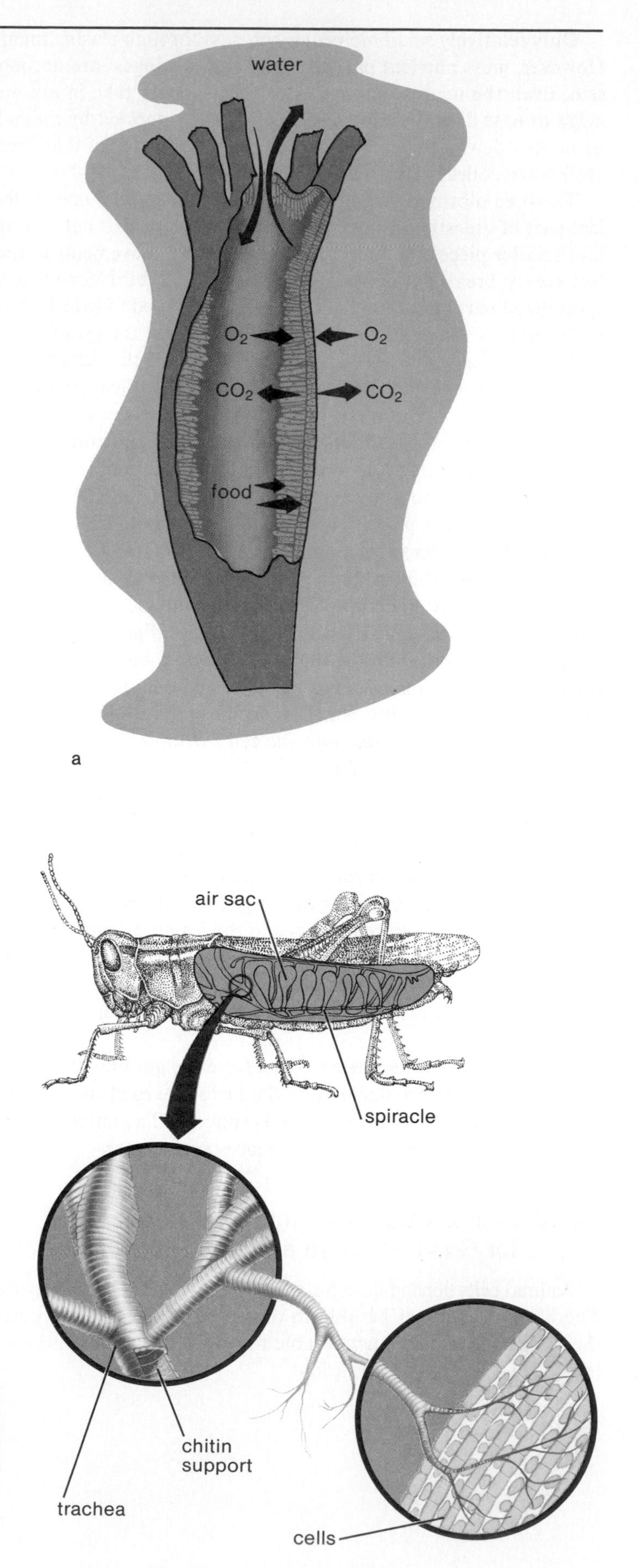

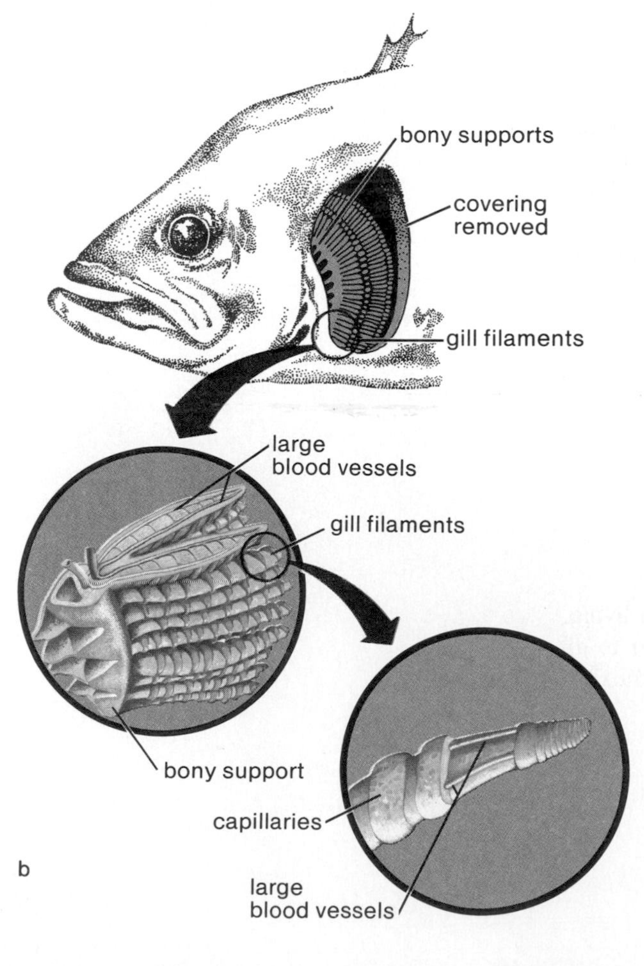

In small animals, such as hydras, gas exchange occurs entirely through the body wall. The body surface is large compared with the volume of living substance. That means that the surface area is large enough to allow sufficient amounts of oxygen to enter the organism by diffusion. As body size increases, however, the ratio of surface area to volume becomes smaller. In general, large animals do not have large enough body surfaces to allow sufficient gas exchange. Thus, they must have organs that increase the surface area through which respiration can occur.

In aquatic animals such organs are usually gills. Most often they are feathery or platelike structures. Dissolved oxygen diffuses in and carbon dioxide diffuses out through the gill cells. Gills are remarkably similar in a wide variety of animals.

Terrestrial animals lose a great deal of water through their respiratory organs, because water can diffuse through any surface that permits diffusion of respiratory gases. Also, cell surfaces must be kept moist so gases can diffuse through them. For that reason, terrestrial animals that breathe through gills (sow bugs, for example) must live in places where air is moist and evaporation is slow. That also is true of land animals that take in oxygen through their body surfaces (slugs, earthworms, and frogs, for example).

Many terrestrial animals live where the air is dry. They need an extensive surface *inside* the body where air can be kept moist. There are two principal ways of meeting that requirement. In insects and some other arthropods, a complicated system of air tubes extends to all parts of the body. The tubes carry oxygen directly to most cells. Body movements help move air through the tube system. In air-breathing vertebrates, air passes into lungs. Lungs are divided into such a large number of tiny air sacs that they appear spongy (see figure 16.19, page 592). Respiratory gases diffuse through the enormous moist surface area provided by those sacs.

In a single-celled organism, movement of the cytoplasm provides an adequate transportation system. In some multicellular organisms such as sponges and coelenterates, almost every cell has part of its surface exposed to the environment. Each cell can obtain its own oxygen and get rid of its own wastes. All cells may not take in food, but no cell is very far from others that do. Diffusion and active transport are sufficient to move substances into cells.

A similar situation exists in free-living flatworms. In roundworms, however, there is a fluid-filled body cavity surrounding the digestive tube. As the roundworm wriggles, the fluid is squeezed about from one place to another. In that way substances dissolved in the fluid are carried to and from the body cells.

Most animals that have body fluid have a circulatory system. Such a system includes a pump and a series of tubes through which nutrients can be delivered and waste products removed from the cells. In arthropods and most mollusks blood is pumped through blood vessels that empty into body spaces. The blood moves about sluggishly through those spaces in contact with the tissues. Eventually it gets back into another set of vessels, which carries it back to the pumping point. Such an incomplete vascular system is called an open circulatory system.

Figure 14.31 Diagrams of fluid transport in four invertebrate animals.

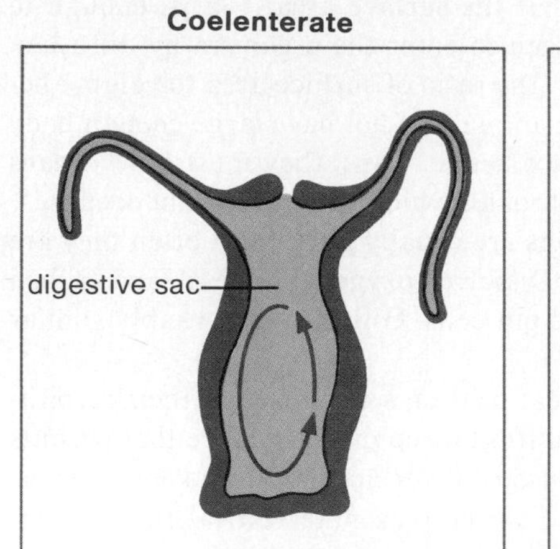

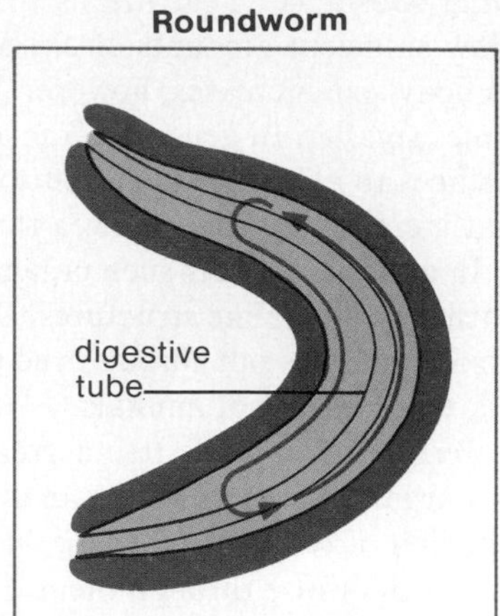

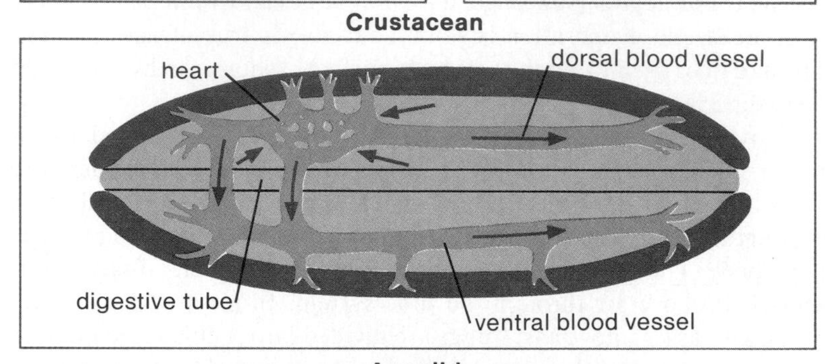

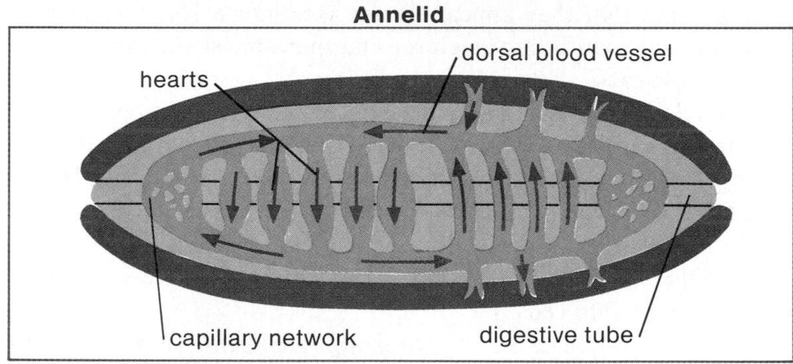

Annelids, on the other hand, have a closed circulatory system, which you can study in investigation 14.3. In that system blood flows within vessels through all of its course. An earthworm has a system with five pairs of hearts and a complex set of finely branched vessels. Those vessels eventually empty into a large dorsal vessel, whch returns the blood to the hearts. Valves in the dorsal vessel keep the blood flowing in only one direction through the system. Vertebrates, including humans, also have a closed circulatory system.

Investigation 14.3 TEMPERATURE AND CIRCULATION

Introduction

The function of the circulatory system of a multicellular animal is affected by many environmental factors. You probably could suggest several hypotheses about the effect of temperature on the rate at which the system pumps blood. How would increasing temperatures affect the rate at which an animal's heart beats? In this investigation you will discover the effects of environmental temperature on the pulse rate of the dorsal blood vessel of an earthworm. In doing so, you also will develop skills in using the inquiry process.

Materials (per team)

large earthworm
thermometer
clean, chemical-free dissecting tray
tap water
paper towels
warm water bath
clock for timing

Procedure

1. Place an earthworm into the pan dorsal side up. The dorsal side will be much darker and rounder than the ventral side.
2. Moisten the earthworm with a few drops of water. Place a damp piece of paper towel gently over the head region, and the worm will wiggle and move very little. Touch the worm as little as possible.
3. Locate the dorsal blood vessel running directly down the center of the dorsal surface. Find the part of the vessel where you can most easily see the actual pulsing of the vessel. Make a trial count of the number of beats in 1 minute.
4. Construct a hypothesis about the effects of various temperatures on the pulse rate of a worm's dorsal blood vessel. Record this hypothesis in your data book.
5. You will expose the worm to 5 different temperatures from nearly freezing (ice water) to uncomfortably warm but not hot. (The worm will die at temperatures greater than 45° C.)
6. Add just enough ice water to the tray to submerge your worm (approximately 1 cm).
7. Lay the thermometer in the pan so that the bulb is submerged.
8. Wait 3 minutes to allow the worm to adjust to the temperature.
9. Read the temperature of the water and immediately begin counting the pulse rate for 1 minute. Record the beat rate/min and the temperature in your data book.
10. Pour off the water and let the worm breathe for 2 minutes.
11. Add water that is about 10° C to the tray as in procedure 6.
12. Repeat procedures 7–10 with the 10° C water.
13. Repeat procedures 6–10 with water at or close to 20° C, 30° C, and 40° C.
14. When you are finished collecting data, return the worm to the place designated by your teacher. These worms will be retired to a nice compost pile.

Discussion

1. Graph your temperature and beat rate/min data in your data book. Remember to plot the independent variable on the horizontal axis.
2. Why is it important to wait a few minutes after adding water to the pans before counting the pulse rate?
3. Why must the water be poured off to allow the worm to breathe?
4. What would be the experimental advantage of starting either with the coldest or warmest temperatures and working gradually in the other direction instead of skipping around to different temperatures?
5. Describe any patterns revealed by the curve on your graph. Does the data support or refute your hypothesis? Explain.
6. To how many other kinds of organisms can you generalize your data?
7. What are some flaws or sources of error in the experimental procedure used here? Be very critical.
8. If you were to test your hypothesis again and had no limit on equipment or materials, how would you design the new experiment?

14.11 Excretory Systems Maintain Water Balance and Chemical Composition of Body Fluids

Waste substances are removed from cells by a process called **excretion** (ek SKREE shun). What do we mean by wastes? Some products of metabolism are poisonous, for example, ammonia, which is formed in the breakdown of proteins. Some substances, however, are toxic only if large amounts accumulate. Sodium chloride is a normal cell substance that is toxic in large amounts. Ordinarily this salt constantly diffuses into cells from the fluid surrounding them. The normal proportion of sodium chloride in cells can be maintained only by continuous excretion. In general, then, any substance can be called "waste" if an organism has too much of it.

In small aquatic animals wastes may simply diffuse out through plasma membranes. Sponges and coelenterates also excrete wastes directly through their body surfaces. That can happen because all their cells are close to a water environment. Most animals, however, have special devices for ridding their bodies of wastes.

Animal cells constantly produce water through cellular respiration. What happens to that water depends on the kind of environment in which an animal lives. For example, the cells of a jellyfish contain a mixture of substances in water. Outside the plasma membranes is another mixture—the salty seawater. Normally the concentration of water molecules inside and outside the jellyfish is almost equal. As fast as metabolic water is produced, it diffuses into the environment. That is true of many other marine invertebrates as well.

In fresh water, on the other hand, there are very few dissolved substances, and the concentration of water molecules is high. In the cells of a freshwater planarian, the concentration of dissolved substances is high, and the water concentration is low. Therefore, water is always diffusing *into* a planarian. Metabolic water is constantly added to this excess. We might expect that all this water would build up inside a cell and increase

Figure 14.32 (a) The excretory system of a planarian. A flame cell and an excretory pore are shown enlarged. Wastes and excess water removed by flame cells are eliminated through pores in the body wall. (b) Excretory tubes in the earthworm. The near side of the body, including the alimentary canal, is cut away. Most of the segments of the body have a pair of excretory tubes, one on either side. Capillaries from the circulatory system surround the excretory tubes.

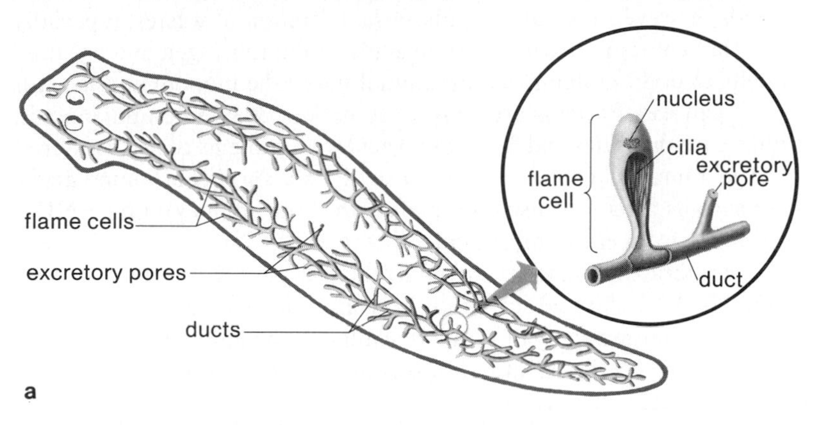

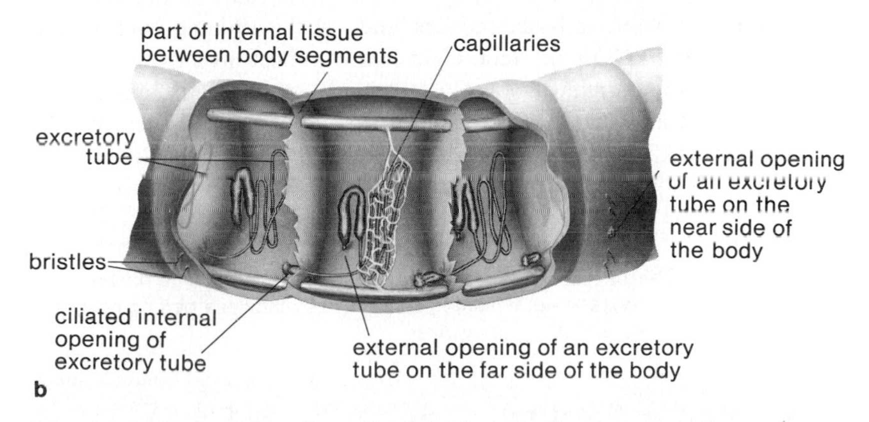

its volume. Eventually, the cell might burst unless water was somehow expelled from it. Experiments have shown that freshwater animals excrete water by active transport.

Terrestrial animals are in a similar situation. You, for example, take in a great deal of fresh water. Your cells also produce water by metabolism. As a land animal, however, your greatest danger is of drying out.

Animals maintain water balance within their cells through a variety of structures. In planarians that function is performed by a system of **flame cells,** shown in figure 14.32a. They are spread throughout the body and are connected by tubules. Each flame cell has cilia that project into a tubule. Wastes enter the flame cell. The waving action of the cilia moves fluid and wastes through the tubule. Many tubules join and eventually empty wastes into the environment through a pore. In this system there are many flame cells and many pores.

Most annelids, mollusks, and crustaceans have a different excretory system. In those animals the functional unit is a tubule leading from the body cavity to the outside (figure 14.32b). Again, there are many tubules. Wastes enter the tubules from the body cavity. Around each tubule there is a network of capillaries, and wastes from the capillaries may be added to the wastes already in the tubule. At the same time, useful materials may be absorbed back into the blood or body fluid. Each tubule leads to the outside where the wastes are emptied. In vertebrates somewhat similar tubules are found in the kidneys, as we will see in chapter 16.

Excretory organs evolved chiefly as water-regulating devices. In most animals, however, they also regulate the excretion of wastes, especially those that contain nitrogen. Amino acids contain nitrogen and are used by cells to build proteins, but an animal may take in more amino acids than it can use. Proteins are constantly broken down into amino acids. Unlike carbohydrates and fats, amino acids and proteins cannot be stored in large amounts. Therefore, there usually is a surplus of amino acids. That surplus cannot be used for energy until the amino group ($-NH_2$) is removed from each amino acid.

In vertebrates, amino groups are removed mainly in the liver. Ammonia (NH_3) is formed in the process. It is quite toxic but also quite soluble. If a large supply of water is available, the ammonia can be carried out of the body in solution. In freshwater fishes, nitrogenous wastes may be excreted through the gills.

In other vertebrates the kidneys are the main route for excretion of nitrogenous wastes. In birds, reptiles, and insects, amino groups are excreted as **uric** (YOOR ik) **acid.** Uric acid is almost insoluble and is excreted with only a small loss of water. In most adult amphibians and mammals, amino groups are converted to a waste called **urea.** Unlike uric acid, urea is soluble. It diffuses into the blood, from which it is removed by the kidneys. It is then excreted in solution in the urine.

Figure 14.33 The insoluble nitrogenous wastes (uric acid) of these brown pelicans paint the rocks white. In some places where many sea birds gather, the wastes are collected and used as fertilizer.

Staley Studio

14.12 Nervous Systems Enable an Animal to Respond to Stimuli and to Coordinate Activities of the Other Systems

In general, the rapid adjustments characteristic of animals are brought about by nervous systems. Although sponges have no nervous systems, they still are able to adjust to changes in their environment, or **stimuli** (STIM yoo ly).

Coelenterates have nerve cells, some of which are specialized to receive only certain stimuli. The nerve cells are connected in a network that permits simple coordinated responses.

Flatworms have nerve networks, but they also have a centralized system of two nerve cords that extend along the length of the body. At the anterior end is a large mass of nerve tissue, a **ganglion** (GANG glee un). A ganglion is a center where nerve impulses are exchanged. Flatworms also have cells specialized for receiving stimuli. The eyespots of planarians are examples. Those eyespots cannot form images, but they can detect the direction and intensity of light.

Annelids have well-developed nervous systems. A main nerve cord extends along the ventral side of the body. Many ganglia occur along the nerve cord. A large ganglion, sometimes called a brain, is found at the anterior end of the body. Although earthworms have no obvious sense organs, they can detect many stimuli. Other annelids have specialized sense organs, including eyes.

Among mollusks and arthropods there is a great variety of nervous systems. All are basically of the annelid type. However, they are more numerous and varied than those of annelids.

A dorsal, tubular nerve cord, usually called a spinal cord, is a distinctive characteristic of the chordate phylum. In vertebrate chordates an anterior enlargement of this nerve cord—the brain—dominates the rest of the nervous system. Nervous systems of several animals are compared in figure 14.34.

Ability to receive and to react to stimuli from the environment is one of the basic characteristics of living things. That ability is developed to different degrees in different organisms. Most animals detect different kinds of stimuli by using specialized receptors. In humans, for example, receptors in the skin of the fingertips are sensitive to pressure but not to light. Receptors in the eyes are light sensitive, but they are not sensitive to sound waves.

In most animals some receptors are concentrated in special organs. You are well acquainted with your principal ones—eyes, ears, and nose. Other kinds of receptors, such as those sensitive to pressure, touch, cold, and heat, are distributed widely in your skin.

No organism has specialized receptors for all the stimuli in the environment. Many cave-dwelling animals have no receptors for light. You have no receptors for electromagnetic waves that carry radio and television signals. Lack of ability to detect light is ordinarily no handicap to cave-dwelling animals. However, if a cave-dwelling animal leaves its cave, its inability to see might mean disaster. You use instruments such as television that change electromagnetic waves to sound and light waves. For those you do have receptors. However, you can suffer from nuclear radiation without being aware of your exposure unless you have an instrument to detect it.

Figure 14.34 Nervous systems in five diverse kinds of animals.

Coelenterate

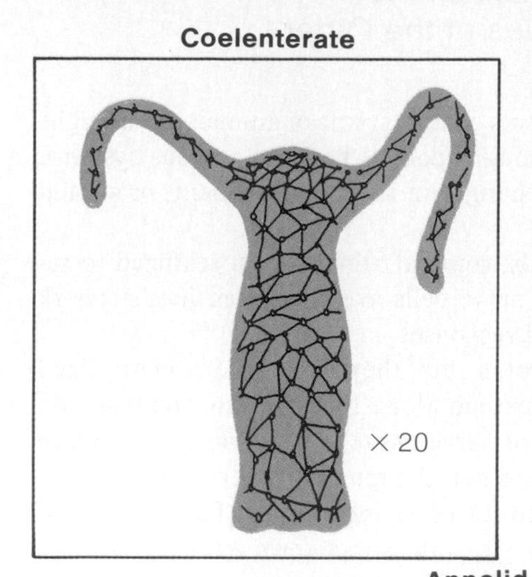

Flatworm

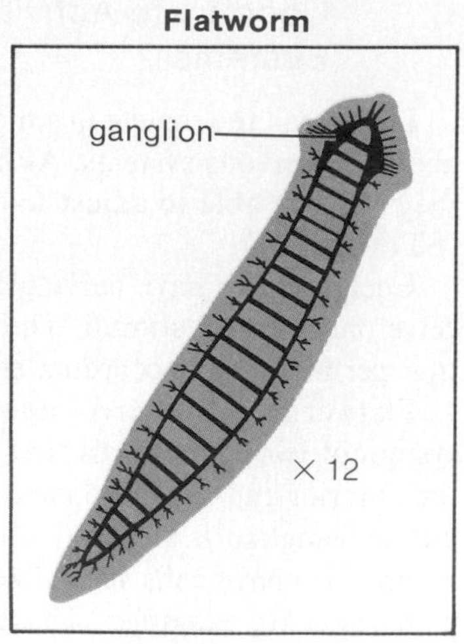

Annelid

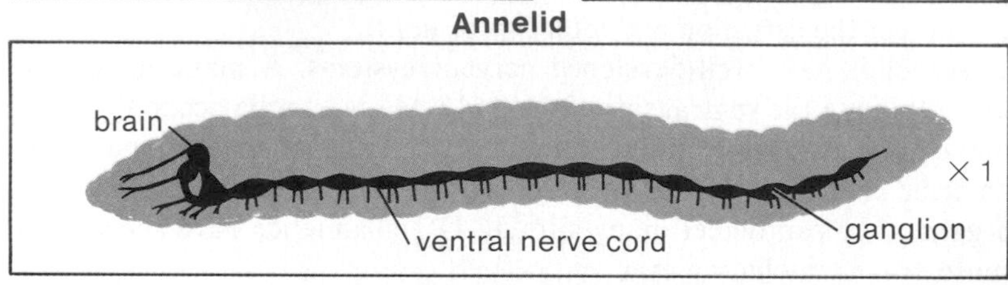

Crustacean

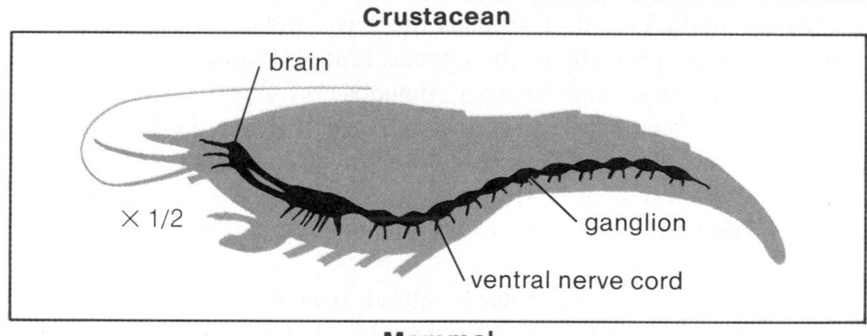

Mammal

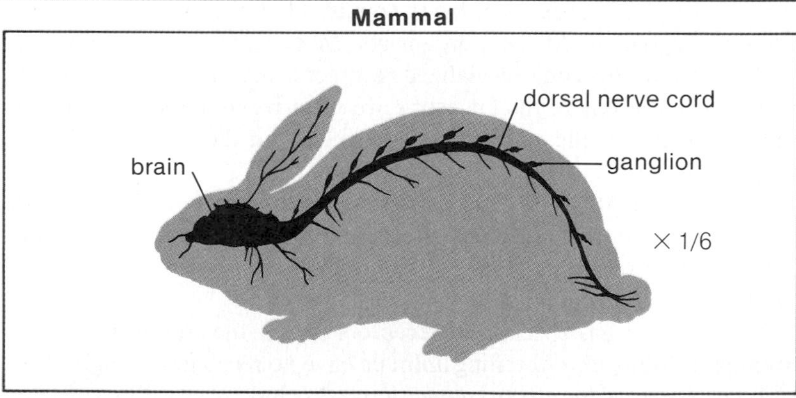

Figure 14.35 Sensory receptors are specialized to detect certain kinds of stimuli. (a) Receptors in the skin detect touch, vibration, heat, cold, and pain. (b) Rods and cones in the retina of the eye detect light. Rods detect light intensity; different cones are sensitive to the different colors of blue, green, and red.

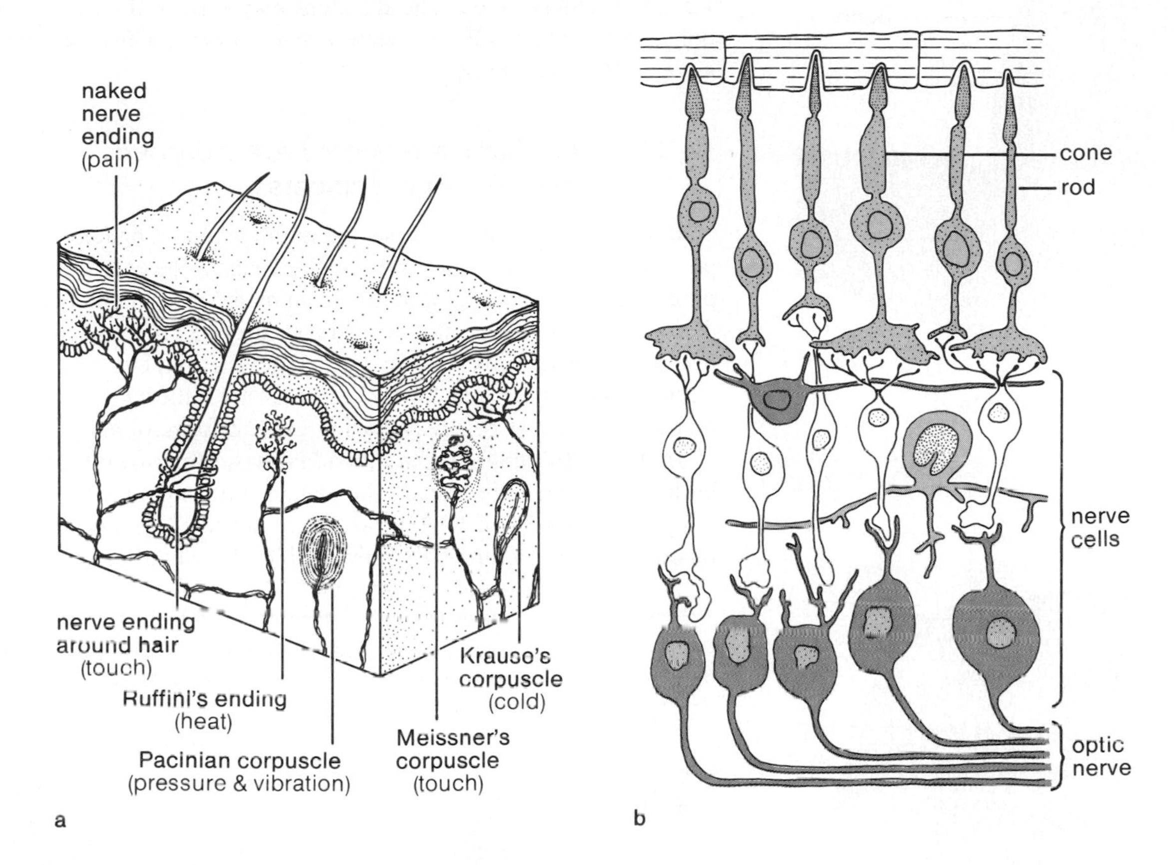

14.13 Muscles and Skeletons Provide Support and Locomotion

In animals, motion usually involves muscle cells. Sponges again are an exception. They have no muscle cells, although individual cells are capable of movement. Their larvae swim by means of cilia, just as many protists do.

Coelenterates have specialized cells that allow the animals to move their tentacles. Flatworms have cells organized into definite muscle tissues, but locomotion still is accomplished largely by cilia. In all other animal phyla, muscle tissues are organized into bundles (muscles). The muscles are controlled by nervous systems.

The skeleton of a sponge consists of small, rigid parts scattered through the soft, living tissues. Those parts support the softer tissues. The stony skeletons built up by corals support the animals and also protect them from predators. In mollusks the skeleton (shells) are chiefly protective.

Support and protection are functions of arthropod and chordate skeletons. In those phyla, skeletons also function in the movements of the animals, especially in locomotion. Arthropod skeletons are external, with the muscles attached to the inner surfaces, as shown in figure 14.36. Those **exoskeletons** (EK soh SKEL eh tunz) are composed of chitin, a tough, flexible material. In many arthropods, calcium compounds, deposited along with the chitin, make the exoskeleton hard and strong.

Figure 14.36 Relation to muscles to skeletons. Why are two muscles shown in each example?

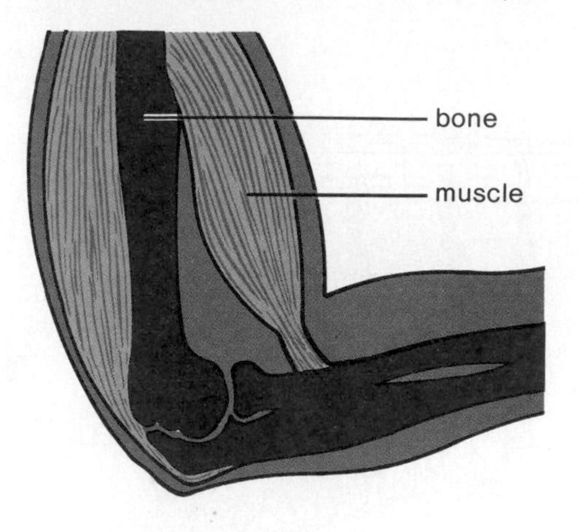

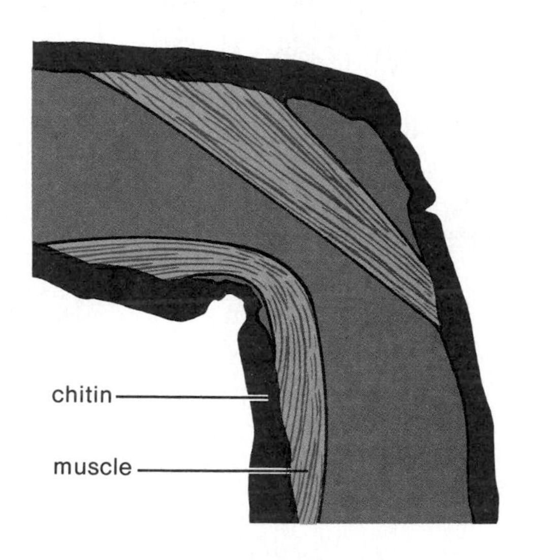

Thin flexible chitin joints permit bending. Although exoskeletons provide good support, they do not allow for growth. Arthropods must periodically shed their exoskeletons and produce new ones.

Vertebrates have **endoskeletons** (EN doh SKEL eh tunz)—skeletons inside their bodies (see figure 14.36). Muscles are attached to the outside of an endoskeleton. The skeletons may consist of either cartilage or bone; both contain cells that secrete new material. Thus the skeleton can grow as the animal does.

14.14 Reproductive Systems Are Adapted to Animals' Environments

Reproduction is primarily sexual in the animal kingdom. Even in species that have asexual methods, such as many coelenterates, sexual reproduction takes place frequently. In animals, alternation of haploid with diploid generations is unknown. In coelenterates there is an alternation of a sexual generation with an asexual generation, but both are diploid. Furthermore, male and female gametes are different in animals, and meiosis occurs just before or during gamete formation.

In most adult animals, an individual has either ovaries or testes, not both. Often that difference in the gonads is accompanied by differences in appearance (figure 14.37), behavior (figure 14.38), or other characteristics. In some animals an individual has both ovaries and testes. That

Figure 14.37 Some secondary sexual characteristics in animals. Can you think of other instances where the male and female of a species do not closely resemble each other?

Figure 14.38 Specialized behavior called courtship precedes mating in many animals.

In the breeding season the ventral surface of the male stickleback develops brilliant color that attracts the female.
× 1/2
The male fiddler crab attracts attention by waving its one large claw.
× 1
× 1/10
The male reddish egret adopts this position when courting.
Male bighorn sheep engage in butting duels.
× 1/25

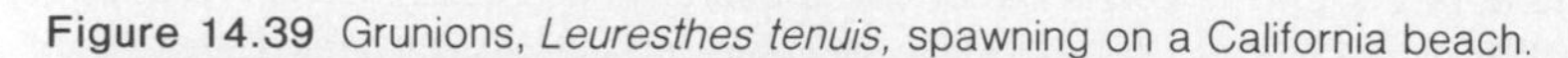

Figure 14.39 Grunions, *Leuresthes tenuis*, spawning on a California beach.

Jeff Foott/TOM STACK & ASSOCIATES

is true of many annelids, most flatworms, and some crustaceans and mollusks. An animal that has both ovaries and testes is called a **hermaphrodite** (her MAF roh dyt). Even among vertebrates, hermaphroditic individuals occasionally occur. However, they are not normal in any vertebrate species.

Sperm cells swim, and that requires a liquid. Animals that live in water can release eggs and sperm directly into their environment (figure 14.39). That is *external* fertilization. However, sperm contain only a very small amount of stored food. Hence, they can survive only a short time after being released from the male parent. Obviously, then, if a sperm is to unite with an egg, both must be released at approximately the same time and place.

In many phyla fertilization is *internal.* In that case the male places sperm directly into the body of the female. There the sperm swim through part of the female's reproductive tract. The two gametes meet at some point between the ovary and the opening to the environment. Internal fertilization is not necessary for aquatic animals, but it does occur among many crustaceans and all cartilaginous fishes. Among terrestrial animals internal fertilization is necessary because sperm cannot swim through air.

In some animals and under certain conditions, an ovum may develop into a new individual without fertilization by a sperm. Such reproduction by **parthenogenesis** (par theh noh JEN eh sis) occurs, for example, among aphids. During summer, many generations of aphids are produced in that manner. There is a problem here, because gametes are generally haploid, and fertilization is necessary to restore the diploid number of chromosomes. What happens when there are successive generations without fertilization? Usually, animals that reproduce by parthenogenesis produce diploid eggs. Therefore, offspring are diploid *without* fertilization. In some species of bees and ants, individuals produced by parthenogenesis are indeed haploid as expected. Those individuals are always male.

Coelenterates reproduce both sexually and asexually. Hydras, for example, reproduce asexually by budding (figure 14.40) through much of the year. Under certain conditions, however, they produce ovaries and testes. Most species are then hermaphroditic, an adaptation that increases the chances of fertilization in sessile or slow-moving animals. Eggs in the ovary are fertilized by sperm shed into the water.

Flatworms have a complex reproductive system. Most are hermaphroditic, but do not fertilize their own eggs. Instead, two worms exchange sperm. Free-living forms also reproduce asexually by fragmentation; even a small piece can regenerate into an entire worm. Parasitic forms such as *Schistosoma* have complex life cycles involving many larval forms and two or more hosts, as you can see in figure 14.41. Parasitic forms produce huge numbers of eggs, an adaptation that increases the chances for survival.

In roundworms, the sexes are separate, and asexual reproduction does not occur. The females may release as many as 200,000 eggs a day, and the egg cases and developing embryos can survive for many years before resuming growth. As with flatworms, parasitic forms have complex life cycles with several hosts.

Earthworms are hermaphroditic, but the ova in an individual are not fertilized by sperm of the same individual. Tubes from the ovaries lead to the surface of one segment. Those from the testes lead to the surface of an adjoining segment. Fertilization is internal. When two earthworms copulate (KOP yoo layt), or mate, sperm of one individual are deposited in a special sac of the other. Likewise, sperm from the second worm are deposited in the first. As ova move from the ovary, they pass the sperm-storage sac. Sperm are released, and the ova are fertilized.

In fishes and amphibians fertilization occurs externally, and the zygote develops in the water. Fertilization is internal in all other vertebrates. The zygote may develop in an egg laid by the female, as in birds and most reptiles, or within the body of the female, as in mammals.

Figure 14.40 A hydra can reproduce either asexually or sexually.

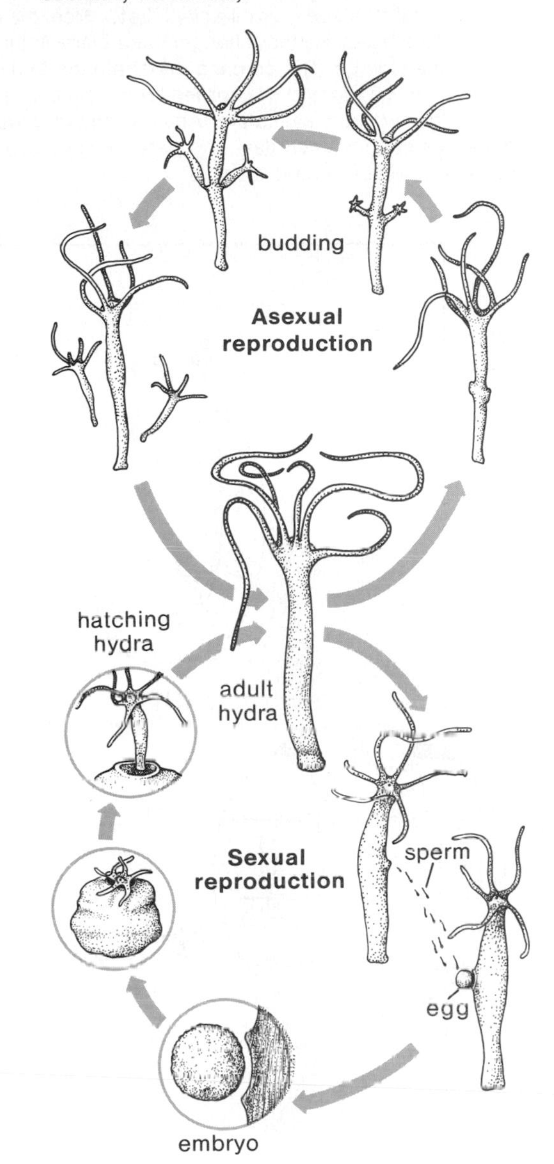

14.15 An Animal's Behavior Helps It Adapt to Its Environment

All living organisms are continually *doing* something. They respond to stimuli from their external environment. They also respond to stimuli within their bodies. Many communicate with other organisms. They feed. They reproduce. They do other things. The sum of all these activities of an organism is what biologists call behavior. Behavior is influenced by other organisms of the same kind, other organisms used as food, and other organisms that try to use *this* organism as food. Behavior also includes all the responses of an organism to things such as the changes in light, temperature, day or night, time of year, and each other characteristic of the ecosystem in which the organism lives.

For example, planarians are frequently found in wet, dark habitats under stones. If you remove one of those stones, the planarians respond to the increase in light intensity by an increase in movement. They wander from side to side as well as move forward. Eventually they come upon another dark spot and the response stops.

When a male moth emerges from its cocoon and detects the odor produced by a female of its species, it flies upwind toward the source of the odor. The first time a tree squirrel sees a nut, it tries to bury the nut, even if it has never seen another squirrel do so. Young spiders weave webs as well constructed as those of older spiders.

[shis toh SOHM uh]

Figure 14.41 Life cycle of *Schistosoma haematobium*. Adult flukes in the veins of a human host produce fertilized eggs that are expelled with the urine. In the water, the larval stages, or miracidia, hatch from the egg and infect snails, the intermediate hosts. Further changes take place in the snail, and immature worms or cercaria emerge. The cercaria penetrate the skin of a human, migrate into the small blood vessels and are carried by the circulatory system to small veins in the bladder, where they mature. Adult worms may live 30 years and produce thousands of eggs each day. This parasite is widespread in many parts of the world and causes serious disease.

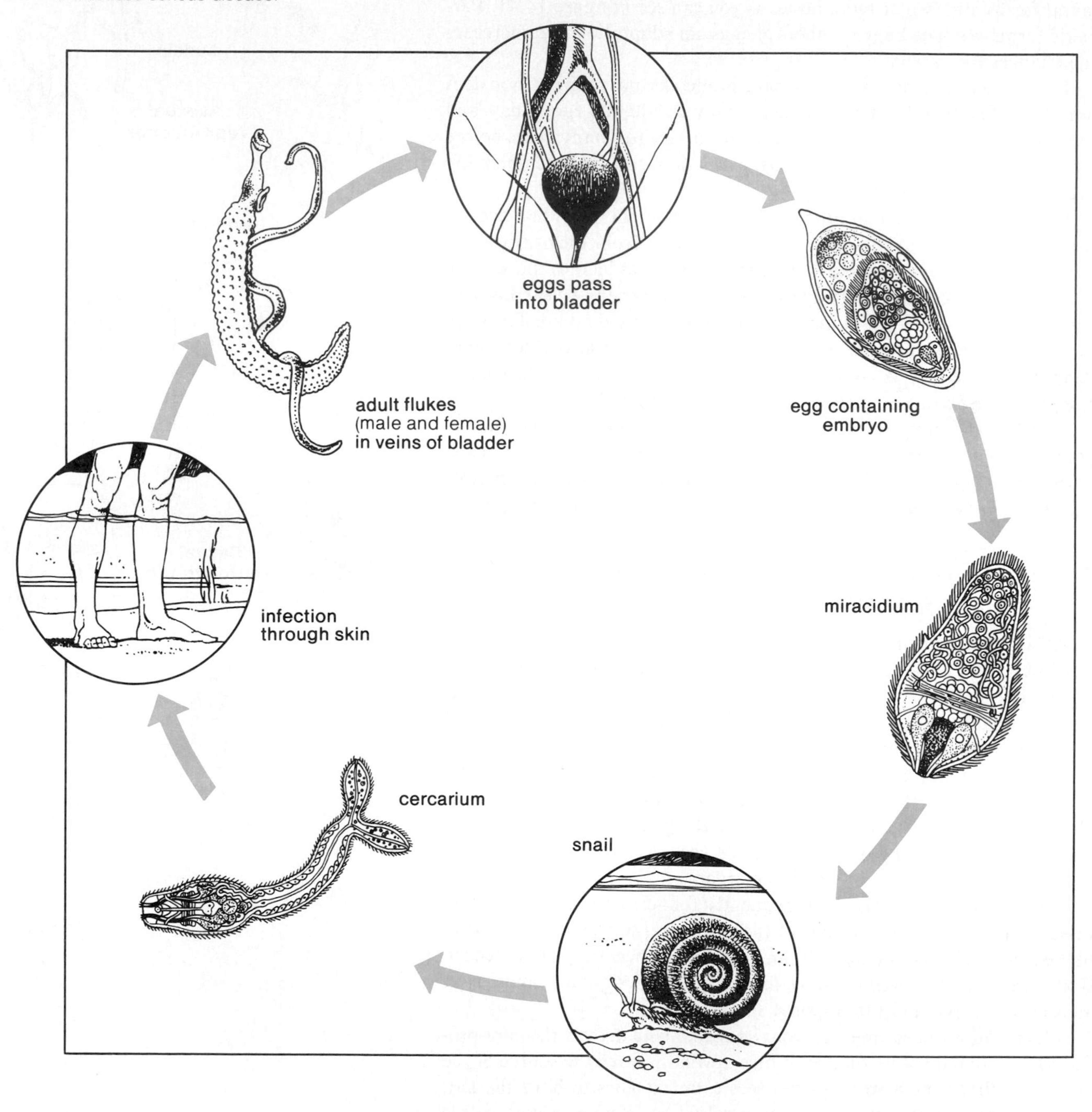

Figure 14.42 Earthworms copulating. The thickened bands aid in the transfer of sperm and later secrete a protective coating around the developing embryos. How many parents does an earthworm have?

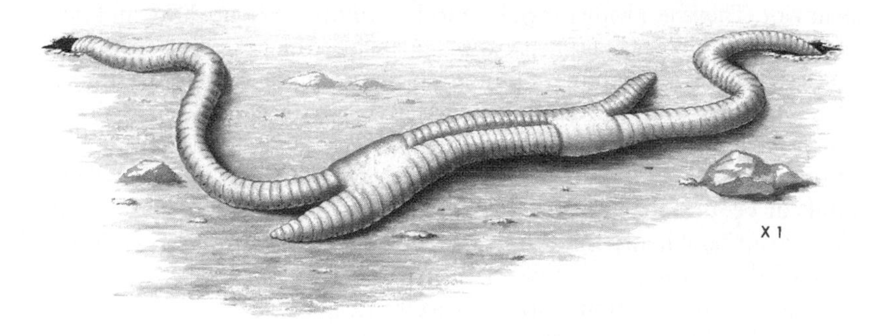

Figure 14.43 The cat's behavior tells an observer that it is aware of the bird's presence.

BSCS by Richard Tolman

Those are examples of **innate** (in NAYT) behavior, or instinct. Behavior is considered to be innate if it occurs in response to a particular stimulus the first time an individual is exposed to that stimulus. Innate behavior has a genetic basis, and it develops as a result of natural selection.

Innate behavior can be modified through experience. For example, a young squirrel opens a nut satisfactorily. As the squirrel becomes older and more experienced, however, its efficiency at opening nuts increases greatly. Chaffinches (figure 14.44) reared from hatching in soundproof rooms develop a song pattern basically like that of wild chaffinches, but their songs never include all the notes of the wild song. When the birds

Figure 14.44 Chaffinch. This is a European species that has been used in behavior studies.

Figure 14.45 Laughing seagulls exhibiting learned behavior—accepting food from tourists on Siesta Key, Florida.

Florida Image File, Inc.

hear the wild song, however, they learn it. Evidently a basic song pattern is innate, but something is added to the innate behavior during the life of the birds. Learning takes place in both squirrels and birds.

Learning occurs when experience brings about a lasting change in behavior. There is a wide range in learning abilities among different kinds of animals. Thus far, it seems possible to explain the behaviors of sponges and coelenterates without assuming that learning has occurred. Studies of planarians, however, have shown that they are capable of a simple kind of learning. On the other hand, learning does not always occur even in organisms with well-developed nervous systems. For example, many kinds of beetles, if put on a tabletop, will crawl to the edge and fall off. No matter how many times that happens, they never learn to avoid the edge of the table.

Learning occurs frequently in vertebrates. For example, along the coast of Florida, gulls feed on a variety of things. They have learned to follow ships to pick up food scraps thrown overboard. The laughing gulls on Siesta Key are fed by visitors to the beaches in the area. The gulls have learned to take food from a picnicker's hand or to pick up scraps tossed on the ground. In general, learning gives an animal flexibility to adapt to a changing environment by acquiring new behavior patterns. Most adaptive behavior, however, has both innate and learned components.

Many biologists are interested in how behavior functions in the survival of individuals and of species. Behavior is a reaction to the environment, both internal and external. Organisms react to many environmental factors—to heat and cold, to the pull of gravity, and to light, sound, and chemicals. An organism also reacts to the objects around it, both living and nonliving. If an animal reacts to its particular environment in a way that helps it to survive, the behavior of that organism can be called successful.

Self-Review

1. How do the various food-getting devices of animals illustrate structural diversity?
2. In what ways do digestive cavities differ among animals?
3. Why does a very small aquatic animal require no breathing system?
4. How do gills and lungs function in gas exchange?
5. What kinds of animals can survive without circulatory systems?
6. Distinguish between open and closed circulatory systems.
7. What are the basic functions of excretory systems?
8. Compare the nervous system of a vertebrate with that of a flatworm.
9. How do skeletons differ in vertebrates and arthropods?
10. Under what circumstances is internal fertilization necessary?
11. How does behavior reflect adaptations?

Summary

Animal form and function are direct results of their heterotrophic life-style. Evolutionary development favored a motile life-style that improved the ability to obtain food. Motility called for streamlining and led to the evolution of bilateral symmetry and a head where sensory organs and nerve cells are concentrated. Larger animals have more choice of food sources but also more cells, requiring more coordination and greater specialization. Systems evolved to handle basic functions such as digestion, gas exchange, transport, excretion, and reproduction. Evolution, through natural selection, results in a variety of adaptations that enable animals to solve the problems of life that different environments impose on them.

In this chapter we have begun to explore some of the diversity of animals, and how they function. In the next section we will look more closely at form and function in one particular animal, the human.

Application Questions

1. Birds and mammals maintain constant body temperature. In what way is that adaptation an advantage?
2. What features of arthropods and vertebrates enabled them to adapt to a terrestrial life?
3. What are the advantages of hermaphroditism?
4. Would you consider parthenogenesis a sexual method of reproduction? Why or why not?
5. One of the major principles of biology is that an organism's structure is related to its function. Choose one organism from any phylum and explain how that organism illustrates that principle.
6. One of the major principles of biology is that an organism and its environment are complementary. Choose one organism from any phylum and explain how that organism illustrates that principle.
7. Suggest how behavior can be a factor in evolution.

Problems

1. Hemoglobin acts as a respiratory pigment in animals of several phyla, but there are other such pigments in the animal kingdom. Investigate this matter, considering the following questions:
   (a) Do all respiratory pigments act in the same way?
   (b) What are the chemical similarities and differences among respiratory pigments?
   (c) Do respiratory pigments provide any clues to the evolutionary relationships among animal phyla?
2. List the principal life functions of animals. Then compare the structures by which each is accomplished in a sponge, a planarian, an insect, and a mammal. Because all of those animals exist in large numbers, we must conclude that despite such diverse structures they all successfully carry on their life functions. Explain how that can be.
3. Make a list of animals from a number of phyla and arrange it in order of the care given the young—from least to most. List the same animals in order of numbers of young produced—from most to least. Explain any relationships you can find between the two lists.

Suggested Readings

B. M. Galdikus, "Living with the Great Orange Apes" *National Geographic* (June 1980). Orangutans, as well as chimpanzees and gorillas, can learn to communicate with humans by signing.

J. D. Ligon and S. H. Ligon, "The Cooperative Breeding Behavior of the Green Woodhoopoe" *Scientific American* (July 1982). Among these East African birds, one pair in each flock breed while the nonbreeding adults assist in the raising of the breeders' chicks.

E. A. Newman and P. H. Hartline, "The Infrared 'Vision' of Snakes" *Scientific American* (March 1982). Infrared and visible-light information are integrated in the brain to yield a unique wide-spectrum picture of the world.

B. L. Partridge, "The Structure and Function of Fish Schools" *Scientific American* (June 1982). Interesting, well-illustrated discussion of fish schools.

S. J. Shettleworth, "Memory in Food-Hoarding Birds" *Scientific American* (March 1983). Interesting experiments were conducted in trying to determine how birds remember where they cache their food.

P. G. Veit, "Gorilla Society" *Natural History* (March 1982). Well-illustrated article dealing with the endangered mountain gorillas of Zaïre, Uganda, and Rwanda.

BSCS by Carlye Calvin

Section Four

Functioning Organisms in the Biosphere

Organisms vary greatly in size. A redwood tree may be 100 m tall and a blue whale may weigh 150 metric tons. A bacterium, though, may be only 0.4 μm wide and weigh a small fraction of a milligram. We have been treating these as equal units interacting with other individuals and with the abiotic environment.

Now we shift to the inside to see how internal structures determine what an organism does. What produces the activities seen from the outside? We have seen how energy goes from one organism to another, but what happens to this energy within each organism? In attempting to answer these questions we will focus on two familiar organisms: humans and flowering plants.

Carlye Calvin

What nutrients are provided by this lunch of hamburger, fries, and soft drink?

CHAPTER **15**

The Human Animal: Food and Energy

Introduction

Did you ever think about what happens to the hamburger, fries, and soft drink you had for lunch? You know that you are growing and that the food you eat is used to build your body. But are you made of cow protein and potato starch? How do the plant and animal tissues you eat become human cells and tissues? Let us follow your lunch through the digestive tract to see what happens to it and how it becomes a part of you.

The processes by which organisms obtain, process, distribute, and use nutrients are known collectively as **nutrition.** This is not to be confused with digestion. Digestion is the process by which nutrients are broken down into molecules that can then be transported to and used by the working cells of your body.

Ingestion and Digestion

Guidepost: How is food prepared for absorption?

15.1 Food Must Be Reduced in Size before Chemical Processes Can Begin

Let us begin with the first bite of that hamburger. Ingestion is the process of taking food into the entrance of the digestive tract. In humans, this entrance is called the **oral cavity** and is bounded by the teeth, tongue, and palate. Here the chewing action of the teeth begins the mechanical breakdown of food. This grinding action breaks the large pieces of hamburger and bun into smaller pieces, much like chopping a log into kindling to help start a fire.

As you are chewing your hamburger, your highly muscular tongue keeps the food in contact with the teeth, moves it to mix it with saliva (a watery secretion that contains digestive enzymes and begins chemical digestion), and manipulates it into position for swallowing. In addition, the tongue is richly supplied with sensory nerve endings in the form of taste buds (figure 15.1) that keep you informed about the taste and tex-

Figure 15.1 A cross section of a taste bud.

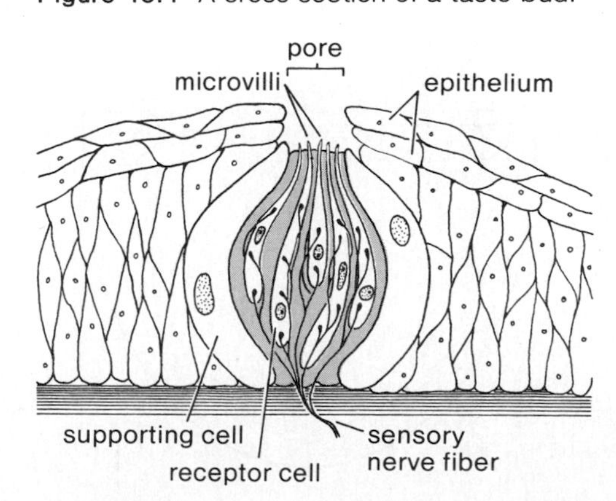

ture of ingested food. The tongue then moves the moistened and ground hamburger to the back of the oral cavity, where it is swallowed. You can observe the sensitivity of the taste buds in your tongue in investigation 15.1.

Investigation 15.1 YOUR CHEMICAL SENSES

Introduction

Many animals have nerve endings that are sensitive to chemical substances. Arthropods have such receptors in their antennae and feet. Vertebrates have them in their mouths and nasal passages where the senses of taste and smell are found.

The study of these senses in nonhuman animals is complicated by a lack of communication. Humans can at least give descriptions of particular stimuli. Even then there are difficulties in interpreting such reports. So a complete understanding of sense organs—even in humans—is not easy.

Materials (per team of 2)

For procedure A

2 ml 10% salt solution
2 ml 5% sucrose solution
2 ml 1% acetic acid solution
2 ml 0.1% quinine sulfate solution
syracuse watch glass
2 beakers filled with water
4 cotton swabs
waste jar for every 6 students

For procedure B

solutions of orange juice, milk, onion juice, 2% vinegar, sugar, dill pickle juice—any 3 or all 6
handkerchief (for blindfold)
3 to 6 paper cups

Figure 15.2

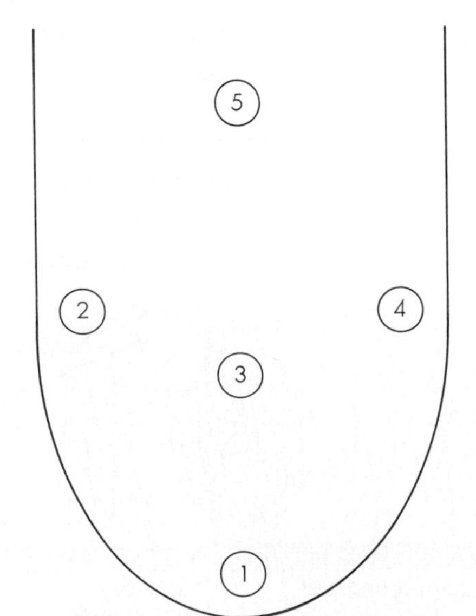

Procedure

Part A—Taste Receptors

During this procedure you will locate the taste receptors on your tongue for four kinds of chemical substances.

1. Decide who will be student A and student B.
2. Read through all the procedures for part A and do not begin with procedure 3 below until you understand your part in the investigation.
3. Student A: Pour about 2 ml of 10% salt solution into a watch glass. Student B: Make a copy of figure 15.2 and label it salt.

4. Student A: Dip a cotton swab into the solution for about 10 seconds. *Thoroughly* drain excess solution from the swab. Touch the swab to the tongue of student B at the point marked 1 in figure 15.2.
   Student B: Keep your mouth open during the testing of all five points on your tongue. Hand signal to your partner: 1 finger if you sense no taste, 2 fingers if you sense a mild taste of salt, and 3 fingers if you sense a strong taste of salt.
5. Student A: At point 1 in the tongue drawing, place a minus sign (−) if your partner signaled with 1 finger, a plus sign (+) if the signal was 2 fingers, and a double-plus sign (++) if 3 fingers were signaled.
6. Student A: As soon as the response at point 1 is recorded, touch the swab to B's tongue at point 2.
   Student B: Use the same hand signals to A to indicate no taste, mild taste, or strong taste of salt.
7. Student A: Record the signaled sensation. Repeat the procedures for points 3, 4, and 5 on B's tongue.
   Student B: Signal in the same way as you did for points 1 and 2.
8. Student A: Record the signaled responses for points 3, 4, and 5.
   Student B: Rinse your mouth thoroughly with water.
9. Student A: Break the swab you have been using and discard it. Pour the salt solution from the watch glass into the waste jar. Rinse the watch glass. Pour about 2 ml of 5% sucrose solution into the watch glass.
   Student B: Make a copy of figure 15.2. Label it sweet.
10. Repeat procedures 2–9 with the sucrose solution.
11. Repeat procedures with about 2 ml of 1% acetic acid solution—sour—and with a 0.1% solution of quinine sulfate—bitter.
12. If time permits, switch the roles of students A and B and repeat the 4 taste tests.

Part B—Taste and Smell

During this procedure you will investigate the relationship between taste and smell. It is important that the student being tested not know what the substance is.

1. Read through all the procedures for part B and do not begin with procedure 2 below until you understand your part in the investigation.
2. Student A: Copy the table shown below in your data book.

Subject	Solution Presented	Nose Closed		Nose Open	
		Taste	Identify	Taste	Identify

   Student B: Blindfold student A. Obtain a paper cup, labeled A, containing a few milliliters of test solution 1.
3. Student A: *Holding your nose tightly,* sip the solution. *While still holding your nose,* report its taste and try to identify the substance in the solution.
   Student B: Record these reports on the chart.

4. Student A: Without holding your nose, sip the same solution. Again report its taste and try to identify the substance.
   Student B: Record these reports on the chart.
5. Repeat the procedure with student B as the subject and use test solution 2.
6. Repeat the procedure with student A as the subject and use test solution 3.
7. Continue alternating the function of students A and B until all the test solutions have been used.

Discussion

On the chalkboard, make 4 large diagrams as in figure 15.2. Label them salt, sweet, sour, and bitter. Assemble all the data obtained in procedure A. At each test point on the diagrams, record the total number of minus, plus, and double-plus responses.

1. What are some of the possible causes for variability in the data?
2. Which kinds of variability are the result of "errors of observation"? Which kinds are the result of physiological variability?

On the chalkboard, list the solutions (1, 2, 3, and so on) used in procedure B. Tally separately the tastes reported with nose closed and with nose open. Also tally the identifications of solutions.

3. Are the kinds of tastes reported with the nose open more varied than those reported with the nose closed? Less varied? Neither?
4. Are the identifications made with the nose open more accurate than those made with the nose closed? Less accurate? Neither?
5. What assumption is involved in holding the nose closed?
6. Do the data from procedure A support the hypothesis that receptors of the four kinds of taste are equally distributed on the surface of the tongue? Explain.
7. If the data fail to support this hypothesis, where on the tongue is each kind of taste receptor located?
8. On the basis of the data from procedure B, write a brief statement relating the sense of taste to the sense of smell.

For Further Investigation

1. Hold a bottle containing oil of cloves about 1.5 cm from your nose and vigorously and continuously inhale, exhaling through your mouth. How much time passes before you can no longer clearly detect the smell of cloves? You now have "olfactory fatigue." Immediately smell peppermint oil. Can you detect its odor?
2. Stick your tongue out and keep it out during the following procedure. Dry your tongue with a piece of gauze or paper towel. Place a few crystals of sugar on your tongue and note the time. How much time passes before you can taste the sugar? Rinse your mouth with water. Again stick your tongue out, but do not dry it before placing sugar crystals on it. How much time passes before you can taste the sugar? Rinse your mouth with water. Try the same procedure with salt crystals. Again measure the time. What conclusions can you draw from your results?

Figure 15.3 Movement of food through the alimentary canal. Peristalsis in the wall of the esophagus forces food through it and into the stomach.

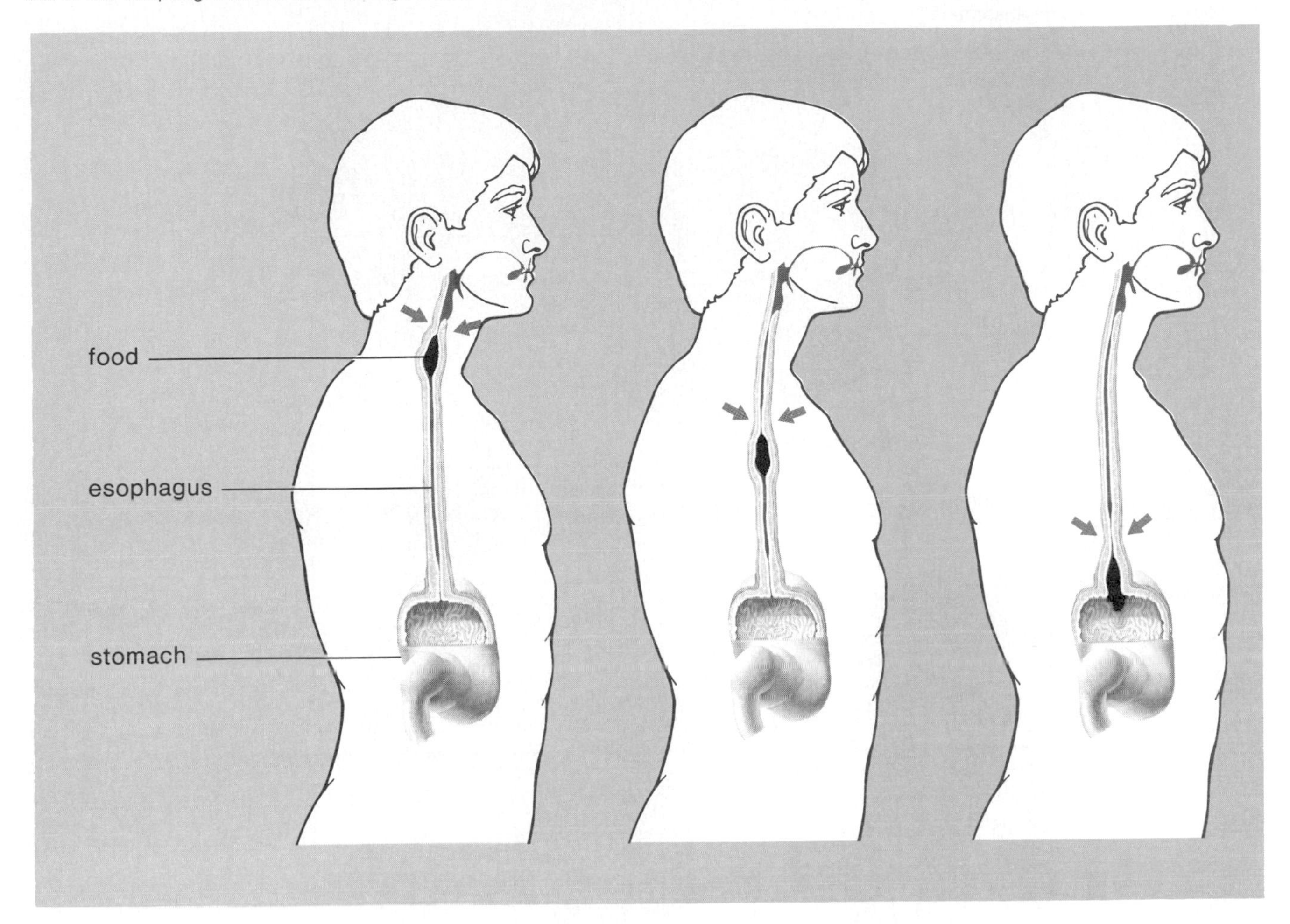

15.2 Specific Actions and Reactions Take Place along the Digestive Tract

The **esophagus** is the tube connecting the oral cavity to the stomach. It is made up of two layers of muscles: an outer one running the length of the esophagus and an inner circular layer. Together, these muscles move the hamburger to the stomach by a process known as **peristalsis** (per ih STAWL sis) (see figure 15.3). Food is pushed along by contraction of the circular muscle immediately behind the swallowed food as the muscle in front of it relaxes. Peristalsis proceeds in a wavelike sequence down the length of the esophagus.

Figure 15.4 The human digestive system is a continuous tube with highly specialized organs and tissues along its length. Mechanical and chemical digestion are followed by absorption.

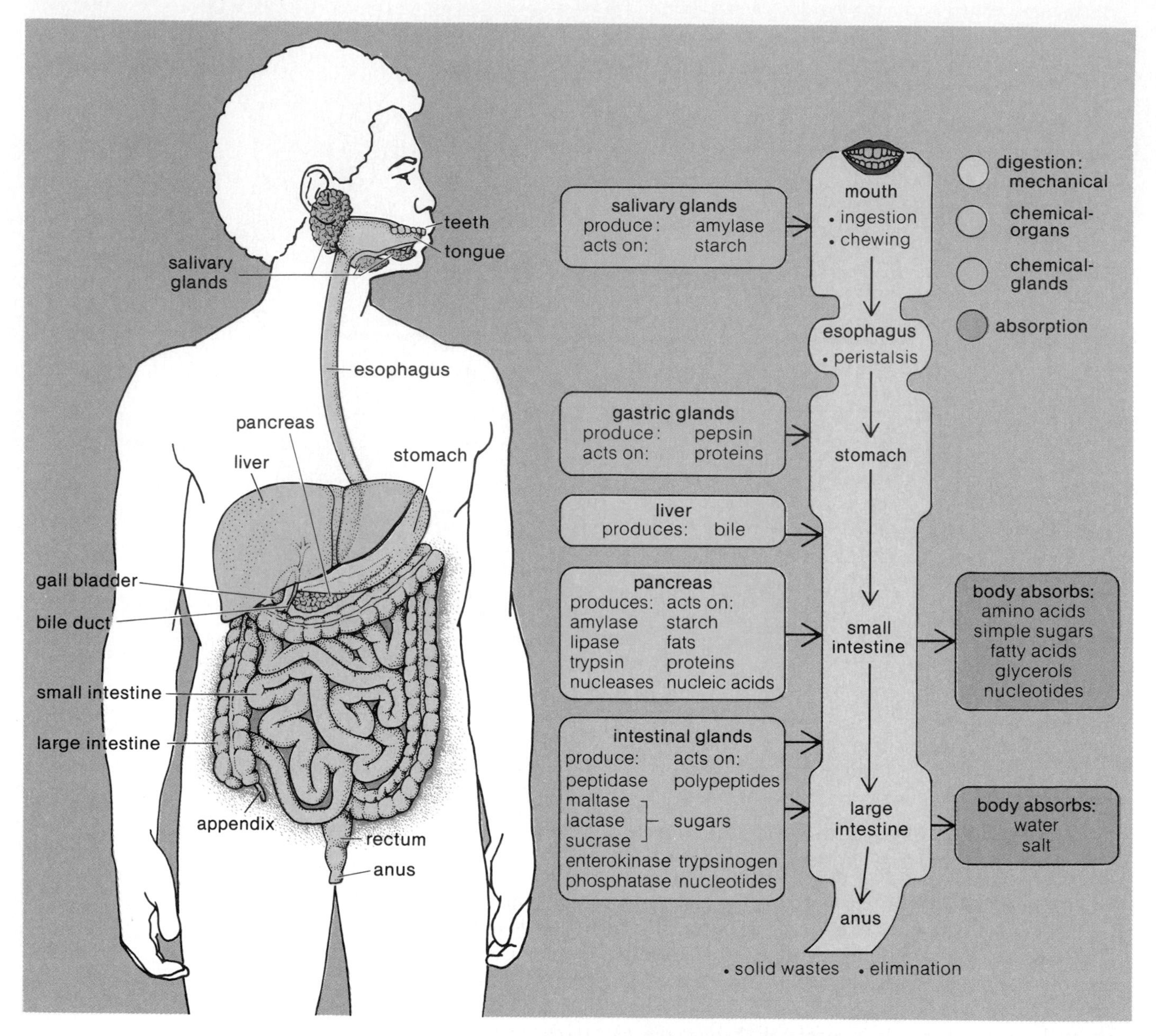

The journey your hamburger takes is normally a one-way passage through a tube, the digestive tract or gut, which begins at the mouth and ends at the anus. Figure 15.4 shows the human digestive tract and summarizes the activities that take place in it. As the food moves along approximately 9 m of digestive tract, it goes through various sections that function as a disassembly line. The **stomach** is an enlargement of the gut between the esophagus and the intestine, and has a circular muscle or **sphincter** (SFINK ter) at either end that closes the opening. The stomach is often thought of as an organ of storage to be packed with food. However, the food remains there only long enough to be prepared for entrance into the small intestine.

15.3 Chemical Digestion Reduces Large Food Molecules to Smaller, Absorbable Molecules

In the stomach the food is churned and diluted to a creamy consistency, the proper pH is established, and enzymatic action is begun. Here your food undergoes further mechanical breakdown with the kneading and churning action of the stomach muscles. This motion also helps mix in a watery fluid known as **gastric juice,** which is secreted into the stomach cavity by glands in the stomach wall (figure 15.4). Gastric juice contains hydrochloric acid, which aids in the breakdown of proteins into polypeptides. The digestive enzymes that catalyze that breakdown require a low (acidic) pH in order to function effectively. The hydrochloric acid in the gastric juice provides an appropriate environment in the stomach.

By means of the churning and the action of gastric juice and digestive enzymes, the contents of your stomach, your hamburger lunch, soon become like a cream soup. The partially digested hamburger is held in the stomach by contraction of the pyloric valve, the sphincter between the stomach and small intestine. The pyloric valve relaxes irregularly, spurting the partially digested food little by little into the small intestine, emptying the stomach in about four hours.

So far, your hamburger has done some traveling, been ground into a soupy mixture, and partially digested. What happens now? Food enters the **small intestine,** a tube approximately 6 m long where chemical digestion is completed and absorption of food molecules takes place. **Absorption** occurs when the molecules move through the intestinal walls and enter the bloodstream. The blood carries the molecules to the cells, where the food finally becomes a part of you.

Food molecules go through their final chemical breakdown in the small intestine. From chapter 4 you will remember that there are four types of molecules used in all living cells as building materials and a source of energy. The four are carbohydrates, proteins, fats (lipids), and nucleic acids. These are the molecules that your body needs and that your food must supply. However, you cannot use cow protein, bread carbohydrates, or the DNA of a potato. Just as an old brick building can be torn down and the bricks reused to pave a patio or to construct a fireplace, so your body tears food molecules apart to form the building blocks it needs. Only these building blocks are absorbed; only they can be used to synthesize the specific molecules that make up your body.

What are those building blocks? They are the small molecules that make up the biological molecules mentioned above. The carbohydrates are strings of simple sugars, proteins are composed of amino acids, and simple fats are made up of a glycerol molecule and three fatty acids.

The small intestine accomplishes the task of splitting the large molecules through the action of digestive enzymes. Enzymes and digestive juices enter the upper part of the small intestine from the pancreas, the liver, and the intestine itself. All have a high (basic) pH and help neutralize the hydrochloric acid of the soupy mixture entering from the stomach. That is important because the enzymes of the small intestine require a neutral environment.

The pancreas delivers its **pancreatic** (pan kree AT ik) **juice** through a duct to the small intestine. Pancreatic juice contains several enzymes that catalyze digestion of polypeptides, fats, and polysaccharides (see figure 15.4). **Intestinal juice,** secreted by glands in the wall of the small intestine, contains other enzymes. These function in the digestion of the dipeptides and disaccharides.

Figure 15.5 A cross section of the small intestine. Intestinal villi are shown enlarged in the photomicrograph and drawing. Digested foodstuffs enter the blood and the lymph through the villi.

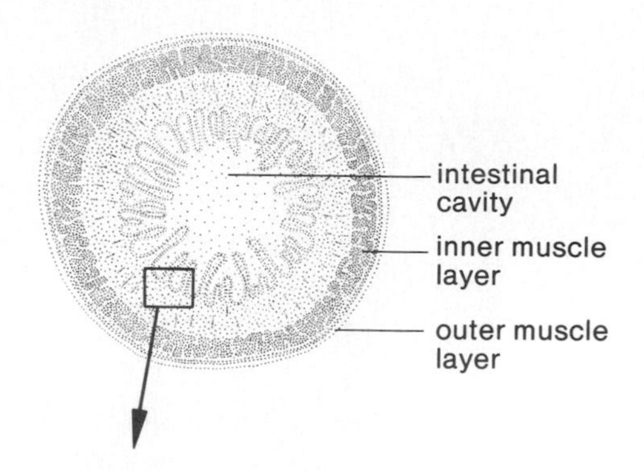

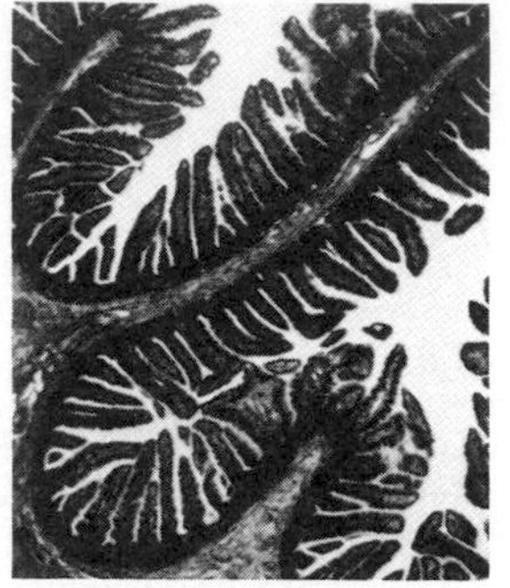

Struwe/Monkmeyer Press

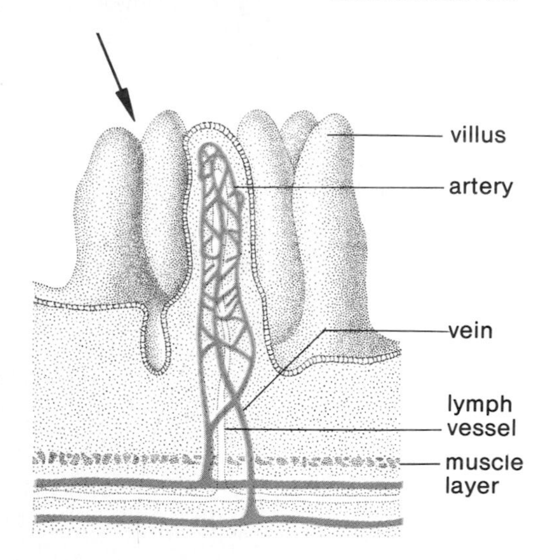

The fats must be pretreated before they can be digested. This function is performed by **bile,** which is secreted by the liver and stored in the gall bladder. Bile breaks down the fat droplets into fine particles that can be reached by the pancreatic enzymes, which then digest the fats into fatty acids and glycerol.

15.4 Absorption Takes Place in the Small Intestine

Almost all absorption of nutrients occurs in the lower part of the small intestine. The process of absorbing food molecules is very much like wiping up a spill—the larger the sponge, the more will be absorbed. If you flattened every wrinkle and bulge of the human small intestine, its total surface area would be about 300 m^2, about half the size of a basketball court. That enormous surface area is possible because of the presence of folds in the intestinal wall that are covered by tiny bulges known as villi (see figure 15.5). These villi are covered by cells whose surface membrane is folded into fine projections called **microvilli.** Amino acids and simple sugars are, respectively, the end products of protein and carbohydrate digestion. These amino acids and simple sugars are absorbed by diffusion or active transport through the walls of the small intestine into the blood.

Most of the fatty acids and glycerol recombine during absorption to form fat. Fatty acids with 12 or fewer carbons are absorbed directly into the blood capillaries and carried to the liver for processing. Those fatty acids with more than 12 carbons do not enter the blood directly. Rather, they are absorbed by the **lymphatic** (lim FAT ik) **system,** about which you will learn in chapter 16.

These absorption processes are selective but not infallible. There is no control mechanism to prevent absorption of excess food, and many harmful molecules can masquerade as useful ones and be absorbed. An example is DDT, an insecticide that was used heavily on food crops until 1972, when its use was prohibited in the United States. When eaten, it was absorbed and stored in fatty tissue and in human milk.

15.5 The Large Intestine Absorbs Water

In a typical diet approximately 800 g of food and 1200 ml of water are ingested per day. To these are added the following digestive secretions: (approximate amounts)

1500 ml saliva
2000 ml gastric secretions
1500 ml intestinal secretions
500 ml bile
1500 ml pancreatic secretions.

Of this total, about 9000 ml, 8500 ml are absorbed in the small intestine and 350 ml in the large intestine. The remaining 100 ml of water plus 50 ml of solids are expelled from the body as solid matter.

Normally, digestion and absorption are completed in four to seven hours. Substances left in the small intestine then pass into the large intestine, where more water is absorbed. No further absorption of food substances occurs in the large intestine. Undigested foods, indigestible substances, mucus, dead cells from the digestive tube lining, and bacteria are concentrated by water removal to form the waste matter, or **feces** (FEE seez). If the fecal matter remains in the large intestine too long, almost all the water is reabsorbed and a very dry feces is passed. The feces leave the digestive tube through the **anus** (AY nus).

But what of the 8850 ml of absorbed solids and liquids? In the next section we will trace the fate of molecules intended as fuel for the energy producing processes.

Self-Review

1. Distinguish between mechanical and chemical digestion.
2. Name the four basic nutrient molecules and the form in which each is absorbed.
3. How does the function of bile differ from other intestinal juices?
4. Distinguish among ingestion, digestion, and absorption.

Cellular Respiration

Guidepost: How do cells obtain energy from food molecules?

15.6 In Cellular Respiration, the Energy from Food Molecules Is Released Gradually

Cells require a continuous supply of energy for cellular work such as maintaining order, moving substances, building organic molecules, and growing. Energy for cells must come either from food or from storage molecules. As a result of the digestive processes described in the previous sections, your hamburger lunch has been reduced to amino acids, simple sugars, fatty acids, and glycerol, and has been delivered to your cells. How do your cells obtain energy from these molecules?

Cells release energy from the basic molecules of food through the process of cellular respiration, a kind of burning. In burning, a great deal of energy is liberated all at once in the form of heat and light. Cells release the same amount of energy gradually, in a stepwise series of reactions controlled by enzymes. As a result, the energy is freed in small amounts that can be captured and stored in ATP molecules. As we discussed in chapter 4, energy stored in ATP is like "small change"—it is readily available for use in cellular work.

In investigation 15.2, you will be able to measure the amount of heat given off as a food substance burns and to calculate the amount of energy that heat represents.

Investigation 15.2 FOOD ENERGY

Introduction

Organisms require both organic and inorganic compounds. Their energy requirements are provided by organic foods. All foods contain energy. How much energy? Do equal amounts of different foods contain the same amount of energy? In this investigation you will use a calorimeter (figure 15.6) to measure the amount of energy in some foods.

This energy will be measured in calories. Recall that a calorie is the amount of heat required to raise the temperature of 1 ml (1 g) of water 1° C. Calorie values of foods in diet charts are listed in kilocalories (1000 calories) or kcals. Accepted caloric values for some common foods will be given to you later by your teacher.

You will measure the difference in temperature (ΔT) of a measured volume of water. The temperature change is caused by the absorption of the heat given off by the burning of a known mass of food.

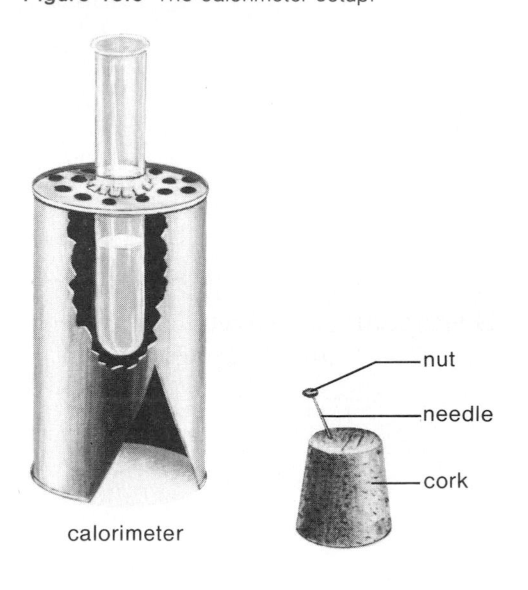

Figure 15.6 The calorimeter setup.

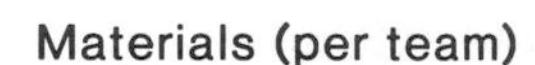

Materials (per team)

For calorimeter:

tin can 6–8 cm wide, 10–12 cm tall
tin snips
hammer and nail
needle-nosed pliers
heat-resistant test tube 18 mm × 150 mm
cork
cork pad or piece of plexiglass
straight pin or needle
thermometer (10–110° C)

For testing food:

3 pieces each of peanuts and walnuts (0.2 g each)
balance
graduated cylinder, 10 ml
safety matches
test tube holder

Procedure

1. Construct the calorimeter, using figure 15.6 as a guide. **CAUTION:** *Tin can edges are sharp.*
   (a) Use the tin snips to cut a V-shaped opening at the base of the can. It should be no more than 1/3 of the height of the can.
   (b) Use a hammer and nail to punch a hole in the center of the closed end of the can. With the needle-nosed pliers, ream this hole until the 18 mm × 150 mm test tube will fit snugly in the can.
   (c) Punch about 10–15 more holes in the closed end of the can.
2. Weigh out three 0.2 g pieces of peanut, and three 0.2 g pieces of walnut.

3. Place one of the peanuts on the needle held up by the cork.
4. Place the calorimeter over the nut, needle, and cork setup. Adjust the test tube so that it is about 2 cm above the nut.
5. Remove the calorimeter from over the nut. Be very careful not to change the position of the test tube. Measure 10 ml of water and put it in the test tube.
6. Copy the table below into your data book.

	Temperature of Water, °C			Food Energy		
	Before Burning	After Burning	Difference	calories	Kcal	Kcal per Gram
Walnut sample 1						
Walnut sample 2						
Walnut sample 3						
Average						
Peanut sample 1						
Peanut sample 2						
Peanut sample 3						
Average						

7. Measure the temperature of the water in the test tube. Record it in the table. Remove the thermometer.
8. Set fire to the nut. Quickly and carefully position the calorimeter over the burning nut.
9. Burn the nut completely. As soon as it burns out, measure the temperature of the water. Record it in your table.
10. Repeat the procedure until you have data for 3 samples of walnut and 3 of peanut. Change the water in the tube each time. Allow the tube to cool off before putting in a new water sample, or use a second tube. **CAUTION:** *Do not touch the tubes or calorimeter while they are hot. Use a test tube holder to handle the hot test tube.*
11. Find the average difference in temperature for each sample. Now calculate the number of kcals produced per gram. To do this, multiply the increase in water temperature (average difference) by 10, the number of ml of water used. Next divide this number by 0.2 (the number of grams of food burned). This will give you the calories produced per gram of food. To convert this into kcals, divide this number by 1000. The kcals listed in most diet charts are per 100 g, per ounce, per cup, or per serving. To compare your results, you may need to convert to common units.

Discussion

1. How do your data (adjusted for 100 g) compare with the values for 100 g of the same or similar food listed by your teacher?
2. How do you account for any differences?
3. If the same amount of each food you tested were completely used in the cells of the human body, what would you expect the energy release to be?
4. Which of the foods you tested seems to be the best energy source?
5. Why might some foods with fewer kcals be better energy sources than other foods with more kcals?
6. What was the original source of energy in all of the foods tested?

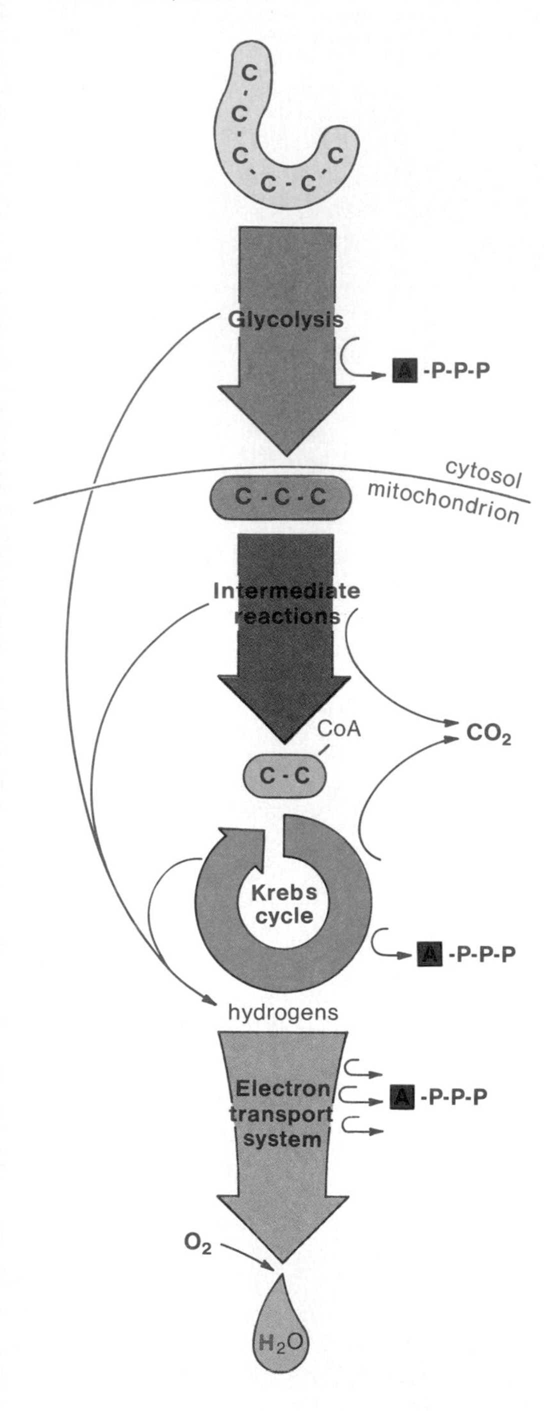

Figure 15.7 Simplified diagram of the reactions in cellular respiration.

15.7 Glucose Is the Primary Source of Energy for Cells

Oxygen is required for many of the reactions of cellular respiration. Oxygen and small food molecules are transported in the blood to every cell. They move across the plasma membrane by diffusion or active transport, and can be used by the cell in a variety of ways. The primary food molecule used in cellular respiration is the simple sugar glucose, which has the formula $C_6H_{12}O_6$. During respiration, the energy stored in the glucose is released as the molecule is gradually broken down to produce six carbon dioxide molecules. The overall reaction may be summarized in the following equation:

$$\underset{\text{(glucose)}}{C_6H_{12}O_6} + \underset{\text{(oxygen)}}{6\ O_2} \xrightarrow{\text{enzymes}} \underset{\left(\begin{smallmatrix}\text{carbon}\\ \text{dioxide}\end{smallmatrix}\right)}{6\ CO_2} + \underset{\text{(water)}}{6\ H_2O} + \text{energy}$$

This equation summarizes a complex series of reactions that involves many steps. We can consider those steps in four groups: (1) glycolysis, (2) intermediate reactions, (3) Krebs citric acid cycle, and (4) the electron transport system. Figure 15.7 is a very simplified diagram of those reactions.

In **glycolysis** (gly KAWL uh sis), glucose is split into two 3-carbon molecules and a small amount of the energy is transferred to ATP. The reactions of glycolysis take place in the cytosol. In the intermediate reactions and the **Krebs citric acid cycle,** the two 3-carbon glucose fragments are disassembled and six carbon dioxide molecules are formed. Hydrogen atoms also are released. They are picked up by specialized molecules known as **carriers** that transfer them to the fourth and last series of reactions. This final series of reactions is the **electron transport system,** during which the relatively large amount of energy in the glucose molecule is stored in several smaller amounts in ATP. In the electron transport system, each hydrogen atom is separated into an electron and a proton and transferred through many small steps to oxygen, finally forming water. The intermediate reactions, the citric acid cycle, and the electron transport system all take place in the mitochondria (see figure 15.8).

15.8 Glycolysis Begins the Energy-Yielding Process

In our study of cellular respiration, we will begin with a single glucose molecule and follow it through the series of reactions known as glycolysis. Three important things happen to the glucose during the glycolysis reactions. First, the carbon chain is broken into two pieces. Second, some ATP is formed. And third, hydrogen atoms are made available for use in the electron transport system. Figure 15.9 presents a simplified diagram of the chemical events of glycolysis. Refer to this figure as you read.

Figure 15.8 (a) A mitochondrion in the pancreas of a bat, as photographed through an electron microscope (×25,000). (b) A three dimensional drawing of the mitochondrion shown in (a).

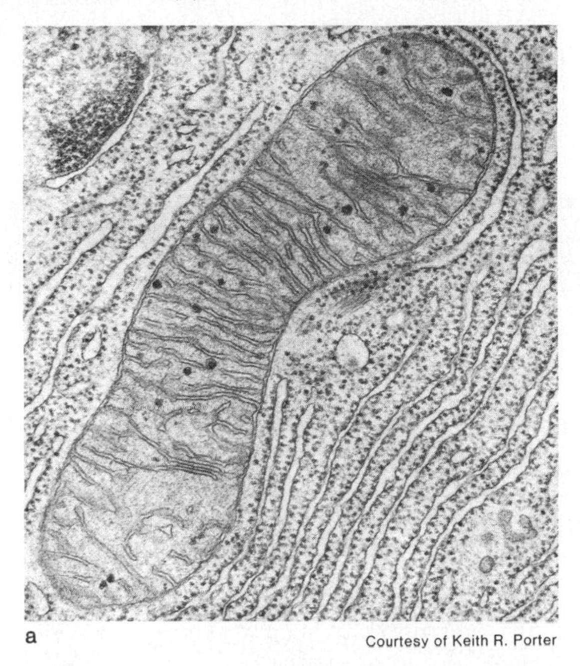

a Courtesy of Keith R. Porter

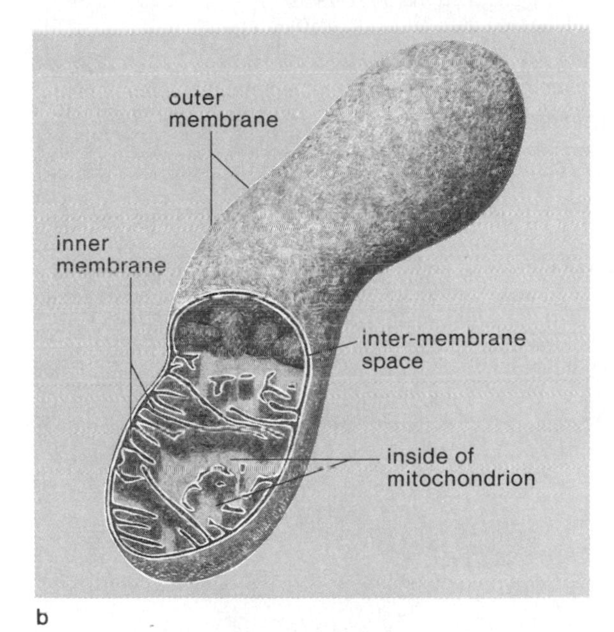

b

Glucose contains a large amount of chemical energy, but it is a relatively stable molecule. Some energy must be expended to start the energy-releasing process, just as energy (in the form of a match) is required to start a fuel burning. The starting energy is provided by the transfer of phosphates from two ATP molecules, converting them to ADP

Figure 15.9 Glycolysis. See accompanying text for explanation.

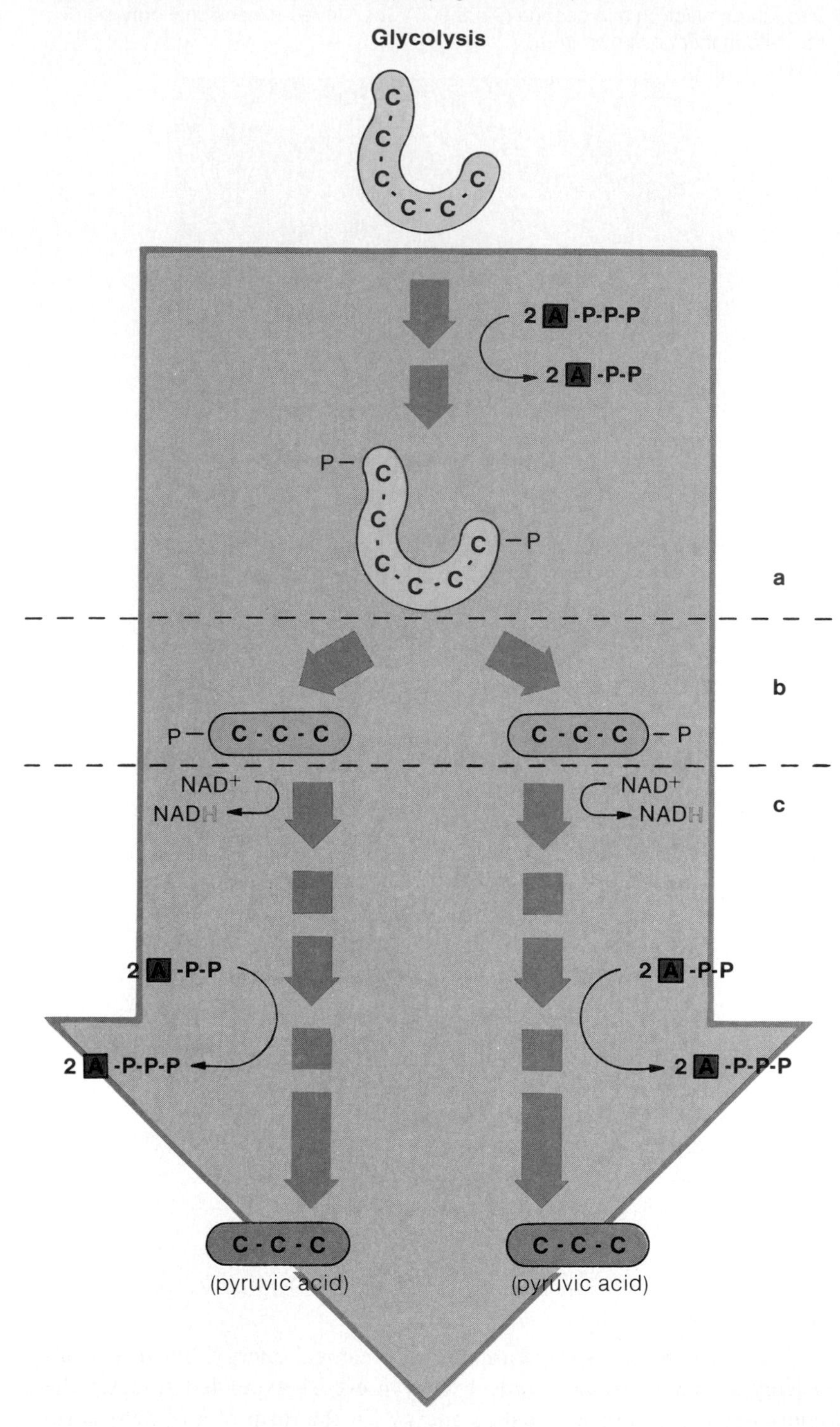

Figure 15.10 Nicotinamide adenine dinucleotide, NAD^+.

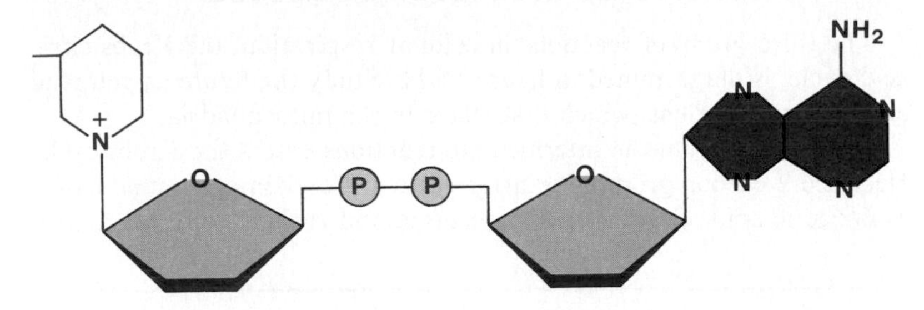

(figure 15.9a). The resulting molecule readily enters into the next reaction (figure 15.9b), in which the 6-carbon chain is split into two 3-carbon molecules. In the remaining reactions of glycolysis (figure 15.9c), these 3-carbon molecules are rearranged to form two molecules of pyruvic acid. In these rearrangements, no further energy is expended. Instead, these reactions *yield* energy.

Four ATP molecules are produced in glycolysis, a net gain of two ATP molecules. In addition, hydrogen atoms released during the reactions are picked up by a carrier molecule called **nicotinamide adenine dinucleotide** (nik uh TEE nuh myd AD uh neen DY NOO klee oh tyd), or **NAD^+**. NADH is formed. The function of a carrier molecule is to transfer substances from one reaction to another, much as a mail carrier transfers letters from the post office to your home. NAD^+ transfers hydrogen atoms (electrons and protons) from the reactions of glycolysis to the electron transport system.

The end products of glycolysis are two molecules of pyruvic acid, two ATP molecules, and the hydrogen atoms picked up by NAD^+. Most of the chemical energy in the original glucose molecule is still retained in the pyruvic acid molecules.

15.9 Intermediate Reactions Prepare Pyruvic Acid for the Krebs Cycle

Pyruvic acid molecules are transported into the mitochondria, but they do not enter directly into the Krebs cycle. First they undergo reactions that link glycolysis and the Krebs cycle. In these intermediate reactions, each molecule of pyruvic acid is broken down, and a molecule of carbon dioxide is released. Hydrogen atoms, also released during these reactions, are picked up by NAD^+. The remaining 2-carbon fragment combines with a carrier called coenzyme A (CoA). A temporary compound known as acetyl CoA is formed. These reactions are shown in figure 15.11a.

15.10 The Krebs Citric Acid Cycle Completes the Breakdown of Glucose

The third group of reactions in cellular respiration, the Krebs citric acid cycle, is diagrammed in figure 15.11. Study the figure as you read about these reactions, which take place in the mitochondria.

Acetyl CoA from the intermediate reactions enters the Krebs cycle. Here the 2-carbon group is transferred to a 4-carbon compound called oxaloacetic acid. Coenzyme A is released and is then available to pick

Figure 15.11 The intermediate reactions and the Krebs citric acid cycle.

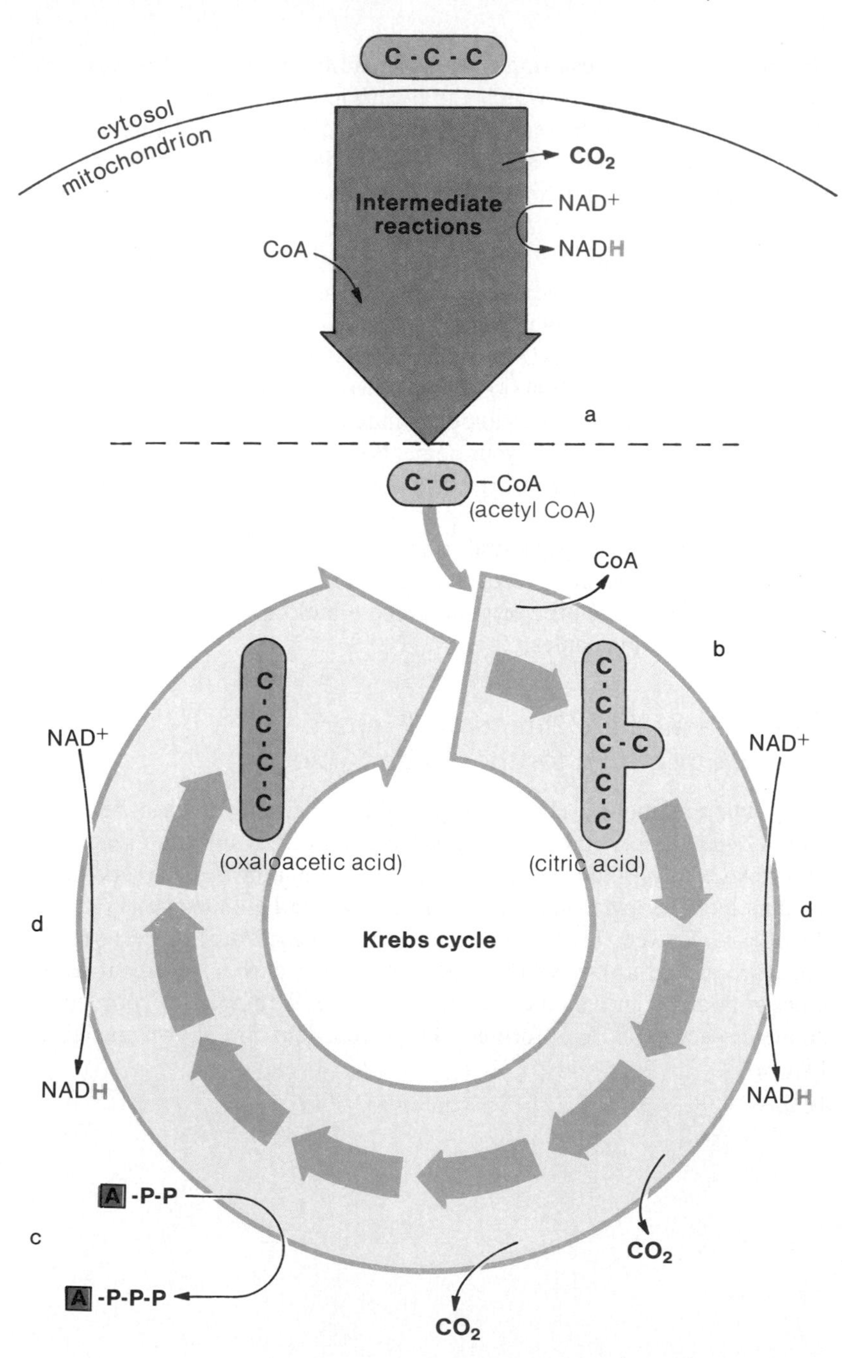

up another 2-carbon fragment from pyruvic acid for transfer to the Krebs cycle. The 6-carbon compound thus formed is citric acid (figure 15.11b).

The formation of citric acid is the beginning of the Krebs cycle. During this sequence of reactions, the remaining two carbons of glucose are released as carbon dioxide. By means of many rearrangements, the oxaloacetic acid is regenerated, allowing the cycle to continue. During one of those rearrangements, sufficient energy is released to combine a phosphate with ADP, forming a molecule of ATP (figure 15.11c). Many hydrogen atoms also are released in the Krebs cycle. These are picked up by NAD^+ or another carrier for transfer to the electron transport system (figure 15.11d).

In the citric acid cycle, breakdown of the carbon chain in glucose has been completed. As a result of glycolysis, the intermediate reactions, and the citric acid cycle, one 6-carbon glucose molecule has been broken down into six 1-carbon molecules: the carbon dioxide you exhale. These reactions are often called the carbon pathway. The direct energy gain has been two ATP molecules produced in glycolysis and another two ATPs formed during the citric acid cycle. Most important, both processes have released hydrogen atoms that are transported to the electron transport system by carrier molecules.

15.11 Energy from Glucose is Packaged as ATP in the Electron Transport System

During this final series of reactions, illustrated in figure 15.12, the hydrogen atoms are separated into electrons and protons. The electrons are passed along a series of electron carriers located on the inner membrane of the mitochondrion. As the electrons move from one carrier to the next in a succession of reactions (central part of the arrow in figure 15.12), energy is released. Some of that energy is used to actively transport protons across the inner membrane of the mitochondrion. The protons become concentrated in the space between the two membranes (right side of the arrow). As a result, a proton gradient is built up, much like the diffusion gradient discussed in section 5.6. Protons then move down their concentration gradient through a group of enzymes in the inner membrane. There, ADP and phosphate combine to form ATP. In that way, much of the energy from the electrons is transferred to ATP.

As the electrons and protons reach the end of these reactions, they are reunited to reform hydrogen atoms. The hydrogen immediately combines with oxygen to form water, ending the process. Normally, 32 molecules of ATP are formed in the electron transport system for each molecule of glucose. With the 4 ATPs formed earlier in glycolysis and the Krebs cycle, a total of 36 ATPs is formed in cellular respiration. That represents approximately 44 percent of the energy available in a molecule of glucose, a remarkable efficiency. An automobile engine, by comparison, converts only about 25 percent of the energy in gasoline into a usable form.

Figure 15.12 The electron transport system. Most of the ATP formation of cellular respiration occurs in this system.

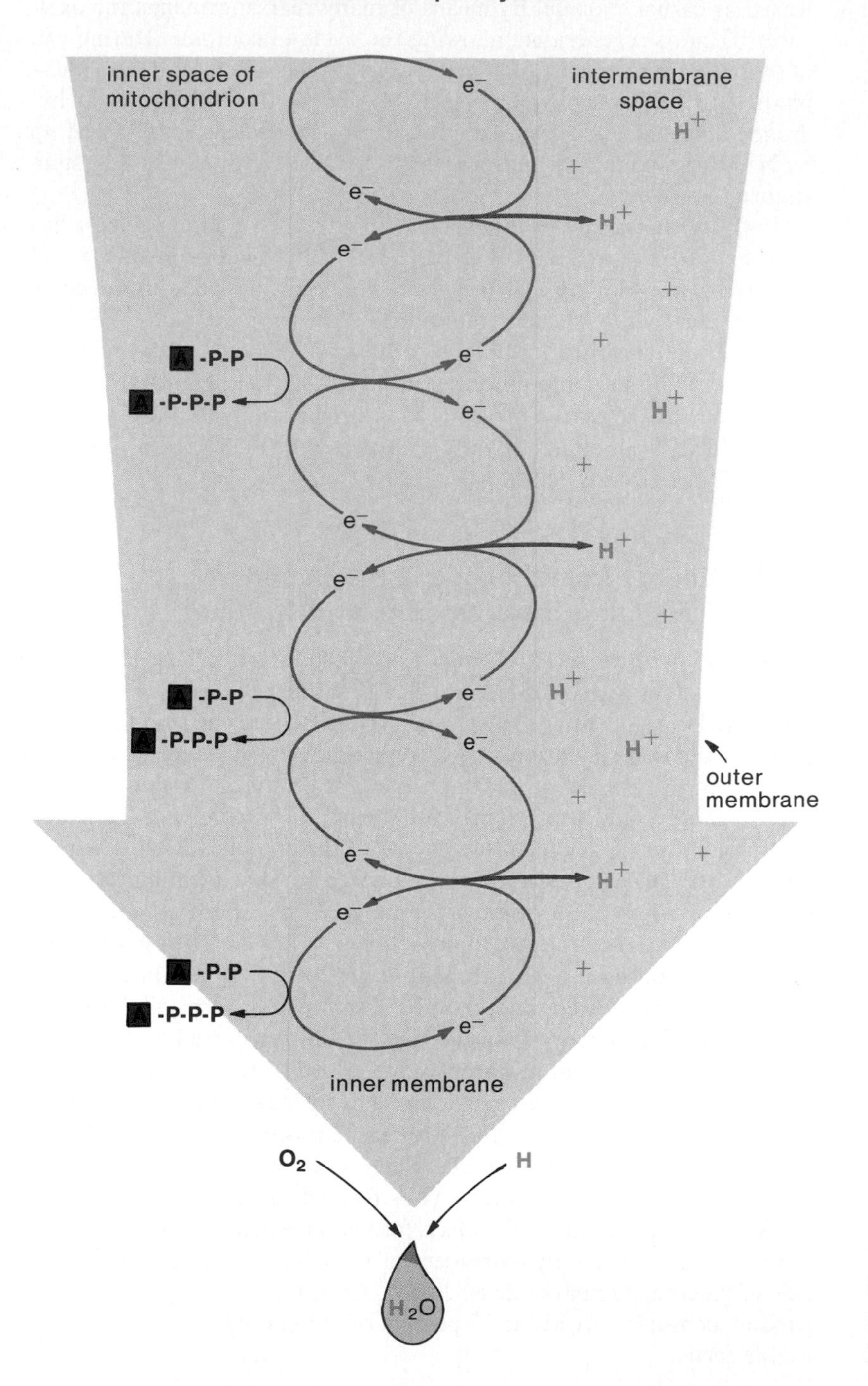

15.12 The Krebs Cycle Plays a Central Role in Cellular Metabolism

All three classes of foodstuffs—carbohydrates, fats, and proteins—may be used as sources of energy in respiration. Breakdown products of all three eventually enter the Krebs cycle. Carbohydrates can enter the carbon pathway as glucose or pyruvic acid. Fats are first separated into glycerol and fatty acids. Glycerol is converted to one of the 3-carbon intermediates of glycolysis and thus enters the carbon pathway. Fatty acids are broken down to the same 2-carbon fragment as carbohydrates and form acetyl CoA. The acetyl group is then decomposed in the Krebs cycle to give off two molecules of carbon dioxide.

When proteins are used in respiration, they are first decomposed to amino acids. The amino group is removed, and the remaining carbon skeletons may be broken down into the same 2-, 3-, 4-, and 5-carbon molecules that are shown in figure 15.13. These compounds then enter the carbon pathway at various points and are finally decomposed by the Krebs cycle to give off carbon dioxide.

As figure 15.13 shows, the Krebs cycle plays a central role in the carbon pathway. Of equal importance, the intermediate compounds of the Krebs cycle, glycolysis, and the intermediate reactions provide carbon skeletons with which cells can synthesize other compounds. These **biosynthesis** (by oh SIN thuh sis) reactions provide the cell with enzymes and all other materials needed for maintenance, cell repair, and growth.

15.13 Energy Releasing Processes Are Essential to Life

The role of oxygen in cellular respiration cannot be underestimated. Without its presence, the entire process stops because all the electron carrier molecules become "loaded" and cannot transfer their loads. Oxygen is the final acceptor of electrons. If oxygen is not present in sufficient amounts, electron flow stops, and the electron transport system backs up like a plugged drain. NAD^+ is unable to transfer the hydrogens it is carrying and is, therefore, unable to pick up more hydrogens. As a result, the Krebs cycle also stops.

When muscles are severely taxed, as in strenuous exercise, the lungs and circulatory system may be unable to meet the oxygen demands of the muscle cells. Under such conditions, glycolysis continues, even without oxygen, producing two ATPs, pyruvic acid, and NADH. The pyruvic acid does not proceed to the Krebs cycle, however. Instead, two

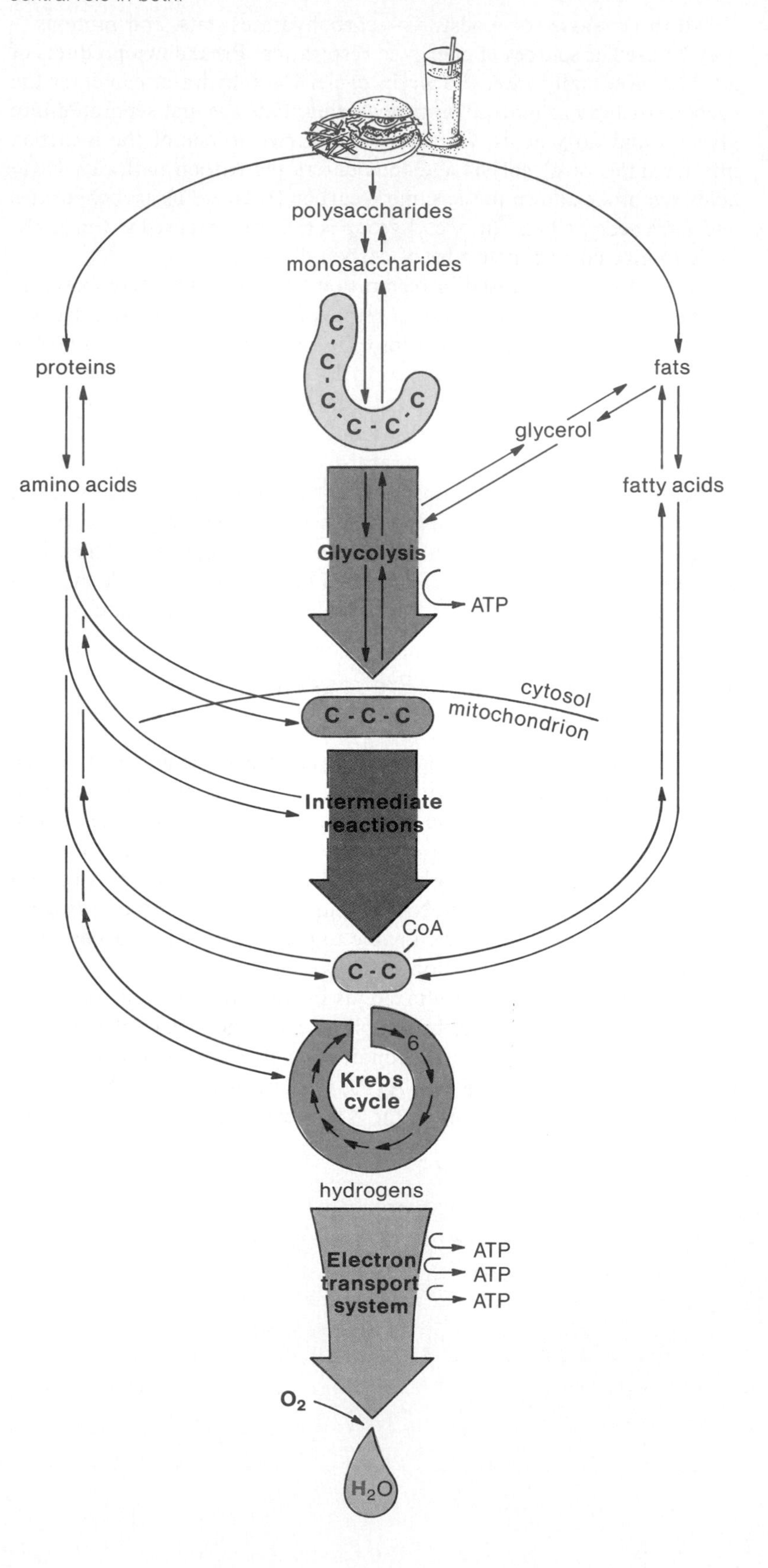

Figure 15.13 Respiratory and biosynthesis pathways. The Krebs cycle plays a central role in both.

Figure 15.14 Conversion of pyruvic acid to lactic acid in muscles. This reaction, in which NADH also is converted to NAD^+, enables glycolysis to continue, supplying energy in the form of ATP to the muscle cells.

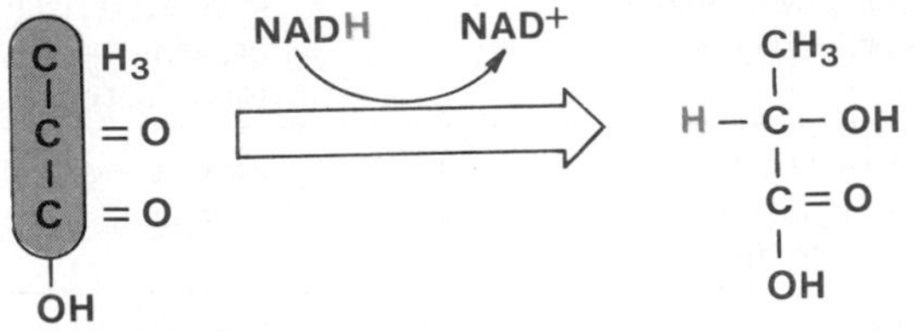

NADH NAD^+

pyruvic acid
(from glycolysis)

lactic acid

hydrogen atoms are transferred from NADH to the pyruvic acid, converting it to the 3-carbon molecule lactic acid (figure 15.14). The NAD^+ is freed to pick up more hydrogen, and glycolysis can continue, providing limited amounts of ATP. The lactic acid accumulates in the muscles, eventually reducing the ability of muscle fibers to contract, and causing muscle fatigue.

To illustrate the vital nature of these processes, consider what happens when they are stopped—for example, by the action of cyanide, one of the fastest acting poisons. It combines chemically with the final carrier in the electron transport system and blocks the production of ATP by the mitochondria. Without ATP, cellular activities cannot continue. A person becomes unconscious within a minute and usually dies within three to six minutes.

Now your lunch has served one of its two purposes—to provide usable energy for your life functions. The second purpose is to reassemble the absorbed molecules into larger molecules to build or repair cells in your body. Usually, this second process, known as biosynthesis, seems to proceed without problems. However, biosynthesis is dependent on the presence of appropriate building materials. Those include the carbon skeletons formed in the carbon pathway as well as various minerals and vitamins that must be obtained in the diet. In the next section we will examine some of the requirements for biosynthesis and some of the ways that today's environment might make it difficult to obtain those requirements.

Self-Review

1. Why can food be considered a fuel?
2. What is the difference between the release of energy in burning and the release of energy in cells?
3. What role does glucose play in cellular respiration?
4. In what chemical compound is energy stored?
5. How are fats and proteins used in cellular respiration?
6. In what ways does the Krebs cycle play a central role in cellular metabolism?

Table 15.1 Vitamins important in humans

Name	Food Sources	Function	Deficiency Symptoms
A, retinol	Liver, green and yellow vegetables, fruits, egg yolks, butter	Formation of visual pigments; cell growth, especially of epithelial cells	Night blindness, flaky skin, lowered resistance to infection, growth stunting, faulty reproduction
D, calciferol	Fish oils, liver, action of sunlight on lipids in skin	Increases calcium absorption from gut; important in bone and tooth formation	Rickets—defective bone formation
E, tocopherol	Oils, whole grains, liver, legumes, green leafy vegetables	Protects red blood cells, plasma membranes, and vitamin A from destruction; important in muscle maintenance	Fragility of red blood cells, muscle wasting
K	Synthesis by intestinal bacteria; green leafy vegetables, cheese, liver	Synthesis of clotting factors by liver	Internal hemorrhaging (deficiency can be caused by oral antibiotics, which kill intestinal bacteria)
B-Complex Vitamins:			
B_1, thiamine	Whole grains, legumes, nuts, liver, heart, kidney, pork	Carbohydrate metabolism	Beriberi, loss of appetite, indigestion, fatigue, nerve irritability, heart failure
B_2, riboflavin	Liver, kidney, heart, yeast, milk, eggs, whole grains	Forms part of electron carrier in electron transport system	Sore mouth and tongue, cracks at corners of mouth, eye irritation, scaly skin
Pantothenic acid	Yeast, liver, eggs, wheat germ, bran, peanuts, peas	Part of Coenzyme A; essential for energy release and biosynthesis	Fatigue, headache, sleep disturbances, nausea, muscle cramps, loss of antibody production
Niacin	Yeast, liver, kidney, heart, meat, fish, poultry, legumes, nuts, whole grains	Coenzyme in energy metabolism; part of NAD^+ and NADP	Pellagra, skin lesions, digestive problems, nerve disorders
B_6, pyridoxine	Whole grains, potatoes, fish, poultry, red meats, legumes, seeds	Coenzyme for amino acid and fatty acid metabolism	Skin disorders, sore mouth and tongue, nerve disorders, anemia, weight loss, impaired antibody response
Biotin	Liver, kidney, yeast, egg yolks, whole grains, fish, legumes, nuts, meats, dairy products; synthesis by intestinal bacteria	Fatty acid, amino acid, and protein synthesis; energy release from glucose	Skin disorders, appetite loss, depression, sleeplessness, muscle pain
Folacin (folic acid)	Liver, yeast, leafy vegetables	Nucleic acid synthesis, amino acid metabolism	Failure of red blood cells to mature, anemia, intestinal disturbances and diarrhea
B_{12}	Liver and organ meats, muscle meats, fish, eggs, shellfish, milk; synthesis by intestinal bacteria	Nucleic acid synthesis	Pernicious anemia
C, ascorbic acid	Citrus fruits, tomatoes, green leafy vegetables	Essential to formation of collagen and intercellular substance; protects against infection; maintains strength of blood vessels; increases iron absorption from gut; important in muscle maintenance	Scurvy, failure to form connective tissue, bleeding, anemia, slow wound healing

Nutrition

Guidepost: What nutrients do humans need for optimal growth and health?

15.14 Our Digestive System Is the Result of Evolution

The function of the digestive system is to break down large molecules and to selectively absorb the resulting smaller molecules, which supply the needs of the cells in your body. However, this system can only utilize the materials that you supply—the food you decide to eat. Assuming that you decided to have that hamburger, fries, and soft drink for lunch, what options have you given your body? Will the food you ingested provide the necessary nutrients for your body to continue growing and functioning?

There are several types of nutrients. Carbohydrates and fats are primary sources of energy. Proteins supply building materials and enzymes but also may be used to provide energy. Vitamins and minerals are essential substances that form cofactors in cellular respiration and other cellular activities. Thus they help to release the energy of carbohydrates, fats, and proteins, and to maintain normal body function. Major functions of the vitamins and minerals are shown in tables 15.1 and 15.2.

Our genes dictate the form and function of our bodies, including the structure and operation of the digestive system. The human genus has existed for about 2 million years, and our prehuman hominid ancestors appeared at least 4 million years ago. During that time the human digestive system evolved in accordance with a dietary selection that changed very little until this century. From the available evidence, that pattern was high in fiber and vegetable matter and low in fat, refined sugar, and salt. During the last 50 years, our diet has become high in fat, refined sugar, and salt, and low in fiber. During that time there also has been a rise in forms of disability and illness that may be partly linked to our new dietary habits.

15.15 Human Dietary Habits Are Related to Health

Recent research indicates that several dietary habits may be responsible for damage to the human body. Those include eating too much processed food, eating too much fat, not eating enough complex carbohydrates, and eating more kcals than are needed or expended.

In 1977, the Senate Select Committee on Nutrition and Human Needs investigated the problem of obesity (excess body fat) and the entire structure of the American diet. Its goal was to promote health and longevity by reducing the incidence of major disorders thought to be linked to our present diet. Among those are heart disease, cancer of the colon, stroke, hypertension (high blood pressure), obesity, diabetes, and diseases of the arteries and the liver. This committee recommended that Americans adopt the following dietary goals:

1. Maintain a balance between kcal intake and kcal expenditure that results in ideal weight.
2. Reduce consumption of sugars that are refined (cane or beet sugar: sucrose) or processed (corn sugar, syrups, molasses, and honey), which are added to foods.

Table 15.2 Minerals important in humans

Name	Food Sources	Function	Deficiency	Excess
Major Minerals				
Calcium (Ca)	Dairy products, green leafy vegetables, eggs, nuts, dried legumes	Development of bones and teeth, muscle contraction, blood clotting, nerve impulse transmission, enzyme activation	Stunted growth, poor quality bones and teeth, rickets, convulsions	Excess blood calcium, loss of appetite, muscle weakness, fever
Chlorine (Cl)	Table salt, most water supplies, bleach	Water balance, hydrochloric acid in stomach	Metabolic alkalosis, constipation, failure to gain weight (in infants)	Vomiting; elemental chlorine is a poison used for chemical warfare
Magnesium (Mg)	Whole grains, liver, kidneys, milk, nuts, green leafy vegetables	Component of chlorophyll; bones and teeth, coenzyme in carbohydrate and protein metabolism	Infertility, menstrual disorders	Loss of reflexes, drowsiness, coma, death
Phosphorus (P)	Dairy foods, egg yolk, meat, whole grains	Development of bones and teeth, energy metabolism, pH balance	Bone fractures, disorders of red blood cells, metabolic problems	As phosphorus increases, calcium decreases; muscle spasm, jaw erosion
Potassium (K)	Whole grains, meat, bananas, vegetables	Body water and pH balance, nerve and muscle activity	Muscle and nerve weakness	Abnormalities in heart beat or stoppage, muscle weakness, mental confusion, cold and pale skin
Sodium (Na)	Table salt, dairy foods, eggs, baking soda and powder, meat, vegetables	Body water and pH balance, nerve and muscle activity	Weakness, muscle cramps, diarrhea, dehydration	High blood pressure, edema, kidney disease
Sulphur (S)	Dairy products, nuts, legumes	Component of some amino acids, enzyme activator	Related to intake and deficiency of sulfur amino acids	Excess sulfur amino acid intake leads to poor growth

3. Increase consumption of complex carbohydrates (polysaccharides) and naturally occurring sugars, which are found in fresh fruits, vegetables, and whole grains.
4. Reduce fat consumption, particularly of saturated fats and those that contain cholesterol.
5. Reduce salt intake.

A comparison of these dietary goals with the current American diet is shown in figure 15.15. What differences and problem areas do you see?

15.16 Fats Play Important Roles in the Body

Lipids are the most concentrated source of food energy available. They release approximately 9 kcals for every gram of fat, compared to only 4 kcals per gram from either proteins or carbohydrates. They aid in cholesterol metabolism and in the absorption of vitamins A, D, E, and K. They are used in the production of hormones and hormonelike substances and structurally, in cellular membranes. They also supply essential fatty acids. **Essential nutrients** are those that the body cannot produce at all or in adequate amounts and that, therefore, must be obtained directly from ingested foods.

Table 15.2 *Continued*

Name	Food Sources	Function	Deficiency	Excess
Trace Minerals				
Cobalt (Co)	Common in foods, meat, milk	Component of Vitamin B_{12}, essential for red blood cell formation	Rare	Dermatitis, excessive production of red corpuscles
Copper (Cu)	Liver, meat, seafood, whole grains, legumes, nuts	Production of hemoglobin, bone formation, component of electron carriers	Anemia, bone and connective tissue disorders, scurvylike conditions, an early death	Toxic concentrations in liver and eyes of persons with genetic inability to metabolize
Fluorine (F)	Most water supplies, seafood	Prevents bacterial tooth decay	Tooth decay, bone weakness	Mottling and brown spots on teeth, deformed teeth and bones
Iodine (I)	Seafood, iodized salt, dairy products	Component of thyroid hormone, which controls cellular respiration	Inadequate synthesis of thyroid hormone, goiter (enlarged thyroid), cretinism	Antithyroid compounds
Iron (Fe)	Liver, meat, eggs, spinach, enriched bread and cereals	Component of hemoglobin (oxygen and electron transport system)	Iron-deficiency anemia, chronic fatigue, weakness	Accidental poisoning of children, cirrhosis of liver
Manganese (Mn)	Liver, kidneys, legumes, cereals, tea, coffee	Ions necessary in protein and carbohydrate metabolism; Krebs cycle	Infertility, menstrual problems	Brain and nervous system disorders
Molybdenum (Mo)	Organ meats, milk, whole grains, leafy vegetables, legumes	Enzyme component	Edema, lethargy, disorientation, and coma	Weight loss, growth retardation, and changes in connective tissue
Zinc (Zn)	Liver, seafoods, common foods	Essential enzyme component; necessary for normal senses of taste and smell	Slow sexual development, loss of appetite, retarded growth	Nausea, bloating, and cramps; depresses copper absorption

Although fats are nutritionally important, Americans in general consume too much and the wrong kind, as you can see in figure 15.15. Two types of lipids are of particular concern: **saturated fats,** which include animal fats such as lard and butter, and **unsaturated fats,** which include most vegetable oils. Fats containing fatty acids with no double carbon bonds (two carbon atoms sharing two chemical bonds) are saturated fats and tend to be solid at room temperature. Fats that contain one or more double carbon bonds in their fatty acids tend to be liquid at room temperature. They are known as monounsaturated or polyunsaturated fats, depending on the number of double carbon bonds present. (Review figure 4.18, page 113.)

Reducing intake of fat, particularly of cholesterol and saturated fat, is important because of the apparent link between high blood cholesterol level and heart disease. Research over the past 30 years has indicated that high dietary intake of both cholesterol and saturated fat tends to elevate blood cholesterol level. Conversely, a diet rich in polyunsaturated fat often has the effect of lowering blood cholesterol. Excess cholesterol can be deposited as bulky fat streaks called plaques on the inner lining of the arteries. The resulting disease, **atherosclerosis** (ATH uh roh skleh roh sis), is caused by an accumulation of plaques that inhibit the flow

Figure 15.15 Content difference between current diets and proposed dietary goals.

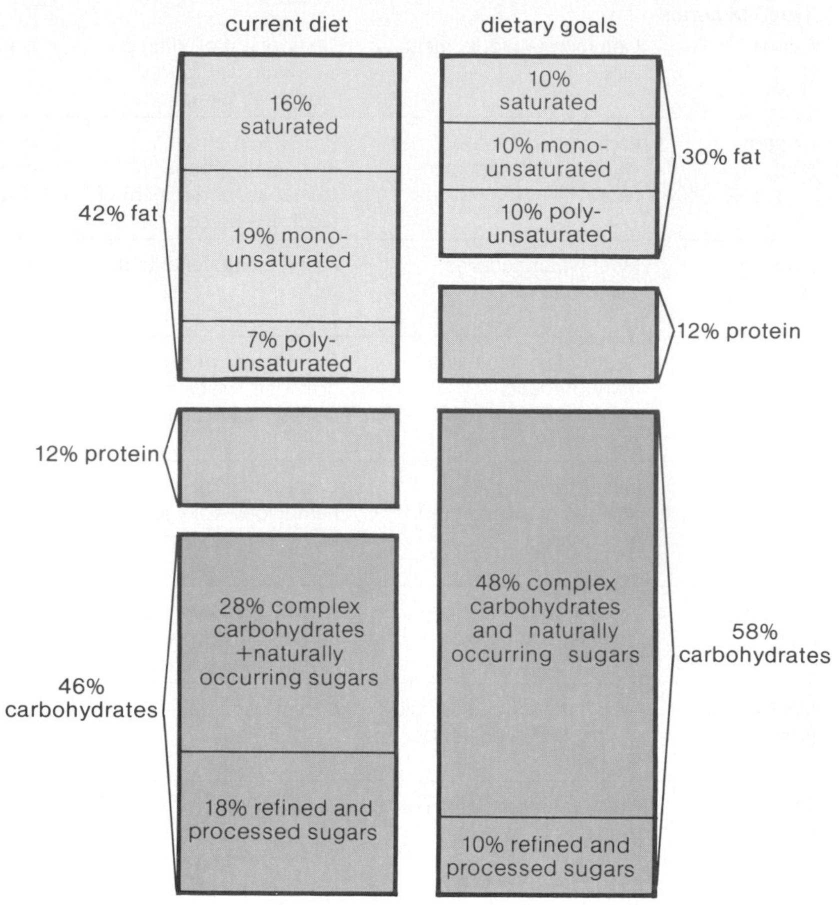

From *Dietary Goals for the United States,* 2nd edition, 1977 (Select Committee on Nutrition and Human Needs).

Figure 15.16 Atherosclerosis occurs as a fatty deposit on the walls of an artery

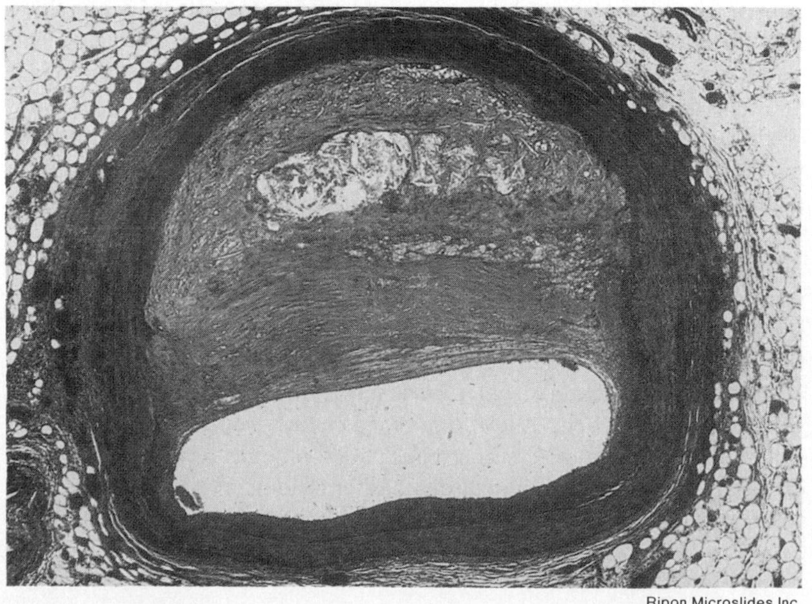

Ripon Microslides Inc.

Table 15.3 Some risk factors associated with heart disease

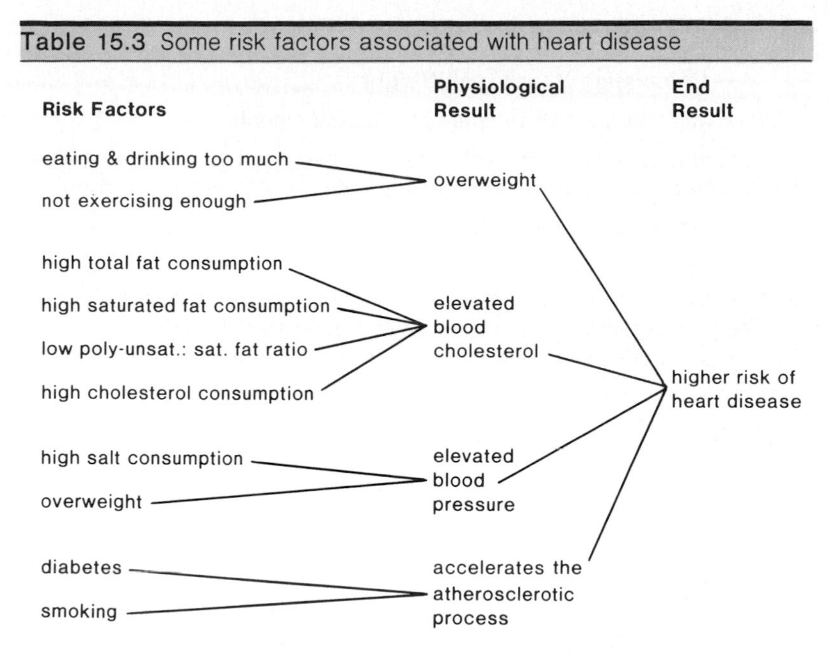

Reprinted from *Dietary Goals for the United States*, 2nd ed, 1977. (Select Committee on Nutrition and Human Needs).

of blood (figure 15.16). A clot might eventually form, blocking the artery and causing a heart attack or stroke. Factors that increase risk of heart disease are shown in table 15.3. Data show that half of all the deaths in the United States are caused by this type of disease.

In the last 30 years, autopsies of individuals between the ages of 18 and 30 have revealed significant development of cholesterol deposits in the arteries. A recent study has shown fatty streaks in arteries of children as young as 2 years, indicating that atherosclerosis might begin in childhood. Thus it becomes important to adopt moderate-fat and moderate-cholesterol diets early in life before life-style patterns have been established. In investigation 15.3, you can evaluate your own risk of developing cardiovascular disease.

Investigation 15.3 ASSESSING RISK FOR CARDIOVASCULAR DISEASE

Introduction

Cardiovascular disease is a leading cause of death in the United States. Several factors are known to contribute to cardiovascular disease. We can control some of these factors, but not others.

In this activity, you will examine your chances of acquiring cardiovascular disease. At your age, you can make appropriate modifications in your life-style that could reduce the risk of developing cardiovascular problems.

Materials (per team of 2 students)

tape measure
bathroom scale
sphygmomanometer (optional)

Procedure

Part A—Calculating Your Ideal Weight

Work with your partner to make the measurements.

1. Measure your wrists in centimeters at their smallest circumferences. Add both measurements and divide them by 2 to get an average.

$$\frac{\text{left wrist} + \text{right wrist}}{2} = \text{average}$$

2. Measure your forearms, calves, and ankles at their largest circumferences. Calculate an average for each as in step 1.
3. Add the 4 averages (wrist + forearm + calf + ankle) and divide the sum by 17.07 for males, 16.89 for females.

$$\frac{\text{wrist} + \text{forearm} + \text{calf} + \text{ankle}}{17.07 \text{ or } 16.89} = \text{quotient}$$

4. Square the quotient (quotient × quotient = _____).
5. Measure your height in centimeters without shoes.
6. Multiply your answer in step 4 by your height.
   height × quotient² = _____
7. Then, multiply the answer in step 6 by 0.0111 to obtain your "ideal" weight. (This answer is in kilograms. To convert this value to pounds, multiply it by 2.2.)

   $\text{height} \times \text{quotient}^2 \times 0.0111 \times 2.2 = \text{ideal weight in pounds}$

8. Determine your actual weight by weighing yourself on a bathroom scale. Compare your actual weight with your ideal weight. Is your real weight over, under, or equal to your ideal weight?
9. Find the difference between your actual and ideal weight.

Part B—A Self-Check

1. Take the self-check below. If you do not have a sphygmomanometer, omit item 6 of the self-check.
2. After completing the self-check, use the self-check score interpretation to determine your risk of cardiovascular disease.

Self-Check

Directions: Please read each item and score the appropriate number in the space to the right of the number.

Points for each item:

1. _____ Statistics show that males are more likely to suffer heart attacks than females. If you are (a) male, score 1 point, or (b) female, score 0.
2. _____ Heredity can influence your chances of heart disease. If one or more of your parents, grandparents, or siblings have suffered a heart attack, you may have an inherited tendency toward this condition. If one or more of your parents, grandparents, or siblings have suffered a heart attack (a) before age 60, score 12 points, (b) after age 60, score 6 points, or (c) neither a nor b, score 0.
3. _____ Diabetes is related to heart disease in that a person with diabetes is more likely to build up fatty deposits in the arteries. If you have (a) diabetes and are now taking insulin or pills, score 10 points, or (b) no diabetes or can control it with diet, score 0.

4. _____ Smoking has been shown to contribute to cardiovascular disease. Substances inhaled during smoking damage the lining of blood vessels. If you (a) smoke 2 packs or more per day, score 10 points, (b) smoke 1–2 packs per day or quit less than a year ago, score 6 points, (c) smoke less than 1 pack per day or quit 1–10 years ago, score 3 points, or (d) never smoked, score 0.
5. _____ High amounts of cholesterol in the diet can clog or narrow the arteries. This places added stress on the heart and arteries. If you eat (a) 1 serving of red meat per day, over 7 eggs per week, use butter, whole milk, and cheese daily, score 8 points, (b) red meat 5–6 times a week, 4–7 eggs per week, use margarine, low-fat dairy products, and some cheese, score 4 points, or (c) poultry, fish, and little or no red meat, 3 or fewer eggs per week, use margarine and skim milk, score 0.
6. _____ High blood pressure increases the heart's work and places wear and tear on blood vessels. If you are able to measure your blood pressure, score this item. Otherwise, omit a score. If your blood pressure at rest measures (a) 160/150, score 8 points, (b) between 160/105 and 140/90, score 4 points, or (c) less than 140/90, score 0.
7. _____ Overweight people run a higher risk of heart disease than those not overweight. (Refer to the calculation of the difference between your ideal and actual weight—item 9 in part A.) If you are (a) 25 pounds overweight, score 4 points, (b) 10–25 pounds overweight, score 2 points, or (c) less than 10 pounds overweight, score 0.
8. _____ Aerobic exercise is that type of activity that temporarily increases your heartrate, stimulates sweat production, and causes deep breathing (jogging, bicycling, swimming, and similar activities). If you engage in aerobic exercise (a) less than once per week, score 2 points, (b) 1–2 times per week, score 1 point, or (c) 3 or more times per week, score 0.

_____ Total Score

Self-Check Score Interpretation

Total Score	Risk of Heart Attack, Stroke, or Cardiovascular Disease
26 points or more	high risk
25–14 points	medium risk
13 points or less	low risk

Use the following information if item 6 (blood pressure analysis) was omitted.

22 points or more	high risk
21–12 points	medium risk
11 points or less	low risk

Discussion

In the first part of this activity, you calculated your ideal weight. The value you obtained is an approximation of what your body weight should be. It is normal for your actual weight to vary 1 to 10 pounds from your ideal weight.

Kcal Tally

Meat

140 Beef pot roast, lean only (2 thin slices, 4″ x 2″)
85 Ham, boiled, 1 slice
245 Hamburger patty
115 Meat loaf, 1 slice
130 Pork chop, 1 lean

Chicken

105 Bread stuffing, ½ cup
215 Chicken breast, ½, fried
185 Chicken, ¼, broiled
485 Chicken potpie, individual
150 Turkey, light, 1 slice
173 Turkey, dark, 1 slice

Fish

40 Fishstick, 1, breaded
230 Halibut, 1 steak, broiled
195 Ocean Perch, breaded, fried, 1 piece
215 Tuna, in oil, ½ cup
110 Tartar Sauce, 1 tablespoon

Dairy

100 Butter or margarine, 1 tbs
59 Cheese, American, 1 slice
60 Cottage cheese, ¼ cup
165 Milk, whole, 1 glass

Main Dishes

460 Beef potpie, 1 individual
180 Beef stew, 1 cup
170 Chili con carne with beans, canned, ½ cup
240 Macaroni & cheese, ½ cup
153 Pizza, cheese, ⅛″ wedge
157 Pizza, sausage, ⅛″ wedge
215 Spaghetti w/meat sauce, ¾ cup

Salads

50 Coleslaw
245 Potato salad, ½ cup
185 Waldorf salad, ½ cup

Sandwiches

280 Bacon and tomato
360 Bologna
330 Cheese
545 Cheeseburger
445 Hamburger
265 Egg salad
280 Hot dog, 1 bun
310 Roast beef
360 Salami

Soups

190 Bean, navy, 1 cup
100 Beef, 1 cup
100 Chicken noodle, 1 cup
140 Split-pea, 1 cup
185 Potato, 1 cup
90 Tomato, 1 cup
80 Vegetable, 1 cup

Vegetables

165 Beans, baked w/pork, 1 cup
15 Beans, green, snap, wax, or yellow, cooked, ½ cup
75 Beans, Lima, ½ cup
35 Beets, diced, ½ cup
15 Cauliflower, ½ cup
5 Cucumber, 6 thin slices
5 Lettuce leaves, 4 small
60 Peas, green, ½ cup
15 Pepper, green, 1 medium
90 Potato, baked or boiled, 1
110 Potato chips, 10 medium
155 Potatoes, French-fried, 10
240 Potatoes, fried, ½ cup
235 Potatoes, hashed brown, ½ cup
115 Potatoes, mashed, ½ cup
15 Sauerkraut, ½ cup
30 Tomato, fresh, 1 medium

Desserts

330 Apple pie, 1 slice
420 Chocolate cake, fudge icing, 2″ wedge
80 Gelatin, plain, ½ cup
300 Lemon meringue pie, 1 slice
265 Pumpkin pie, 1 slice

Breakfast Dishes

95 Bacon, 2 crisp strips
76 Bread, white, 1 slice
85 Cornflakes, 1 cup
135 Doughnut, cake type
100 Egg, fried
80 Egg, poached, hard cooked
110 Egg, scrambled
60 Griddle cake, 4-inch cake
110 Oatmeal, cooked, ¾ cup
170 Pork sausage, 2″ patty
95 Pork sausage, 1 link
100 Shredded wheat, 1 biscuit

Fruits

70 Apple, raw, 1 medium
75 Grapefruit
70 Orange
35 Peach
100 Pear
35 Raspberries, red, ½ cup
30 Strawberries, ½ cup

Drinks

117 Apple juice, 1 cup
175 Cocoa (all milk), ¾ cup
0 Coffee or tea
144 Cola, 12 ozs
1 Cola, diet, 12 ozs
75 Grape juice, ½ cup
190 Milk, skim, chocolate, 1 glass
135 Orange juice, 1 cup

Candies/Cookies/Snacks

110 Animal Crackers, 10
97 Brownie, plain, w/nuts
103 Brownie, frosted, w/nuts
145 Candy bar, chocolate, 1 oz
100 Chocolate kisses, 5
110 Cookie, plain, 3″
90 Marshmallow
50 Oreo
105 Peanuts, 10
23 Popcorn, plain, 1 cup
41 Popcorn, oil & salt
134 Popcorn, sugar coated
50 Pretzels, 3-ring, 10

The second part of this activity dealt with an assessment of your chances of acquiring cardiovascular disease. The information you obtained in this section should be used only as a guide. However, this information can be useful in examining your life-style. Using this information, please respond to the following questions:

1. Based on your self-check score, do you appear to have a high, medium, or low risk of cardiovascular disease?
2. What aspects of your life that could increase your chances of cardiovascular disease are you incapable of changing?
3. What modifications, if any, can you make in your life-style to reduce your chances of having cardiovascular disease?

For Further Investigation

Does your daily diet have the proper number of kcals to maintain your ideal weight? To find this out, keep a record of what you eat for 5 days. Obtain an average of your kcal intake for the 5 days. Find out if your average kcal intake is appropriate for your weight. (A quick calculation to determine your approximate kcal needs per day is: ideal weight $\times$ 15 = kcal needs per day.)

15.17 Carbohydrates Provide Energy, Nutrients, and Fiber

Fruits, vegetables, and whole grains are important in the diet because, in addition to providing the carbohydrates that are the body's primary source of energy, they provide minerals and vitamins essential to good health. Refined sugars, on the other hand, provide only kcals—"empty" kcals with no other nutrients. In the United States between 1910 and 1976, the annual consumption of refined sugar and related sweeteners increased 32 percent. During the same period, consumption of fresh fruit decreased by 43 percent, while that of processed fruits increased 275 percent. Consumption of soft drinks doubled between 1962 and 1975, and in 1980, carbonated beverages accounted for 20 percent of all refined sugar used. Other reports indicate that 3 of every 5 kcals ingested by Americans come from fats or added sugars.

Figure 15.17 Some high-fiber foods.

BSCS by Doug Sokell

In the American diet, processed and convenience foods with their high content of refined sugar are increasingly replacing more nutritious foods that supply vitamins and minerals. Refined and processed sugars are added to almost every type of processed and convenience food. The food industry has many terms for the sugars and sweeteners it uses, such as sucrose, raw sugar, turbinado sugar, brown sugar, total invert sugar, corn syrup, honey, fructose, levulose, dextrose, lactose, and others. All can contribute significantly to obesity and to the $10 billion-a-year dental bill for cavities alone. In some cases, because of the current labeling laws, it is not possible for consumers to determine how much refined or processed sugar they actually consume.

Fruits, vegetables, and whole grains are also sources of dietary fiber or roughage. Dietary fiber consists of cellulose and other carbohydrates that are abundant in plants and in unprocessed plant foods. Humans do not have the necessary enzymes to digest those substances. Instead, fiber absorbs water rather like a sponge, causing bulkier feces that move more quickly and easily through the large intestine.

The current emphasis on fiber intake began with some observations made by a number of British physicians. They noted the reduced incidence of diseases such as cancer of the colon and atherosclerosis in certain African rural villages. The diet of those villagers is low in processed food and high in fiber. However, when those villagers moved to urban areas and began eating the low-fiber, high-fat diet of Western cultures, they suffered occurrences of the same diseases as longtime urban dwellers. The physicians proposed the hypothesis that a high-fiber diet would protect against the diseases of Western cultures. That hypothesis, however, is still being tested, and caution is advised in adding large amounts of fiber to the diet. Bran, in particular, may interfere with absorption of calcium and other minerals.

15.18 Protein Provides Your Body Framework

Protein is needed daily for repair and maintenance of body tissues, as well as for normal growth and development. Protein is important in the diet because it supplies the amino acids we need to make our own protein. Humans can synthesize 8 to 10 of the 20 amino acids they need.

Figure 15.18 Beans are rich in lysine (LYS) but deficient in the sulfur-containing amino acids methionine (MET) and cystine (CYS). Wheat is deficient in lysine but strong in methionine and cystine. When eaten together in a 1:1 ratio, beans and wheat provide a good balance of these essential amino acids.

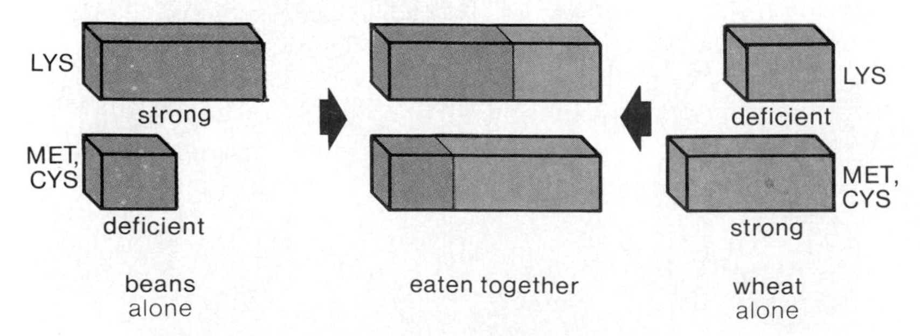

The others—the essential amino acids—must be present in our food. Eggs, milk, fish, soybeans, cheese, meat, and poultry provide **complete proteins.** Complete proteins are those that contain all of the essential amino acids in the proportions needed by the body. Grains, nuts, and seeds also are good sources of protein, but they usually provide neither all of the essential amino acids nor the required amounts or proportions. However, it is possible to obtain complete protein by combining those foods so that a missing amino acid in one is provided by the other. Grains and milk, grains and legumes (beans, peas, and peanuts), and legumes and nuts are examples of such combinations. Vegetarian diets should contain a balance of soybean products, leafy dark-green vegetables, and some dairy products to supply the necessary balance of amino acids.

Most Americans exceed the protein requirement of 0.5 to 0.8 g per kilogram body weight per day. Contrary to popular claims, excess protein does not cause "muscle building." Instead, it is respired to provide energy or converted to fat and stored.

15.19 Eating Disorders Are Widespread

In attempting to reduce caloric intake and, thereby, lose weight, many individuals fall victim to eating disorders. These victims are usually teenage girls and young women. One of these disorders is **bulimia** (byoo LIM ee uh). Typically, the individual will overeat and then attempt to get rid of the kcals through self-induced vomiting or by using laxatives.

Another disorder, **anorexia** (an oh REX see uh), is characterized by a rapid and substantial weight loss due to self-starvation or extreme dieting. Some individuals may exhibit eating patterns of both bulimia and anorexia. This is referred to as **bulimarexia** (byoo lih muh REX see uh). Since 1980, these disorders have increased at a rate unparalleled in medical history. It is now estimated that 1 out of 5 college-going women suffers from bulimia, and 1 in every 100 teenage girls or young women exhibits anorexic habits. Only 1 out of every 10 persons suffering from an eating disorder is a male.

Those persons who suffer from either of these diseases have an irrational fear of being fat, have low self-esteem, and are unable to see themselves as they actually are. Even in advanced cases, where the individuals may weigh only half of their original weight, they still perceive themselves as fat. The disease may result in the cessation of the menstrual cycle, skin rashes and dry skin, loss of hair and nail quality, dental cavities, and gum diseases. The sufferer may require hospitalization and therapeutic interventions such as behavior modification and individual or group therapy. In its extreme form, affected individuals may die from damage to vital organs, heart failure, rupture of the esophagus, or other causes. The mortality rate of these disorders is, perhaps, the highest of any condition classified as a psychiatric disorder. Even diagnosis of these disorders is a problem. It is important to consult a doctor if an eating disorder is suspected.

Figure 15.19 Anorexia—an eating disorder that can, if untreated, lead to death.

15.20 Americans Consume too many Kcals and in the Wrong Proportion

Americans now consume about 3 percent fewer kcals than they did in 1910, but they have become so sedentary that 2 out of every 5 are overweight. Furthermore, the intake of refined sugars and animal fats has increased, with the result that some overweight individuals are actually malnourished due to the absence of essential nutrients in their diets. The problem is that the average American takes in more food than his or her body requires but does not ingest the proper amounts of basic and essential nutrients.

Table 15.4 Analysis of a fast food lunch

	Kcals	Protein (grams)	Carbohydrates (grams)	Fats (grams)
Hamburger	606	29	51	32
Fries	215	3	28	10
Soft drink	145	0	41	0
Totals:	966	32	120	42

Age	Sex	Recommended Daily Kcal Intake	Kcals in this Meal		Percentage of Total Kcals
15–18	Male	2800	966	=	34.5
15–18	Female	2100	966	=	46.0

Nutrient (energy content)	Grams	×	Kcal/g	=	Total Kcals	Actual Percentage of Daily Kcal Intake	Recommended Percentage of Daily Kcal Intake
Protein (4 kcal/g)	32	×	4	=	128	4.6 (male) 6.1 (female)	12 12
Carbohydrates (3.8 kcal/g)	120	×	3.8	=	456	17.1 (male) 22.9 (female)	58* 58*
Fats (9.1 kcal/g)	42	×	9.1	=	382	13.5 (male) 18.0 (female)	30** 30**

*Only 10% of the total carbohydrate intake should be refined carbohydrates—77% of the carbohydrate in this lunch is refined.

**Only 10% of the total fat intake should be saturated fats—all of the fat in this lunch is saturated.

Does your diet supply you with all the nutrients you need? Look at table 15.4, an analysis of your fast food lunch. If you are a male between the ages of 15 and 18 years, you have consumed 34.5 percent of your daily recommended kcal allowance. But if you are a female in the same age group, you took in 46 percent of your kcals for the day. Those kcal recommendations are based on activities for the average high school student, which include walking to school and some daily physical activity, such as physical education class. If you are on one of the athletic teams and work out regularly, your allowance would be increased. If you are less active, then the number of kcals may have to be decreased to avoid gaining weight.

Of the carbohydrates in your lunch, only 28 g, or 23 percent, are complex carbohydrates. The 92 g of refined carbohydrates represents 77 percent of the total carbohydrate intake, rather than the recommended 10 percent. All of the 378 kcals of fats eaten are probably saturated fats. Current recommendations state that only 10 percent of the total daily intake of fats should be saturated fats.

Many questions about diet and nutrition remain to be answered by research. Until more information becomes available, the most reasonable recommendation is to eat a variety of foods in moderation and to reduce intake of processed and convenience foods.

Self-Review

1. What are the basic food molecules the human body needs to function properly?
2. What are the three major causes of dietary damage to the human body?
3. What are the major sources of refined sugar in our diet?
4. What are the possible problems related to excess fat intake?
5. What is the role of cellulose in our diet?
6. What problems are associated with taking in too many or too few kcals?

Summary

Digestion is the process by which food is broken down into small molecules. The process begins with mechanical breakdown in the mouth, and successive stages take place in the various compartments of the gut. Most of the chemical breakdown occurs in the upper part of the small intestine, in the presence of specific digestive enzymes. The end products of digestion are absorbed from the small intestine and delivered to the cells by the blood and lymph. Inside the cell, the food molecules may be stored, respired to obtain usable energy, or used to synthesize other necessary molecules.

In cellular respiraton, the energy stored in food molecules is converted to the "small change" of ATP molecules. The reactions of respiration take place in the cytosol and mitochondria, and in addition to providing usable energy in the form of ATP, provide carbon skeletons for biosynthesis. Carbohydrates, especially glucose, are the major source of energy in respiration, but fats and proteins also can be respired. These nutrients, as well as vitamins and minerals that are required in small amounts, must be supplied in the diet. Increased intake of processed foods, fats, and refined sugars by Americans and people of other industrialized nations appears to be related to major health problems such as obesity and heart disease.

Application Questions

1. How is chemical digestion related to the chemical syntheses carried on by cells?
2. What changes occur in the pH of the human digestive system as food passes through it?
3. Why are feces semisolid though digested food in the small intestine is semiliquid?
4. Contrast the major events of glycolysis and the Krebs cycle with the electron transport system. Which of these reactions yields more energy?
5. Explain the central role of the Krebs cycle in both cellular respiration and cellular synthesis reactions.
6. Why do we need complete proteins in our diet?
7. In what ways are vitamins and minerals important to health?

Problems

1. What are some of the factors in our society that might cause a high school student to become anorexic or bulimic?
2. People living in different parts of the world have very different diets. Most of the population in Africa, Asia, and Australia cannot drink milk. Investigate why that is so.
3. Because of the success of the artificial kidney a biomedical engineer wished to design an artificial digestive system. What major functions would you have to build into the artificial digestive system?

Suggested Readings

M. S. Brown and J. L. Goldstein, "How LDL Receptors Influence Cholesterol and Atherosclerosis" *Scientific American* (November 1984). Explains what LDL receptors are and why Americans have too few of them.

S. B. Eaton and M. Konner, "Paleolithic Nutrition: A Consideration of Its Nature and Current Implications" *The New England Journal of Medicine* (31 January 1985). Discusses the diet of early humans and how it has affected our current genetic composition, and compares modern nutrition with that for which we are genetically programmed.

G. Kolata, "How Important Is Dietary Calcium in Preventing Osteoporosis?" *Science* (1 August 1986). Reports on the latest research on the importance of dietary calcium.

T. Monmaney, "Vitamins: Much Ado About Milligrams" *Science 86* (January/February 1986). Concerns the controversy of establishing and revising Recommended Dietary Allowances (RDAs).

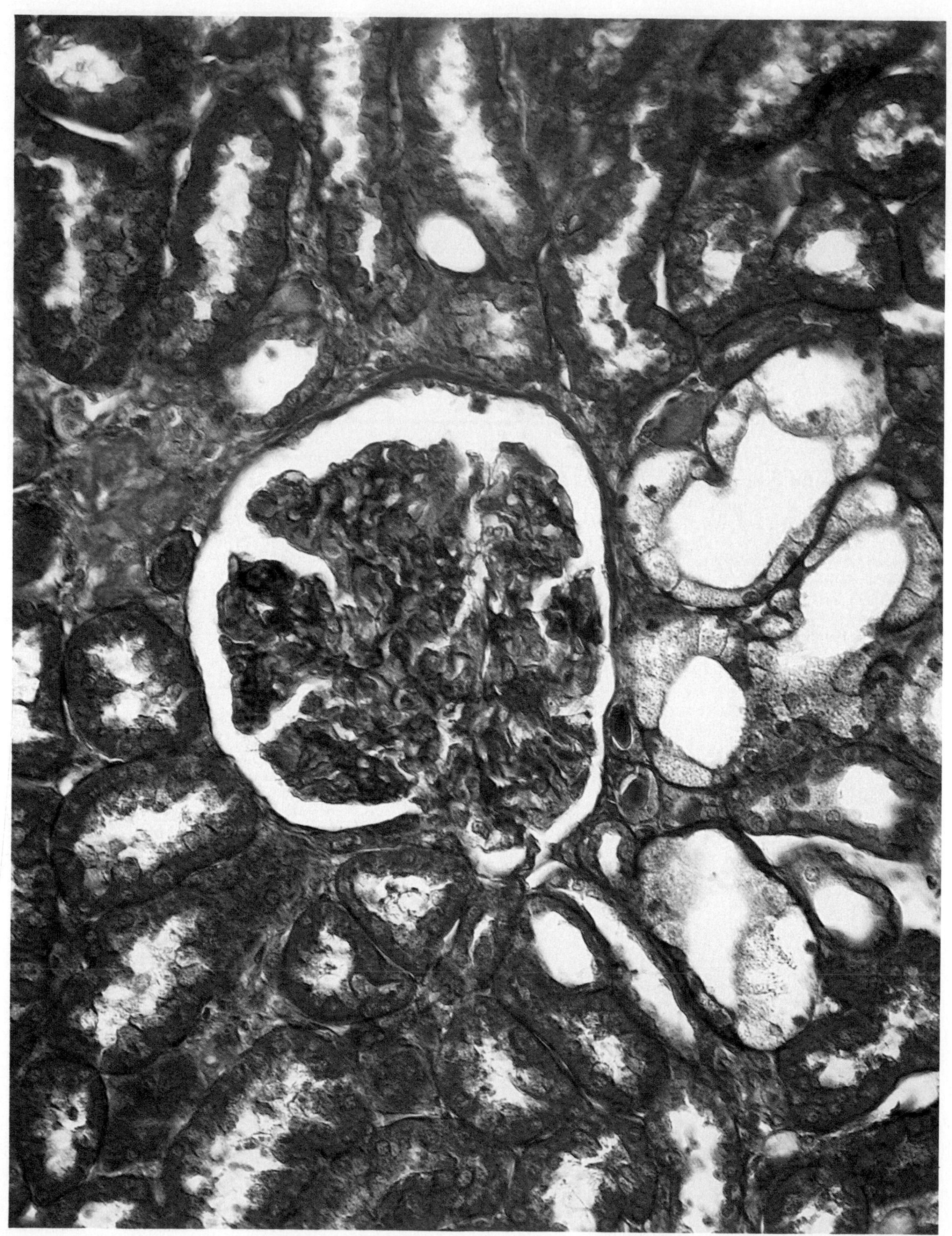

Ed Reschke

The kidney plays a major role in maintaining homeostasis. Kidney tubules surround a glomerulus in this stained cross section.

CHAPTER 16

The Human Animal: Maintenance of Internal Environment

Introduction

Once you have eaten, digested, and absorbed a meal into the cells of the digestive tract, there still remains the process of distribution. Not only must the absorbed food molecules be delivered, but they must be carefully controlled so the supply of food suits the needs of the cells. Excesses may be as harmful as shortages. This balance is part of the homeostasis of the body.

In the last chapter we followed the fate of a typical luncheon as it became the source of building materials and energy for your body. In this chapter we will trace the route by which this food is delivered to the working cells of your body by the circulatory system. We will examine how cells are supplied with oxygen and other necessary substances, and how wastes are removed. Because the warm, liquid environment of the cells is very desirable to hostile organisms, we will study how the immune system defends your body against them. We will see how the circulatory, respiratory, excretory, and immune systems interact to regulate the internal environment of the body.

Circulation

Guidepost: How does the circulatory system distribute materials to all functioning cells?

16.1 Pushed by the Heart's Pumping Action, Blood Circulates through a Series of Tubes

Humans, like most animals that have a body fluid, have a system of tubes through which fluid flows—a circulatory system. A muscular pump (heart) propels a fluid containing special cells (blood) through tubes (vessels). The direction of flow is controlled by valves inside the tubes.

The basic function of a circulatory system is to transport materials throughout an organism's body. This system provides the raw materials needed by the cells and removes wastes from the cells' environment.

Human circulation occurs in a closed system. A single, muscular heart with four chambers pumps blood through the system. There are three kinds of blood vessels. **Arteries** have rather thick muscular walls and carry blood away from the heart. **Veins** have relatively thin walls with less muscle. They carry blood toward the heart. **Capillaries** (KAP ih layr eez) are thin-walled, narrow tubes that connect arteries and veins.

Figure 16.1 A simplified drawing of the human circulatory system. Oxygen-rich blood is shown in red, oxygen-poor blood in blue.

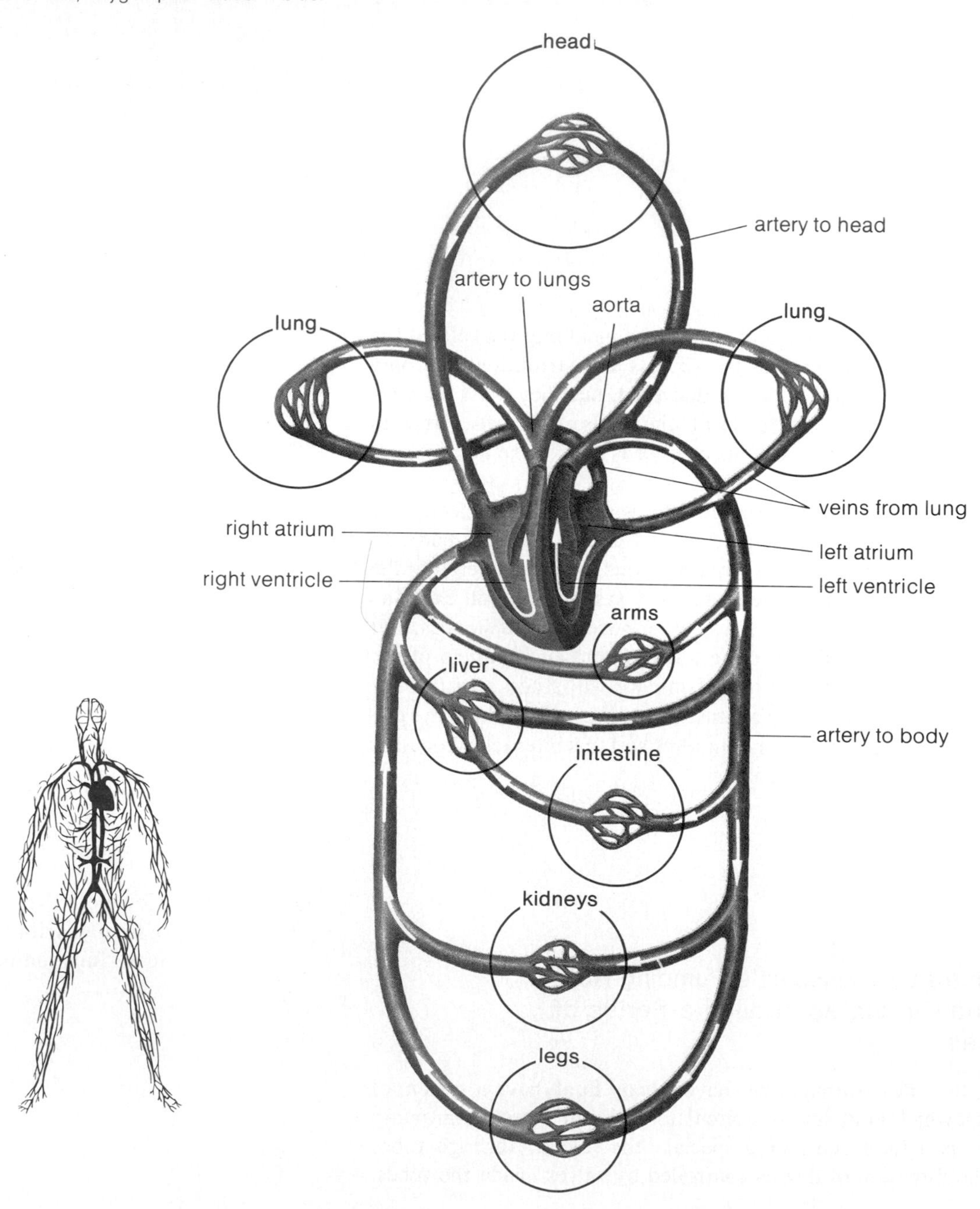

By ingenious experiments, William Harvey in the 17th century showed that blood leaves a vertebrate heart through arteries and returns to the heart through veins. He reasoned that blood circulates, but never actually saw blood passing from arteries to veins, because the use of microscopes was not yet widespread. Later in the century, another scientist first observed capillaries connecting the arteries and veins (figure 16.2). This observation confirmed Harvey's reasoning about circulation.

In humans, as in all mammals and birds, the heart is separated into right and left sides. Each side has its own set of veins and arteries. In humans, the right side receives blood from almost all parts of the body and then sends it to the lungs. The left side receives oxygenated blood from the lungs and returns it to all parts of the body. Each side has two chambers. The first chamber, or **atrium** (AY tree um), forms the upper part of the heart and receives incoming blood from the tissues of the body. The thin-walled atrium bulges with this blood, and as the lower heart muscle relaxes, the blood flows into a second chamber, the thick muscular **ventricle** (VEN trih kul). These structures show clearly in figure 16.3.

Figure 16.2 A typical capillary bed.

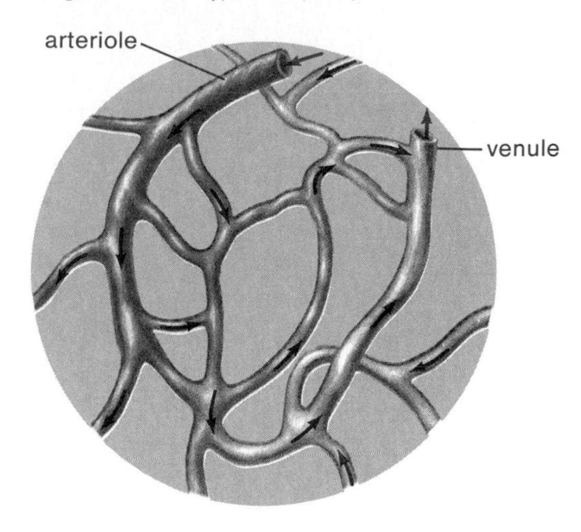

Figure 16.3 A drawing of a section through a human heart and the blood vessels leading to and from it.

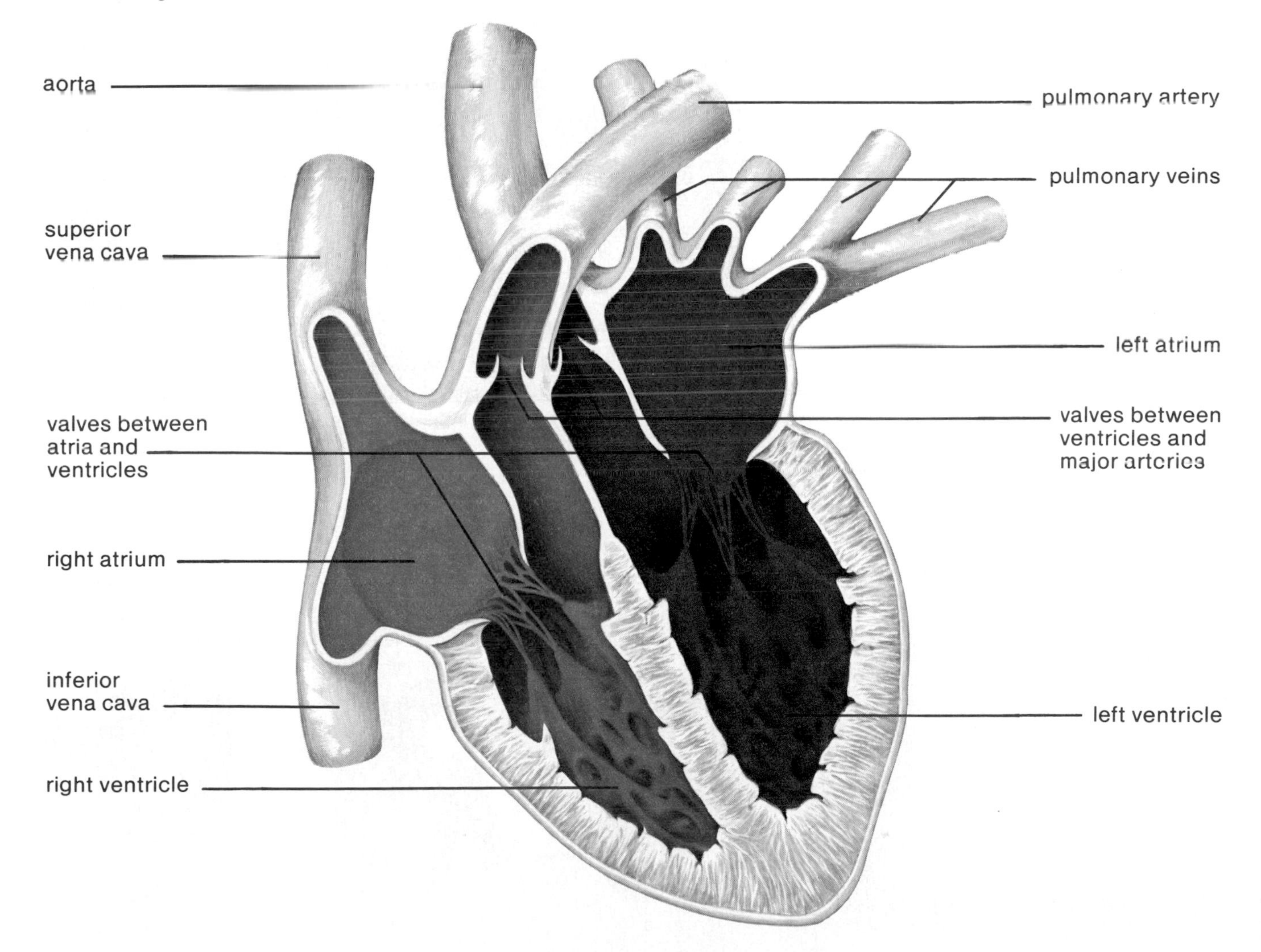

The atrium and the ventricle are separated by tissue flaps called valves (figure 16.4). The structure of these valves prevents blood from flowing back into the atrium when the ventricle contracts. When the contraction occurs, the muscular wall of the ventricle squeezes the blood, forcing closed the tissue flaps between the two chambers. That prevents backflow into the atrium, and the blood is forced out of the heart into an artery. When blood is pumped from the heart, the flaps at the entrance to the artery are forced against the artery wall. Blood then can flow through the vessel away from the heart. When the ventricles relax between heartbeats, back pressure of the blood forces the flaps away from the artery wall. They block the artery so that blood cannot flow back toward the heart. In the veins, blood flow is helped by contraction of surrounding muscles, as shown in figure 16.6. Valves prevent backflow, so the blood flows only toward the heart.

Figure 16.4 Valves of the human heart.

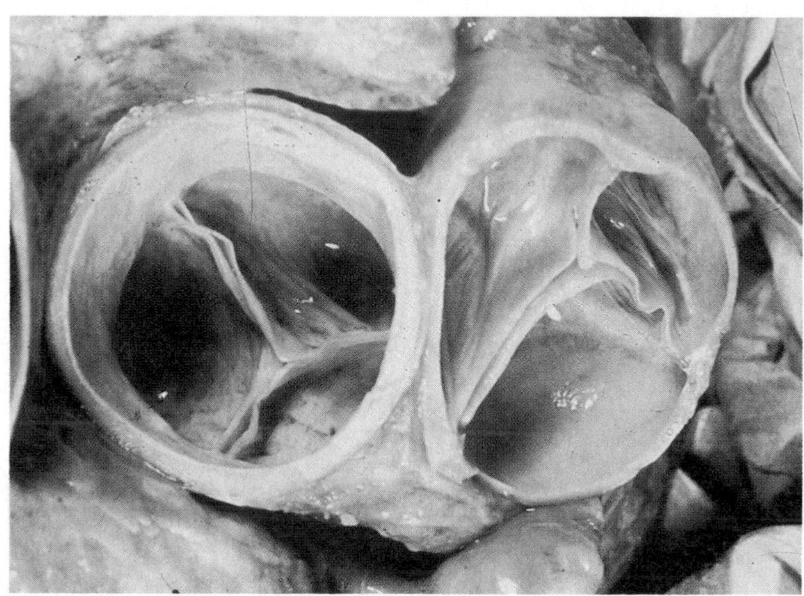

C. Yokochi and J. W. Rohen, Photographic Anatomy of the Human Body, 2nd ed., 1978.

Figure 16.5 Three steps in the pumping action of a mammalian heart. Why does the blood not flow back into the arteries when the ventricles contract?

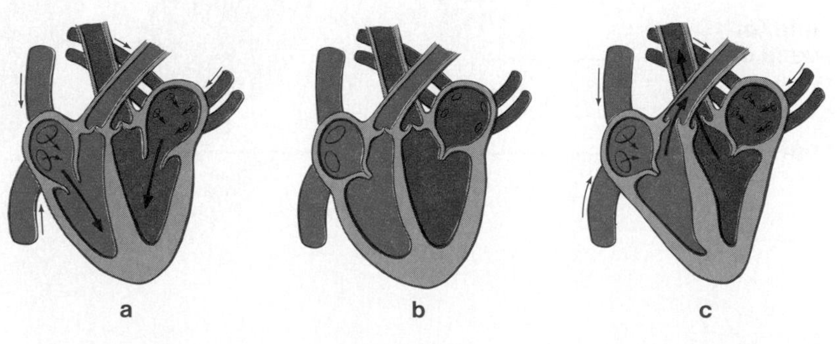

Figure 16.6 Movement of blood in veins is brought about by pressure from adjacent muscles. Compression forces blood in both directions, but valves prevent blood from flowing backward, away from the heart.

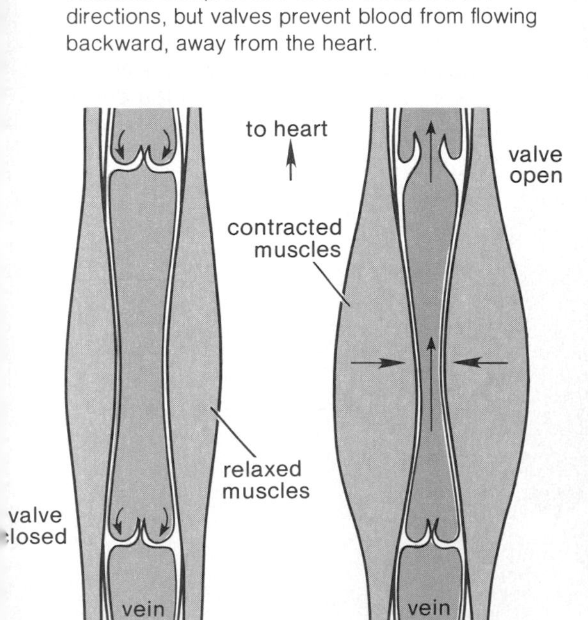

Capillary walls are only one cell layer thick. As blood flows through the capillaries, some substances move from the blood through the thin walls into the body tissues. Other substances move from the tissues into the blood at the same time. The exchange of materials occurs by diffusion, because substances in the tissues and in the blood are present in unequal concentrations.

16.2 Blood Consists of Cells Suspended in a Liquid Known as Plasma

Blood is a complex tissue formed of cells and other substances suspended in **plasma** (PLAZ muh), a clear straw-colored liquid. Plasma is 90 percent water and 10 percent dissolved substances. The dissolved substances consist of about 8 percent proteins, called plasma proteins, and 0.9 percent minerals. The other 1.1 percent includes absorbed food molecules such as simple sugars, amino acids, and fatty acids, as well as respiratory gases (oxygen and carbon dioxide), waste products, and regulatory substances (hormones and enzymes).

Some of the plasma proteins play important roles in homeostatic functions, such as blood clotting and maintenance of blood osmotic pressure. Others are essential products of the immune system, which protects the body against invasion by organisms or foreign particles.

The two types of human blood cells, red cells and white cells, are manufactured in the bone marrow. Red blood cells are specialized for the transport of oxygen. As a red cell matures, it loses its nucleus and other cell structures. It becomes filled with **hemoglobin** (HEE moh gloh bin), an iron-containing pigment that combines readily with oxygen.

Figure 16.7 The exchange of materials at a capillary. What do you think is happening at points 1, 2, and 3?

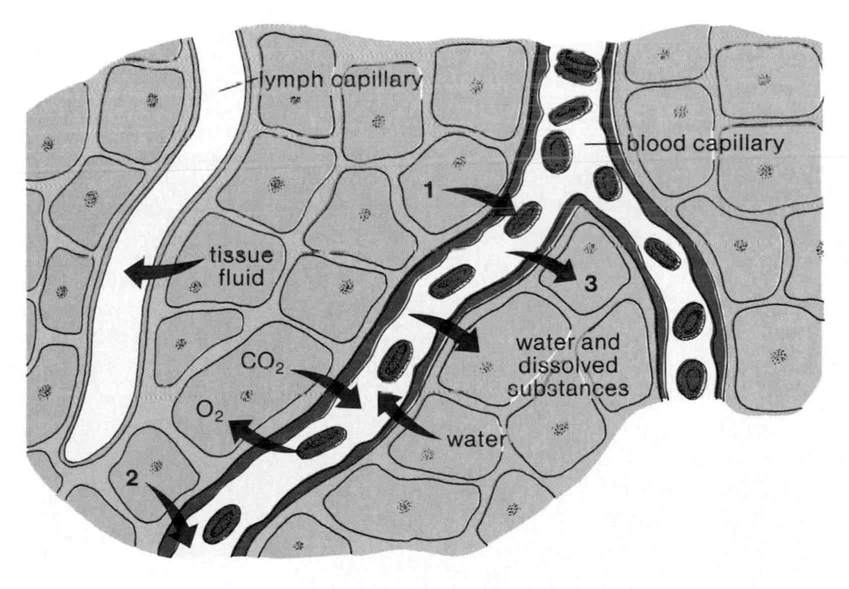

Later in this chapter we will see how hemoglobin acts in transport of respiratory gases. Because they lack a nucleus, human red cells live only 110 to 120 days. Then they are removed from circulation and destroyed in the liver and spleen. Iron from the hemoglobin is salvaged in the liver and used by bone marrow cells to make new red cells.

White blood cells (figure 16.9) play a major role in defending the body against invading pathogens. There are several kinds of white cells that differ in size and function, but all contain a nucleus. Because they lack hemoglobin, white cells are colorless unless stained. Their differential reaction to stains aids in their microscopic identification. White cells can move about like an amoeba, slipping through the thin walls of

Figure 16.8 A comparison of some characteristics of blood elements. This is a term used by those who wish to emphasize that platelets are only fragments of cells.

Element	Diameter (in μm)	Number (per mm^3)	Main function
red blood cells	7-8	4,500,000-5,500,000	oxygen transport
white blood cells	9-12	7,000-10,000	defense against microorganisms
platelets	2-4	300,000 (much variation)	blood-clotting

Figure 16.9 Human blood from a healthy individual. Some red blood cells appear to have holes because they are thinner in the middle. White blood cells are stained a darker color; the white blood cell in (a) is a lymphocyte; that in (b) is a macrophage. Both are important in the immune response.

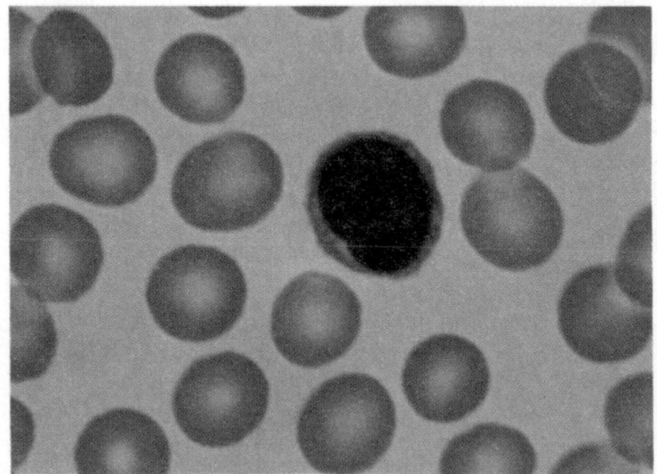

a

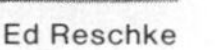

Ed Reschke

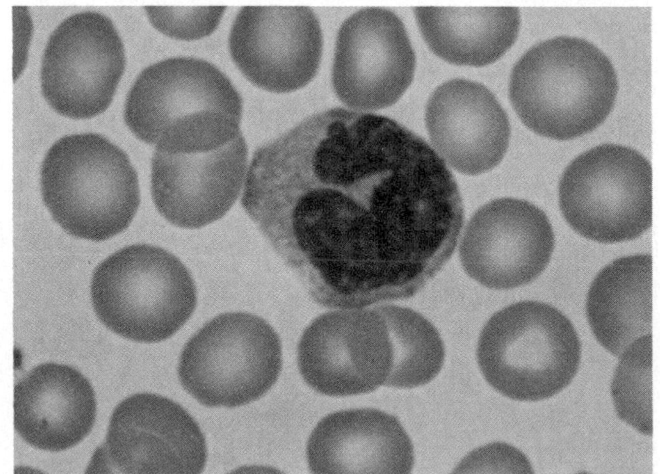

b Ed Reschke

capillaries and wandering among cells and tissues. Some white cells engulf bacteria or other pathogens as an amoeba does. Others synthesize antibodies, complex proteins that react with pathogens and other foreign substances. We will discuss these cells in more detail in section 16.6.

16.3 Clotting Is an Interaction between Platelets and Plasma Proteins

Normally, when you suffer a small wound, the blood at the skin surface clots or hardens. Blood clotting is a complex sequence of events that involves some thirty factors, as well as small cell fragments called **platelets** (PLAYT lets). Clotting begins when plasma and platelets come in contact with a rough surface, such as a torn tissue. The platelets become sticky and attract more platelets, forming a plug that partially seals the wound. They also release substances that act with clotting factors in the plasma to begin a chain of chemical reactions (figure 16.10a). As a result of these reactions, a substance called **prothrombin** (proh THROM bin) activator is formed. In the presence of calcium, prothrombin activator catalyzes the conversion of prothrombin, a plasma protein, to **thrombin.** Thrombin then acts as an enzyme to convert the soluble plasma protein **fibrinogen** (fy BRIN oh jen) to its insoluble

Figure 16.10 The fibrin strands provide a network in which platelets are trapped, forming a blood clot. A blood clot is the result of a complex cascade of enzymatic reactions that ends when the soluble protein fibrinogen is converted to insoluble fibrin strands.

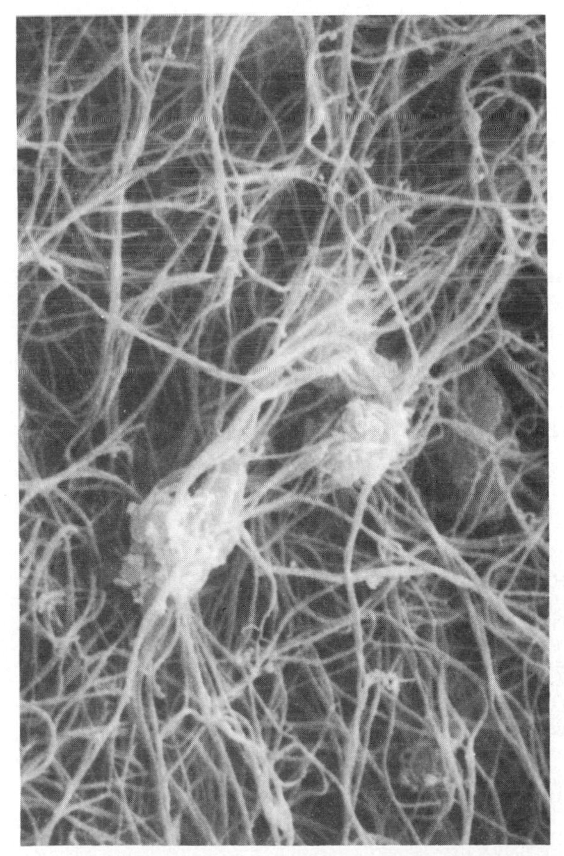

Micrograph taken by Richard G. Taylor in the laboratories of Dr. Jon C. Lewis and Dr. Roy R. Hantgan of Wake Forest University.

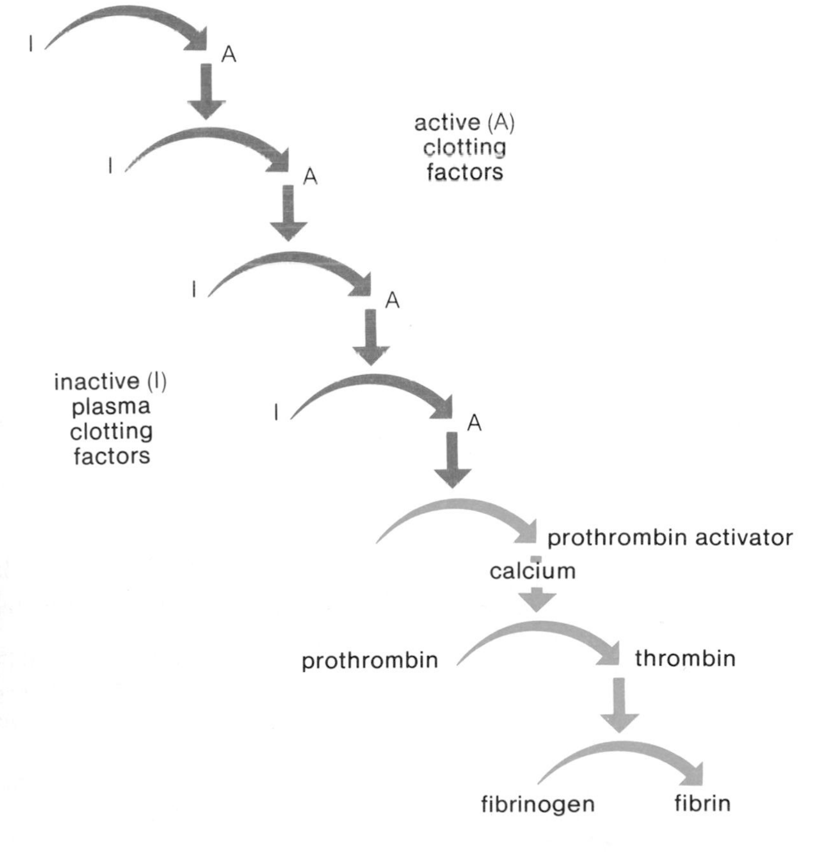

Figure 16.11 The heart attack and possibilities for recovery.

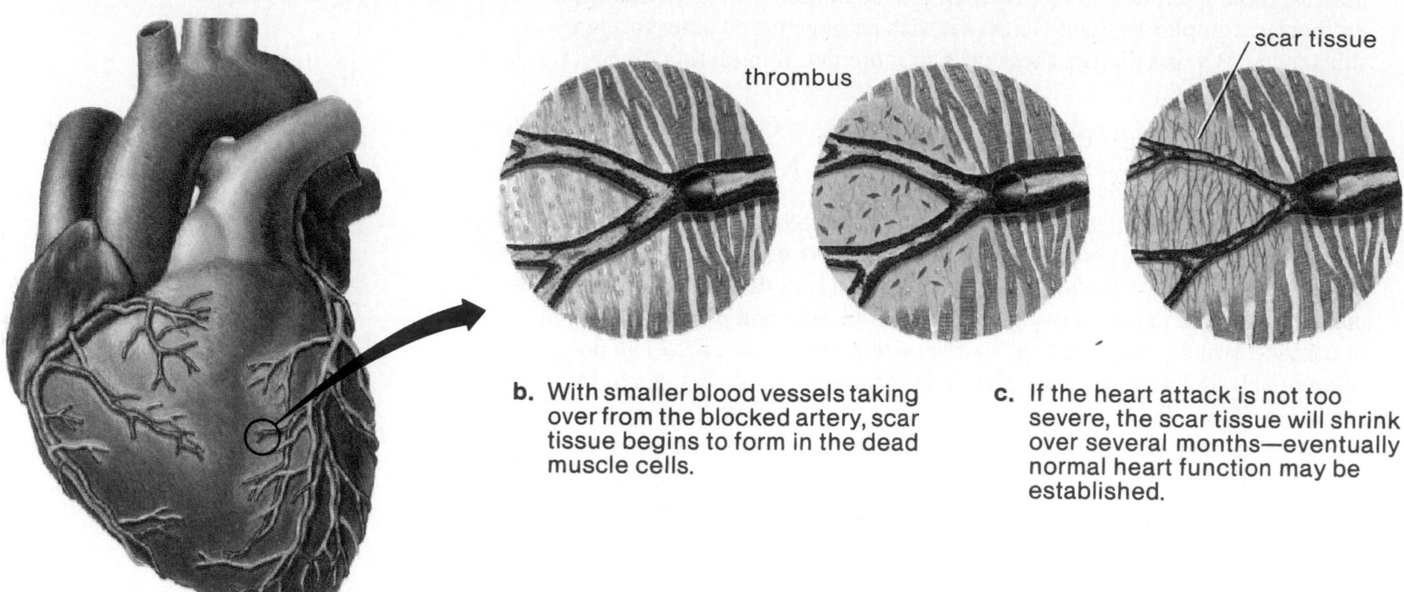

b. With smaller blood vessels taking over from the blocked artery, scar tissue begins to form in the dead muscle cells.

c. If the heart attack is not too severe, the scar tissue will shrink over several months—eventually normal heart function may be established.

a. The hearts own system of blood vessels supplies the muscular walls of this powerful pump with food and oxygen. Sometimes blood flow may be blocked (circled area). The muscles are damaged by lack of oxygen and foods.

form, **fibrin** (FY brin). The fibrin forms a network of threads that trap platelets and other materials and form the clot (figure 16.10b).

Clotting also may occur within uninjured blood vessels, forming a clump of cells known as a **thrombus.** A heart attack may be caused when a thrombus blocks one of the arteries that delivers blood to the heart itself. As a result, blood flow to an area of the heart is cut off. Muscle cells stop contracting and may die due to lack of nutrients and oxygen. Smaller blood vessels then begin to enlarge and take over the role of the blocked artery. Scar tissue forms in the dead cells. Over a period of several months, the scar tissue shrinks, and normal heart function may be reestablished. The processes leading to formation of these internal clots are still being investigated, but the presence of cholesterol deposits inside an artery seems to be one causative factor, as we have seen in section 15.15.

16.4 Cells and Materials Move between Blood Vessels and Tissue

The water and minerals of plasma normally pass through capillary walls to and from body tissues. White cells also move freely between blood vessels and tissues. Red blood cells, however, do not leave the blood vessels, and only small amounts of plasma proteins are found in tissues. Thus the fluid that bathes tissue cells is lower in protein content than the blood plasma.

Some of this tissue fluid may ooze back into the blood capillaries. Most of it collects in a set of vessels different from those in which blood is carried. Here the liquid is called **lymph** (LIMF), and the tubes that carry it are called **lymph vessels.** These vessels join to form larger vessels. As you move, muscle contractions squeeze the vessels and move the lymph along. In the walls of the small intestine, lymph vessels in the villi absorb fats. Many of the metabolic wastes of cells also pass into the lymph. Thus it has a higher fat content and a higher waste content than does blood.

At many points the vessels of the lymph system divide into tiny twisted passages, forming **lymph nodes.** Lymph flows slowly through the nodes. Here pathogenic organisms and other foreign materials that have entered the body are engulfed by white blood cells in the lymph. The lymph system thus is a part of your defense system. It is shown in figure 16.12 on page 581.

Eventually all lymph vessels join, forming a duct in the region of the left shoulder that empties into a vein. The fluids that moved into the tissues at the capillaries return to the blood before it enters the heart.

Self-Review

1. What are the differences among arteries, veins, and capillaries?
2. Explain how our four-chambered heart functions.
3. How is blood kept flowing in one direction?
4. How does plasma differ from whole blood?

Investigation 16.1 HEART RATE IN A MAMMAL

Introduction

In investigation 14.3, you studied the heart rate of the earthworm. The pulsing blood vessel was so close to the very thin body wall of the animal that you could observe the heart action without dissection. In most large animals such direct observation of the heart is impossible. There are, however, a number of indirect ways by which the heart rate in a mammal can be determined.

In investigation 14.3, you also studied the effects of varying environmental temperatures on heart rate. In birds and mammals (after hatching or birth) the heart lies in an internal environment where a relatively stable temperature is maintained independently of the external environment. Thus, the problems and methods that are suitable for the study of heart rate in mammals are quite different from those suitable for such study in earthworms.

This situation provides an opportunity. You have had several months of experience carrying out experimental procedures and drawing conclusions from data. You should now be able to set up a problem, work out a procedure for gathering data, carry out the procedure, and then draw conclusions.

Materials

watch or clock with second hand

Procedure

1. In carrying out this investigation, the only requirements are:
   (a) Your problem and your procedure must deal with the heart rate in a mammal.
   (b) Your equipment must be limited to a watch or clock with a second hand.
2. The following statements may help you:
   (a) Humans are mammals.
   (b) An increase or decrease in the activity of an animal may be reflected in changes of heart rate.
   (c) Physicians use stethoscopes to listen to the heart rate. With only a watch, nurses can easily determine the rate.

Guidepost: How does the immune system protect the body from invasion?

Immunity

16.5 The Body Has Several Defenses against Foreign Invaders

Immunity is the capacity of the human body to resist most foreign invaders—organisms or toxins that might damage tissues and organs. The body has two types of immunity against these foreign substances. The first is nonspecific immunity, which involves intact skin and the inflammatory process. The second is a specific immune response made by the immune system.

The layer of intact skin and mucous membranes that covers the outer and inner surfaces of the body provides a barrier against invasion. Mucous membranes are protected by secretions of mucus. Some membranes consist of ciliated cells that sweep foreign objects away. Other surfaces are washed by fluids such as saliva or tears that contain substances active against microorganisms.

If the skin barrier is breached, the inflammatory response is activated. Substances in the circulating blood and lymph initiate this response. For example, if you cut your finger, the injured cells release histamine and other substances that cause nearby capillaries to swell and become "leaky." Various kinds of white blood cells pass through the capillary walls and gather at the site of injury, where they engulf microorganisms that may have entered through the cut.

16.6 Protection by the Immune System Is Very Specific

In contrast to the nonspecific defenses described in section 16.5, the response of the immune system to foreign invaders is very specific. The immune system includes the structures shown in figure 16.12 as well as the bone marrow and a variety of interacting white blood cells.

Figure 16.12 The human immune system. In addition to the entire lymphatic system, the tonsils, thymus, and spleen are important components of this system.

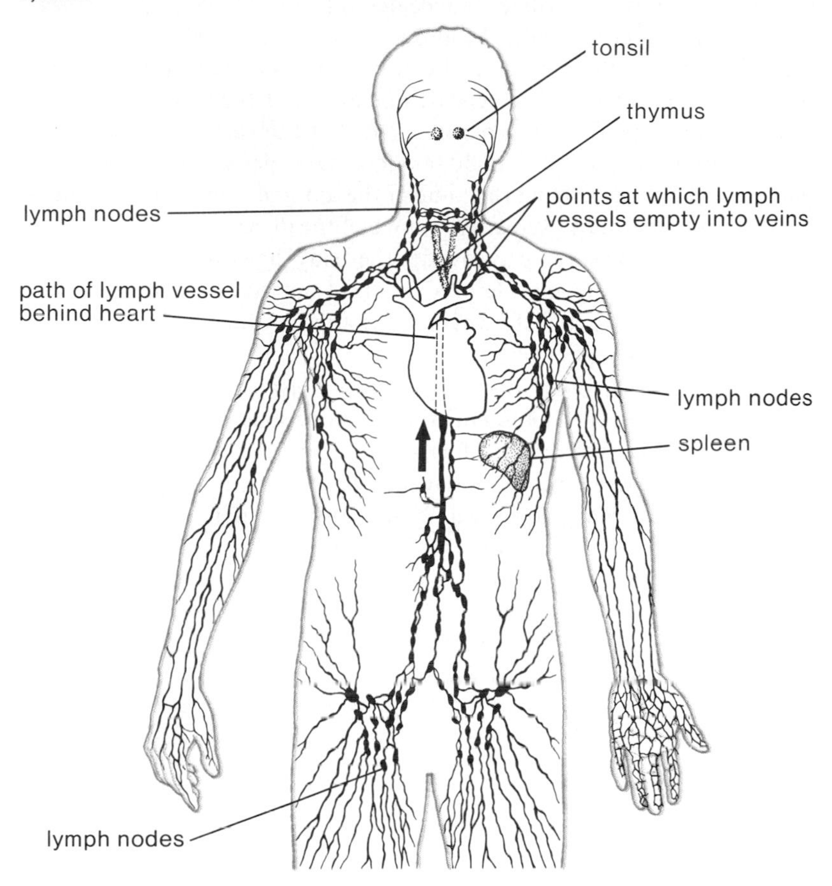

The primary cells of the specific immune system are small white blood cells called **lymphocytes** (LIM foh syts). Like other blood cells, they develop in the bone marrow. **B cell** lymphocytes mature in the bone marrow. **T cell** lymphocytes migrate to the thymus gland and mature into at least three different types of T cells. B cells and T cells interact closely, though they take part in different forms of the immune response. B cells secrete large proteins called antibodies that act against foreign substances in the blood. T cells serve to regulate the immune response. They act primarily against infected host cells, but they also act to reject organ transplants.

Both B cells and T cells are activated by **antigens** (ANT ih jens)—substances the body recognizes as being foreign. Antigens are usually large proteins or carbohydrates that make up the cell walls or other parts of microorganisms such as viruses, fungi, and bacteria. Other large molecules or parts of molecules also can serve as antigens.

Each circulating B cell displays on its surface several copies of a specific antibody. If an antigen with a shape that fits the antibody enters the blood, the two combine, or bind together. A T cell then combines with the B cell-antigen complex and stimulates the B cell to enlarge and divide rapidly. Two types of offspring cells that produce the same kind of antibody are formed: plasma cells and memory B cells. Plasma cells secrete thousands of antibody molecules into the bloodstream. There, the antibodies combine with the antigens that stimulated their production. Memory B cells remain in the circulation for many years, even a lifetime, and protect against repeated invasions of the same antigen.

The production of mature plasma cells that can secrete antibodies at the maximum rate of 3,000 to 30,000 molecules per cell per second requires about 5 days. During this time, if the antigen—for example, measles virus—also is multiplying, symptoms of the disease are present. The second time the measles virus invades the body, however, memory cells immediately begin large-scale production of antibodies, and the infection usually is overcome before symptoms appear. Thus we say a person is **immune** to measles.

This immunity, brought about by the rapid response of memory cells, is the basis for vaccination against many infectious diseases. Vaccines are prepared from weakened, killed, or closely related or modified pathogens. When injected into the body, the vaccine stimulates production of plasma and memory cells, usually without producing disease symptoms. The immunity is very specific. Immunity to measles does not provide immunity to other diseases such as chicken pox or mumps.

Figure 16.13 The cells involved in the immune response, B cells, T cells, and macrophages, all arise from unspecialized cells in the bone marrow. The B cells (plasma cells and memory B cells) and the macrophages are released directly to the body. The T cells (helper, inducer, cytotoxic, and suppressor T cells) are modified in the thymus before being released.

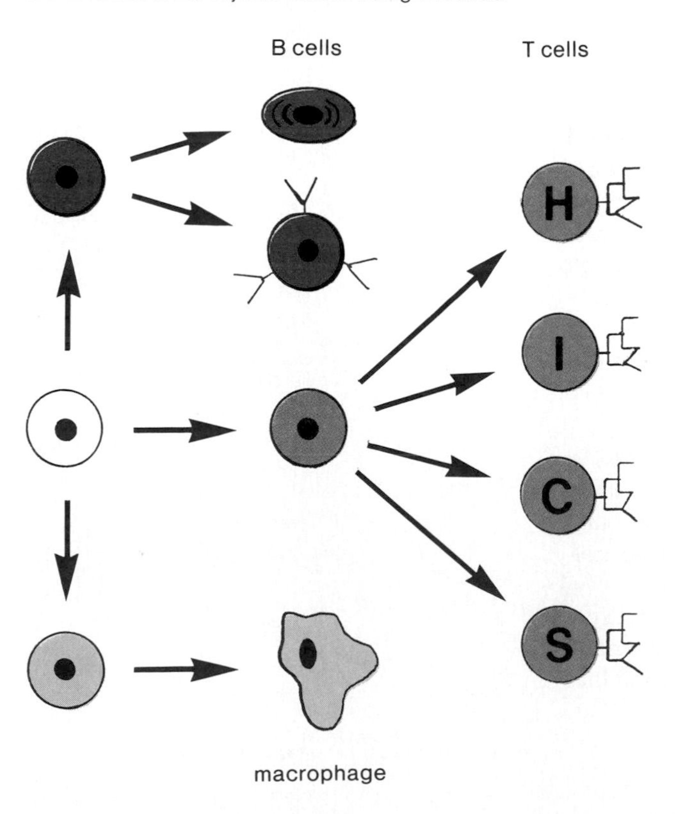

Figure 16.14 Activation of B cells begins with a macrophage, which processes and displays viral antigens. Helper T cells recognize these surface antigens and activate B cells. The B cells produce memory B cells and antibody-producing plasma cells.

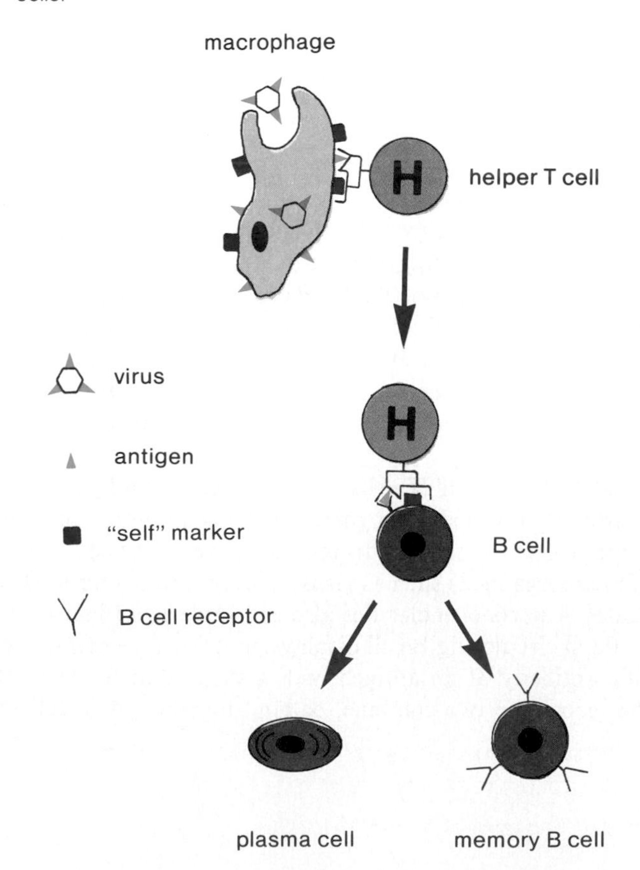

Biology Today

Monoclonal Antibodies

Antibodies are proteins produced by the immune system to fight infection. They are highly specific. That is, they are effective against only one type of antigen, or infectious agent. Antibodies are produced in large quantities in the body during an infection. Until recently, biologists were unable to produce large quantities of a given antibody artificially. That changed in 1975, when two immunologists, Georges Kohler and Cesar Milstein, developed a technology that uses two different kinds of cells.

Antibodies are produced by B cells—one kind of specialized cell in the immune system. B cells do not grow well in culture. They tend to die off after a few generations. Cancer cells, however, are immortal: they grow in culture almost indefinitely. In fact, that is the problem with cancer cells in the body. They grow in an uncontrolled manner and ultimately invade surrounding tissue.

Kohler and Milstein developed a technique to fuse B cells and cancer cells. The process (see figure) begins by injecting mice with a specific antigen—for example, the virus that causes hepatitis. The mice produce B cells (antibody-producing cells) against the virus. The B cells then are collected and fused in culture with a special type of cancer cell called a myeloma cell. The resulting hybrid cells are called hybridoma cells. They are grown in a special culture that eliminates both the parent B cells and the myeloma cells. Only the fused hybridoma cells remain. Those cells have the characteristics of both parent cells: they produce the specific antibody of the B cell, and they have the essential immortality of the myeloma cell.

The hybridomas are grown, or cloned, in culture, to produce large quantities of the desired antibody. The resulting product is called a monoclonal antibody.

The technology developed by Kohler and Milstein, for which they won the 1984 Nobel Prize in physiology and medicine, has allowed biologists to produce many highly specific antibodies for medical diagnosis and treatment and for use in research. Because they are chemically uniform, monoclonal antibodies are superior to antibodies extracted from animals (the conventional method).

The antigen used to stimulate antibody production does not have to be an infectious agent. For example, researchers at the National Institute of Health have produced a monoclonal antibody against a blood protein that is present in high levels in persons who have the genetic disorder cystic fibrosis. The antibody can be used for early diagnosis of the disorder. Cancer specialists think that monoclonal antibodies can be produced against specific antigens on the surface of cancer cells. It might be possible to use the antibodies to carry drugs or radioactive treatments directly to the site of the cancer. That process would reduce the damage to other cells and tissues that often results from less well-targeted use of drugs and radiation. Monoclonal antibodies are now used to screen donor blood for hepatitis virus and may someday be used to detect the virus that causes acquired immune deficiency syndrome (AIDS).

The applications of monoclonal antibodies increase almost daily. This technology is but one example of our growing knowledge about the regulation of genetic and cellular events.

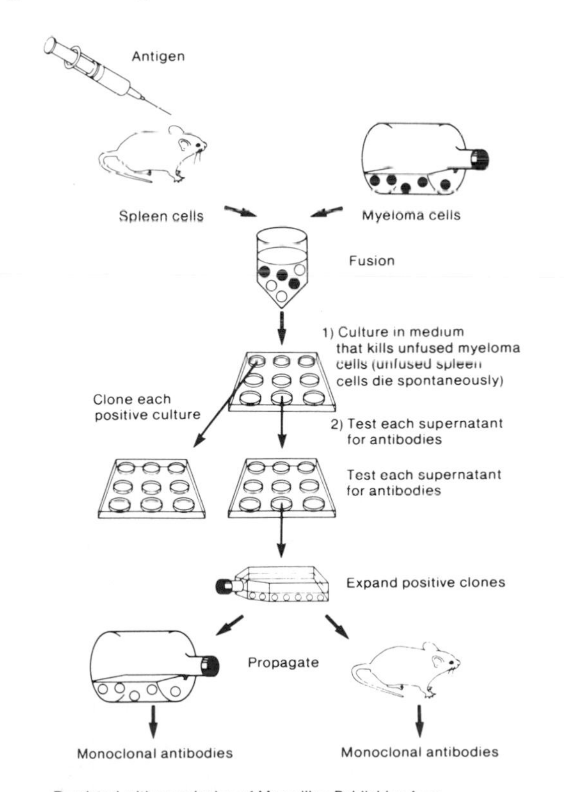

Figure 16.15 Macrophages initiate the destruction of virus-infected cells. A macrophage displaying viral antigens activates cytotoxic T cells, which directly destroy infected cells, and helper T cells, which activate B cells (see figure 16.14). The B cells produce plasma cells, which in turn produce antibodies. The antibodies bind to the antigens, forming a clump of particles that can be consumed by other macrophages.

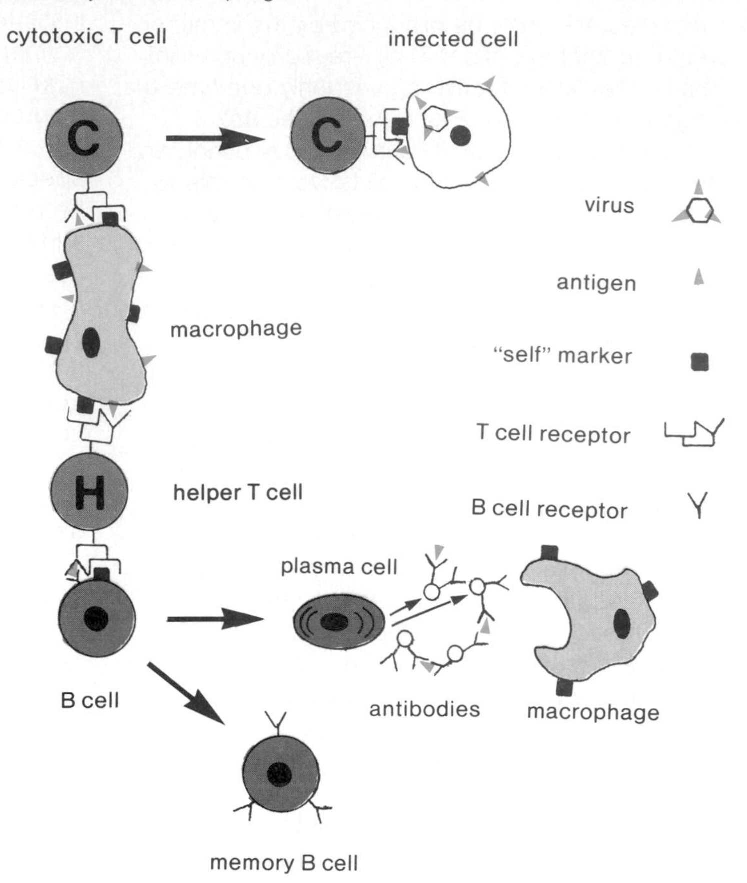

Antibodies themselves do not destroy antigens. Instead, by combining with the antigens, they prepare them for destruction by other components of the immune system. The antigen-antibody complex may be engulfed and digested by white blood cells called **macrophages** (MAK roh fayj ez), or acted on by a group of blood proteins known as **complement** (KOM pleh ment) that can digest holes in foreign cells, causing them to burst.

Unlike B cells, T cells do not bind directly to antigens. The antigen must be engulfed by a macrophage and presented on its surface in an appropriate way before binding can take place. After binding, T cells divide and develop into functional cells specific to antigen. Memory T cells also are formed. **Cytotoxic** (syt oh TOKS ik) or "killer" T cells act against the body's own cells that are infected by a virus or other microorganism. A virus inside a cell cannot be acted on by antibodies. As the virus multiplies, however, virus antigens appear on the cell surface. Cytotoxic T cells bind to these antigens and cause the cells to burst, exposing the viruses to antibody action (figure 16.15).

Other types of T cells, **helper** T cells and **suppressor** T cells, play regulatory roles. Helper T cells serve to activate both B cells and other T

Figure 16.16 Activation of T cells begins with macrophages that process viral antigens. After a macrophage has engulfed a virus, it displays viral antigens on its surface. Helper T cells are activated when they encounter these surface antigens. The activated helper T cell can produce all the T cell types (helper, inducer, cytotoxic, and suppressor T cells) as well as activating B cells (see figure 16.14).

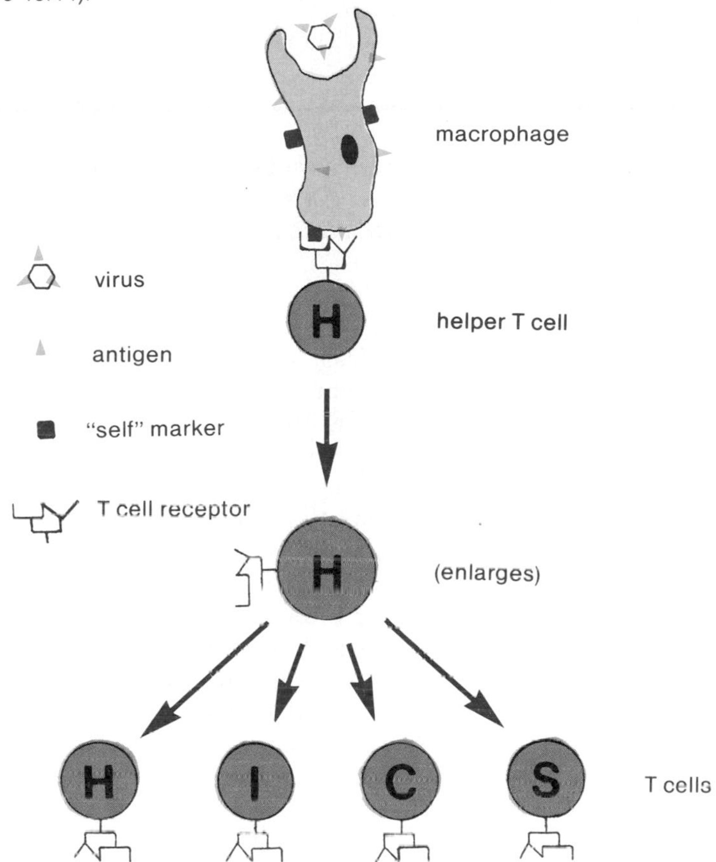

cells. They enable B cells to manufacture and secrete antibodies. Suppressor T cells moderate the activities of B cells and other T cells and help to terminate the immune response.

Acquired immune deficiency syndrome (AIDS) is caused by a virus that destroys helper T cells, so the other cells of the immune system cannot function or function poorly. As a result, the patient loses protection against infections of all kinds.

16.7 Many Problems Can Arise with the Immune System

The primary role of the immune system is to distinguish "self" from "nonself." In the developing embryo, the immune system learns to recognize substances that are present as "self." Sometimes this recognition breaks down, and the immune system makes antibodies against the individual's own body cells. Such disorders are known as **autoimmune** diseases. In one autoimmune disease, antibodies are formed that interfere with nerve stimulation of muscles, which results in muscular weakness.

Table 16.1 ABO blood group antigens and antibodies

Blood Group	Antigen on Red Blood Cell	Antibody in Plasma
0	none	anti A, anti B
A	A	anti B
B	B	anti A
AB	A, B	none

In another, antibodies are produced against the individual's own DNA, thus disrupting many body functions. An autoimmune response is suspected in a number of other disorders, such as rheumatoid arthritis and multiple sclerosis.

Allergies are an apparently maladaptive response of the immune system to foods or substances commonly found in the environment, such as pollen and dust. Sensitive individuals produce a class of antibodies that combine with specialized cells found in the skin and membranes of the eye, nose, mouth, respiratory tract, and intestines. These cells, in turn, release histamine and other substances that cause the congestion, sneezing, and itching typical of "hay fever," or cramps and diarrhea in the case of food allergies. Treatment involves use of antihistamines, which suppress some of the allergic symptoms, but which also cause side effects such as drowsiness.

Problems may arise with blood type. You learned in chapter 8 about the ABO blood groups of humans. The different blood groups are not compatible, and transfusing blood of one type into blood of another type can cause a fatal reaction. The incompatibility comes about because antibodies in the plasma of one blood type react with antigens on the red cells of another. The reaction causes the red blood cells to clump or **agglutinate** (uh GLOOT in ayt). Unlike other antibodies that are produced only in response to an antigen. ABO blood group antibodies develop spontaneously and are normally present in the blood. Each blood group is characterized by the presence of a particular antigen and a different antibody, as shown in table 16.1.

Blood group systems other than ABO also are present in humans, and sometimes cause problems in transfusions. The Rh system is the most widely known of these. Individuals who are Rh positive have Rh antigens on their red blood cells; those who are Rh negative do not. Antibodies to Rh antigens are not normally present in plasma, as are those of ABO blood groups, but may develop if Rh positive blood is transfused into an Rh negative individual.

Serious problems may arise in pregnancy when an Rh negative woman has an Rh positive baby. In the first pregnancy, there is usually no problem for the fetus unless the woman was previously sensitized by a transfusion of Rh positive blood. During birth, however, red cells from the infant may enter the mother's blood, stimulating formation of Rh antibodies in her plasma. During a subsequent pregnancy, those antibodies may pass into the fetal blood, causing destruction of fetal red cells. Those problems are prevented by injecting an Rh negative mother, within 72 hours of delivery of her first child, with Rh antibodies. The Rh antibodies destroy the fetal Rh positive red cells in her body, and her immune system is not stimulated to form antibodies.

Figure 16.17 The events leading to Rh disease. Fetal red cells may enter the maternal blood during childbirth, stimulating formation of Rh antibodies in the mother's plasma. Those antibodies may pass into the fetal blood during a subsequent pregnancy, destroying the fetal red cells.

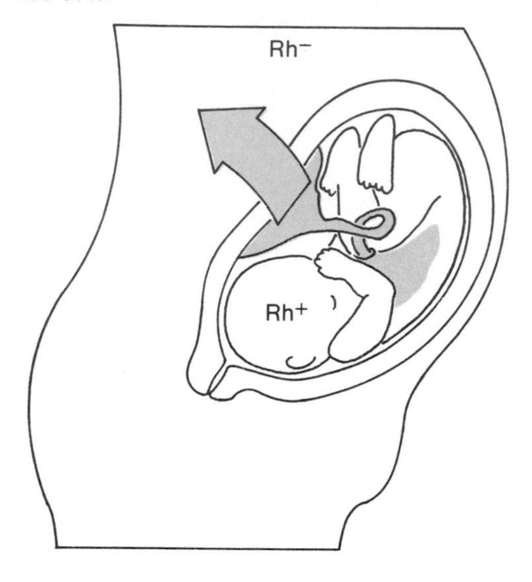

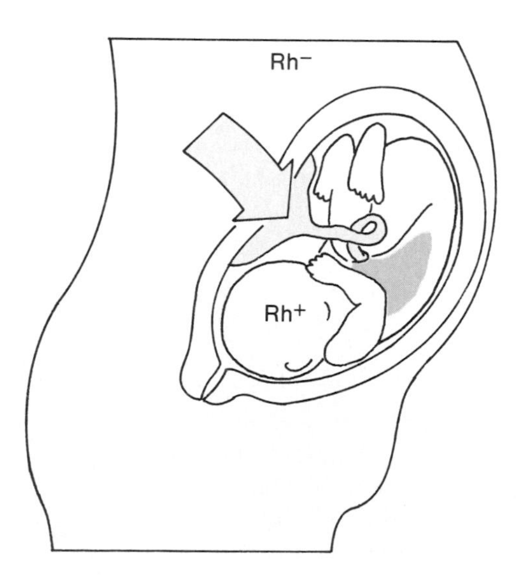

fetal red blood cells with Rh antigen

maternal antibodies against Rh antigen

The immune system also is responsible for rejection of organ transplants. Rejection is due to T cells, which identify the transplanted organ as foreign antigen. Within a few days after transplantation they invade the tissue and begin to destroy it. To prevent this reaction, drugs are given to suppress the immune response. This makes the transplant recipient very vulnerable to infection, the chief cause of death among kidney transplant recipients. Efforts to control the immune response and to match more closely donor and recipient tissues are active areas of research.

Self-Review

1. What is the difference between specific and nonspecific immunity?
2. In what ways do B cells and T cells differ?
3. How are antibodies produced?
4. Why does the second exposure to a pathogen usually not produce disease?
5. What are some problems that can arise with the immune system?

Investigation 16.2 BLOOD AND IMMUNITY

Introduction

Your blood serves a variety of functions. Some of the most important of those functions are related to immunity. Whole blood is slightly heavier than water and 3 to 4 times thicker than water. It contains a number of complex chemical components. Its cells, which are formed mostly in the red marrow of bone, include red cells, white cells, and cell fragments called platelets. In this investigation, you will examine some components of blood and discuss how they relate to certain aspects of immunity.

Materials

Part A

1 sterile blood-letting lancet
1 alcohol prep pad
2 toothpicks
1 clean microscope slide
substances 1 & 2
piece of paper towel

Part B

prepared slide of stained human blood
charts, photographs, and diagrams of blood components

Part A—Identification of Blood Components

Procedure

1. Place your slide on the paper towel and label the towel 1 at one end of the slide and 2 at the other end.
2. Carefully cleanse one of your middle fingers with the alcohol prep pad and allow the alcohol to dry. (If you do not wish to draw your own blood, use the human blood your teacher has available for you.)

3. Puncture your finger with the sterile lancet and wipe away the first drops of blood with the alcohol pad. **CAUTION:** *Never use the same lancet more than once.*
4. Gently squeeze your finger and place one drop of blood at the end of the slide labeled 1 and a second drop at the end labeled 2.
5. Gently press the alcohol pad against your finger and the bleeding will stop, if it has not already done so.
6. Obtain the vial labeled substance 1 and place a drop of this next to the drop of blood labeled 1. Place a drop of substance 2 next to the drop of blood labeled 2.
7. Use a toothpick to mix subtance 1 with the blood. Use a different toothpick to do the same with substance 2. Try to avoid spreading the mixture of blood and substance too much, because this may cause the blood to dry too rapidly. Take care to prevent mixing of substance 1 with substance 2 as you mix these components.
8. Observe the blood and substance mixtures. What, if anything, do you see happening? Check with 2 or 3 of your classmates and notice whether they have similar or different reactions. Record what you see in your data book.
9. Your teacher will collect the data from each student and record results on the chalkboard. Reactions or the absence of visible reactions with blood and substances 1 and 2 will be recorded.

Discussion

In small groups of 2–4 students, consider the following:

1. What seems to be happening (or not happening) when blood is mixed with 1 of the 2 substances?
2. Develop 3 hypotheses (more, if possible) that might explain how blood and the substances cause the type of reaction you have observed.
3. If substance 1 caused a reaction with the blood with which it was mixed, would that type of reaction be desirable in a blood transfusion? Why or why not?
4. From the data recorded on the chalkboard, formulate a statement that might account for the following observations:
   (a) Blood will react with substance 1 but not 2.
   (b) Blood will react with substance 2 but not 1.
   (c) Blood will react with substances 1 and 2.
   (d) Blood will react with neither substance, 1 or 2.
5. Be prepared to discuss your hypotheses and statement with the entire class.

Part B—Examination of Stained Blood

Procedure

1. Examine the prepared slide of stained human blood under the high-power objective of the microscope. Identify the red blood cells. They are small and have biconcave edges. How is this shape related to the function of these cells, which are rich in hemoglobin?
2. After you have examined and considered the structural and functional properties of red cells, look for cells that will appear different in number, size, and staining reaction in contrast to red blood cells. Find as many different types of these white cells as possible.
3. The size and characteristic shape of the nuclei will help you identify some of these white cells. With the aid of photographs, charts, and diagrams of blood cells provided by your teacher, identify as many different kinds of white cells as possible.

Discussion

1. Although a red cell has a nucleus during its development within bone marrow, the nucleus is lost as the red cell matures and takes on its function in support of the life of the individual. This lack of a nucleus seems to increase the cell's efficiency. Damaged red cells are destroyed by macrophages. This occurs mainly in the liver and spleen. What is the specific function of red cells?
2. White cells do most of their work outside of the circulatory system, but they are transported by blood to areas of need. What particular role do white blood cells perform?
3. What do you think might happen to the number of white cells during an infection?
4. Which blood components are involved in the immune response?
5. Why do so many diagnostic tests for disease conditions involve blood analysis? Identify as many conditions as you can that can be diagnosed by blood tests.

Part C—A Liver Transplant

Procedure

Read the following true story and discuss the questions in small groups.

A Life on Standby

Their suitcases are always packed as 11-year-old Tommy and his parents wait for a phone call. That phone call will make the difference between life and death for Tommy. This family awaits word from Children's Hospital that a donor has been found for a liver transplant—an operation that Tommy needs to save his life. The family has been told that the call will likely come within the next 3 months, and the parents will have less than 6 hours to get Tommy to the hospital. Nearby companies have volunteered the use of their aircraft to fly Tommy and his parents to the hospital. Plans for a special charter flight have also been made in the event that these planes are not available when the call comes.

Tommy's parents discovered their son's affliction when he was only 2 weeks old and doctors became concerned about the yellow tone of his skin. Tommy was born without bile ducts; he had his first operation before he was 3 months old. He has undergone 12 operations and has been hospitalized about 60 times. He was near death several times. Although Tommy is afraid that he is going to die, his mother says that her son's attitude is terrific. He still enjoys the pastimes of other children his age and passes the school vacation time by fishing, bicycle riding, and playing with his friends—and waiting for that important phone call.

The only symptoms that Tommy is dealing with a life-and-death struggle are his yellowed eyes and a pouch he must wear on his side. Doctors have decided to do the liver transplant now because Tommy faces a growth spurt that his liver may not be able to withstand.

(Adapted from the article "Lakewood Boy, 10, on 'Standby' Status for Liver Transplant," *The Denver Post* [16 July 1985].)

Tommy's medical expenses thus far have exceeded $1 million. The liver transplant operation could cost as much as $300,000. The family's medical insurance does not begin to cover all of these bills. About $7000 has been raised through local fund-raising activities, and contributions are still being sought to help pay for an operation needed to save the life of a young boy.

Discussion

1. Why must Tommy wait so long for an operation that is so desperately needed?
2. When the phone call finally does come, what further problems or complications might occur as a result of the operation?
3. How might Tommy's physicians increase the chances that he will not reject the transplanted liver?
4. The cost of transplant surgery is exceedingly high. Most medical insurance plans do not provide coverage, because the insurers consider transplant surgery as experimental. Discuss this issue with members of your group.

Guidepost: What role do the respiratory and excretory systems play in maintenance of homeostasis?

Gas Exchange and Excretion

16.8 Cellular Respiration and Gas Exchange Are Not the Same

Cellular respiration often is confused with the process that exchanges vital gases with the environment. Cellular respiration is primarily a process of energy release. However, because it uses oxygen and releases carbon dioxide, gas exchange also is involved. As the carbon dioxide accumulates, it produces acid conditions that are poisonous to cells and, therefore, must be removed. Oxygen is present in the environment surrounding you. The overall process of exchanging oxygen and carbon dioxide with the environment and the blood is accomplished by the respiratory system and is called respiration. Respiration may be studied in three stages. The first is the process of breathing that involves the movement of air in and out of the lungs. The second stage is the exchange of gases between the internal surface of the lungs and the blood. The third is the exchange of gases between the blood and the tissue cells.

16.9 Air Moves from the External Environment into the Lungs because of Pressure Differences

The respiratory organs function to exchange gas molecules between the inner surface of the lungs and the blood. Breathing moves the air that has been inhaled by the mouth and nose through a series of air tubes into the lungs.

Movement of the air is accomplished by the action of two groups of muscles. The first is the **diaphragm** (DY uh fram), a muscular wall that divides the body cavity into two parts. The second is the rib muscles. These muscles act together to change the size of the chest cavity. When you inhale, your diaphragm moves down, your ribs move up and out, and the cavity enlarges. When the chest cavity expands, the pressure within the chest falls. As a result, the pressure within the chest cavity is lower than the atmospheric pressure outside, and air rushes in. When you exhale, the volume of the chest cavity is reduced, the internal pres-

Figure 16.18 Movements of breathing in humans.

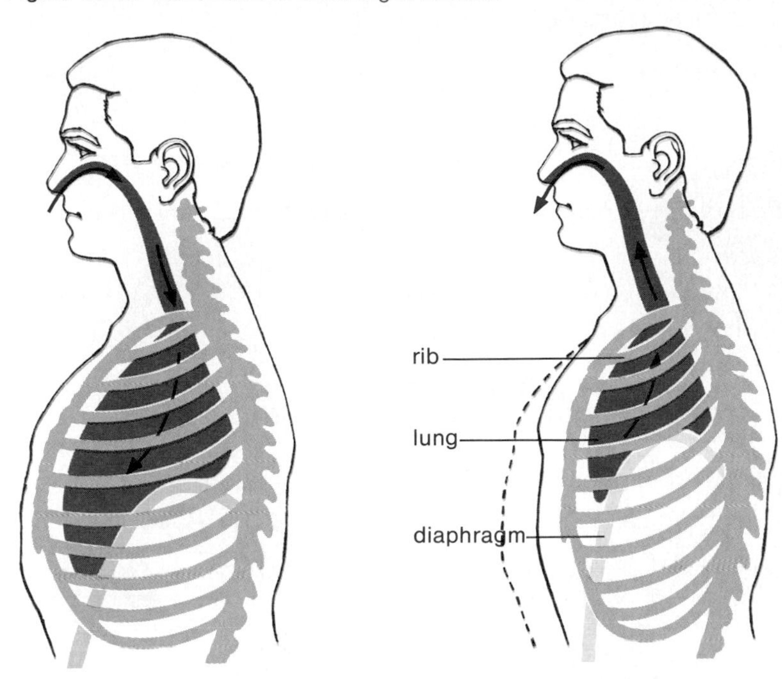

sure becomes greater than the atmospheric pressure, and air is forced out. The rhythmic increase and decrease in the volume of the chest cavity is the mechanical pump that drives air in and out of the lungs.

Atmospheric air is dry, sometimes cold, and often dirty. The air you breathe passes through your nose and down the **trachea** (TRAY kee uh), or windpipe. The air is moistened, warmed, and cleaned by cells lining the air passageways. These passageways enter the lungs and end in the **alveoli** (al VEE oh ly). The alveoli are grapelike clusters of cavities formed by one-layered sheets of cells. Each lung has millions of these cavities, whose walls are enveloped by a network of capillaries. The human respiratory system and details of the alveoli are illustrated in figure 16.19. It is through the alveolar walls that oxygen diffuses into the bloodstream. The lung can exchange large volumes of gases in a very short time because the many alveoli of the lung provide an enormous amount of surface area. If all the alveoli of the human lungs were spread out flat, the surface would cover an area of about 70 m^2—the size of about five parking spaces.

Some diseases may affect the normal functioning of the respiratory system. In the disease emphysema, the alveolar walls lose their elasticity. It becomes difficult to empty the lungs of air low in oxygen and high in carbon dioxide. This, in turn, decreases the amount of fresh air, containing more oxygen and less carbon dioxide, that may be brought in for air/blood gas exchange. This disease is associated with smoking or living in areas of high air pollution. The condition becomes progressively worse, and sufferers may become completely incapacitated.

Figure 16.19 The parts of the human respiratory system involved in breathing. The lung has been cut away to expose the branching system of bronchial tubes. Part of the lung has been enlarged to show air sacs and their relation to capillaries. Millions of air sacs in each lung give the tissue a spongelike appearance.

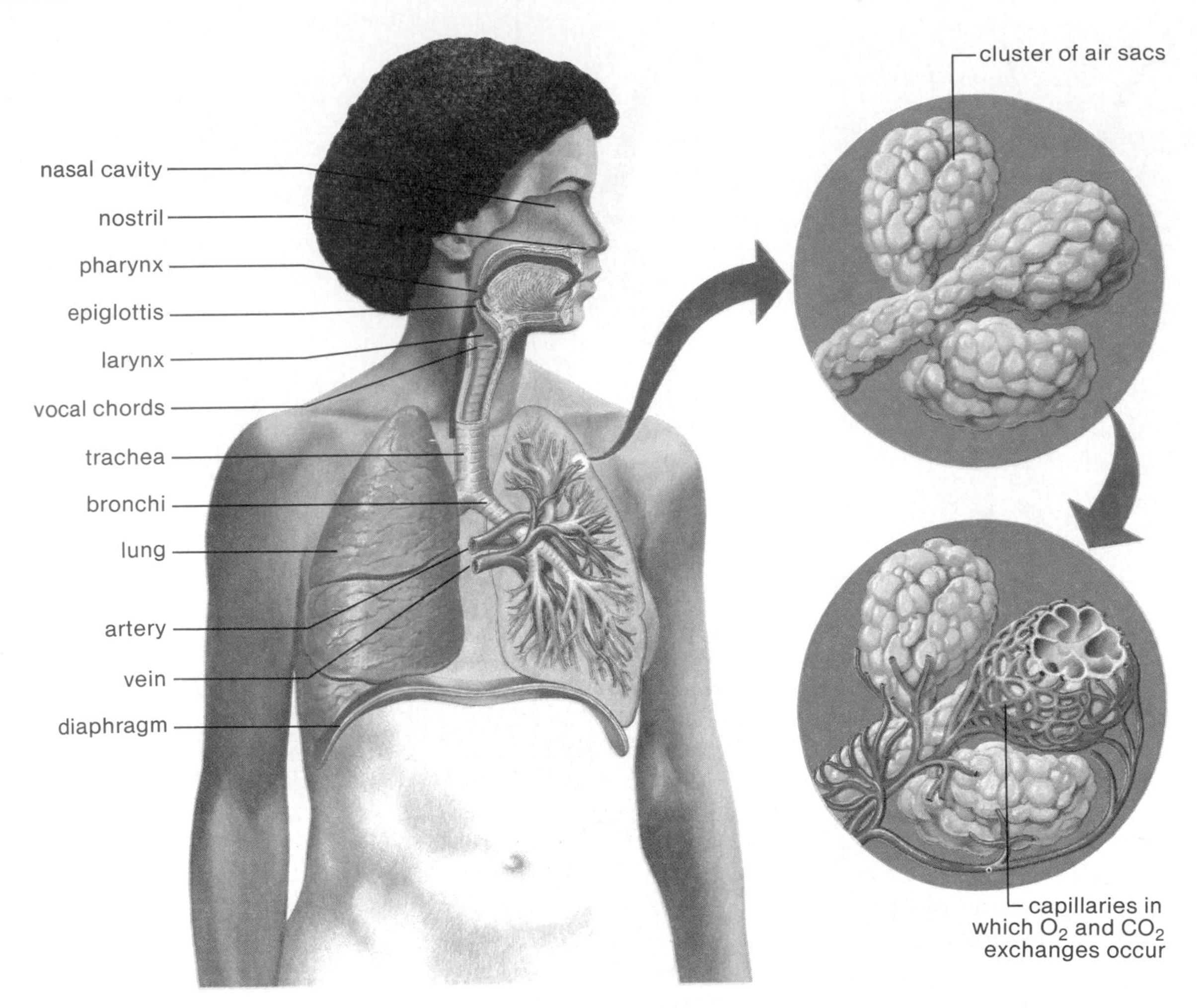

16.10 Respiratory Gases Are Transported in the Blood

Once oxygen has diffused from the alveoli into the blood, it must be transported to the tissues, where cellular respiration takes place. Because oxygen does not dissolve readily in plasma, special oxygen-transporting molecules are required. In humans and all other vertebrates, the red blood cells are packed with hemoglobin molecules, as we noted in section 16.2. When the concentration of oxygen is relatively high, as in the alveoli, each hemoglobin molecule combines with four oxygen molecules. In the tissues, the concentration of oxygen is relatively low, and the hemoglobin readily gives up its oxygen. Hemoglobin enables our blood to carry about 60 times more oxygen than it could by plasma alone.

Figure 16.20 Oxygen and carbon dioxide transport. Oxygen from the alveolus enters red blood cells and combines with hemoglobin (Hb) to form oxyhemoglobin (HbO_2). The oxygen is carried in this form to body cells, where it is released (see left side of illustration). Carbon dioxide diffuses from body cells into the red cells. There it combines with water to form carbonic acid (H_2CO_3), which ionizes to bicarbonate (HCO_3^-) and hydrogen (H^+) ions. The bicarbonate diffuses into the plasma. The hydrogen ions combine with hemoglobin (H.Hb). Some of the carbon dioxide combines directly with hemoglobin ($HbCO_2$). In the lung capillary, the reverse reactions occur. Bicarbonate ions from the plasma are converted to carbon dioxide and diffuse into the alveolus.

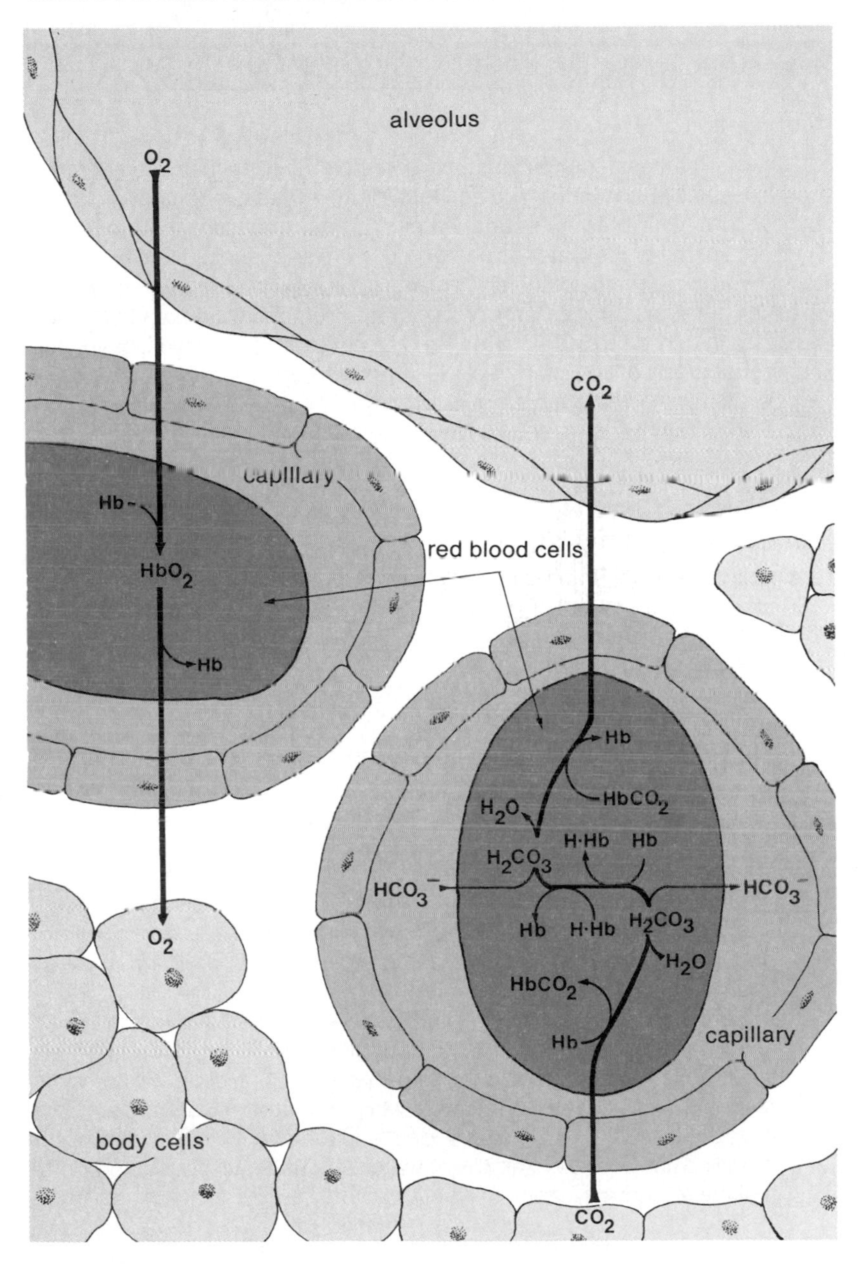

Carbon dioxide is more soluble than oxygen in the blood, and a small amount dissolves in the plasma. About 25 percent is transported by hemoglobin. Most of the carbon dioxide, however, is carried in the blood as bicarbonate ion (HCO_3^-). Carbon dioxide first reacts with water in the blood to form carbonic acid. The carbonic acid then ionizes to form hydrogen and bicarbonate ions. As with oxygen transport, relative concentrations of carbon dioxide in the alveoli and the tissues determine the direction of this reversible reaction. You can observe some of these reactions in investigation 16.3.

Investigation 16.3 CARBON DIOXIDE AND YOU

Introduction

Organisms constantly produce carbon dioxide when they use energy. It combines easily with water. You can test for the presence of carbon dioxide by bubbling your breath through water. You can measure the amount of carbon dioxide in the water using two chemicals: phenolphthalein and sodium hydroxide. Phenolphthalein remains colorless when carbon dioxide is present but turns pink as carbon dioxide is removed. Sodium hydroxide reacts with carbon dioxide in water and removes it. In this investigation the number of drops of sodium hydroxide needed to bring water to a pink color will be used to indicate the amount of carbon dioxide in that water. If you have time, both partners should do all the steps in the investigation.

Materials (per team of 2)

1% phenolphthalein solution in dropping bottles
0.4% NaOH solution in dropping bottles
100 ml graduated cylinder
2 flasks, 250 ml each
rubber stoppers to fit flasks
soda straws
piece of white paper
stop watch (or watch with second hand)

Procedure

1. Measure 100 ml of tap water and transfer it to a flask.
2. Add 5 drops of phenolphthalein solution to the tap water and swirl the flask to mix the materials. If the mixture is pink, there is very little or no CO_2 in the water. Save this sample of water. Cork it and use it as your standard of pinkness (control).
3. If there was no color change, the tap water must have some CO_2 in it. To find out how much, add NaOH solution drop by drop. It will help if you do this over a piece of white paper—the pink color will be easier to see. Swirl the water constantly while adding the NaOH. Count the drops. Stop when you have added enough NaOH to turn the water slightly pink. Cork this sample of water and use it as your standard of pinkness (control).

4. Copy the table below in your data book and record the number of drops of NaOH you added to get your control.

Activity	Drops of NaOH Needed to Remove CO_2 from Water
Control	
Sitting	
Mild exercise	
Vigorous exercise	

5. In the following steps, try to match the color of the control sample.
6. Prepare a second flask with water and phenolphthalein as you did the first flask.
7. Sit very quietly for 1 minute. Put a soda straw in the water. Blow air from your lungs into the water through the straw for 10 seconds.
8. Swirl the water gently while adding NaOH drop by drop (count the drops), until the water turns pink. If the pink disappears, add more NaOH. When the water stays at the pink that matches your control, record the number of drops of NaOH you used.
9. Discard this sample and clean the flask.
10. Prepare a new 100 ml water sample with 5 drops of phenolphthalein. Exercise for 1 minute by walking in place. Immediately, bubble air through the water sample for 10 seconds. Record the number of drops of NaOH needed to get the standard pink color. Discard the sample and clean the flask.
11. Repeat procedure 10. This time, exercise more vigorously for 1 minute. (Run in place, dance, or do jumping jacks.)

Discussion

1. If you had to add drops of NaOH to tap water to get a pink color to use as a control (procedure 3), what must you do to the number of drops you recorded for sitting, mild exercise, and vigorous exercise?
2. Make a bar graph of your corrected experimental data. Include 1 bar for each of the 3 experimental conditions.
3. How is the production of carbon dioxide related to activity?
4. What factors other than exercise might play a part in determining the amount of carbon dioxide given off?

16.11 The Kidneys Are Major Homeostatic Organs

The internal chemical environment of the body must be closely regulated at all times. Such regulation involves excreting cellular wastes, controlling concentrations of ions and other substances, and maintaining water balance. Carbon dioxide and nitrogen compounds are the chief cellular wastes. In the previous sections we saw how the lungs function to excrete carbon dioxide. Excretion of nitrogen compounds, regulation of ion concentrations, and maintenance of water balance are functions of the kidneys.

Figure 16.21 Urinary system in the human.

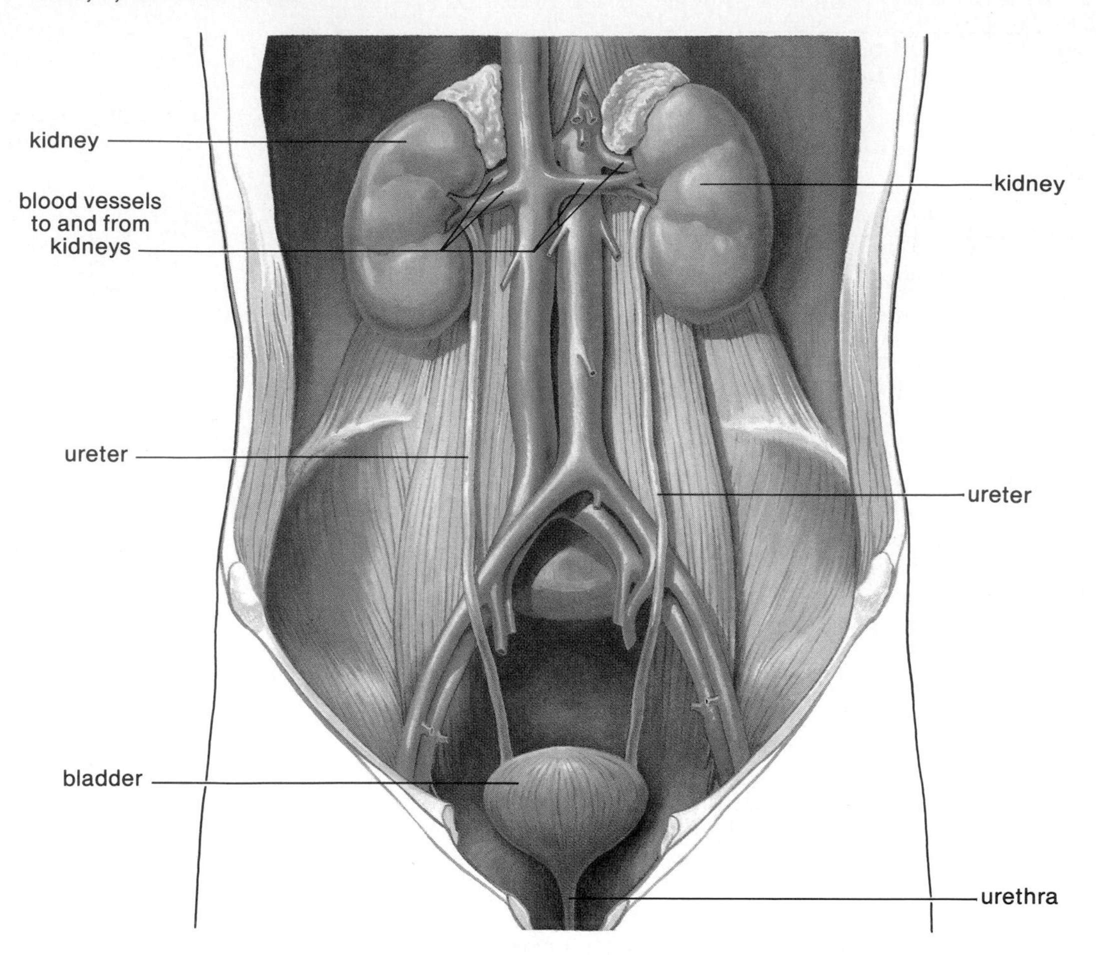

Figure 16.21 shows the urinary system of a human. The kidneys are dark red, bean-shaped organs about 10 cm long. They are located on each side of the back wall of the body cavity, just above waist level. Each kidney contains about a million working units, or **nephrons** (NEF rahnz). A nephron is a long, coiled tubule, one end of which opens into a duct that collects urine. The other end of the tubule forms a cup that encloses a mass of capillaries. Other capillaries form a network that closely surrounds the entire nephron, as seen in figure 16.22. This intimate relationship between the blood and the kidneys is essential to kidney function, as we will learn in the next section.

The cup of the nephron is called **Bowman's capsule.** The ball of capillaries in the cup is a **glomerulus** (glah MER yoo lus). The tubule wall is just one cell thick, and is in direct contact with a capillary wall, also a single cell thick. Often the tubule and capillary walls appear to merge into one undivided structure.

The tubule of each nephron leads into a collecting duct. Collecting ducts of all the nephrons empty into the **ureter** (YOOR et er), a large tube that leads from each kidney to the urinary bladder. Urine is stored in the bladder until it is discharged to the outside through another tube called the **urethra** (yoo REE thruh).

Figure 16.22 A section through the human kidney and an enlarged view of one nephron with its surrounding capillaries.

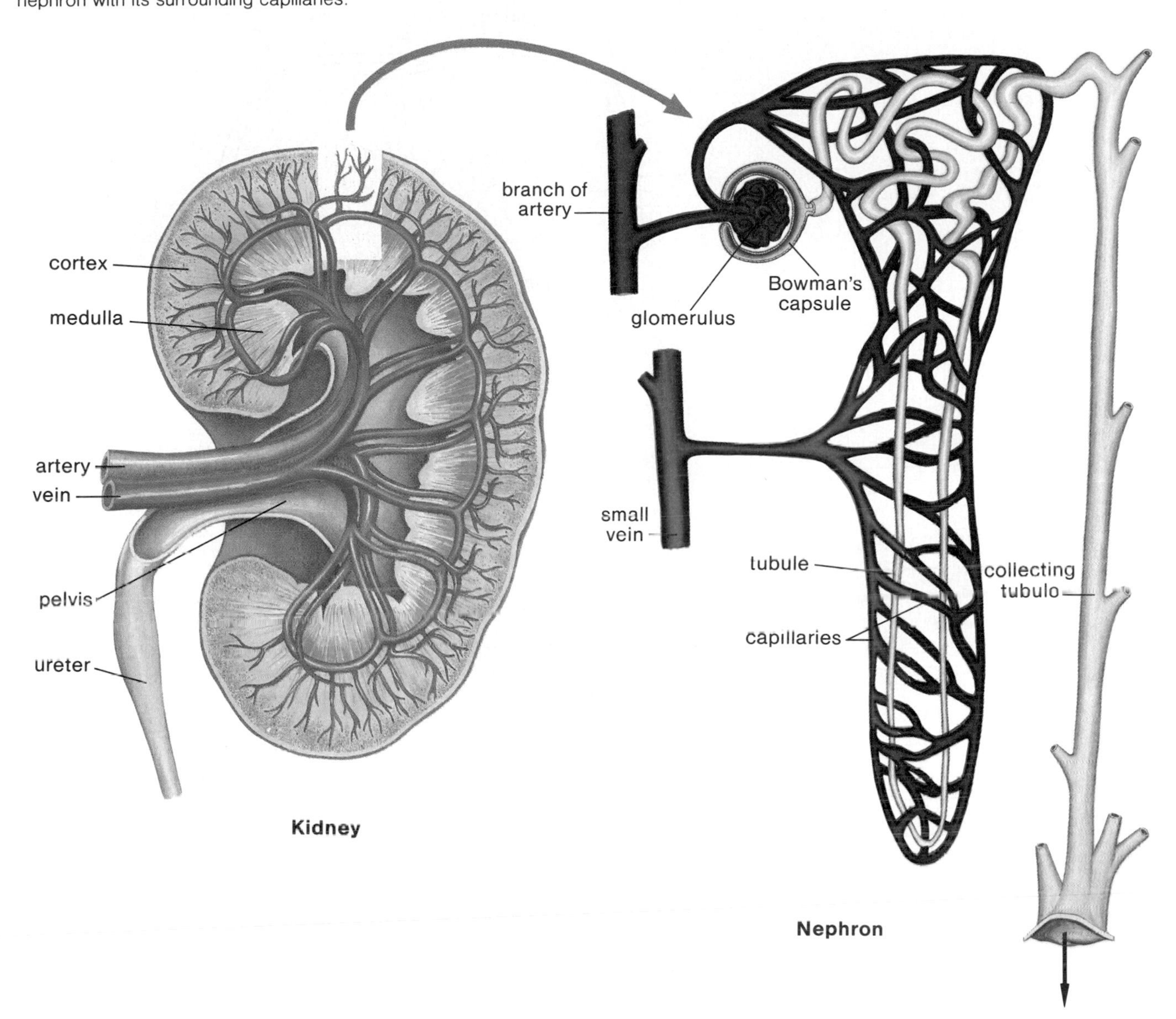

16.12 Nephrons Filter the Blood

Three processes are involved in the function of the nephrons: filtration, secretion, and reabsorption. These processes are summarized in figure 16.23. Filtration occurs in the glomerulus, where the fluid portion of the blood is forced into Bowman's capsule. Blood cells and most of the plasma proteins are retained in the glomerulus. The filtrate in Bowman's capsule contains nitrogenous wastes, ions, and much of the blood's water content. About 150 to 180 l of fluid enter the nephrons each day, yet only about 1.5 l of urine are eliminated from the bladder. That means that more than 99 percent of the fluid arriving in Bowman's capsule is returned to the blood.

Figure 16.23 Major steps in the formation of urine.

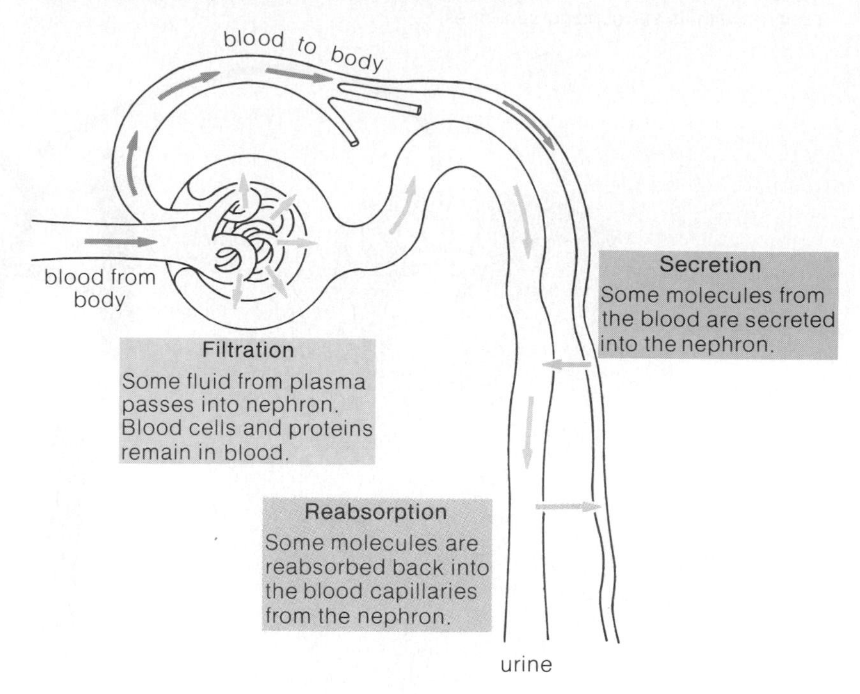
blood to body
blood from body
Filtration
Some fluid from plasma passes into nephron. Blood cells and proteins remain in blood.
Secretion
Some molecules from the blood are secreted into the nephron.
Reabsorption
Some molecules are reabsorbed back into the blood capillaries from the nephron.
urine

Secretion and reabsorption take place in the tubule of the nephron. As the filtrate moves through the tubule, cells of the tubular wall selectively remove from the surrounding capillaries substances left in the plasma after filtration. The cells then secrete these substances into the filtrate. Penicillin is removed from the blood in this manner.

Cells of the tubular walls also reabsorb useful substances from the filtrate and transport them back into the blood. Glucose, amino acids, essential ions such as sodium and potassium, and most of the water are conserved in this manner. Secretion and reabsorption require active transport for this exchange of materials.

The nephrons maintain appropriate blood-sugar level by glucose reabsorption. If the concentration rises too high, as in patients with diabetes, not all of the glucose can be reabsorbed, and some will be excreted in the urine. If the blood-sugar level is low or normal, almost all the glucose in the nephrons will be reabsorbed into the blood and no glucose will be present in the urine.

Water/salt balance is regulated at the far end of the tubule and in the collecting ducts. Here, about 99 percent of the water that has left the capillaries and entered the nephrons is reabsorbed into the blood. The mechanism is complex and involves maintenance of a high salt concentration in the tissues surrounding the tubule and collecting ducts. As a result, water leaves the collecting duct by osmosis. The reabsorption of water is under hormonal control, and the final concentration of the urine occurs in the collecting duct.

As a net result of the kidney's activities, blood-sugar level is regulated; nitrogenous wastes are removed from the blood; water/salt balance is regulated (and water reabsorbed into the blood); and excess salt, within limits, is excreted. However, the kidneys cannot excrete high concentrations of salt—nor can the skin glands, through perspiration. Normally, in a nutritious diet containing few processed foods, you do not eat or drink many substances with high salt concentrations. However, people shipwrecked on the ocean can easily die from dehydration by drinking the salt water. Instead of replenishing their body water, they will lose still more water than before as the kidneys attempt to excrete the salt.

The kidneys have still other functions, such as pH regulation, but the three we have just discussed—blood-sugar regulation, water/salt balance, and nitrogenous waste excretion—are the major ones. If the kidneys fail, the balance of vital and poisonous blood constituents cannot be maintained, homeostasis fails, and death follows. Investigation 16.4 develops the relationship between structure and function in the kidney.

Self-Review

1. What is the difference between respiration and cellular respiration?
2. Describe the mechanism by which air is moved into and out of human lungs.
3. Describe how oxygen and carbon dioxide are carried in your blood.
4. List the major regulatory functions of the kidneys.
5. Describe the structure of the nephron.
6. Explain how filtration, secretion, and reabsorption contribute to formation of urine.

Investigation 16.4 THE KIDNEY AND HOMEOSTASIS

Introduction

The cells of the human body are surrounded by liquid that is remarkably constant in its properties. The continued regulation of the many dissolved compounds and ions in this internal environment is referred to as homeostasis.

The kidneys are extremely important in maintaining homeostasis. They function rapidly and sensitively in regulating blood composition and maintaining optimum concentration of dissolved substances. About 1700 l of blood flows through the kidneys of an average person in a single day. Of this amount, about 170 l is filtered through the glomeruli into the nephrons, but only about 1.5 l of this filtrate is excreted as urine. The amount varies, depending on the individual's health, activity, water and salt intake, temperature, and many other factors.

Part A—Blood v. Urine

Procedure

The relationship of structure and function in the kidney is illustrated in figure 16.22, page 597. Use it and the data given in table 16.2 to answer the discussion questions.

Table 16.2 Comparison of materials in blood and urine

	% in Blood as It Enters Kidney	% in Urine as It Leaves Kidney
Water	91.5	96.0
Protein	7.0	0.0
Glucose	0.1	0.0
Sodium	0.33	0.29
Potassium	0.02	0.24
Urea	0.03	2.70

Discussion

1. What do the data for water indicate?
2. Protein molecules are not normally found in the urine. Give some possible reasons for this.
3. The information for glucose is similar to that for protein. Can you explain these data?
4. Look at the sodium data. Based on these data, what may happen to the sodium content in the urine of a person who increased his or her intake of sodium chloride?
5. How does the data for potassium differ from that of sodium?
6. How would you interpret the data given for urea?
7. Summarize the functions that take place between blood and urine and the structures where these functions occur.

Part B—Filtration, Reabsorption, and Secretion

Procedure

The micropuncture method was used in a second study of the 6 materials presented in table 16.2. A very fine pipette was used under a microscope to withdraw samples of fluid at 4 points along the nephron and collecting tubule. Study table 16.3, which shows the data that were collected using this technique. Use the data to answer the discussion questions.

Discussion

1. Which function, secretion or reabsorption, is greatest as far as the movement of water is concerned in the kidney?
2. Proteins are involved in which of these 3 functions?
3. Compare the protein and glucose data. What is different? Explain this difference.
4. In some samples glucose is found in the urine. What might cause this?
5. Why are excess glucose molecules in the blood excreted?
6. The data tells us that the concentration of sodium in the blood is greater than in the urine, yet most of the sodium molecules in the urine move back into the blood. What process makes this movement possible?

Table 16.3 Comparison of materials at 4 points along the nephron

	In Blood Entering Glomerulus	In Tubule* from Glomerulus	In the Urine	In Blood Leaving** Nephron
Water	100	30	1	99
Protein	100	0	0	100
Glucose	100	20	0	100
Sodium	100	30	1	99
Potassium	100	23	12	88
Urea	100	50	90	10

*The numbers in this column represent proportions, not actual numbers of molecules. For every 100 molecules of water in the blood, 30 are found in the tubule.

**The numbers in this column were obtained by subtracting the proportionate number of molecules of the substance in the urine from the proportionate number of molecules of the substance originally in the blood (100).

7. Urea is a by-product of amino acid metabolism. Next to water, urea is the most abundant material found in urine. If urea were allowed to accumulate, what might happen?
8. Homeostasis is the maintenance of a relatively stable internal environment in an organism. Discuss your ideas about how the kidney functions as a homeostatic organ.

Temperature Regulation

Guidepost: How do humans maintain a constant internal body temperature?

16.13 The Rate of Chemical Reactions Is Influenced by Temperature

Metabolism is the sum of all the chemical reactions that occur within a cell or organism. Like other chemical reactions, these enzyme-controlled reactions are influenced by changes in temperature. Within limits, they slow down at low temperatures and speed up at high temperatures. Therefore, maintaining a constant internal temperature is an advantage; it allows for more efficient chemical processes to take place. It also permits an animal to be active when environmental temperatures are low.

In humans and other animals that are able to maintain a constant internal temperature, the temperature of the skin and the tissues just beneath it may fluctuate. Internal body temperature in most individuals, however, changes very little in the course of a day. On arising, your temperature is usually about 36.2° C, and it increases to perhaps 37.6° C by late afternoon, averaging about 37° C. It is important that body temperature be maintained within these narrow limits.

In order to accomplish this, the body must balance the amount of heat it produces with the amount it loses. Therefore, when you become overheated, as during strenuous exercise, the extra heat must be dispelled from the body. Otherwise, the body temperature could increase to the point at which enzyme functions would be impaired.

In chapter 15, we learned that one of the by-products of cellular respiration is heat. It is this heat, produced by the breakdown of foods, that maintains our body temperature. Because muscles and organs such as the kidneys are the most active tissues, they carry on more cellular respiration, and, thus, produce more heat than any of the other body tissues. Therefore, the activity of the muscles determines the rate of heat production. When you sleep, there is little muscular movement, and heat production decreases. As you exercise or shiver, your active muscles produce more heat.

16.14 Major Heat Loss Occurs through Evaporation and Radiation

Most of the heat loss, 80 percent or more, occurs through the skin. The balance takes place through the normal function of the respiratory, digestive, and excretory systems.

Figure 16.24 Exchanges that take place between internal and external environments.

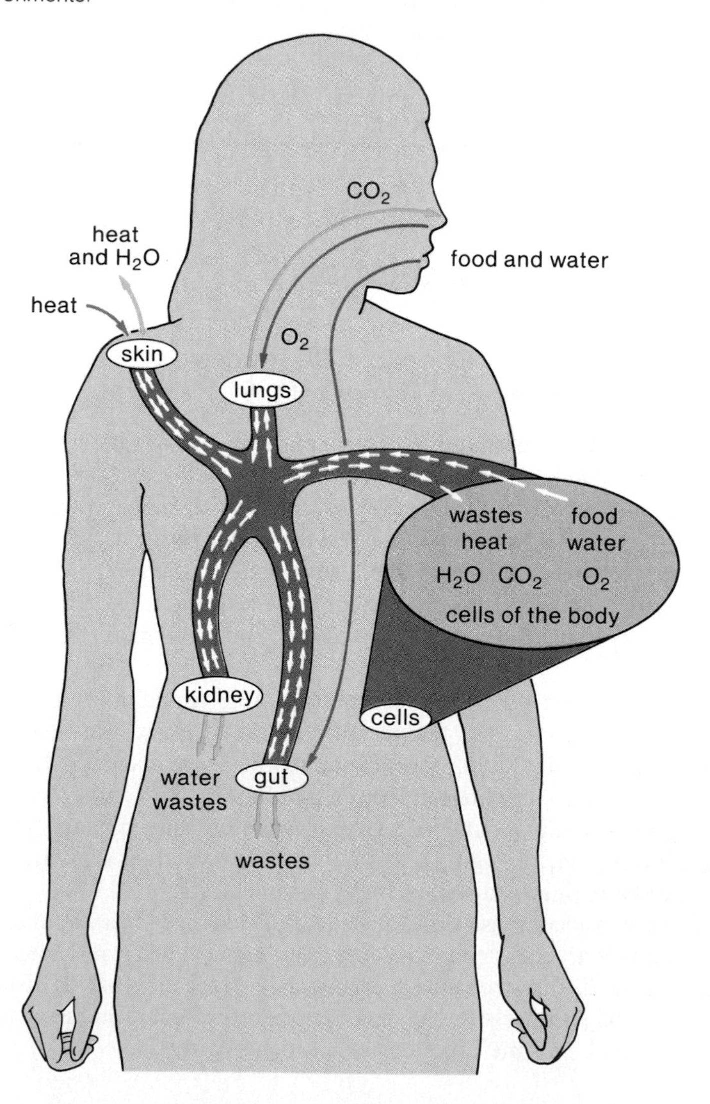

Figure 16.25 Lizard absorbing radiated heat. Animals such as this do not have internal mechanisms to regulate body temperature.

BSCS by Carlye Calvin

Evaporation at average temperatures and normal rates of activity is only one of the methods of cooling the body. However, at very high temperatures or during vigorous activity, it is the only method by which heat can be lost through the skin. Have you ever noticed that the same temperature on two different days may feel hotter on one of the days? At a temperature of 38° C (100° F) and a high humidity of 90 percent, you would feel hotter than at the same temperature with a humidity of 45 percent. That is because evaporation takes place more rapidly in a dryer environment, thus cooling your skin more efficiently.

Radiated heat is transferred from one object to another even when the two do not touch. You can feel the radiant heat of the sun without actually being in contact with the sun's surface. The skin gains or loses heat through radiation depending on the environment. If the environment is cool, body heat is lost through radiation, and conversely, in a hot environment heat is gained by radiation from hot surfaces.

16.15 Internal Temperature Is Controlled by the Brain

Heat loss or gain also may be affected by the amount and type of clothing worn, the ingestion of hot or cold food or liquid, or even by standing in a breeze. Internal body temperature can remain constant only if the rate of heat loss is the same as that of heat production. Receptors that respond to temperature changes are necessary to keep body temperature constant. In the hypothalamus, an area of the brain that we will discuss in the next chapter, there are receptors that detect changes in blood temperature. These receptors act as a thermostat to regulate body temperatures, much as a thermostat controls a furnace, air conditioner, or water heater.

Figure 16.26 How heat dissipating and heat conserving mechanisms operate to maintain normal body temperature.

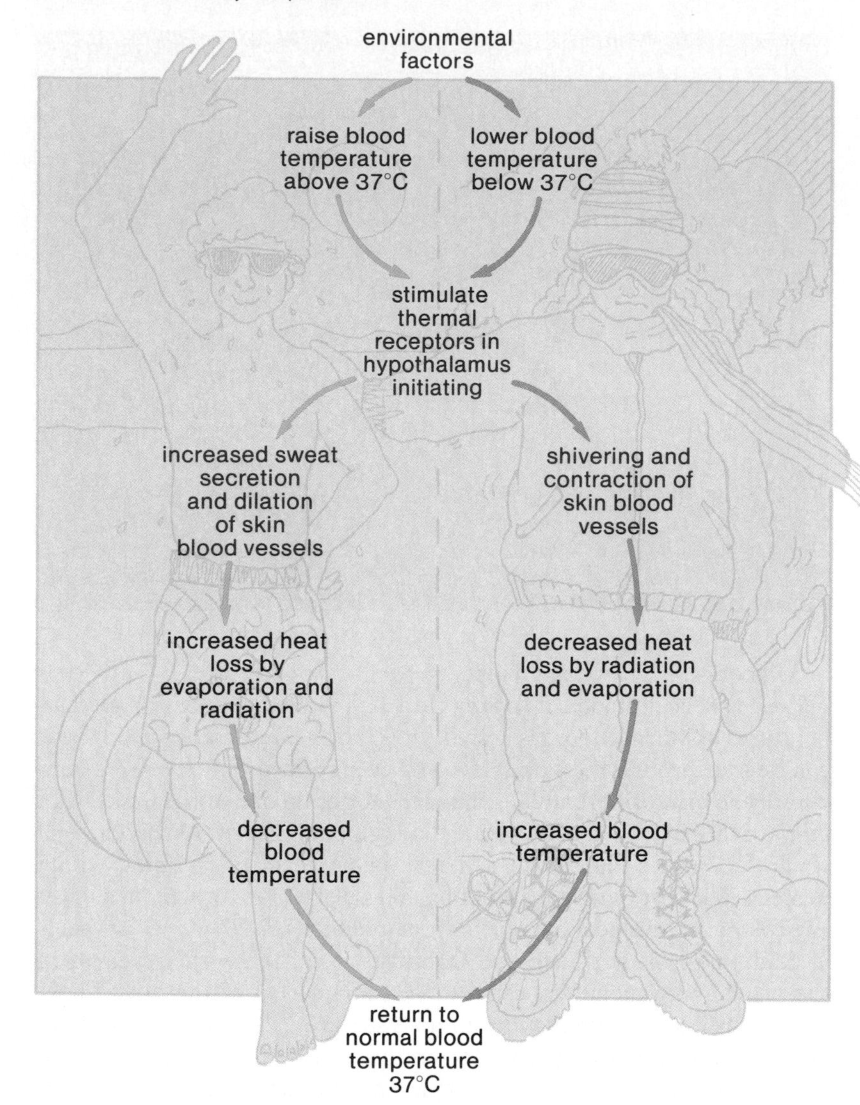

The body thermostat is set at 37° C. When the temperature of the blood increases by as little as 0.01° C, the cells of the hypothalamus send messages to the sweat glands and blood vessels of the skin. In response the sweat glands increase their rate of secretion. The blood vessels in the skin begin to dilate, or become larger, allowing for greater blood flow to and heat loss from the body surface. If body temperature continues to increase, this process will speed up the rate of sweating and dilation, causing more heat loss from the skin.

In a very cold environment, the reverse of this process occurs. When the temperature of the blood reaching the hypothalamus drops, messages are sent that slow production of sweat and that constrict, or narrow, the blood vessels in the skin. If this reaction does not raise the temperature sufficiently, a second mechanism is initiated. Shivering and voluntary muscle contractions cause an acceleration of cellular respiration and heat production. That is why when you are very cold, you use more oxygen and tire more quickly.

The use of hypothermia (the lowering of body temperature) is often called for in open-heart surgery and other prolonged surgical procedures. The purpose is to lower the body's activity rate until after surgery. However, the mechanisms involved in survival of extremely low body temperatures are still poorly understood.

Self-Review

1. What is the advantage of maintaining a constant body temperature?
2. What are some of the mechanisms by which your body attempts to keep you warm in very cold weather?
3. How does the body prevent damage from overheating as you are vigorously exercising?
4. How does the human body regulate its body temperature?
5. How is body temperature related to homeostasis?

Summary

The body requires a constant internal environment so that its cells can function effectively. Homeostasis, the maintenance of this stable environment, is achieved by cooperative action of all body systems. The heart and blood vessels that make up the circulatory system are specialized to deliver raw materials and remove wastes. The immune system serves to protect the body from foreign invaders. The respiratory system supplies the body with oxygen, and aids the excretory system in eliminating wastes. In addition, the excretory system plays a central role in regulating the concentration of many essential substances in the blood. Constant internal temperature enables chemical reactions to proceed at optimum rates. These systems all are coordinated by the nervous and endocrine systems, which we will examine in detail in the next chapter.

Application Questions

1. Describe the route followed by a molecule of oxygen as it moves from the air of your external environment to a mitochondrion in one of your muscle cells.
2. A temporary reddening of the skin surface is sometimes called a flush and sometimes a blush. The first term often is used in cases of fever, the second, to describe a reaction to some situation in the external environment. Is the body mechanism the same in both cases? If it is, how does it operate? If it is not, what are the differences?

Problems

1. In cases of kidney failure, the patient must undergo periodic hemodialysis on a kidney machine. How does this machine function? Compare it with the functions of the human kidney.
2. Why do surgeons place their patients in hypothermia before procedures such as open-heart surgery? What are the advantages?
3. Because the heart is often damaged by disease, much work has been done on designing artificial hearts. What problems must be overcome in order to design an effective artificial heart?

3. Trace the pathways of the hamburger, fries, and soft drink you might have had for lunch. Describe what happens to the food molecules from the time they are absorbed in the intestine until their remains are excreted in the urine or eliminated through the anus.
4. Distinguish among excretion, secretion, and elimination. Explain which system(s) of the body are involved in each.
5. Construct a diagram or concept map indicating the relationship between the circulatory and respiratory systems.
6. What is the effect of the presence of respiratory pigment such as hemoglobin on the transport of oxygen?
7. How are breathing and gas transport affected by climbing to high altitudes?

4. Under what circumstances would you apply cardiopulmonary resuscitation (CPR)? What are the precautions you must observe in exhaled air ventilation and external cardiac compression?

Suggested Readings

P. D. Buisseret, "Allergy" *Scientific American* (August 1982). A very interesting article investigating the reasons why people suffer from allergies.

B. Dixon, "Overdosing on Wonder Drugs" *Science 86* (May 1986). Reckless use of antibiotics is creating tougher germs worldwide.

R. L. Edelson and J. M. Fink, "The Immunologic Function of Skin" *Scientific American* (June 1985). Examines the various roles of the body's largest organ.

P. Huyghe, "Your Heart: A Survival Guide" *Science Digest* (April 1985). Examines the various characteristics of and prevention of heart disease.

N. R. Rose, "Autoimmune Diseases" *Scientific American* (February 1981). Occasionally the immune system malfunctions and attacks the body's own tissues.

R. B. Schlesinger, "Defense Mechanisms of the Respiratory System" *BioScience* (January 1982). Provides an overview of the defense mechanisms of the mammalian respiratory tract.

R. A. Stallones, "The Rise and Fall of Ischemic Heart Disease" *Scientific American* (November 1980). Since the 1960s, deaths due to heart attack and other results of the obstruction of the arteries has decreased. The reasons are investigated in this article.

Tom Stack/TOM STACK & ASSOCIATES

The gymnast displays coordination involving the nervous, hormonal, muscular, and skeletal systems.

CHAPTER 17

The Human Animal: Coordination

Introduction

In performing any activity involving movement, you must integrate several systems of your body. Have you ever wondered how a gymnast is able to execute such complex moves with so few mistakes? One answer is practice, but how does simply repeating an action result in such precision? If we wish to analyze a gymnast's routine or even your ability to run, we must consider the function and integration of the skeletal, muscular, nervous, and hormonal systems. Both conscious and unconscious mental processes are needed simply to initiate the behavior that results in movement. Behavior may be defined as any action that occurs in response to a signal, either internal, such as a thought, or external, such as visual stimuli from the environment. Before the gymnast can begin her demanding and precise exercise routine, she must marshal the many internal and external factors that affect movement and behavior. In this chapter we will examine some of the mechanisms that make such integration possible.

Human Movement

Guidepost: How do muscles and bones enable humans to move?

17.1 Muscle Contraction Depends on Energy from ATP

Humans and other animals have three types of muscles, each with a different function. **Striated** (STRY ayt ed) **muscle** moves the skeleton in response to conscious control, and is thus called voluntary muscle. This type of muscle is involved in adjustments to the external environment such as raising your arm to swat an annoying mosquito. **Smooth muscle** is found in the walls of blood vessels, the digestive tract, and portions of the lower respiratory tract. Smooth muscle functions in the

Figure 17.1 (a) Skeletal muscle, showing the characteristic striations. (b) Smooth muscle showing contraction bands. This tissue contracts in wavelike motions. (c) Drawing of several smooth muscle cells. Smooth muscle has clearly defined cells with a central nucleus. (d) Cardiac muscle.

a Ed Reschke

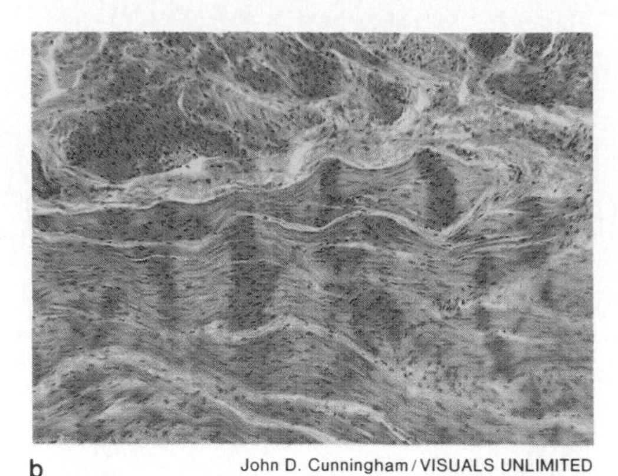

b John D. Cunningham/VISUALS UNLIMITED

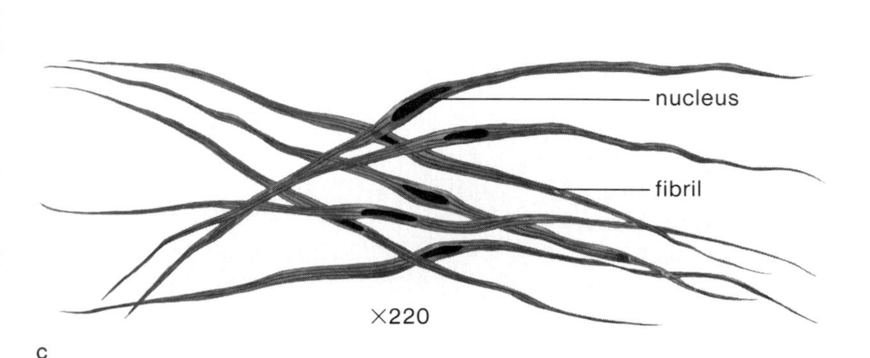

c

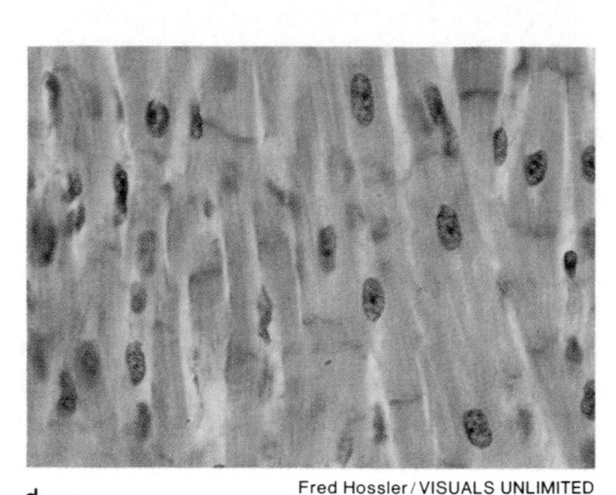

d Fred Hossler/VISUALS UNLIMITED

operation and regulation of the internal environment. **Cardiac** (KARD ee ak) **muscle** is specialized striated muscle found only in the heart. Smooth muscle and cardiac muscle are not generally under the conscious control of the individual; they are involuntary muscles.

Figure 17.2 shows a striated muscle at successively greater magnifications. As you can see in (a), the muscle consists of individual fibers that run the entire length. Each muscle fiber, the equivalent of a muscle cell, is made up of many parallel fibrils (c), and each fibril is composed of protein organized into thick and thin filaments (d). The thick and thin filaments are arranged in an overlapping pattern (e) that gives striated muscle its characteristic appearance under the microscope. In muscle contraction, portions of the thick filaments attach to the thin filaments and pull the thin filaments toward each other (f).

Muscle contraction is initiated by a nerve impulse and requires the presence of calcium ions. ATP provides the energy. The supply of ATP in a muscle fiber, however, can sustain full contraction for only about a second. In order for a muscle fiber to continue contracting, the ATP must be rapidly regenerated. This is made possible by utilizing three energy sources. The first is **creatine phosphate** (KREE uh tin FOS fayt), a substance in the muscle cell that can pass its energy to ADP. Creatine phosphate provides *immediate* regeneration of ATP. The second energy source is the ATP formed during normal cellular respiration, and the third is **glycogen** (GLY koh jen), the storage form of the glucose you take in. Glycogen is stored in muscle and in the liver. In the muscle cells, when glycogen is broken down to glucose, it is respired to produce more ATP. In the liver, when glycogen is broken down to glucose, it is released into the blood in the presence of chemical messengers known as hormones. As an athlete mentally prepares for exertion, he triggers the release of these hormones, which prepare the body for action. Later in this chapter we will discover how the brain initiates the secretion of those hormones.

17.2 Interaction of Bones and Muscles Produces Movement

Movement is achieved by the contraction of muscles that are attached to the bones. The skeleton consists of two kinds of tissue, cartilage and bone. The hardness of bone results, in part, from deposits of calcium and magnesium compounds. Both cartilage and bone contain cells that secrete these compounds. These living cells and their secretions enable the skeleton to grow as the child grows. Though most of the skeleton begins as cartilage, nearly all of it is gradually replaced by bone. At your age

Figure 17.3 Nerve endings on striated muscle fibers. Nerve impulses stimulate the nerve endings to secrete their chemical messengers, initiating the events that result in contraction of the muscle fibers.

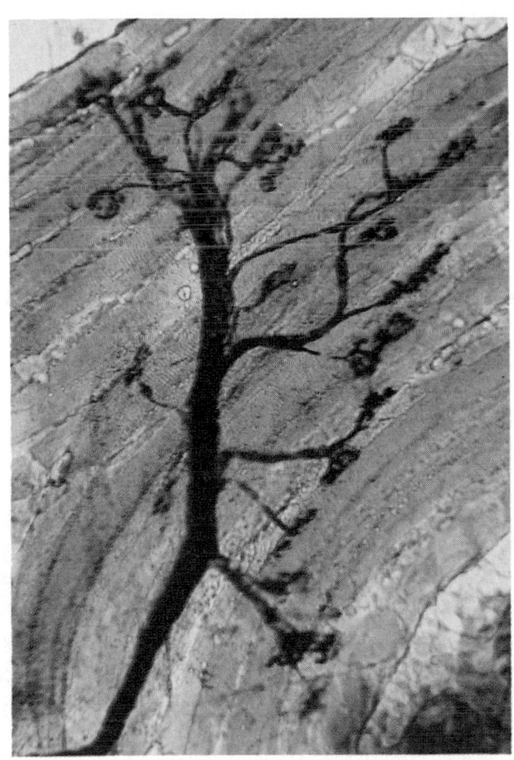

John D. Cunningham/VISUALS UNLIMITED

Figure 17.2 Successive magnifications from muscle to fiber to fibril to filaments. Striated muscle contracts when the thick filaments temporarily attach to the thin filaments and pull them toward each other.

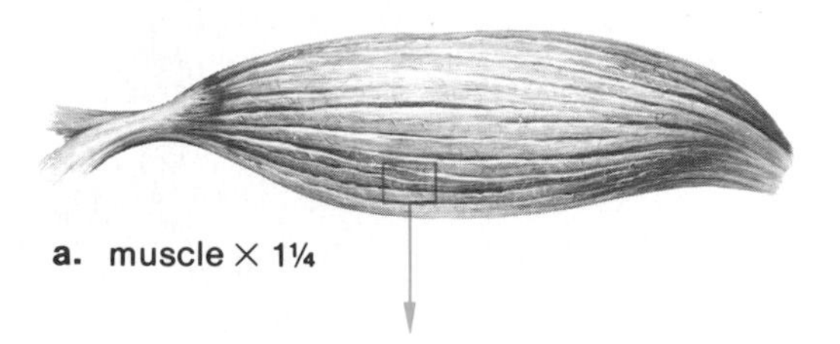

a. muscle × 1¼

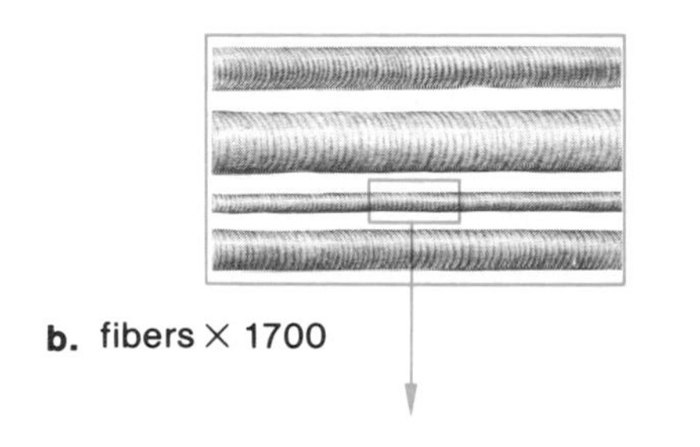

b. fibers × 1700

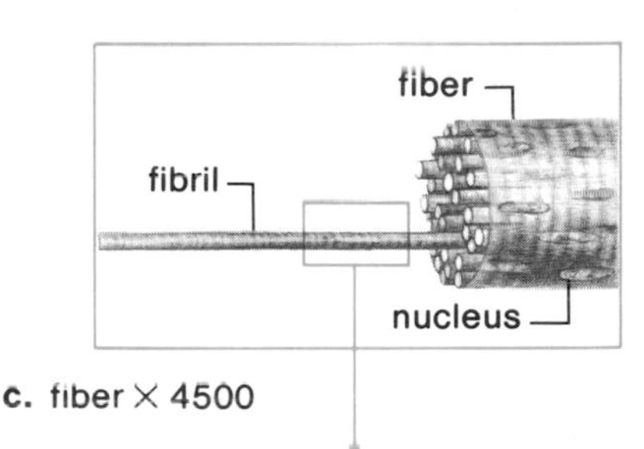

c. fiber × 4500

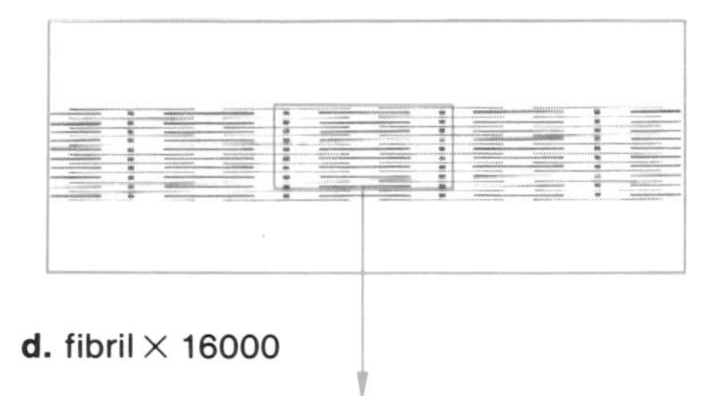

d. fibril × 16000

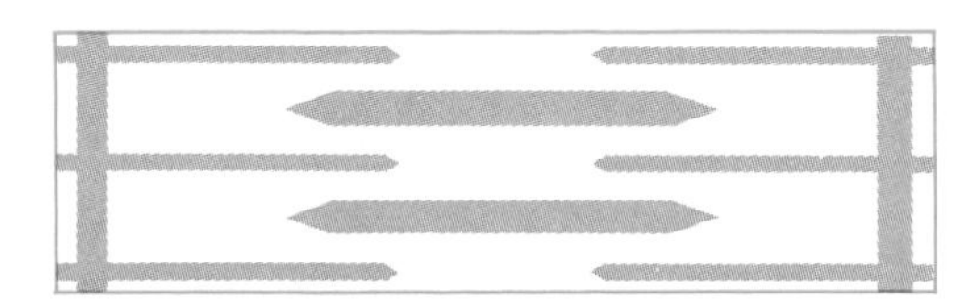

e. filaments – relaxed position

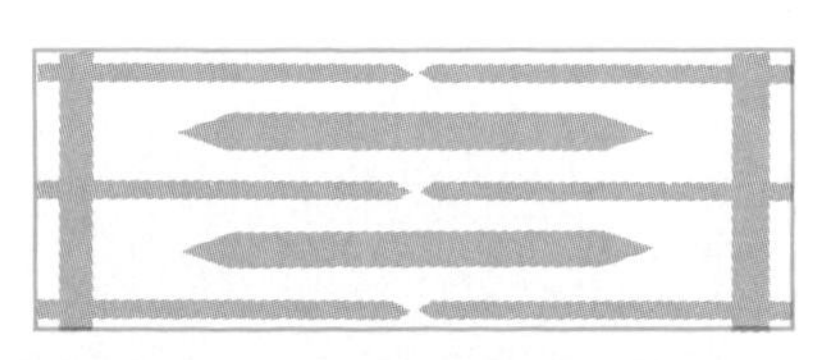

f. filaments – contracted position

Figure 17.4 Human skeletal and muscular systems.

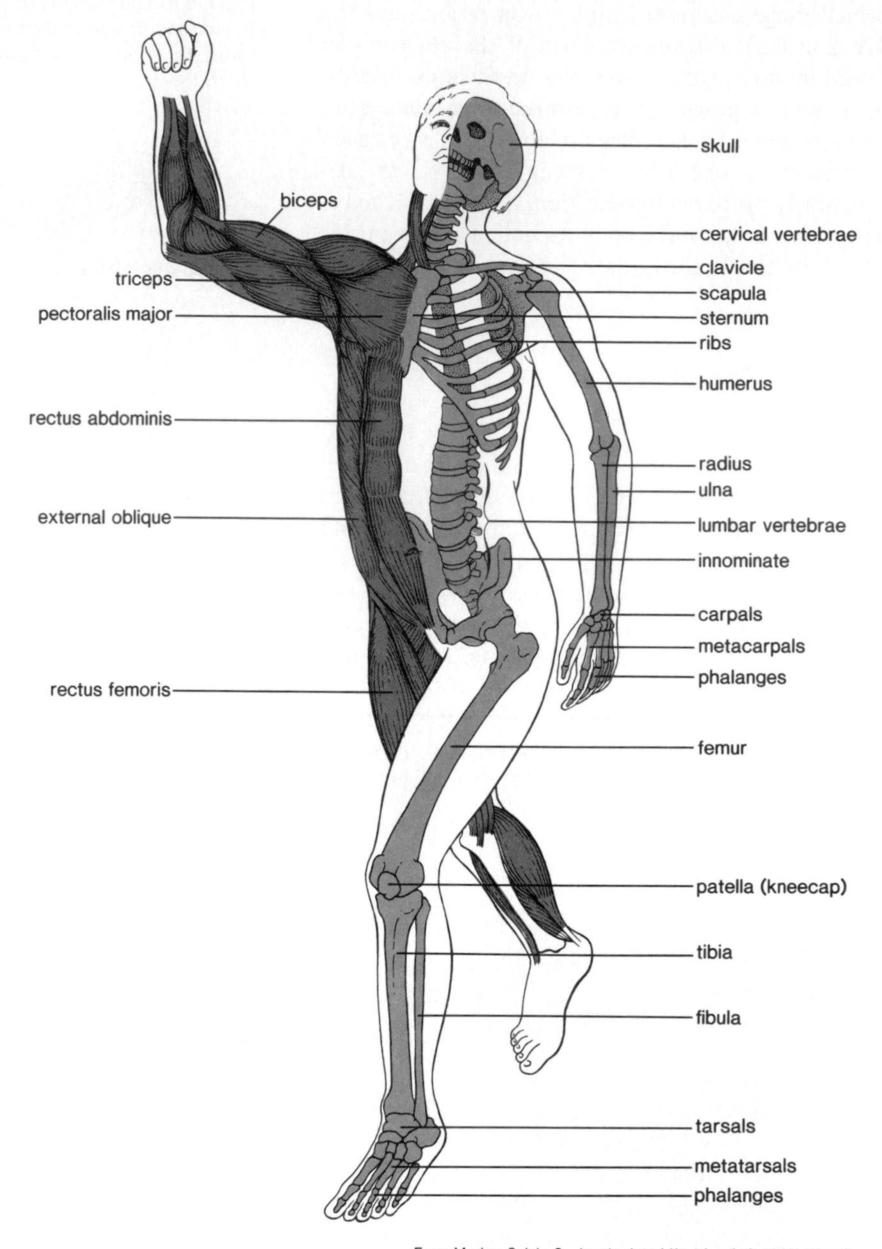

the replacement process is well advanced. Some parts of the skeleton, however, remain as cartilage. The tip of your nose and the external parts of your ears will never become hard bone and will continue to grow to some extent.

The jointed bones of a vertebrate skeleton act together with muscles to produce movement. A **joint** is where two or more bones meet and allow for some type of movement. Muscles supply the force to move these parts.

Figure 17.5 A flexor-extensor muscle pair in the human arm. Flexors bend a limb at a skeletal joint; extensors straighten the limb again.

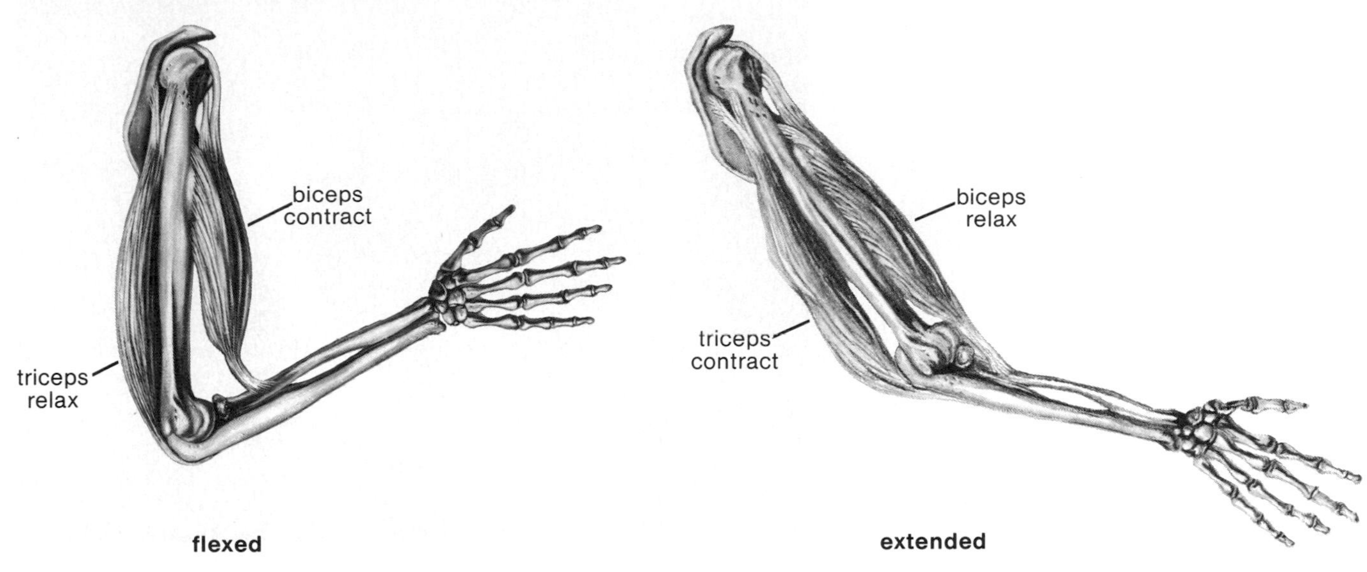

A muscle attached to a bone is like a rope attached to a wagon. With a rope you can pull an object, but you cannot push it. If you want to move the wagon back to its original position, you must attach a rope to the other end and again pull it. Muscles act in the same way—in pairs (see figure 17.5). To touch your hand to your shoulder, you contract one set of muscles. When you return your hand and arm to the extended position, you contract another set of muscles and relax the first set. These two sets of muscles work in opposition to each other. All your skeletal movements are performed by contraction and relaxation of opposing sets of muscles.

17.3 Cardiovascular Fitness Depends on Regular Exercise

Even when an animal appears to be at rest, its muscles are not completely relaxed. The muscles of any healthy organism are always in a state of partial contraction that is called **muscle tone.** This produces the firmness that can be felt even in "relaxed" muscles.

Today, physical fitness is a household word and a large business. For many, fitness means losing weight, whereas for others it means building muscles or improving muscle tone. The primary benefit of fitness, however, is to improve the ability of the lungs, heart, and blood vessels to deliver oxygen to the cells. This is known as **cardiovascular** (KARD ee oh VAS kyoo ler) **fitness,** an expression that refers to the fitness of the heart (cardio) and the vessels (vascular).

The American Heart Association recommends exercising 20 to 30 minutes a day, 3 days a week, as one way to prevent coronary problems. The heart, like any muscle, gets stronger when it is exercised. The average person's heart pumps about 5 l of blood per minute. During intense

Figure 17.6 A muscle builder.

BSCS

Figure 17.7 The use of technology in athletic training.

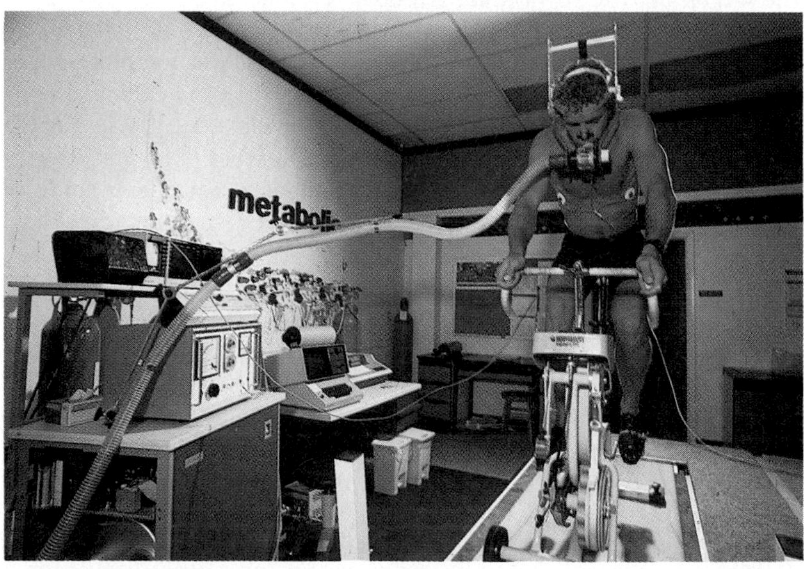

John Morgan

exercise that may rise to 30 l per minute. At that rate a marathon runner's heart can deliver as much as 4000 l of blood to the body during a 43 km race—enough to fill a 12 gal gas tank 80 times.

Cardiovascular fitness is important for everyone's health. To achieve movements of an Olympic calibre athlete, however, requires a great deal more. Centers such as the U.S. Olympic Training Center in Colorado Springs, Colorado, use the latest in modern electronic technology. Athletes are subjected to a battery of tests by sports psychologists and exercise physiologists. The test equipment that is used includes the

electroencephalograph (ee LEK troh en SEF uh loh graf), which monitors electrical brain activities, and computers, which provide dynamic computer-enhanced images of body functions. Here the human body is treated as if it were a machine, and its muscles and limbs were pulleys and levers. Because of progress in sports medicine, experts believe that the 1996 Olympics will see athletes reach the limits of human performance in those events involving a short burst of energy. Researchers also predict that within a decade or two, women will equal or surpass men in marathon events.

Self-Review

1. Name the three types of muscles, where they are found, and how they are controlled.
2. How is the supply of ATP in muscle regenerated?
3. How does cardiovascular fitness differ from physical fitness?

Investigation 17.1 EXERCISE, ENERGY, AND MUSCLES

Introduction

As we become more aware of our personal physical fitness and its importance in competitive athletics, we place greater emphasis on learning about the interaction between exercise, energy, and muscles. Rather than asking how muscles work, we ask questions concerning energy/muscle relationships. We also ask how energy-producing processes interact, or which physiological aspect has the greatest influence on performance levels during specific activities.

In this investigation you will examine results from two experiments concerned with energy/muscle relationships. You will then use these data, together with your readings in chapters 15 and 17, to determine how cellular respiration relates to muscle structure and function.

Procedure

Part A—Energy Production During Physical Activity

Energy can be produced by two different cellular processes, anaerobic (without 0_2) and aerobic (with 0_2) respiration. How much energy does each contribute during physical activity? To answer this question, human subjects were asked to perform running and bicycling exercises for different lengths of time. For each time period, total energy production (output) was measured and the amount contributed by anaerobic and aerobic respiration determined. The results are shown in table 17.1.

1. Using the results in table 17.1, form a hypothesis to describe the relationship between anaerobic and aerobic respiration during exercise.
2. (a) In terms of muscle chemistry, which is more important for initiating exercise—creatine phosphate or glycogen?
   (b) Which one is more important in continuing exercise? Explain.

Table 17.1 Relative energy contributions of aerobic and anaerobic processes

Work Time Maximal Exercise	Energy Output (kcal)		
	Anaerobic Processes	Aerobic Processes	Total
10 sec	20	4	24
1 min	30	20	50
2 min	30	45	75
5 min	30	120	150
10 min	25	245	270
30 min	20	657	677
60 min	15	1200	1215

From Gollnick, P. D. and Hermansen, L.: "Biochemical adaptations to exercise: Anaerobic metabolism," *Exercise and Sport Science Reviews,* Vol. 1. Edited by J. H. Wilmore. New York, Academic Press, 1973.

Part B—Muscle Structure and Activity

Muscles consist of fiber bundles containing 2 fiber types: slow and fast. Because muscles of different individuals vary in their percentage of slow and fast fibers, it would be important to ask: Does muscle structure influence physical performance? One experiment to test this possibility used 2 groups of athletes. Muscles in 1 group consisted of 67% fast fibers and 33% slow fibers. The other group had 21% fast fibers and 79% slow fibers. While group members performed 100 knee extensions, strength measurements were made for each knee extension. Figure 17.8 shows the results of the experiment.

1. Based on Figure 17.8, what conclusions can be made about the role of muscle structure during physical activity?
2. Similar results were obtained when 2 types of runners, sprinters and marathoners, performed a similar test. What types of muscles would you expect sprinters to have? Marathoners? Explain.
3. (a) Compare sprinters and marathoners in terms of their physical differences.
   (b) Would you expect it to be possible to retrain a world-class runner of one type to be competitive at the same level in the other event? Why or why not?

Figure 17.8 Comparison of leg strength changes in high (67%) and low (21%) fast muscle fiber groups during knee extension exercises.

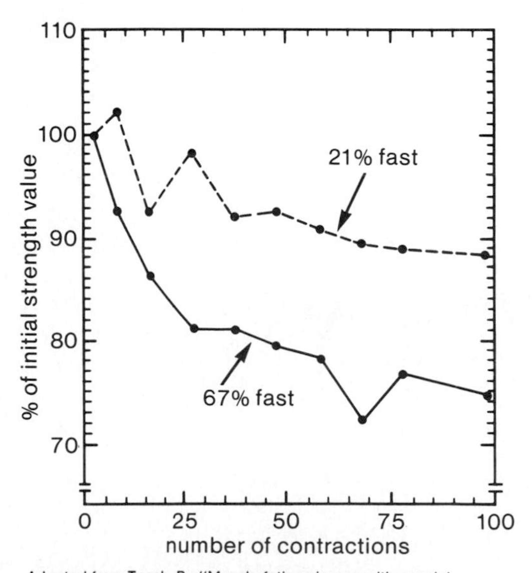

Adapted from Tesch, P.: "Muscle fatigue in man with special reference to lactate accumulation during short term intense exercise," *Acta Physiol. Scand.* 480:44, 1980.

Discussion

1. Based on the data in table 17.1 and figure 17.8, how would you describe the relationship between energy production and muscle structure?
2. Examine the list of sports people below and rank them from 1 to 12 in terms of their aerobic energy demands.

_____ football players	_____ basketball players
_____ swimmers	_____ cyclists
_____ recreational runners	_____ tennis players
_____ ice hockey players	_____ cross-country skiers
_____ untrained persons	_____ soccer players
_____ elite distance runners	_____ gymnasts

The Nervous System

Guidepost: How does the brain coordinate body movements and behavior?

17.4 Neurons Transmit Nerve Impulses

In general, rapid adjustments of animals to the environment are brought about by the nervous system. These adjustments or movements are initiated by an internal or external signal known as a **stimulus** (STIM yoo lus). The information is carried through the nervous system by **neurons** (NYOO rahnz), or nerve cells (figure 17.9). Each neuron has an enlarged region, the **cell body,** that contains the nucleus. Most cell bodies are located in the brain or spinal cord. From the cell body extend one or more long projections called **nerve fibers.** In humans, the fibers of some neurons are almost a meter long. **Nerves** are bundles of nerve fibers.

Neurons transmit **nerve impulses.** A stimulus occurring at the end of a nerve fiber starts a process of chemical and electrical changes that travels like a wave over the length of a neuron. This wave of change is the nerve impulse.

The chemical reactions that occur in the nerve impulse require oxygen and energy and produce carbon dioxide and heat. Electrical changes also take place. The plasma membrane of a resting neuron is electrically more positive on the outside than on the inside (figure 17.10a). This difference in electrical charge is due to the differential permeability of the membrane to sodium and potassium ions.

Stimulation of a neuron causes a small segment of the plasma membrane to become more permeable to sodium ions. As positively charged sodium ions rush into the neuron, there is a sudden change in electrical charge of the membrane (figure 17.10b). That local change is the nerve impulse, and it starts a similar change in the next small segment. In that manner, the impulse moves from one end of the neuron to the other as a wave of local chemical and electrical changes (figure 17.10c).

Neurons are separated by a very small space called a **synapse** (SIN aps). When an impulse reaches the end of a neuron, it causes the release of a **neurotransmitter** (NYOOR oh trans MIT er). That is a chemical substance that diffuses across the synapse and causes a new nerve impulse to start in the next neuron. Because transmission across a synapse takes place only in one direction, neurons conduct impulses only in one direction. Neurotransmitters also cause muscles to contract and certain glands to secrete hormones.

Nerve impulses may travel at speeds greater than 100 m per second in large fibers. The impulses are of short duration—usually a few tenthousandths of a second. However, the neuron cannot carry another impulse until it has had time to recover. To restore the resting state, sodium ions must be pumped back outside the plasma membrane by means of active transport. Only after recovery can the neuron respond to a new stimulus.

In humans three kinds of neurons can be distinguished by their functions. **Sensory neurons** receive impulses from a **receptor.** Receptors are specially modified sensory neurons such as the cells in the retina of the eye that react to light. Sensory neurons then transmit nerve impulses to an **associative neuron,** which transmits impulses from one type of neuron to another. **Motor neurons** carry the impulses to an **effector**—that is, a muscle or a gland. The effector responds to the impulse with movement or secretion.

Figure 17.9 In this typical neuron, note that the axon always carries impulses away from the cell body.

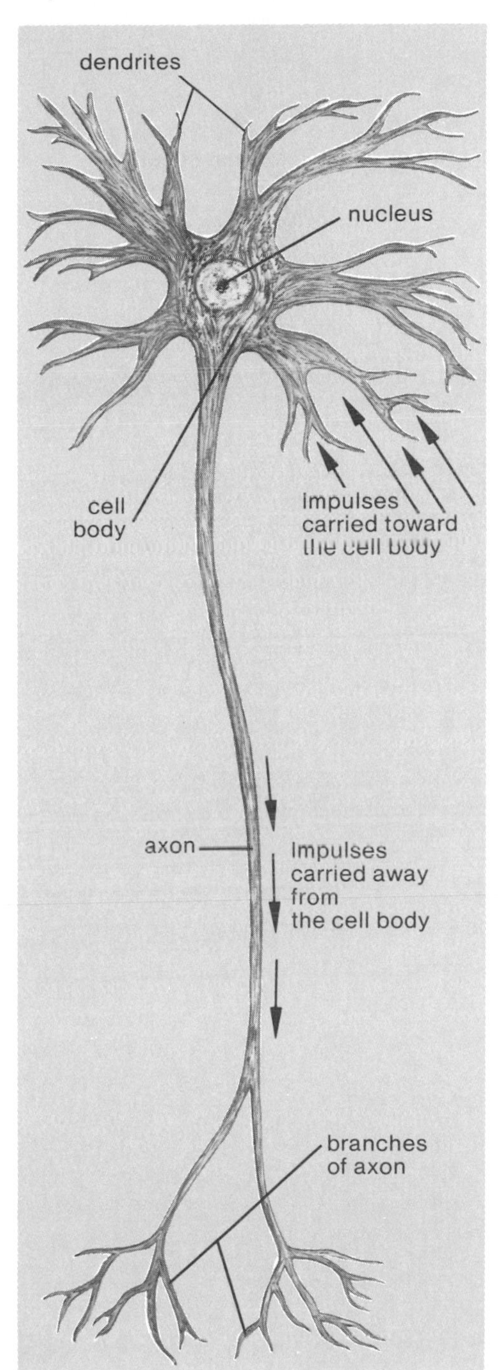

Figure 17.10 (a) A resting neuron. The plasma membrane is more positive on the outside than on the inside; plus and minus signs indicate the relative difference in electrical charge. (b) A stimulus is applied. The electrical state reverses as the impulse is initiated. (c) The impulse moves as a wave of changes in electrical charges. (d) A second stimulus is applied after recovery. (e) Both impulses, spaced apart, move along the axon.

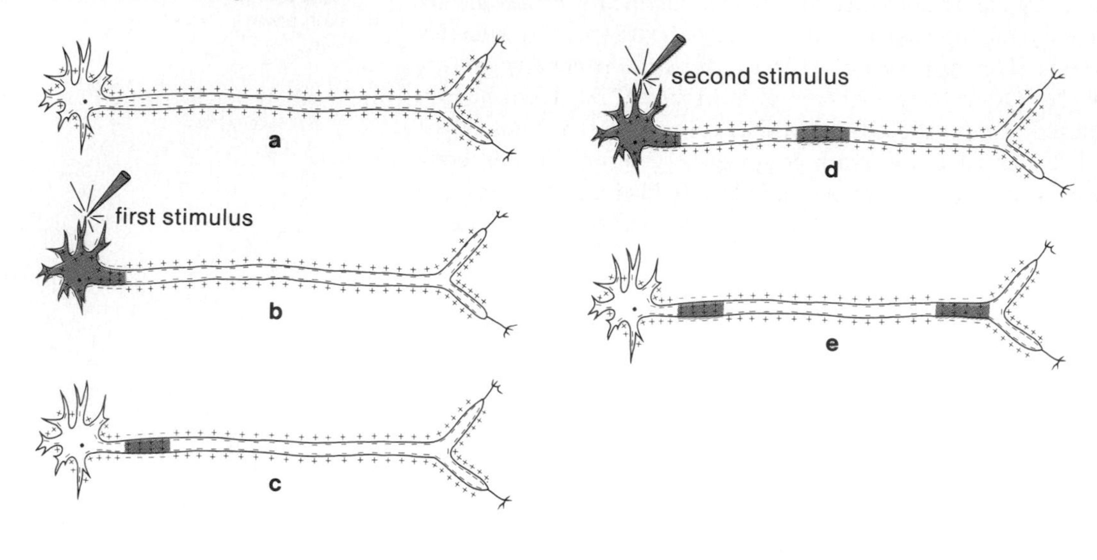

Figure 17.11 Kinds of neurons.

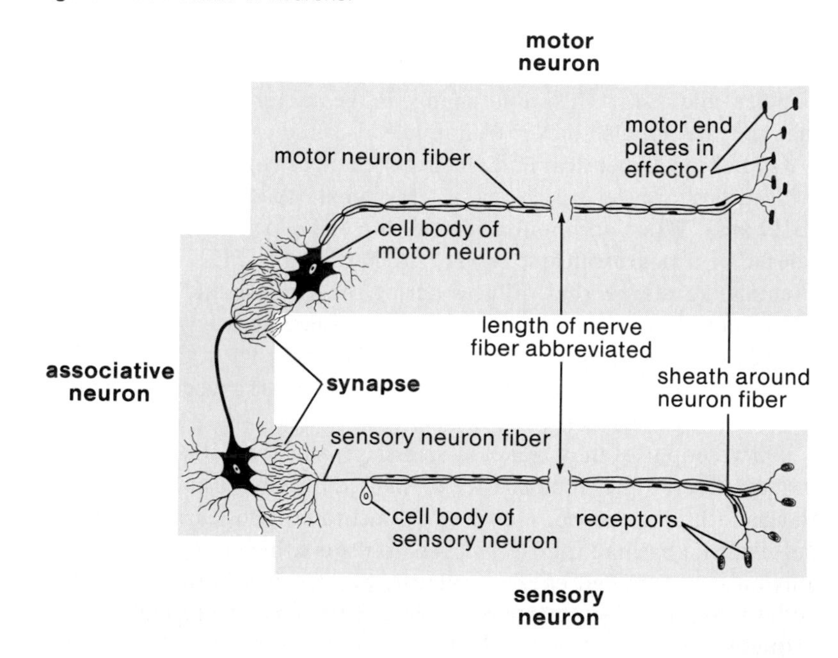

Figure 17.12 Some functional areas of the human cerebrum.

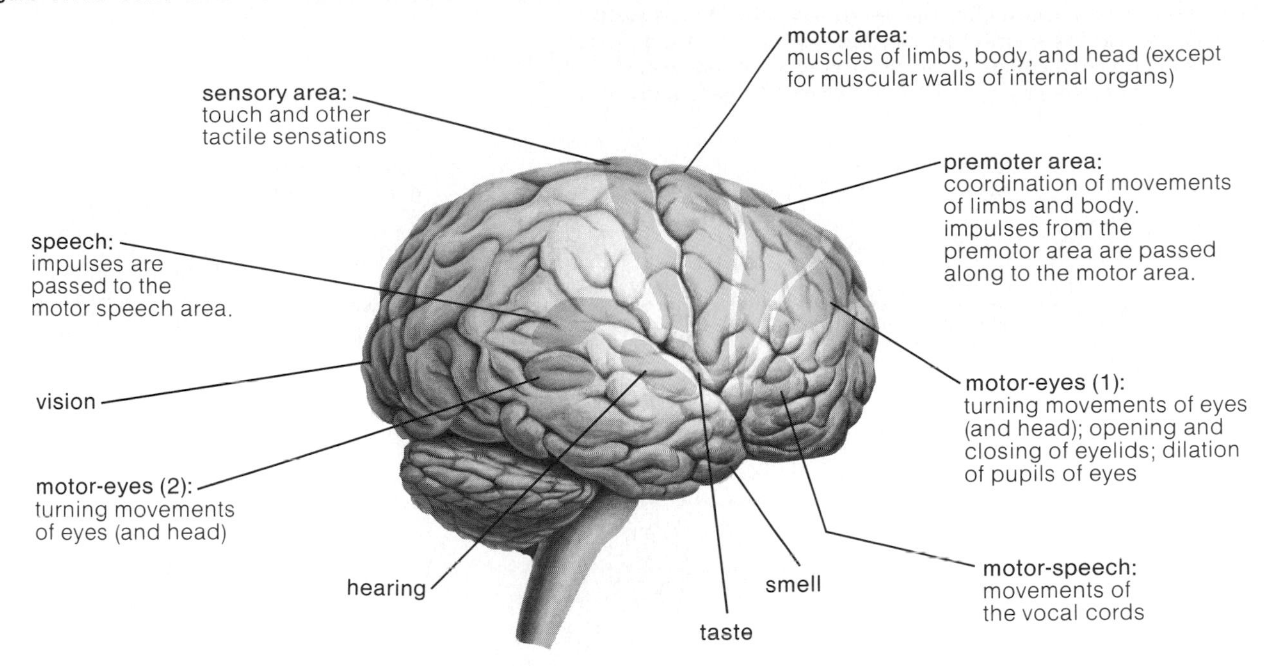

17.5 The Central Nervous System Coordinates Conscious Functions

The activities that you can control are coordinated by the **central nervous system.** This system consists of the brain and spinal cord, which connect directly with many nerves. The central nervous system receives and processes incoming sensory information, and determines and initiates the appropriate motor response. Thinking, reading, speaking, and learning are functions that involve the **cerebrum** (seh REE brum) and its outermost layers, the **cerebral cortex** (seh REE brul KOR teks). The coordination of muscles involves the **cerebellum** (ser eh BEL um) as well as the cerebrum. The central nervous system coordinates some activities that you can control in part but do not usually think about, such as your rate of breathing.

17.6 The Autonomic Nervous System Coordinates Unconscious Functions

Much activity in your nervous system happens without your being aware of it. Most of this unconscious activity is under the control of the **autonomic nervous system.** The autonomic system helps to control blood pressure, stomach movements and secretions, urine formation and excretion, body temperature, and many other functions necessary to the maintenance of a steady state. It coordinates the activities of the internal environment through a system of interconnecting neurons. The autonomic system also enables the body to respond to emergencies, and plays a major role in emotions. Some of the actions of the autonomic nervous system are shown in figure 17.13.

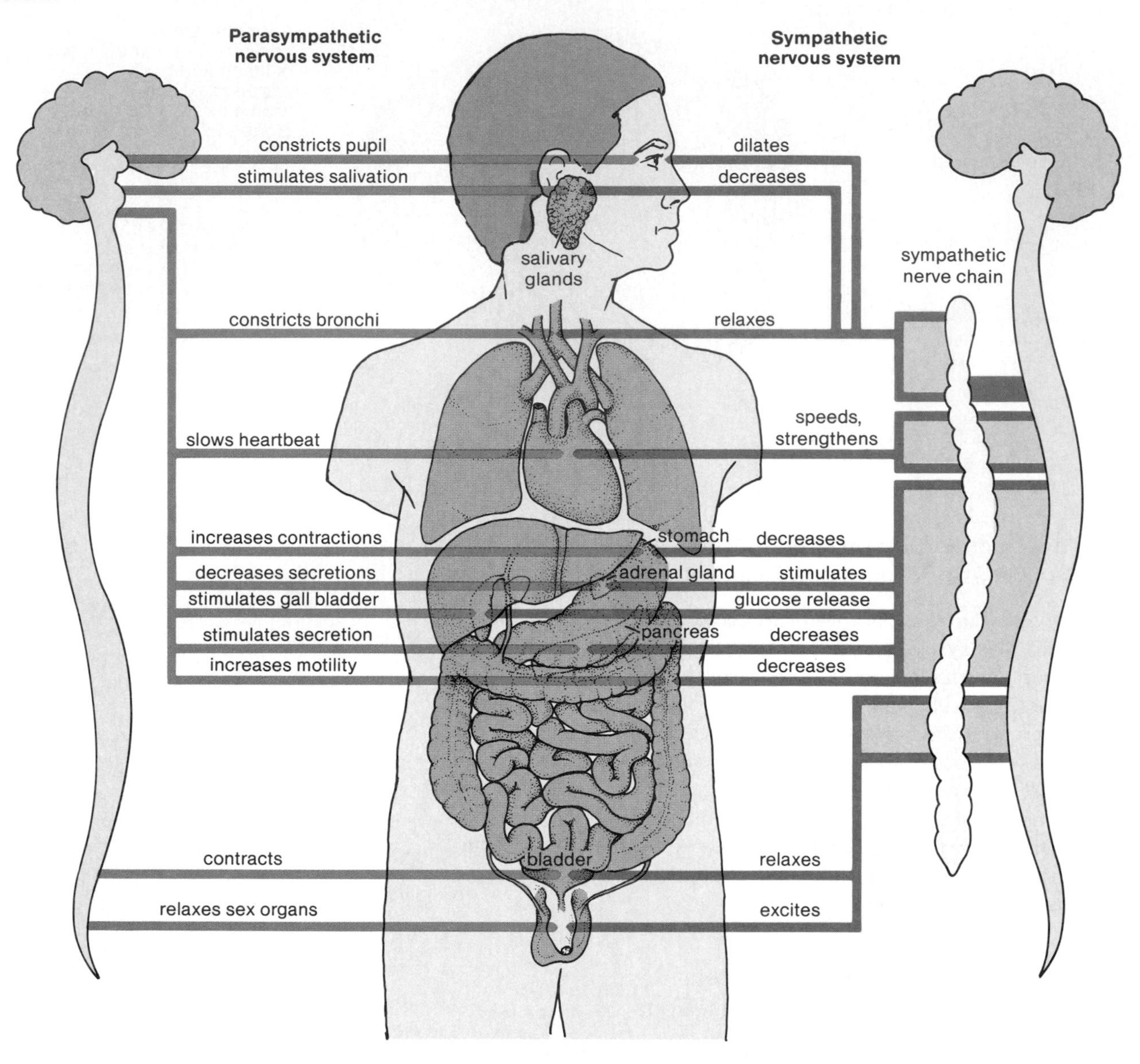

Figure 17.13 The autonomic nervous system is made up of two divisions that act like a brake and an accelerator. The parasympathetic nervous system generally acts to maintain normal body function. The sympathetic nervous system acts to prepare the body for emergency—it is the fight or flight system. The two divisions have opposing effects on a variety of organs and body functions.

The functions of the autonomic nervous system are, in turn, controlled by the **hypothalamus** (hy poh THAL uh mus), a part of the brain located under the cerebrum. The hypothalamus also is part of the system of glands that produces hormones. Thus it links the nervous system and the hormonal system in coordinating many body activities.

17.7 Complex Interactions Prepare the Body for Muscular Activity

Suppose that you had to run to catch the school bus. The sudden muscular activity exerts pressure on the veins in your extremities, increasing the rate at which blood returns to the right atrium of your heart. The

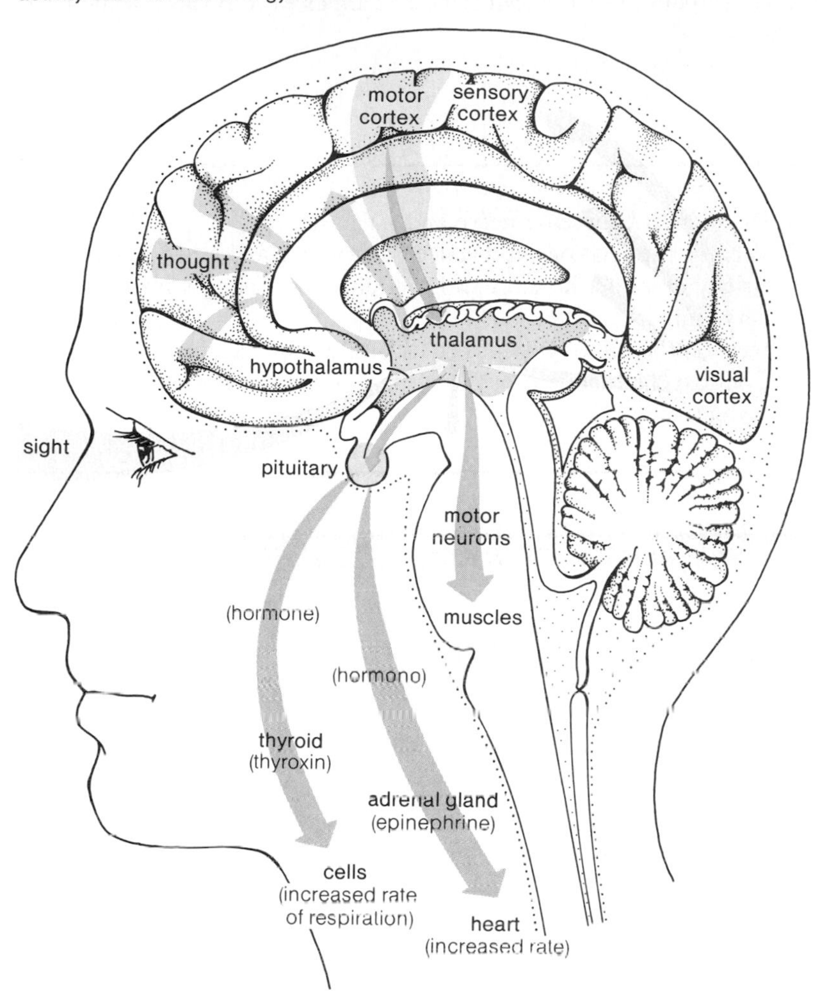

Figure 17.14 Some of the pathways involved in preparation for muscular activity such as that of a gymnast.

extra blood stretches the walls of the atrium, stimulating sensory neurons located there. Impulses are sent through the sensory nerve fibers to your brain. There, motor neurons leading to your heart are stimulated to fire nerve impulses. As a result, your heart contracts more rapidly. All this occurs in a fraction of a second, but for the athlete, this delay could be critical.

As the gymnast prepares to begin a routine, her heart starts to beat faster due to direct stimulation of the cardiac muscle by the autonomic nervous system. How does this occur when the endings of the sensory nerves are in the walls of the heart and cannot receive direct stimulation from the external sights and sounds? As the gymnast sees the crowd and concentrates on the first step, her brain prepares her body for action. In response to practice during which a series of brain pathways has been repeatedly stimulated, her brain unconsciously coordinates not just the muscles but all the services, including her heart and respiratory rates, that the body must supply to make possible the exercise. The gymnast takes the first step, and familiar neuronal pathways take over.

The coordination of the nervous and muscular systems is elegantly portrayed in the actions of the gymnast. Such coordination evolved not simply as a mechanism to catch prey and avoid predators, but also as a mechanism to direct human behavior for survival and reproduction.

Human behavior, however, is not a product of the nervous system alone. It is strongly influenced by the presence of chemical substances—hormones—produced by the endocrine system, as we will learn in the next section.

Self-Review

1. Distinguish between a nerve and a neuron.
2. What is the relationship between a stimulus and a nerve impulse?
3. Briefly describe the electrical and chemical changes involved in a nerve impulse.
4. How do the three types of neurons differ in function?
5. Contrast the functions of the cerebrum and the autonomic nervous system.

Investigation 17.2 SENSORY RECEPTORS

Introduction

How do we know about the world in which we live? We receive information through receptors. The activities of these various receptors, coordinated by the brain, are called the senses: touch, sight, hearing, smell, and taste, for example. In this investigation you will test some aspects of the senses involved in touch and sight.

Materials (per team of 2)

centimeter ruler
blunt dissecting needle (or probe)
colored pencils (red, blue)
meter stick

Part A—Touch

Procedure

It is advisable to work in pairs during the test situations that follow. One partner applies the stimulus while the other indicates the sensation evoked. All the data should be recorded in your data book.

1. On a sheet of notebook paper 4 cm square, trace with a ruler a 1 cm square. Cut out the 1 cm square so that the larger square has a hole in it that is 1 cm^2 in area. This paper template can be used to find the number of touch receptors in 1 cm^2 of skin surface.
2. The subject should close his or her eyes. Then place the template on the underside of the subject's wrist and with a probe touch the skin *very lightly*. Try not to depress the skin surface. The subject should indicate by saying "yes" whenever he or she feels the touch.
3. Trace a similar template in your data book. Map the subject's touch receptors by using a red dot to represent a touch receptor (a "yes" response) and a blue dot to represent an area touched without sensation.
4. Try 3 different areas on the wrist. Record responses in the same way as in procedure 3.
5. Count the number of receptors (a "yes" response) in each area and divide by the number of areas tested.

6. Proceed in a similar manner to locate touch receptors on the upper arm, back of the neck, and the fingertips. Record your data as before.

Discussion

1. (a) How many touch receptors per cm^2 of wrist surface did you find?
   (b) Of upper arm surface?
   (c) Of back of the neck surface?
   (d) Of fingertip surface?
2. Which area had the greatest number of touch receptors? The fewest receptors?
3. Suggest some hypotheses for the differences in receptor frequency in these various areas.
4. What is the relationship, if any, between hairs on the skin and touch receptors?

Part B—Sight

Procedure

Each student should work alone in this part.

1. Take a piece of paper and place a cross (+) and a circle (O) on the paper 6.5 cm apart. Make the cross and circle about the size of the ring holes in your notebook paper.
2. Enclose these marks within a 5 by 10 cm rectangle.
3. Hold the paper about 60 cm away from your eyes and close your left or right eye. Slowly bring the paper closer while keeping your open eye fixed on the cross. Record in your data book what happens to the circle and the cross as you bring the paper nearer.
4. Draw a line from the cross almost to the circle, interrupting it in the vicinity of the circle and continuing it again on the other side of the circle.
5. Now repeat procedure 3. Record what happens to the line in the vicinity of the circle.

Discussion

1. What happened to the circle and the cross as you brought the paper nearer your eye in procedure 3 above?
2. What happens to the line in the vicinity of the circle in procedure 5 above?
3. What do these experiments indicate about the sense of sight?

Part C—Reaction to Stimuli

Procedure

Work in pairs for part C.

1. The subject will sit down with an arm resting on the desk so that the hand is extended past the edge of the desk. Then curl the last 3 fingers of the extended hand into a fist, leaving the thumb and forefinger free. The thumb and forefinger should be parallel to the ground and 3 to 4 cm apart.
2. The experimenter will stand and hold a meter stick vertically between the thumb and forefinger of the subject. The lowest number on the meter stick should be between the subject's thumb and forefinger.
3. Without any warning, the experimenter will drop the stick.
4. The subject will try to catch it with just the thumb and forefinger of the extended hand.
5. Record the point on the meter stick at which the subject caught it.

6. Repeat the test 4 more times, recording this distance each time. Determine the average for the 5 trials.
7. Repeat the exercise while the subject is counting by 3s to 99. Average the time (distance on the meter stick) it takes the subject to catch the meter stick while counting.
8. Repeat the procedure while the subject's eyes are closed. The experimenter will snap his or her fingers to signal when the stick is released. Calculate the average for these 5 trials.

Discussion

1. In the 1st test, what happens in other parts of your body before you react and catch the meter stick?
2. What receptors are involved?
3. In the 2nd test, what effect does thinking have on the reaction time?
4. Compare the reaction time in the 1st test with that in the 3rd test. In which situation was reaction time shortest?
5. What can you conclude about the reactions to the different signals?

Guidepost: How do chemical messengers influence internal and external events?

The Endocrine System

17.8 Hormones are Chemical Messengers

Some cells secrete chemicals that influence the growth, development, or behavior of other cells. Chemicals that are produced by one set of cells and that affect other cells are known as hormones. Hormones may be secreted by individual cells scattered among other cells of the human body. Usually, however, the secreting cells are grouped into tissues or distinct organs known as glands. Glands that secrete tears, sweat, and saliva empty their products into a tubule or duct and are called **exocrine** (EK soh krin) glands. Glands that secrete hormones generally have no ducts. They empty their secretions directly into the circulatory system. The hormones then are carried in the bloodstream throughout the body. Because these **endocrine** (EN doh krin), or ductless, glands interact with each other, we can say that there is an endocrine system. Endocrine glands are capable of sensing the level of specific hormones in the blood and responding by increasing or decreasing their own secretions. The endocrine system is slower to respond than the nervous system, but its response is of longer duration. Thus the two complement each other very well.

17.9 The Hypothalamus and the Pituitary Control Many Other Endocrine Glands

Once known as chief among the endocrine glands is the **pituitary** (pih TYOO ih ter ee), often called the master gland because it secretes hormones that control the rate at which some of the other endocrine glands function. However, the pituitary itself is controlled by hormones from the hypothalamus. Some of these hormones pass through blood vessels into the pituitary, causing the pituitary to release its own hormones. Other hypothalamic hormones pass through secretory neurons and are released from the pituitary. Thus, the hypothalamus is a major link between the nervous and endocrine systems. Its hormones affect the pituitary and

Figure 17.15 The major endocrine glands in the human body. The dotted lines show organs such as the stomach and kidneys.

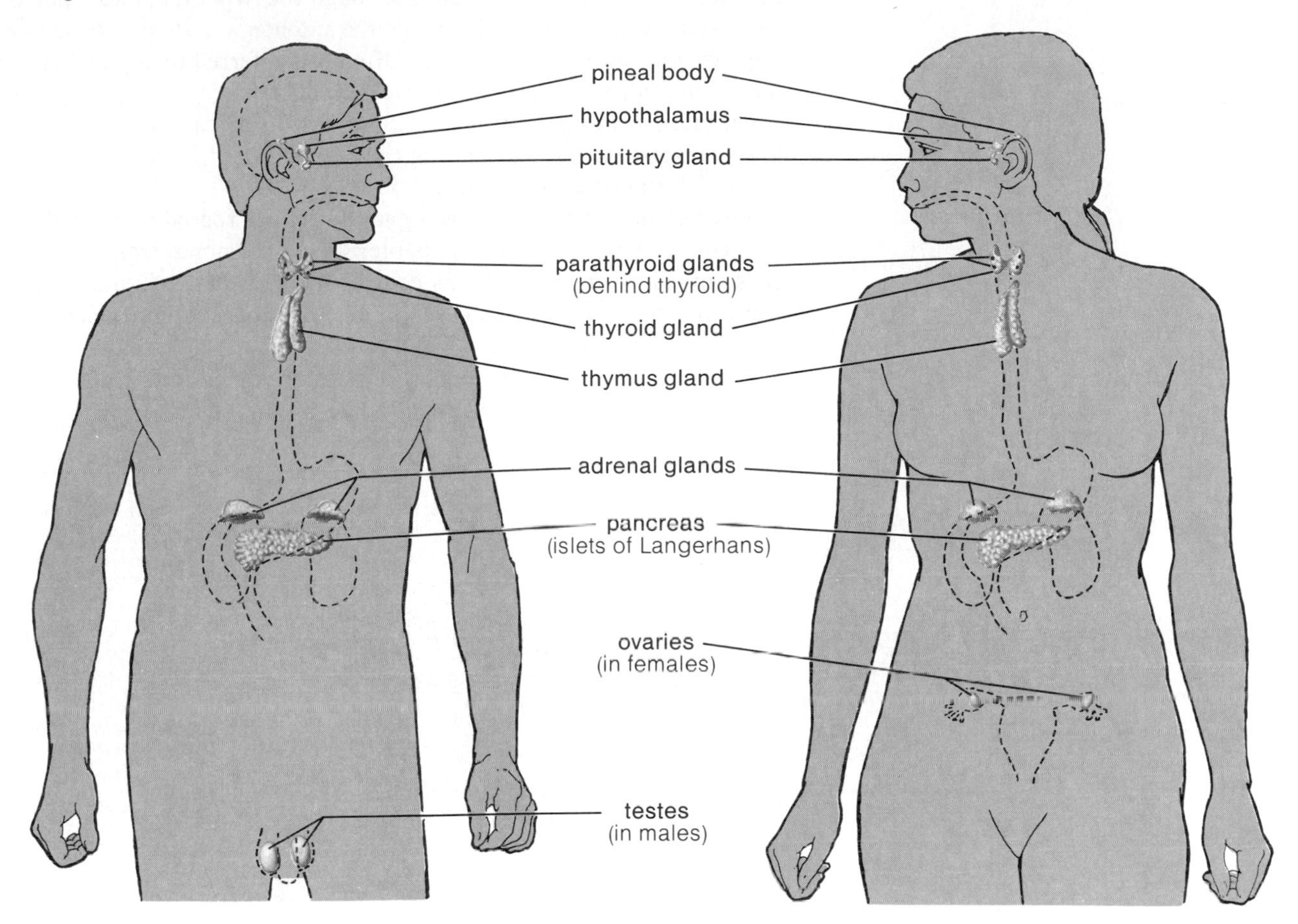

some other glands. In turn, pituitary hormones control the thyroid and the adrenal glands and, through the gonads, also regulate reproductive activities such as the menstrual cycle and ovulation, sperm production, embryonic development, and the production of the secondary sex characteristics.

The thyroid gland is located at the base of the neck and secretes hormones, one of which, **thyroxin** (thy ROK sin), regulates the rate of cellular respiration. If too little of this hormone is produced, the rate of cellular respiration decreases. A person with too little thyroxin stores food rather than using it in energy release, which results in an increase in weight. Other effects are sluggishness, sleepiness, and lowered body temperature. Too much thyroxin, on the other hand, increases the rate of cellular respiration, so very little food is stored. A person with this condition generally loses weight, has excess energy, and is very nervous. The thyroid is controlled by the hypothalamus and pituitary in the feedback system shown in figure 17.16.

The adrenal glands are found adjacent to the kidneys and are also under the control of the hypothalamus and pituitary. The adrenal glands produce important hormones that regulate salt and water balance and also enable the body to respond to stress. In investigation 17.3, you can examine the interaction of those hormones to stress conditions.

Perhaps the best known adrenal hormone is adrenalin, or **epinephrine** (ep ih NEF rin), which is secreted in response to nerve signals from the autonomic nervous system, acting through the hypothalamus. Epinephrine works both directly and through the autonomic system to raise blood pressure and speed up heart rate. Often it is referred to as the "fight or flight" hormone because it increases an individual's chance of survival when faced with an emergency. Epinephrine also can enhance an athlete's performance by stimulating the breakdown of glycogen, thus providing additional energy sources to the cells.

Ovaries and testes are the organs in which reproductive cells are formed. We have discussed in chapter 6 how hormones from endocrine cells embedded in those organs control an individual's sexual development and function. Secretion of the sex hormones is under control of specific pituitary hormones.

Table 17.2 presents a summary of hormones produced in the human and their roles in coordination and homeostasis.

Figure 17.16 The feedback mechanism between the pituitary and the thyroid glands. This mechanism controls the level of thyroxin in the blood.

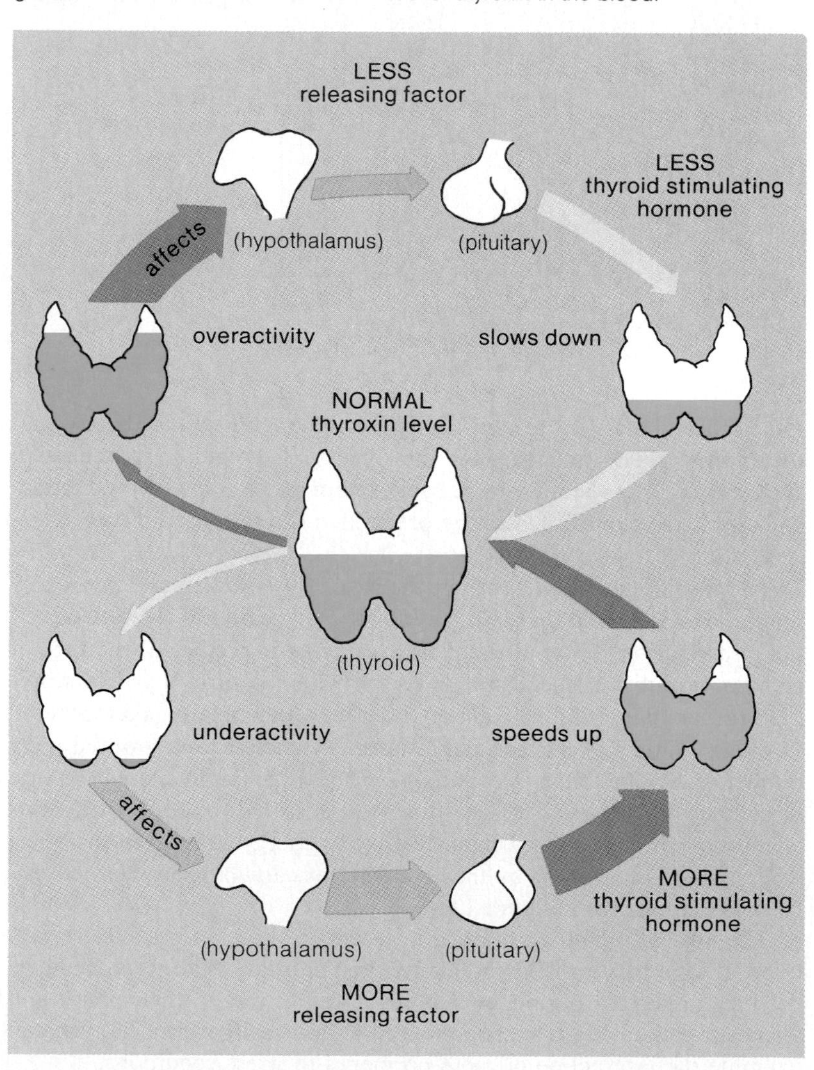

Table 17.2 Origins and effects of hormones

Gland/Organ	Hormone	Target	Principal Action
Adrenal cortex (outer portion)	cortisol	general	increases glucose, protein, and fat metabolism; reduces inflammation
	aldosterone	kidneys	affects water and salt balance
Adrenal medulla (inner portion)	epinephrine, norepinephrine	general (many regions and organs)	increases heart rate and blood pressure; activates "fight or flight" mechanism
Gonads			
ovaries	estrogen	general	development of secondary sex characteristics; bone growth; sex drive
	progesterone	uterus (lining)	maintenance of uterus during pregnancy
testes	testosterone	general	development of secondary sex characteristics; bone growth; sex drive
Heart	atrial natriuretic factor (ANF)	blood vessels, kidneys, adrenal glands, regulatory areas of the brain	regulates blood pressure and volume; excretion of water, sodium, and potassium by the kidneys
Hypothalamus (via posterior lobe of pituitary)	antidiuretic hormone (ADH, vasopressin)	kidney	controls water excretion
	oxytocin	breasts, uterus	stimulates release of milk; contraction of smooth muscle in childbirth
Pancreas (Islets of Langerhans)	glucagon	liver	stimulates breakdown of glycogen to glucose
	insulin	cell membranes	lowers blood sugar level; increases storage of glycogen
Parathyroid	parathyroid hormone (parathormone)	intestine, bone	stimulates release of calcium from bone; decreases excretion of calcium by kidney and increases absorption by intestine
Pineal	melatonin	unknown in humans—perhaps hypothalamus and pituitary	regulation of circadian rhythms (day/night cycles)
Pituitary (anterior lobe)	adrenocorticotropic hormone (ACTH)	adrenal cortex	secretes steroid hormones
	growth hormone (GH)	general	stimulates bone and muscle growth, amino acid transport, and breakdown of fatty acids
	thyroid stimulating hormone (TSH)	thyroid	secretes thyroxin
	prolactin	breasts	stimulates milk production and secretion
	follicle stimulating hormone (FSH)	ovarian follicles, testes	stimulates follicle; estrogen production; spermatogenesis
	luteinizing hormone (LH)	mature ovarian follicle, interstitial cells of testes	stimulates ovulation in females, sperm and testosterone production in males
Thymus	thymosin	lymphatic system	possibly stimulates development of lymphatic system
Thyroid	thyroxin	general	stimulates and maintains metabolic activities
	calcitonin	intestine, kidney, bone	inhibits release of calcium from bone; decreases excretion of calcium by kidney and increases absorption by intestine

Investigation 17.3 HORMONES AND STRESS

Introduction

During periods of stress humans rely on their endocrine system to counteract increased physiological demands that could result in serious health problems. While some stress responses are relatively dramatic and fast, for example the fight or flight response, most develop over time and involve subtle changes in cell chemistry that make them difficult to detect and study.

Although stress conditions present unique sets of problems, they also share a common response called the "stress syndrome." That involves the chain reactions of many hormones in meeting stress conditions found by an organism. In this investigation you will compare 2 types of stress conditions to determine their degree of similarity. You also will develop hypotheses to explain the physiological changes induced by stress.

Procedure

Part A—Endocrine Interactions in Response to Stress Due to Cold Temperature

Individuals with normal adrenal and pituitary glands were found to survive much longer when exposed to prolonged cold temperatures than those having abnormal adrenal or pituitary glands. Early mouse studies found that survival in cold temperatures also was reduced by tying off the connection between the hypothalamus and pituitary. The mice with tied off connections did not have the hormones ACTH or cortisol, which are found in mice surviving cold stress. Table 17.3 summarizes a series of mouse experiments to determine the relationship between the adrenal and pituitary glands as well as which one produced the hormones ACTH and cortisol. Human studies later produced results similar to those in the mouse study. Use the data to answer the questions below.

1. (a) Which hormone, ACTH or cortisol, was produced by the adrenal gland? Explain.
   (b) Which hormone, ACTH or cortisol, was produced by the pituitary gland? Explain.
2. Outline the sequence of events resulting in cold stress survival in terms of the glands and hormones studied in the cold shock experiment.

Part B—Cortisol Levels of Trained and Untrained Humans During Graded Exercises

Two groups of humans, a 10-member group of 22- to 27-year-old trained cyclists and a 10-member group of 25- to 33-year-old nonathletes, were first tested to determine their maximum work capacity. Work capacity is the amount of energy that the heart converts to work while pumping blood into the arteries. Both groups were then studied during a 32-minute exercise period during which their workloads were increased from 30 to 45, to 60, and then to 75% of their predetermined maximum levels at 8-minute intervals. Figure 17.17 compares the cortisol changes in the groups. Use the data to answer the questions below.

1. Based on the data in figure 17.17, develop a hypothesis to explain the relationship between exercise and cortisol production.
2. How does this experiment indicate that the cortisol response may be beneficial?
3. Prepare a list of experimental factors that could alter the results reported for this experiment.

Table 17.3 Cortisol production during cold stress

Exp.	Stimulus	Pituitary	Hypothalamus	Substance Injected	Adrenal Gland Weight (g)	Cortisol in Plasma (mg/100 ml)	Stress Result
I	cold	normal	normal	none	7.5	30.5	survival
II	cold	removed	normal	none	3.4	0.0	death
III	cold	normal	injured	none	3.5	0.0	death
IV	none	removed	normal	ACTH	7.4	30.6	survival

Figure 17.17 Effect of graded exercise on plasma cortisol levels.

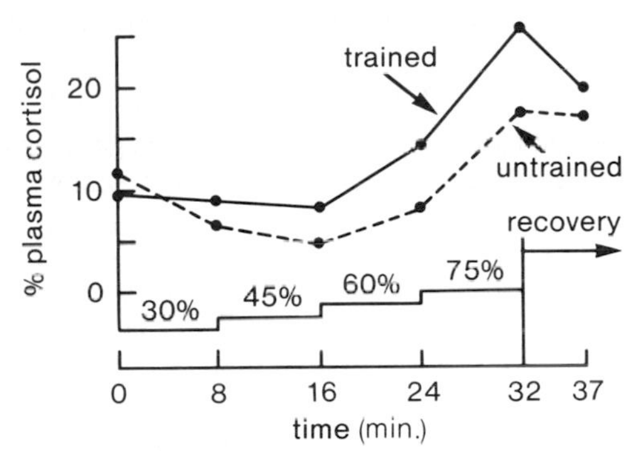

From S. R. Bloom, R. H. Johnson, D. M. Park, M. J. Rennie, and W. R. Sulaiman, "Differences in the metabolic and hormonal response to exercise between racing cyclists and untrained individuals" *Journal of Physiology* 258:1-18 (1976, p. 11).

Figure 17.18 Effect of graded exercise on blood glucose levels.

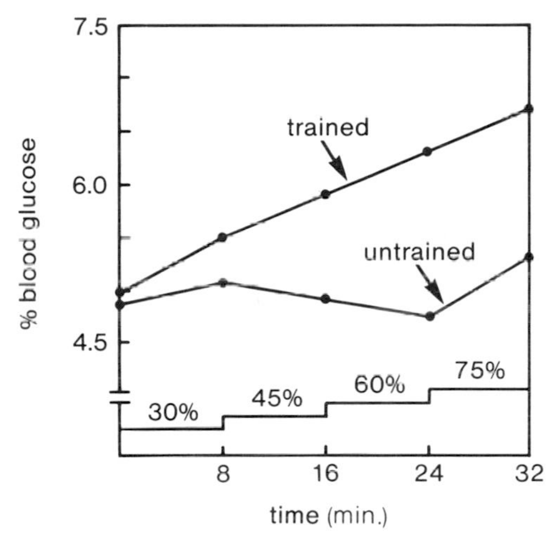

From S. R. Bloom, R. H. Johnson, D. M. Park, M. J. Rennie, and W. R. Sulaiman, "Differences in the metabolic and hormonal response to exercise between racing cyclists and untrained individuals" *Journal of Physiology* 258:1-18 (1976, p. 5).

Part C—Cortisol Function

Cortisol activity results in increased energy production. One indication of increased energy production is provided by blood glucose level. Figure 17.18 shows the results obtained when this was measured in the experiment described in part B. Use the data to answer the questions below.

1. What information does figure 17.18 provide about plasma glucose levels during graded exercise?
2. Do the results of the experiment shown in figures 17.17 and 17.18 reflect the role of cortisol? Explain.
3. Based on the results shown in figures 17.17 and 17.18, what would you conclude about the relationship between cortisol and glucose?

Discussion

1. What do the cold stress and graded exercise experiments have in common?
2. Epinephrine and cortisol are both produced by the adrenal glands. Individuals with Addison's disease have considerable adrenal gland damage and adjust poorly to stress situations in general. However, they do have a near normal fight or flight response. How would you account for this?
3. Cortisol is now known to cause a marked increase in protein decomposition. Why would this be beneficial during stress?

Figure 17.19 Hormonal regulation of blood glucose. When blood glucose levels are high, the pancreas releases insulin. Insulin lowers blood glucose by promoting its entry into cells and its storage in the liver. When blood glucose levels are low, the pancreas releases glucagon, which stimulates the liver to release glucose. During stress conditions, the adrenal gland releases epinephrine and other hormones that act to raise blood glucose.

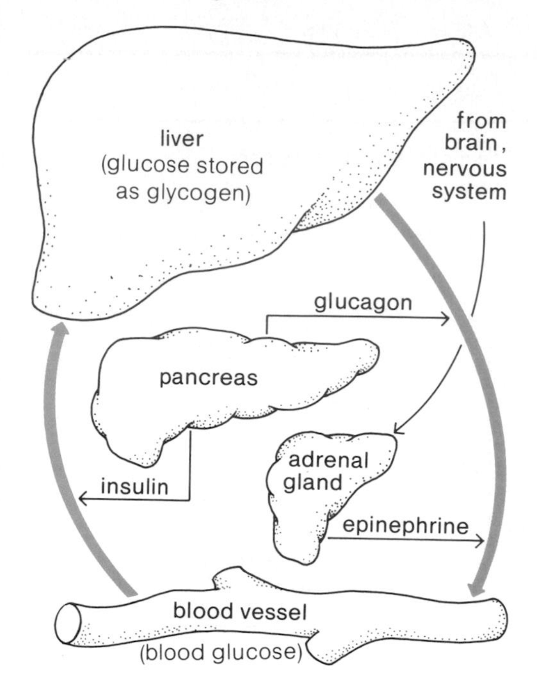

17.10 Several Hormones Act Together to Control Blood Glucose Levels

Endocrine tissues embedded in the pancreas produce two hormones: **insulin** (IN suh lin) and **glucagon** (GLOO kuh gahn). These along with epinephrine are the primary regulators of glucose levels in the blood. Insulin is secreted in response to a rise in blood glucose, as after a meal, and facilitates entry of glucose into the cells. In the absence of insulin, cells are unable to absorb glucose, and glucose is excreted in the urine. Without glucose, the cells use fats and proteins in respiration to provide energy. Some of the products of this process have undesirable side effects when they appear in the blood. Very high levels of these products may even cause coma and death.

Glucagon and epinephrine both act to raise blood glucose levels and prevent **hypoglycemia** (hy poh gly SEE mee uh), or low blood sugar. Hypoglycemia is dangerous because brain cells must obtain a constant supply of glucose from the blood. If the supply is cut off, an individual may lose consciousness.

The disease **diabetes** (dy uh BEET eez) results from insufficient insulin secretion. Because the cells then are unable to absorb glucose and instead must use fats and proteins for energy, changes occur in many body systems. Particularly critical are changes in the circulatory system that can lead to heart disease or blindness if the disease is not controlled.

Self-Review

1. How are the endocrine glands controlled?
2. Why is the pituitary gland often called the master gland?
3. Describe the feedback loop that controls secretion of thyroxin by the thyroid.
4. What are the functions of the adrenal hormones?
5. How do hormones interact to control blood glucose levels?
6. Why can the ovaries and testes be considered endocrine in function?

Guidepost: What is the relationship between the mind, the brain, and human behavior?

Human Behavior and the Nervous System

17.11 The Mind Is a Major Aspect of Who We Are

At the moment a gymnast's brain is signaling the hypothalamus to alert the body for action, the mind is controlling the brain. How does the mind differ from the brain?

The brain is made of tissue that is organized into distinct parts with specific functions. The brain's functions can be traced through its electrical activities during life, and its structure determined by dissection after death. No trace of a "mind," however, will be seen in either observation. What, then, *is* the mind? It seems to emanate from our brains and is a major aspect of who we are. Perhaps we can tentatively define "mind" as the result of actions of one or more parts of the brain, both conscious and unconscious.

The mind is often associated with intelligence, the ability to learn. Intelligence is sometimes linked with brain size, but studies have not confirmed such a relationship. The average weight of the adult male brain is about 1380 g and of the adult female about 1250. In that mass there are on the order of 10^{11} (100 billion) neurons, give or take a factor of 10. The cerebrum, where all conscious thought, learning, and memory take place, constitutes about seven-eighths of the total weight of the human brain and occupies most of the area of the skull. Brain size increases with body size and decreases as an adult ages or during long periods of illness.

17.12 The Human Brain and Human Behavior Evolved Together

Humans have the most intricate brain and exhibit the most complex behavior patterns of any animal. We cannot trace the evolution of human behavor, but we have evidence of a rapid (in evolutionary terms) increase in cranial capacity. This rapid development of the brain signifies to many researchers strong selection pressure for the survival of intelligent human forms.

A factor that made more learning possible was the lengthening of prenatal and postnatal dependent life. Longer prenatal life allowed time for the brain to develop and enlarge. Longer postnatal dependency provided time for the offspring to learn the resources of their environment from accumulated family knowledge. That, in turn, made necessary the use of some form of communication.

At an early stage in our history, we added two immensely powerful tools to our other abilities. The first was language, which is a common scheme of sounds for communicating with one another. The second was writing, a technique for storing information in symbols so that it can be passed along from generation to generation. The verbal and written transmission of information made possible the development of the learned pattern of thought and behavior we call **human culture.**

Human language is the most complex animal communication system known to us at present. Our minds, which govern the vast majority of our actions, function through the use of language. Some psychologists, people who study human behavior, believe that we cannot think what we cannot say. Others believe that language is only one of the functions of thought.

Figure 17.20 How bees communicate.

a. A foraging honeybee returns to the hive after finding a nectar source. Other bees soon leave the hive and fly to the same source. How does the first bee inform other bees about the food source?

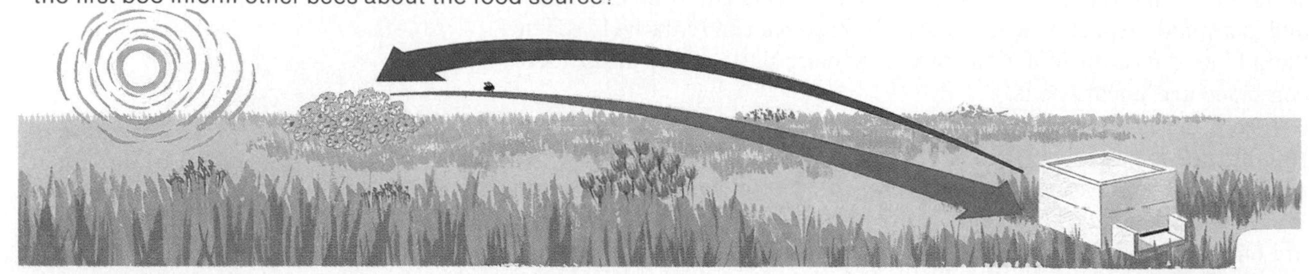

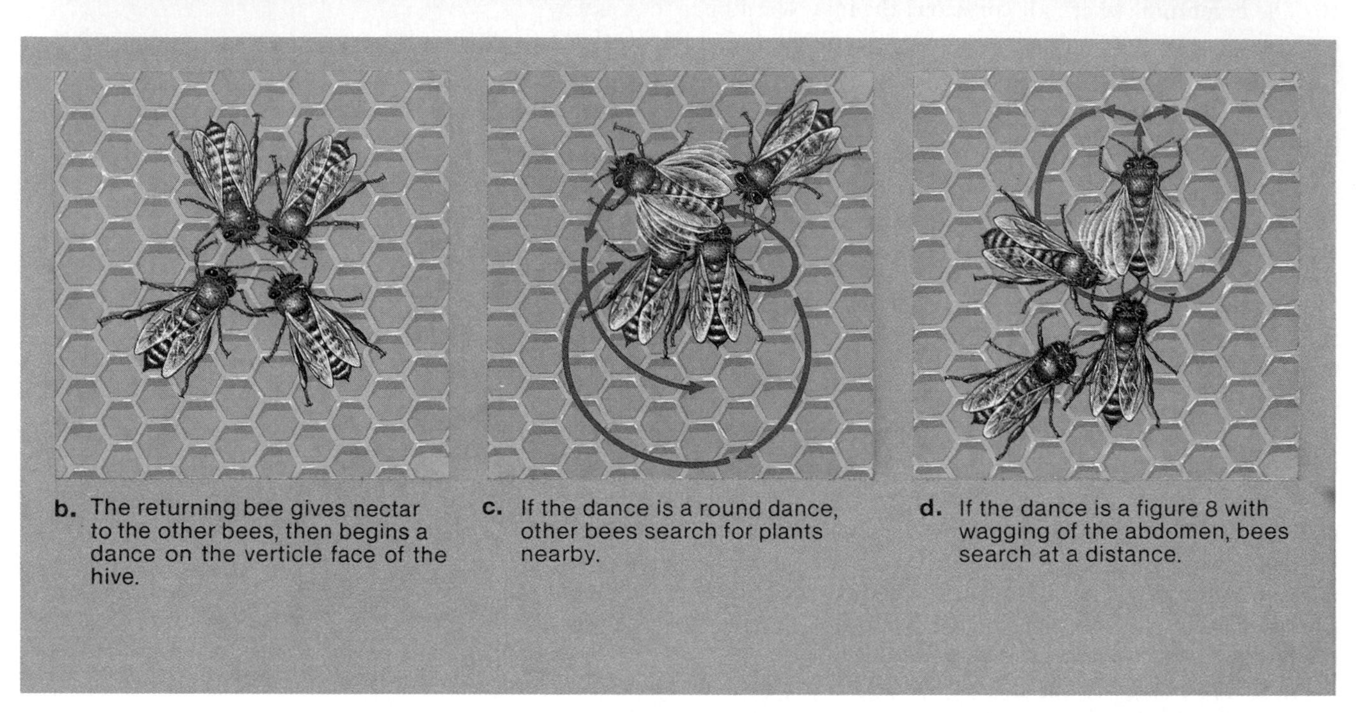

b. The returning bee gives nectar to the other bees, then begins a dance on the verticle face of the hive.

c. If the dance is a round dance, other bees search for plants nearby.

d. If the dance is a figure 8 with wagging of the abdomen, bees search at a distance.

The development of culture is thought to be an outgrowth of the development of at least a rudimentary language. The two are mutually dependent and probably evolved together. Development of language and culture allowed for rapid changes in response to the environment, both natural and human-made. Significant genetic change normally requires millions of years. Cultural adaptation occurs much more rapidly. Furthermore, such adaptation can be passed to the next generation.

17.13 Other Animals Communicate and May Have Conscious Thoughts

Though human beings possess the most complex brain and language, they are not alone in the ability to communicate and form societies. Bees have a very complex communication signal known as the bee dance (figure 17.20). Through this dance, a bee can communicate to other bees in the hive the location of food (nectar) in the form of flowers. Therefore, the bee dance describes an event distant in both time and space.

Evidences of conscious behavior exist in primates other than humans. In an attempt to relieve a hunger problem in a macaque troop on the Japanese island of Kashima, scientists threw wheat grains on a sandy beach. The effort of separating wheat grains one by one from sand grains easily could use more energy than eating the collected grains would provide. Perhaps accidentally, perhaps in anger, a female monkey named Imo threw handfuls of the mixture into the water. She noted that the wheat floated and the sand sank, and she scooped up and ate the cleaned wheat grains. The younger monkeys imitated her discovery, and the practice spread. All macaques on Kashima are now competent at water sifting.

The active passing of information, if not teaching as such, was exhibited by Washoe, a chimp who was taught American Sign Language as an infant. She has shown her own adopted infant the sign for chair and has signed "food" to him and then molded his hands with hers into the sign for food. Though not all researchers agree, some of the data from these and other studies seem to suggest a mental and social consciousness in apes as well as humans.

Figure 17.21 Chimp using sign language to communicate.

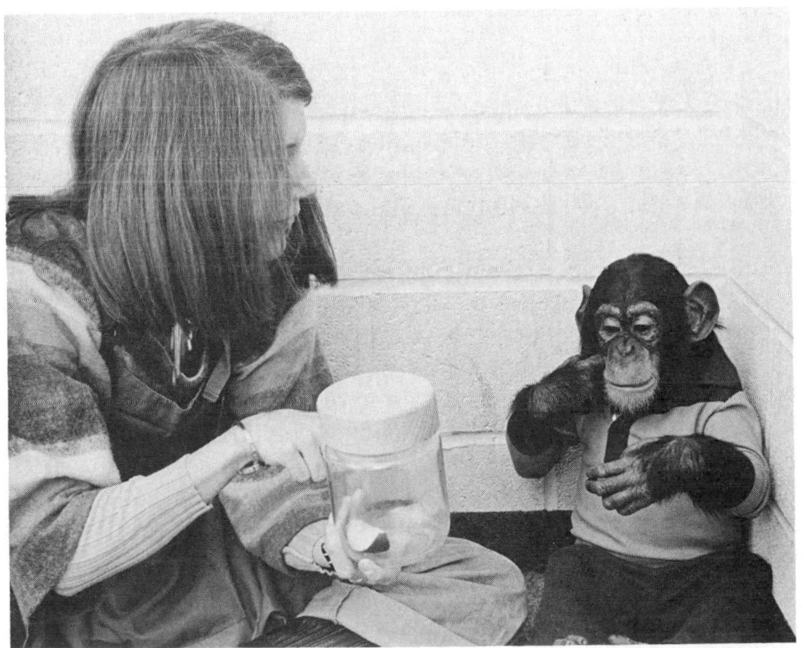

H. Terrace/Anthro Photo

Biology Today

Bird Migration and Biological Clocks

The flight of birds migrating south in the fall or north in the spring is familiar to everyone. What guides these birds toward warmer climates in the winter and back to their breeding grounds in the spring? There are two general answers to this question. One is that migration is triggered by external factors, such as changes in temperature and photoperiod, the number of daylight hours, from season to season. The other is that there are genetically determined internal factors that control this seasonal behavior.

For the past 20 years, behavioral scientists in southern Germany have been studying migration of several species of warblers that migrate at night and rest during the day. The scientists observed that caged warblers were intensely active at night during the fall or spring. This behavior, called "migratory restlessness," could be measured and used to determine the beginning and end of migration.

The scientists first investigated three groups of warblers. One group was held in the laboratory at constant temperature and a constant photoperiod of 12 hours per day. A second group was transported to the birds' normal wintering range. The third group was in the laboratory throughout the winter at constant temperature but with variations in photoperiod typical of temperate regions.

All three groups exhibited behavior typical of warblers in the wild. In further experiments, the scientists exposed each of three groups of warblers to different photoperiods of a constant length for several years. Migratory restlessness continued in the typical yearly pattern for all the groups for the length of the experiments. In addition, the scientists observed that molting occurred as it would in the wild.

These experiments showed clearly that internal factors control the onset of migration in warblers. Such rhythmic internal timekeepers are known as biological clocks. Many other organisms, exhibit annual rhythms similar to those of birds.

Under constant environmental conditions, the period of such a biological clock usually is not exactly a year. The caged warblers, for example, molted about every 10 months rather than every 12. Yet, in nature, seasonal activities such as molting and migration always occur at the same time of year. What factor could synchronize the approximately annual internal rhythms with the solar year?

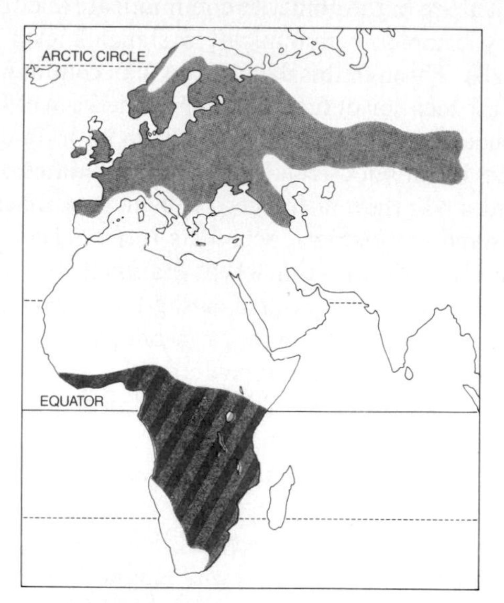

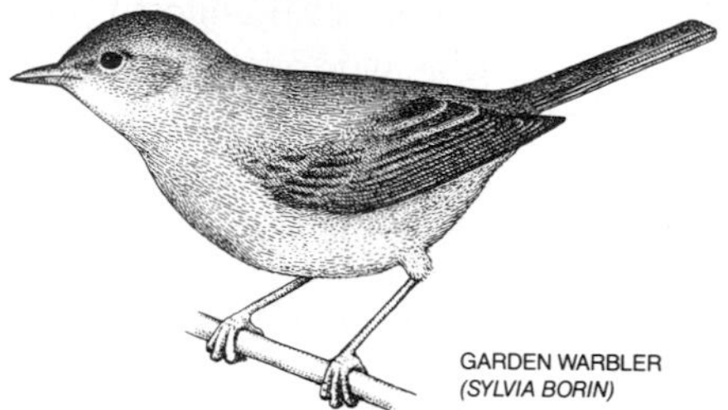

Reprinted with permission of W. H. Freeman and Company from "Internal Rhythms in Bird Migration" by Eberhard Gwinner. SCIENTIFIC AMERICAN, April 1986.

Further experiments with warblers showed the synchronizer to be photoperiod. When the environment of the caged birds simulated that of their natural breeding range, they underwent migratory restlessness and molted on an exact annual schedule. In addition, if the photoperiod was increased and decreased on a 6-month cycle instead of a 12-month cycle, the internal rhythm was shortened to half its normal duration.

Thus it seems clear that internal factors, synchronized by external factors, particularly photoperiod, control migration of birds. Evidence continues to accumulate that this is true for annual behaviors of other organisms as well.

17.14 Our Slowly Evolving Control Systems Might Not Be Appropriate for Modern Living

Human behavior, like other human characteristics, is the result of evolution and adaptation, and thus has a genetic basis. It is strongly influenced by the environment, and scientists disagree about the relative importance of heredity and environment in the determination of human behavioral traits.

For example, the problem of stress currently receives a great deal of attention. Many blame stress on the rapid rate of technological advances and the demand this places on the individual to keep pace with the resulting changes. However, the way our glandular and nervous systems function is also partly to blame. These systems have not changed significantly from the earliest hunter-gatherer stages when the appropriate response to any threat was fight or flight.

Today, when an individual perceives a threat, real or imagined, the fight or flight response is activated. The autonomic nervous system and the hypothalamus initiate a series of nervous and endocrine events that

Figure 17.22 The sympathetic division of the autonomic nervous system stimulates a number of organs in the "fight or flight" response.

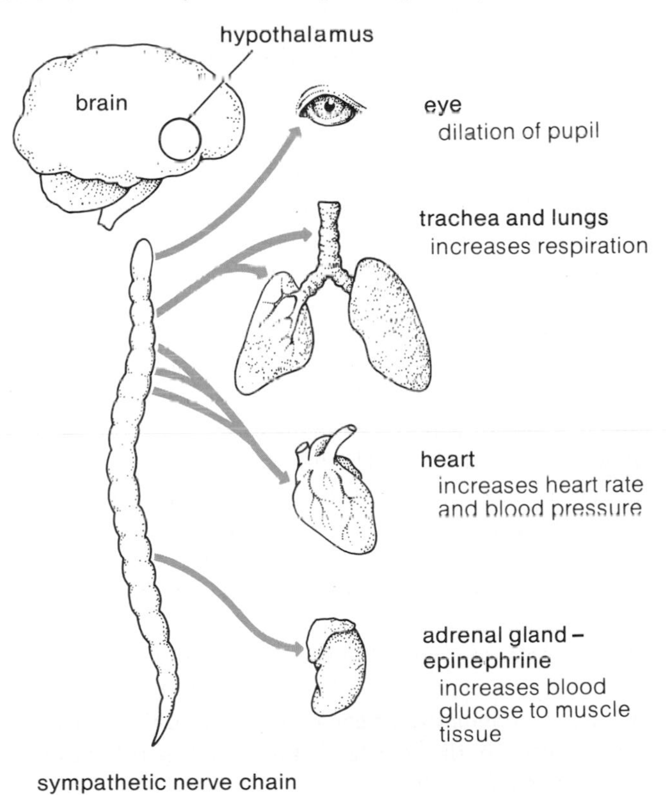

enable the body to perform vigorous muscular activity. Specific responses to threat include increased breathing rate and heart rate, a rise in blood pressure and blood clotting ability, and increased blood glucose levels, mental activity, and muscle strength. Because threats in today's society do not often involve situations where either fight or flight is appropriate, the net result to the body is like stepping on the accelerator of a car while the brake is depressed. A lot of fuel is burned, but you do not get anywhere. Some researchers believe that repeated stressful situations are related to the incidence of heart problems in relatively young people. Psychological problems such as insomnia, anxiety, and depression also appear to be related to stress.

Habits acquired in your teen years set the patterns of behavior that you are likely to follow as an adult. You are at a stage of life at which you can evaluate your behavior and determine what type of adult you would like to become. You may find it interesting to think about your own life and the lives of relatives and friends you have known for several years. Can you recognize any trends of behavior in your family and friends? Compare the behavior of students in the lowest and highest grades in your school. Can you see any changes that may be the result of "growing up?" Are there signs of increased stressful behavior in your peer group? To what extent are those changes based on experience, education, or pressures from society?

17.15 Artificial Intelligence Is a Possibility in the Future

Many investigators are trying to find the limits of the human brain. Some neurobiologists believe that its capabilities are infinite and are beyond our ability to duplicate in computers. Others, however, feel that the brain is like a machine—a giant, complicated computer. If that is true, it should be possible to construct a computer capable of creating ideas—an artificial intelligence. The responses of the brain are relatively slow compared to the millionths of a second it takes for a computer to react. At the present time, however, there is no known way of duplicating in a computer the versatility of the 10^{14}, or 100 trillion, synapses of the brain. Only the future will determine whether it is possible. Today we are faced with the question of whether this is even a desirable goal.

The gymnast's mind influences her behavior through determination and practice. Her practice is often painful and always time-consuming, time she could be spending in less painful and demanding activities—such as watching TV. Her rewards are in knowing she has performed to the best of her ability.

For many people, the mental and physical efforts necessary for that feeling of accomplishment are too high a price to pay. They attempt to gain satisfaction, confidence, or even escape through the use of various chemical substances. In the next section we will look at some of the drugs that influence human behavior.

Self-Review

1. What kinds of activities take place in the cerebrum?
2. How can we define mind? intelligence?
3. How does a longer prenatal and postnatal life relate to greater human intelligence?
4. What two tools enabled humans to develop their society and culture?
5. What evidence do we have that animals other than humans may have minds?
6. How does stress result in a fight or flight response in the body?

Drugs and Behavior

Guidepost: What are drugs and how do they affect the functions of the human body?

17.16 Drugs Can Be Helpful or Harmful

Drugs are substances that change the way the body or mind functions. Used properly, they are important in maintaining physical and mental health. Drugs include medicinal substances, such as antibiotics and aspirin, that are used to cure or treat diseases or to relieve minor discomforts. Drugs also include mind-altering or **psychoactive** (sy koh AK tiv) substances such as tranquilizers, opiates, barbiturates, alcohol, and tobacco. Some are prescribed to relieve severe pain, aid sleep, and calm nervousness. Because these substances work on the mind and the senses, they can change the way a person thinks, feels, or acts. Many of them are used illegally, without a prescription, for their pleasurable side effects.

Any drug can be abused, that is, used in a way that causes personal or social problems. For example, overuse of aspirin can lead to severe abdominal bleeding. Consumption of too much caffeine in coffee, tea, cocoa, or cola drinks can lead to irritability and sleeplessness. Abuse of psychoactive drugs, in addition to causing a variety of physical effects, can lead to physical or psychological dependence.

Psychoactive drugs can be described in three general groups: depressants, stimulants, and hallucinogens. Many of the psychoactive drugs induce tolerance, so that larger and larger amounts are required to produce the same effect. Many also are addictive, producing physical or psychological dependence. In physical dependence, the body becomes unable to function normally without the drug. Withdrawal may produce symptoms ranging from discomfort to convulsions, and they can be fatal. In psychological dependence, the user exhibits an intense craving for the drug and its effects. Table 17.4 summarizes information about the more commonly used psychoactive drugs.

Table 17.4 Sources, uses, and effects of some psychoactive drugs

Psychoactive drugs affect body and nervous functions and may change behavior. This table lists some of the drugs most commonly abused in the United States today. Effects vary a great deal from person to person; only a few are described.

Name	Source and Use	Effects
Depressants		
Alcohol (in wine, beer, ale, spirits, liquors, mixed drinks, and so on).	Synthesized or produced naturally by fermentation of fruits, vegetables, or grains.	Affects brain in proportion to amount in bloodstream. Small dose produces euphoria, drowsiness, dizziness, flushing, and release of inhibitions and tensions. Slurred speech, staggering, and double vision may result from large dose. Impairs driving in any dose and exaggerates effects of other drugs. Liver damage, vitamin deficiencies, and brain damage can occur with excessive use. Use of 3 oz or more during pregnancy may result in underweight babies with physical, mental and behavioral abnormalities. May produce tolerance and addiction. Most common form of drug abuse, particularly among teenagers.
Tranquilizers—valium, librium, and miltown.	Produce calm without sleepiness. Used to treat anxiety, nervousness, tension, and muscle spasm.	Produces mildly impaired coordination and balance, reduced alertness and emotional reactions, loss of inhibition. May produce sleep disturbances or depression. Use during pregnancy may cause congenital malformations. Use with alcohol or while driving is dangerous. Tolerance-inducing and addictive.
Opiates—opium, morphine, codeine, and heroin; dope, horse, smack, and skag.	Seed capsules of the opium poppy (*Papaver somniferum*) produce a milky juice. From this juice, many drugs can be prepared, including morphine and codeine. Heroin is formed by chemical synthesis from morphine. Taken by smoking, by mouth, or by injection. Used as pain killers.	Injection produces surge of pleasure, state of gratification and stupor. Sensations of pain, hunger, and sexual desire are lost. Physical effects include nausea, vomiting, insensitivity to pain, constipation, sweating, slowed breathing. Long-term effects include severe constipation, moodiness, menstrual irregularities, and liver and brain damage. Use with alcohol very dangerous. Tolerance-inducing and highly addictive.
Barbiturates—pentobarbital, seconbarbital; also called goof-balls, downers, yellow jackets, red devils, and so on.	Many compounds, developed to suppress pain, treat sleeplessness, anxiety, tension, high blood pressure, convulsions, and to induce anesthesia. Taken by mouth or injected into muscles.	Effects similar to alcohol: release from tension and inhibition, followed by interference with mental function, depression, and hostility. Overdoses cause unconsciousness, coma, and death. Extremely dangerous in combination with alcohol. Long-term effects include liver damage and chronic intoxication. Addictive.
Stimulants		
Caffeine.	White, bitter, crystalline substance, found in coffee beans, tea leaves, cocoa leaves, and kola nuts. Ingredient in many pain relievers, cold remedies, and stimulant mixtures.	Increases metabolic rate, blood pressure, urination, and body temperature; shortens sleep, decreases appetite, and impairs coordination of movement. Long-term or heavy use can cause insomnia, anxiety, depression, or birth problems. Regular consumption of 4 cups of coffee a day can produce a form of physical dependence.

Table 17.4 Continued

Name	Source and Use	Effects
Stimulants		
Tobacco.	Shredded, dried leaves of tobacco plant. Contains tar and nicotine and cancer-causing substances. Smoke contains carbon monoxide. Generates 2000 different chemical compounds. Smoked or chewed.	Increased heart and breathing rates and blood pressure; decreased appetite. Nicotine enters bloodstream; tars accumulate in lungs. Carbon monoxide interferes with ability of blood to transport oxygen. Long-term effects include narrowing or blockage of blood vessels, respiratory disease, cancers of lung, mouth, or throat, stomach ulcers, and reduced immunity. Chewing tobacco increases the risk of oral cancer by 40 times. Smoking during pregnancy increases risk of miscarriage, low birth rate, and developmental problems. Causes psychological and physical dependence.
Amphetamines—Benzadrine, dexedrine, methedrine; speed, splash, uppers, bennies, dexies, and crystal.	Human-made drugs taken by mouth or injected into veins.	Increased alertness and energy, feeling of well-being, rapid heart rate and breathing, and increased blood pressure. Restlessness and feelings of power, aggression, or hostility common. Very large doses can produce irregular heartbeat, hallucinations, or heart failure. Long-term use can produce mental illness, kidney damage, or lung problems. Produces powerful psychological and physical dependence.
Cocaine— coke, snow, nose candy, crack.	Comes from the leaves of the coca plant. Sniffed, ingested, injected, or smoked as freebase.	Effects similar to amphetamines but of shorter duration. Toxic; can cause hallucinations, muscle spasms, convulsions, and death. Use produces restlessness, insomnia, hallucinations, delusions, and weight loss. Produces powerful psychological and physical dependence.
Hallucinogens		
Cannabis—hashish and marijuana; also called pot, grass, weed, reefer, and joint.	Flowers, leaves, oils, or resin of *Cannabis sativa*. Smoked in pipe or hand rolled cigarette, or ingested by mouth.	Impairs concentration, short-term memory, coordination, and motor skills. Enhances sensory perception and feelings of relaxation. Distorts space-time sense and induces withdrawal, fearfulness, anxiety, depression, or hallucinations. Long-term effects include loss of motivation, interest, memory, and concentration. The smoke can cause chronic lung disease and lung cancer. Psychological dependence common.
LSD—lysergic acid diethylamide or acid; mescaline and psilocybin; mind-expanding drugs.	LSD is an artificial chemical compound developed in the 1940s. Mescaline is a natural product of peyote (a cactus) long used by American Indians in religious practices. Psilocybin is formed by a mushroom. Usually taken by mouth.	Vivid psychic effects, including hallucinations. Sensations intensified and distorted. Extreme mood swings, including joy, inspiration, depression, anxiety, terror, and aggression. Long-term effects of LSD include decreased motivation and interest, prolonged depression, and anxiety. Fetal abnormalities may result from use during pregnancy.

17.17 Psychoactive Drugs Affect the Brain in Three General Ways

Depressants reduce the activity of the central nervous system, some of them by blocking nerve transmission. Alcohol is the most widely used and abused depressant. It releases inhibitions and produces feelings of happiness. Tranquilizers dull the emotions and reduce anxiety by calming and relaxing the individual. Overuse can lead to psychological or physical dependence. Opiates (opium, morphine, and heroin) are used to relieve pain and in addition produce effects similar to tranquilizers. Opiates, however, induce tolerance and are physically addictive. Barbiturates dull the mind and are used to induce sleep and relax tensions. Like opiates, they induce tolerance and are addictive. Barbiturates are especially dangerous when used with alcohol, opiates, anesthetics, or tranquilizers.

Stimulants increase activity of the central nervous system and generally induce a feeling of well-being. Caffeine and the nicotine in tobacco are both stimulants. Amphetamines are used to increase alertness and reduce hunger. They induce tolerance and produce powerful psychological dependence. Physical dependence also can develop. The effects of cocaine are similar to those of amphetamines.

Hallucinogens are drugs that change sensation, thinking, self-awareness, emotion, and space-time perception. Marijuana is the most widely used of all illegal drugs. It contains substances that affect transmission of nerve impulses in the brain. Long-term use may lead to loss of motivation and interest in daily life. LSD blocks nerve impulses and distorts sensory perceptions, producing hallucinations and mood swings. Peyote and psilocybin are naturally occurring substances that have been widely used in religious ceremonies. The effects of all hallucinogens are related to the expectations of the user, the setting in which use takes place, and the potency of the drug.

Figure 17.23 An opium poppy.

BSCS by Doug Sokell

Figure 17.24 Many of the complex behavior patterns of animals can be disturbed by chemical substances. A female spider builds webs in the characteristic regular form shown on the left. Several hours after feeding on sugar water containing a small dose of an amphetamine, the spider built the unusually small, irregular web shown on the right. Although we cannot compare directly the behavior patterns of invertebrate animals and humans, experiments such as this provide important evidence about the effects of chemical substances on brain function.

Peter N. Witt, Raleigh, N.C.

Peter N. Witt, Raleigh, N.C.

Self-Review

1. What are drugs and what effects can they produce?
2. What is meant by drug abuse?
3. How do psychoactive drugs affect the brain?
4. Contrast physical and psychological dependence.
5. What are the general effects of depressants, stimulants, and hallucinogens?

Summary

We have seen some of the ways in which internal homeostasis is maintained despite outward actions of the body. Muscle contractions are initiated by nerve impulses triggered by external signals, such as the noise of an expectant audience, and by internal signals, such as thought about the action to be performed. Muscles and bones work together to bring about the desired movements. Practice reinforces certain nerve pathways, so that those movements become automatic. The nervous and endocrine systems interact to coordinate the specific movements required.

The excitement of competition activates the autonomic nervous system, and the fight or flight response prepares the body for intense physical activity. Other hormones, secreted in response to signals from the hypothalamus-pituitary pathway, aid in preparation of the body.

Scholars, artists, scientists, and athletes all strive for excellence. Some never attain the level of perfection they had hoped for, and some attempt to enhance their performance by using psychoactive drugs. Those drugs may eventually take their toll—in performance or health. When the gymnast begins a double twisting back flip, only a fully operational mind and brain can coordinate all the systems to prevent injury and produce a flawless performance.

Application Questions

1. Describe how quickly the food you ate 24 hours before any exertion could affect the amount of energy available for the muscles. What would be the effect of food eaten 4 hours before?
2. Explain the action of the muscles of the neck as you bring your left ear to your left shoulder and then move the right ear to the right shoulder.
3. Beginning with a stimulus and ending with a movement, place the following in order: synapse, effector, receptor, sensory neuron, motor neuron, associative neuron, and muscle.
4. Describe how a pituitary tumor in a teenager could affect the onset of maturation/puberty.
5. Describe the effects of a pregame pep rally on fans and players during the rally and as the game starts.
6. What would be the results of a drug that heightens perception but depresses the function of the hypothalamus? How would it affect the performance of a high-wire walker, a musician, or a basketball player?

Problems

1. With the current emphasis on physical fitness, research any one fad, such as jogging, racketball, or aerobics, and determine its relative value for cardiovascular fitness.
2. Biofeedback has been used to control functions such as blood pressure and pulse. Research the validity of claims to control autonomic or subconscious functions.
3. In 1986, two young, strong, apparently well-conditioned athletes died from heart attacks caused by cocaine. What might be the physiological mechanism?

Suggested Readings

B. Fellman, "A Clockwork Gland" *Science 85* (May 1985). Examines the role the pineal gland plays in human biological clocks.

A. J. Hudspeth, "The Hair Cells of the Inner Ear" *Scientific American* (January 1983). Well-illustrated article dealing with these very important structures of the inner ear.

P. Knudtson, "Painter of Neurons" *Science 85* (September 1985). Working in the unlikely environs of 19th-century Spain, a physician/artist revealed the fundamental structure of the human brain.

G. Kolata, "Scrutinizing Sleeping Sickness" *Science* (23 November 1984). Interesting discussion of this ancient disease that, to date, defies vaccination.

J. H. Schwartz, "The Transport of Substances in Nerve Cells" *ScientificAmerican* (April 1980). The role of the axon in regulating impulses between the cell body and the nerve endings.

Scientific American (September 1979). This entire issue is devoted to the brain and nervous system.

S. H. Snyder, 1986, ***Drugs and the Brain*** (New York: Scientific American Books). Comprehensive discussion of how drugs work and their uses and misuses.

B. M. Sweeney, "Biological Clocks—An Introduction" *BioScience* (July/August 1983). Explains what biological clocks (circadian rhythms) are and what function they might serve.

L. Torrey, "How Science Creates Winners" *Science Digest* (August 1984). Describes how biomechanical evaluation can improve an athlete's performance.

Doug Sokell

The Parry primrose, *Primrose parryi,* is a typical flowering plant.

CHAPTER **18**

The Flowering Plant: Form and Function

Introduction

Most plants live in two different environments at the same time: air and soil. Leaves and stems generally live above ground, surrounded by air. Light, carbon dioxide, and oxygen are readily available in that environment. Roots live in the soil, which supplies water and minerals. Each part of the plant is adapted for its environment and for a specific function in the life of the entire plant. Leaves carry out photosynthesis, stems support the leaves and transport materials to other plant parts, and roots anchor the plant and absorb water and minerals.

The plant uses sugars produced during photosynthesis to build its structure, beginning with the embryo inside a seed. How is that structure produced, and how are the parts of the plant adapted to their environments? How does each part function, and how are the activities of all the parts coordinated in the plant as a whole? In this and the next chapter, we will begin to answer these questions. We will confine our study to the flowering plants, which are the most familiar and also the most important to humans.

Leaves and Photosynthesis

Guidepost: How are the parts of a leaf adapted for photosynthesis?

18.1 The Arrangement of Leaf Cells Allows for Movement of Carbon Dioxide

The main function of a leaf is to produce food through photosynthesis. How is leaf structure adapted for that function? The leaf of a flowering plant consists of an enlarged flat portion, the **blade,** usually connected to the plant stem by a **petiole** (PET ee ohl). The blade may be in one piece or divided into separate leaflets. A large surface allows for maximum exposure to light.

Figure 18.1 (a) Simple leaves and (b) a compound leaf.

a BSCS by Carlye Calvin

b Gordon E. Uno

Figure 18.2 A portion of a leaf blade showing internal structures. Colors are diagrammatic only.

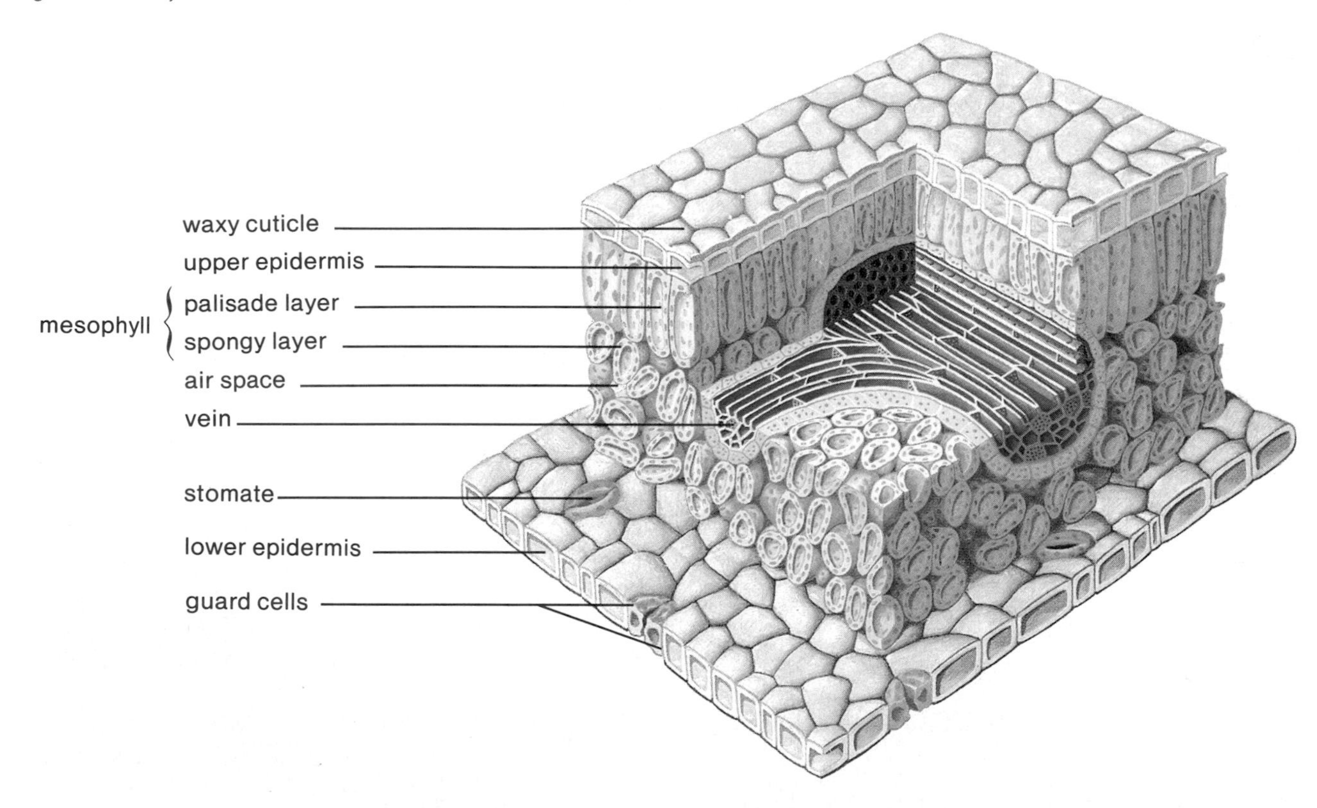

The cellular structure of a leaf blade is shown in figure 18.2, and you can observe it directly in investigation 18.2 (page 658). Several different tissues can be distinguished. Covering both surfaces of the leaf is a transparent layer of cells called the epidermis. Epidermal cells secrete a waxy substance that forms a waterproof coating, the cuticle. Photosynthesis occurs mainly in the **mesophyll** (MEZ oh fil) cells, which contain many chloroplasts. There are two types of mesophyll cells. In the upper, palisade layer, elongated cells are arranged side by side. This space-saving plan exposes a maximum number of cells to the light in a minimum amount of space. In the lower, spongy layer, the cells are loosely packed, with many empty spaces between them. Gases can move freely around and into all the mesophyll cells, as clearly shown in the scanning electron micrograph in figure 18.3.

Substances enter and leave the leaf by two different routes: veins and stomates. Water and minerals are supplied to the leaf cells by the veins, vascular tissues that are continuous with those of the stem and root. Gases move into and out of a leaf by diffusion through stomates, slitlike openings in the epidermis (figure 18.4). Most stomates are located on the underside of a leaf, and there may be millions of them per leaf. The stomates open into the air spaces of the spongy mesophyll. Thus, the carbon dioxide used in photosynthesis and the oxygen used in respiration can reach all the photosynthetic cells of the leaf.

The concentration of carbon dioxide in the air is relatively constant. Within the leaf, however, the concentration varies. Respiration goes on at all times in leaf cells, producing carbon dioxide as a waste product.

Figure 18.3 Scanning electron micrograph of a leaf cross section. Note that air can move freely throughout the interior of the leaf.

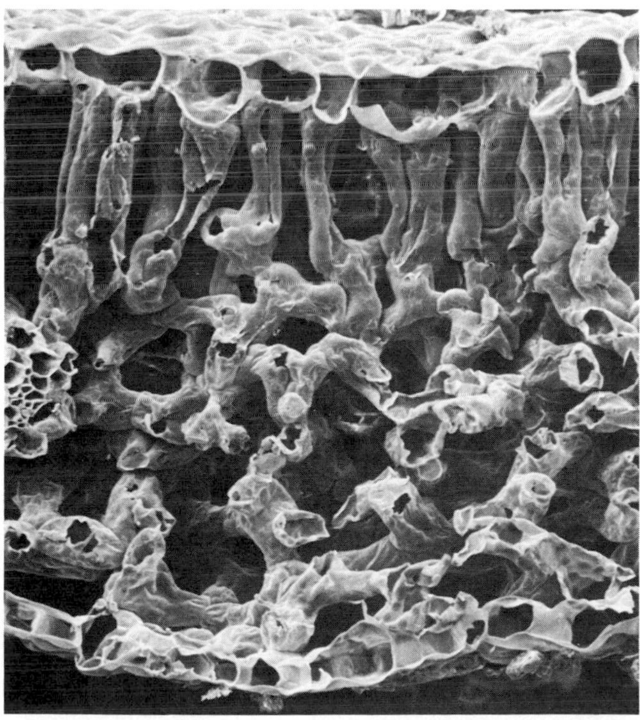

J. H. Troughton

Figure 18.4 Scanning electron micrograph of the surface of a leaf showing stomates.

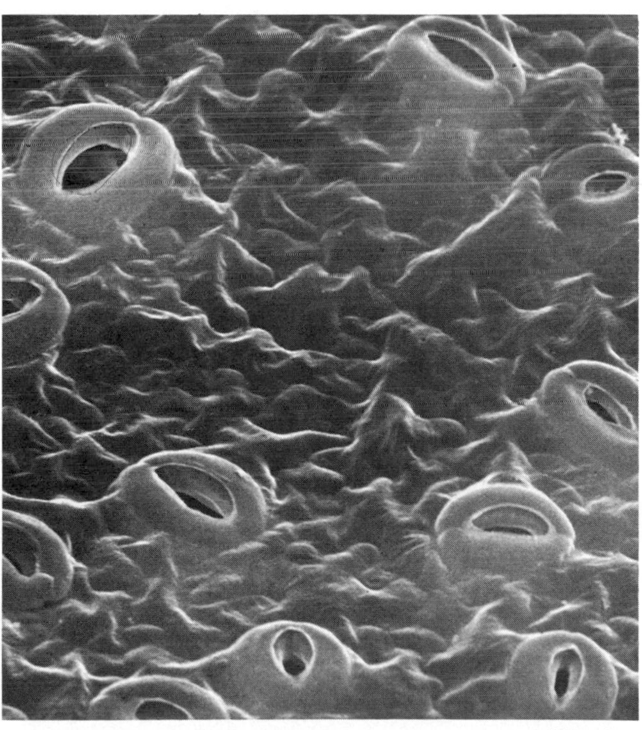

J. H. Troughton

During the day, mesophyll cells use up that carbon dioxide in photosynthesis. As a result, the concentration of carbon dioxide becomes lower in the leaf than in the air, and carbon dioxide diffuses in through the stomates. At night, photosynthesis does not occur. As a result of respiration, the level of carbon dioxide builds up in the leaf. Eventually, it becomes higher than the level in air and diffuses out.

18.2 Guard Cells Control the Rate of Transpiration

Although water molecules are present in the air as water vapor, they are never as abundant in the air as they are in the leaf. Thus, the plant loses water that diffuses into the air through the stomates. This loss is called **transpiration** (trans pih RAY shun).

Figure 18.5 Guard cells control the opening of stomates. Because they are attached to each other at both ends and encircled by rigid cellulose fiber, the guard cells elongate and bend outward when they take up water.

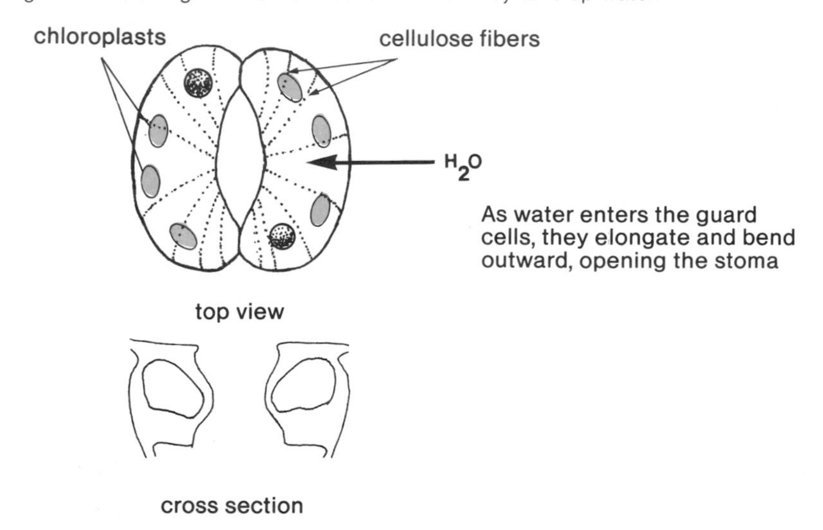
chloroplasts
cellulose fibers
H_2O
As water enters the guard cells, they elongate and bend outward, opening the stoma
top view
cross section

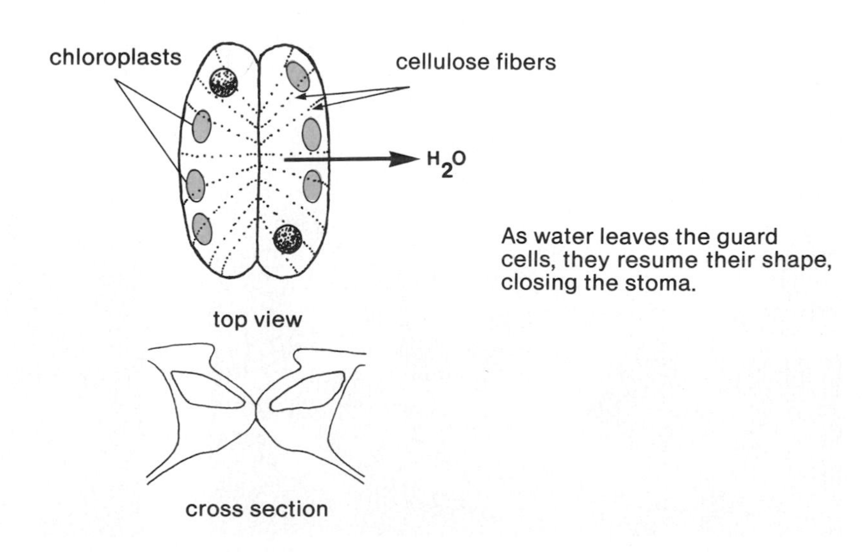
chloroplasts
cellulose fibers
H_2O
As water leaves the guard cells, they resume their shape, closing the stoma.
top view
cross section

When plant cells have adequate supplies of water, the water exerts a pressure, known as **turgor** (TER ger) **pressure,** against the cell walls. Turgor pressure provides support for the stem and leaves. If more water is lost from a plant by transpiration than is replaced by the roots, the cells lose turgor pressure and the plant wilts. As a result, the stem and leaves are no longer held upright. If water is not replaced quickly, the plant cells and the plant will die. In investigation 18.1, you can see the effects of turgor pressure on plant tissue.

How can the plant conserve water, yet allow carbon dioxide to enter? Each stomate is surrounded by a pair of specialized cells called **guard cells.** When the guard cells fill with water, they bend outward (figure 18.5, top). As they bend, the stomate opens and carbon dioxide diffuses into the leaf. When a plant loses more water than it can replace, the turgor pressure of the guard cells decreases. The guard cells no longer bend outward, and as a result, the stomates close (figure 18.5, bottom). In that manner, the plant is able to reduce the loss of water under dry conditions. During those times, however, little photosynthesis takes place.

Self-Review

1. How is the arrangement of the two kinds of mesophyll cells in the leaf important to photosynthesis?
2. What controls the direction of carbon dioxide diffusion through the stomates?
3. How does turgor pressure provide support for a leaf?
4. How do guard cells function to prevent water loss through the stomates?

Investigation 18.1 WATER AND TURGOR PRESSURE

Introduction

Some plants maintain a position above ground, resisting the forces of gravity, wind, rain, and snow, because of the rigidity (firmness) of the plant body. This is true in woody plants in which much of the body consists of nonliving thickened cell walls.

In herbaceous plants many cell walls are thin and structurally weak. Their support depends on the turgor pressure that the contents of individual cells exert against their walls. This turgor pressure varies as the volume of the cell contents changes when water is taken in or lost. In such plants, maintaining position is directly related to maintaining shape, which depends on turgor pressure. Turgor pressure, in turn, depends on the water relationships of individual cells.

Materials (per team)

white potato, large
sucrose solutions, 0.2 *M*, 0.4 *M*, 0.6 *M*, 75 ml of each
4 petri dishes, 100 mm × 20 mm
beaker, 250 ml
balance
knife, with 12 cm blade
cork borer, 1 cm diameter, with rod
heavy cardboard, 15 cm square
glass-marking pencil
paper towels
graph paper
refrigerator
metric ruler
distilled water

Procedure

1. Read the procedure and then state a hypothesis appropriate to the design of the experiment.
2. Using the knife, cut off one end of a potato perpendicular to its long axis. Then make a 2nd cut parallel to the 1st one about 7 cm from it. Discard the end pieces.
3. Place one cut surface on top of the cardboard square on the laboratory table. Cut a core of tissue by forcing the cork borer down through the potato, with a twisting motion. Then, using the rod, force the core out of the borer into the bottom half of a petri dish. Repeat this coring procedure 3 more times.
4. Place the cores in petri dishes. Line up the dishes and label them 0.0 *M*, 0.2 *M*, 0.4 *M*, and 0.6 *M*. (*M* = molar.) A molar solution (1.0 *M*) of sucrose contains 342 g of this sugar per liter.
5. Weigh and record the mass of each core. Measure and record the length of each core. Determine the rigidity of each core by holding it at each end between your fingertips and gently bending it. Are there any marked differences in rigidity among the cores? If so, record them. Replace each core in its dish.
6. Now add to dish 0.0 *M* enough water to cover the core. Add to each of the other 3 dishes enough of the appropriate sucrose solutions to cover the cores.
7. After 30 minutes remove the core from dish 0.0 *M*. Dry it gently by rolling it between 2 pieces of paper towel and lightly pressing each end on the paper. Repeat for each of the other cores.
8. Determine whether there has been any change in rigidity among the cores. If so, devise a system to describe the differences and record them.
9. Return each core to its dish. Then place the dishes in a refrigerator.
10. After 24 hours remove the dishes from the refrigerator. Repeat the drying procedure for each core and immediately determine and record rigidity, mass, and length.
11. Calculate the differences, if any, between initial and final mass and initial and final lengths of each core. Record these, using a + sign to indicate increase and a − sign to indicate decrease.
12. Graph these differences, using a grid as shown in figure 18.6 below.

Figure 18.6

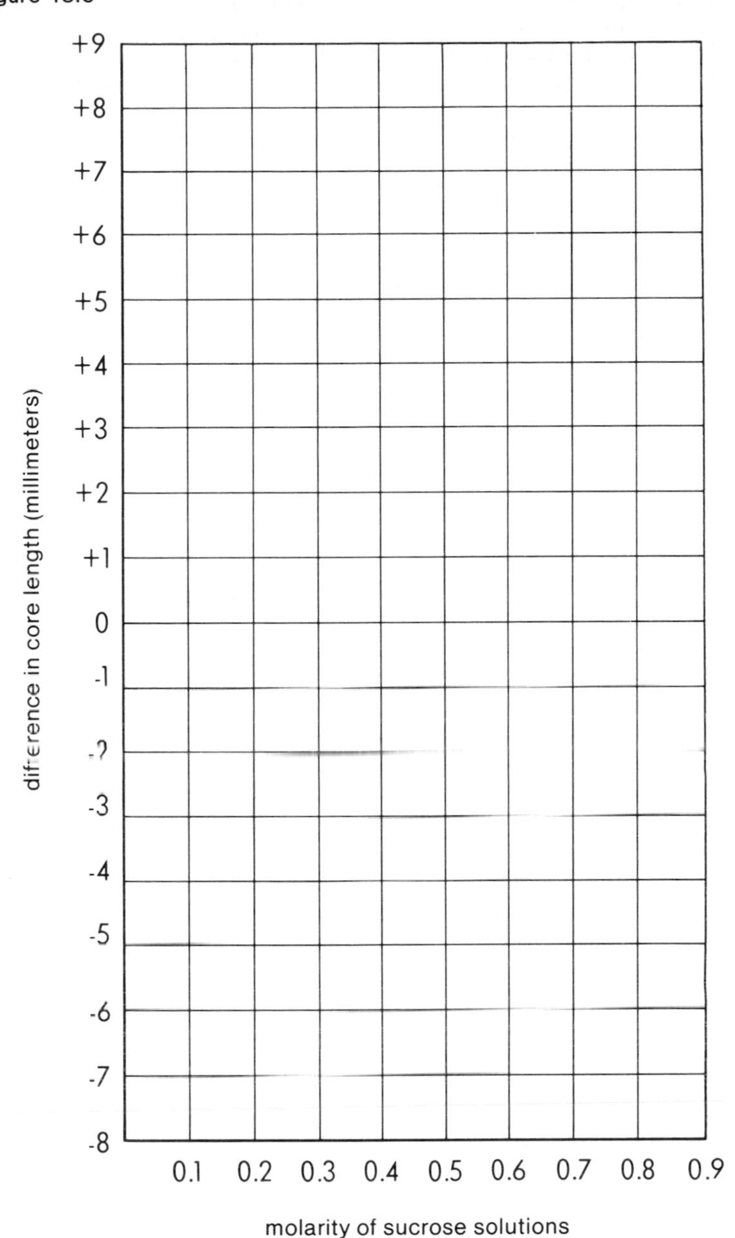

Discussion

Review the discussion of diffusion in section 5.7, pages 144–145, and in investigation 5.2. Plasma membranes of potato are highly permeable to water and highly impermeable to sucrose molecules. The thin cell walls are highly permeable to both. The walls of these cells can be stretched or contracted only to a limited extent. Their shape when contracted, however, can be readily changed.

1. On what basis can you explain differences in rigidity, if any, among the cores placed in various concentrations of sucrose?
2. For each of the cores, compare the rigidity change, if any, after 30 minutes.
   (a) Which core showed the greatest change in rigidity?
   (b) Which showed the least change?

3. (a) Is there any relationship between your observations on rigidity and differences between initial and final lengths of the cores? If so, explain.
   (b) Between initial and final mass? If so, explain.
4. Do your data support the hypothesis you stated at the beginning of this investigation?
5. What is the relationship between water content and rigidity of plant structures that have thin-walled cells?

For Further Investigation

1. Using the same experimental approach, investigate the effects of sucrose solutions having concentrations of 0.8 *M* and 1.0 *M*. Compare data obtained with those derived from your original experiment.
2. Investigate the effects on elodea leaves of sucrose solutions of the same range of concentrations as used in this investigation. Mount detached leaves on a microscope slide in the sugar solution, and add a cover slip. Observe this first under low power and then under high power for 5 minutes.

Guidepost: How are stems adapted for conduction and support?

Stems and Conduction

18.3 Stems Support the Leaves and Conduct Water and Sugars

The plant stem connects the leaves and roots, and supports the leaves and reproductive organs in the light and air. It carries water and minerals from the roots to the leaves and sugars from the leaves to nonphotosynthetic parts of the plant. Air diffuses into stems through **lenticels** (LENT ih selz), small openings on the surface. Some stems also store food in their tissues. Stems may be either herbaceous or woody. Herbaceous stems are rather soft and are supported primarily by turgor pressure, as we explained in section 18.2. Woody stems have cells with thick, stiff walls that provide support.

Figure 18.7 Structural adaptations of underground stems. What do you think is the principal function of each type?

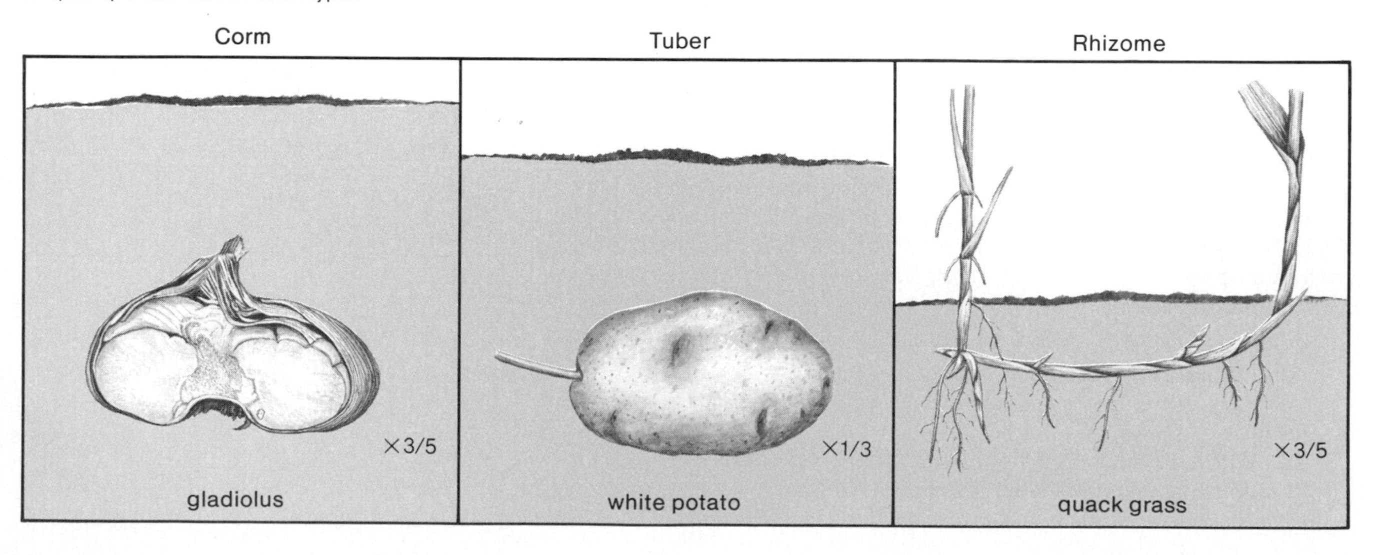

Stems differ greatly in structure, but all have buds. A bud is a miniature shoot consisting of a short stem, tiny immature leaves, and sometimes flowers. The "eyes" of a white potato are really buds. The potato, therefore, is an underground stem. A sweet potato has no buds; it is a root. Most stems, however, grow above ground.

If we examine a woody twig from a deciduous tree after the leaves have fallen, the buds are usually conspicuous. Growth from a terminal (tip) bud lengthens the twig. Growth from a lateral (side) bud starts a new branch. During the winter, a bud is usually covered with protective scales, which are modified leaves. Bud scales fall off when growth starts in the spring, leaving scars where they were attached. Because these bud scales are formed only in the fall, one can determine the age of a branch by counting the number of scars. Each ring of bud scale scars indicates where growth began for that year.

Figure 18.8 (a) A dormant woody twig, (b) a terminal bud and lateral buds, and (c) a diagram of a longitudinal section of a terminal bud.

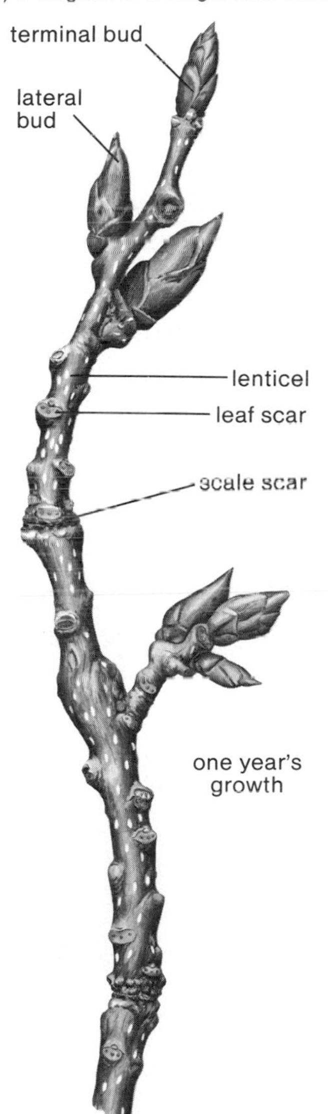

BSCS by Doug Sokell

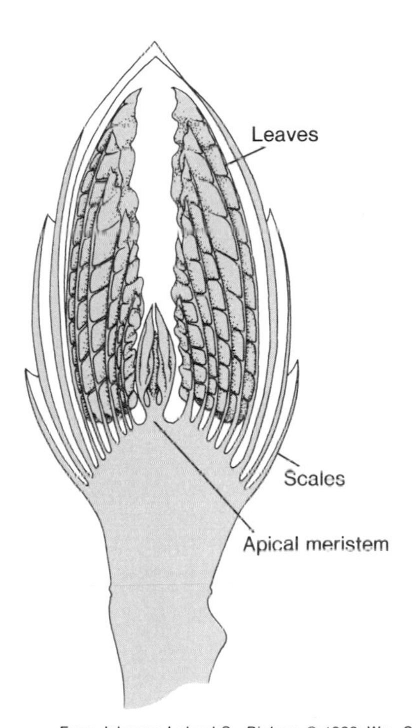

From Johnson, Leland G., *Biology*, © 1983. Wm. C. Brown Publishers, Dubuque, Iowa. All Rights Reserved. Reprinted by permission.

18.4 Water and Sugars Move through Different Kinds of Cells in the Stem

Figure 18.9 shows the microscopic structure of a young dicot stem in three dimensions. At the very center of the young stem there may be a group of loosely collected cells called the **pith.** The pith stores food in young stems and is usually destroyed as the stem grows older.

The epidermis forms the outside "skin" of the young stem. It is a single, protective layer of cells that will be replaced by the **bark** as the young stem grows older. The **cortex** tissue is formed of thin-walled cells that can serve as either a storage area or a photosynthetic area, depending on the stem.

Sugars produced by photosynthesizing leaf cells are transported throughout the plant in the phloem. Sieve cells in the phloem form tubes. As each sieve cell develops, many small holes form in both end walls.

Figure 18.9 A young stem showing microscopic structures. Colors are diagrammatic only.

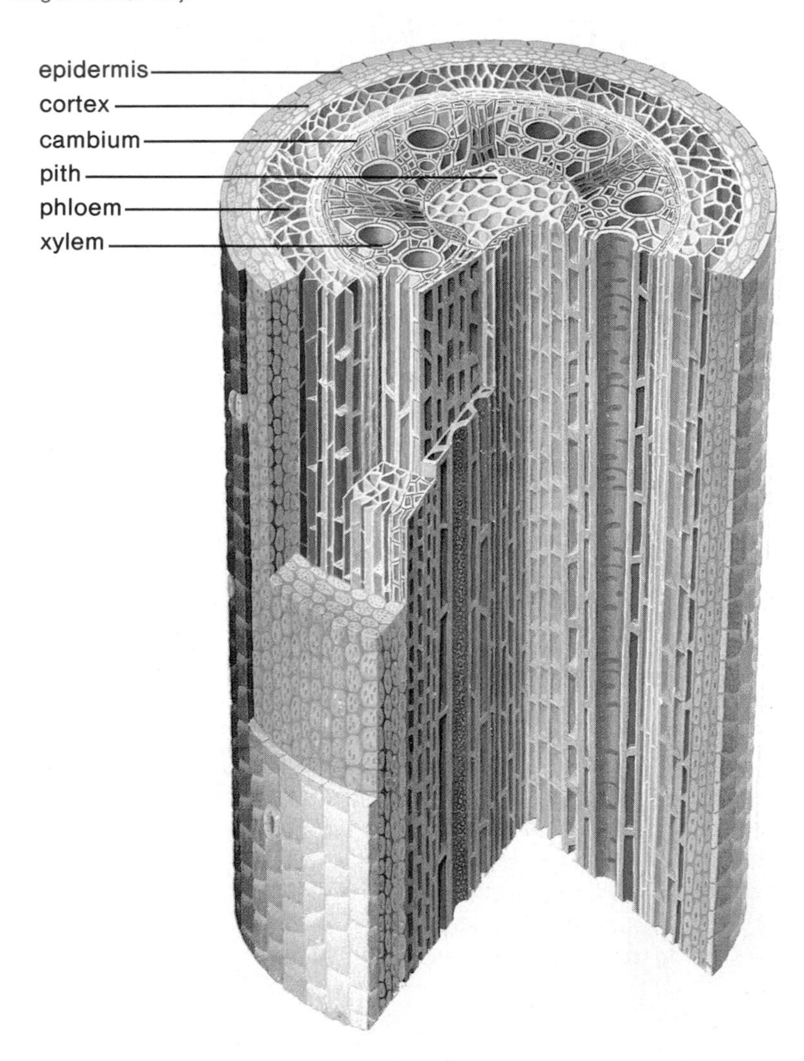

Figure 18.10 Stained cross section of a young dicot stem showing pith, cortex, and fibrovascular bundles.

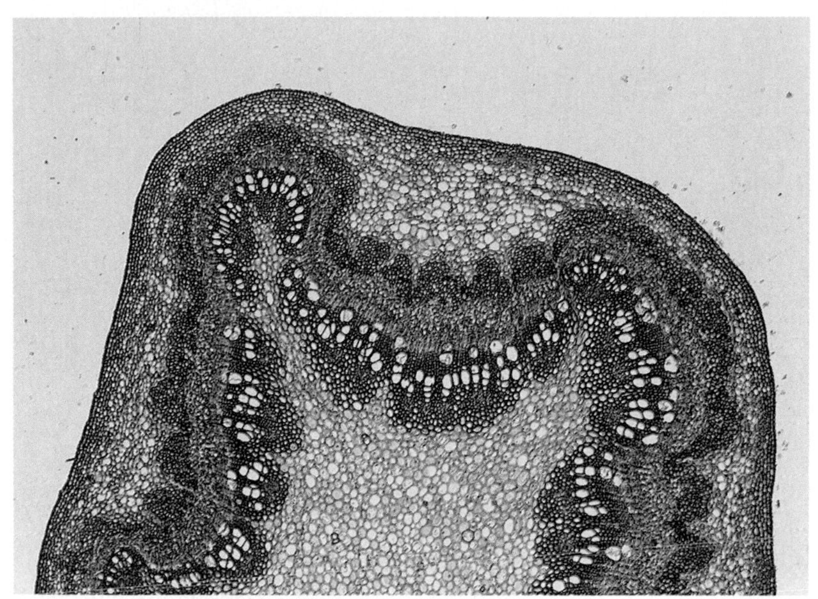

Ripon Microslides Inc.

Through these holes the cytoplasm of one cell connects with the cytoplasm of adjacent cells, making a continuous cell-to-cell system. As a sieve cell matures, its nucleus disintegrates. Located beside each sieve-tube cell is a smaller, companion cell that has a nucleus. Botanists think that companion cells regulate the activity of sieve-tube cells.

The vascular **cambium** (KAM bee um) tissue lies between the phloem and xylem cells. It consists of cells that undergo mitosis and divide, forming other plant tissues. When a cambium cell divides into two new cells, one of these cells eventually becomes a conducting or supporting cell. The other cell remains a part of the cambium tissue and divides again. Phloem cells are formed continually at the outer surface of the cambium. Xylem cells are formed continually at the inner surface of the cambium. Fiber cells also are formed by the cambium. They are interspersed with the vascular xylem and phloem, and they strengthen and support the stem.

Most of the stem eventually consists of xylem, which serves two important functions. Xylem transports water and minerals, and its thick-walled cells are the major supporting structures of the stem. Wood, which is found only in older stems, is made completely out of xylem cells. Xylem may be made of two kinds of cells—tracheids and vessels. Tracheids are thick-walled long cells that grow to their full size and then die. The walls of these dead cells contain thin areas called pits. Pits in adjacent tracheids are paired, so that water and dissolved substances can pass easily from one tracheid to another. Vessels are made of long, thick-walled cells joined end-to-end to form tiny, elongated pipes that extend through the

Figure 18.11 (a) Cells from conducting tissues of flowering plants. (b) Scanning electron micrograph of a stem cross section showing xylem vessels.

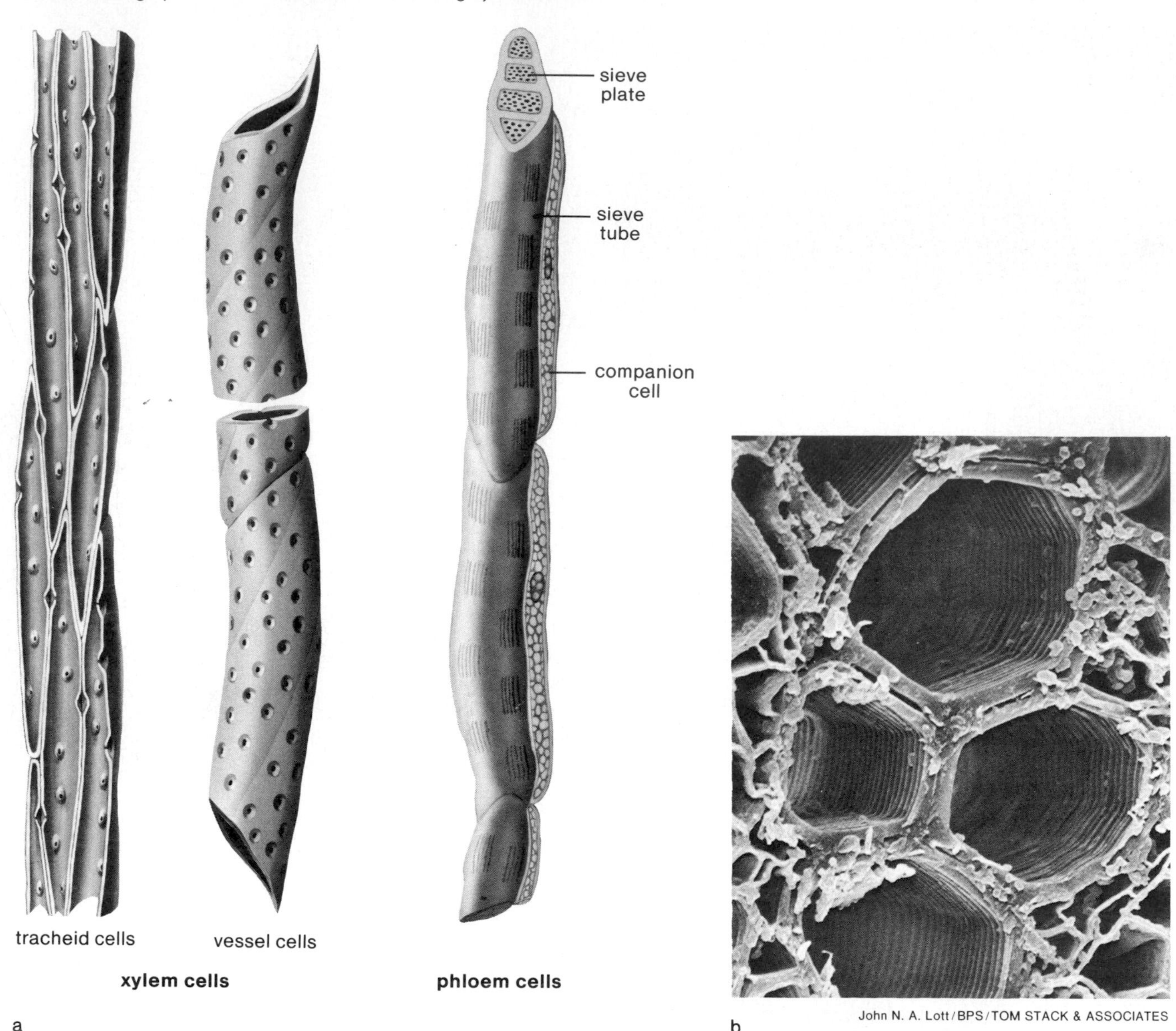

stem (figure 18.11b). The end walls of vessel cells disintegrate, and they, like tracheids, die. Both tracheids and vessels are arranged to form a continuous conducting system from the root, up through the stem, and out into the veins of the leaf. You will be able to observe these structures in investigation 18.2 on page 658.

18.5 Transpiration Pulls Water Up through the Xylem of a Plant

Water must travel more than 100 m to reach the top of the tallest trees (see figure 13.2, page 438). Many experiments have shown that water from roots rises through root xylem to stem xylem to the xylem in the veins of leaves. This movement is against the force of gravity.

Imagine that you are standing with a long soda straw on top of a building three stories tall. The straw extends down into a bottle of root beer on the ground. No matter how hard you try, you cannot suck the root beer up from the bottle. You could not do this even with a vacuum pump. How then do water and dissolved materials in the water move up to the top of a tree?

Water is thought to move by a process known as **cohesion-transpiration.** Under certain conditions, water can be pulled up a narrow tube if the water is in a continuous column. One condition is that the tube must have a very small diameter. A second condition is that the tube must be made of a material to which water molecules will adhere, or stick. These conditions exist within the xylem cells of plants. In addition, water molecules exhibit **cohesion:** they are attracted to adjoining water molecules. As a result of the cohesion of water molecules, an unbroken column of water is maintained in each xylem tube. When water molecules are lost by transpiration from the upper end of the column in the leaves, a pull results. The pull is transmitted through the length of the column, and water is pulled from the roots up the plant to the leaves.

18.6 Pressure within Phloem Cells Helps Move Sugars Down a Plant

Sugars move from the leaves to roots and other nonphotosynthetic parts of the plant through the phloem cells. Phloem cells contain living cytoplasm through which water and dissolved sugars must pass. The rate at which the fluid moves through phloem is thousands of times faster than diffusion alone could account for. What is the mechanism of phloem transport?

The best explanation of movement of sugars through the phloem is the **pressure-flow** hypothesis. According to this hypothesis, water and dissolved sugars flow through the sieve tubes from an area of higher pressure to an area of lower pressure. Mesophyll cells in the leaf secrete sugars by active transport into the phloem cells. The resultant high sugar concentration causes water to diffuse into the phloem cells, increasing their turgor pressure. An area of higher pressure is thus formed, which forces the sugar-water solution to move into the next phloem cell. In this manner, sugars are moved from cell to cell—from higher pressure area to lower pressure area—until they reach a cell where they will be used or stored. There, sugars are removed from the phloem, again by active transport. When this happens the water also leaves the phloem cell. Thus, the flow of sugar water from the leaves to the root can continue.

Figure 18.12 A hypothesis based on fluid pressure, for the transport of food and water in phloem.

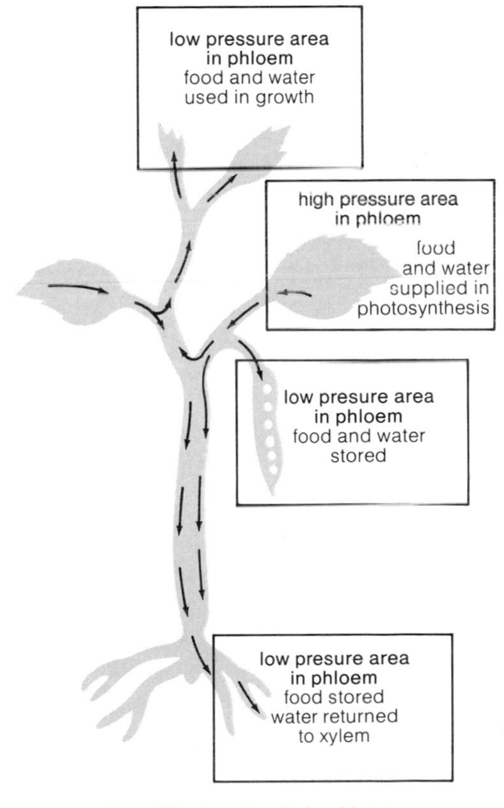

Self-Review

1. What are the major differences between xylem and phloem?
2. How do vessels and tracheids differ?
3. What roles do cohesion and transpiration play in water movement?
4. How does the pressure-flow hypothesis explain the movement of sugars in the phloem?

Investigation 18.2 LEAVES, STEMS, AND ROOTS: STRUCTURAL ADAPTATIONS

Introduction

The leaves, stems, and roots of flowering plants have structural adaptations that enable them to perform efficiently their specific functions. In this investigation, you will examine those plant structures and attempt to deduce the functions for which they are adapted.

Materials

compound microscope
dissecting microscope
variety of mature plants
prepared cross section of a leaf
young bean plant
prepared cross section of an herbaceous dicot stem
radish seedlings germinating in a petri dish
grass seedlings germinating on water
bunch of carrots
prepared cross section of a root
colored pencils (red, blue, brown, green)

Procedure

Part A—Leaf Structure and Function

1. Look at the various plants and the different kinds of leaves. What might be the advantage of a flat, thin leaf blade to the photosynthetic capacity of a plant?
2. How are the leaves arranged on the stems of different plants? Relate this arrangement to the photosynthetic capacity of the plant.
3. Examine a prepared cross section of a leaf under the high power of your microscope. Compare your slide with figure 18.3 on page 647 to become familiar with the various regions of the leaf. Consider its structures in relation to the functions of light absorption, water supply, and carbon dioxide absorption.
4. Locate chloroplasts in the leaf cells.
   (a) What shape are they?
   (b) Which leaf cells contain the chloroplasts?
   (c) What difference in abundance of chloroplasts among those cells can you see?
5. Locate a cross section of a small vein in the center tissues of the leaf. The vein is surrounded by a sheath of cells that also are photosynthetic. Notice some empty cells with thick walls in the upper part of the sectioned vein. What might be the function of these cells?
6. Examine the covering layers of the leaf—the upper epidermis and the lower epidermis. These single layers of cells are covered by cuticle, which may have been removed when the slide was made. How might the cuticle affect the efficiency of photosynthesis?
7. Locate a stomate and its guard cells. Locate the spongy tissue just above the lower epidermis. How does the structure of the spongy tissue differ from that of the other leaf tissues?
8. Note how the stomates are located in relation to the spongy tissue. What does that relationship suggest about the function of the spongy tissue?

Part B—Stem Structure and Function

1. Observe the stem of the bean plant. Notice how the leaves are attached to the stem. The site of attachment is called the node (figure 18.13).
   (a) What color is the stem?
   (b) Judging from its color, what do you think might be the function of a herbaceous stem?
   (c) Should this be listed as a function of all stems? Why or why not?
2. Using low power, study a cross section through the internode of a stem. Compare your slide with figure 18.9 on page 654 to become familiar with the general regions of the stem. Like a leaf, an herbaceous stem is covered by an epidermis. How many cells thick is the epidermis?
3. The most noticeable feature of the cross section is a ring of vascular bundles. Each bundle is usually wedge shaped with the narrow end of the wedge directed toward the center of the stem. The center of the stem is made up of large, thin-walled cells. This is the pith. Between the outer edges of the vascular bundles and the epidermis is the cortex. Draw a circle about 15 cm in diameter. In the circle, outline the vascular bundles as they appear in your slide. Do not draw in any cells.
4. Using high power, look in the cortex and vascular bundles for thick-walled, empty cells. Show their location in red on your diagram. Suggest a possible function for these cells.
5. The leaves need water for photosynthesis. Water is absorbed by the roots and is conducted through the xylem of the stem to the leaves. Use a blue pencil to color the xylem in your drawing.
   (a) In what structures of the stem did you look for xylem cells?
   (b) What other functions might these cells have?
   (c) What relation do these cells have to those previously noted in your stem drawing?
6. Materials manufactured in the leaves are transported to other parts of the plant through the phloem. With a brown pencil, color the part of the diagram that represents the phloem.
   (a) Where in the stem is the phloem tissue?
   (b) Was phloem also present in the leaf you observed earlier?
7. Food in the form of starch is stored in stems. Using high power, carefully examine the stem tissues to find cells that store food. Color the storage cells in the diagram green.
   (a) How is the presence of stored food indicated in these tissues?
   (b) What region of the stem is devoted primarily to storage?

Figure 18.13

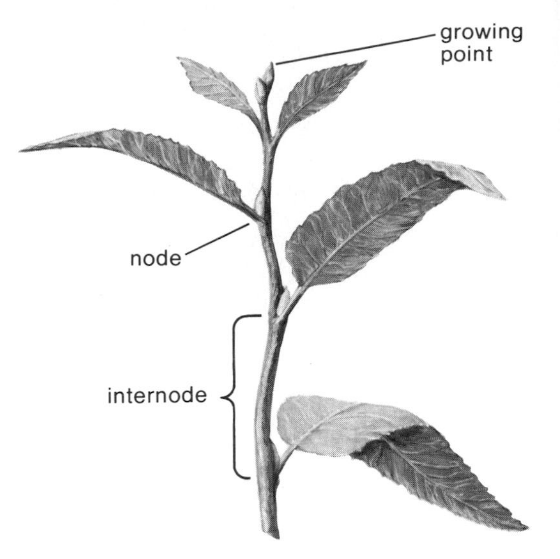

Part C—Root Structure and Function

1. What part of a plant absorbs water?
2. Recall your study of the absorbing surfaces of animal digestive tracts (chapter 15). What would you expect one of the characteristics of water-absorbing structures of a plant to be?
3. Some roots store more food than others. Look at the root system of the grass plant and the carrot. Which probably contains more stored food?
4. Examine the radish seedlings in the petri dish. (Do not remove the cover from the dish.) Use the dissecting microscope and look through the cover of the dish at the fuzzy mass of tiny structures around the root. These structures are called root hairs.
   (a) On what part of the root are the root hairs longest?
   (b) What probably happens to the root hairs if a plant is pulled out of the soil?

5. With forceps, pick up a young grass seedling. Mount the seedling in a drop of water on a clean glass slide without a cover glass. With the low power of your compound microscope, find the root tip. (You can see that the root differs from the young shoot, which is green.) Look along the root for root hairs.
   (a) Is a root hair made up of one or many cells?
   (b) What relationship do root hairs have to the epidermis of the young root? (To answer this question, you may have to put a cover glass on the specimen and examine it with high power.)
   (c) Are root hair cells living or dead?
   (d) What important process is involved in the absorption of water by root hair cells?
6. Observe with low power the prepared slide of a cross section of a mature root. Locate the epidermis, cortex, xylem, and phloem. Draw a circle to represent the root cross section. Color the location of the xylem blue on your diagram. Color the location of the phloem brown. Where is the phloem in relation to the xylem?
7. Examine the cells and tissues of the root with high power, looking for stored food. Color the region of food storage on your diagram with a green pencil.
   (a) What region of the root contains the greatest amount of stored food?
   (b) In what form is the food stored in the root?

Discussion

1. (a) On the basis of your observations of chloroplast location in the leaf, which are the main photosynthetic cells?
   (b) How might the location of chloroplasts in these cells be advantageous in light absorption?
2. How are the leaf structures you observed adapted for leaf functions?
3. According to your observations, what are the major functions of the stem?
4. What stem structures are adapted for each of those functions?
5. How does the function of root epidermis compare with the function of stem and leaf epidermis?
6. How does the position of xylem in the root compare with its position in the stem?
7. What function of stems and roots is lacking in most leaves?
8. What function of leaves and young stems is lacking in roots?
9. What structures would a molecule of water pass through from the soil to the air just outside a leaf? List them in order.

Guidepost: How are roots adapted for absorption of water and minerals?

Roots and Absorption

18.7 Roots Anchor the Plant

Anchorage and absorption are the two main functions of a root, but roots also conduct materials and serve as storage organs. Figure 18.14 shows the microscopic structure of the tip of a root. The vascular tissues form a cylinder in the center. Surrounding the vascular tissues is the cortex, which may form part of the bark around an older root. Sometimes food is stored in the cortex in the form of starch or sugars. Carrots, sugar beets, radishes, and turnips are examples of storage roots.

Anyone who has pulled weeds from the ground knows that the roots of a plant anchor it firmly in the soil. In some species there are many branching roots growing from the bottom of the plant. This is a **fibrous-root system.** It is characteristic of plants such as corn, beans, and clover. In other species, the plant is anchored by a long, tapering root with slender, short, side branches. This is a **taproot system,** found in such plants as dandelions, mesquite, and carrots. Fibrous root systems are relatively close to the soil surface. Therefore, rainwater does not have to penetrate the soil very deeply before it can be absorbed. Rainwater must penetrate soil farther to be absorbed by a taproot system because the root hairs are deeper in the ground. On the other hand, taproots can use water sources that are deeper in the soil.

Figure 18.14 The terminal portion of a root. Colors are diagrammatic only.

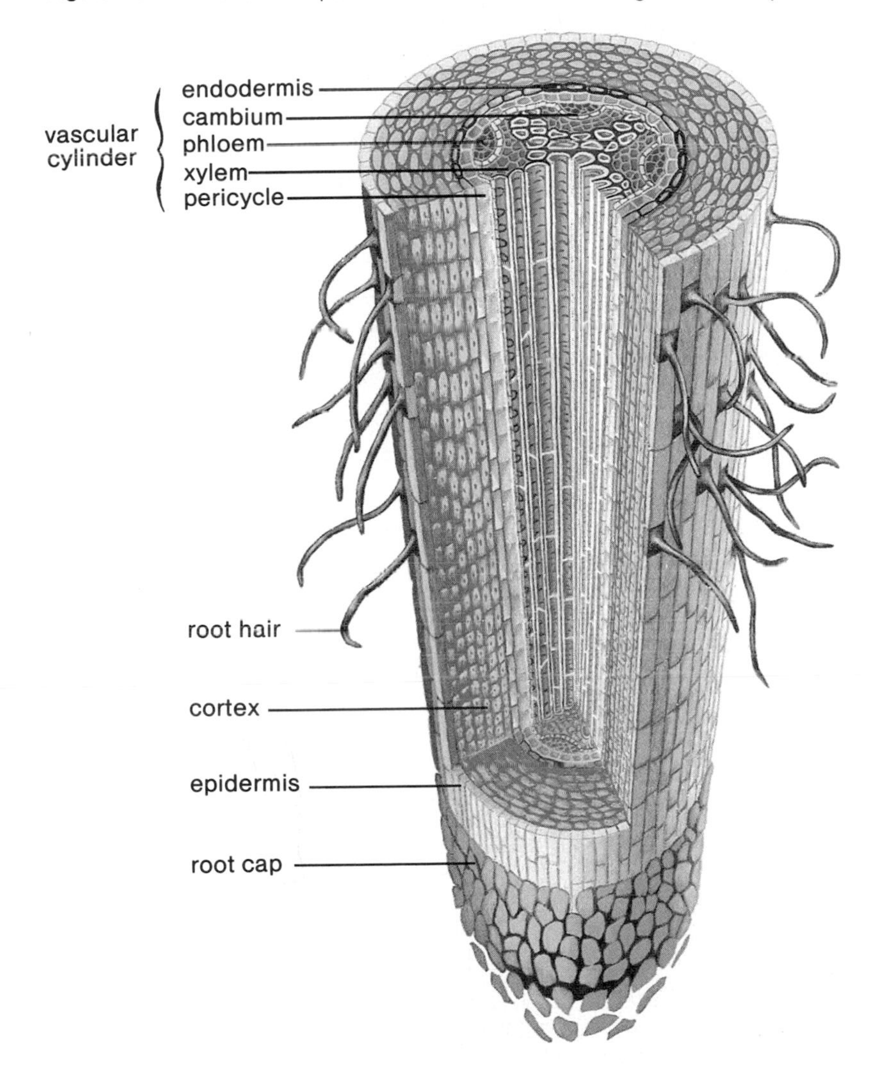

Figure 18.15 When large quantities of food are stored, both taproots (left) and fibrous roots (right) may be thickened.

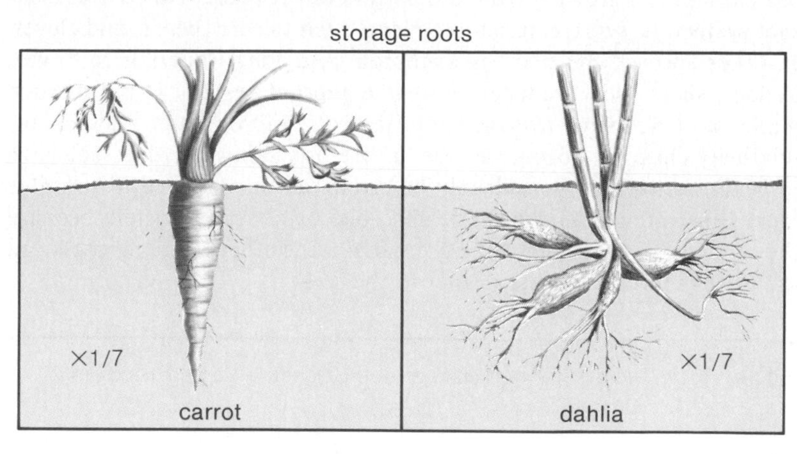

Figure 18.16 Two kinds of root systems.

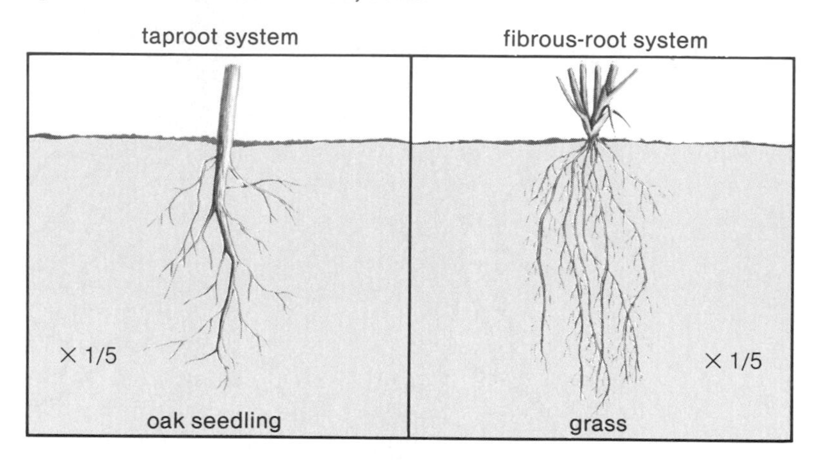

Figure 18.17 A radish seedling showing root hairs.

BSCS by Doug Sokell

18.8 Root Hairs Greatly Increase the Surface Area of a Root System

Most water absorption occurs through **root hairs,** each of which is a thin-walled extension of a single epidermal cell. The root hairs appear in figure 18.17 as a fuzzy white zone just behind the tip of the seedling root. Root hairs penetrate the spaces between soil particles and absorb the water and minerals required by a plant through a huge surface area. A single rye plant only 60 cm tall is estimated to have a root system with a total length of 480 km and a total surface area of more than 600 m^2—twice that of a tennis court. Much of its length and surface area is due to root hairs.

If a plant is pulled up roughly out of the soil, most of its root system remains behind. That is why some plants wilt after being transplanted from one pot into another. Most of the root hairs have been pulled off during the transplant operation, and without them the plant cannot absorb enough water to prevent wilting.

Figure 18.18 Root hairs penetrating into soil. On the left are conducting tissues of the root.

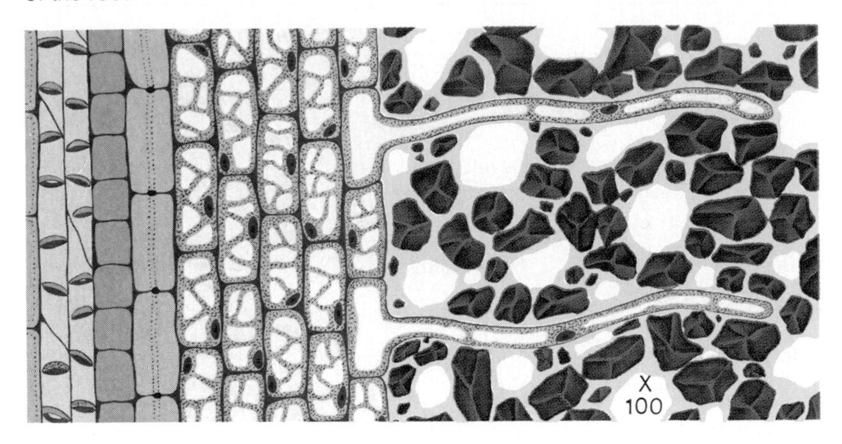

The cell walls of root hairs absorb water from the soil, much as paper towels "drink up" liquid spills. From the cell walls, water diffuses into the inner part of the root hair cell. On their inner sides, root hair cells are in contact with other root cells. Diffusing from cell to cell, the water eventually makes its way to a xylem cell. Here, the water begins its upward journey to the leaves of the plant, pulled by transpiration, as we described in section 18.5.

18.9 Minerals Move into a Plant by Active Transport

In addition to water, a plant requires mineral nutrients for growth and maintenance. These elements enter roots in soil water as dissolved ions. Roots take in nitrogen, for example, in the form of ammonium or nitrate ions. Mineral nutrients such as nitrogen that a plant needs in relatively large amounts are called **macronutrients.** Other minerals such as iron are required in extremely small amounts. These are called **micronutrients.** Plant physiologists have been able to identify these essential minerals by growing plants in solutions lacking a particular mineral (figure 18.19). They have learned how the minerals are absorbed and used by the plant, and what effect is produced when a particular nutrient is missing. Table 18.1 summarizes that information.

The mineral nutrients are generally more concentrated in root hairs than in soil water. Absorption of minerals thus involves active transport, the transport of dissolved substances *against* a concentration gradient, or in a direction opposite to that of diffusion. Active transport requires energy. If root cells are deprived of oxygen and are thus unable to respire, the absorption of minerals slows greatly. Absorbed minerals move deeper into the root by active transport from one layer of cells to another. Eventually, minerals reach the xylem cells, through which they are conducted to the stem and leaves.

Figure 18.19 Tomato plants showing symptoms of mineral nutrient deficiency. From left: potassium, phosphorus, and nitrogen deficient plants. The plant on the right was grown in medium supplying all mineral needs.

Gordon E. Uno

Table 18.1 Mineral elements required by plants

Element	Function	Deficiency
Macronutrients		
Calcium	Component of cell walls; enzyme cofactor; involved in cell membrane permeability; encourages root development.	Characterized by death of the growing points.
Magnesium	Part of the chlorophyll molecule; activator of many enzymes.	Development of pale, sickly foliage, an unhealthy condition known as chlorosis.
Nitrogen	Component of amino acids, chlorophyll, coenzymes, and proteins. An excess causes vigorous vegetative growth and suppresses food storage and fruit and seed development.	Early symptom is yellowing of leaves, followed by a stunting in the growth of all parts of the plant.
Phosphorus	Promotes root growth and hastens maturity, particularly of cereal grains.	Underdeveloped root system; all parts of plant stunted.
Potassium	Enzyme activator; production of chlorophyll.	Pale, sickly foliage.
Sulfur	Component of some amino acids.	Chlorosis; poor root system.
Micronutrients		
Boron	Pollen germination; regulation of carbohydrate metabolism.	Darker color; abnormal growth; malformations.
Chlorine	Evolution of oxygen during photosynthesis.	Small leaves; slow growth.
Copper	Component of some enzymes.	Lowered protein synthesis.
Iron	Needed for chlorophyll production.	Chlorosis, appearing first in youngest leaves.
Manganese	Activates Krebs cycle enzymes.	Mottled chlorosis.
Molybdenum	Part of enzymes for nitrate reduction.	Severe stunting of older leaves.
Zinc	Component of some enzymes; internode elongation.	Small leaves; short internodes.

Self-Review

1. How do fibrous-root and taproot systems differ?
2. What role do root hairs play in water absorption?
3. What is the evidence that minerals move into and through the root by active transport?

Guidepost: What are the characteristics of growth in plants?

Plant Growth

18.10 A Seed Protects and Nourishes the Embryo Inside

To begin our study of plant growth, let us examine the seed of a dicot. Each seed contains one offspring of a parent plant, the embryo, and stored food. The embryo is protected within the seed by a **seed coat.** Some seed coats are extremely thick, making digestion difficult for seed predators. Other seed coats contain chemicals that inhibit germination until appropriate growing conditions occur.

Figure 18.20 As a bean seedling develops from a seed, it grows both above and below the cotyledons.

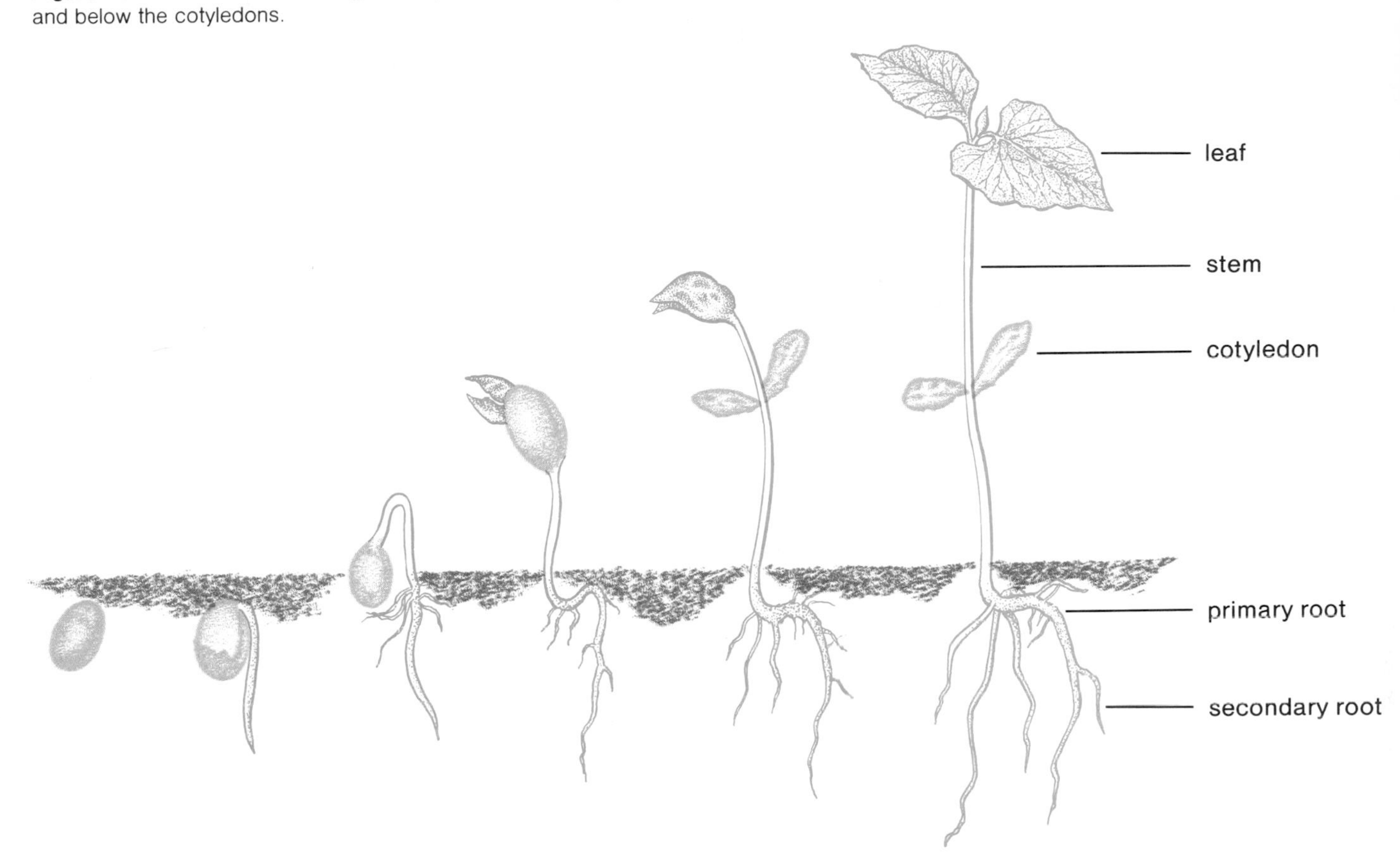

When most seeds germinate, the first structure to appear is the embryonic root. The root turns downward into the soil, anchoring the seedling and absorbing water and minerals. The stem appears next and, in the case of many dicot seeds, carries up two green cotyledons with it. Each of those cotyledons contains energy and nutrients for the young, developing seedling. As the seedling grows, it uses those stored reserves. After the seedling has grown true leaves that can produce food through photosynthesis, the cotyledons shrink and fall off. The seedling continues to grow and differentiate into all the tissues of a mature plant. You can observe some of those events occurring in bean plants in investigation 18.3.

Investigation 18.3 SEEDS AND SEEDLINGS

Introduction

A seed is a packaged plant. Within it is a complete set of instructions for growing a maple tree or a geranium. The seed contains all the parts and materials needed to establish the plant in the soil. How does that take place? In this investigation you will have an opportunity to find out.

Materials

Parts A and B

soaked bean seeds
bean seeds, germinated 1, 2, 3, and 10 days
hand lens
dilute iodine solution
sharp single-edge razor blade

Part C

soaked germinating corn grains
petri dish with starch agar—dish A
petri dish with plain agar—dish B
petri dish with starch agar and germinating corn grains—dish C
petri dish with starch agar and corn grains killed in FAA—dish D
iodine solution
sharp single-edge razor blade

Part A—The Seed

Procedure

1. Examine some of the external features of a bean seed. Notice that the seed is covered by a tough, leathery coat. Look along one edge of the seed and find a scar. This scar marks the place where the seed was attached to the parent plant.
2. Remove the seed coat. Inside the seed coat you will find the embryo. Two fleshy halves called cotyledons make up part of the embryo.
3. Cut a little sliver from one of the cotyledons. Test the sliver with iodine solution. Record the results in your data book.
4. Separate the two halves of the cotyledon and find the little plant attached to one end of one of the cotyledons. Take a closer look at it with a hand lens. You will see that this part of the embryo has two miniature leaves and a root. The small leaves plus a tiny short tip make up the **epicotyl** of the embryo. The root portion is the **hypocotyl.**

Discussion

1. What do you think is the function of the seed coat?
2. What would you guess to be the function of a connection between a parent plant and a developing seed?
3. What would you deduce is the primary function of the cotyledons?
4. What was the original source of the substance of the cotyledons?

Part B—The Seedling

Procedure

1. Look at bean seedlings that are 1, 2, and 3 days old.
2. Then compare the 10-day-old seedling with the 3-day-old seedling.

Discussion

1. What part of the plant becomes established first?
2. What part of the embryo gives rise to the root of a bean plant?
3. Where are the first leaves of the 3-day-old seedling?

4. What part of the embryo produces the first leaves?
5. What has happened to the cotyledons in the 10-day-old seedling?
6. Where is the seed coat in this plant?
7. Which part or parts of the embryo developed into the stem?
8. How are the first 2 tiny leaves arranged on the stem?

Part C

Procedure

1. Cut a soaked, germinated corn grain lengthwise with the razor blade.
2. Test the cut surfaces with iodine solution. Record the results in your date book.
3. Test the starch agar and plain agar in petri dishes A and B with iodine solution. Record the results in your data book.
4. On petri dish C, 2 or 3 corn grains have started to germinate on starch agar. Each grain was cut lengthwise and the cut surfaces were placed on the starch agar for about 2 days. Petri dish D also contains starch agar and corn grains, but these have been killed. Remove the corn grains from both petri dishes.
5. Cover the surface of the starch agar in each dish with iodine solution.
6. After a few seconds, pour off the excess.

Discussion

1. When you tested the cut surface of corn grains what food was present?
2. What other foods might be present in corn that were not demonstrated by the test?
3. What difference did you observe when you tested the agars in petri dishes A and B?
4. Suggest hypotheses that might account for the appearance of the areas in petri dish C that were covered by the germinating corn grains.
5. What kind of food would you expect to find in the clear areas?
6. What did you observe in petri dish D?

For Further Investigation

1. Devise an experiment that might give evidence for your hypotheses in number 4.

18.11 Primary Growth Increases the Length of the Plant

Plants continue to increase in size throughout their lives. A plant grows in length and in diameter, or girth. Growth in length is called **primary growth** and produces primary tissues. Primary tissues are always herbaceous, or nonwoody. Young plants contain only primary tissues. Growth in girth is called **secondary growth.** Secondary tissues increase the diameter of the plant and are often woody.

In plants, cells that have differentiated do not usually duplicate. Instead, new cells are formed by specialized tissues called **meristems** (MER ih stemz) that are found throughout the plant. A meristem is a tissue that undergoes mitosis and cell division to form other cells and tissues. Cell division continues in the meristems as long as the plant lives. Meristems are located at the tip, or **apex,** of stems and roots; in buds; and between the xylem and phloem along the length of a stem.

Figure 18.21 Diagram showing location of principal meristems.

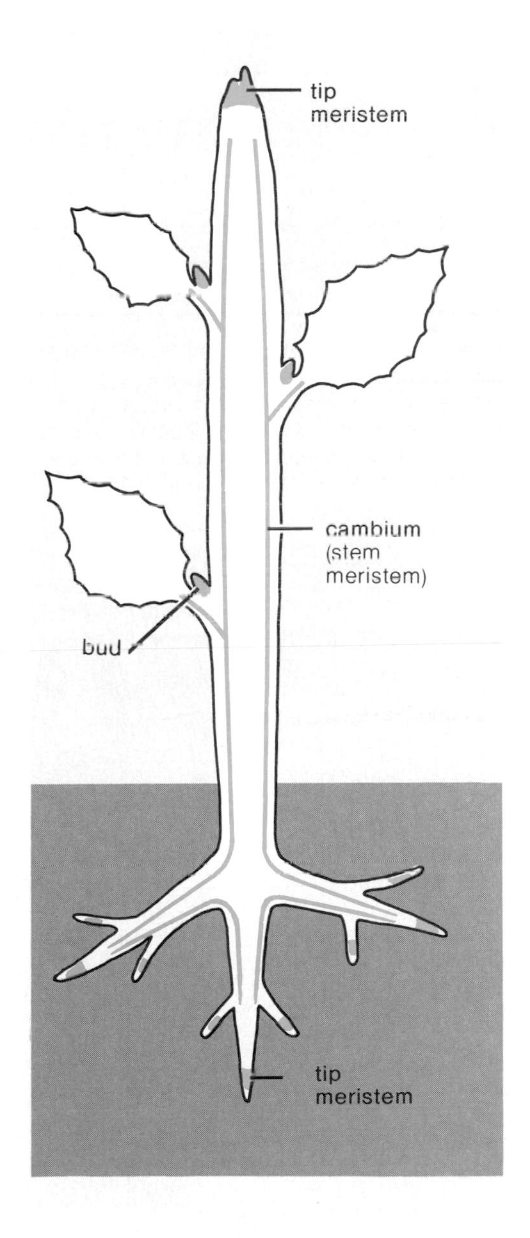

The meristem responsible for stem elongation is at the apex. Just behind the meristem is a zone of elongation in which the newly formed cells grow longer. Behind this is a zone in which the cells differentiate into all the specialized tissues of the stem. Thus, the meristem gives rise to all stem tissues, including the cambium that produces new xylem and phloem cells.

The meristem responsible for root elongation is located just behind the **root cap,** a layer of protective cells covering the root tip. Part of this meristem forms the root cap cells, which are rubbed off as the root pushes through the soil. The root meristem also forms cells that differentiate into all the specialized root tissues. The meristems in the root and stem tips increase the length, or primary growth, of the plant. Thus, a plant grows from its top upward and from its bottom downward. You can observe growth of a root in investigation 18.4.

In most leaves all the cells differentiate into the leaf tissues (including xylem, phloem, and mesophyll) at an early stage in leaf formation. In late summer deciduous woody plants develop tiny, fully formed leaves inside their buds. The next spring the buds open and the new leaves expand mostly by the enlargement of the small cells. Leaves of grasses and some other plants are an exception: they grow continually from a meristem at the base of the leaf. These plants evolved where they were constantly grazed by large herbivores. The meristem at the leaf base is an adaptation that allows the plant to survive repeated grazing: a leaf can grow even after most of the blade has been bitten off.

Figure 18.22 (a) A longitudinal section of a stem tip. Notice the correspondence between the zones here and in the root at the right. The differentiation of vascular tissue appears to take place independently in the stem and in the young leaves. (b) A longitudinal section of a root tip. How well do the zones of growth and differentiation correlate with the changes in spacing of India ink marks on the root in investigation 18.4?

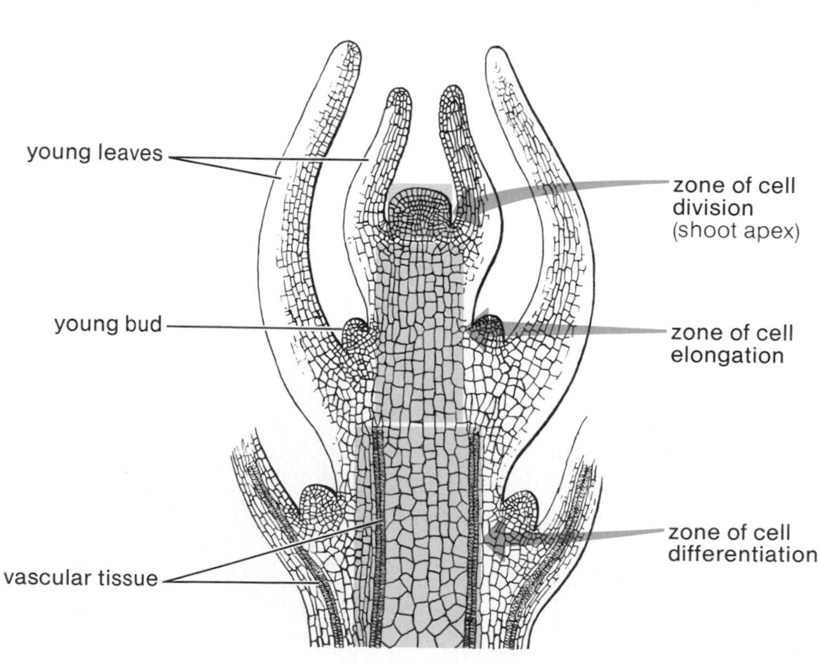

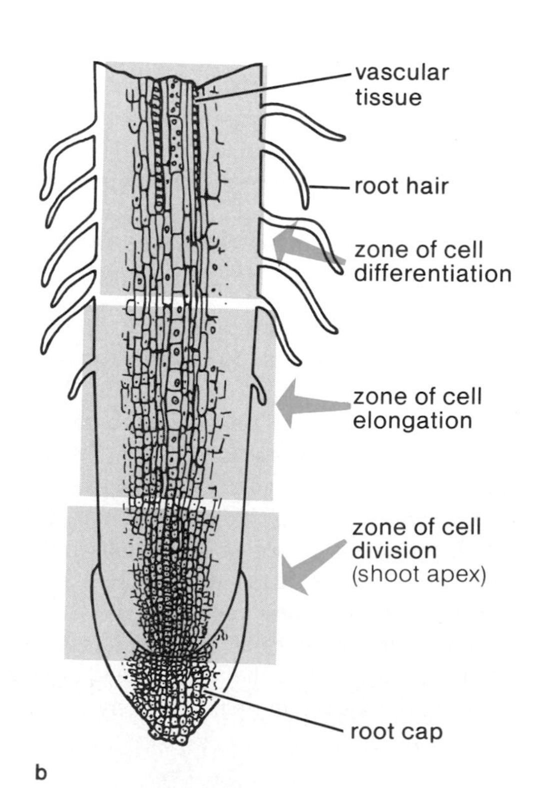

Investigation 18.4 ROOT GROWTH

Introduction

In this investigation, you will observe the growth patterns of corn seedlings just a few days after they have germinated. Are all parts of the root involved in growth? Do any parts of the root grow faster than others?

Materials (per team)

2 petri dishes
4 pieces filter paper (to fit petri dishes)
12 germinated corn seeds
glass-marking pencil
fingerprint ink or any waterproof ink
distilled water
single-edge razor blade
8 cardboard tags
metric ruler
toothpick

Day 1

Procedure

1. Place a piece of filter paper in the bottom of each of 2 petri dishes marked with your team's symbol and label them dish 1 and 2. Add distilled water to dampen the paper. Pour off any excess water.
2. Select 4 seedlings. Using a toothpick and ink, carefully mark the shortest root with a straight, very narrow line exactly 2 mm from the tip. (You do not have to mark the entire circumference of the root.) Be careful not to crush or damage the root. Draw as many lines as possible, 2 mm apart, behind this 1st mark. Repeat for the other 3 roots. All roots should have the same number of marks.
3. Measure the distance from the tip to the last mark. This is the initial root length.
4. Carefully place your 4 marked seedlings on the moist filter paper in petri dish 1. Place them so that the markings are visible.
5. Mark the remaining 8 seedlings as follows: using a toothpick and ink, place a dot 5 mm from the tip of each root. Be sure to handle the roots carefully, and do not let them dry out.
6. Using a razor blade, cut off 1 mm of the tip of 2 corn seedling roots; cut off 3 mm of the roots of 2 others; cut off 5 mm of 2 others. Leave the remaining 2 seedlings untreated.
7. Label each seedling as to the amount of root cut off. To do this, use a small cardboard tag tied to each seedling. Place all of these seedlings in petri dish 2.
8. Cover the seedlings in both dishes with a piece of filter paper. Add water to moisten them. Press down lightly to ensure that the paper is firmly placed in the dishes. Then pour off any excess water. Place the dishes away from direct sunlight and heat. Do not let the paper dry out during the experiment.

Day 2

Procedure

1. After 24 hours, uncover the seedlings you prepared in dish 1. Examine each seedling. Measure the distance between the tip of the root and the last mark. Measure the distances between each of the lines, in order, from the tip to the base. Record your measurements.

2. Note the appearance of all the lines. Are all the lines as clear as they were yesterday?
3. Discard these seedlings, and clean or discard the dishes.

Discussion

1. Add together the lengths of all 4 roots, from tip to last mark. Divide by 4. Subtract from this length the initial root length in procedure 3 from Day 1. What is this average amount of growth for each seedling?
2. In your roots, did growth occur at the tip, at the base, or all along the root?
3. (a) How much growth occurred between the tip of the root and the 1st mark?
   (b) Between the last 2 marks?
4. How do you explain the smears or wider marks at or near the tip of the roots?
5. On the basis of these results, what do you predict will be the results of cutting off the root tips?

Day 3

Procedure

1. After 2 days, examine the roots in petri dish 2. Measure and record the distance from the original 5 mm mark to the tip of the root for each seedling.
2. Discard the seedlings and clean or discard the dish.

Discussion

1. Add the measurements for the 2 seedlings that were not cut and determine the average. Has there been any growth in these 2 seedlings?
2. Prepare a bar graph of the class data showing the amount of growth of the roots cut at 1 mm, 3 mm, and 5 mm. Compare with the growth of the uncut roots.
3. How important is the tip for growth of the root?
4. What information do these observations give you that the earlier observations did not?

For Further Investigation

1. Is the growth pattern of peas or beans the same as that of corn? Germinate some of these seeds and conduct the same experiment that you did on corn.
2. Design and carry out an experiment to measure the growth rate of a leaf of a common houseplant.

18.12 Secondary Growth Increases the Diameter of a Plant

Vascular cambium is the meristem responsible for secondary growth. Located between the xylem and phloem in the stem and root, vascular cambium continues to produce new xylem and phloem cells throughout the life of a plant. Because these new cells increase the diameter of the stems and roots, this process is known as secondary growth.

Ray cells, thin-walled living cells in the xylem and phloem, allow for horizontal transport in large stems. Pits in the walls of ray cells communicate with pores in both xylem and phloem. Ray cells supply water and minerals to the phloem and sugars to the cambium cells.

Figure 18.23 Section of a woody stem. How old was this tree? What separates bark from wood?

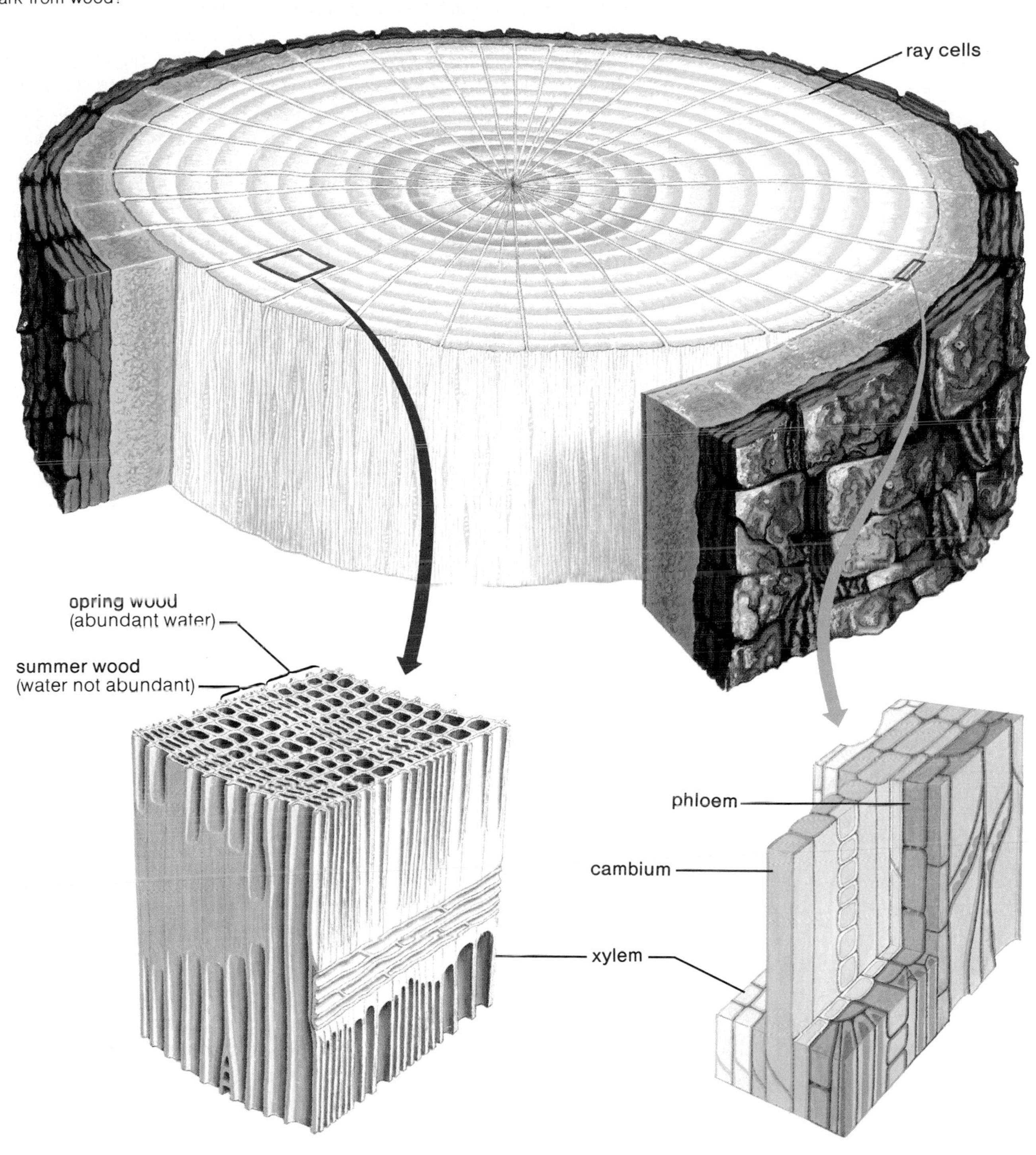

Phloem cells, which are much more fragile than xylem cells, are crushed each year as the stem increases in diameter. The tough xylem cells, on the other hand, remain in the stem, forming a ring of cells each year. These **annual rings** can be used to determine the age of a tree—one year for each ring. Annual rings also can reveal the growing conditions during a particular year. An extremely narrow ring could indicate bad growing conditions during the year the ring was formed. There could have been a drought or an infestation of leaf-eating caterpillars. In either case, the tree was unable to grow very much, and, therefore, the ring was small. The annual rings of xylem cells are the wood of the tree.

In older stems, the cambium remains as a boundary between the central core of wood (xylem) and the phloem and bark. Bark is made up of tough, dead cells that protect the thin layers of living phloem and cambium underneath. The rest of the stem of a tree, except for ray cells, is composed of dead cells. Bark forms within the first few years of a tree's life, replacing the epidermis. Bark usually can be peeled easily from a tree trunk because the walls of cambium cells are thin and easily broken.

Self-Review

1. What is the role of the cotyledons in a dicot seed?
2. What are the functions of cambium and other meristems?
3. How does primary growth differ from secondary growth?
4. What can annual rings tell about the life of a tree?

Guidepost: In what ways are roots, stems, and leaves adapted to special environments?

Morphological Adaptations to Different Environments

18.13 Spines Reduce Transpiration

Although the major function of a leaf is photosynthesis, there are many leaves that photosynthesize little, if at all. They have other functions. Stems also may have functions other than support and conduction. These modified leaves and stems are adapted to the environmental conditions in which the plants live. For instance, photosynthesis in a cactus takes place in the stem, and the spines on cacti are actually modified leaves. These leaves are hard, nonphotosynthetic, and often dangerous to touch. Because transpiration occurs mostly from leaves, plants with small leaves lose less water than do plants with large ones. In the dry habitats in which cacti are found, spines reduce water loss. The spines also help protect the cactus from herbivores.

In some plants, spines are modified stems. Examples are the spines of the hawthorn (*Crataegus*) and honey locust trees (*Gleditsia*), seen in figure 18.24b.

Figure 18.24 (a) Cactus spines, which are modified leaves. (b) Locust spines, which are modified stems.

Gordon E. Uno

BSCS by Doug Sokell

Figure 18.25 A succulent of the genus *Sedum*.

BSCS by Faith Hickman

18.14 Some Leaves Are Involved in Storage, Support, and Nutrient Collection

Many plants in dry habitats have modified leaves or stems that store water. Such **succulent** (SUK yoo lent) plants have juicy tissues, and water actually can be squeezed from them. After a rainstorm the roots of succulents quickly absorb more water than the plant can use immediately. The water then is stored within the leaves of succulents such as the *Sedum* in figure 18.25, and within the stems of cacti. The leaves also have a waxy cuticle so thick it can be scraped off with a fingernail. The cuticle helps to hold in the stored water until the plant needs it.

Figure 18.26 This tendril is a modified stem.

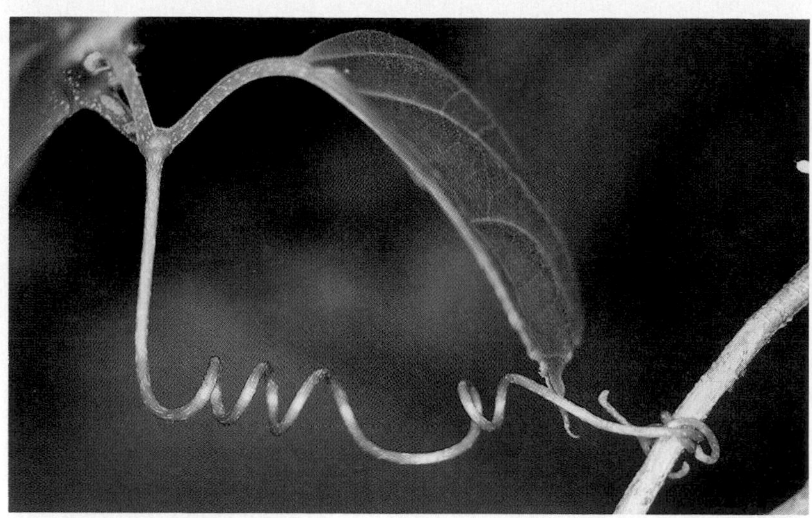

Gordon E. Uno

Although roots are important storage organs for many plants, in some plants the stems and leaves are modified for storage. An onion bulb is a small stem with modified leaves attached. The upper part of each leaf is green and produces sugars through photosynthesis. The bottom part of the leaf is white (underground) and stores the sugars in the form of starch. Another starch-containing modified stem is the white potato.

Tendrils can be either modified stems or leaves. A **tendril** is a whiplike organ that supports a plant by growing around an upright structure as shown in figure 18.26. A grape has a stem tendril, and a sweet pea has a leaf tendril. Without tendrils these plants could grow only along the ground, shaded by other plants above. With tendrils they are able to grow off the ground where more light is available.

Bogs are watery habitats with soil that often lacks nitrogen. Yet most bogs are populated with great numbers of plants—including insectivorous plants. These plants have leaves adapted for their environment. The Venus's-flytrap, the sundew, and the pitcher plant are all bog plants. Each has different modified leaves that help attract and capture insects. The insects are then digested within the leaf, and their nutrients, including nitrogen-containing compounds, are absorbed by the plant. In this way, insectivorous plants can live in the nitrogen-poor soils of the bogs.

Figure 18.27 The leaves of the sundew are adapted to capture and digest insects.

John D. Cunningham/VISUALS UNLIMITED

Self-Review

1. What advantage do small leaves have over large leaves in a dry habitat?
2. In what way are the leaves of succulents and the leaves of onions alike?
3. What advantage do plants with tendrils have over those that do not have them?
4. How do leaves of insectivorous plants help them live in nitrogen-poor soils?

Summary

Each part of a flowering plant is adapted for a specific function. The leaf uses carbon dioxide, water, and light in photosynthesis. The mesophyll of the leaf is organized so that light and carbon dioxide can reach all the cells. Water loss through transpiration is reduced by the action of guard cells surrounding the stomates. The arrangement of the vascular tissues in stems provides support as well as transport of materials to all parts of the plant. Roots anchor the plant in the soil, and their thousands of root hairs are specialized to absorb water and minerals. Water moves through the root cells until it reaches the xylem, where it is pulled up the root and stem by the force of transpiration. Pressure created by the sugar-water solution in phloem cells moves sugar to non-photosynthesizing parts of the plant. Leaves, stems, and roots may be modified for a variety of other functions as well.

A flowering plant begins its life as an embryo within a seed. The seed germinates, and the seedling develops characteristic plant structures. The plant grows in length and girth, forming new cells in meristems throughout its body. Growth depends on the production of sugars in photosynthesis and is regulated by the coordination of external and internal factors. We will examine those processes in the next chapter.

Application Questions

1. Water lily plants are rooted in mud at the bottom of ponds, but their leaves float on the water surface. How might the cellular structure of the roots, stems, and leaves of water lilies differ from that in terrestrial vascular plants?
2. In what ways do the usual environments of a plant root and a plant shoot differ?
3. What are the principal substances that pass into and out of plants through the leaves? What are the forces involved with this movement?
4. During the growing season farmers spend considerable time cultivating their crops—loosening the soil between plants. What advantage does this have for the crop plants?
5. How would you distinguish a root, a leaf, and a stem from each other?
6. Explain how root hairs illustrate the biological principle of the complementarity of structure and function.

Problems

1. Investigate how growth in plants differs from growth in animals.
2. Ten years ago a farmer built a fence 1.5 m high and attached one end of it to a tree that was 7 m high. Now the tree has grown to a height of 14 m. How far above the ground is the attached end of the fence? Explain.
3. In a middle-latitude biome, a pine and an apple tree are growing side by side. Compare amounts of water lost by these two trees and their growth rates throughout the year.
4. The following questions concern lateral growth in woody stems:
   (a) Within a given biome, how would the annual ring formed in a wet year differ from one formed in a dry year?
   (b) Sometimes two rings are formed in one year. How might that happen?
   (c) What is the science of dendrochronology and how is it used?
   (d) Would you expect to find annual rings in the bark of the tree? Why, or why not?

Suggested Readings

See also the Suggested Readings for Chapter 19.

B. H. Beard, "The Sunflower Crop" *Scientific American* (May 1981). Comprehensive article dealing with the plant itself and its importance in worldwide agriculture.

R. E. Cook, "Long-lived Seeds" *Natural History* (February 1979). Interesting, well-illustrated article dealing with dormant seeds.

R. Robinson, "Rings of Flowers" *BioScience* (June 1986). Uniquely Californian, vernal pools host a diversity of endemic species often threatened by their habitat's destruction.

T. E. Weier, C. R. Stocking, M. G. Barbour, and T. L. Rost, 1982, *Botany: An Introduction to Plant Biology* (New York: John Wiley and Sons). Well-illustrated text deals extensively with flowering plants.

BSCS

Sunlight absorbed by these willow leaves provides energy for photosynthesis.

CHAPTER 19

The Flowering Plant: Maintenance and Coordination

Introduction

Although plants may seem to be fairly simple organisms, they are complex systems made of millions of cells. Like all living and growing cells, plant cells require energy to do their work and to maintain themselves. Energy is made available for cellular work through the process of cellular respiration, as we have seen in chapter 15. In that process, energy stored in sugars is transferred to ATP. The energy is first stored in sugars during photosynthesis, the process by which green plants convert light energy to chemical energy. In addition to sugars, photosynthesis provides the oxygen gas necessary for cellular respiration. Thus, photosynthesis maintains not only the plants themselves, but also all the consumers of the biosphere.

Each plant cell has a function that contributes to the life of the entire plant. Activities of all the individual plant cells must be coordinated in order for the plant to grow, mature, flower, and form fruit. That coordination is provided by a variety of plant growth substances called hormones. In this chapter, we will study some of the internal activity or functioning of plants, which is called **plant physiology** (fiz ee OL uh jee).

Photosynthesis

Guidepost: How is the sun's energy changed into chemical energy in photosynthesis?

19.1 Photosynthesis Takes Place in Chloroplasts

Photosynthesis is a series of reactions in which plants use the sun's energy to synthesize complex, energy-rich molecules from smaller, simpler molecules. In eukaryotic cells, all of these reactions take place in the structures known as chloroplasts. Even when removed from the cell in a laboratory, chloroplasts can carry on the entire process of photosynthesis by themselves.

Figure 19.1 Electron micrograph of a chloroplast in a leaf of timothy grass. ×31,000. The drawing shows the structure of a granum enlarged still more.

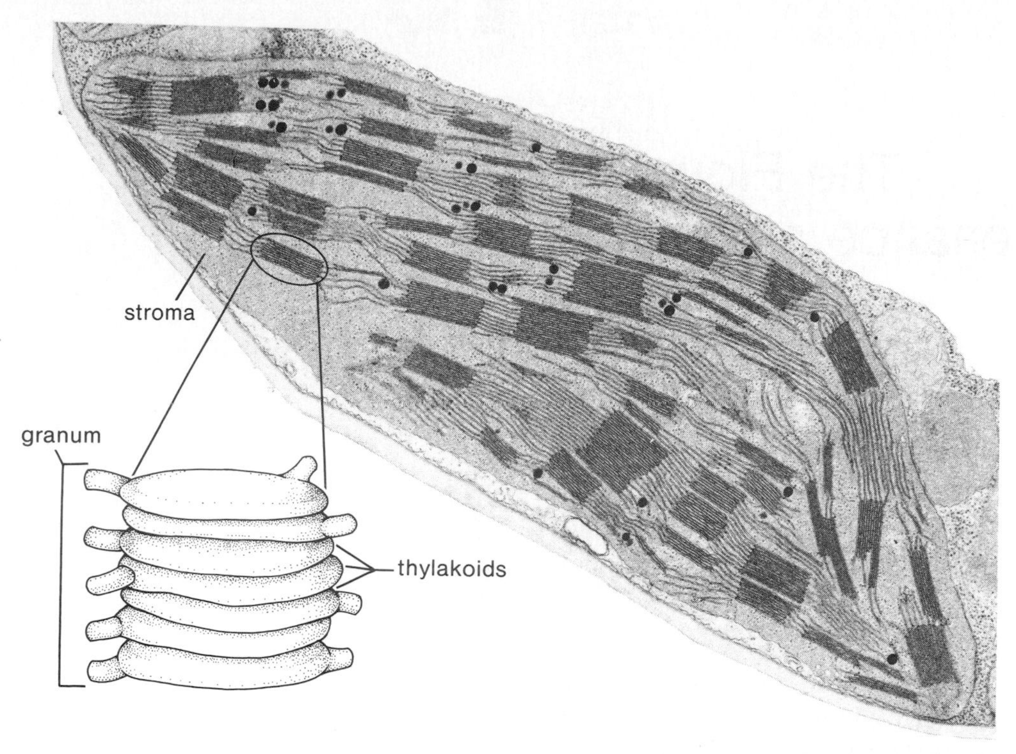

W. P. Wergin/BPS/TOM STACK & ASSOCIATES

The internal structure of chloroplasts is revealed in electron micrographs such as the one in figure 19.1. They show a highly organized array of internal membranes composed of flattened sacs called **thylakoids** (THY luh koyds). Many of the thylakoids are arranged in stacks, forming structures called **grana** (GRAY nuh) (singular: granum). Chlorophyll, other pigments, and enzymes are embedded in the thylakoids. Between the thylakoids is a colorless substance, the **stroma** (STROH muh). Other enzymes, DNA, RNA, and ribosomes are present in the stroma.

19.2 Light Is Used in Photosynthesis

Life on earth continues only because our sun constantly releases light energy. Some of that energy travels the 93 million miles to the earth. Of the sunlight that reaches our planet, only about one percent is actually involved in photosynthesis. Some of the sunlight is absorbed or reflected by clouds or dust in the earth's atmosphere. Much of the light energy that reaches the earth is absorbed and then radiated back into space.

Visible light is only a small fraction of light energy, as can be seen in figure 19.2. The visible light consists of a spectrum of colors, each with a different wavelength and energy content. Red light has the longest wavelength and the least energy; violet has the shortest wavelength and the most energy of visible light.

Figure 19.2 Radiations from the sun form a continuous series, from those of very short wavelengths to those of very long wavelengths. Different parts of the series have been given names. The range of radiations that organisms can detect with their eyes—visible light—is roughly the same range used by plants.

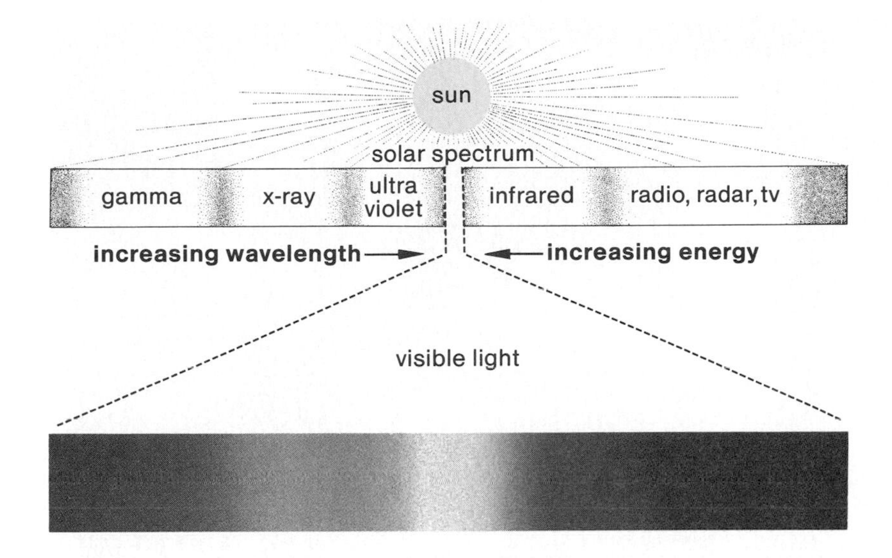

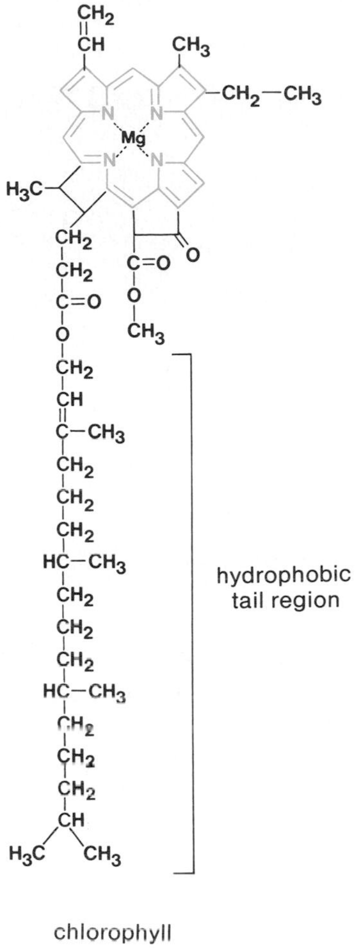

When light strikes an object, it may be transmitted, absorbed, or reflected. Light energy is absorbed by several different pigments in plant cells. Each pigment is a chemical compound that absorbs only certain wavelengths of light and reflects or transmits all others. Green plants, for example, appear green because chlorophyll absorbs most wavelengths of visible light except green. Most of the green light is reflected.

Chlorophyll is the complex green pigment molecule found in all plants. Five different kinds of chlorophylls are known, all of which appear green. Scientists think that chlorophyll *a,* the most common and most important, is present in all photosynthetic plants. The other four chlorophylls, *b, c, d,* and *e,* may be present in different plants in different combinations.

An **absorption spectrum** (ab SORP shun SPEK trum), such as the one in figure 19.4, is a simple graph that shows the percentage of light absorbed by a pigment at each wavelength or color. As you can see, all of the chlorophylls absorb much of the light in the blue-violet and orange-red wavelengths, but very little or none in the green-yellow wavelengths. Plants can utilize only the energy from absorbed wavelengths. The **action spectrum** at the top of figure 19.4 shows this clearly. An action spectrum measures the rate of photosynthesis at certain wavelengths of light. In those wavelengths that are strongly absorbed, the rate of photosynthesis is high. In green light the rate of photosynthesis is much lower, because chlorophyll reflects those wavelengths.

In addition to chlorophylls, plants may contain other pigments. These are called accessory pigments because they work with chlorophyll to trap and absorb additional wavelengths of light. Their absorbed light energy is transferred to chlorophyll for use in photosynthesis. Some of the accessory pigments are responsible for fall coloration of leaves and become more visible as the chlorophyll content declines. In investigation 19.1, you will be able to observe some of those pigments.

Figure 19.3 The structure of chlorophyll.

hydrophobic tail region

chlorophyll

Figure 19.4 The upper curve shows the action spectrum for photosynthesis. The lower curves show absorption spectra for chlorophylls *a* and *b*. It is clear from the graph that both the chlorophylls absorb the wavelengths of light used in photosynthesis. What wavelengths (colors) do these chlorophylls absorb least?

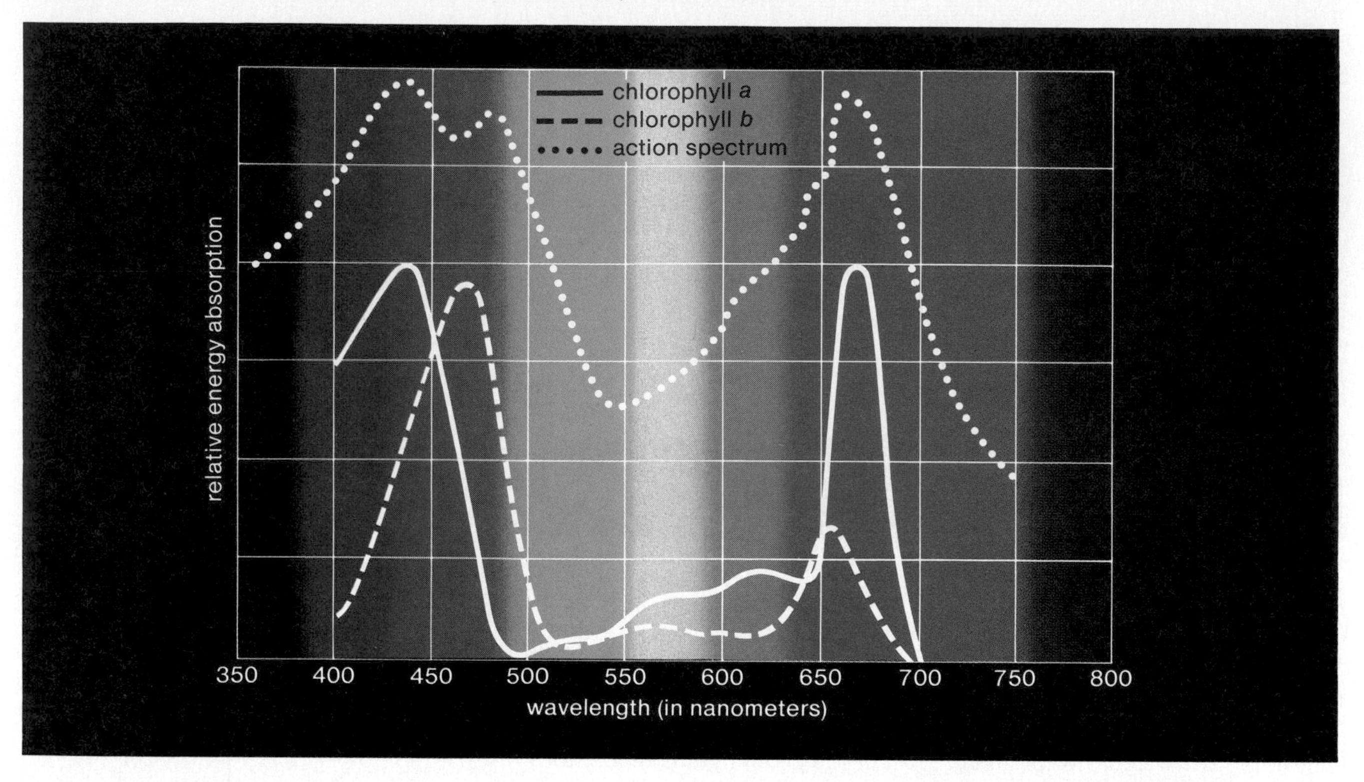

Figure 19.5 These coleus leaves contain visible accessory pigments.

BSCS by Carlye Calvin

Biology Today C

Florist

Rick Rigg's hobby is also his life's work; he owns a florist shop and greenhouse. Rick was studying biology in college when he started working at a florist shop. Rick received his master's degree in biology, but he became so interested in the business of growing plants that he left the university and bought the shop before finishing work on his Ph.D.

In his shop Rick has many young potted plants. He realizes, however, that it is often hard for a customer to imagine what the young plants will look like when they mature. To help his customers, he has placed full-grown plants next to the young ones, all growing in the right light conditions. People may come in and choose the small inexpensive plants. They can see that, in time and with proper care, their plants can be tall, healthy, and beautiful.

Rick offers plants in a variety of colors, shapes, and sizes. He grows many of today's popular houseplants in his greenhouse. Rick thinks one of the most rewarding and delightful aspects of his job is to be able to produce a plant from a seed or cutting, watching with satisfaction as it grows to full form. The job requires an understanding of plant physiology, ecology, and horticulture. There is a lot of common sense involved, too.

One area of the greenhouse is devoted entirely to cactus plants. Another is devoted to exotic flowering plants from the tropics. Rick also has several very uncommon plants. Many of these are only for display, such as the *Dioscorea,* which looks like a large turtle shell, in the photo on the right.

The Riggses' home is right behind the shop. That makes it easy for Rick, his wife, Carol, and their children to work at the shop. High school students work there part-time, as do college students who are majoring in plant biology. Some students earn work-study credits through their work in the greenhouse. They may help plant and landscape the garden, arrange displays, or help maintain displays by removing dead leaves and blossoms. Their work provides experience that can lead to careers in related fields, such as landscaping.

BSCS by Carlye Calvin

For their shop Rick and Carol have built an outdoor botanic garden with a beautiful pond and walkways through an herb and vegetable garden, with hanging baskets decorating the area. It just so happens that all this is the Riggses' backyard, too.

The Riggs family have found that working together can be enjoyable and profitable—as long as you have "green thumbs."

BSCS by Carlye Calvin

Investigation 19.1 SEPARATION OF LEAF PIGMENTS

Introduction

Chlorophyll is the most obvious pigment in leaves. Five different chlorophylls have been identified as *a, b, c, d,* and *e.* Chlorophyll *a* is believed to be present in all photosynthetic plants. The other chlorophylls may be present in different plants in various combinations. Accessory pigments also may be present, but are masked by chlorophyll. In this investigation you will use a process called thin layer chromatography (TLC) to separate the pigments of a leaf.

Materials (per team of 2)

2 prepared TLC plates
1 chromatojar containing chromatographic solution
2 Pasteur pipets
1 dark-colored jar with cover containing leaf extract

Procedure

Part A—Placing Extract on Slide

1. Place a Pasteur pipet into the leaf extract and allow the solution to move into the pipet by capillary action.
2. Place the pipet on the silica gel layer about 1 mm from the bottom of the slide and allow the solution to run onto the gel.
3. As soon as the spot of solution dries, add another drop of solution to the spot.
4. Repeat this procedure until a dark green spot is obtained.

Part B—Developing the Slide

1. Place the slide in the chromatojar containing the solution and quickly cover. Separation of the pigments will occur in 3 to 4 minutes.
2. When the leading edge of the solvent nears the top of the silica gel, remove the slide from the chromatojar and allow to dry.

Discussion

1. Is there any evidence that more than 1 pigment is present in the leaf extract you placed on the gel slide?
2. Examine the chromatogram (separated pigments on the slide). How many bands of color can you see?
3. How many bands might be made up of chlorophylls?
4. What other colors can you see in the chromatogram?
5. Why were you unable to see these colors in the leaf?
6. Suggest a hypothesis to explain the change of color that often occurs when a leaf dies.
7. From what point did all the pigments start as the developing solution began to rise?
8. When did the pigments start to move, and when did they stop?
9. In what characteristic, then, must the pigments have differed?

19.3 Photosynthesis Involves Many Interdependent Reactions

Three major events occur in photosynthesis: (1) absorption of light energy, (2) conversion of light energy to chemical energy, and (3) storage of chemical energy in sugars. The reactions by which those events occur may be considered in two distinct but interdependent groups: the light-dependent reactions and the Calvin cycle. Those reactions are summarized in figure 19.6.

In the **light-dependent reactions** light energy is absorbed and converted to chemical energy in short-lived energy-rich molecules. These molecules are then used to make 3-carbon sugars from carbon dioxide in the series of reactions known as the **Calvin cycle.** In this cycle, chemical energy is stored in the sugars, and new carbon is incorporated into the plant for future growth.

The overall reactions of photosynthesis may be summarized as follows:

$$\underset{\left(\substack{\text{carbon}\\\text{dioxide}}\right)}{3\,CO_2} + \underset{\text{(water)}}{3\,H_2O} \xrightarrow{\text{light energy}} \underset{\left(\substack{\text{3-carbon}\\\text{sugar}}\right)}{C_3H_6O_3} + \underset{\left(\substack{\text{oxygen}\\\text{gas}}\right)}{3\,O_2}$$

This summary equation indicates only the major raw materials and some of the end products. It does not show the many chemical steps and other substances involved. The next sections explain those steps in more detail.

Figure 19.6 Diagrammatic summary of the reactions of photosynthesis.

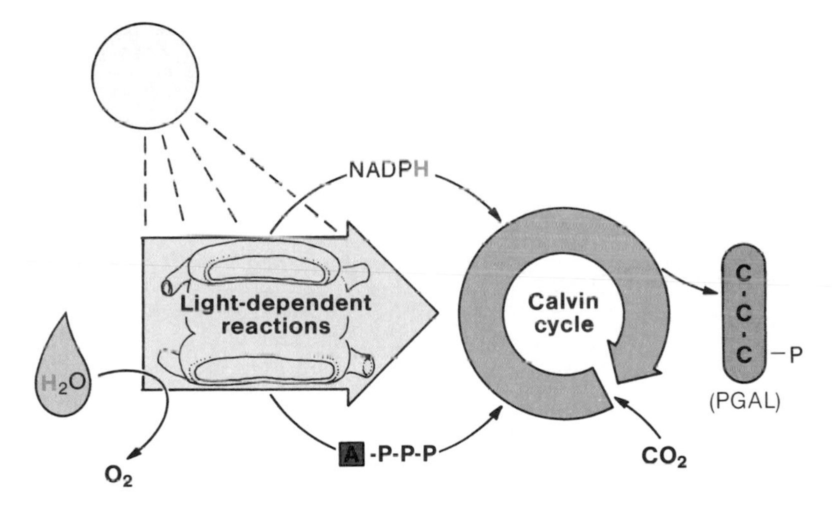

19.4 Oxygen Gas Is a By-Product of the Light-Dependent Reactions

In the light-dependent reactions, light energy is absorbed by two groups of pigments embedded in the thylakoid membranes. These pigment groups are called Photosystems (PS) I and II. They are connected by an electron transport system similar to the one in cellular respiration. Both photosystems absorb light, but of slightly different wavelengths. When light energy is absorbed, chlorophyll molecules in both systems lose energy-rich electrons, which are captured by carrier molecules. Water also is separated into oxygen, protons, and electrons. These reactions are summarized in figure 19.7.

A flow of electrons is set up. Electrons from water replace the ones lost by PS II. Electrons lost by PS II replace the ones lost by PS I. As electrons are passed from carrier to carrier along the electron transport system, some of the energy they originally captured from the sun is used to make ATP from ADP and phosphate. When that occurs, light energy has been converted to chemical energy.

Figure 19.7 The light-dependent reactions of photosynthesis. Electrons flow from water to PS II to PS I to NADP+. ATP is formed as electrons flow between the two photosystems. The NADPH that is formed has a hydrogen ion and two electrons originally derived from water.

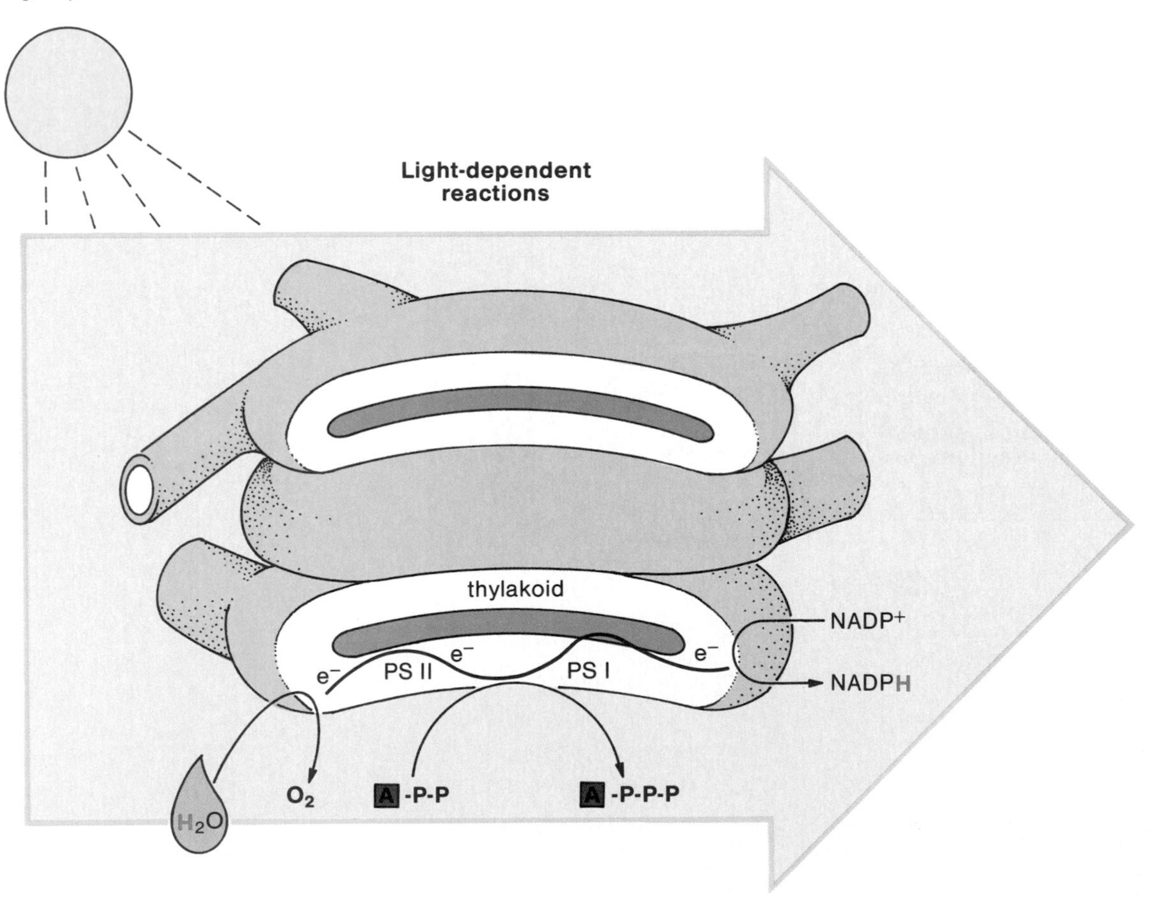

At the end of the electron flow, the electrons, along with protons from water, combine with a hydrogen carrier called **nicotinamide adenine dinucleotide phosphate** (nik uh TEE nuh mid AD uh neen DY NOO klee oh tyd FOS fayt), **$NADP^+$.** $NADP^+$ is very similar to NAD^+, which serves as a hydrogen carrier in cellular respiration. When electrons and protons combine with $NADP^+$, NADPH is formed. The oxygen from water is given off as oxygen gas, O_2.

In the light-dependent reactions, the first two events of photosynthesis occur: absorption of light energy and conversion of light energy to chemical energy. Three products are formed. One is oxygen gas, which is released to the atmosphere through the stomates of the leaf. The other two are the energy-rich molecules ATP and NADPH, both of which are used in the Calvin cycle.

Figure 19.8 Structure of $NADP^+$. Compare this to the structure of NAD^+ in figure 15.10, p. 547.

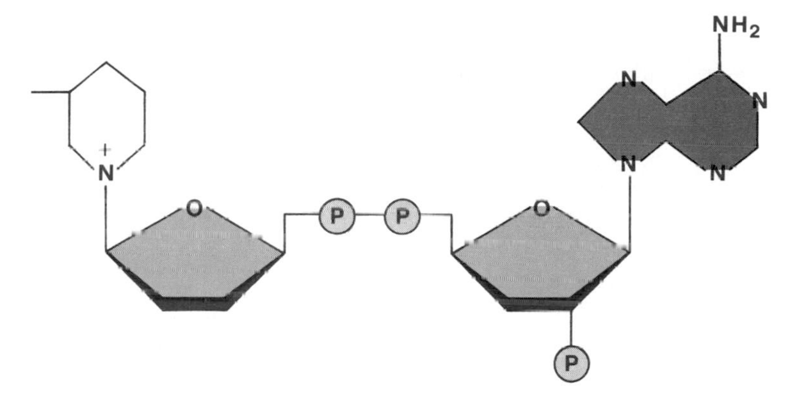

Figure 19.9 Algae giving off bubbles of oxygen.

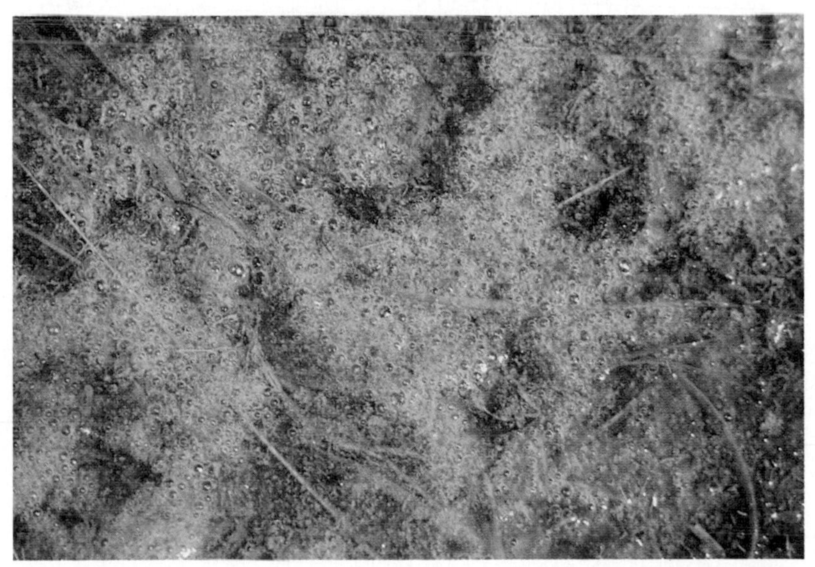

John D. Cunningham/VISUALS UNLIMITED

19.5 Sugars Are Formed in the Calvin Cycle

The reactions of the Calvin cycle do not involve the absorption of light energy. However, they do require the products of the light-dependent reactions, ATP and NADPH. The Calvin cycle is a series of reactions in which carbon dioxide is combined with the hydrogen split from water in the light-dependent reactions. Energy for these reactions is provided by the ATP formed in the light-dependent reactions.

The reactions of the Calvin cycle take place in the stroma of the chloroplasts. To begin the cycle, a molecule of carbon dioxide combines with a 5-carbon molecule, forming a 6-carbon molecule that immediately splits

Figure 19.10 A summary of the reactions in the Calvin cycle, and of the ways that PGAL can be used.

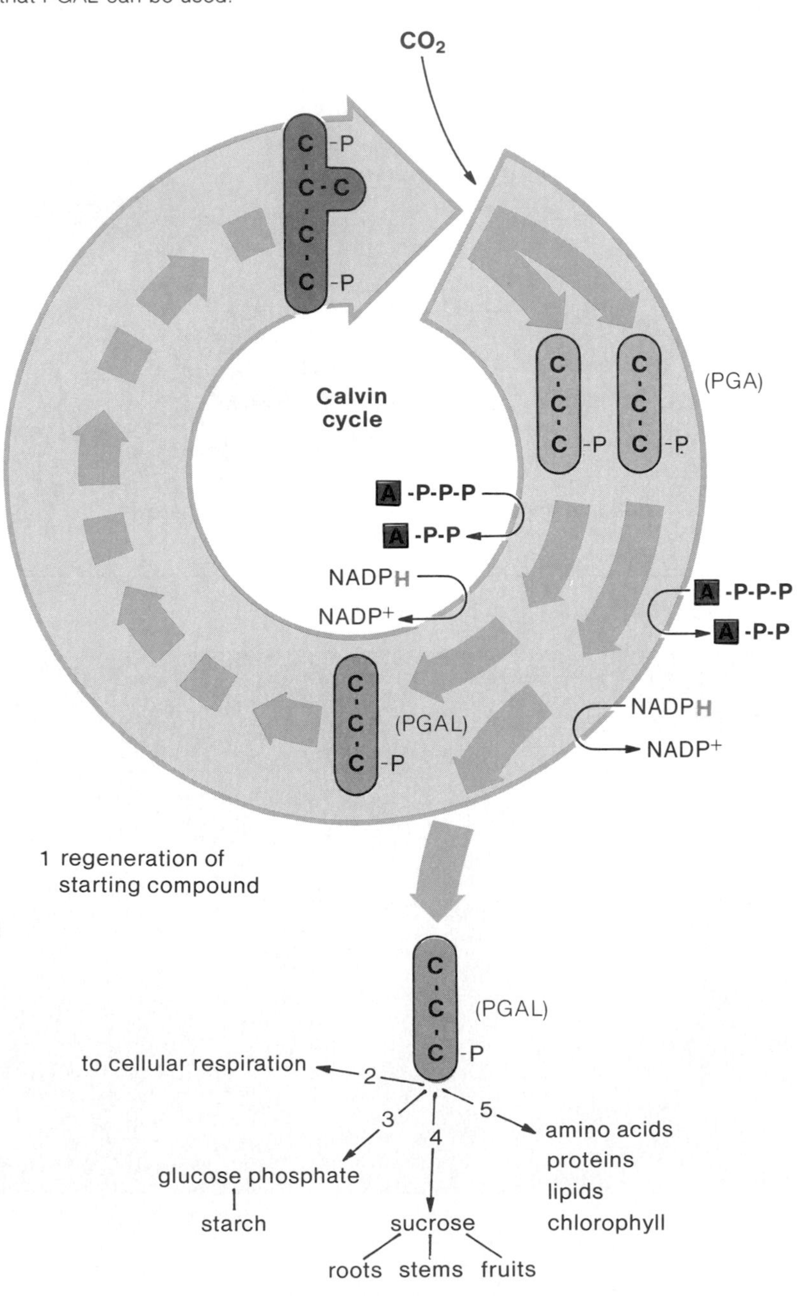

into two 3-carbon molecules. Each of those accepts a hydrogen from NADPH and a phosphate group from ATP to form a 3-carbon sugar called **phosphoglyceraldehyde** (fos fo glis uh RAL deh hyd), or **PGAL.** PGAL is the first stable, usable sugar formed from carbon dioxide in the Calvin cycle. Those reactions are summarized in the diagram in figure 19.10.

Several things can happen to the PGAL. First, it can undergo many transformations in the Calvin cycle to regenerate the original 5-carbon molecule with which the cycle began. Without that molecule, the cycle would stop. Second, the PGAL can leave the chloroplast and enter the pathway of glycolysis and cellular respiration to provide energy for the cell. Third, two molecules of PGAL can combine to form a molecule of glucose-phosphate. Many molecules of glucose-phosphate are combined to form starch, the major plant storage compound. Fourth, the PGAL can be used to make the sugar sucrose, which is transported, via phloem, to roots, stems, fruits, and growing regions of the plant. Last, PGAL can be used to synthesize amino acids, proteins, lipids, chlorophyll, enzymes, and other compounds used in the plant cell. Thus, in the Calvin cycle, chemical energy is stored in sugars, as well as in other compounds synthesized by the plant cells.

The Calvin cycle and the Krebs citric acid cycle are similar in involving many rearrangements of carbon chains. Both provide carbon skeletons for use in biosynthesis reactions. Carbon dioxide is used in the Calvin cycle and released in the Krebs cycle. ATP is used in the Calvin cycle and formed in the Krebs cycle, and NADPH is used in the Calvin cycle while NADH is produced in the Krebs cycle. Relationships between photosynthesis and respiration are summarized in figure 19.11.

Figure 19.11 The relationships between photosynthesis and cellular respiration.

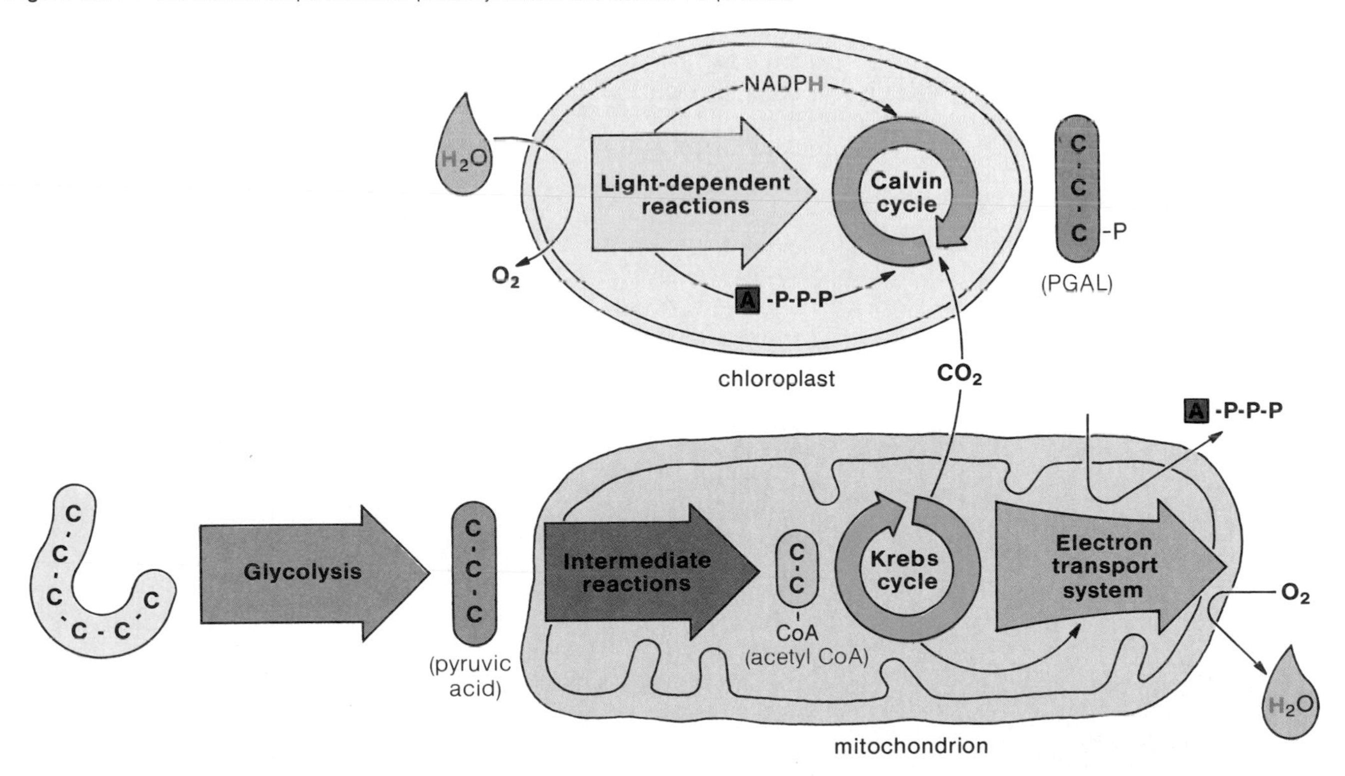

Self-Review

1. Why is chlorophyll considered the most important plant pigment?
2. What are accessory pigments, and what role do they play in photosynthesis?
3. What is the difference between an absorption spectrum and an action spectrum?
4. What major events occur in the light-dependent reactions? In the Calvin cycle?
5. What are the major products of the light-dependent reactions of photosynthesis?

Investigation 19.2 GAS EXCHANGE AND PHOTOSYNTHESIS

Introduction

Following the principles of diffusion, carbon dioxide would normally flow into a leaf during the day and oxygen would flow out as photosynthesis proceeds. In this investigation, you will disrupt the normal gas exchange process and observe the effects.

Materials (per team)

For Part A

fresh leaves, several kinds
single-edge razor blade
microscope
microscope slide
coverslip
forceps
dropping pipet

For Part B

2 potted plants
alcohol (95%)
iodine solution
xylene
3 beakers, 400 ml
beaker, 1000 ml
4 petri dishes
forceps
scissors
hot plate
water, at room temperature
petroleum jelly
paper towel
absorbent cotton
white paper

Procedure

Part A—Number of Stomates

1. Tear a leaf at an angle while holding the lower surface upward. The tearing action should peel off a portion of the lower epidermis. It will appear as a narrow, colorless zone extending beyond the green part of the leaf.
2. Using a razor blade, cut off a small piece of this epidermis. Immediately place it in a drop of water on a slide. Add a coverslip. Do not allow the fragment to dry out.
3. Using the low-power objective of your microscope, locate some stomates. Then switch to the high-power objective. Make a sketch to show the shape of a stomate, its guard cells, and a few adjacent cells in the epidermis.
4. Count the number of stomates in 10 different fields of the microscope under high power and average them. (Refer to appendix 2 to calculate the diameter of the high-power field. Use this figure to calculate the area of the leaf observed under the microscope.) Calculate the average number of stomates per mm^2 of leaf surface.
5. In the same manner, count the stomates on the upper epidermis of the same leaf. Examine as many other kinds of leaves as possible. Compare the number of stomates per mm^2 on the upper and lower surfaces of each kind of leaf.

Part B—Light and Photosynthesis

1. Select 2 healthy plants of the same species. Place 1 plant where it will receive no light. Place the other where it will be exposed to sunlight.
2. After 3 days remove a leaf from each plant. Place a small notch in the margin of the illuminated plant.
3. Immediately drop the leaves into a beaker of boiling water.
4. When they are limp, transfer the leaves to a beaker half full of alcohol. Place this beaker in an electrically heated water bath. **CAUTION:** *Never heat alcohol over an open flame or permit its vapor to come into contact with an open flame.*
5. Heated alcohol extracts chlorophyll from leaves. It also makes them brittle, because most of their water is removed. As soon as the leaves are no longer green, use forceps to take them out of the alcohol. Then drop the leaves into a beaker of water at room temperature. After a minute or so, they will become quite soft.
6. Spread each leaf out in a petri dish and cover it with iodine solution.
7. Allow the iodine solution to act on the leaves for several minutes. Then remove both leaves. Rinse them in water, and spread them out in water in petri dishes placed on a piece of white paper. Record the color of each leaf.
8. Select 4 similar leaves on the plant that has been kept in the dark. Do not remove them from the plant. Thoroughly coat the upper surface of 1 leaf with petroleum jelly. (A layer of petroleum jelly, though transparent, is a highly effective barrier across which many gases cannot pass.) Cut one notch in the leaf's margin.
9. Coat a 2nd leaf on its lower surface and cut 2 notches in its margin.
10. Coat a 3rd leaf on both upper and lower surfaces and cut 3 notches in its margin.
11. Do not coat the 4th leaf, but cut 4 notches in its margin. Place the plant where it will be exposed to sunlight.

12. After 3 days remove all 4 leaves and place them on paper towels. Remove the petroleum jelly by gently rubbing the leaves with absorbent cotton saturated with xylene.
13. Following the procedure used before, perform the iodine test on each leaf. Compare the color reactions of the 4 leaves, and record your observations.

Discussion

1. How did the number of stomates per mm^2 in different areas of the same side of a piece of leaf epidermis compare? On opposite sides?
2. Did the stomates vary in the amount they were open? How can you explain this?
3. What would you do to assure a reliable comparison of the number of stomates per mm^2 for 2 species of plants?
4. What do your data suggest about the distribution of stomates in leaves of your species of plant?
5. What assumption must you make in drawing this conclusion?
6. What was the purpose of the 1st set of iodine tests?
7. If you use this test as an indication of photosynthetic activity, what assumption are you making?
8. What is the purpose of the leaf that is marked with 4 notches?
9. In which of the leaves coated with petroleum jelly did photosynthetic activity appear to have been greatest?
10. In which of the leaves did photosynthetic activity appear to have been least? Do your data support your hypothesis?

For Further Investigation

Compare the number of stomates and their locations on leaves of 2 different species. Select 1 species that usually grows in full sunlight and 1 that grows in shade.

Guidepost: How do plant cells obtain energy for cellular activities?

Respiration in Plants

19.6 Fermentation Is Less Efficient than Aerobic Respiration

As we have seen, the sugars produced in photosynthesis can be used as a source of energy and of carbon building blocks for the plant. Cellular respiration in plant cells is essentially the same as in animal cells. We saw in chapter 15 that in the presence of oxygen much of the energy from sugars, as well as from fats and proteins, can be used to make ATP molecules. When oxygen is lacking, however, the reactions of the Krebs cycle and the electron transport system stop. Under such anaerobic conditions, much less usable energy is made available.

In animals, aerobic respiration of 1 glucose molecule usually forms 36 ATP molecules. (In plants, slightly more ATP may be formed.) By contrast, under anaerobic conditions only 2 ATP molecules are produced per 1 glucose molecule. Under these conditions, both animal and plant cells carry out **fermentation** (fer men TAY shun), or anaerobic respiration. Glycolysis continues, but the pyruvic acid is converted to lactic acid or alcohol. Animal muscle cells form lactic acid. Plant cells usually form alcohol, but can form lactic acid as well. A general equation for fermentation is shown below.

$$ADP + P + \underset{\text{(3-carbon sugar)}}{C_3H_6O_3} \xrightarrow{\text{enzymes}} \begin{cases} ATP + \underset{\text{(lactic acid)}}{CH_3CH(OH)COOH} \\ ATP + \underset{\text{(carbon dioxide)}}{CO_2} + \underset{\text{(alcohol)}}{C_2H_5OH} \end{cases}$$

Wineries make use of this process. In anaerobic containers yeast cells ferment grape sugar to alcohol in wine. The yeast in the wine eventually are killed by their own waste product, alcohol, when kept in anaerobic conditions. As soon as the yeast die, the alcohol content of the wine stops increasing.

The cells of most organisms can survive only a short time on the limited amount of energy released by anaerobic respiration. Eventually the cells will die, unless oxygen becomes available for the more efficient aerobic respiration to take place. Some organisms, however, exist entirely by anaerobic respiration. Many of the bacteria described in chapter 11 are anaerobic. Organisms such as yeast can exist well anaerobically, but if oxygen is available, they switch to the more efficient aerobic method. Large organisms, such as humans and trees, require the large amounts of energy made available in aerobic respiration.

Figure 19.12 Yeast cells produce a dustlike "bloom" on these grapes. When the grapes are crushed, the yeast cells mix with the juice. Under anaerobic conditions, the yeast break down the sugar in the grape juice to alcohol.

BSCS by Doug Sokell

Figure 19.13 The rate of photosynthesis depends on the amount of CO_2 available, the intensity of light, and the temperature.

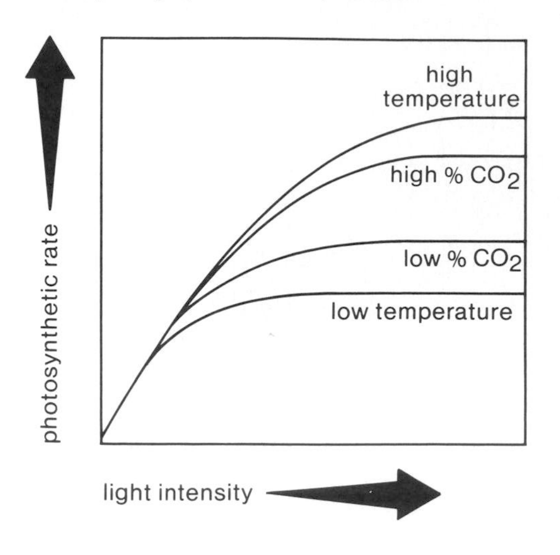

Figure 19.14 The comparative rates of photosynthesis and respiration in leaves of Irish potato.

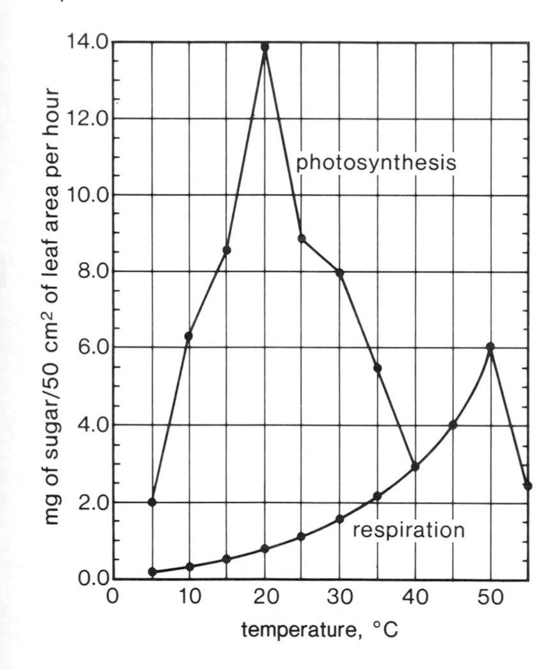

19.7 Many Environmental Factors Affect Photosynthesis and Respiration

Many environmental factors affect the rates of respiration and photosynthesis. If any of those factors is present at less than optimum levels, that factor limits the rate of the reaction. For example, at optimal temperature and carbon dioxide concentration, the rate of photosynthesis is limited by the light intensity. If temperature and light intensity are optimal, then carbon dioxide concentration becomes the limiting factor. And if light intensity and carbon dioxide concentration are adequate, the temperature controls the overall rate of photosynthesis. You can observe how some of these factors affect the rate of photosynthesis in investigation 19.3.

In general, higher temperatures speed up, and lower temperatures slow down, the rate of chemical reactions. For instance, potatoes are good crops for Idaho, but not for southern Florida, because of the temperature during the growing season. The rate of photosynthesis drops sharply at temperatures above 20° C, whereas the rate of respiration continues to increase, as shown in the graph in figure 19.14. That means that more sugars are used up by respiration than are being produced by photosynthesis. Thus, the potato tuber can store little sugar as starch. In the cooler north, however, the rate of photosynthesis in potatoes is higher than the rate of respiration, and potatoes grow very well. In addition, low temperature stimulates a plant to store food in tubers or fruits.

Photosynthesis provides both the carbon compounds to build cells and the chemical energy that cellular respiration uses to produce ATP molecules. Those ATP molecules then are used for maintenance and growth of cells within the plant. The growth of a plant is controlled by a variety of growth regulators called plant hormones. In the next section we will discuss the most important plant hormones and some of the ways they interact with environmental factors.

Self-Review

1. Compare the amounts of energy trapped in ATP by aerobic respiration and fermentation.
2. How do wineries use the process of fermentation?
3. Why can few organisms live using only fermentation?
4. What are some of the environmental factors that affect rates of respiration and photosynthesis?

Investigation 19.3 PHOTOSYNTHETIC RATE

Introduction

There are several ways that the rate of photosynthesis can be measured. This investigation calls for the use of a sprig of elodea, a common aquatic plant. You may want to collect and use some other aquatic plant found in your area. If you live near the coast, you may even want to try to measure the photosynthetic rate of seaweed in seawater. After all, most of the photosynthesis on earth takes place in the ocean.

Materials (per team)

2 rubber stoppers, 2-hole, no. 4
2 glass tubes, 8 cm long
4 pieces of new rubber tubing, 6 cm lengths
2 screw-type pinch clamps
2 glass tubes, 20 cm long
2 pipets, 1 ml
2 test tubes, 22 mm × 175 mm
2 l beaker
250 ml flask
drinking straw
2 sprigs of young elodea, 15 cm
2 ring stands
2 ring stand clamps
syringe with fine needle
lamp with 150 watt light bulb

Procedure

Part A—Manometric Assembly

Prepare 2 manometers as shown in figure 19.15.

1. Fill a 2 l beaker with tap water and let stand while assembling the rest of the apparatus.
2. Insert an 8 cm long glass tube into 1 of the holes of each rubber stopper.
3. To the outside end of each tube, attach a 6 cm length of rubber tubing to serve as a mouthpiece.
4. Put a screw-type pinch clamp on each mouthpiece.
5. Into the other hole of each stopper, insert a 20 cm long glass tube so that it reaches almost to the bottom of the test tube that will become part of the manometer.
6. To the outside end of each tube, attach a 6 cm length of rubber tubing.
7. Connect a 1 ml pipet to each piece of tubing.
8. Put 125 ml of distilled water into a flask and use a drinking straw to blow your breath into the water for 2 minutes.
9. Place 2 sprigs of elodea, cut end up, into 1 of the test tubes (experimental tube).
10. Fill both tubes with the water that you bubbled into earlier.

Figure 19.15 Manometer set up.

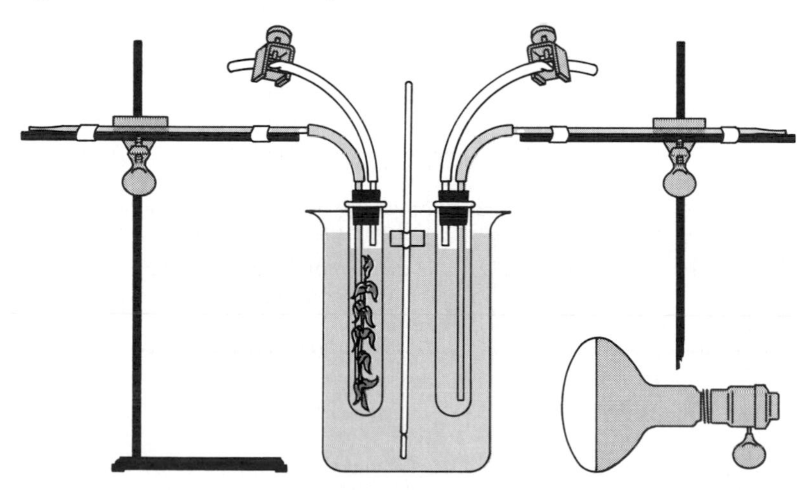

11. Press a 2-hole stopper assembly tightly into each test tube. Close the screw clamps partway.
12. Stand the test tubes in the 2 l beaker you filled with water in step 1 of these procedures so that the water just covers the outside surface of the 2-hole stopper.
13. Support the pipets in a horizontal position by means of the ring stands and ring stand clamps, as shown in figure 19.16.
14. Blow gently through the mouthpiece until the water comes out the end of the pipet. Close the screw clamp completely while blowing. (If the water backs out of the pipet into the test tube, it means there is a leak somewhere in the system. Check all fittings to be sure they are tight.)
15. Let the entire assembly stand for about 10 minutes to permit temperature equilibration throughout the system.
16. During this time, introduce a *small* air bubble into each pipet at the end where it is attached to the test tube portion. To do this, gently force the fine needle of an empty syringe into the rubber tubing, which connects with the pipet, and inject a *small* bubble of air. Use the mouthpiece to move the air bubble into the pipet so it can be seen.

Part B—Basic Photosynthetic Rate

1. Use the scale on the pipets to record the position of 1 end of the air bubble in each manometer.
2. Place the lamp 30 cm from the beaker and illuminate the 2 manometers.
3. Use the scale on the pipets to record the position of the air bubbles in each pipet every 2 minutes over a period of 20 minutes.

Part C—Effects of Light Intensity on Photosynthetic Rate

Repeat the procedures of part B with the light source 10 cm and 50 cm away from the manometer assembly.

Discussion

1. What is the purpose of the 2nd manometer set-up?
2. What chemical change occurred in the water that was bubbled into for 2 minutes?
3. What is produced in the test tubes that causes the air bubble to move in the pipets?
4. The test tube without the elodea is called a thermobarometer. What 2 environmental factors are being controlled by this set-up?
5. How would you use the distance the thermobarometer air bubble moved to correct the distance the experimental air bubble moved?
6. Use the corrected distance the experimental air bubble moved and calculate the volume of O_2 produced during the 20-minute period. Determine the rate of photosynthesis by calculating O_2 produced per minute.
7. Plot the data. What variable goes on the horizontal axis? What variable goes on the vertical axis?
8. Calculate the volume of O_2 produced with the light source 10 cm and 50 cm away from the manometer assembly. Plot this data on the graph you prepared in discussion number 7.

Biochemical and Environmental Control of Plant Growth

Guidepost: How are chemicals involved in plant growth and development, and what role does the environment play?

19.8 Plant Hormones Interact to Regulate Plant Processes

As a plant grows, it increases in size, but it also differentiates, forming a variety of cells, tissues, and organs. Although genes determine the basic form of a plant, the environment can strongly modify its development. Many of a plant's activities are coordinated with the changing seasons. Regulatory substances (hormones) produced by the plant play critical roles in these responses. Plant growth and development thus depend on the interaction of many internal and external factors.

Figure 19.16 Some of the hormonal interrelationships among various portions of a plant.

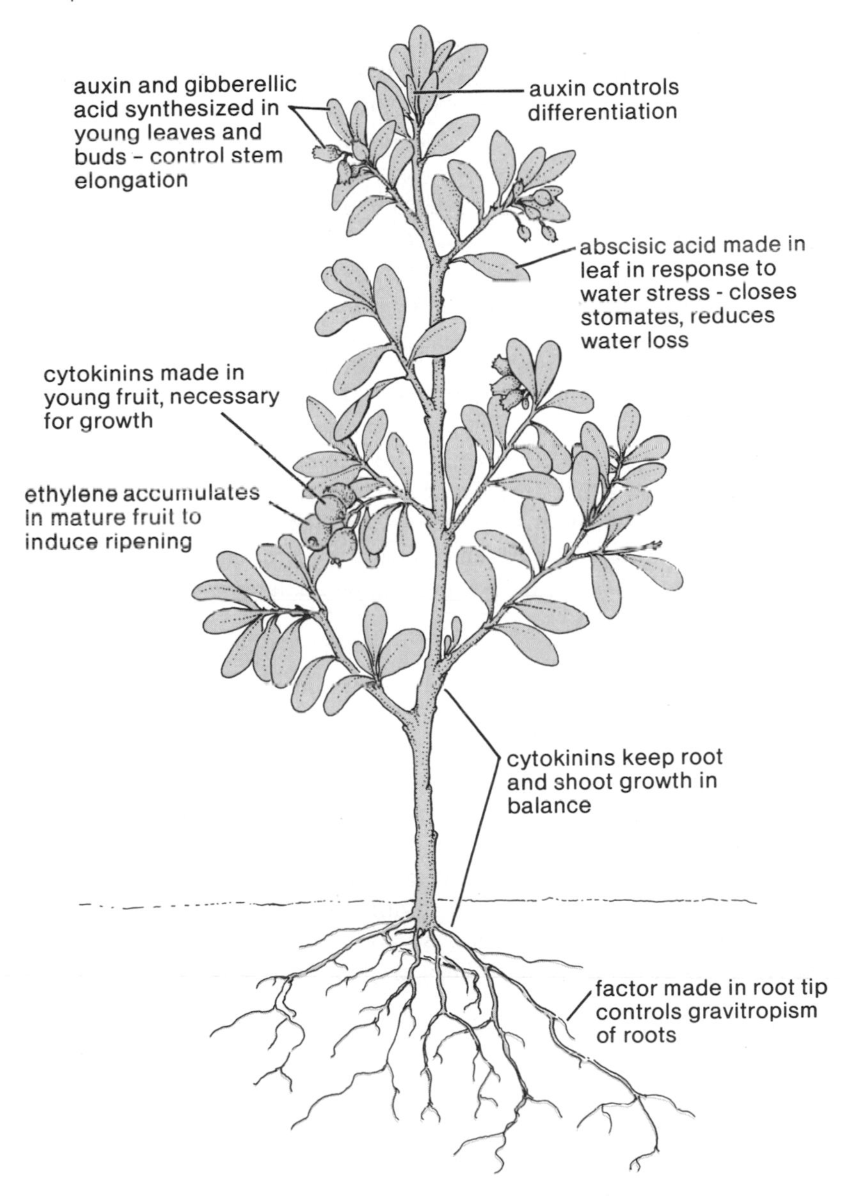
auxin and gibberellic acid synthesized in young leaves and buds - control stem elongation
auxin controls differentiation
abscisic acid made in leaf in response to water stress - closes stomates, reduces water loss
cytokinins made in young fruit, necessary for growth
ethylene accumulates in mature fruit to induce ripening
cytokinins keep root and shoot growth in balance
factor made in root tip controls gravitropism of roots

Plant hormones have a number of characteristics in common. First, they are produced in one place and transported to another place, where they exert their effects. Second, they are produced and are effective in extremely small amounts. Third, hormones may interact with other hormones or chemical substances to bring about a particular response. Many plant processes require interaction among several hormones. Finally, a plant hormone may affect the responses of many plant parts, and each part may respond differently to the hormone. In general, the response to a particular hormone is influenced by a variety of factors, including concentration and the presence of other hormones. These characteristics have made it extremely difficult to determine the roles of the hormones in the plant. Although physiologists have been experimenting for more than 100 years, many questions remain unanswered.

19.9 Auxins Influence Many Aspects of Plant Growth

Five groups of plant hormones are presently recognized. The first of these to be discovered was the **auxins** (AWK sins), in particular one auxin that seemed to cause curvature of certain stems toward the light, as we will explain in section 19.12. Today physiologists have identified one to perhaps three naturally occurring auxins, and they have synthesized several others.

Auxins are thought to be produced in actively growing regions such as the tip ends of shoots. They are moved by active transport to other parts of the plant. Auxins may cause cells in the growing region of the shoot to elongate. In contrast, the same concentration of auxins applied to root cells inhibits their elongation. Root cells elongate only in response to extremely low concentrations of auxins. Thus, the effect of an auxin appears to depend on its concentration as well as on the particular plant part it acts on.

Auxins can be applied to cuttings to stimulate the formation of **adventitious** (ad ven TISH us) **roots.** An adventitious root is one that arises from an unusual place, such as from a stem that has been cut off a plant and placed in water. When such a cutting is placed in water containing a natural or synthetic auxin, root production is stimulated, as in the holly cuttings in figure 19.17.

A synthetic auxin called 2,4-D is used to kill dicot weeds. At the concentrations generally used, 2,4-D does not affect members of the grass family (monocots), so it can be used to control weeds such as dandelions in lawns and grain fields.

Applied auxins also can promote fruit growth. A fruit develops after a flower has been pollinated and its ovules have been fertilized. Normally, if pollination or fertilization does not occur, the fruit will not develop. However, scientists discovered that they could "fool" certain flowers into developing fruit by spraying them with an auxin. The fruit is produced without fertilization, so no seeds develop inside. Seedless tomatoes and cucumbers have been produced this way.

Figure 19.17 The top row of holly cuttings was treated with an auxin. The bottom row was not treated. How might this growth substance be used commercially?

USDA

Figure 19.18 Effect of gibberellic acid (GA_3) on dwarf maize plants. Each dwarf plant was treated with the indicated dosage of GA_3 and allowed to continue growing for seven days. Note the increase in height of the plant with increase in dosage. Normal growth is exhibited by plants treated with 10 and 100 μg GA_3.

B. O. Phinney

19.10 Other Plant Hormones Also Have Diverse Effects

A second group of plant hormones, **gibberellins** (jib uh REL ens), was discovered many years ago when Japanese rice farmers noticed that rice plants sometimes grow gigantically tall and then fall over and die. Japanese botanists studied this "foolish seedling" disease and found that the rice plants were infected with a fungus. The fungus produced a chemical that caused the strange growth of rice. Many plants are now known to produce their own gibberellins. In fact, more than 60 gibberellins have been identified. When treated with gibberellins, many kinds of plants grow to double or triple their normal height. However, the stems are very thin and the leaves are often pale.

Natural gibberellins may be involved in seed germination. After a seed has absorbed water, the embryo begins to produce gibberellins. The hormone appears to trigger the production of enzymes that digest the stored food in the seed, converting it to sugars and amino acids. These are then absorbed and used by the developing embryo. Gibberellins also cause certain plants to **bolt,** or to produce flowers and seeds prematurely (figure 19.19). Bolting in garden plants such as spinach and cabbage is

Figure 19.19 Bolting caused by gibberellic acid. The cabbage plants at left are untreated. Treatment with gibberellic acid caused bolting and flowering in the plants at right.

Sylvan Wittwer

normally a response to temperature changes, but can be initiated by applications of a gibberellin. Application of gibberellins can cause some flowers to develop seedless fruit. Gibberellins are used commercially to produce larger fruits, as in the grapes seen in figure 19.20.

A third group of plant hormones, **cytokinins** (syt oh KY ninz), promote cell division and organ formation. They are found mostly in plant parts with actively dividing cells, such as root tips, germinating seeds, and fruits. Cytokinins appear to be necessary to promote stem and root growth, as well as chloroplast development and chlorophyll synthesis. Cytokinins and auxins interact closely to regulate the total growth pattern of the plant.

A fourth kind of plant hormone, **ethylene** (ETH ih leen), promotes fruit ripening and aging of tissues. It is different from other hormones because it is a gas. Ethylene was used unknowingly hundreds of years ago by Chinese farmers, who ripened their fruits in rooms in which they were burning incense. The incense produced small amounts of ethylene gas. Ripening fruits and other plant parts produce this hormone. Bananas, tomatoes, and other fruits often are picked while still green and then treated with ethylene to ripen them when they are ready to be sold. In addition to promoting fruit ripening, ethylene appears to inhibit elongation of stems and roots, as well as flowering in most species.

A fifth kind of plant hormone is **abscisic** (ab SIS ik) **acid,** which is thought to be involved in the dormancy of buds and seeds. In the dormant state, seeds are able to survive extremes of temperature and dryness, thus ensuring survival of the embryo. Abscisic acid also affects stomate closing and is sometimes called the stress hormone because it helps protect the plant against unfavorable environmental conditions.

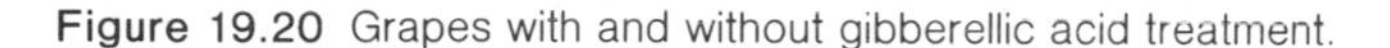

Figure 19.20 Grapes with and without gibberellic acid treatment.

Fred Jensen

Figure 19.21 Mimosa plant before (a) and after (b) being touched.

a BSCS by Carlye Calvin

b BSCS by Carlye Calvin

19.11 Plants Respond to Environmental Stimuli

Although we do not usually think about plants as moving objects, plants do have movements. Plant movements are often the result of differential growth, and most occur in response to stimuli such as changes in the environment. The movements are generally very small and take place over a period of time. It is usually necessary to use time-lapse photography in order to see the movements. Nevertheless, these movements are particularly important to proper growth and development.

Consider some of the more dramatic movements of plants. The rapid closing of a Venus's flytrap leaf is a response to the stimulus of an insect crawling over trigger hairs in the leaf. The insect is quickly trapped within the leaf and then slowly digested by enzymes secreted from the leaf. The sensitive plant, *Mimosa pudica,* has compound leaves. When any part of the leaf is touched, the leaflets droop together suddenly, as shown in figure 19.21. This movement is the result of a sudden loss of water from certain cells at the base of the leaves and leaflets. The significance of this movement is not completely apparent, but it may help to make the plant unattractive to herbivores or to help the leaves conserve water in the droopy condition.

19.12 Tropisms Are Plant Movements

If you leave your houseplants next to a window they will bend toward the outdoors. That is because the most intense light comes through the window. For a long time biologists have observed that most green plants grow toward light. Charles Darwin studied this response, which is called **phototropism** (foh toh TROH piz um). **Tropisms** are movements of plant parts in response to a stimulus. In most plants, tropisms are closely associated with growth and vary according to the intensity of the stimulus.

Figure 19.22 Seedlings bending toward light.

David Newman/VISUALS UNLIMITED

Figure 19.23 Differential elongation of cells on opposite sides of a shoot produces bending.

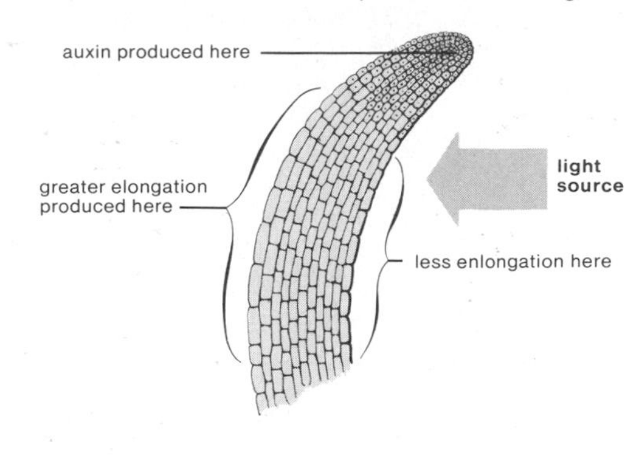

Figure 19.24 One of the classic experiments in coleoptile growth. A very small piece of mica was inserted between the growing tips and the rest of two coleoptiles, one on the left side, one on the right side. One coleoptile was left untouched. The tips of all three plants were illuminated from the right side only. The normal plant grew and curved to the right. The plant with the mica on the right grew in a similar manner. The plant with the mica on the left side failed to grow.

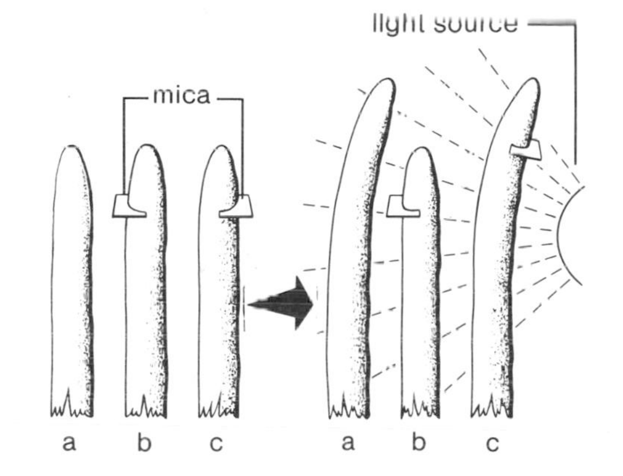

Since Darwin's time, many experiments have been carried out in an attempt to explain the mechanism of phototropism. That mechanism, however, is still unclear. In the phototropic response, cells on the lighted side of the shoot stop growing, while those on the shaded side continue to elongate. That differential growth seems to cause the bending, but what causes the differential growth?

Experiments designed to answer that question have been carried out on grass **coleoptiles** (koh lee OP tilz). A coleoptile is a specialized leaf that forms a sheath around the first true leaves of a monocot. The direction of coleoptile growth is influenced by gravity and light. In uniform lighting or in the dark, grass seedlings grow straight upward, or in the direction opposite to gravity. With one-sided lighting, bending occurs.

Evidence from the experiments indicated that the tip of a growing shoot produces a chemical that causes bending. Darwin's experiments showed that if the tip was covered, the shoot would not bend. Other researchers found that a substance produced in the tip could cause the shoot to bend even in the dark, if placed on only one side of the shoot.

Eventually the substance was isolated and found to be an auxin. It appeared that the auxin was synthesized in the tip and transported to the shaded side, where it stimulated elongation of the cells. That hypothesis is now being questioned, and at the present time it is not clear how, or even whether, light and auxin interact to produce bending.

Gravitropism (grav ih TROH piz um) is growth movement toward or away from the earth's gravitational pull. Stems and flower stalks are negatively gravitropic, that is, they grow in a direction away from gravity. If stems are placed in a horizontal position, they bend upward. The response is variable, and auxins are thought to play a critical role, as are calcium ions. Roots are positively gravitropic, and the evidence indicates that perception of gravity occurs in the root cap. There, plastids filled with starch grains migrate to the bottom of certain cells, and their movement initiates a sequence of events that leads to downward growth or curvature. Again, auxins appear to be involved, along with abscisic acid and, perhaps, other chemicals. You can observe some of these tropisms in investigation 19.4.

Figure 19.25 When an upright plant is turned on its side, in time the roots bend down and the stem bends up. Thus, roots demonstrate positive gravitropism and stems demonstrate negative gravitropism.

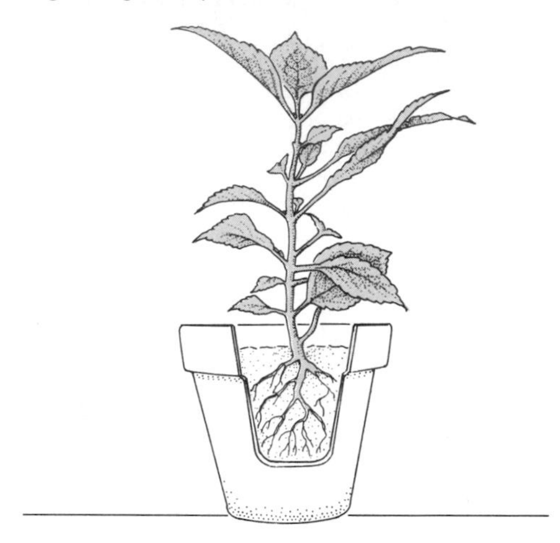

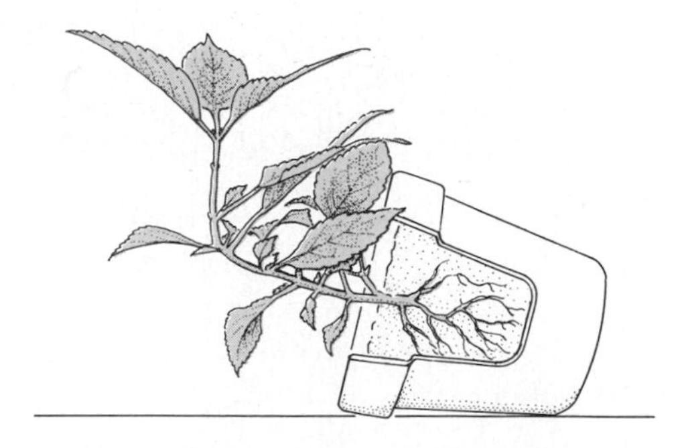

Investigation 19.4 TROPISMS

Introduction

This investigation consists of 2 separate investigations. Each part will be conducted by some teams in each class. Before you begin the part your team will conduct, read through all the procedures for parts A and B and form a hypothesis for each. All members of the class should observe the results and participate in a discussion of the outcome of each part.

Materials (per team)

For Part A

4 soaked corn grains
petri dish
cotton
scissors
heavy blotting paper
cellophane tape
glass-marking pencil
modeling clay

For Part B

4 flowerpots, about 8 cm in diameter
4 cardboard boxes, at least 5 cm higher than the flowerpots
40 radish seeds
soil
red and blue cellophane
scissors
cellophane tape

Part A—Orientation of Shoots and Roots in Germinating Corn

Procedure

1. Place 4 soaked corn grains in the bottom half of a petri dish. Arrange them cotyledon side down, as shown in figure 19.26.
2. Fill the spaces between the corn grains with wads of cotton to a depth slightly greater than the thickness of the grains.

3. Cut a piece of blotting paper slightly larger than the bottom of the petri dish. Fit it snugly over the grains and the cotton.
4. Hold the dish on its edge and observe the grains through the bottom. If they do not stay in place, repack with more cotton.
5. When the grains are secure in the dish, wet the blotting paper thoroughly. Seal the 2 halves of the petri dish together with cellophane tape.
6. Place the dish on edge in dim light.
7. Rotate the dish until 1 grain is at the top. With the glass-marking pencil, write an A on the dish beside the topmost grain. Then, proceeding clockwise, label the other grains B, C, and D.
8. Use modeling clay to support the dish as shown in figure 19.26.
9. When the grains begin to germinate, make sketches daily for 5 days, showing the direction in which the root and the shoot grow from each grain.

Figure 19.26

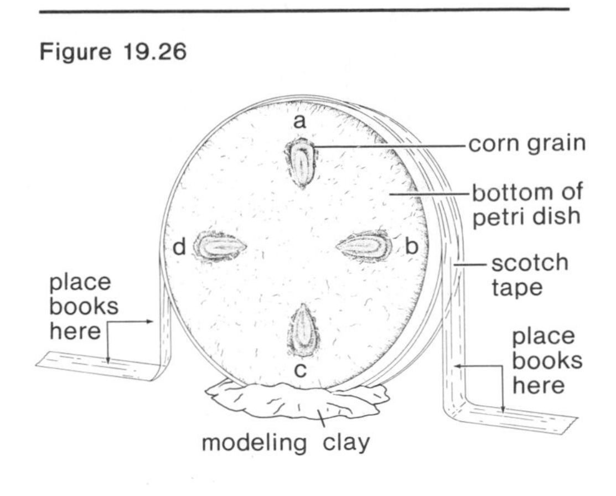

Discussion

1. From which end of the grains did the roots grow?
2. From which end did the shoots grow?
3. Did the roots of all grains eventually turn in 1 direction? If so, what was the direction?
4. Did the shoots of all 4 grains eventually turn in 1 direction?
5. To what stimulus did the roots and shoots seem to be responding?
6. Were the responses positive (toward the stimulus) or negative (away from the stimulus)?

Part B—Orientation of Radish Seedlings

Procedure

1. Turn the 4 cardboard boxes upside down. Number them 1 to 4. Label each with your team symbol.
2. Cut a rectangular hole in 1 side of each of 3 boxes. (Use the dimensions shown in figure 19.27.)
3. Tape a strip of red cellophane over the hole in box 1. Tape a strip of blue cellophane over the hole in box 2. Leave the hole in box 3 uncovered. Do not cut a hole in box 4.
4. Using a pencil, number 4 flowerpots 1 to 4. Label each with your team symbol. Fill the pots to 1 cm below the top with soil.
5. In each pot, plant 10 radish seeds about 0.5 cm deep and 2 cm apart. Press the soil down firmly over the seeds and water the pots. Place them in a location that receives strong light but not direct sunlight.
6. Cover each pot with the box bearing its number. Turn the boxes so the sides with holes face the light.
7. Once each day remove the boxes and water the pots. (Do not move the pots; replace the boxes in the same position.)
8. When most of the radish seedlings have been above ground for 2 or 3 days, record the direction of stem growth in each pot—upright, curved slightly, or curved greatly. If curved, record in what direction with respect to the hole in the box.

Figure 19.27

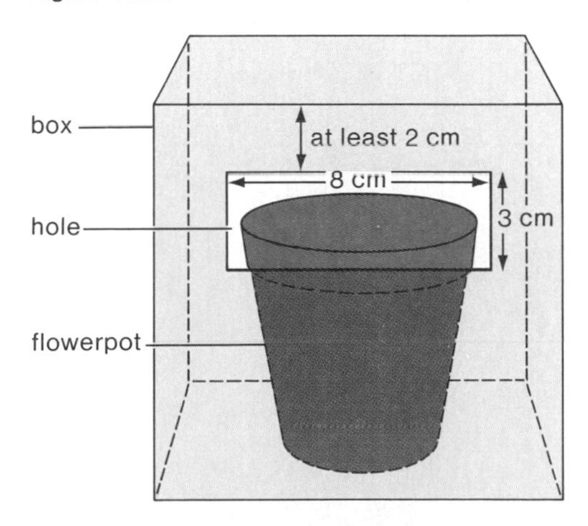

Discussion

1. In which pot were the stems most nearly perpendicular?
2. Were all the stems curved in one direction in any pot?
3. If so, in which pot and in what direction? If not, in what direction did most of the stems curve?
4. To what stimulus do you think the stems responded?
5. What effect, if any, did the red and blue cellophane have on the direction of the stem growth?

For Further Investigation

Will centrifugal force overcome the response of plant parts to gravity? To test this idea, mount the setup used in part A on the turntable of a phonograph.

19.13 Many Plants Respond to the Length of Day and Night

The changing seasons are an important environmental cue for all terrestrial organisms. Birds migrate, insects produce dormant eggs, animals hibernate, and deciduous trees lose their leaves as winter approaches. Those activities are triggered by changes in day length, and organisms have mechanisms that allow them to respond to the relative amount of light and dark in a 24-hour period. This response is called **photoperiodism** (foh toh PIH ree ud iz um).

Many plants show the effects of photoperiodism in flowering. There is no single "best" time for all plants to flower: it depends on the individual species of plant. Spring-flowering plants can reproduce before other plants do. Fall-flowering plants can reproduce after they have grown and stored energy all summer long. Then they can use this energy in the fall

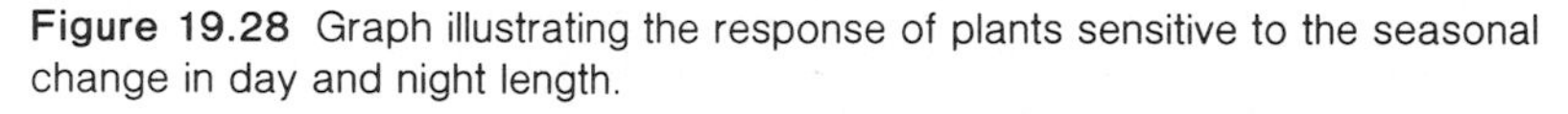

Figure 19.28 Graph illustrating the response of plants sensitive to the seasonal change in day and night length.

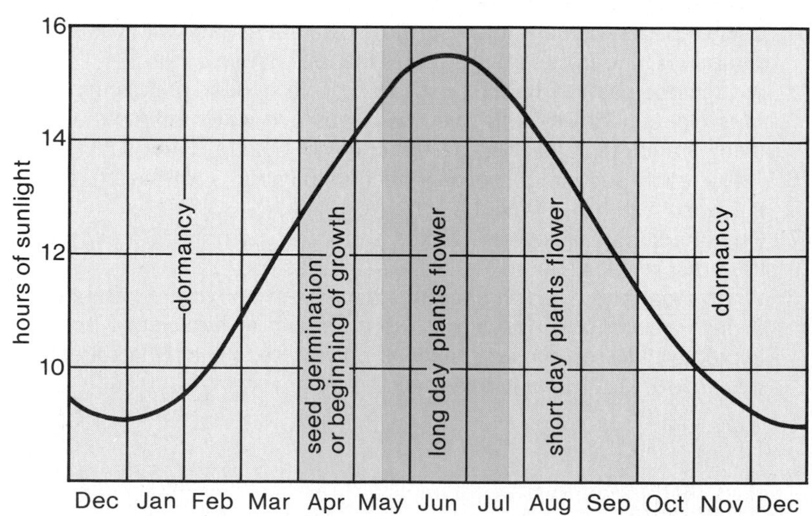

to quickly form flowers, fruits, and seeds before winter comes. Spring-flowering plants flower as the days are getting longer. They are called long-day plants. Fall-flowering plants flower when the days are shorter and are called short-day plants. *Most* plants flower whenever they become mature, regardless of the day length. They are day-neutral, although temperature may play an important role in their flowering.

A plant pigment called **phytochrome** (FYT oh krohm) is involved in photoperiodism. Phytochrome changes from one form to another when it absorbs certain wavelengths of light. In the dark, it changes back to the original form. Depending on the plant, one form or the other will trigger certain responses. In long-day and short-day plants, phytochrome is sensitive to the changing day length and, at the appropriate time, triggers internal changes that bring about flowering.

Figure 19.29 Flowering of some plants is controlled by day length. The columbine (a) is a long day plant, the rose (b) is day neutral, and the aster (c) is a short day plant.

a Doug Sokoll

b Margaret Drucker

c Staley Studio

Figure 19.30 An experiment illustrating the effect of different photoperiods on the flowering of Maryland mammoth tobacco.

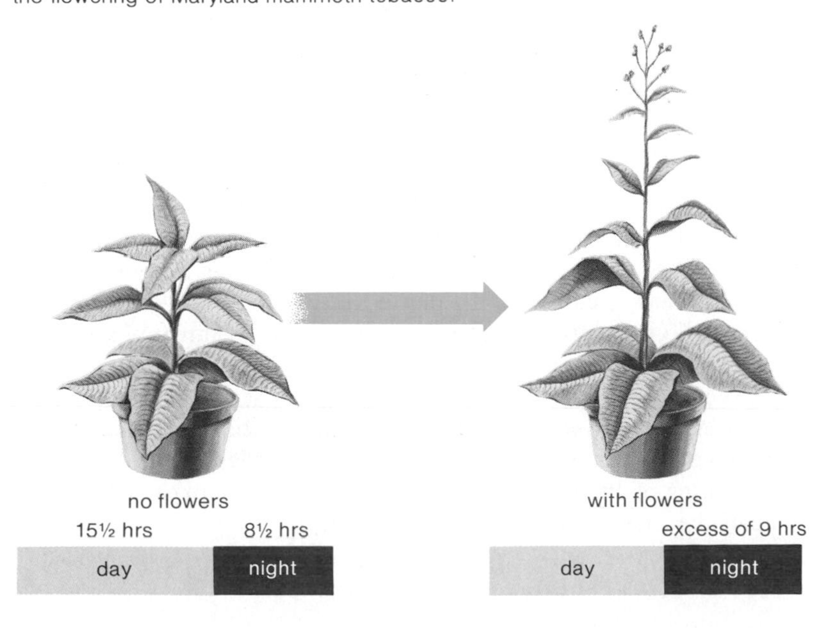

Figure 19.31 Diagram of the effects and interaction of auxin and cytokinin. Pieces of tobacco pith tissues were grown in cultures supplemented with various levels of the two hormones.

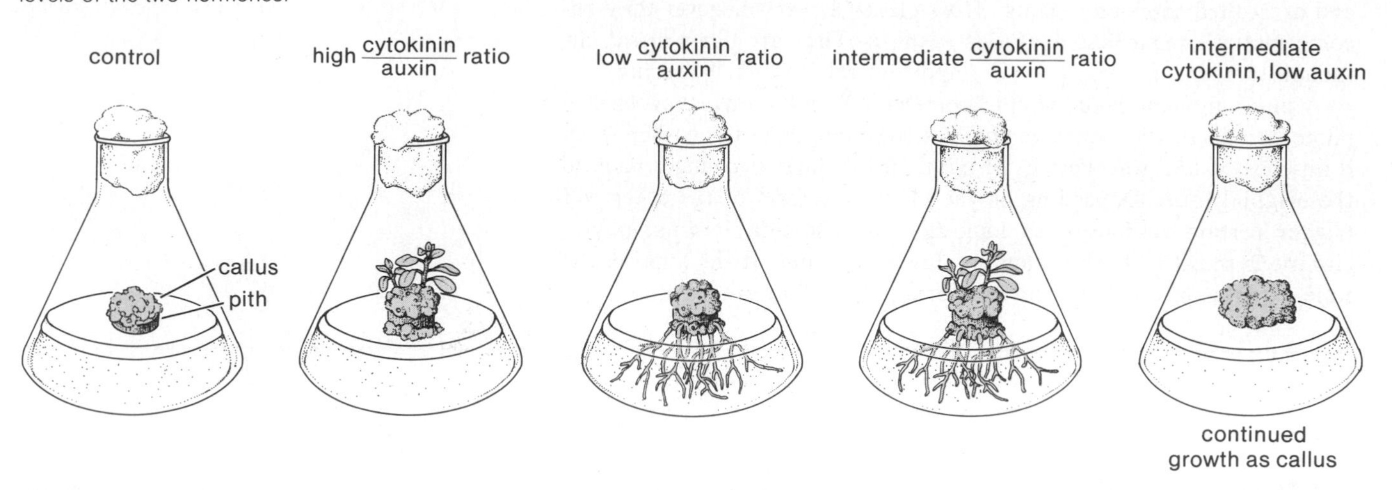

19.14 Knowledge of Plant Hormones Is Important in Research

Use of plant hormones has enabled plant physiologists to devise new methods of growing plants. In the technique known as **tissue culture,** single cells or groups of cells are placed in sterile containers with minerals, water, and hormones to stimulate growth and development. At equal concentrations of auxins and cytokinins, many cells in culture continue to divide, forming an undifferentiated tissue called a **callus** (KAL us). By adjusting the relative concentrations of auxins, cytokinins, and other growth substances, the callus cells can be induced to form roots or buds and, in some cases, to grow into a complete plant (see figure 19.31). Because one plant can contribute many cells, it is possible to develop many identical plants. These plants are **clones** of each other—genetically identical individuals. Tissue culture has been used to clone many different plants, but few have developed into adult plants. The cloning of animal cells, including those of humans, is not a reality at the present time.

Cloning has an important advantage in the development of new plant varieties. Because there is much variation in most plant populations, there may be just one plant out of thousands that has a particular combination of desirable characteristics. An example might be a new variety of rose or an unusually tasty carrot. If that one plant is crossed with another to get seeds, there is no guarantee that the offspring would have the same characteristics as those of the desired parent. Cloning, however, could produce duplicate copies of the desired plant. Cloned plants then can contribute to the culturing of many more clones. In this way an entire field of identical plants could be developed.

Tissue culture is just one of many ways that scientists develop new and better crops. In **selective breeding,** plant and animal breeders allow only those individuals with the "best" characteristics to breed. Most of the offspring of the individuals allowed to breed are expected to have some of the characteristics of the two parents.

Figure 19.32 These protoplasts have been removed from their cell walls in preparation for fusion.

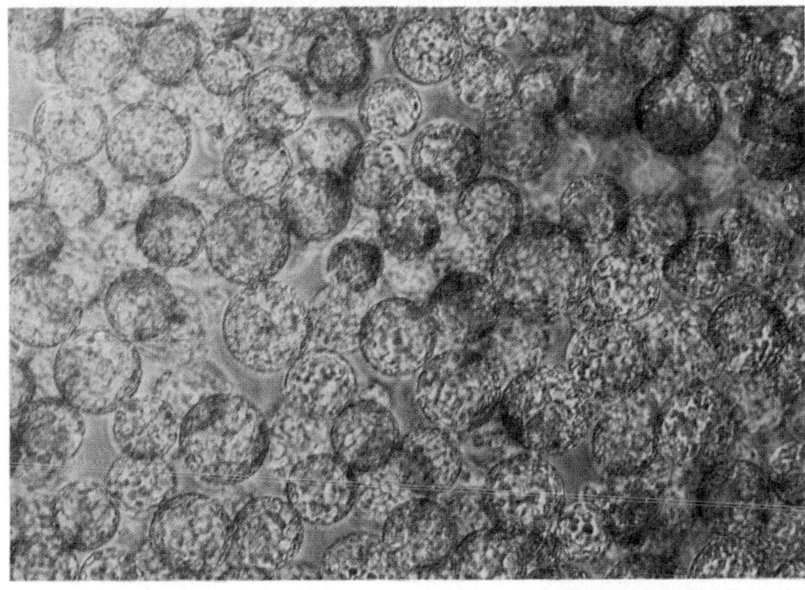

DNA/Plant Technology Corporation

A new technique for crop development is **protoplast fusion** (PROH toh plast FYOO zhun). In this technique cells from two different plants are placed in a special liquid in the same container. Enzymes are used to digest the cell walls away, leaving intact the living contents, or protoplasts. In the liquid some of the protoplasts can be induced to fuse. The fused protoplast may then develop a cell wall and begin to grow, forming a hybrid cell.

A hybrid is the offspring of two different organisms, as you learned in section 8.4. You, for example, are a hybrid of your two parents. In many cases the formation of a hybrid is impossible. Individuals of two different species cannot form viable offspring, or hybrids. For example, it has not been possible to produce a hybrid offspring by placing pollen grains of a potato on the pistil of a tomato. However, a hybrid cell between these two plants can be formed using protoplast fusion. This has raised hopes that extremely different plants might be combined into "superplants" or "supercrops." For instance, a supercrop of the future might be a corn plant with greater drought resistance or lower nitrogen requirements than the present varieties. Unfortunately, protoplast fusion has not been entirely successful.

Self-Review

1. In what way are gibberellins and auxins similar?
2. How do phototropism and gravitropism affect plant growth?
3. What role does phytochrome play in plant photoperiodism?
4. What is the advantage of using cloning in the production of a crop?

Summary

In the light-dependent reactions of photosynthesis, light energy is absorbed by a variety of plant pigments, primarily chlorophyll. A series of reactions follows in which energy-rich molecules are formed as the light energy is converted to chemical energy. In addition to these molecules, oxygen gas is released into the atmosphere as a by-product. In the Calvin cycle, the energy-rich molecules are used to make 3-carbon sugars from carbon dioxide. During cellular respiration the energy from these sugars is released. Environmental factors such as temperature, oxygen and carbon dioxide concentration, and light intensity interact to affect the rates of both photosynthesis and respiration.

Growth and development of plants result from the interaction of plant hormones and environmental factors, such as light and gravity. Auxins, gibberellins, cytokinins, ethylene, and abscisic acid are the groups of natural plant hormones. Some of these have been produced synthetically by humans and are used in research and agriculture.

Application Questions

1. In what ways are photosynthesis and respiration essentially opposite sets of reactions?
2. Trace the production of ATP molecules in both respiration and photosynthesis.
3. What roles do photosynthesis and respiration play in the cycling of carbon?
4. How are plant hormones used to bring about differentiation and growth of a new plant from a callus?
5. Deciduous trees lose their leaves in the fall. Describe possible hormonal and environmental stimuli that might bring about this response.

Problems

1. Investigate some of the practical uses of auxins and synthetic growth substances as they apply to farming and the raising of fruits and vegetables.
2. Many botanists are searching for plants that synthesize fuel-related carbon compounds. Part of our energy needs could be met by growing these plants commercially. What other types of useful compounds are produced by plants? Report your findings to the class.
3. Experiments with photosynthesizing vascular plants have shown that when they are grown in an atmosphere without oxygen they take up carbon dioxide at 1.5 times the rate at which they do so in natural atmosphere, which is about 20 percent oxygen.
   (a) What does this indicate about the relationship between photosynthesis and cellular respiration?
   (b) How might this relationship affect the composition of the earth's atmosphere?

Suggested Readings

Refer also to the Suggested Readings for Chapter 18.

D. Bardell, "Bacterial Photosynthesis Without Chlorophyll" *The American Biology Teacher* (May 1982). Short article dealing with this little-known process.

T. Boddé, "Genetic Engineering in Agriculture: Another Green Revolution?" *BioScience* (July/August 1982). The present impact and the future of genetic manipulation on agriculture is discussed.

R. Robinson, "Rings of Flowers" *BioScience* (June 1986). Uniquely Californian, vernal pools host a diversity of endemic species often threatened by their habitat's destruction.

Doug Sokell

Section Five

Patterns in the Biosphere

An ecologist must study living things not as isolated objects and events, but as interrelated patterns. Individuals are members of populations, and populations are members of communities and ecosystems.

An ecosystem makes more sense if it is seen across time as well as space. The patterns of the present are the result of interacting patterns of the past. Furthermore, ecosystems change continuously, and ecology often includes predictions about future environments.

Our study of biology began with broad patterns in the web of life. Then we examined the organisms in the web as individuals and as cell-based systems. Now it is time to close the circle by returning to patterns of populations—of the past, present, and future.

Ed Reschke

What adaptations enable the Joshua tree, *Yucca brevifolia,* to survive in the harsh desert environment?

CHAPTER 20

Selection and Survival

Introduction

Organisms are what they are because the genes they share with their ancestors allowed those ancestors to survive and reproduce. Environmental selection may act in favor of some genes, but it removes others from the gene pool. If the surviving genes in a population make individuals fit for the environment, the genes will be retained. If the environment changes, however, the genes may be removed.

Because each population is part of the biotic environment of other populations, a change in one population's gene pool may cause selection for or against genes in other populations. Selection and survival in interacting populations help to form the dynamic pattern in any ecosystem.

Populations and Environments

Guidepost: What is the relationship between limiting factors and organismal tolerance?

20.1 Organisms Must Be Able to Tolerate Conditions in Their Environments

How do environmental factors result in the selection of certain organisms and populations for survival? Selection results from the action of specific environmental factors that set limits for growth. As you will recall from chapter 2, these limiting factors affect mortality, natality, emigration, and immigration.

One important limiting factor is temperature. If a household geranium is left outdoors during a Minnesota winter, it will die. If a blacksnake in a shadeless cage is exposed to the July sun of Georgia, it will die. Household geraniums cannot tolerate long periods of freezing temperatures. Blacksnakes cannot tolerate long periods of high temperatures. If an organism cannot tolerate the highest or lowest temperature

Figure 20.1 A typical bell-shaped curve showing the tolerance range of a given organism, in this case, a geranium.

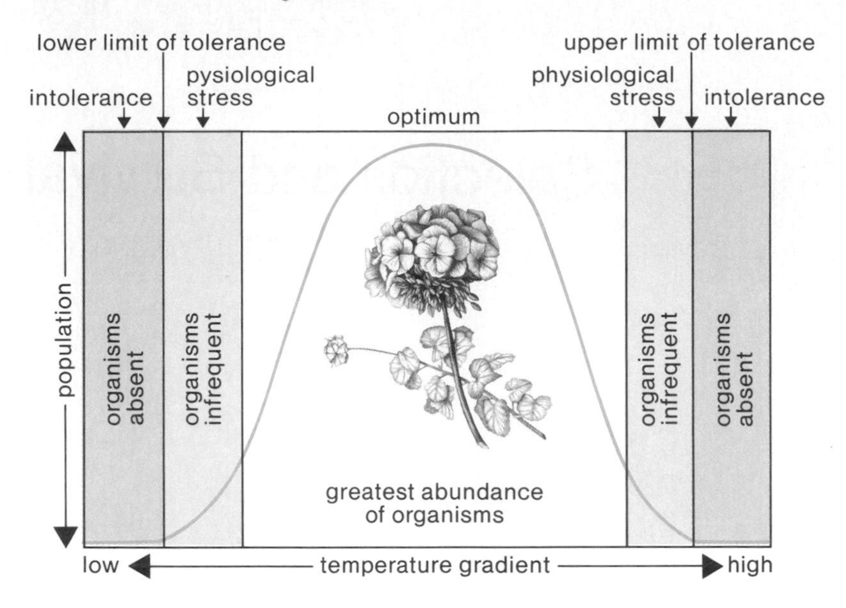

in an area, it will die or move elsewhere. Thus, **tolerance** is the ability of an individual or a species to withstand particular environmental conditions.

Working with any one measurable environmental factor, we can determine by experiment the tolerance limits of a species. To do this, we must find the upper limit (maximum) and the lower limit (minimum) of tolerance. Those values and any values between them make up the **range** of tolerance of the species for that environmental factor. Likewise, we can determine the range of conditions most favorable for growth and reproduction for that species. These are called the **optimum** conditions for the species. This seems clear-cut, but several complications arise.

The **duration** of the condition is important. Duration is especially important in determining maximum and minimum limits. For instance, geraniums can withstand short periods of freezing temperature, but not long ones. The limiting factor of temperature selects for geraniums that can grow in moderate climates.

20.2 Organisms Vary in Their Tolerance

Within any population, individuals vary (differ) genetically for some characteristics, including tolerance. Within a species, also, populations of organisms vary in their tolerance for conditions. Populations that come from different parts of a species' geographic range vary in their tolerance as well. A population of the jellyfish *Aurelia aurita* (figure 20.2), which lives off the coast of Maine, can tolerate temperatures between 5° C and 18° C. For the *Aurelia* population off the southern coast of Florida, however, the optimum varies between 28° C and 30° C. Both the northern and the southern jellyfish have been selected for survival in their particular environments.

Figure 20.2 *Aurelia aurita.*

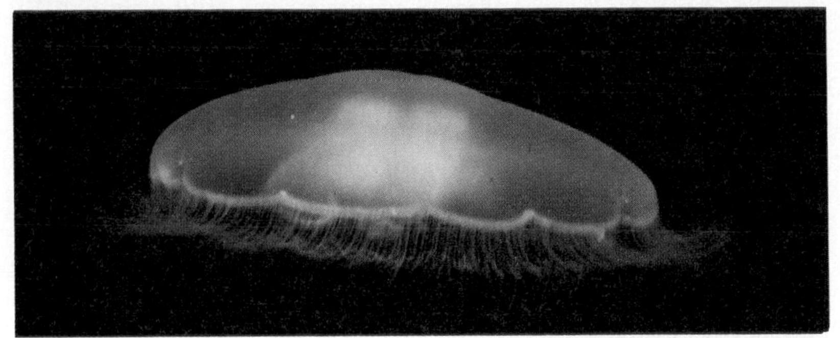

Figure 20.3 The tolerance ranges for 2 populations of *Aurelia aurita,* one in Florida, and one in Maine. Even though they are the same species, they no longer can live in water that is the same temperature.

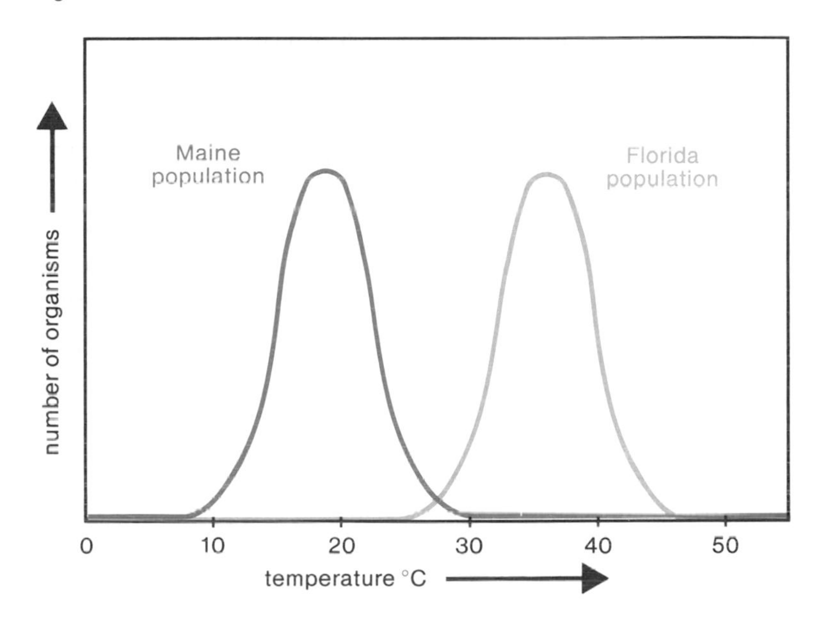

Such variation in a population, of course, arises by mutation or genetic recombination in some individuals. Jellyfish that can tolerate temperatures of about 18° C are already adapted to a southern environment, whether or not the water is ever that warm.

20.3 Organisms Meet the Environment as a Whole, Not as Separate Factors

Now consider the interrelationship of tolerances in determining geographic range. Field sparrows (*Spizella pusilla*) can survive northern winter temperatures in the United States if they have enough food for energy. Sparrows need more food in the winter because more heat is lost from their bodies than in summer. Sparrows can hunt food only during the day, and winter days are short. Is it the temperature, the food supply, or the length of day that sets the northern winter boundaries of field sparrows? It could be any one or any combination of those factors.

Figure 20.4 Field sparrow.

Figure 20.5 Hessian fly.

Agricultural Research Service, USDA

Abiotic conditions within a species' tolerance limits may allow it to survive in a particular ecosystem. But those conditions do not guarantee that the species can survive there. The species may fail because of the selection by the biotic environment. It may have to compete with other organisms, or be affected by them in other ways. For example, white bald wheat was grown in New England before the Revolutionary War, and it did well in the abiotic conditions there. But when the Hessian fly (figure 20.5) was inadvertently brought in by Europeans during the war, the flies attacked the wheat fields. By 1800, wheat farming in New England had ended. Later, different varieties of wheat were introduced, and they were planted just before the first frost. Because the frost killed adult flies, the wheat could survive. By that time, however, wheat farming had moved westward.

Examples like this remind us that the whole organism encounters the whole environment. Individuals respond in certain ways when a particular environmental factor is changed. Ecologists can begin to understand the entire situation of an organism by studying those factors one at a time. One major aspect of ecology is the study of the tolerance limits of different species. You will be able to observe the tolerance of four kinds of seeds for different combinations of environmental factors in investigation 20.1.

Investigation 20.1 ENVIRONMENTAL TOLERANCE

Introduction

The seeds of some desert plants will not germinate (sprout) until sufficient rainfall washes out chemicals in the seeds that inhibit germination. Other seeds must pass through the digestive tracts of animals before they will germinate. Some wheat seeds will not germinate until they have been exposed to low temperatures for a certain period of time. In this investigation you will examine the tolerance that some seeds have to some environmental abiotic factors.

Before beginning work, read through the procedure and then set up several hypotheses on the basis of the experimental design.

Materials (per team)

4 beakers, 50 ml
seeds of radish, vetch, tomato, and lettuce (50 each)
150 ml fungicide
5 petri dishes
5 clear plastic bags
5 pieces of string (20 cm each)
2 shallow cardboard boxes with covers
20 pieces of paper towel, cut to fit petri dishes
20 cardboard strips, cut to fit the diameter of petri dishes
forceps
glass-marking pencil
refrigerator
incubator
2 thermometers (−10° to +110° C)

Procedure

1. Label the beakers tomato, radish, vetch, and lettuce. In each beaker, place 50 seeds of the species named. Add enough fungicide to cover the seeds. Soak them for the period of time recommended by your teacher.

2. Place 4 disks of paper towel in each petri dish. Moisten the paper thoroughly with distilled water. Divide each dish into 4 sections by inserting cardboard dividers, as shown in figure 20.6.
3. Pour the fungicide solution from the beakers and rinse the seeds with water.
4. Using forceps, place 10 tomato seeds in 1 section of each dish. Repeat with the other 3 kinds of seeds in the remaining 3 sections of each dish.
5. Label the dishes with your team symbol and number them from 1 to 5. Place each dish in a clear plastic bag. Tie the bag closed with a piece of string.
6. Place each dish in a different environment, as follows:
   Dish 1—continuous light and cold—a refrigerator that has the light adjusted to remain on when the door is closed. (Maintain a temperature of 10° to 12° C.)
   Dish 2—continuous dark and cold—a light-tight box in a refrigerator (10° to 12° C).
   Dish 3—continuous light and warm—an incubator with a light (30° to 32° C).
   Dish 4—continuous dark and warm—a light-tight box in an incubator (30° to 32° C).
   Dish 5—variable temperature and light—on a windowsill.
7. Each day, count the number of seeds that have germinated. Record the counts in your data book. A suggested form:

Dish No. ________ **Environment** ________________

Kind of Seed	Number Germinated			
	Day 1	Day 2		Day 10
tomato				
radish				
vetch				
lettuce				

8. After 10 days, combine the data of all teams.

Figure 20.6 Experimental setup.

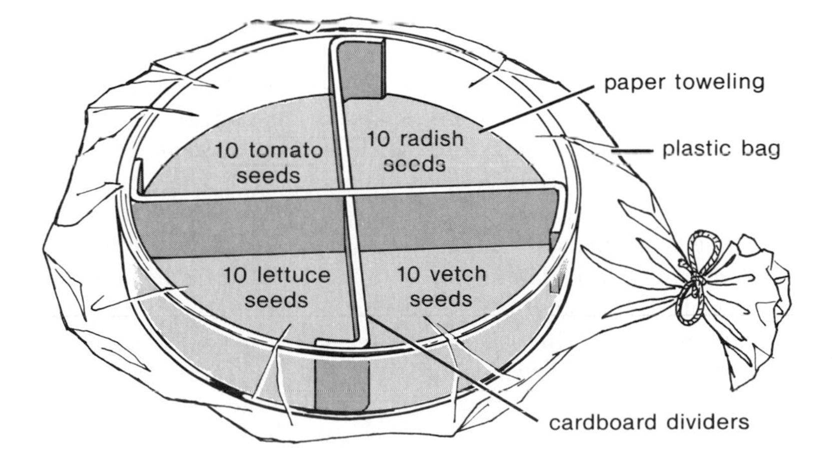

Discussion

1. Why should the data from all the teams be combined?
2. In which environment did the greatest percentage of the following seeds germinate?
   (a) tomato seeds?
   (b) radish seeds?
   (c) vetch seeds?
   (d) lettuce seeds?
3. (a) Did any seeds of one species germinate fastest in one environment, but have the greatest number of germinated seeds in another environment?
   (b) If so, which species and environment are involved?
4. Which species has the greatest tolerance for continuous light?
5. Which species has the greatest tolerance for low temperature?
6. (a) Did any species germinate similarly in all the experimental environments?
   (b) If so, which?
7. Compare your results with your hypotheses. Recall that the establishment of a species in an ecosystem depends on both its tolerances and its competition with other species.
8. (a) Which factor do you think would give a species a greater advantage—rapid germination or germination of a large percentage of seeds?
   (b) Why?
9. On the basis of your experimental results, describe ecosystems in which each species you studied in this investigation might have an advantage.

For Further Investigation

From a grocery store, obtain seeds of plants that grow in a variety of climates, such as avocados, dates, grapefruits, oranges, pomegranates, lentils, and many kinds of beans. Test these for germination in experimental environments. In some cases you may have to lengthen the time allowed for germination.

20.4 Human Populations Are Limited by Environmental Factors

Like other organisms, humans are affected by limiting factors in the environment, such as food and water. Some limiting factors have even worked together over long periods to select for certain human characteristics. Modern African populations, for example, have a high percentage of alleles for "sickling" of red blood cells. That is true even though persons homozygous for the sickling allele usually develop sickle-cell anemia and die before they reproduce. A single sickling allele, however, protects against malaria and, thus, is of value to the individual. Because heterozygous individuals do not breed true, a quarter of their offspring is susceptible to malaria, and a quarter suffers from sickle-cell anemia.

For humans, even more than for other organisms, energy is an important limiting factor. Our usual energy sources—coal, oil, and natural gas—are finite. Many scientists think that depletion of these resources will limit the amount of food that can be raised in the future.

Figure 20.7 (a) Red blood cells of a person who does not have the sickling allele. (b) Cells of a person who has a single sickling allele. Such heterozygous persons are protected against malaria. (c) Cells of a person who has sickle-cell anemia. These individuals are homozygous for the sickling allele.

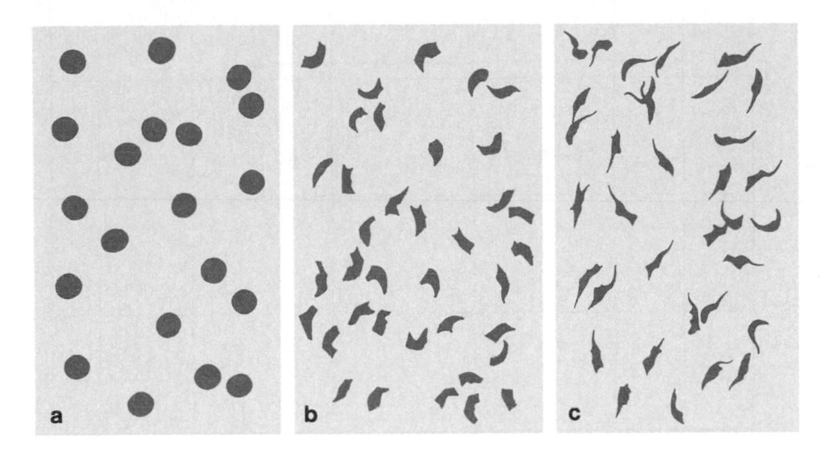

Figure 20.8 Energy use in the United States. The sources of energy used have become increasingly varied. The use of synthetic and nuclear fuel is expected to increase in the future while both domestic and foreign oil and gas consumption is expected to decrease.

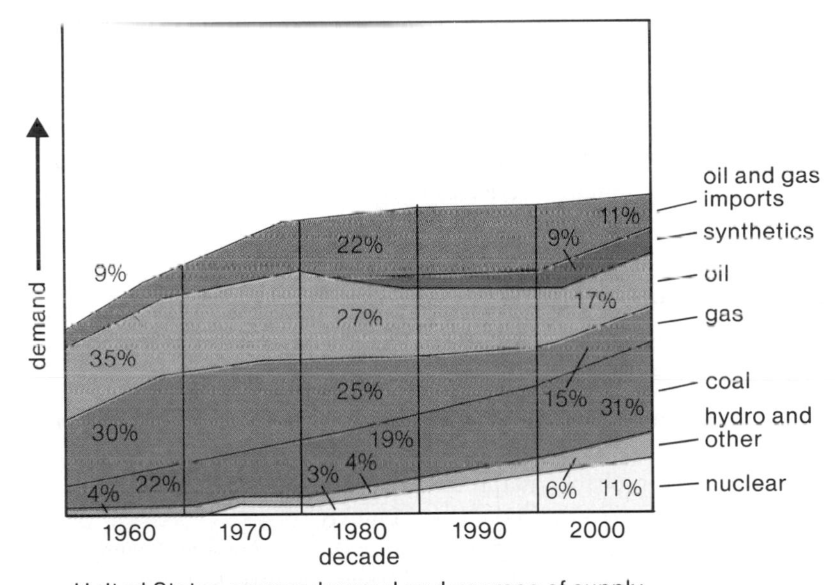

United States energy demand and sources of supply

Space is another important requirement. Humans tend to congregate, to prefer living near others. Some "standing room" is necessary, however. Some scientists see severe overcrowding as the limiting factor for human populations.

The earth's carrying capacity is finite. Biologists do not know whether food, energy, space, or a combination of these, will limit the number of persons on earth. Already, food is a limiting factor in many African countries. The Chinese may be limited by space: on the average, there are 461 persons for every square kilometer in China, as compared with

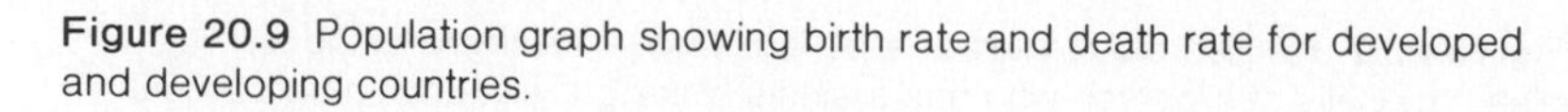

Figure 20.9 Population graph showing birth rate and death rate for developed and developing countries.

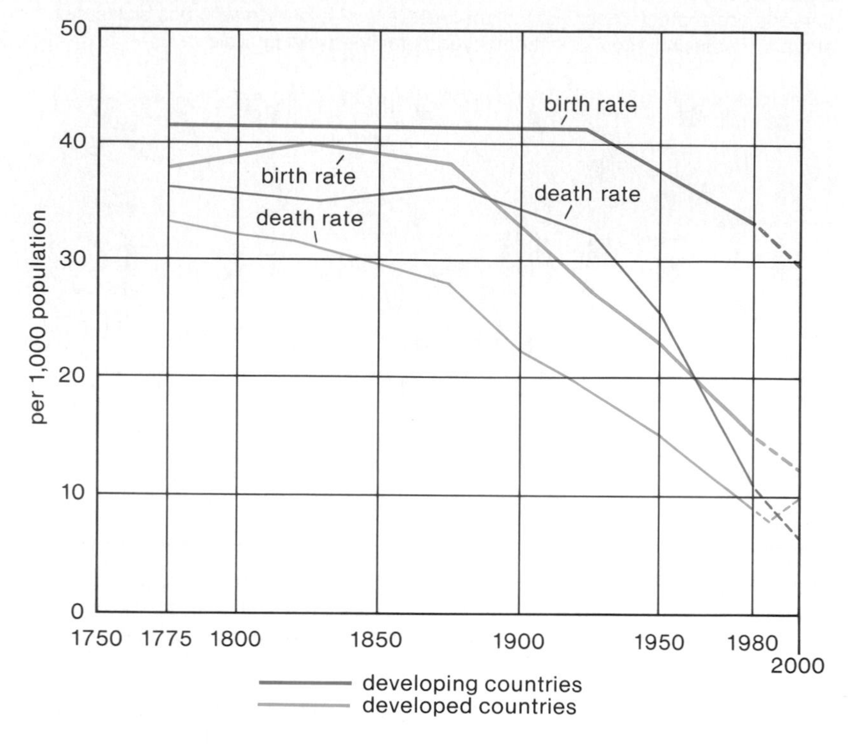

25 in the United States. Everything known about populations indicates that the number of Earth's human residents *will* be limited. The only question that seems unanswered is "How?" Will mortality, through starvation, disease, and war, rise to equal present-day natality? Or will natality be lowered to match today's low death rates?

20.5 Limiting Factors May Act at Different Points in the Life Cycle

Some limiting factors act only in certain parts of a population's life cycle. For example, predation by coyotes on prairie dog populations affects mainly young prairie dogs. Thus, the individuals that survive to adulthood were probably adapted at a young age to react promptly to parental warning cries and take cover quickly.

Early in their lives some organisms tolerate environmental conditions well; others are unlikely to survive that period. Figure 20.10(a–c) shows three different patterns of mortality. Figure 20.10a is a pattern typical of humans in Western nations. A large proportion of the population survives childhood and middle age, but relatively few live beyond 65.

Just the opposite is the situation shown in figure 20.10c, which is characteristic of populations of organisms such as oysters and redwood trees. Many fail to survive the early years, but those that do survive are likely to live a long life. For redwoods, that may be 2500 years.

Still a third sort of mortality pattern is that in figure 20.10b. A population of organisms with this sort of pattern loses individuals at a constant rate. A chickadee, for example, is just as likely to die between the ages of 5 and 6 years as it is between the ages of 1 and 2 years.

Figure 20.10 Mortality graphs for three kinds of organisms.

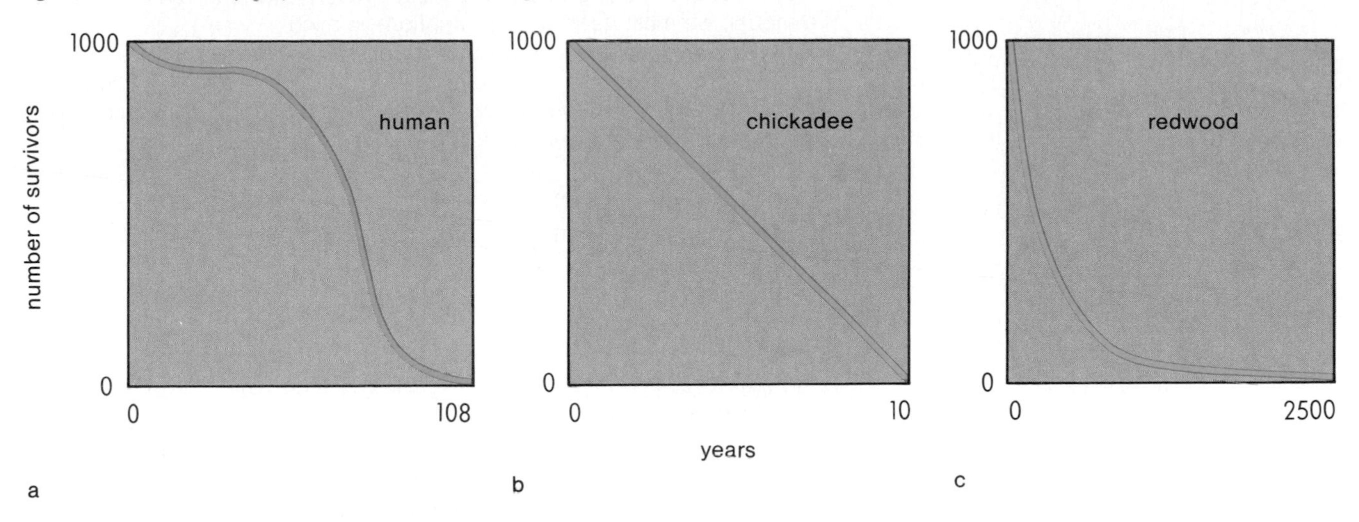

Many persons use such patterns of mortality to make predictions about populations. For example, knowing the pattern of human mortality and the numbers of humans in various age groups in a population, you can predict how many persons will be in each age group in 10 years' time. Such predictions are made routinely by persons who build schools or write textbooks.

Using the mortality pattern and related information for an insect species, a person who wants to use an insecticide at the most efficient time can do so. If most of the insects survive the larval stage (when some insects do their greatest damage), then applying the insecticide before the larvae are expected to hatch would be more effective than waiting until hatching has occurred.

Self-Review

1. What is a limiting factor?
2. What is meant by an organism's range of tolerance?
3. What are some limiting factors for human populations?
4. How might limiting factors interact to affect a population?

Investigation 20.2 POPULATION CHANGES: A MODEL

Introduction

Just as we need physical tools such as microscopes to extend our powers of observation, we also need mental tools to extend our thinking. One such mental tool is called a **model.** Here the word does not mean an object. Instead, it means something we construct in our minds. A mental model simplifies a complex real situation, so that we can understand it more easily. For example, the board game Monopoly is a very simple model of real estate investment. Because a model is a simplification, it differs in some respects from the real situation. To simplify a situation, we make **assumptions.** That is, for the model we assume certain things that might not be entirely true in the real situation. (In Monopoly, for example, we assume that the cost of putting a house on Boardwalk is always the same.) In using a model, we must keep our assumptions in mind.

If a specific model gives results similar to the observations we make in some real situation, we assume tentatively that the real situation works in the same way the model does. We must keep in mind, however, that a different model might give the same results.

Materials (per student)

4 sheets arithmetic graph paper
1 sheet semilogarithmic graph paper

Procedure

1. Let us begin with real organisms—house sparrows. For our model we will start with a hypothetical (imaginary) population of house sparrows. In the spring of 1987, there were 10 sparrows (5 males and 5 females) living on an isolated island. Our assumptions are:
   (a) All the sparrows form permanent pairs, and all pairs have offspring.
   (b) Every breeding season (spring), each pair produces 10 offspring (5 males and 5 females).
   (c) Each year, before the next breeding season, all the breeding (parent) birds die.
   (d) Each year all offspring live through the next breeding season. (In most real situations some parents would live and some offspring would die. But taken together, assumptions c and d balance each other to imitate the real situation.)
   (e) During the study, no other sparrows arrive on the island, and none leave it.
2. Now let us use this model. Calculate the size of the hypothetical population at the beginning of each breeding season. According to assumption b, in the spring of 1987 there are 5 pairs of birds. Each of the 5 pairs produces 10 offspring, a total of 50 (25 males and 25 females). According to assumption c, the 10 breeding birds of 1987 die before the next spring. According to assumption d, all 50 offspring live to the spring of 1988. Thus, at the start of the 1988 breeding season, there are 25 pairs of house sparrows on the island. Using these assumptions, calculate the island's sparrow population at the beginning of the breeding season in 1989, 1990, 1991, and 1992.
3. To check your figures, type the following program into a computer:

```
10      REM POPMODEL
20      N = 10
30      PRINT "First year?"
35      INPUT YF
40      PRINT "Last Year?"
45      INPUT YL
50      FOR YR = YF TO YL
60      0 = N / 2 * 10
62      N = 0
65      PRINT "How many"
70      PRINT "offspring are"
75      PRINT "produced by the"
80      PRINT "beginning of "YR + 1"?"
90      INPUT NH
100     IF NH = 0 THEN PRINT "Good!"
105     IF NH = 0 THEN GOTO 170
110     IF NH < > 0 THEN GOTO 65
115     N = 0
170     NEXT YR
180     END
```

Figure 20.11 House sparrow.

4. You now have a series of numbers. To get a clearer idea of the population change, plot the numbers on a line graph. Show the years along the horizontal axis (x), and the number of birds along the vertical axis (y). Be sure to make the vertical scale large enough to show the 1992 population. Plot as many generations as you can. (This is an arithmetic graph.)
5. Now plot your data using another tool—semilogarithmic (usually called semilog) graph paper. You do not need to understand fully the mathematics of logarithms to use this tool. Your teacher will explain what you need to know to plot the data.

Discussion

1. Look first at the arithmetic graph. How does the slope of the line change as you read from left to right (from year to year)?
2. What does this mean in terms of rate of population change?
3. Now compare the graphs. What advantage(s) does the semilog graph have over the arithmetic graph for plotting population growth data?
4. What kind of line shows the same thing on the semilog graph?
5. If you continued using the same assumptions to calculate populations for an indefinite number of years and plotted them on a graph, what would happen to the slope of the line on the arithmetic graph?
6. On the semilog graph?
7. In a sentence or two, summarize the change that is supported by the assumptions stated in the model.
8. Do you think any real population might change in this way? Why or why not?

For Further Investigation

Sometimes a model gives results that are very different from any observed situation. To make the model more useful, you can change one or two of the assumptions and compare the new results with reality. The closer the results of a model are to the observed situation, the more useful the model is. Some suggestions for changing assumptions follow. In each case, calculate the populations, plot the data on arithmetic and semilog graph paper, and compare these results with your original graphs. (To check your data, you must modify your computer program. Work together to determine what modifications are necessary.) Describe how the change of assumption has affected the hypothetical population.

1. Change assumption c as follows: Each year 2/5 of the breeding birds (equally males and females) live to breed again a second year and then die. All other assumptions remain unchanged.
2. Change assumption d as follows: Each year 2/5 of the offspring (equally males and females) die before the beginning of the next breeding season. All other assumptions remain unchanged.
3. Change assumption e as follows: Each year 20 new house sparrows (equally males and females) migrate to the island. None leave. All other assumptions remain unchanged.
4. Change assumption e as follows: Each year 40 house sparrows (equally males and females) emigrate from the island. None arrive. All other assumptions remain unchanged.
5. You can devise more complex problems by changing 2 or more assumptions simultaneously. If you are testing your calculations with a computer program, you should be able to modify the program also.

Guidepost: How do limiting factors determine the size and geographic range of populations?

Changes in Populations

20.6 Populations May Be Open or Closed

Any population of organisms has a built-in, characteristic growth rate. However, that rate is limited by environmental factors. The interaction of the population's natural growth rate and selection by the environment determines the density of the surviving population.

If you measure the density of a population at intervals over a period of time, you seldom find that any two consecutive measurements are the same. Density increases or decreases continually. Biologists have made many such studies of population densities, and they have been able to make some **generalizations** about how populations change. That is, they have summarized many specific observations in a few general statements that hold true for most of the data.

Under the original assumptions, the hypothetical house sparrows in investigation 20.2 were a **closed population.** That is, they could not emigrate, nor could others immigrate.

Many closed populations of small organisms have been set up in laboratories to test hypotheses about population changes. Figure 20.12 is based on data from an experiment involving diatoms (small photosynthetic organisms). A few diatoms were placed in a favorable medium, and samples from the population were counted on succeeding days. Experiments with closed populations of other small organisms have produced similar data. Notice that the growth of the diatom population during the first eight days was similar to the growth of the hypothetical house sparrow population. The model used in your investigation agrees, then, with a real situation—up to a point. Unlike the model, a real population does not continue to grow indefinitely.

Closed populations are not typical; they are found chiefly in laboratories or on islands. Most natural populations are **open populations.** Individuals are free to enter or leave. Therefore, we cannot assume that patterns represented by the diatom graph apply to natural populations.

Figure 20.12 Changes in a laboratory population of a type of diatom.

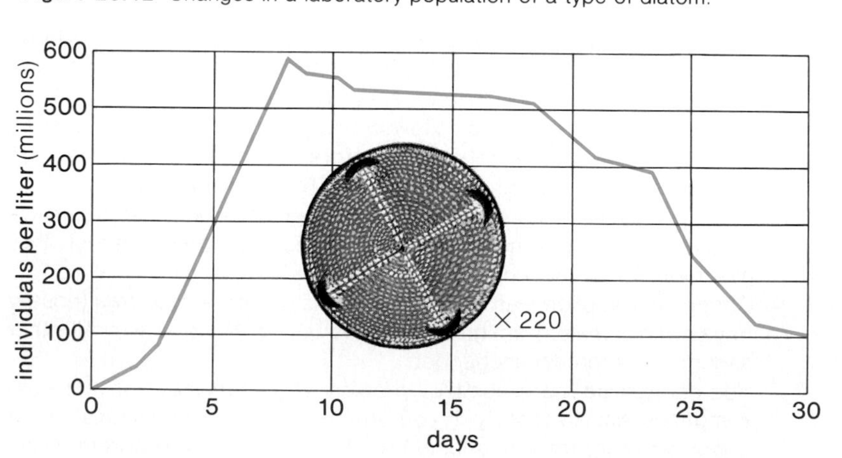

20.7 Population Sizes Fluctuate

The graph in figure 20.13 is based on data collected during population studies of Norway rats in Baltimore, Maryland. In 1942, the city health department conducted a poisoning campaign that apparently wiped out the rat population in the city block from which the data were collected. Because it is difficult to count individuals in natural populations, a few rats may have survived, or a few may have immigrated later from elsewhere. In either case, a "new" rat population was increasing by early in 1945. Compare the graph of figure 20.13 from early 1945 to 1946 with your graphs from investigation 20.2 and figure 20.12.

In the rat population graph the line from mid-1945 to the end of 1946 is somewhat similar to the first part of the graph line of the diatom population. Look at the line for the later years of the rat study, though. As with the closed population of diatoms in the laboratory, the population decreased after a peak density was reached. The decrease in the rat population, however, did not continue. Open populations usually increase again—as the rat population did. After such a population peaks, it again decreases, and then it may stabilize. Natural populations show such **fluctuations** (fluk shoo AY shunz)—ups and downs—on graphs of population counts. These fluctuations are caused by variables in the environment—often in climate, available food, or the activities of natural enemies.

In the past, human populations undoubtedly have fluctuated like open populations of other organisms. During the Middle Ages the population of western Europe decreased sharply as a result of plagues such as the

Figure 20.13 Changes in the Norway rat population of a city block.

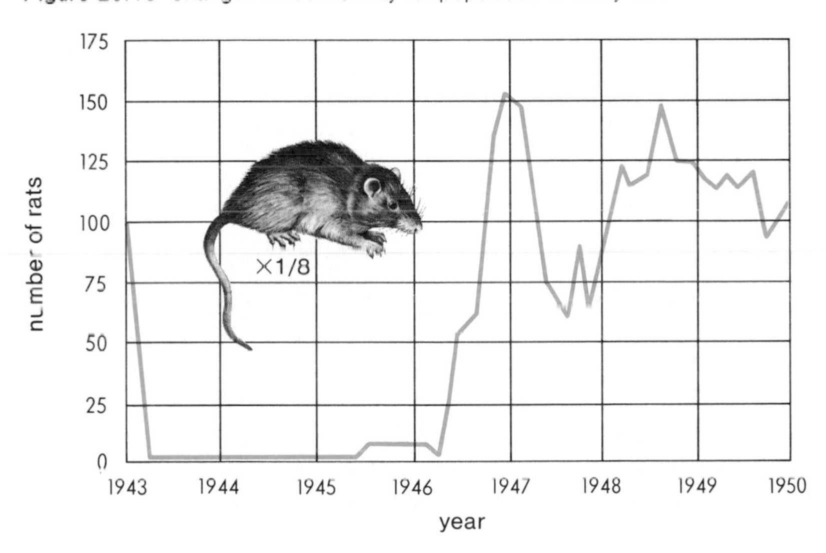

Figure 20.14 World and U.S. population growth.

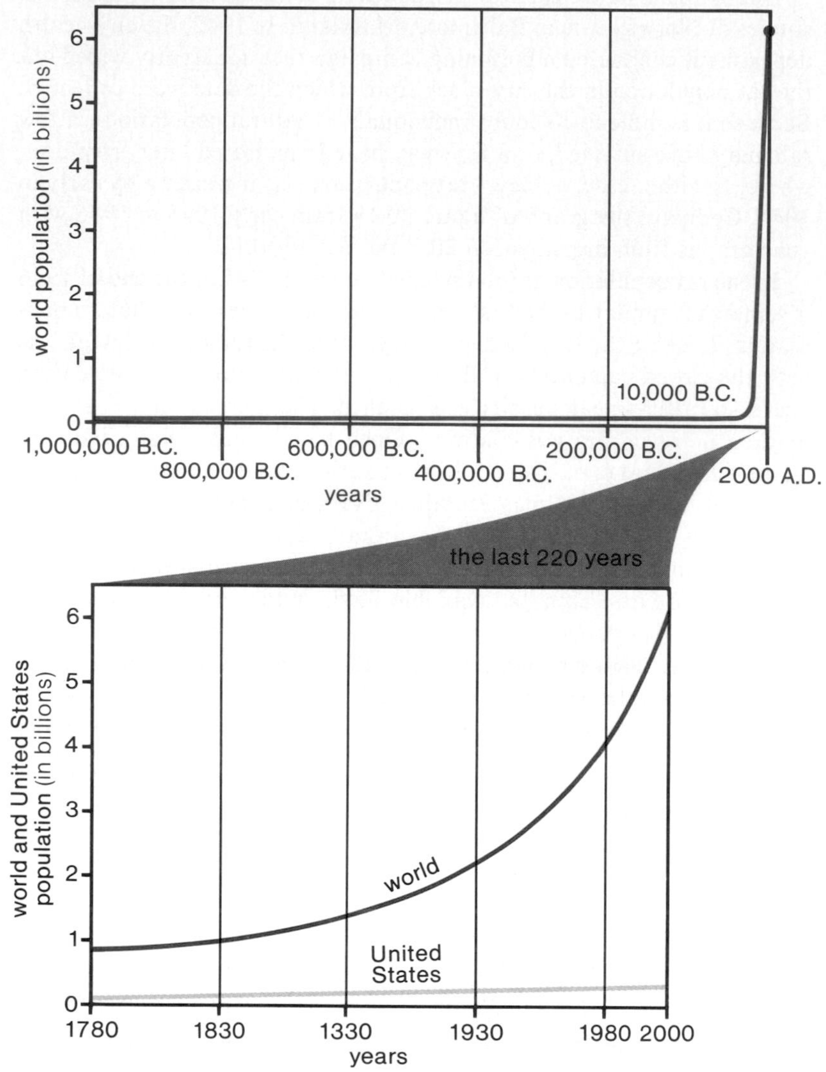

Black Death, and then rose again. Within the last few centuries, however, such fluctuations have disappeared in many countries. For the world as a whole, we have a human population that looks rather like your graph of the hypothetical population in investigation 20.2.

As cooperative animals, humans have been able to tolerate a high level of crowding. It is usually only when we are limited by food or other resources that we become concerned about population density.

20.8 Some Population Changes Occur in Cycles

Sometimes population fluctuations are very regular, and the peaks on a graph are at approximately equal distances. Data gathered in Canada show that populations of snowshoe hares peak about every 10 years (figure 20.15). Similarly, populations of lemmings reach peaks every 3 or 4 years. A number of other organisms also have such **population cycles.** Most of them are animals that live in the northern parts of Europe, Asia, and North America. These observations, however, do not explain why

Figure 20.15 Changes in the snowshoe-hare population (Canada) based on the number of skins traded at Hudson's Bay Company posts.

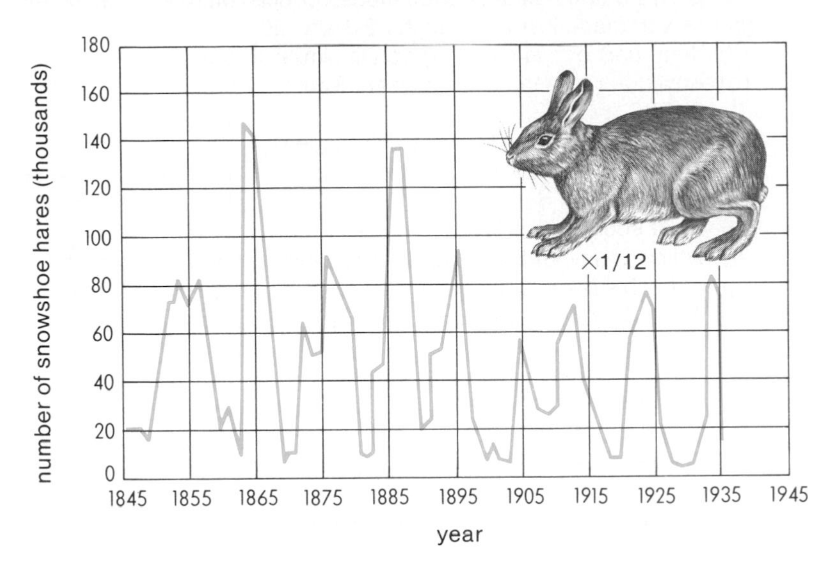

such cycles occur. Although the data show very regular cycles when plotted on a graph, some biologists think that this regularity is misleading. They point out that a combination of purely chance events can produce apparently regular cycles.

As you have seen, many populations change cyclically. You can study several examples in investigation 20.3. Some population changes are permanent—if a population becomes a new species or becomes extinct, for example. And any permanent change in a population is a change in the ecosystem to which the population belongs.

Figure 20.16 Lemming. These mouselike animals live in the northern parts of North America and Eurasia.

Investigation 20.3 POPULATION CHANGES: FIELD DATA

Introduction

Gathering data on natural populations requires a lot of time and patience. You can observe some of the characteristics of population changes by using data that have already been obtained by biologists. Then you can compare these population data with the data from your hypothetical sparrow populations and from the laboratory yeast population that you investigated in chapter 2.

Materials (per student)

2 sheets graph paper (arithmetic)
red pencil

Procedure

Part A—Cotton Mouse

The data in table 20.1 came from a study of cotton mice. The density is given as the number of mice caught per 100 traps per night. As is often the case in studying natural populations, the actual number of animals present in the area is not known. Thus, even in this real situation, we have to make an assumption. We assume that the number of mice caught was always in proportion to the actual density of the population.

Figure 20.17 Cotton mouse.

1. Plot the data on a sheet of graph paper, using a vertical scale that will place the highest density figure near the top of the graph.
2. Compare the graph of the cotton mouse population with the arithmetic graphs you made in investigations 2.3 and 20.2.
   (a) What part of this mouse graph is similar to the other graphs?
   (b) How does the mouse graph differ from your graph in investigation 20.2?
   (c) What could account for the differences?
   (d) How does the mouse graph differ from your graph of the yeast population?
   (e) What could cause the difference?
   (f) Which, if any, of the 3 populations was an open population?
   (g) In which season of the year do you think natality was the highest?
   (h) When do you think mortality and emigration were greatest?

Table 20.1 Data on density of cotton mice (Florida)

Date	Number of Mice Caught per 100 Traps per Night
September 24, 1949	25
October 9	45
October 30	38
December 4	30
January 7, 1950	20
February 26	14
March 12	13
April 16	8
May 8	7
June 16	11
July 16	4
August 16	13

Part B—Ring-necked Pheasant

A few ring-necked pheasants (native to Eurasia) were introduced on Protection Island, off the coast of Washington, in 1937. They were brought in as game birds for hunters. Counts of the population each spring and fall for the five years following introduction are presented in table 20.2.

1. Plot the data on a sheet of graph paper and connect the points with a lead pencil. How do you explain the regular fluctuations shown on the graph?
2. Using a red pencil, connect all the points representing spring counts, skipping the fall counts.
   (a) What does this line tell you about the population?
   (b) Remembering that this is a natural population, if spring counts had been made after 1942, what do you think they might have shown?

Table 20.2 Numbers of ring-necked pheasants (Washington)

Year	Season	Population Size
1937	spring	8
	fall	40
1938	spring	30
	fall	100
1939	spring	90
	fall	425
1940	spring	300
	fall	825
1941	spring	600
	fall	1520
1942	spring	1325
	fall	1900

Figure 20.18 Heath hen (left) and ring-necked pheasant (right).

Part C—Heath Hen

Heath hens were once common birds along the Atlantic coast from New England to Virginia. By 1880 they had disappeared from all locations except Martha's Vineyard, an island off Cape Cod. Figure 20.19 shows the result of a careful study of this population. Biologists believe several factors account for changes in the heath hen population: pressure of hunting by humans (followed by extreme efforts at preservation), disease, effects of forest fires, and an excessive number of males.

1. What caused the heath hen population to increase beginning about 1907?
2. How might an excess of males affect the limiting factors of a population?
3. What might have happened to this population if there had been an excess of females?
4. What happened to this species of bird about 1932?

Figure 20.19 Numbers of heath hens (Martha's Vineyard, Massachusetts).

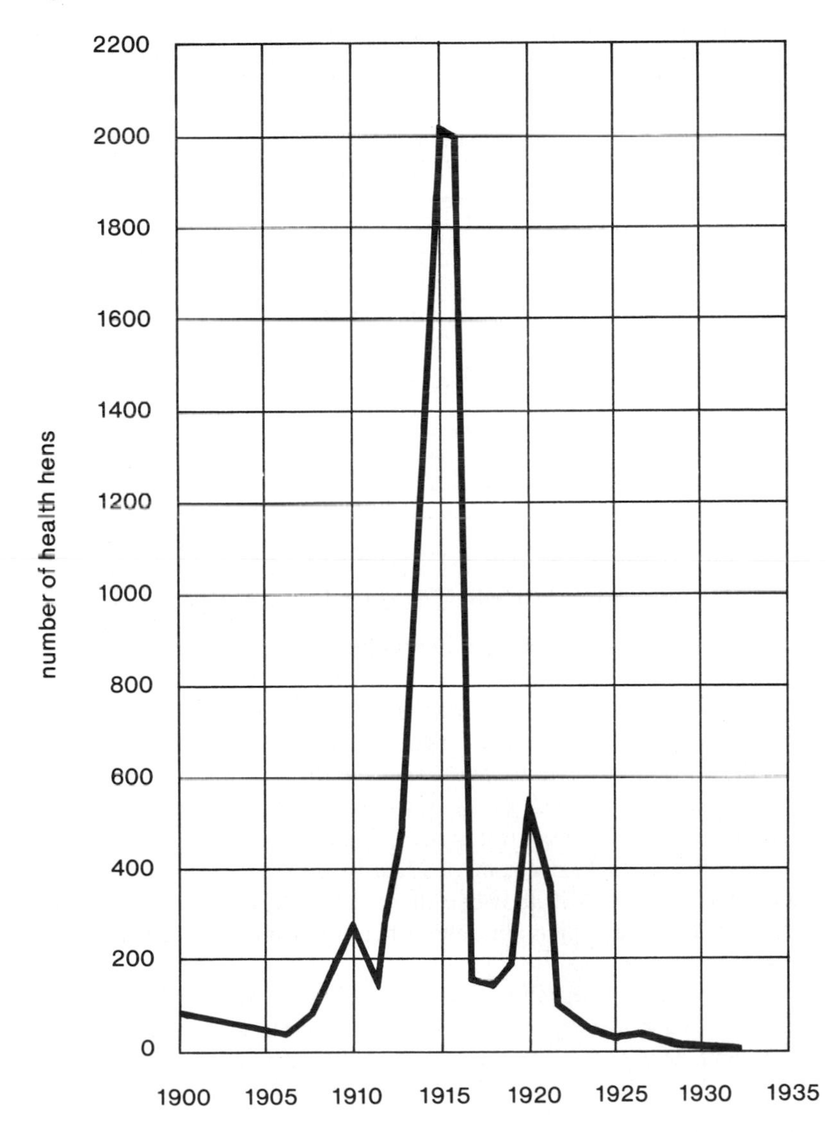

Discussion

You should now be able to draw some general conclusions from your investigations of population change.

1. Does the growth of a population tend to follow a basic pattern? If so, what are the characteristics of this pattern?
2. What is the chief difference between the graph for the hypothetical population (investigation 20.2) and the graphs for the real populations (investigations 2.3 and 20.3)?
3. How do you account for the difference?
4. How does the web of life (chapter 1) affect populations?

For Further Investigation

Table 20.3 presents data on a population of Italian bees. Plot the data on arithmetic graph paper.

Table 20.3 Numbers of Italian bees in an experimental colony

Days	0	7	14	21	28	35	42	49	56	63	70	77	84	91	98	105	112	119
Population of Colony (in Thousands)	1	1.5	2.5	4	8	16	22	32	40.5	50.3	55	62.5	72	72.5	71	82	78	81

1. Does this graph most closely resemble the graph for the house sparrow, the yeast, or the cotton mouse population?
2. On the bee graph, what is beginning to happen toward the end of the graph line?
3. Can you predict what probably happened soon after the collection of data was discontinued?
4. Which of the population determiners mentioned in the text is involved in your prediction?

20.9 Geographic Ranges Depend on Several Factors

In the Arctic and Antarctic, climate and other abiotic factors are similar, yet the organisms differ. Only in the Arctic do polar bears roam the ice floes. In the Antarctic they are absent. Only in the Antarctic do penguins waddle about. In the Arctic there are none. Why are no polar bears near the South Pole, and no penguins near the North Pole?

From observations such as these, we must conclude that tolerance to environmental factors does not entirely explain geographic ranges of organisms. Because an organism *can* live in a particular place does not necessarily mean that it *does* live there. To understand the geographic ranges of polar bears, penguins, and other organisms, we need additional facts.

We can start our search with two hypotheses. First, perhaps all species once occurred everywhere and later disappeared from some places. Or, second, each species may have originated in a particular place and

Figure 20.20 Polar bears.

Paul Howlott

Figure 20.21 Emperor penguin.

Dr. James B. McClintock, Institute of Marine Sciences, University of California, Santa Cruz, CA 95064.

then spread into other places. Biologists have little evidence for the first hypothesis. For the second, the evidence is strong. Scientists have studied fossils from all parts of the world. The evidence indicates that populations of species originated in small areas and then spread.

20.10 Populations Disperse to New Areas

Early in U.S. history, Europeans settled on the east and west coasts. The central areas of the country, with tens of thousands of Native Americans, had almost no people of European origin. By 1890, however, the national census showed that all parts of the country were inhabited by Europeans to a considerable extent. In all populations it is easy to observe this tendency of living things to spread from places where they are to places where they are not. This spreading of organisms is called dispersal.

In the case of motile organisms, dispersal may be accomplished by flying, swimming, walking, running, crawling, or burrowing. In the case of nonmotile organisms, dispersal is passive. Seeds, spores, and eggs can remain in a dormant state for long periods. During this time they may be carried great distances by currents of air or water, or they may travel in the mud on a bird's foot. Even motile organisms may be carried much farther than they could travel themselves. A polar bear may be carried hundreds of kilometers on floating ice. A spider may be blown long distances on the wind.

Dispersal alone, of course, does not change a species' geographic range. Unless the organisms survive and reproduce in the new location, the range has not changed. In other words, viability of individuals is not enough. It must be followed by fertility.

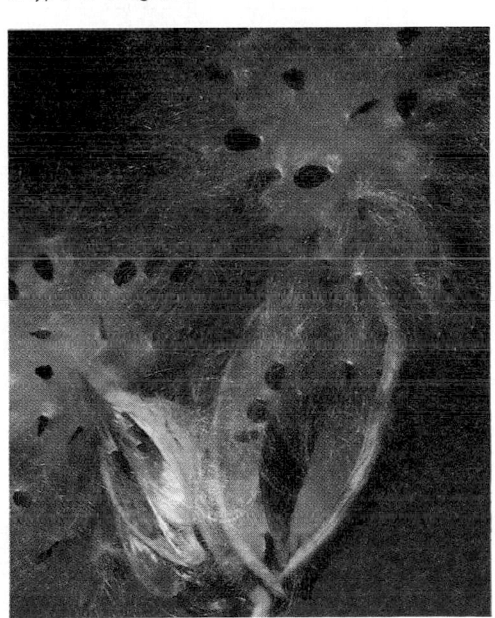

Figure 20.22 The dispersal of milkweed seeds, a type of emigration.

Russell C. Dohrmann

20.11 Many Kinds of Barriers Can Prevent Dispersal

Each kind of organism has some means of dispersal. It seems reasonable, therefore, to expect that eventually all species might be found wherever environmental conditions are suitable. Actually, such a broad geographic range is the exception rather than the rule. What, then, limits the dispersal of organisms? In the case of early Americans, it was often a mountain range—a **barrier.** For other animals, too, barriers prevent dispersal.

For most terrestrial animals large areas of water are effective barriers. For aquatic animals the land may be a barrier. Mountains and rivers are barriers to many organisms. Besides such physical barriers

Figure 20.23 Kirtland's warblers can fly very well yet they are found only in the small areas shown on the map. How might you explain this situation?

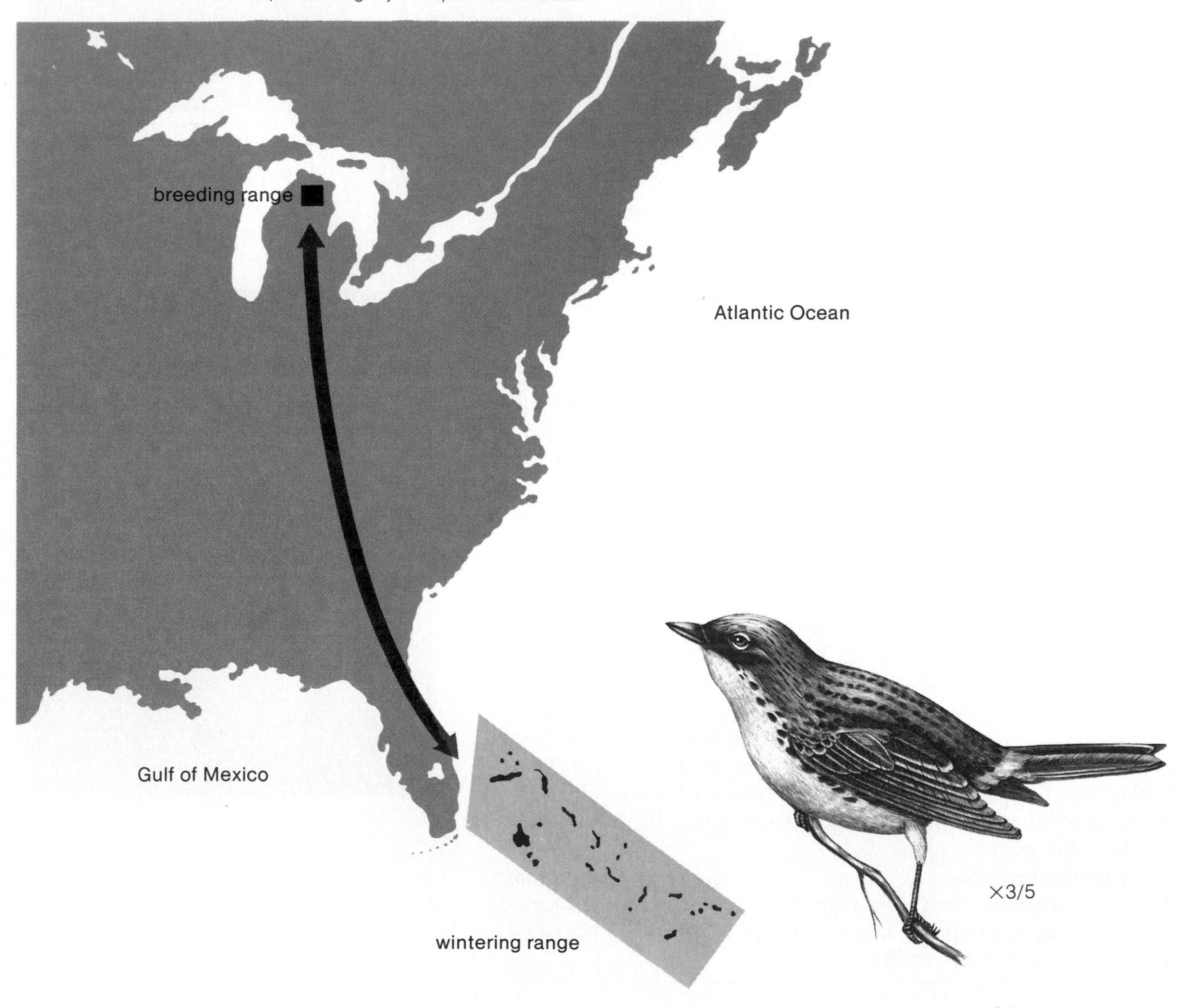

there also are ecological barriers. For organisms adapted to forest life, grassland or desert areas may be barriers. For grassland species, a forest region may limit dispersal.

Some barriers are behavioral. It seems reasonable to suppose, for instance, that flying birds would be found almost everywhere. However, many birds that can fly great distances remain in very restricted regions. Their distribution apparently is limited by the behavior of individuals in selecting their habitat. For example, the tree pipit (*Anthus trivialis*) and the meadow pipit (*A. pratensis*) have similar requirements, except that the tree pipit breeds only in areas having at least one tall tree. Both pipits nest on the ground, and they feed on the same kinds of organisms. Both have similar aerial songs. However, the tree pipit ends its song by perching on a tree, whereas the meadow pipit lands on the ground as shown in figure 20.24. This difference in behavior, therefore, limits the dispersal of the two species.

An increase in the population of a motile species encourages emigration to less populated areas, where there may be more resources available. Dispersal may take place rapidly as the population grows. However, when barriers are great, dispersal may be slow even though the population is increasing rapidly. In passive dispersal the means of transportation may be the most important factor in determining rate of spread. Species of trees whose seeds are carried away and buried by squirrels have been estimated to spread only about 1.6 km in 1000 years. By contrast, organisms swept up in a tornado may be carried 30 km in a few hours.

If our reasoning about dispersal and barriers is correct, we can now explain the absence of polar bears from the Antarctic. We first assume that polar bears originated in the Arctic and tended to disperse. But polar bears would find a tropical environment much too hot, so the tropics would act as a barrier to their dispersal. This wide barrier has existed throughout the existence of the polar bear species. Thus far no part of the population has been able to move across the barrier. Therefore, no polar bears are found in the Antarctic. Similar reasoning can be applied to the lack of dispersal by penguins.

Thus, we see that limiting factors shape not only whether populations survive, but also in what areas they can live. If a population has characteristics needed for survival in an area, environmental selection operates in favor of the population. If not, selection removes the population from that area.

Figure 20.24 The distribution of tree and meadow pipits is limited by behavioral barriers.

Self-Review

1. What is the difference between an open population and a closed population?
2. How is a species' geographic range affected by dispersal?
3. When does a limiting factor become a barrier?
4. How is the likelihood of dispersal affected by an increase in population size?
5. What is an example of a behavioral barrier?

Figure 20.25 Mount St. Helens before and after eruption.

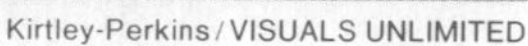
Kirtley-Perkins/VISUALS UNLIMITED

USDA, Forest Service

Guidepost: How does selection produce changing patterns in ecosystems over years and over geologic eras?

Succession and Evolution in Ecosystems

20.12 Ecosystems Are Not Permanent

Landscapes, mountains, and seascapes may seem like eternal ecosystems, but they are not. The great sheets of ice that once covered the northern parts of North America and Eurasia have melted. In many spots they left bare rock and soil. In all regions of the world, erosion constantly exposes bare rock. In many areas, fire is a natural factor. Floods, blowing sand, and volcanic eruptions also may destroy the vegetation of an area and leave bare ground or create new land.

Tests of nuclear explosives also can destroy much life. In the 1950s, some biologists began a five-year study of the effects of earlier nuclear explosions at the Nevada test site. (Atmospheric nuclear tests were stopped in 1958.) The explosions had removed the topsoil at ground zero and destroyed all the desert vegetation within a 1-km radius, as seen in figure 20.26b. Farther out from ground zero, only a few hardy species (such as the creosote bush and the ground thorn) survived.

A year after the last explosion, some spring annuals (stickleaf, stork's-bill, and desert pincushion) appeared. These grew from seeds carried in by wind or birds. Small plants began covering the area, as shown in figure 20.26c.

As the plants died, their remains were added to the sandy soil. The plants changed the abiotic environment in other ways, too. Their roots held more moisture in the soil. The soil temperature became suitable for the germination of seeds of other plant species. By 1961, there was a community of plants, including foxtail chess, wild buckwheat, and others. This community was not the pre-explosion community, however. It was similar to the community that eventually appears in a grassland area previously swept by fire.

Figure 20.26 The aftereffects of atomic testing. (a) Before testing at ground zero, showing typical vegetation. (b) After testing. The exposed rocks indicate extensive soil removal. (c) Russian thistle was the only species that grew within ½ km of ground zero in the first year. Its presence indicates the start of recovery.

a Lora Mangum Shields, New Mexico Highlands University, Las Vegas, New Mexico 87701.

b Lora Mangum Shields, New Mexico Highlands University, Las Vegas, New Mexico 87701.

c Lora Mangum Shields, New Mexico Highlands University, Las Vegas, New Mexico 87701.

20.13 Communities Succeed Each Other over Long Periods of Time

The process by which one community replaces another is called **succession. Primary succession** begins with bare soil or rock and ends with a community that is determined by the climate. **Secondary succession** begins in a disturbed area, such as the Nevada test site described on page 736. The community that ends a succession, at least for a long period of time, is called the **climax community.** It differs from the other communities in the succession process because it is not replaced by any other community unless a disturbance or a change in climate occurs. If a single spruce dies of old age, the space that it occupied is too shaded by neighboring spruces for aspen to grow. A young spruce, tolerant of shade, will probably take its place. Thus, once established, the climax community is relatively permanent.

Figure 20.27 Successional stages and animals of a coniferous forest.

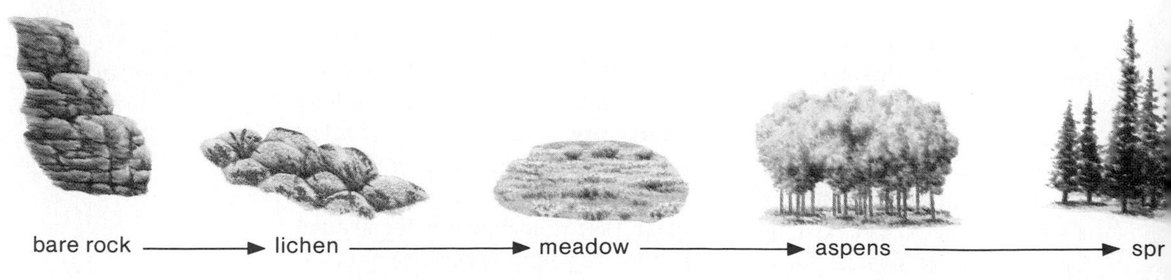

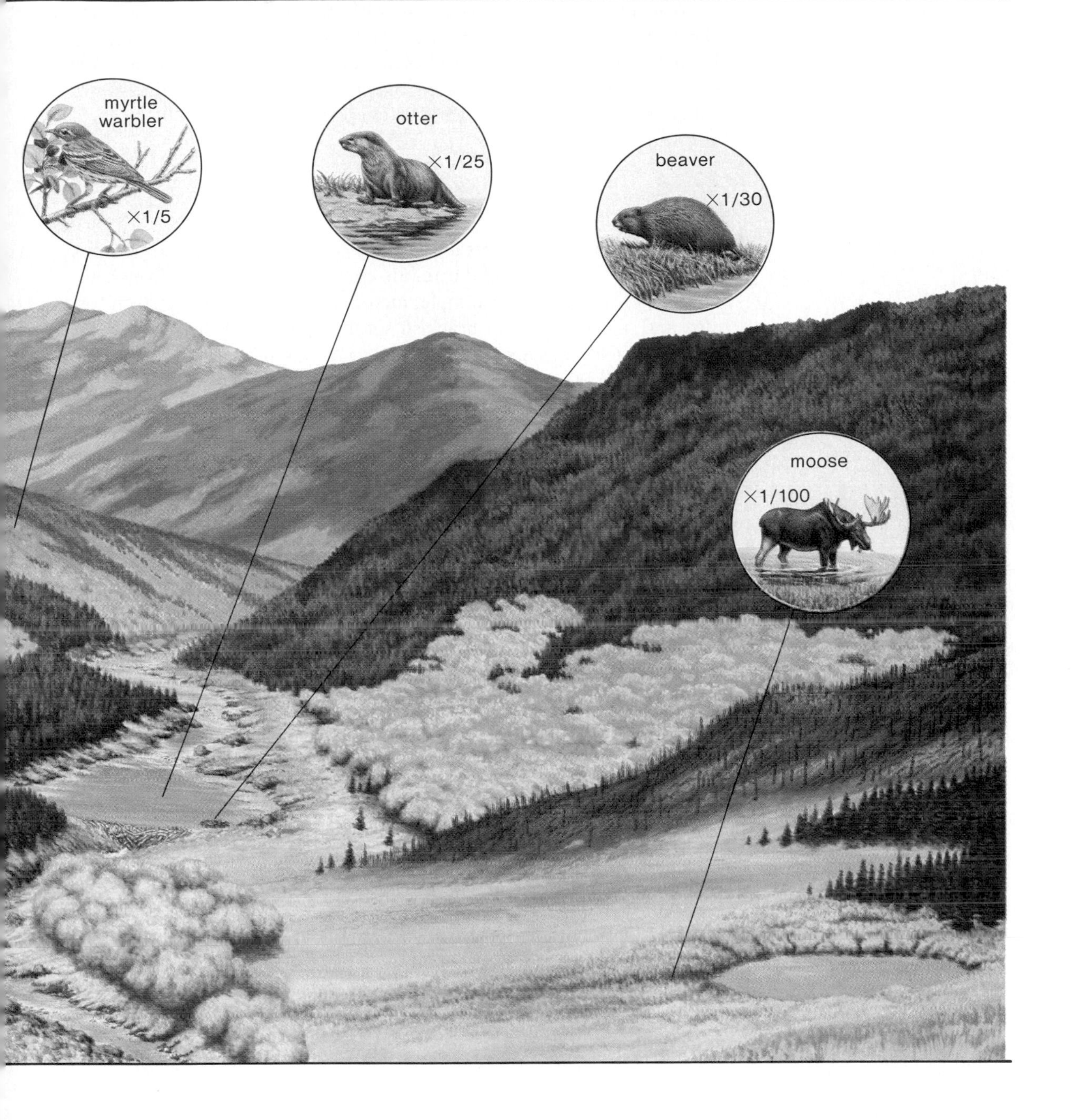
myrtle warbler
×1/5
otter
×1/25
beaver
×1/30
moose
×1/100

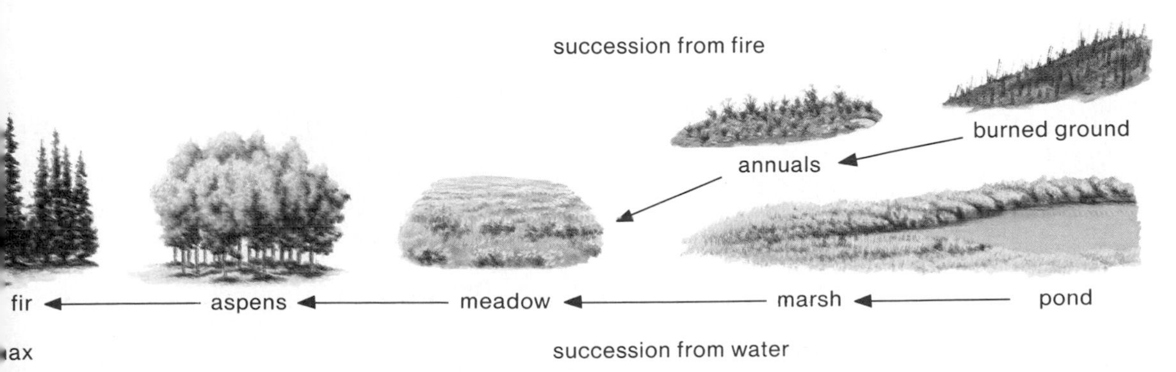
succession from fire
burned ground
annuals
fir
aspens
meadow
marsh
pond
ax
succession from water

Although other factors (such as soil) may play important roles, the climax community is determined mainly by the climate of the region. In some areas, for instance, the climate is unsuitable for trees and the climax community is dominated by grasses. We will examine major climax communities of the world in chapter 22.

20.14 The Animals in a Community Depend on the Plants

Animals depend on plants for food and for shelter. Thus, in any climax community, the plants and the abiotic environment determine which animals can live there. For example, moose live in northern evergreen forests, and manatees live in brackish southern waters. When the former Nevada test site was invaded by plants again, animals soon followed. No forest animals or tropical animals appeared—the animals were the pocket mice (figure 20.28), kangaroo rats (figure 22.35a), and others feeding on desert plants.

Over hundreds or thousands of years, the climate in an area may change. If it grows colder or drier, some animals may die or move elsewhere. Other animals may find the area more hospitable than it was earlier. The selective effect on the animals depends on what adaptations the animals possess. The adaptations may be to climatic factors. Or, animals may be adapted to certain plants that are, in turn, adapted to a certain climate. In that case, a change in climate may affect animals indirectly through changes in the plant life.

The genetic variation present in a natural population means that some individuals will, by chance, prove to be well suited to a change in the environment. Such individuals are, in effect, preadapted to the new environment.

Two species may co-evolve if each is important in the biotic environment of the other. For example, for more than 100 million years flowering plants and flower-pollinating insects have evolved together. The new plants provided more food for the insects, and the new insects pollinated the plants. Each group was a selective force for the other group (see figure 20.29). In the next chapter, you will see more examples of ancient communities in changing environments. In investigation 20.4, you can study the effects of climatic change on a model ecosystem.

Figure 20.28 Pocket mouse.

Figure 20.29 (a) An elk thistle (*Cirsium foliosum*) and (b) its pollinator the bumble bee (*Bombus*). The elk thistle flower is formed of a large head of complex tube flowers. The feeding bee lands on the flowerhead and inserts its tongue into an individual flower to extract the nectar from the base of the tube. Pollen collects all over the bee while it is sucking nectar, and dusts the next flower the bee visits.

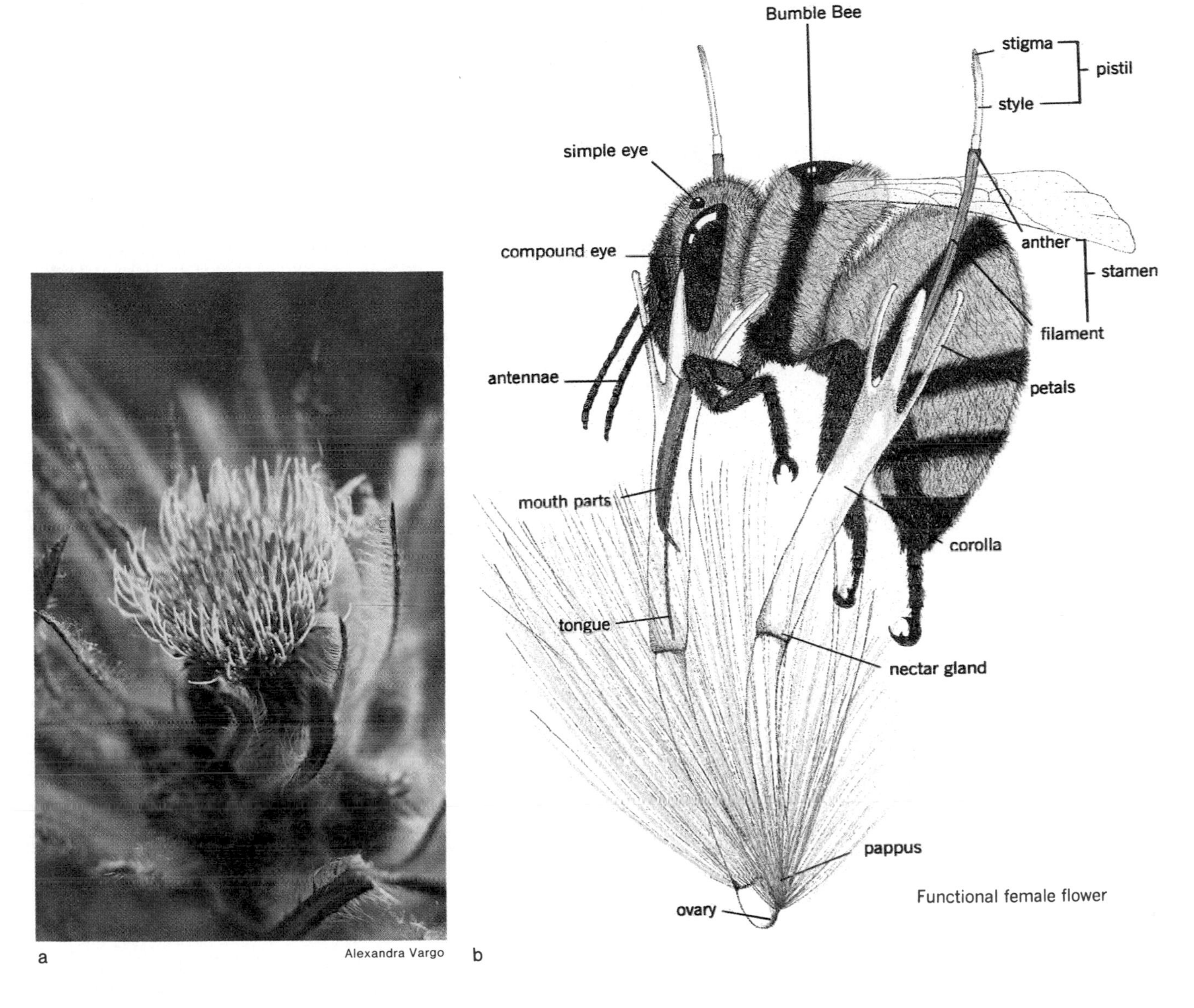

Self-Review

1. What is succession?
2. What kinds of conditions start natural ecological succession?
3. What is meant by a climax community?
4. How does geography help determine the members of climax plant communities?
5. How does geography influence the animals associated with a plant community?

Investigation 20.4 LONG-TERM CHANGES IN AN ECOSYSTEM

Introduction

Over many years, one biotic or abiotic factor in an ecosystem may change. That causes a second factor to change, which, in turn, changes a third factor. Eventually the entire ecosystem may be quite different from what it was earlier.

In this investigation, you will trace the effects of a gradual climatic change on a model ecosystem. The model is much simplified from a real situation.

Procedure

1. Read the following information and diagram the food web in the ecosystem that is described.

   An oak grows next to a shallow stream in a grassy area. There are no shrubs here. Grasshoppers and blacktail jackrabbits feed on the little bluestem grass. Duckweed grows in the water, providing some of the food for wood ducks. These birds also feed on grasshoppers, acorns, and grass. The ducks are a major food source for red wolves.

   The average annual precipitation is 84 cm. The average annual temperature is 10° C.

2. Working as a team, set up a chart like the following:

Round	Years	Average Annual Precipitation	Average Annual Temperature	Changes in Organisms
1	200			
2	400			
(etc. to 50 rounds)				

3. Now fill out the chart, using the following additional information:

   To the west of the grassy area is a desert. There glossy snakes eat Merriam pocket mice. These mice must burrow under shrubs or cacti to hide from the snakes; so the mice cannot live in a grassy area. In the desert they burrow under mesquite shrubs and eat the seeds. Grasshoppers and blacktail jackrabbits eat the mesquite leaves.

   The climate is changing in the grassy area. For the next 10,000 years (50 rounds in your chart), the average annual precipitation will decrease by 1.25 cm every 200 years, and the average annual temperature will increase by 0.3° C every 200 years.

   An average annual temperature of more than 22° C or an average annual precipitation of less than 51 cm will cause the stream to begin drying up and the oak trees to die.

   If the average annual temperature reaches 31° C, or the average annual precipitation is less than 34 cm, the water table will be too low for the grass.

In filling out the chart, assume that organisms in the desert area are trying to disperse to the grassy area at all times, and that they will invade it whenever conditions allow it.

4. After filling out the chart, diagram the food web for the same area at the end of 10,000 years.

Discussion

1. When did the first changes in the ecosystem take place? What changes occurred?
2. What subsequent changes occurred, and in which years?
3. What similarities or differences are there between the initial and final food webs?
4. What is a barrier to dispersal for Merriam pocket mice?
5. What limited the red wolves' population size?
6. What climatic factor was responsible for the other changes?
7. Why does the use of average annual values for temperature and precipitation make this model very artificial?

The Study of Populations

Guidepost: Why do ecologists use a wide variety of techniques and borrow the methods of other scientists?

20.15 Early Humans Studied Their Environment

The earliest humans must have had a keen interest in what we now call ecology. By studying the interactions of predators and prey, they learned where to look for freshly killed meat and what areas might hold dangerous carnivores. By seeing the effects of poisonous plants on other animals, they learned which plants to avoid. Although early humans had no "scientific method," their observations were tests of their hypotheses about food organisms. Such observations of interacting organisms and environments may have been the earliest scientific studies.

Throughout human history, an interest in the communities and ecosystems around us has been necessary for our survival. Eventually, we also learned to appreciate our environment as a focus of art and science. Late in the nineteenth century, the general description of animals and plants called **natural history** evolved into the science of ecology. While natural history emphasized description for its own sake, and sometimes became sentimental or religious, ecology emphasizes experimentation. Though description is often used in ecology, observations are made primarily to test hypotheses.

Figure 20.30 Early humans were the first ecologists.

20.16 Ecologists Study Interactions among Organisms and Environments

Ecologists use many biological techniques. They emphasize experimental studies of interactions among organisms, as well as between the organisms and their environments. To test their hypotheses, they ask questions such as: How many and what kinds of organisms are in this area? What are they doing? What food chains can be found here? How is the community changing over time? How did the organisms come to be like they are now? An ecologist might hypothesize that on any one island of Hawaii, the many niches and the variation in climate would lead to the formation of many species of *Drosophila,* rather than to one population with varying characteristics. To test the hypothesis, it would be necessary to collect drosophilas from many areas, to test their fertility, to do microscopic comparisons of their anatomy, and so on.

Figure 20.31 Two of the many species of *Drosophila* that have evolved in Hawaii. (a) *Drosophila heteroneura;* (b) *Drosophila silvestris.*

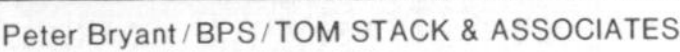

Peter Bryant/BPS/TOM STACK & ASSOCIATES

K. V. Kaneshiro/VISUALS UNLIMITED

Such studies have been aided by the development of new scientific instruments such as modern microscopes and cameras, new techniques for staining organisms and tissues, and by the ability to study variations in DNA. Thus, it has become possible to carry out studies over long periods of time on organisms of all sizes.

20.17 Population Studies Require Special Techniques

Every 10 years, the U.S. Bureau of the Census asks questions of each householder. How many people are in the household? How old are they? How are they employed? The data from all the households in the country are combined. From the results we can describe the population's characteristics and note how they have changed during the 10 years since the previous census.

Taking a human census is difficult enough, even with the help of computers. There are greater problems with taking the census of animal populations, however. Yet such information is essential for **population biologists,** who need to determine the characteristics of a population. For example, they may want to see if a population is evolving in its adaptations for living in a cold environment. One of the things they would need to do is to count the number of organisms in various temperature ranges in that environment.

Many ecological questions are concerned with changes in population size and composition. Some populations, however, may contain thousands of moving organisms. For that reason, ecologists needed to devise reliable ways to estimate the total population size for an area without actually counting every organism. One technique is called sampling, because only a typical sample of the population is counted. For example, if a population is scattered through an area of 10,000 km^2, then a sample of organisms in 1 km^2 should number 1/10,000 of the total population. Of course, many parts of the area would contain atypical numbers. Choosing a sample that is typical of the entire population is difficult, but very important.

Now, suppose a biologist wanted to test the effect of **thermal** (heat) **pollution** on the trout in a lake. One thing the biologist would need to know is how many trout were in the lake before and after the temperature rose. Because it would be hard to find a typical part of the lake to use for a sample, even if the fish did not move around, biologists tag some fish and release them after recording their count. This is the **tagged population.** Later, they collect a sample of fish and count the number having tags. Using the equation

$$\frac{\text{tagged fish in sample}}{\text{total sample}} = \frac{\text{tagged population}}{\text{total population}}$$

they can estimate the total trout population.

To measure environmental factors affecting a population, the biologist needs techniques that might be borrowed from chemistry or geology. It might be necessary, for instance, to test the pH of soil or water, to measure wet-bulb and dry-bulb temperatures, or to determine how much oxygen is dissolved in water.

In some cases, individual organisms of the past are clues about populations of the present. Fossils tell ecologists what kinds of organisms lived in certain places. Rock layers and their fossils indicate what the organisms' environments were like. Sometimes there is also evidence of what the organisms ate, how old they were, and so on. Studies of those organisms and their environments are called **paleoecology** (pay lee oh ee KOL uh jee).

Once the relevant data about a population and its environment are gathered, the ecologist must process the results. Often the average is determined for a characteristic of an organism or an environmental factor. The data are recorded in tables and examined in various ways. For example, in the thermal pollution study, the ecologist might look at the

Figure 20.32 Tagging a brown trout.

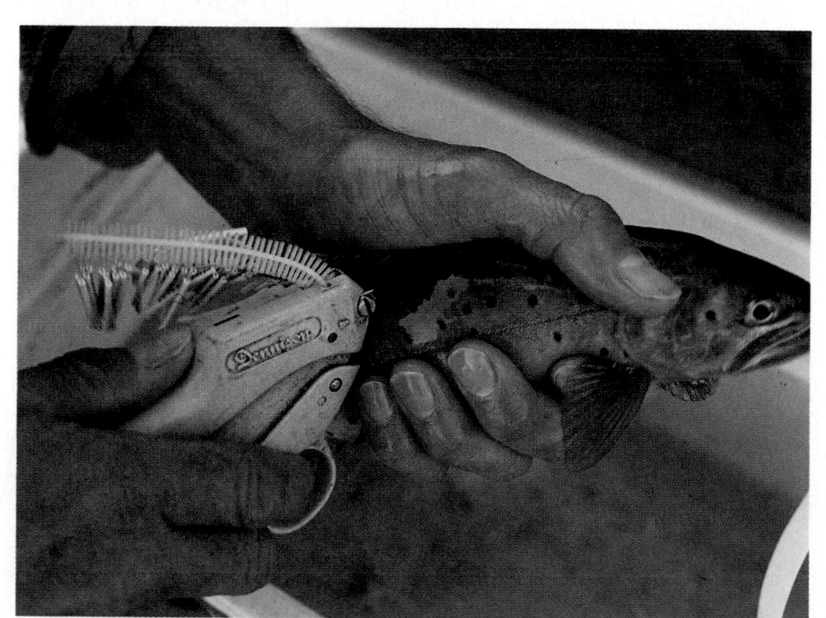

Bruce D. Rosenlund, U.S. Fish & Wildlife Service

total number of living trout before and after the polluting event. Or, the total number could be broken down into large trout and small trout. For any experiment, an enormous number of variables is possible. These can be shown in the form of graphs or charts.

20.18 Human Ecology Reaches into Many Areas

The pressures on the environment from the growing human population have made ecologists very conscious of *human* ecological questions. Today, many ecologists must study economics, engineering, energy relationships, psychology, sociology, and other areas that may sound distant from ecology. By studying the details of what humans do, what we build, and how we interact with each other, ecologists can learn more about how humans affect the world ecosystem.

By definition, ecology has no limits. It integrates all of science and all of life itself. Thus, ecologists use knowledge and techniques from other scientific areas—geology, anthropology, population biology, paleontology, botany, zoology, animal behavior, taxonomy, computer science, and genetics, among others. As knowledge in those sciences has grown, and as their methods have become more mathematical, ecology also has changed in character. Many studies are mathematical, based on calculus and statistics.

20.19 Ecology Is Still Changing

Changes in technology helped change nineteenth-century natural history to modern ecology, and to make ecology more mathematical. Today, technology is again contributing to the character of ecology. The growing

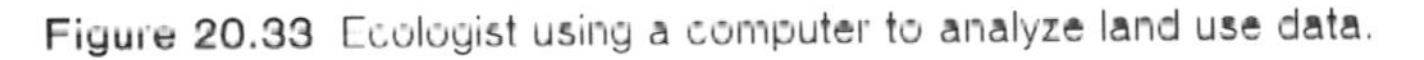

Figure 20.33 Ecologist using a computer to analyze land use data.

Wildlife Resource Information System / Colorado Division of Wildlife

Figure 20.34 Computerized LANDSAT photo of Great Salt Lake. Note the change in color-tone from north to south. The line is caused by a change in salinity in the lake and is directly related to the construction of the Southern Pacific Railroad causeway, which obstructed the circulation in the lake.

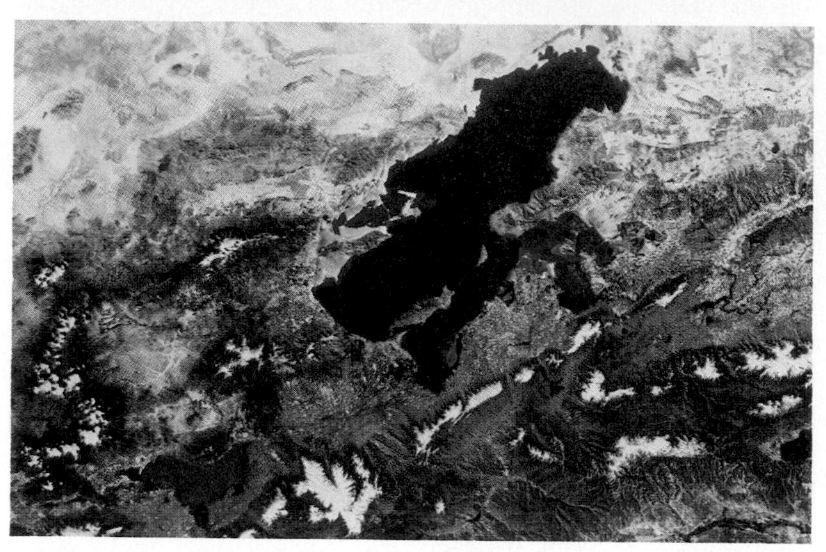

NASA

use of powerful computers has helped ecologists greatly. Elaborate calculations can be done quickly now, freeing scientists to formulate the questions and to interpret the results. Space satellites provide photographs, revealing patterns that were previously difficult or impossible to obtain, as shown in figure 20.34.

The ecological questions themselves have grown. They now include questions such as: How has humankind changed the planet? What will our current activities do to the world in the future? How can we best use current technology to solve problems of human ecology?

In studying selection and survival of populations, ecologists look objectively at patterns of life. The ecologists themselves are part of that pattern, however. What they discover and recommend may help to determine the characteristics of future ecosystems.

Self-Review

1. Why did early humans need to study their environments?
2. What is the purpose of sampling?
3. Why are most ecologists increasingly concerned about questions of human ecology?

Summary

Populations grow in accordance with built-in growth rates, but their growth is usually limited by environmental factors. Such limiting factors result in the selection of individuals for survival or death. Thus, limiting factors determine what the organisms' characteristics are and what the population size can be. Selection is most dramatic when a population is closed, when there is no immigration or emigration. Selection also operates on open populations, as individuals move into new environments. Then limiting factors act as barriers to dispersal, and only organisms with the necessary adaptations to tolerate the new limiting factors are able to survive and migrate to the new area. Over a long period, the interacting populations in an area are shaped by their biotic and abiotic environments. In the absence of disturbance, a climax community of plants appears. That community depends on the climate and geography of the region; typical animals, in turn, depend on the climax community. Dependence of early humans on the plants and animals surrounding them led to practical natural history as a means of survival, and natural history led to modern ecology. As our power to shape the environment increases, so, too, does the strength of ecological methods.

Application Questions

1. Suppose a farmer knows that an insect feeds on apples during its larval stage. A potent insecticide applied to green apples will destroy the insect eggs before they hatch. Or, a safe oil can be sprayed on the trees in the late winter, destroying the insect pupae. Which method would be more effective in controlling the insect population size? Which would probably be safer for people eating the apples?
2. Suppose two populations of a protozoan are grown in an aquarium but are separated by a barrier. Each population reaches 1000, the maximum that can be supported. Then the barrier is removed. If population A is a killer species that attacks population B, what will happen to the two populations in terms of dispersal and eventual population size?
3. Suppose human beings transported living polar bears to Antarctic regions. What do you think would happen? Would you regard the action as a desirable one? Explain.
4. At about the same time as the disappearance of dinosaurs in the fossil record, the earth may have grown colder, and the large primitive forests may have been replaced by flowering plants. What adaptations would the dinosaurs have needed to survive those environmental changes?
5. An ecologist wanted to determine whether adding scarecrows to a golf course would discourage coots (small waterfowl) from landing on the ponds and irritating the golfers. What steps would be necessary to test the hypothesis?

Problems

1. Make a list of terrestrial organisms that human beings have brought into your area. Divide the list into two parts: organisms that (in your opinion) survive because of human activities, and organisms that would survive without human help. Give reasons for your decision on each organism.
2. Explanations of the present geographic ranges of organisms may depend not only on expansion from former ranges but also on reduction of former ranges. What are some factors that might decrease a species' range?
3. Consider the factors that bring about death among humans in modern urban and suburban environments. Include factors that kill individuals before, during, and after the age of reproduction. Consider also factors that reduce health or impair development, and factors that reduce fertility or the survival rate of offspring. Speculate on the possibility that these factors could cause changes in characteristics of future human populations.

Suggested Readings

J. Arehart-Treichel, "Life Expectancy: The Great 20th-Century Leap" *Science News* (13 March 1982). Examines one more facet of a growing human population.

A. T. Bergerud,"Prey Switching in a Simple Ecosystem" *Scientific American* (December 1983). The decline of the caribou in Newfoundland was a clue to a complex cycle of predators and prey.

D. R. Gwatkin and S. K. Brandel, "Life Expectancy and Population Growth in the Third World" *Scientific American* (May 1982). Examines how life expectancy affects population size.

R. A. Kerr, "Periodic Impacts and Extinctions Reported" *Science* (23 March 1984). Investigates one possible explanation for the large-scale extinctions that have occurred periodically throughout Earth's history.

"State of the Species" *Science 86* (January 1986). Three articles relate to current issues in population of the human species.

Smithsonian Institution Photo No. 62.1446

This mural, painted by Jay H. Matternes, depicts some of the better-known mammals of Wyoming in the middle Eocene.

CHAPTER 21

Ecosystems of the Past

Introduction

Ecologists study the size, shape, and other characteristics of organisms in the present. These characteristics may change quickly or may persist for hundreds of years. Selection by the environment may promote one population's survival but extinguish another. And, if the same area were seen once every million years, few populations would have remained just like their ancestors of a million years before. The entire pattern of the ecosystem would have changed greatly, or have evolved. In this chapter we will learn how scientists study the earth's history and what their study has revealed about past ecosystems.

Reconstructing the Past

Guideposts: What evidence do paleontologists study, and how do they reach conclusions?

21.1 Fossils Are Evidence of Organisms in the Past

When organisms of the distant past died, most of them decayed and disappeared forever. Here and there, however, skeletons, teeth, and other decay-resistant structures remained. Sometimes parts of organisms were replaced by minerals, or **petrified** (PEH trih fyd). Sometimes a mold, or cast, of an organism was formed in mud that hardened. Any such impression or remains of an organism that lived in a past age is called a fossil (see figure 21.1).

Figure 21.1 A variety of fossils. (a) *Archaeopteryx,* generally accepted as the oldest known bird, (b) petrified wood, (c) seed fern leaf, (d) frozen remains of a baby woolly mammoth, found at Cripple Creek, Alaska, (e) starfish.

a Neg. No. 319836, Courtesy Department of Library Services, American Museum of Natural History.

b American Airlines

c

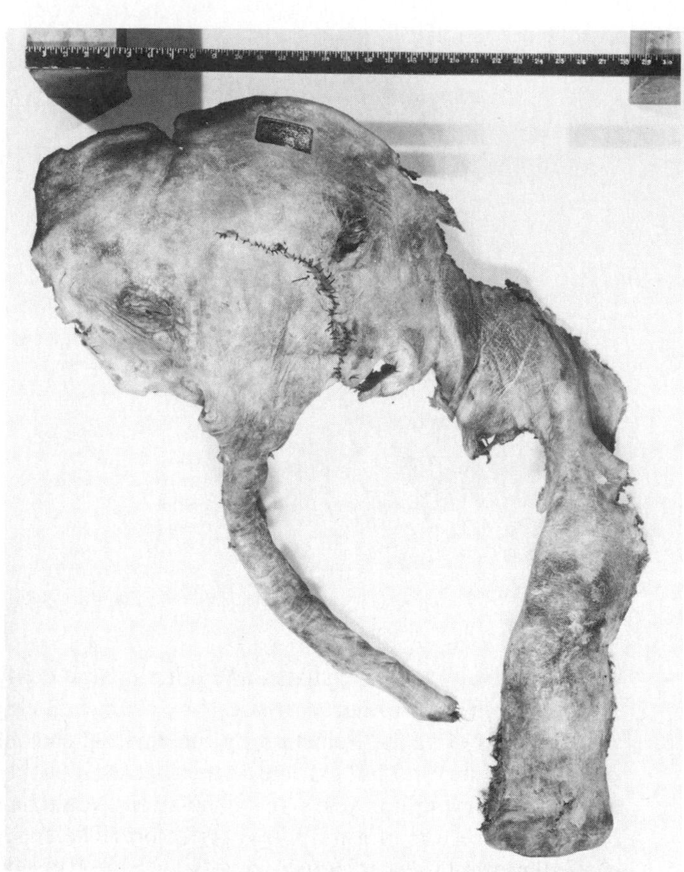

d Neg. No. 320539 (Photo: Thane L. Bierwert), Courtesy Department Library Services, American Museum of Natural History.

e Smithsonian Institution Photo No. Departmental Negative

Figure 21.2 Fossil formation. (a) Underwater sediments are oxygen-poor. Thus, there may be few of the oxygen-requiring microorganisms that decay plant and animal remains. Dead fish, or their skeletons, may remain intact in those sediments over long periods of time. Eventually minerals circulating in underground water replace the bone substance of the fish's skeletons. The mineralized skeletal replacements are fossils. (b) Buried fossils may be exposed by any of the forces that uplift segments of the earth's crust and expose those segments to erosion.

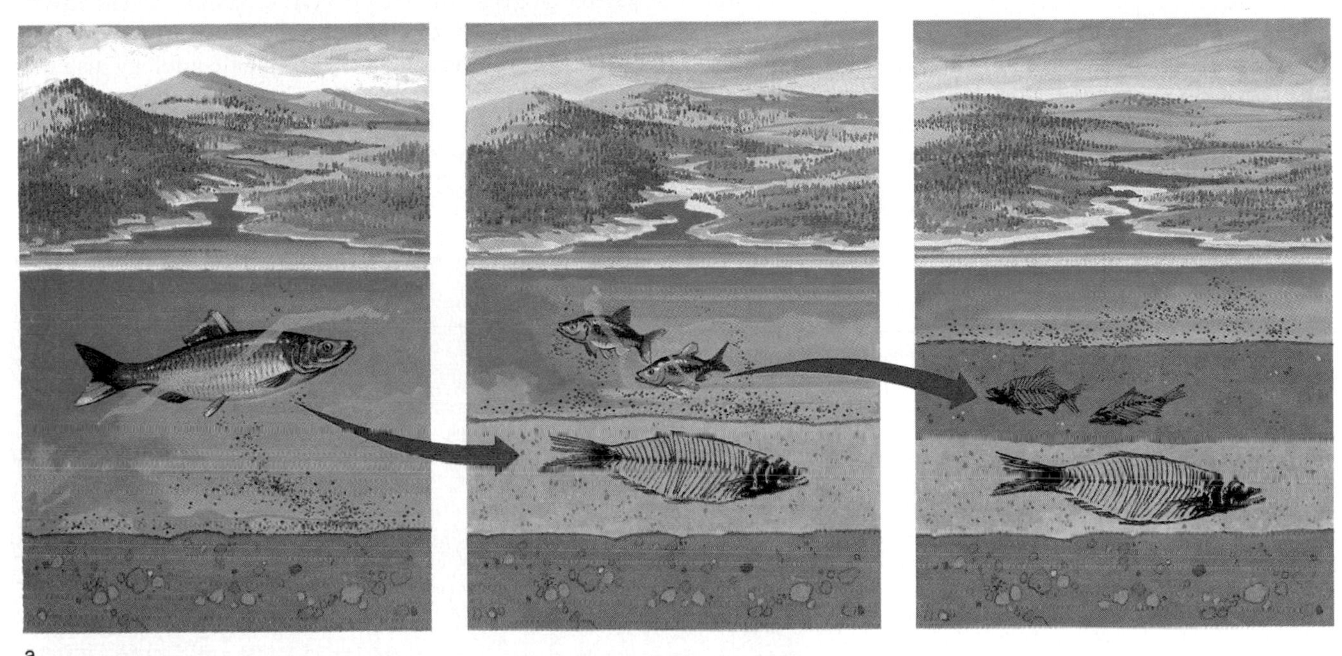

a

b

Even as fossils were forming they were covered with sand or mud that hid them from view. In some cases millions of years passed, with many layers of sediment being added. The layers, or **strata** (STRAYT uh), turned to rock. Finally, some event, such as the erosion of the Grand Canyon or the building of a highway (figure 21.3), exposed some of the fossils to view. There we can study them as evidence of the past.

Layers of rock are all that is left from ecosystems of past ages. They are studied by **paleontologists** (pay lee un TOL uh jists)—scientists who study fossil remains to reconstruct the long drama of life. Ecologists, geologists, and geographers whose fields overlap paleontology also may study fossil evidence.

Figure 21.3 The stratification of rock layers in this mountainside was exposed when a highway was built.

BSCS by Carlye Calvin

Figure 21.4 Excavating dinosaur bones at Dinosaur National Monument on the Colorado–Utah border. What information do you think is important enough to be recorded?

C. Allan Morgan

Paleontologists and geologists have pieced together information from many parts of the world. In this way they have been able to put most of the known rock strata in sequence. But how old are the strata?

The most reliable method for dating rocks depends on the presence of **radioactive** (ray dee oh AK tiv) chemical elements such as uranium. The atomic nuclei of radioactive elements are unstable and emit radiation. They break down to stable elements at a constant rate known as the **half-life,** the time it takes for half of the element to break down. Uranium breaks down to lead; its half-life is 4.5 billion years. Paleontologists can use the half-life of uranium to calculate the age of a rock. To do that, they remove a sample of rock from a stratum and measure the amount of uranium and lead in it. For example, if they find equal parts of lead and uranium, the rock is 4.5 billion years old. Half of the uranium that was present when the rock was formed has had time to break down to lead.

By measuring the ratios between uranium and lead, we can estimate the ages of rocks that are millions of years old. The measurements are not perfect, but they have provided a time scale (table 21.1) that is more accurate than any previous one. Similar calculations have been made using radioactive potassium and rubidium. Radioactive carbon (^{14}C) has been used to determine the age of plant and animal remains. New techniques measure directly the ^{14}C atoms in the sample and allow the dating of materials up to 70,000 years old.

Figure 21.5 Strata of sedimentary rock are usually piled on each other like pages in a book. In general the oldest strata are at the bottom and the newest on top. Geologists fit together strata from different places to construct the "book of the earth."

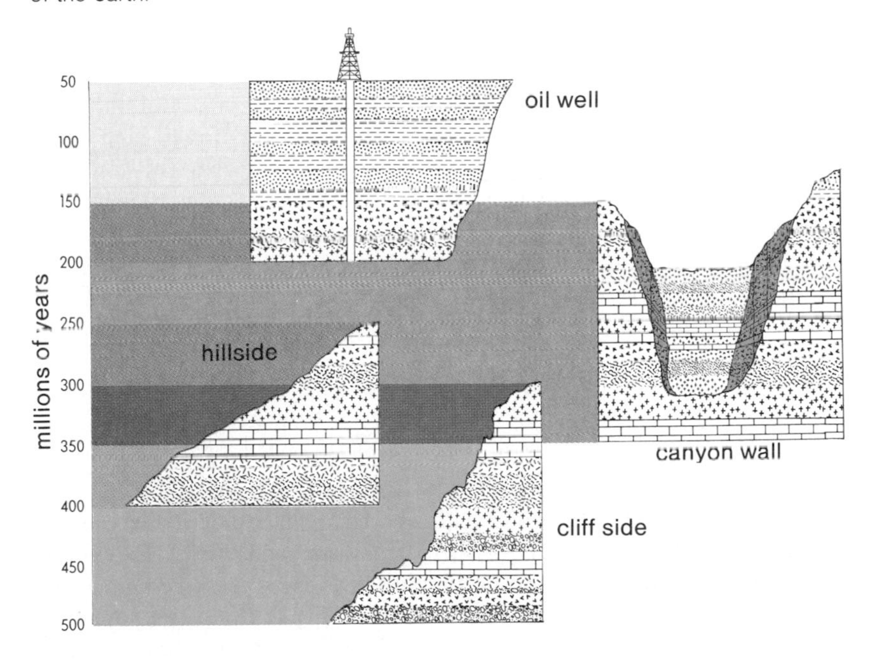

Table 21.1 Geologic time scale

Eras	Periods	Epochs	Years in Millions Since Beginning of Period or Epoch (MYA)
Cenozoic	Quaternary	Recent	.1
		Pleistocene	1.6
	Tertiary	Pliocene	5
		Miocene	22
		Oligocene	36
		Eocene	55
		Paleocene	65
Mesozoic	Cretaceous		144
	Jurassic		192
	Triassic		245
Paleozoic	Permian		290
	Carboniferous		360
	Devonian		408
	Silurian		435
	Ordovician		485
	Cambrian		570
Precambrian			4600

21.2 Paleontologists Study the Evidence

Inferences about ancient ecosystems are based on studies of ancient rock layers and the fossils within them. Early paleontologists were puzzled by fossils that did not resemble any living forms until the theory of evolution made it possible to link fossils with living forms. Then fossils could be seen as clues to the history of life.

Soft parts of an organism usually decay, and even when all the hard parts are preserved, they are seldom found in perfect condition. They usually must be reassembled and placed in proper relation to each other. To do this well, paleontologists must know modern organisms and how the parts are arranged. Then, to picture fossil organisms as they were in life, paleontologists must determine the placement of structures that have disappeared, such as muscles or leaves. Finally, paleontologists may paint a reconstruction of the animal—a life-size model based on fossils. The choice of colors is guesswork: guesses are based on our knowledge of color in modern organisms.

In all this work it is possible for different paleontologists to interpret the evidence differently. The farther we go from the basic evidence—the fossils themselves—the greater is the possibility of differing interpretations, as you can see in figure 21.6.

In reconstructing the evolution of species, paleontologists need to determine relationships among modern organisms and fossils. Today they even can study the DNA and protein in some fossils preserved in ice and mud and can calculate the amount of similarity to those compounds in other organisms. Biochemical studies, however, are a recent development. Morphological characteristics are still widely used for determination of relationships and for classification.

Consider the problem posed by a fossil from the early Mesozoic era, about 225 million years ago. It looks like a reptilian jaw, but can we be sure? Mammals were beginning to appear then. Many characteristics

Figure 21.6 *Stegosaurus,* a late Mesozoic reptile. ×1/50 (a) Fossil bones mounted in a museum, (b) an artist's reconstruction, (c) another artist's reconstruction.

a

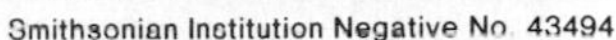

Smithsonian Institution Negative No. 43494

b Smithsonian Institution Negative No. 28531

c Peabody Museum, Yale University

are used to distinguish present-day mammals from reptiles. Mammals have simple jawbones, incisors and molars, hair, and mammary (milk) glands. Reptiles have none of these characteristics. But if mammals evolved from reptiles, there once must have been animals with a combination of mammalian and reptilian characteristics. Such problems make the work of paleontologists and taxonomists difficult but interesting.

21.3 The Evidence Must Be Interpreted

No one can examine a large collection of fossils without being impressed by change. That is especially true if the fossils of one general type are arranged in chronological order.

Figure 21.7 Artist's conception of the animals along the main line of evolutionary descent from primitive bony fishes to mammals: *Eusthenopteron*, a primitive lobe-finned fish; *Ichthyostega*, a large primitive amphibian; *Varanops*, a primitive mammal-like reptile; *Probelesodon*, a more advanced mammal-like reptile showing distinct mammalian characteristics; and *Megazostrodon*, the small, shrew-like first mammal.

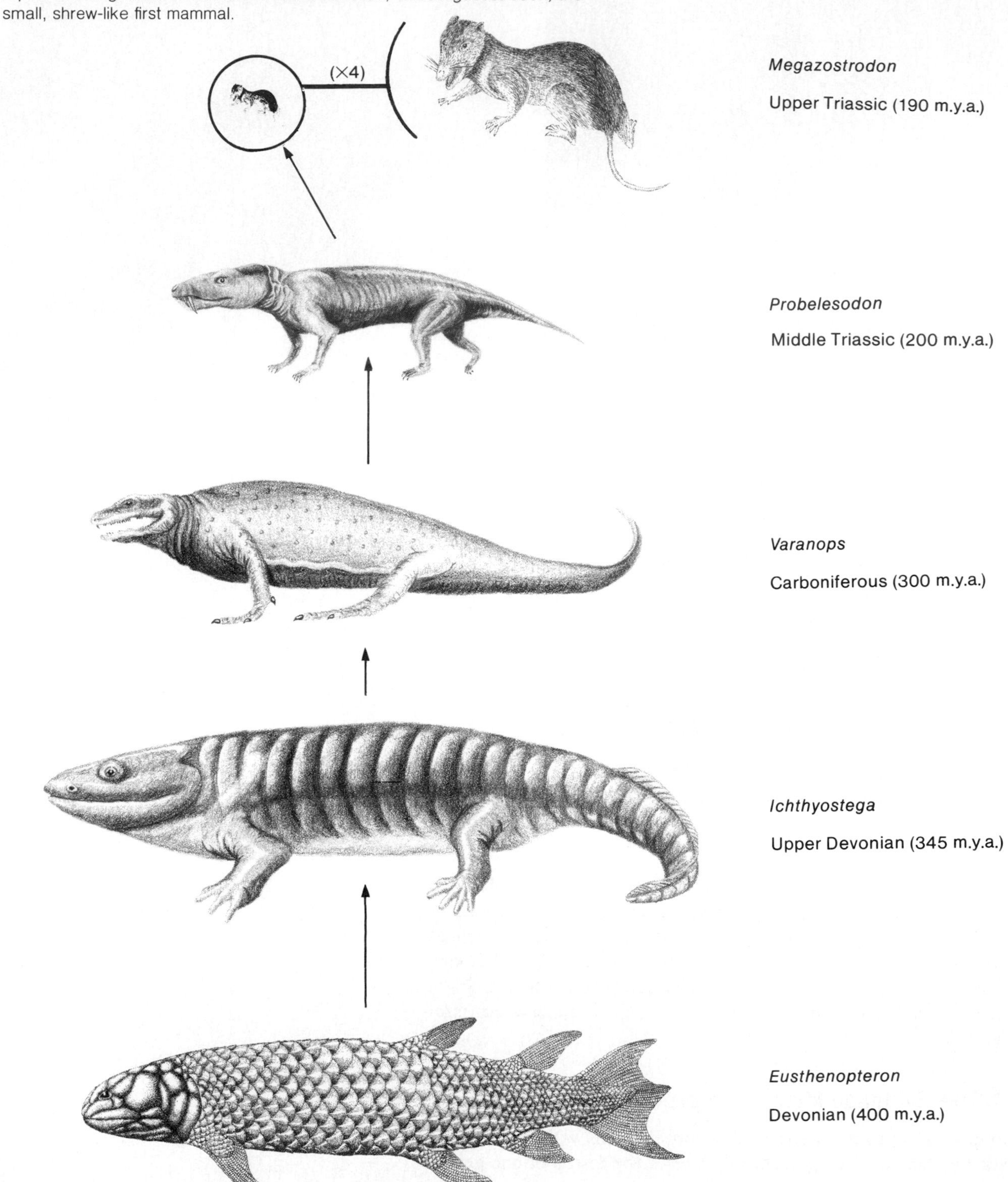

Many species have died out and left no descendants. Others seem to have changed so much through many generations that the successive forms are given different species names.

The fossil record shows that advanced forms in one geological period have descended from primitive ancestral forms in preceding periods. For example, mammals are considered more advanced than reptiles. However, the advanced reptiles of the Mesozoic did not give rise to mammals in the Cenozoic. On the contrary, the ancestors of those reptiles were apparently also the ancestors of the mammals.

At least 130,000 species of animals are known only indirectly from their fossil remains. Dinosaurs and many other groups have become extinct, that is, the entire group died out. In the Cambrian, trilobites (figure 21.8) were varied and very numerous, according to their fossils. They disappeared suddenly from the geological record.

There have been many large-scale extinctions on earth. The trilobites perished in one of those catastrophes. Other groups, including the dinosaurs, died out in other extinctions. What caused such extinctions? Paleontologists have puzzled over this problem for a long time. There have been many hypotheses, but testing paleontologic hypotheses is especially difficult. Although we may never learn what caused the extinction of dinosaurs and other organisms, new evidence continues to be found.

Figure 21.8 A fossil trilobite. Its actual size was about that of a paperclip.

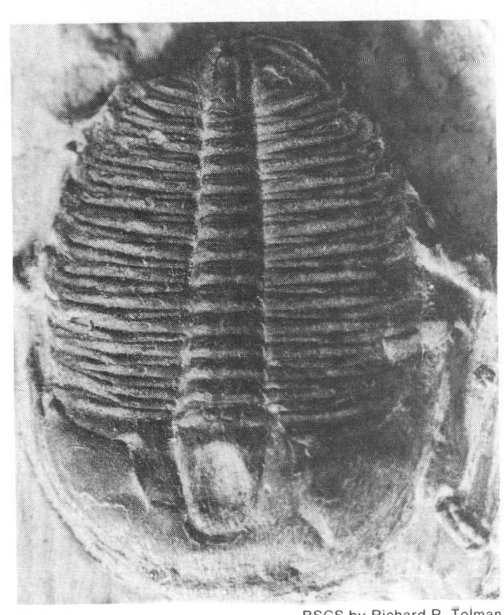

BSCS by Richard R. Tolman

21.4 Interpretations Are Based on Principles

Whole ecosystems also have changed, another example of ecological succession. Change in ecosystems depends on the changes in a particular environment. It also depends on the adaptability of the organisms living in it. A structure that adapts an organism to one environment might be a hindrance in a different environment.

Though the fossil record shows abundant evidence of change, it also provides evidence of great stability. Brachiopods much like those of the Paleozoic seas (figure 21.9) are found in twentieth-century oceans, for example. Ocean environments are generally more constant than land environments. Thus, many of the adaptations that allowed the early forms to survive apparently are still useful.

Figure 21.9 (a) A present day brachiopod. (b) Fossil casts of brachiopods.

Frank T. Awbrey/VISUALS UNLIMITED

a

Smithsonian Institution Departmental Negative

b

Throughout the history of life on Earth, the descendants of small groups of organisms have dispersed into a great variety of ecosystems. That process is known as **adaptive radiation,** because it involved adaptation of the organisms as well as dispersal into many environments. Each original small group may have been adapted to a narrow range of ecological conditions. Their descendants in new ecosystems, however, must have had slightly different adaptations. Adaptive radiation is well demonstrated by mammals, as shown in figure 21.10.

The fossil record also shows examples of **adaptive convergence** (kun VER jents). In such cases, descendants of quite different ancestors have converged (developed similar structures) as they adapted to similar ways of life. Compare (figure 21.11) the spiny, leafless euphorbia of the African desert with a cactus of the Mexican desert. Their body forms are similar, yet flower structure shows that they are members of two different families.

Figure 21.10 Adaptive radiation in the class Mammalia. Representative animals from the orders included are (1) pangolin, (2) squirrel, (3) bat, (4) lion, (5) buffalo, (6) horse, (7) elephant, (8) armadillo, (9) rabbit, (10) monkey, (11) mole, (12) whale, (13) aardvark, (14) manatee, (15) kangaroo, (16) mastodon, (17) litoptern, (18) creodont, (19) *Brontotherium,* (20) *Uintatherium.*

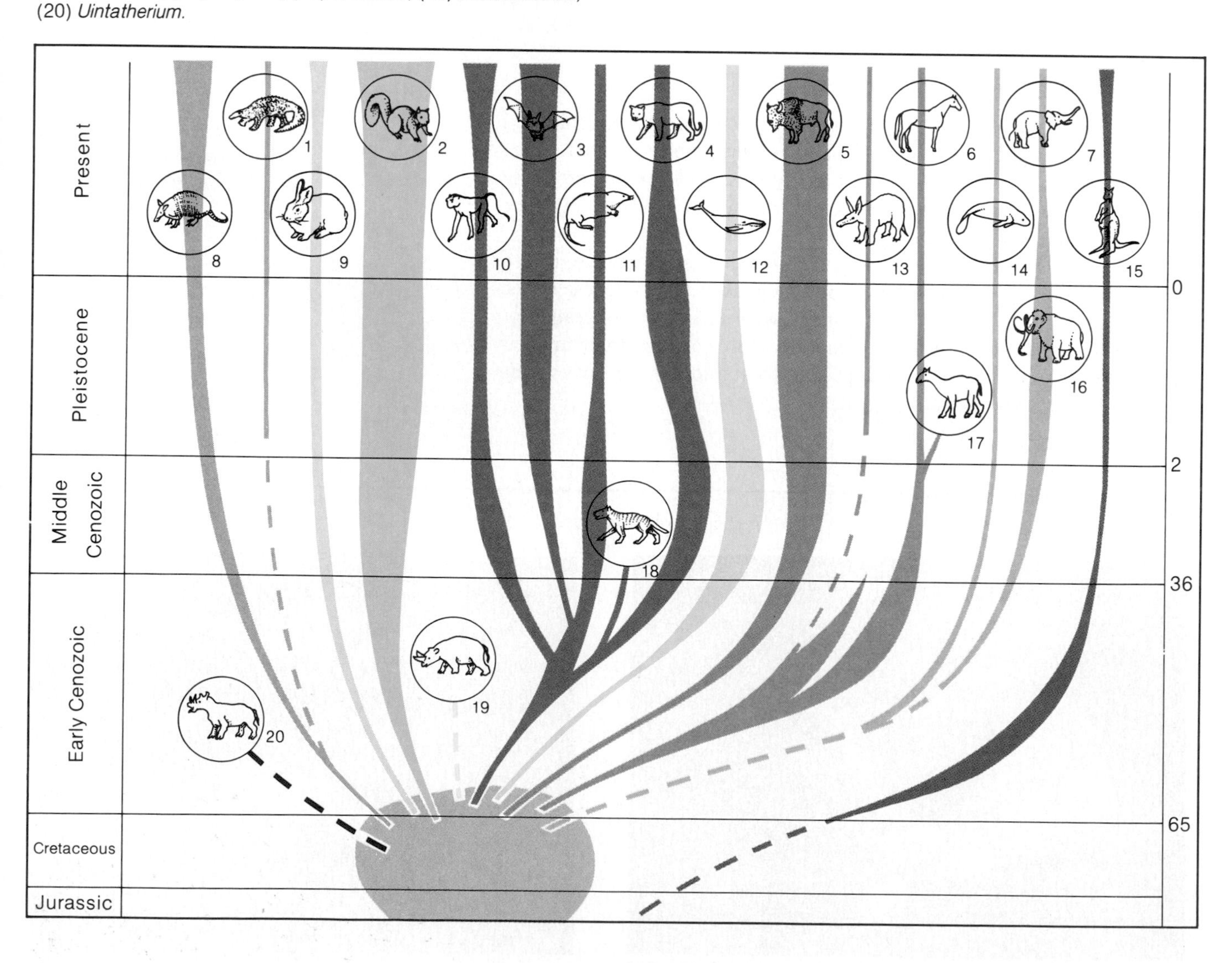

Figure 21.11 Adaptive convergence in plants. Cactus is on the left, euphorbia on the right. Note the similarities in general appearance and in the spines, and the differences in the flowers.

On the whole, fossil evidence favors the hypothesis that each species originated in one place and spread into others. But some species undoubtedly were more widespread at one time than they are today. As a result, there are **discontinuous** (dis kun TIN yoo us) **distributions:** members of the same species are found today in widely separated regions (see figure 21.15 on page 769).

Self-Review

1. What are fossils and how are they formed?
2. Why is collecting fossils only the beginning of a paleontologist's work?
3. How can the age of a fossil be determined?
4. How would a paleontologist decide whether a particular fossil represented a reptile or a mammal?
5. How does the fossil record support both the idea of change and the idea of stability in living things?
6. What problem does the extinction of large groups of organisms—such as the dinosaurs—present to paleontologists?
7. How do adaptive radiation and adaptive convergence differ?

Investigation 21.1 PALEONTOLOGIC COMPARISON

Introduction

The first laboratory task of paleontologists is to remove specimens carefully from surrounding rock. The next task is to describe the cleaned specimens, which includes accurately measuring them. This investigation shows one of the ways that measurements are useful in the interpretation of fossils.

Members of the early Eocene genus *Hyracotherium* are the oldest known animals of the horse family, Equidae. Numerous fossil remains of this family have been found in rocks of the late Eocene and of succeeding Cenozoic epochs. Paleontologists have classified the animals represented by these fossils into 17 genera (figure 21.12). Classification is based on the comparison of many kinds of structural evidence. In this investigation you will study only one of the many anatomical characteristics that paleontologists have used, and determine whether this characteristic is useful in developing an evolutionary scheme for this family.

In horses the grinding teeth are in the back of the mouth, separated from the front teeth by a toothless space. On each side of each jaw, the grinding teeth (cheek teeth) consist of 3 premolars and 3 molars (figure 21.13). The span of the cheek teeth has been measured in many horse fossils. Averages of the data are presented in table 21.2.

Materials (per student)

1 sheet graph paper
pencil

Figure 21.12

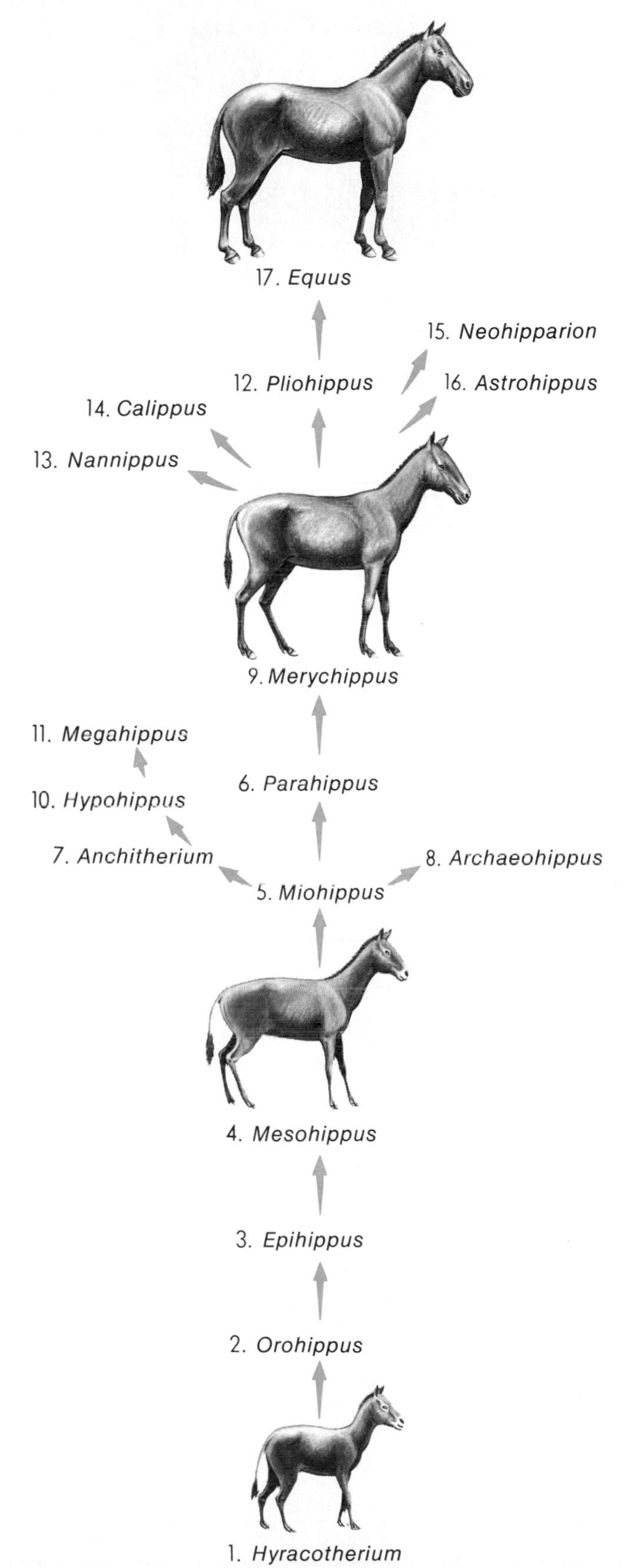
17. Equus
15. Neohipparion
12. Pliohippus
16. Astrohippus
14. Calippus
13. Nannippus
9. Merychippus
11. Megahippus
6. Parahippus
10. Hypohippus
7. Anchitherium
8. Archaeohippus
5. Miohippus
4. Mesohippus
3. Epihippus
2. Orohippus
1. Hyracotherium

Figure 21.13

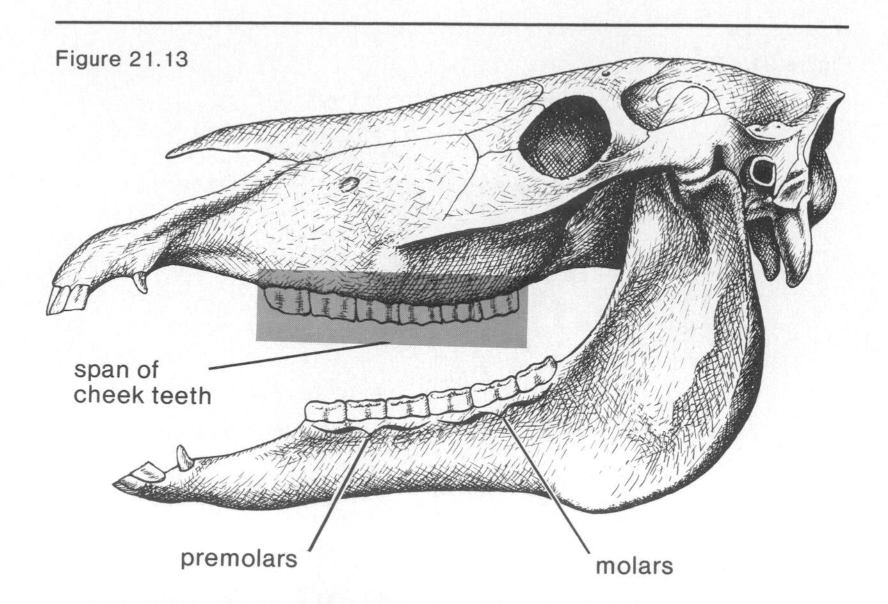

Table 21.2 Average span of cheek teeth in equidae

Genera of Equidae	Time of Existence	Span of Cheek Teeth (in cm)
1. *Hyracotherium*	Early Eocene	4.3
2. *Orohippus*	Middle Eocene	4.3
3. *Epihippus*	Late Eocene	4.7
4. *Mesohippus*	Early Oligocene	7.2
	Middle Oligocene	7.3
5. *Miohippus*	Late Oligocene	8.4
	Early Miocene	8.3
6. *Parahippus*	Early Miocene	10.0
7. *Anchitherium*	Early Miocene	11.3
8. *Archaeohippus*	Middle Miocene	6.5
9. *Merychippus*	Middle Miocene	10.2
	Late Miocene	12.5
10. *Hypohippus*	Late Miocene	14.2
11. *Megahippus*	Early Pliocene	21.5
12. *Pliohippus*	Early Pliocene	15.5
	Middle Pliocene	15.6
13. *Nannippus*	Early Pliocene	11.0
	Late Pliocene	10.7
14. *Calippus*	Early Pliocene	9.3
15. *Neohipparian*	Middle Pliocene	13.1
16. *Astrohippus*	Middle Pliocene	11.8
	Late Pliocene	11.8
17. *Equus*	Late Pliocene	18.8
	Pleistocene	17.6

Procedure

1. When plotted on a graph, the data in table 21.2 suggest certain relationships. Figure 21.14 shows a convenient type of grid to use. Construct a grid twice this size on a full sheet of paper, so that the plotted points will not be crowded. On the grid, plot the cheek-teeth span measurements of the 17 Equidae genera. As each point is plotted on the graph, place beside it the number of the genus it represents.
2. Connect the points representing the genera *Hyracotherium, Orohippus, Epihippus, Mesohippus,* and *Miohippus* (genus 1 through genus 5). What seems to have been the trend of evolution in the span of cheek teeth during Eocene and Oligocene times?
3. (a) Without drawing any lines, describe the general trend of evolution in cheek-teeth span during the Miocene, Pliocene, and Pleistocene.
   (b) Is it possible to connect all of these points with a single line? Why?
4. Now you can find out whether the data on this span of the cheek teeth fit other relationships among the equid genera. To do this, draw lines between the plotted points, so that they correspond to the arrows in figure 21.12. For example, draw a line from the dot for *Miohippus* to that for *Megahippus,* connecting genera 5, 7, 10, and 11. Draw another line from the dot for *Miohippus* to that for *Archaeohippus,* connecting genera 5 and 8. Draw a 3rd line from *Miohippus* to *Equus,* connecting genera 5, 6, 9, 12, and 17. Then draw in the remaining four branches from *Merychippus,* genus 9 (late Miocene) as indicated.

Discussion

If data on a single characteristic conflict with relationships worked out from other characteristics, the data will produce a set of crossing lines when graphed.

1. Do the data on the span of the cheek teeth support the relationships shown in figure 21.12, or do they conflict with those relationships?
2. What was the average change in the span of the cheek teeth per million years from *Hyracotherium* (genus 1) to *Miohippus* (genus 5)?
3. What was the average change per million years from *Miohippus* to *Megahippus* (genus 11)?

Figure 21.14

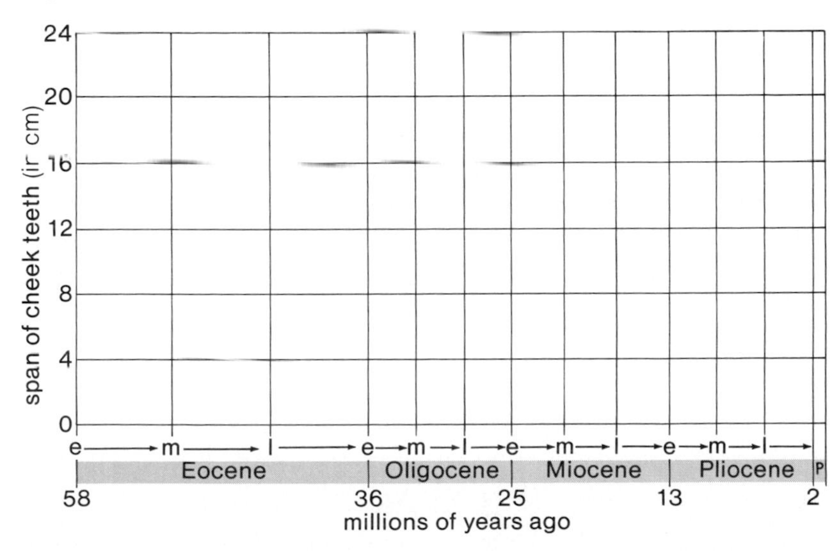

4. From *Miohippus* to *Equus* (genus 17)?
5. From these results, what generalization can you make about the rate of evolutionary change within the Equidae?
6. What evidence do you have that the direction of an evolutionary change may be reversed?
7. From figure 21.12, what would you say was the general trend in the evolution of body size from *Hyracotherium* to *Equus?*
8. How many years passed between the time of the *Hyracotherium* and the early *Equus* horses?
9. If each horse lived 5 years before it reproduced, how many generations of horses were there between *Hyracotherium* and *Equus?*
10. What does this tell you about the rate of evolution?

Guidepost What steps led to the broad array of organisms found on earth today?

The "Entangled Bank" of Life Today

21.5 All Life Has Come from a Simple Beginning

At the end of his famous book on the origin of species, Charles Darwin provided his readers with a poetic summary of how evolution by natural selection has resulted in the many organisms surrounding us:

> It is interesting to contemplate an entangled bank, clothed with many plants of many kinds, with birds singing on the bushes, with various insects flitting about, and with worms crawling through the damp earth, and to reflect that these elaborately constructed forms, so different from each other, and dependent on each other in so complex a manner, have all been produced by laws acting around us. . . . There is grandeur in this view of life, with its several powers, having been originally breathed into a few forms or into one; and that, whilst this planet has gone cycling on according to the fixed law of gravity, from so simple a beginning endless forms most beautiful and most wonderful have been, and are being evolved.
>
> —Charles Darwin, *On the Origin of Species by Means of Natural Selection*

Darwin, of course, wrote about evolution before the heterotroph hypothesis described in section 10.12 was formed and long before scientists duplicated the conditions in which life is thought to have originated. But his comments apply to the evolution of all living forms, starting with those first simple tide-pool heterotrophs and ending with the varied forms about us today.

21.6 Evolution Has Occurred on Moving Plates

The paleontologist's work is complicated by certain geological events. Those events have been involved in cases like the ones shown in figure 21.15. *Nothofagus* (noth oh FAYG us) is a flowering plant sometimes called southern beech. It is, and apparently always has been, absent from the northern hemisphere. A similar pattern of distribution is shown by fossils of *Glossopteris* (glah SOP ter is), a genus of Paleozoic seed ferns, except that they occur also in India and South Africa. Other Paleozoic and early Mesozoic terrestrial organisms have similar patterns of distribution.

The areas are separated by thousands of miles of ocean. The seeds of the plants are not adapted to such long-distance travel over the ocean. Then how did the plants and their fossils get where they are now?

Figure 21.15 Distribution map of extinct *Glossopteris* ferns and living *Nothofagus* trees.

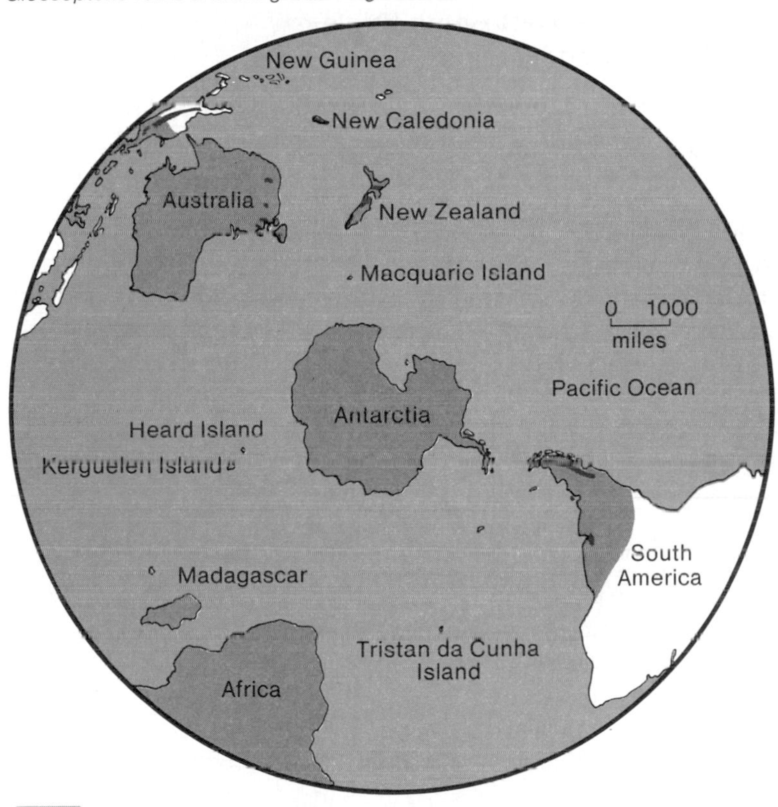

The answer to that and similar puzzling questions was provided by Alfred Wegener, a German scientist, who in 1912 suggested that the continents have not always been where they are now. His idea was that these big land masses might be slowly "floating" over the earth's hot liquid interior. Few accepted his idea at that time. More than 40 years later, though, geologists found great cracks in the middle of the ocean floors. The cracks seemed to have resulted from the rock separating and moving in opposite directions. To the geologists that also indicated that some continents were moving away from each other. Many other observations supported a theory of **continental drift,** illustrated in figure 21.16.

The world's continents were probably joined together at one time in a giant continent geologists call **Pangaea** (pan JEE uh). Figure 21.17 shows how Pangaea was formed and then broke up, and how that helped affect the distribution and evolution of organisms. The continental drift theory is now part of a broader theory of **plate tectonics** (tek TON iks). According to the broader theory, land masses are the highest parts of huge plates that make up the earth's crust.

21.7 Continental Drift Helps Explain Ancient Ecosystems

If the theory is correct, then the discontinuous distribution of organisms such as *Nothofagus* and *Glossopteris* can be explained. They lived and dispersed when the southern continents still were joined as Gondwanaland. When that ancient continent began to break up, the plants and their fossils were carried toward their present positions.

A general principle of paleontology is "The present is the key to the past." In the study of discontinuous distribution, we can see that sometimes the past sheds light on the present. The patterns in today's ecosystems result from events in past ecosystems. In the next section, we present a broad overview of some of those **paleoecosystems** (pay lee oh EE koh sis tumz) (ecosystems of the past).

Self-Review

1. How does continental drift explain some cases of discontinuous distribution of organisms?
2. What was Pangaea?
3. Where is Gondwanaland today?
4. What principle guides the interpretation of paleontologic evidence?

Figure 21.16 Diagram illustrating the mechanism of continental drift. Magma, or molten rock from the earth's interior, forces its way through the thin oceanic crust and forms new crust. This new crust moves away from the mid-oceanic ridge as the process continues. Where the heavy oceanic crust meets the lighter continental coast it is subducted, or forced to slide beneath the continental crust, resulting in volcanoes and island arcs.

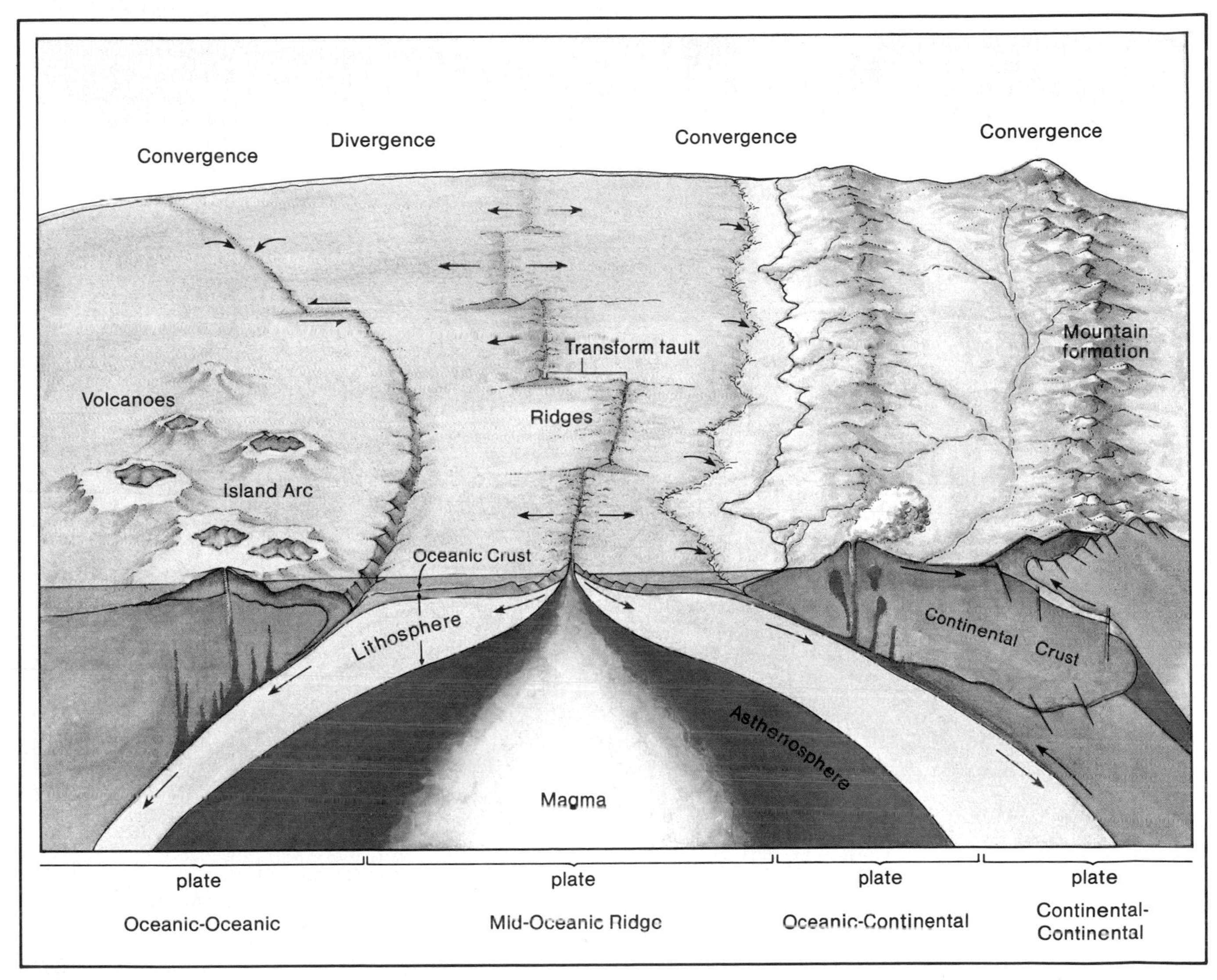

Figure 21.17 The formation and breakup of Pangaea correlated with events in evolution.

CAMBRIAN EARTH

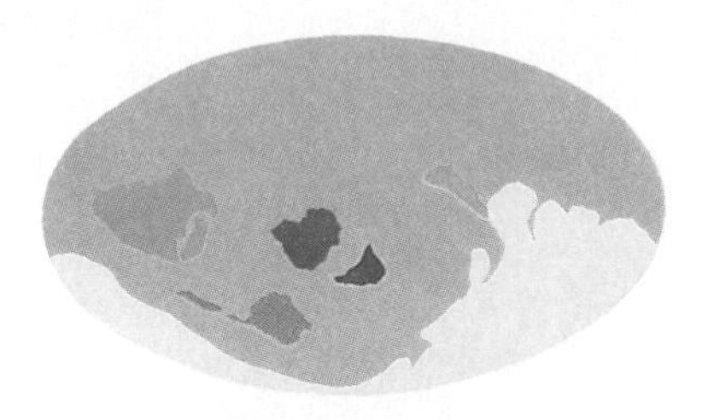

Four large (and two small) continents had been formed and were moving toward each other. Sea levels were high. Vermont mountains were formed.

DEVONIAN EARTH

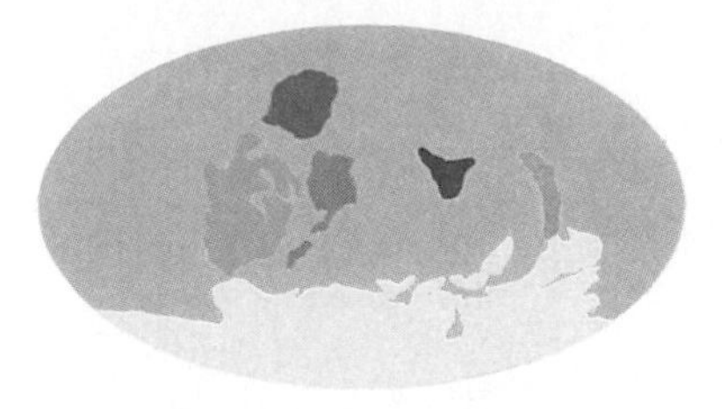

Laurentia and Baltica had collided to form one continent. Sea levels were low. In some regions there were periods of drought.

CARBONIFEROUS EARTH

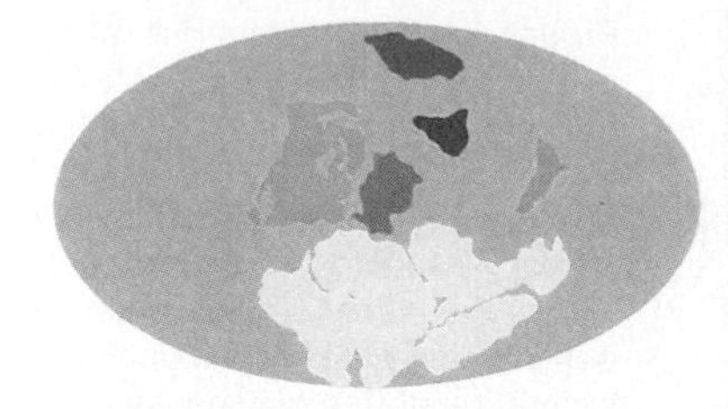

Because of high humidity, swamps and forests covered much of the land.

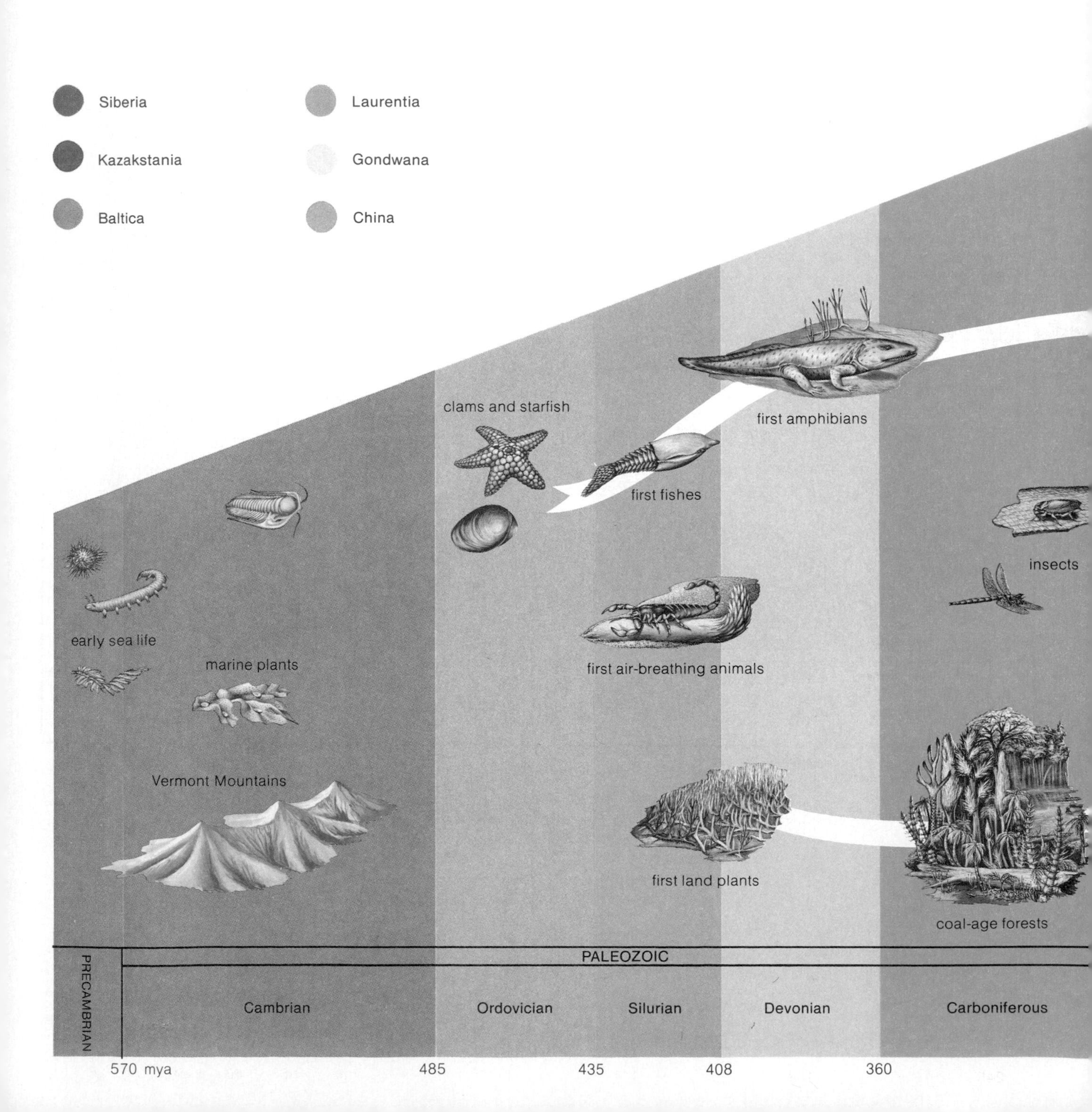

TRIASSIC EARTH

Pangaea had been formed by the four major continents. Sea levels were low and there were many deserts. Appalachian mountains were formed.

CRETACEOUS EARTH

North America and Europe began splitting apart and South America and Africa separated. The sea level was high. Formation of the Rocky Mountains began.

PLEISTOCENE EARTH

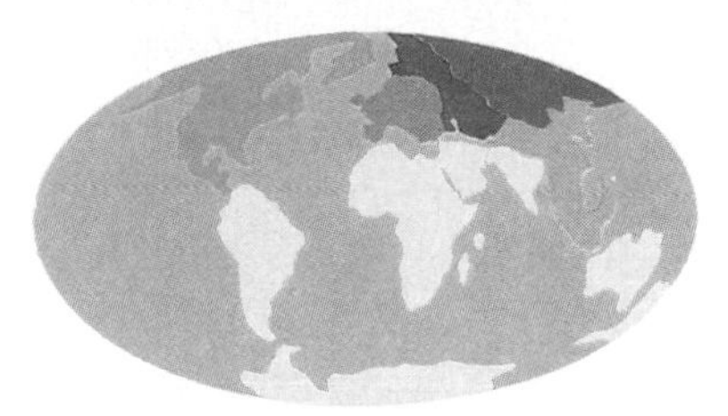

During each of four "ice ages" the sea was very low. Warm periods followed periods of glaciation. The continents had drifted almost to their positions of today.

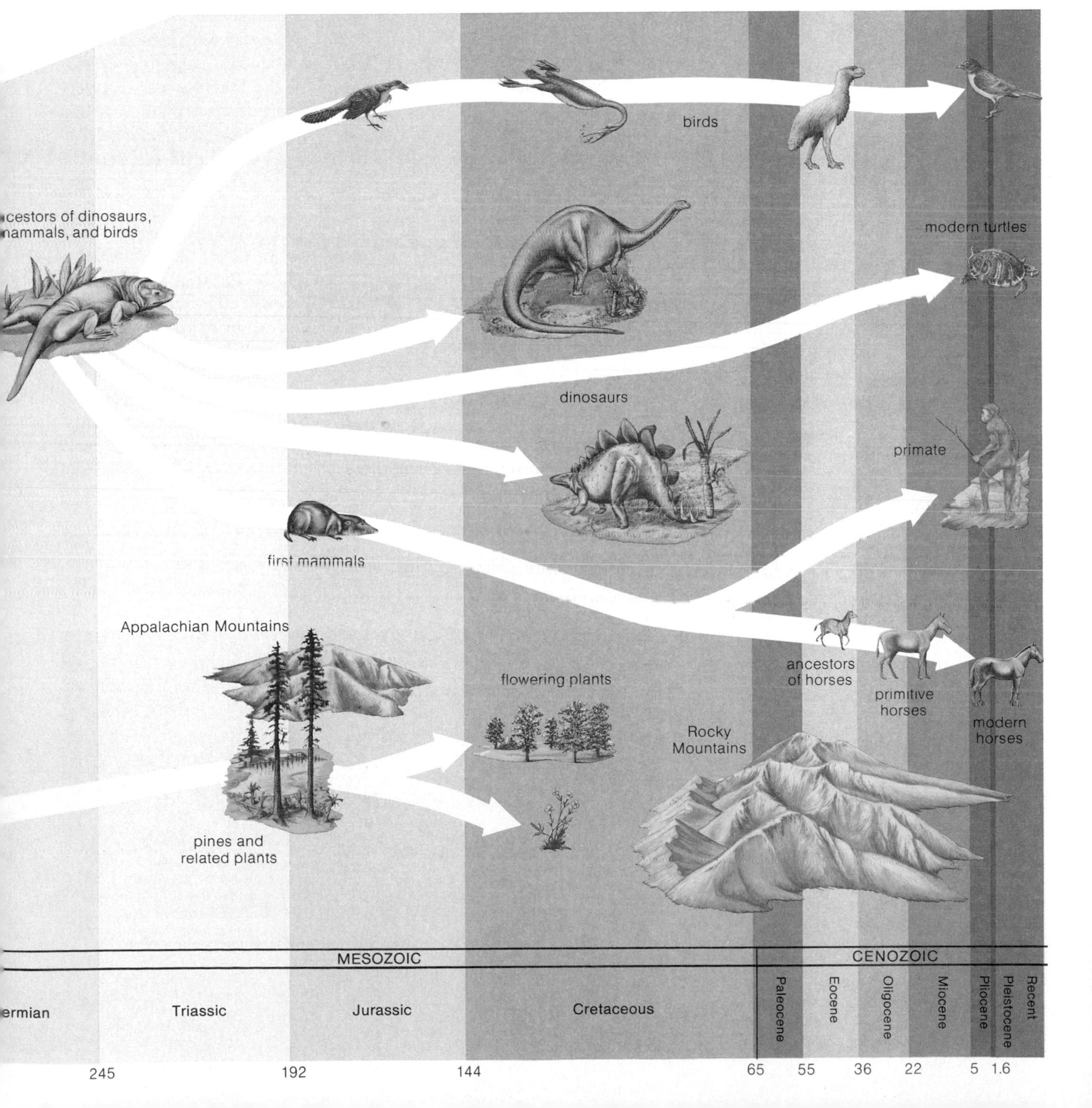

Guidepost: What organisms dominated various ecosystems in the past?

A Series of Ecosystems

21.8 Cambrian Communities Were Aquatic

If this textbook had been written during the Cambrian period, around 570 million years ago, the contents would be very different. The chapter "Biomes Around the World" would be missing, for there is no evidence of terrestrial life during the Cambrian. Marine ecosystems, however, were well developed (figure 21.18). There were shallow- and deep-water organisms—floating, swimming, and bottom-dwelling kinds. The chief marine producers then, as now, probably were microscopic species that floated near the surface.

There are no chordates in the Cambrian fossil record. Otherwise, representatives of the major animal phyla known today were present. There were sponges and coelenterates. The most abundant animals were marine brachiopods and arthropods. Many of the brachiopods were very similar to species living today. But the arthropods were so different that none of them can be placed in modern arthropod classes. Among Cambrian arthropods, the ones that left the most abundant fossils were the trilobites.

21.9 Amphibians Appeared in the Devonian

After the Cambrian, the seas receded a little. In the still-widespread seas, microscopic plants thrived and the first fish appeared. In fact, the Devonian is often called the "Age of Fishes." Many fishes were covered with armorlike plates. Sharks and the ancestors of modern bony fish appeared then, also.

About 417 million years ago, mountains began to rise in parts of Laurentia and Baltica that are now America and Europe. Most of the land, however, was low and flat. There the first vascular plants, such as early relatives of our ferns and horsetails, evolved. Insects crawled around and flew above them.

Figure 21.18 An artist's reconstruction of life in a Cambrian sea. How many kinds of organisms can you identify?

Neg. No. 318465/(Photo: Charles H. Coles) Courtesy Department Library Services, American Museum of Natural History.

Some fish had adaptations—"preadaptations," we might say—for life on land: lungs, internal nostrils, and skeletons that better supported their paired fins. In some fish, lobe-shaped fins became modified into stumpy, leglike paddles. Some of those fish were able to crawl out of a swamp onto land. During dry seasons they could move from pool to pool in search of water and food. Amphibians probably evolved from such fish, as shown in figure 21.7 on page 760. Amphibians even today lay their eggs in the water and spend the early part of their lives there. With their appearance in the Devonian, the vertebrate invasion of land had begun.

21.10 Giant Forests Grew during the Carboniferous

By the Carboniferous (coal age) period, about 350 million years ago, the first forests fringed the shallow seas that still covered most of Laurentia (North America). The trees were unlike those in our forests, though. They were mostly huge relatives of the present-day horsetails, club mosses, and ferns (figure 21.19). Strata of the late Carboniferous age contain some gymnosperm fossils, but the familiar flowering plants of today were absent.

The plants suggest to paleontologists that the climate was warm and humid, like that in today's tropical forests. There was probably little seasonal change.

Invertebrates were numerous. Some predatory insects that darted about were similar to modern dragonflies. One—with a wingspread of almost 75 cm—was the largest insect ever known. Cockroaches were abundant; some species were nearly 10 cm long. (How many inches is that?)

Figure 21.19 Reconstruction of a forest in the Carboniferous period.

Trans. No. K 10234. Courtesy Department Library Services, American Museum of Natural History.

The only large animals were the amphibians, which had been very successful since their appearance in the Devonian. Many kinds were present. Most had four legs, but they could not really stand. Looking a little like modern salamanders, they preyed on fishes in the streams and ponds.

In the seas, trilobites still were present. They would disappear from the fossil record around the end of the Paleozoic era.

21.11 Dinosaurs Dominated Triassic Ecosystems

Following the Carboniferous, Pangaea was formed. Most of the seas covering Laurentia drained away, and by the Triassic, about 115 million years later, large areas were dry or mountainous. By then the amphibians had some formidable competitors.

Evidence of the Triassic period (about 245 million years ago) can be found in the Connecticut Valley of New England, where certain rocks contain the large, three-toed footprints seen in figure 21.20a.

The characteristics of the rocks cause geologists to think that a slow, winding stream flowed through a dry valley. The stream carried materials from highlands on both sides to a broad, flat plain, where it deposited them. Narrow bands of coal-like rocks indicate that small ponds were present. Almost all the fossil plants are from such rocks.

Aquatic insects and several kinds of fishes lived in the ponds. There are fossils of lungfish (figure 21.21), which could obtain oxygen directly from the air. This suggests that many ponds sometimes dried up, just as do ponds where modern lungfish live.

Figure 21.20 The fossil track in the photo could have been made by a bipedal dinosaur such as the one below.

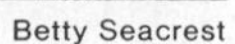

Betty Seacrest

Dinosaurs and other large reptiles were abundant. Lizardlike creatures scurried among the plants. The structure of their leg bones suggests they moved quickly, and their small, sharp teeth indicate they ate insects. In addition, several species of slender dinosaurs about 2.5 meters high roamed the mud flats. They made the three-toed tracks that first called attention to this paleoecosystem.

21.12 Large Mammals Roamed North America in the Pleistocene

The Cenozoic Era is often called the "Age of Mammals," because mammals have become so widespread in the last 60 million years. Though the first small, ratlike mammals lived at the same time as the dinosaurs, larger mammals did not evolve until the dinosaurs died out. Whatever killed the dinosaurs spared some ancestral mammals.

Figure 21.21 An Australian lungfish.

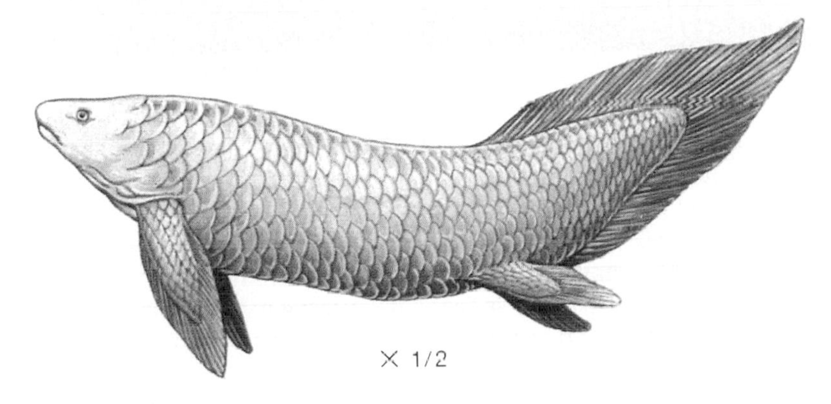

Figure 21.22 A Cenozoic landscape (Pliocene epoch, about 3.4 million years ago).

Smithsonian Institution Photo No. 75-7811

Figure 21.23 The La Brea tar pits.

Photo courtesy of the Greater Los Angeles Visitors and Convention Bureau.

Figure 21.24 Cenozoic animals. From top to bottom: *Diatryma*, saber-tooth cat, *Synthetoceras*, and ground sloth.

× 1/25

× 1/50

× 1/25

× 1/50

In what is now Los Angeles, the La Brea tar pits—molasses-like pools of asphalt—still may entrap unwary small animals. Today these tar pits are enclosed with fences that protect most animals (figure 21.23). However, 30,000 years ago, the huge animals that roamed the area often bogged down in similar pools of asphalt and died there.

Many rabbits, rodents, shrews, and perching birds, all similar to modern species, were trapped in the asphalt. Their similarity to modern forms tells paleontologists that the climate of that ecosystem was probably like the warm, comfortable climate of southern California today. Bishop pines and cypresses grew there, along with juniper and coast live oak trees.

Western horses and other herbivores were there—peccaries, tapirs, antelope, bison, camels, and deer. Ground sloths ate yucca and other plants. Perhaps the most impressive remains, however, are those of mastodons and mammoths. Some of the mammoths were more than 4 m high at the shoulders.

Small reptiles and amphibians also lived in the La Brea ecosystem, eating insects such as flies and crickets. There were small carnivorous mammals. The most obvious carnivores, though, were saber-toothed cats and dire wolves. (Dire wolves were somewhat like modern timber wolves.)

Are you surprised to find no humans here, considering the relatively recent age of this ecosystem? Remains of humans dating from this period are rare. However, evidence indicates that the first Americans crossed a bridge of land or ice that connected North America with Asia as long as 30,000 years ago. They may have been hunters who followed the mammoths and eventually brought about their extinction.

Self-Review

1. In what kind of environment did all the organisms known from Cambrian fossils live?
2. What preadaptations of some fish may have led to the evolution of amphibians during the Devonian?
3. Compare a forest of Carboniferous time with a forest of today.
4. What does the presence of coal beds indicate about decomposers?
5. What class of land vertebrates apparently originated between Carboniferous and Triassic times?
6. In which vertebrate class are most of the fossils of the Triassic ecosystem placed?

Investigation 21.2 PRIMATE BRAIN EVOLUTION

Introduction

Like other tissue, neural tissue changes as a result of genetic mutations. If a change in an organism's nervous system brings about some harmful change in its sensory or motor capability, then the individual is unlikely to survive. If the change gives the organism a selective advantage, however, it will be more likely to survive and reproduce than it would have been without the change. For example, the brains of advanced members of the horse family, when compared with the brains of primitive members, show an expansion of the area of the cerebral cortex controlling lip sensitivity. Probably that change was an advantage for animals that grazed on a variety of plants.

During primate evolution, changes have occurred in the size and organization of the nervous system. We can compare the brains of primates such as modern chimpanzees and humans by dissecting and measuring them; but how can we compare the soft brain tissues of individuals that decomposed thousands or millions of years ago? We can study **endocasts** (EN do kasts), casts of braincases. As organisms decomposed, their soft tissues sometimes filled up with lime-containing sediment. When the sediment dried, a cast of the inside of the skull was formed. Such an endocast looks much like the original brain looked when it was covered with membranes and blood vessels: tiny details of the brain surface cannot be seen, but the major features are clear. One of the first natural endocasts to be studied was of the Taung baby.

Anthropologist Ralph Holloway has devised a technique for making endocasts of any skull. He lines the skull with liquid latex. The latex then solidifies and makes a balloonlike endocast that can be pulled out of the braincase.

Primate brains have generally increased both in complexity and in size (though the average modern human brain is smaller than the average Neanderthal's). In general, a larger organism is likely to have a brain larger than that of a smaller organism. To make comparisons of advancement, biologists determine the ratio of brain volume to total body weight for each organism and then compare the ratios.

In this investigation, you will compare the brains of some extinct and modern primates.

Materials

graph paper

Procedure

1. Examine the 5 endocasts shown in figure 21.25. What is the volume of each?
2. Using the following information, plot the brain volume : body weight ratio for the 5 species on graph paper.

Table 21.3 Body weight of selected species

Species	Average Body Weight (in Grams)
Tarsius	900
Australopithecus	22,700
Homo erectus	41,300
Pan troglodytes	45,360
Homo sapiens	63,500

3. The area circled in color on the *Homo sapiens* endocast is Broca's area, an enlargement of the frontal lobe of the cerebrum. If a person is injured in that part of the brain, normal speech is impossible. Note that Broca's area can be seen in the endocast of *Homo erectus* also, but not in *Pan*.
4. Convert the ratios of brain weight to body weight shown in table 21.4 to decimal fractions and then draw a histogram of the fractions.

Table 21.4 Brain weight : Body weight ratio for selected mammals

Mammal	Brain Weight : Body Weight Ratio
Tree shrew	1 : 40
Macaque	1 : 170
Blue whale	1 : 10,000
Human	1 : 45
Squirrel monkey	1 : 12
House mouse	1 : 40
Elephant	1 : 600
Porpoise	1 : 38
Gorilla	1 : 200

Figure 21.25

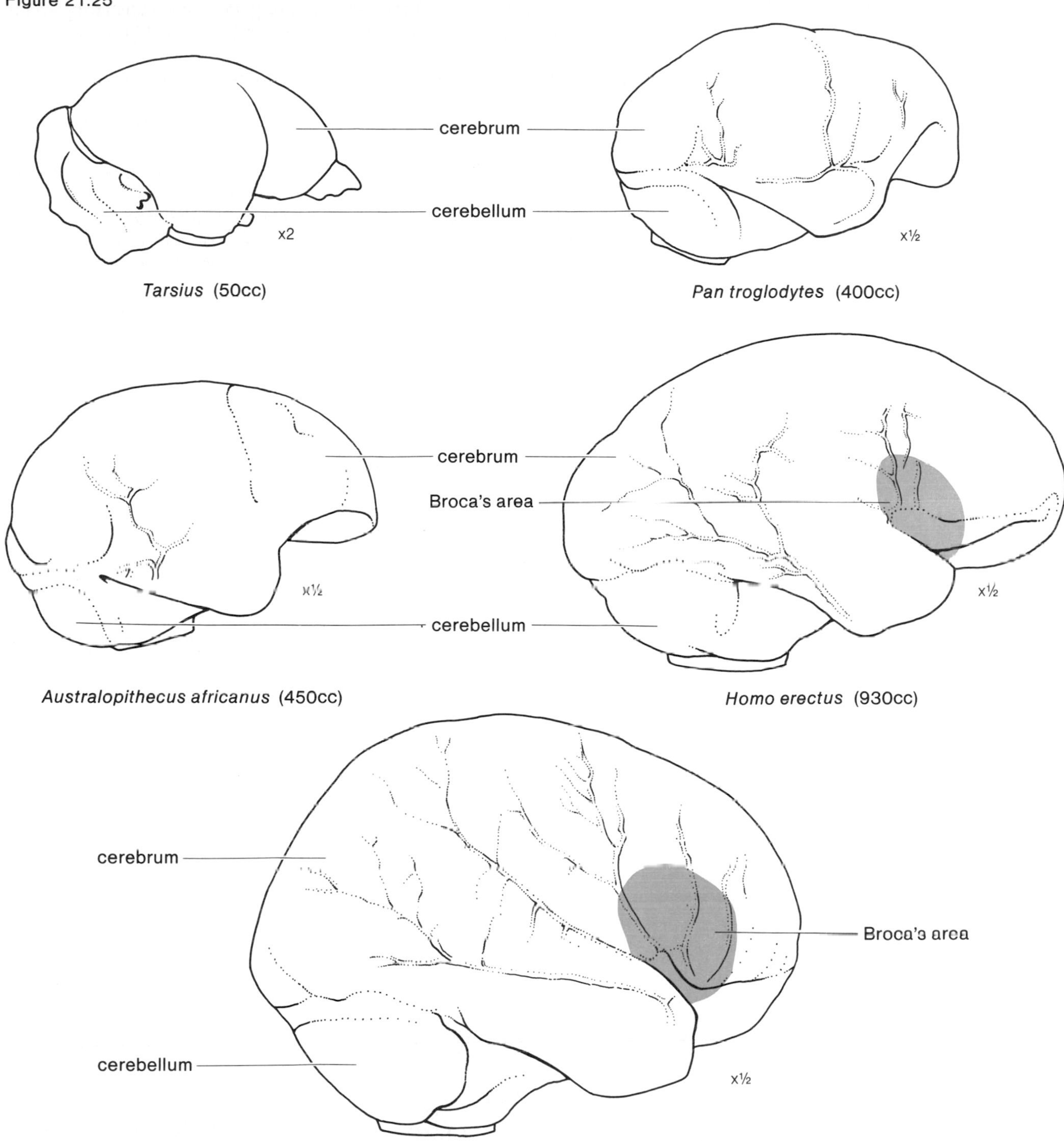
cerebrum
cerebellum
x2
x½
Tarsius (50cc)
Pan troglodytes (400cc)
cerebrum
Broca's area
cerebellum
x½
x½
Australopithecus africanus (450cc)
Homo erectus (930cc)
cerebrum
Broca's area
cerebellum
x½
Homo sapiens sapiens (1400cc)

Discussion

1. Based on your 1st graph, what is the general relationship between evolutionary advancement in primates and the ratio of brain volume to body weight?
2. What major division of the brain has become most noticeably enlarged during primate evolution?
3. Do you think the endocast of *Australopithecus* indicates that this hominid had a Broca's area in its brain?
4. How does the answer to question 3 affect the possible reason for *Australopithecus* disappearing and *Homo* surviving?
5. How does your histogram affect your answer to question 1?
6. Find and compare illustrations of the brains of *Homo sapiens* and other species listed in table 21.4. In addition to Broca's area, what changes are evident?

Guidepost: How do humans differ from other primates?

The Emergence of Humans

21.13 Humans Are Classified in the Order Primates

Humans, monkeys, and apes are very similar in the details of their anatomy. They are, therefore, grouped together in the order Primates, along with animals such as lemurs and tarsiers. Most primates are arboreal (tree climbers) and possess structures and behaviors that relate to the arboreal way of life. That life is dangerous and demanding, and mistakes are likely to be fatal. Therefore, natural selection of adaptations to that life must be severe.

Figure 21.26 Skeletal proportions and postures of a gorilla and a human.

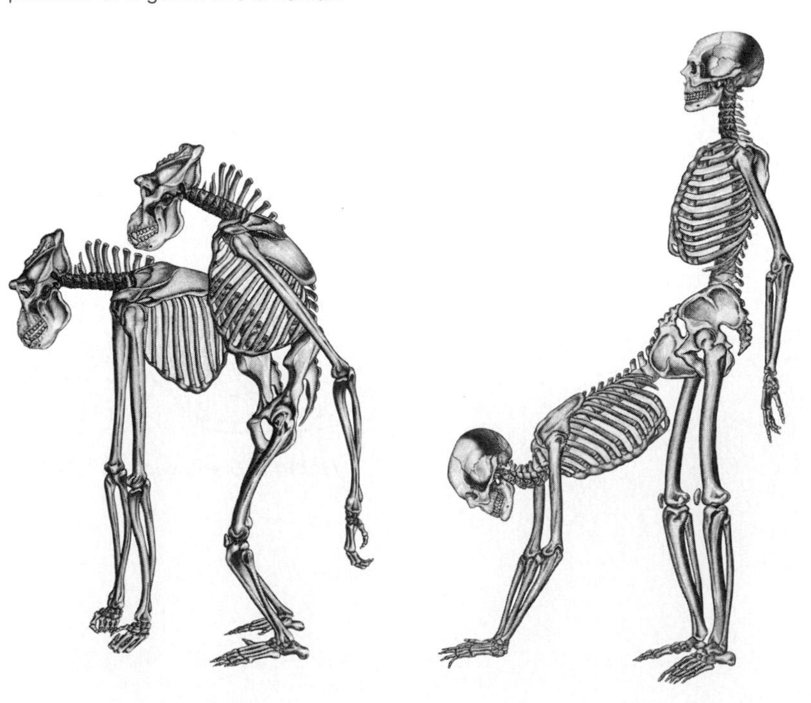

The digits of primates are well developed and give the animal a powerful grasp. They have nails rather than claws. In addition to being powerful, the digits are very sensitive. They can easily tell if a surface is crumbly or slippery.

The eyes of primates are directed forward instead of to the side, as in most mammals. Both eyes view the same object from slightly different angles. That allows the brain to perceive the object in three dimensions so accurate judgments of distance can be made. The brains of most primates are exceptionally large compared with those of all other mammals except whales, dolphins, and porpoises. Primates have a sense of color that is lacking in most mammals.

Bearing one young at a time is the rule among primates, though twins are not unusual. An active arboreal animal cannot carry many offspring.

Figure 21.27 Primate characteristics. Note the binocular vision in the bush baby, tarsier, and squirrel monkey in (a), and the grasping ability of the gibbon in (b).

To feed those young, a female primate has two mammary glands. Young primates, unlike young horses or jackrabbits, are given much maternal care for a long time. Primate young do not have to learn most of their activities by trial and error; they are taught much by their parents.

Primates tend to be omnivorous. They gather food in social groups, often communicating by vocal signals.

21.14 Hominoids Are More Human-Appearing than Other Primates

The first human beings on this continent migrated here from Asia, but the human species probably did not arise in Asia. Early Asians may have come from Africa, through the Mideast. Fossil evidence and early tool sites suggest that it was in Africa that **hominoids** (HOM ih noydz)—humanlike primates—became **hominids** (HOM ih nidz)—hominoids that walked upright—and that early hominids became human.

Modern hominoids include monkeys and apes as well as hominids. Though monkeys and apes do not habitually walk upright, in many ways they closely resemble us. Probably all modern hominoids arose from the same ancestral group.

21.15 Hominoids that Walk Upright Are Hominids

Figure 21.28 The Taung baby.

Photograph by Carolina Biological Supply Company

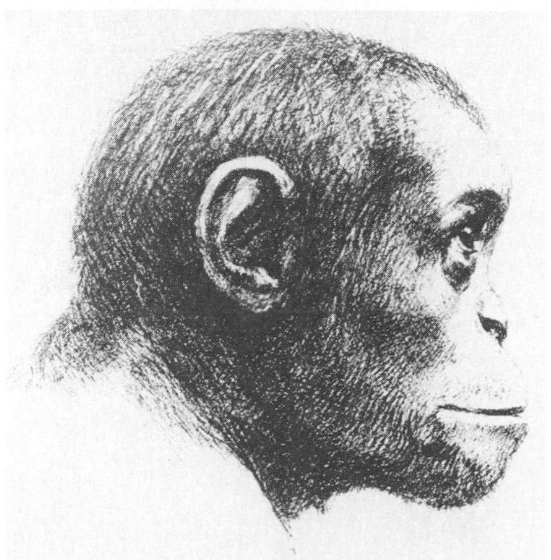

Reconstruction Neg. No. 313484. (A Forestier restoration) Courtesy Department Library Services, American Museum of Natural History.

Between 1 and 3 million years ago, in the area of South Africa now called Taung, a child died. When the child's fossil skull was found in 1924, the child was nicknamed the "Taung baby." We now refer to the Taung baby's species as *Australopithecus africanus* (ah stray loh PITH eh kus aa frih KAN us). The **australopithecines** (ah stray loh PITH eh seenz) are the earliest hominids known. Their fossil remains date to more than 3 million years ago.

The Taung baby had a small brain. However, he stood upright, as humans do, and his face was as much humanlike as apelike. The Taung baby and his family lived on the savanna, a grassy plain with scattered trees. They may have retreated to the trees after foraging in the open for food. The australopithecines had large, well-worn molar teeth, which suggests they ate more seeds, meat, and roots than their ancestors did.

No tools were found with the child's skull. Some paleontologists, however, think australopithecines used crude tools of wood or other organic materials, which might not have been preserved as fossils. Probably they hunted small mammals, such as rabbits. It seems likely that the australopithecines were scavengers, stealing meat of large animals that had been killed by predators.

It was once thought that enlargement of the cerebrum had heralded the appearance of the hominids. However, the fossil skulls of australopithecines show that their brains were little larger than the brains of apes of comparable size. Biologists today define hominids as primates that walk upright, a position that frees the hands for using tools. Thus hominids include all members of the genera *Homo* and *Australopithecus,* while hominoids also include the pongids—the modern apes and their ancestors.

True humans are classified in the genus *Homo,* but the earliest humans do not appear greatly advanced over the australopithecines. Their brains were a little larger and their teeth and jaws appear more human.

Biology Today C

Anthropologist

Mike Hoffman is a biological anthropologist who teaches at an undergraduate liberal arts college. His major interest is the study of the human skeleton, both prehistoric and modern.

As a child he was always picking up bones and loved to visit the dinosaur and fossil human displays in museums. During a family vacation he visited Mesa Verde National Park and saw on display in the park's museum the artifacts and skeletal remains of prehistoric Southwestern Indians. These made a lasting impression on him.

BSCS by Doug Sokell

Professor Hoffman was a biology major in college but took a number of courses in anthropology, mostly in archaeology and biological anthropology. It was at this time that he began to see how a background in biology could be very useful for understanding some questions asked by anthropologists. As his senior year in medical school began, he found he was really more interested in being an anthropologist than in practicing medicine. Following graduation from medical school, Mike started graduate school in biological anthropology.

After completing his Ph.D. in anthropology, Mike taught for several years at universities in Arizona and California before settling in Colorado. While in California he became interested in some of the diseases found in prehistoric California Native Americans. Since then he has maintained a professional interest in human skeletal studies.

Today Mike teaches a variety of courses in biological anthropology, including human

BSCS by Doug Sokell

evolution, biological variation and adaptation, prehistory of the American Southwest, and his real love—bones. His current research on prehistoric skeletons involves material from California and Colorado, the latter from an archaeological site next door to Mesa Verde. A major area of interest is explaining the patterns of diseases present in prehistoric populations, at least those that can be seen from the skeleton. For example, why does a population living in a particular environment at a particular time have certain specific diseases? Are the differences in those patterns related to the age of the individual, to male and female differences, to dietary differences, or to different activities? Commonly seen diseases include arthritis, tooth cavities and abscesses, infectious diseases, and occasionally tumors. (Tumors are rare, because prehistoric peoples died at an earlier age than when most tumors occur.)

Mike's knowledge of human skeletons also allows him to be helpful to police and coroners who often call on him to help identify unknown human skeletons. Using a variety of techniques, he can tell the age at death, sex, stature, race, right versus left handedness, general body build, and other distinguishing characteristics of individuals. He often works closely with dentists to help in this identification process. When doing this kind of work Mike is wearing the hat of a forensic physical anthropologist.

In Mike's words, "Make no bones about it, this is a very interesting profession. It also happens to be great fun."

No sharp physical distinction can be drawn between human and hominid, however.

Humans are the only living species in the family Hominidae. This entire taxonomic family has been set aside for human beings and whatever upright-walking primates are discovered from fossils. Fossil skulls, along with backbones and hip girdles, are enough to make this determination.

Anthropologists (an throh POL uh jists), scientists who study human evolution and culture, use several additional characteristics to distinguish hominoids from hominids: brain size, head shape, teeth and facial characteristics. Some of those characteristics are compared in table 21.5. You can observe the greater skeletal differences between a human and a cat in investigation 21.3.

Table 21.5 Characteristics of the two groups of hominoids

Characteristic	Pongids	Hominids
Posture	bent over; "knucklewalking" common	upright
Leg and arm length	arms longer than legs; adapted for brachiating	legs longer than arms; adapted for striding
Feet	low arches; opposable big toes—capable of grasping	high arches; big toes in line with others; adapted for walking
Canine teeth	prominent	reduced
Skull	bent forward from spinal column	upright on spinal column
Face	jaw juts out, flat nose, lips without a mucous membrane	vertical profile, distinct chin; nose prominent; lips with mucous membrane
Brain size	280–705 c^3 (living species)	400–2000 ^3c (fossil to present)
Breeding season	estrus at definite times	no definite time for modern humans; unknown for early hominids
Average lifespan	relatively short	relatively long
Age at puberty	usually 10	usually 13 or less

Investigation 21.3 A STUDY OF SKELETONS

Introduction

Every vertebrate skeleton is composed of 2 major divisions. One is the **axial** (AK see uh) **skeleton,** and the other is the **appendicular** (ap en DIK yuh lar) **skeleton.** The axial skeleton consists of the skull and the column of vertebrae arranged along the long axis of the body. It includes the ribs, which are attached to certain of the vertebrae. The appendicular skeleton consists of the shoulder and hip girdles. Attached to the girdles are the bones of the appendages.

In this investigation you will compare a human skeleton with that of a 4-footed mammal.

Materials (per class)

mounted human skeleton
mounted cat skeleton
2 rulers

Procedure

In this procedure you will make observations on both cat and human skeletons. When you are directed to examine a part of the skeleton, examine that part in both animals.

1. Begin with the axial skeleton. Examine the general outline of the skull.
   (a) Which occupies the greater volume—the braincase or the bones of the face?
   (b) With respect to the rest of the skull, are the eye sockets directed forward, downward, backward, sideward, or upward?
2. Viewing the skeleton from the side, hold a ruler along the axis of the vertebrae in the upper part of the neck.
   (a) In which skeleton is the axis of the vertebrae closer to the vertical midline of the skull? Holding the 1st ruler in position, place a 2nd ruler along the base of the teeth.
   (b) In which skeleton is the angle formed by the rulers closer to a right angle?
3. The **articulation** (ar tik yoo LAY shun) or jointing of the skull with the 1st vertebra occurs around the **foramen magnum** (foh RAY men MAG num), meaning the "big opening". Through the foramen magnum the spinal cord connects with the brain.
   (a) In which skeleton is the foramen magnum closer to the posterior end of the skull? If you look closely, you will notice roughened areas and ridges on the bones. These are places where muscles were attached. Examine the back of the skull.
   (b) In which skeleton does there seem to be a greater area (in proportion to skull size) for muscle attachment?
4. Examine the vertebral column.
   (a) Which skeleton has the greater number of vertebrae?
   (b) In what portion of the column does the number of vertebrae differ?
   (c) In general, which skeleton (in proportion to its size) has the thicker vertebrae?
   (d) How do the vertebrae in the region of the hip girdle differ in the human and the cat?
   (e) Observe the vertebral column from the side. In which skeleton does the vertebral column form a single arch from shoulder to hip girdle?
5. Now consider the appendicular skeleton. The posterior legs are attached to the **pelvis.** This is a set of bones that, in adults, have grown together.
   (a) In proportion to its size, which skeleton has the heavier pelvis?
   (b) Is the pelvis articulated with the vertebral column, or are the 2 structures fused together?
6. The forelegs, or arms in humans, are attached to an anterior girdle. This girdle is made up of 2 broad, flat **scapulas** (SKAP yoo luhz) or shoulder blades, 2 collarbones, and a **sternum** (STER num) or breastbone.
   (a) In which skeleton are the bones of this girdle more closely associated?
   (b) How are these bones attached to the vertebral column?
   (c) With respect to their attachment to each other, how do the bones of the anterior girdle differ from those of the pelvis?

7. Compare the bones of the human hand with the bones of one of the cat's front feet.
   (a) In which skeleton are the bones of the **digits** (fingers and toes) longer in proportion to the total length of the appendage?
   (b) In which skeleton is the inside digit articulated in such a way that it is opposable to (can be pressed against) the other digits?
8. Compare the cat's posterior appendages with the human's.
   (a) In which skeleton is the knee joint in normal standing position closer to a straight line?
   (b) Consider each leg to be made up of upper leg, lower leg, and foot (including toes). Make a comparison of the length of the foot with the length of the upper leg.
   (c) Which animal normally stands with its heels raised from the ground?

Discussion

The following questions will help you interpret your observations and organize your thoughts. You may need to refer to earlier observations made in the procedure.

1. What nonskeletal human characteristic is implied by your answer to procedure 1 (a)?
2. Procedure 1 (b) is related to what characteristic of vision found in many primates?
3. Observations recorded in procedure 2 are concerned with structural adaptations that support a relatively heavy head in an upright position. Assume that the structure of distant human ancestors was somewhat like that of the cat.
   (a) What mutations in that structure would have been changes favorable to the development of a large brain?
   (b) Of upright posture?
4. (a) In a cat, where is most of the weight of the anterior part of the body supported?
   (b) Where is the anterior weight supported in a human?
5. How does relative thickness of the vertebrae and strength of the pelvis relate to how the anterior weight is supported in each skeleton?
6. (a) Judging from the structure of its anterior girdle, do you think a cat could easily support its weight on its forelegs?
   (b) Can a human being?
7. Humans have the same kind of strong anterior girdle that many primates use in moving about through trees. How is this structural characteristic an advantage to humans, who walk upright on the ground?
8. Notice that the position of the legs in a person who is poised to start a race is similar to the normal position of the posterior appendages in a cat. What advantage does this position have for the athlete and cat?

For Further Investigation

Aristotle described humans as "featherless bipeds." The adjective was necessary because birds also are entirely bipedal. (Aristotle, of course, knew nothing of dinosaurs, some of which were bipeds, or of kangaroos.) Using a mounted skeleton of a pigeon or a chicken, make a comparison with the human skeleton.

21.16 The Genus *Homo* Includes "True" Humans

While the australopithecines were somewhat human, and at one time were thought to be human ancestors, they were not like us. They were more primitive than the earliest human species, *Homo erectus*. *H. erectus* and other early humans learned to use fire, a discovery that certainly set them apart from hominids that could not control fire.

Paleontologists can tell from fossils whether an individual can be classified as a hominid. But to go further and say that an upright-walking species was human requires more than this. Here paleontologists are helped by anthropologists.

Anthropologists seek evidence found along with the fossil skeletons. They look for evidence such as the following: stone tools; collections of bones from food animals (indicating that food killed elsewhere was

Figure 21.29 Four types of stone tools made by *Homo erectus*.

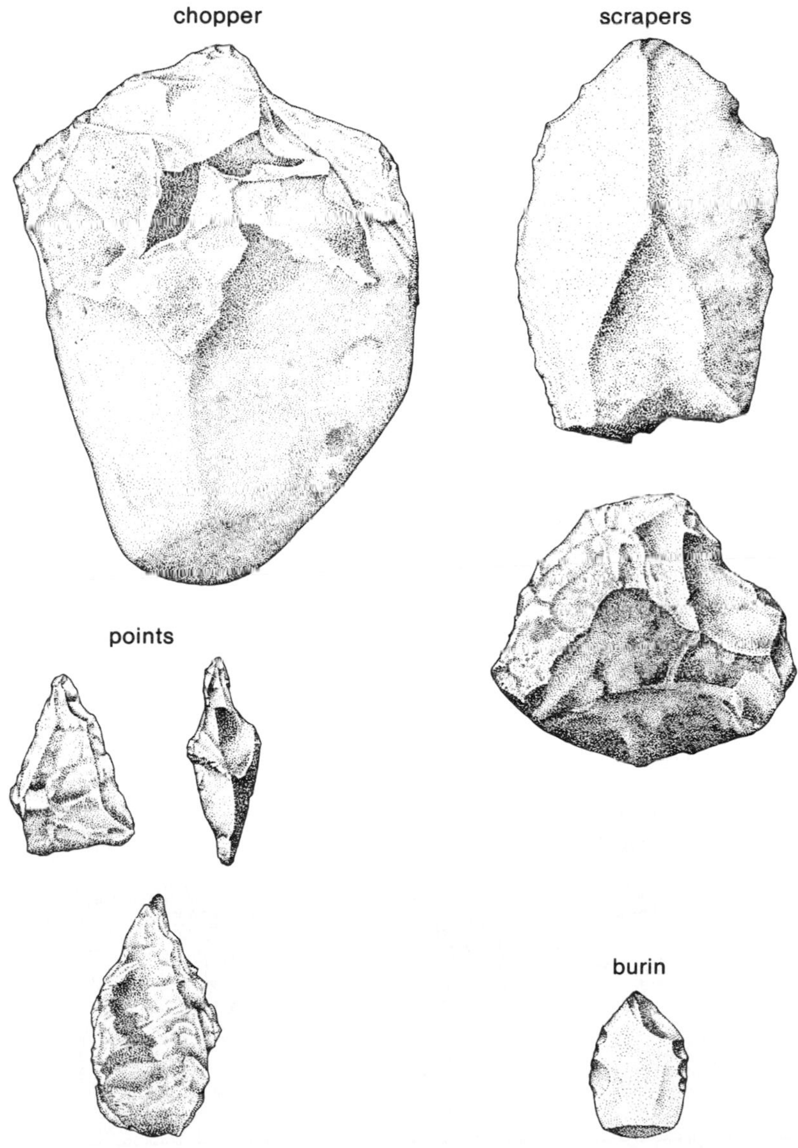

Figure 21.30 One hypothesis of human evolution. It is impossible to define the exact phylogeny of humans because numerous theories are being presented and many debates are taking place. Only recently, new discoveries have thrown doubt on previously accepted theories.

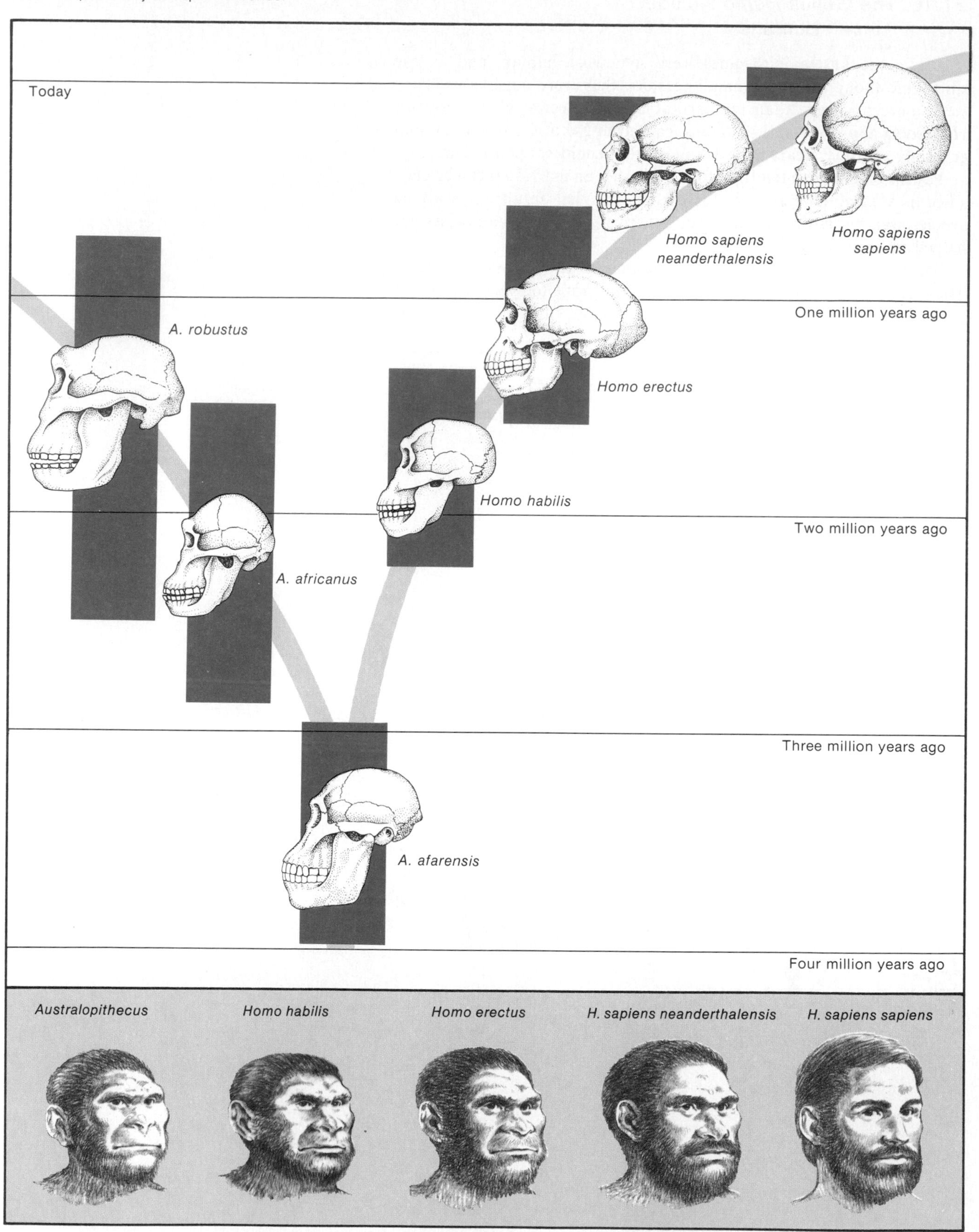

brought to a home site and shared); charcoal from campfires; art on cliff and cave walls; and graves (indicating a burial custom).

Crude stone tools alone do not necessarily indicate humans. But stone tools along with collections of animal bones are considered tentative evidence of humans. If charcoal, art, or graves also are found, the fossils are considered definitely to be human.

Physiological characteristics help define human beings as clearly as do structural characteristics. Behavioral characteristics, however, are also important in defining humans.

One typical human behavior is our tendency to live near other persons rather than alone. As an individual, a person is often helpless. Imagine the plight of a person alone in the forests of Europe during one of the ice ages. Groups of early humans, however, could survive.

Social behavior in humans can be traced, in part, to the long period of growing up. During this period of dependency on parents, children are woven into the social group.

The transfer of knowledge depends on communication among individuals. Human beings may communicate by gestures, but these are usually just a substitute for language. Human language is more complicated than other forms of communication and sets us apart from other animals. Language depends on unusual capabilities of the human brain and the human vocal cords. We have no knowledge of how or when speech began.

21.17 *Homo Sapiens* Has a Large Brain

When Charles Darwin published *The Descent of Man* in 1871, no science of paleontology existed. At least one fossil hominid skull was known, but it remained unidentified. It was only a mysterious skull, unearthed in 1856 in the Neander Valley of Germany. Today the Neanderthals are classified in our own species, as the subspecies *H. sapiens neanderthalensis*. They became prominent as *H. erectus* gave way to *H. sapiens*, some time between 150,000 and 200,000 years ago.

Later discoveries provided evidence that these Neanderthal people had many cultural customs. They lived in the open, in caves, and in skin tents throughout Europe and the Middle East. Remains of mixed bouquets of flowers have been found on their graves.

At first the Neanderthals coexisted with *H. erectus*. Before they disappeared around 50,000 years ago, they coexisted with our own subspecies, *H. sapiens sapiens*, the Cro-Magnon peoples. Thus, the Neanderthals bridged ancient and modern humans.

Neanderthals and Cro-Magnons both had brains of larger size than our own. The Cro-Magnons also looked like us. They lived in the same places Neanderthals did, from 25,000 to 50,000 years ago. They made beautiful cave paintings in full color. They engraved delicate designs on bone and ivory tools they had made. Only the use of agriculture and metal tools distinguished later peoples from the Cro-Magnons. Table 21.6 lists the major hominoid fossil discoveries.

Figure 21.31 Caves in France and Spain contain examples of the oldest known paintings done by Cro-Magnons. This is from Lascaux in France; the originals are in full color.

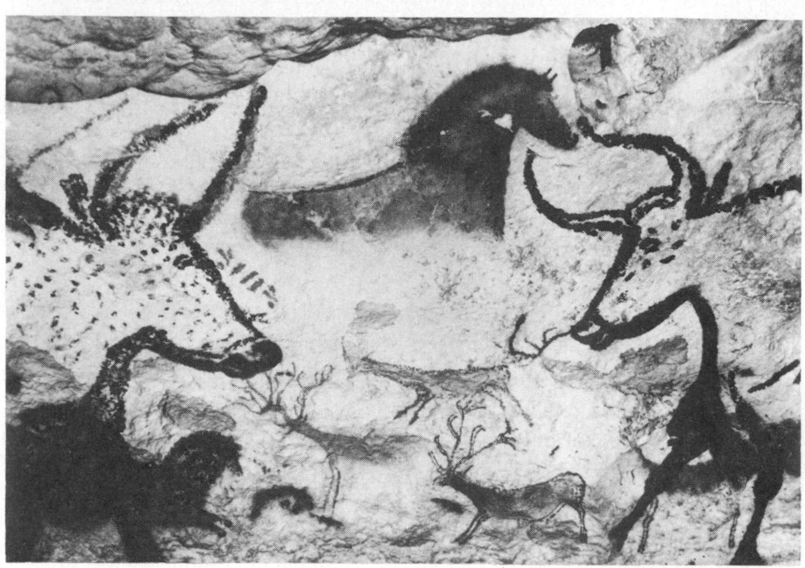

French Government Tourist Office

Table 21.6 Some hominoid fossil discoveries

Date of Discovery	Place	Discoverers	Species (common name)	Current Status
1857	Germany	Quarry workers	*Homo sapiens neanderthalensis*	Among earliest members of *H. sapiens*
1868	France	Road builders	*H. sapiens sapiens* (Cro-Magnon human)	Modern human
1891	Java	Eugene Dubois	*Pithecanthropus erectus* (Java man)	Now included in *H. erectus*
1912	England	Charles Dawson	("Piltdown Man")	Found to be fraudulent; ape jaw and human skull
1924	South Africa	Raymond Dart	*Australopithecus africanus* (Taung baby)	"Gracile" australopithecine; no longer considered a human ancestor
1927	China	Davidson Black	*Sinanthropus erectus* (Peking man)	Now included in *H. erectus*
1930s	Africa, Europe	L. Leakey	(Proconsul)	*Dryopithecus*, ancestors of apes
1934	India	G. E. Lewis	*Ramapithecus*, *Sivapithecus*	Unclear. Somewhat apelike, somewhat humanlike
1938	South Africa	Robert Broom	*Paranthropus*	"Robust" australopithecine, *A. robustus*
1959	Africa (Olduvai)	Mary Leakey	*Zinjanthropus* ("nutcracker man," "Zinj")	Another "robust" australopithecine, *A. boisei*
1964	Africa (Olduvai)	Leakey family	*H. habilis*	Early tool-user. Considered an australopithecine by some, an ancestor of *H. erectus* by the Leakeys
1972	Africa (Koobi Fora)	Richard Leakey	*H. ?* (skull)	Earliest generally accepted fossil *Homo* skull; disputed whether *H. habilis*
1974	Africa (Afar region of Ethiopia)	Donald Johanson	*A. afarensis* ("Lucy")	Disputed
1985	Africa (Lake Turkana)	Alan Walker	*A. boisei* (KMN-WT 14000)	Oldest specimen of *A. boisei* (2.5 million); may affect current theories of human lineage.

21.18 All Living Hominids Are *Homo sapiens*

Humans wander about extensively. Thus, gene flow among human populations has been much greater than among populations of other organisms. However, mass migrations of humans occurred before about A.D. 1500. Before then there was a rough correlation between geographical areas of the world and variations in certain human characteristics. In other words, varieties of *H. sapiens* showed geographical patterns, just as do varieties of other organisms.

The first Europeans and Asians were probably descendants of dark-skinned Africans who migrated north and east. Why did those who left Africa lose some of their skin pigment? One theory is that the pigment protects against skin cancer and is needed in the sunny African environment. In the Scandinavian countries, however, the pigment would no longer be a useful adaptation. Further, it could be a handicap. Heavily

Figure 21.32 Humans have been grouped in as many as 30 varieties on the basis of traits such as body hair and skin color. Today anthropologists emphasize the gradual transitions from each population to others. The original inhabitants of widely separated areas, however, were quite different in appearance. Some of their descendants still are good examples of five human populations: (a) South of the Sahara in Africa, the Negroid people had dark skins, very curly head hair, relatively thick lips, and wide noses. (b) In Europe and western Asia, Caucasoid people were lighter skinned and had thin lips. The males had heavier beards and body hair. (c) Native Australians, Australoids, were similar to Europeans, but had dark skin. (d) Mongoloids of eastern Asia had dark or light yellowish skin; brown eyes; little facial or body hair; straight, black head hair; and a fold in the upper eyelid. (e) In the Americas, the Amerind population was similar to the Mongoloids, but with a less-developed eye fold.

a BSCS by Al Morgan

b BSCS

c C. Benjamin/TOM STACK & ASSOCIATES

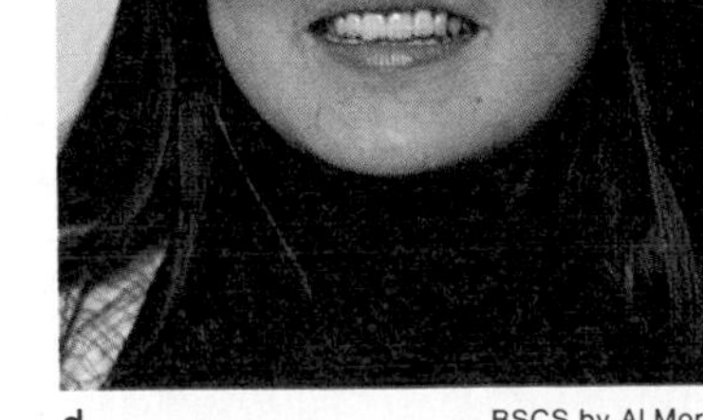

d BSCS by Al Morgan

e BSCS by Carlye Calvin

pigmented skin can prevent a person from manufacturing enough vitamin D, which is necessary to prevent the disease rickets. So, there may have been selection for light skin in northern latitudes, where the relative lack of sunlight lessens the amount of vitamin D the body can make.

In investigation 21.4 you can use gene frequencies of human blood types to make inferences about relatedness of human populations.

Investigation 21.4 BIOLOGICAL DISTANCE

Introduction

Anthropologists use gene frequencies as a basis for classifying human populations. The degree of similarity in the gene frequencies of two or more populations is known as **biological distance.** The more similar the gene frequencies of two populations, the less the biological distance between them, and the more genetically related they are. Conversely, the less similar the gene frequencies, the greater the biological distance.

An American biochemical anthropologist proposed a human classification system based on frequencies of the genes that determine blood types. There are several advantages to using blood types for this purpose. First, the ways in which the blood-type genes are inherited are well known (section 8.9). Second, the blood type of an individual does not change with age or with changes in the environment. Third, natural selection does not seem to cause any rapid changes in the frequencies of blood-type genes. Therefore, present frequencies indicate to some extent how human populations have mixed with one another in the past. Fourth, blood types are rather easy to determine from blood samples taken for various medical purposes. So, data for a large number of individuals representing many human populations are readily available for study.

In this investigation you will consider the following questions: To what extent are three selected North American populations genetically related to each other? How do the migrations of human populations affect gene frequencies? How can the mixing rate of two different populations be calculated? Why is this information useful?

Procedure

1. The 4 blood types, A, B, AB, and O, are determined by allelic genes, I^A, I^B, and i. Figure 21.33 shows the frequencies of the 3 alleles in an Eskimo population inhabiting Barrow, Alaska, in the Indian population of British Columbia, Canada, and in the Navajo population of New Mexico. These gene frequencies have been calculated from the blood-type frequencies found in samples of the populations.
   (a) Do you think these 3 human populations should be classified as 1 variety or as 3?
   (b) Explain your answer.
2. Examine the data.
   (a) On the basis of the I^A gene frequencies, which 2 populations are most alike?
   (b) On the basis of the I^B frequencies, which 2 are most alike?
   (c) On the basis of the i frequencies, which 2 are most alike?
   (d) Would you now classify these 3 populations in a single human variety? Explain your answer.

Figure 21.33

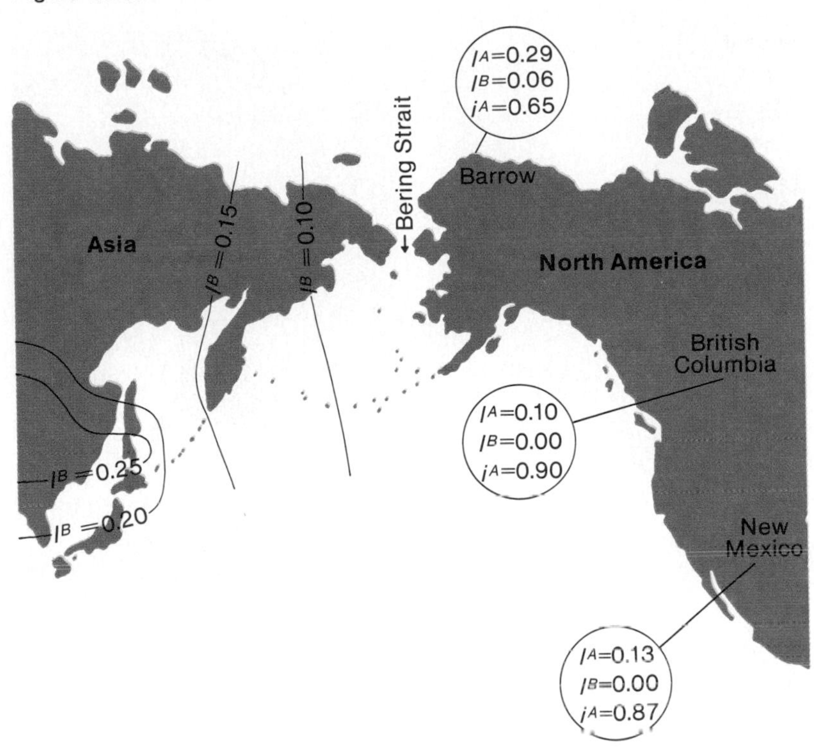

3. Look again at figure 21.33. It shows the frequency of the I^B gene in Asia.
   (a) As you move westward and southward into Asia from the Bering Strait, what happens to the frequency of the I^B gene?
   (b) As you move eastward and southward in North America from the Bering Strait, what happens to the frequency of the I^B gene?

Over much of central Asia, the frequency of I^B is 0.25 to 0.30. Westward from central Asia into Europe, the frequency declines (figure 21.34). Several hypotheses account for this situation, but we shall consider only one. Briefly, this hypothesis states that: (1) at first the population of Asia had all 3 alleles; (2) Europe and America were populated from central Asia; and (3) the 1st emigrant populations from the Asian homeland either lacked the I^B gene or lost it along the way.

How could an interbreeding population lose a gene? Loss by selection seems highly improbable. Blood types apparently have neither selective advantages nor disadvantages. The Hardy-Weinberg principle, discussed in investigation 9.3, states that gene frequencies remain constant. That is true if, in large interbreeding populations, neither mutation nor natural selection occurs. But what about small populations—the kind very probably involved in early human migrations?

Figure 21.34

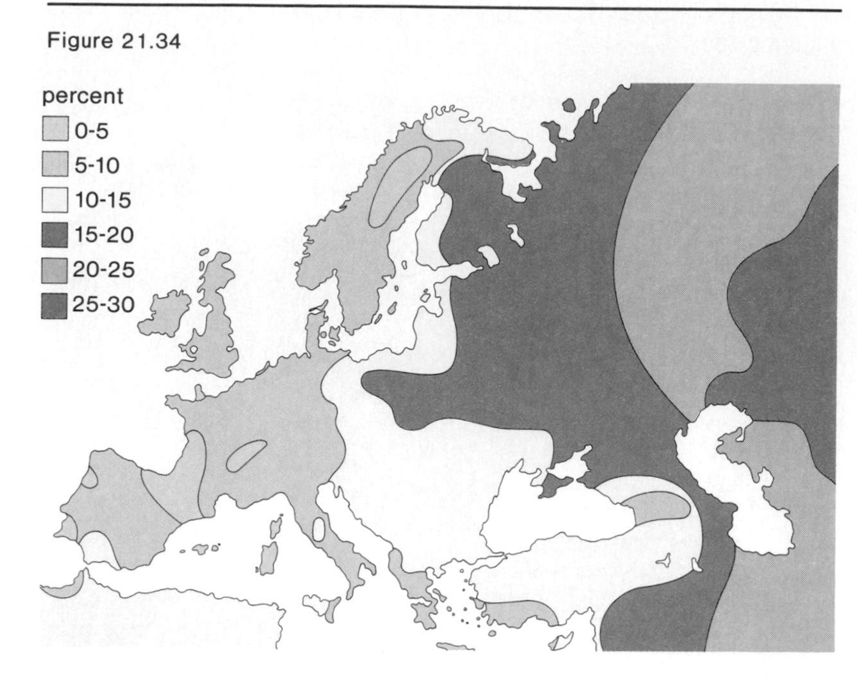

Consider a hypothetical human population with ABO blood-type genes distributed in the following frequencies: 25% I^A, 10% I^B, and 65% *i.* Suppose it is a very small population of only 50 persons per generation. Of course, each individual has 2 genes for blood type. According to the Hardy-Weinberg principle, then, we should expect to find among the 50 children of one generation 25 I^A, 10 I^B, and 65 *i* genes. Yet, from your experience in penny-flipping and genetics experiments, you know that you do not always get exactly what is expected on the basis of probability. In penny-flipping, you expect to get heads as often as tails. But if you flip a penny only 10 times, you might obtain 9 heads and 1 tail—or even all heads or all tails.

You might find similar results in a small population of people. Instead of getting expected results, you might find that purely by chance there were 28 I^A, 4 I^B, and 68 *i* genes. If this occurred, what should we expect in the next generation? We would expect a repetition of the new frequencies—28 I^A, 4 I^B, and 68 *i.* Of course, in a 3rd generation the frequencies might by chance return toward the original ones. But they might result in a further reduction of the I^B gene in the population. This might even happen several times, until the I^B gene disappears from the population. Then it could never return unless reintroduced by mutation or by immigration of I^B genes in individuals coming from some other population.

4. This process of change in gene frequency is called genetic drift. Thus, the first small populations of *Homo sapiens* to reach Europe and America may have had genes I^A and *i* only.
   (a) What blood types could they have had? According to the hypothesis, other populations emigrating from central Asia later reintroduced the I^B gene into American and European populations through interbreeding. Consider the difficulties of primitive travel.

(b) Where would you expect these later emigrant populations to be most numerous?
(c) Least numerous?

5. Consider the I^B gene frequencies.
   (a) Which of the North American populations shown in figure 21.33 probably has had the most recent genetic contact with populations of Asia? The frequency of the I^B gene is 0.00 in the Basque population of southwestern France.
   (b) On the basis of the I^B gene only, what can you say about the biological distance between the Basques, the natives of central Asia, and the Navajos?
   (c) Does this mean that the Basques and the Navajos represent one variety? Why?
6. Now we will study the rate of gene flow from one population to another. To compare 2 populations, they must have the following characteristics:
   (a) Both populations must be large.
   (b) They must differ considerably in the frequencies of alleles at one or more loci.
   (c) The traits determined by these genes must be easily and precisely identifiable. The populations must interbreed. All of these characteristics are found in the Caucasian (Caucasoid) and black (Negroid) populations that have come into North America during recent centuries.

The genetic trait best suited for this study involves another blood characteristic. In 1940, in a series of experiments, the blood of rhesus monkeys was injected into rabbits. Material from the blood of these rabbits caused the red blood cells of some people to clump. Such persons are said to be Rh positive (Rh for rhesus monkeys). Persons whose red blood cells do not clump are Rh negative. Further study showed that the Rh blood types are genetically more complex than the ABO types. Among the genes involved is one that has been symbolized ***Rh***^{o}. This gene can easily be identified, and its frequency differs greatly in the 2 populations that you are considering.

In black populations of Africa, the frequency of the ***Rh***^{o} gene is about 0.60. In Caucasian populations of Europe, it is about 0.03. In the American black population, it is about 0.44.

   (a) What is the difference between the frequencies of the ***Rh***^{o} gene in the African and European populations?
   (b) In the African and American black populations?
   (c) The amount of mixing between the Caucasian and black populations in North America may be expressed as a percentage. To do so, divide answer 6(b) by answer 6(a), then multiply by 100.
   (d) What is the meaning of this percentage?
7. The year 1625 may be taken as the beginning of the genetic mixing between Caucasian and black populations in America. The frequency of the ***Rh***^{o} gene among the American black population was obtained from data gathered about 1950.
   (a) Assuming an average generation length of 25 years, how many generations of mixing could have occurred?
   (b) On the basis of this number of generations, what was the average amount of mixing per generation?

From calculations like this—crude though they may be—anthropologists can estimate the biological distance between populations, the routes of human migration, and the rates at which genetic differences among populations change. And from these studies anthropologists can deduce some aspects of the biological history of humans.

21.19 Culture Is a Unique Trait of Humans

Human uniqueness is based not on structure or physiology, but on behavior and achievement. It lies in the human way of life, in our culture. The word "culture" is used by anthropologists to cover all human knowledge. Culture describes all the human ways of doing things that are passed from one generation to the next by teaching and learning. Our uniqueness comes from the vast bank of information that our species has built up and shared among its members through the years.

Physiologically, we are animals. It is not easy, however, to separate the animal from the cultural human. Everything we do is affected by our culture. We eat, for example, because, as animals, we have to have food. But whether we eat oysters, rice, ham, grasshoppers, potatoes, or spaghetti depends on our cultural attitudes toward those things. The physical aspect of humans has modified human culture. On the other hand, human cultures have modified human biology and evolution. Our use of information has led now to the possibility of affecting future evolution. Genetic engineering, for instance, could change the gene pool on which natural selection acts.

Such power to affect the environment and ourselves can easily lead us to a false sense of importance and independence. Like all organisms, we are products of our heredity and subject to selection by the environment. The genotypes and environments we are changing today will shape the evolution of our descendants.

Self-Review

1. What structural characteristics of primates are related to an arboreal habitat?
2. What characteristics separate the members of the family Hominidae from the rest of the order Hominoidea?
3. In human evolution, did brain expansion or upright posture occur first?
4. Why would dark skin not have been a useful adaptation for human populations moving into northern Europe?
5. How is the slow development of a human being related to culture?

Summary

Paleontologists interpret fossil evidence to reconstruct the organisms and interactions of ancient ecosystems. The evolution, from simple beginnings, of the invertebrates, the flowering plants, the reptiles, the amphibians, and the mammals of today are apparent in those ecosystems. Radiation and convergence of living things, the results of natural selection of organisms carried on moving continents, accounts for the variety and distribution of today's plants and animals. Our own group, Hominoidea, is a subgroup of primates. Ancestors of both humans and apes radiated from early hominoids, evolving into hominids and pongids. We share many characteristics with other primates, but also have distinct differences. Chief among them are our upright posture, brain size and head shape, speech, and the development of culture.

Application Questions

1. Decide whether each of these situations is an example of adaptive radiation or adaptive convergence:
   a. the many varieties of house sparrows across the United States
   b. the similar appearance of dolphins and sharks
   c. the 150 kinds of viruses causing common colds
2. New World and Old World monkeys are quite different in appearance. What geological event helps to explain that?
3. What is wrong with this description of a Cambrian sea? "Microscopic organisms floated on the surface of a gently undulating sea. Trilobites crawled over brightly colored sponges. Coelenterate tentacles waved near some unwary small fish."
4. If you found a fossil skeleton having a brain case of 550 c^3 and a foot with a high arch, would you classify it as a hominid? Why?
5. Would a fossil hominid having a brain case of 600 c^3 and holding an axelike stone be classified as a hominid?
6. Why are the characteristics of the original Amerind and Mongolian populations fairly similar?

Problems

1. Why are tropical forests poor sources of fossil evidence? Consider both the conditions for fossilization and the conditions for finding fossils.
2. Construct a food web for the La Brea ecosystem.
3. On September 23, 1789, 9 Englishmen and 17 Tahitians left Tahiti and sailed to Pitcairn—an isolated, uninhabited island in the South Pacific. For 24 years they and their descendants had no visitors, and they have been largely isolated since. The effects are described in H. L. Shapiro, 1976, *The Heritage of the Bounty,* rev. ed., (New York: AMS Press). Can you find any evidence of random genetic drift among the Pitcairn Islanders?
4. Consider the causes of death in modern urban and suburban environments. Include factors that kill individuals before, during, and after the age of reproduction. Consider also factors that reduce health or impair development, and factors that reduce fertility or the survival rate of offspring. Speculate on the possibility that these factors could cause changes in characteristics of future human populations.

Suggested Readings

R. C. Burchfiel, "The Continent Crust" *Scientific American* (September 1983). A good general discussion of continental drift, focusing on the crust of the continents.

J. Francheteau, "The Oceanic Crust" *Scientific American* (September 1983). The study of this part of the earth's crust is essential to an understanding of continental drift.

R. Hékinian, "Undersea Volcanoes" *Scientific American* (July 1984). Volcanic processes taking place on the ocean floor play an important role in continental drift.

W. Langston, "Pterosaurs" *Scientific American* (February 1981). Very interesting article about these flying reptiles, the largest animals ever to fly.

D. Pilbeam, "The Descent of Hominoids and Hominids" *Scientific American* (March 1984). Uses the latest findings to trace human evolution; includes fine illustrations.

W. Rukang and L. Shenglong, "Peking Man" *Scientific American* (June 1983). Describes how information was gathered on *Homo erectus pekinensis* from a cave near Beijing (Peking), China.

R. Siever, "The Dynamic Earth" *Scientific American* (September 1983). This entire issue deals with the changes that have taken place, and will continue to take place, in the history of the Earth.

E. Trinkaus and W. W. Howells, "The Neanderthals" *Scientific American* (December 1979). Excellent discussion of this close relative to modern humans.

Doug Sokell

Mountain biomes include grassland (alpine meadow), taiga, and tundra.

CHAPTER 22

Biomes Around the World

Introduction

Imagine for a moment that you are in the small town of White River, Ontario, Canada. White River is about 20 km from the northeast shore of Lake Superior and is surrounded by a forest of spruce, fir, and some pine. Winters in White River can be very cold. In fact, a sign with a large thermometer down its middle proclaims that White River is the coldest town in Canada. The temperature painted at the bottom of the sign reads "72 degrees below zero." White River is located at 48 degrees north latitude.

Now, imagine that you are in another town, better known than White River, but at the same latitude—48 degrees north. You are in Paris, France. What is the climate in Paris? Is it as cold? Do the same kinds of trees grow here as in White River? In this chapter we will examine the reasons for the differences in vegetation, not only in these two examples, but throughout the world.

Figure 22.1 White River, Ontario.

Paul McIver

Climate and Biomes

Guidepost: What are the abiotic factors that influence the climate of an ecosystem?

22.1 Climate Determines the Distribution of Earth's Major Biomes

Large ecosystems can be described in terms of their climate, or long-term weather patterns. The climate of an ecosystem results from the interaction of several abiotic factors. These include radiant energy, temperature, wind, precipitation, humidity, and evaporation.

Radiant energy is important to an ecosystem for two reasons. First, radiant energy is the form of energy that producers trap and use to make food. Almost all organisms in the ecosystem depend on food made by

Figure 22.2 The distribution of solar energy on the earth's surface.

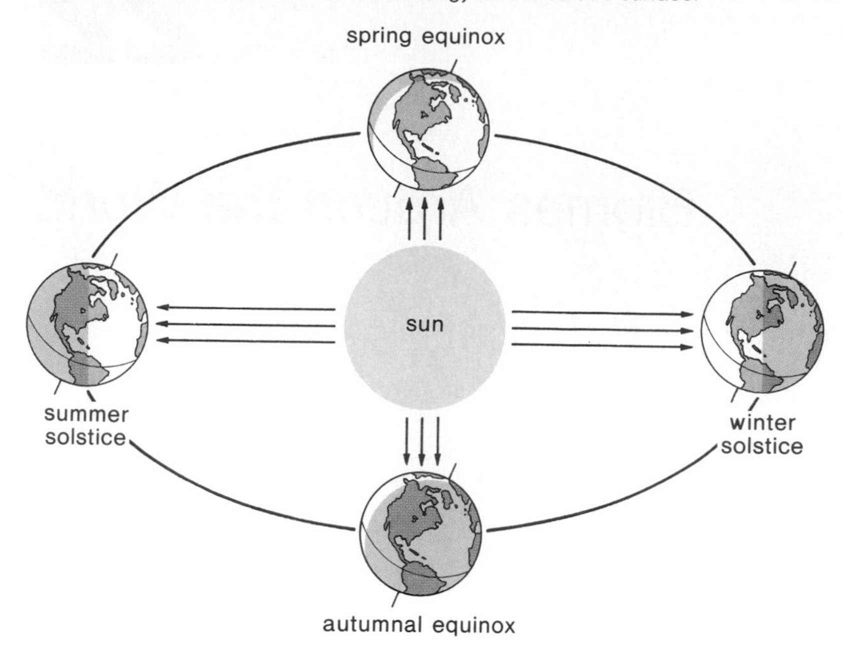

producers. Second, the temperature of the ecosystem is determined by the amount of radiant energy it receives and retains. The energy is absorbed at the earth's surface and is radiated to the air as heat.

The earth is nearly spherical, and it is tilted with respect to its orbit around the sun. At the summer solstice, about June 21, the northern hemisphere is tilted 23.5 degrees toward the sun. As a result, the northern hemisphere receives more solar energy than the southern hemisphere, so it is summer north of the equator and winter south of the equator. At the winter solstice, December 21, the southern hemisphere receives more solar radiation than the northern hemisphere and the seasons are reversed.

Because it is tilted on its axis, the earth receives unequal amounts of solar energy at different places on its surface. The circulation of air in the atmosphere is powered by solar energy. The movement of the air helps to distribute the heat that comes to the earth as radiant energy. At the same time, the circulating air currents carry water vapor from the oceans over land surfaces, where it falls as rain.

Climates occur in broad belts that encircle the earth. The boundaries of these belts are disrupted by land and oceans. Climates are modified further by mountains and ocean currents. Because ocean currents vary in temperature, they can have a profound effect on the type of climate. It is rather easy to map the distribution of a particular factor of climate. It is difficult, however, to map a climate as a whole. This is because climatic factors overlap and interact with one another in complex ways. The overlap of the abiotic factors mentioned earlier makes it difficult to measure climates. To simplify this task, ecologists frequently use **climatograms.** Climatograms are graphs that summarize only two of the factors: monthly measurements of temperature and precipitation. In investigation 22.1 you can prepare climatograms for your area like those in figure 22.3.

In each major kind of climate, a characteristic kind of vegetation develops and maintains itself. For example, warm, arid climates—those

Figure 22.3 Climatograms. Average monthly temperatures are in °C; average monthly precipitation is cm.

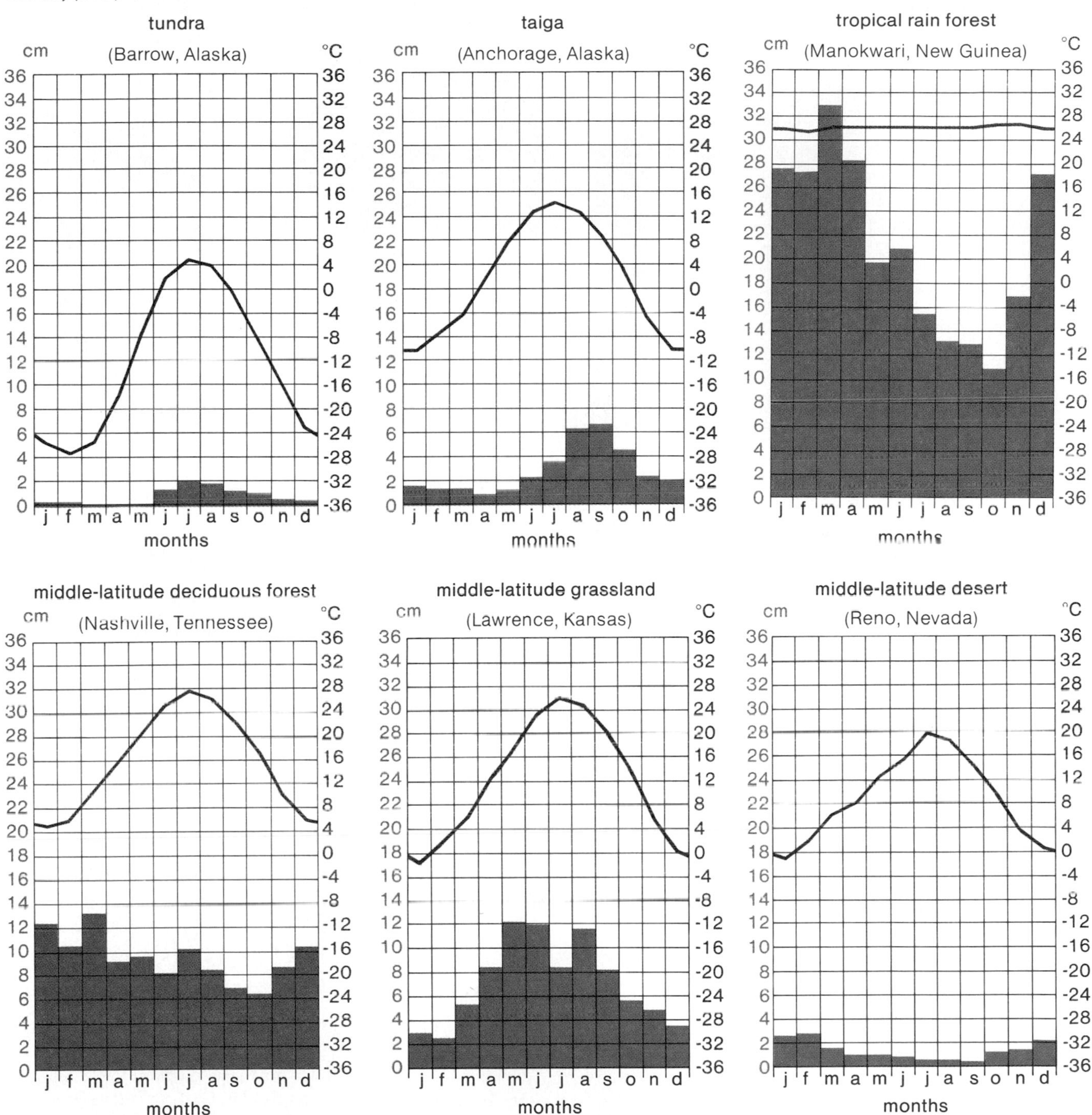

with little rainfall—are associated with desert vegetation. Semiarid climates usually support grasslands. Moist climates support forests. Each kind of plant life, in turn, supports a characteristic variety of animal life. The resulting ecological community of plants and animals is called a **biome.** Biomes extend over large natural areas, as shown in the map in figure 22.4. In the next sections, we will examine some of the distinctive organisms found in each of the major biomes.

Figure 22.4 Major biomes of the earth. Many parts of the earth have not been thoroughly studied, and even where observations are plentiful, ecologists sometimes disagree about their interpretation.

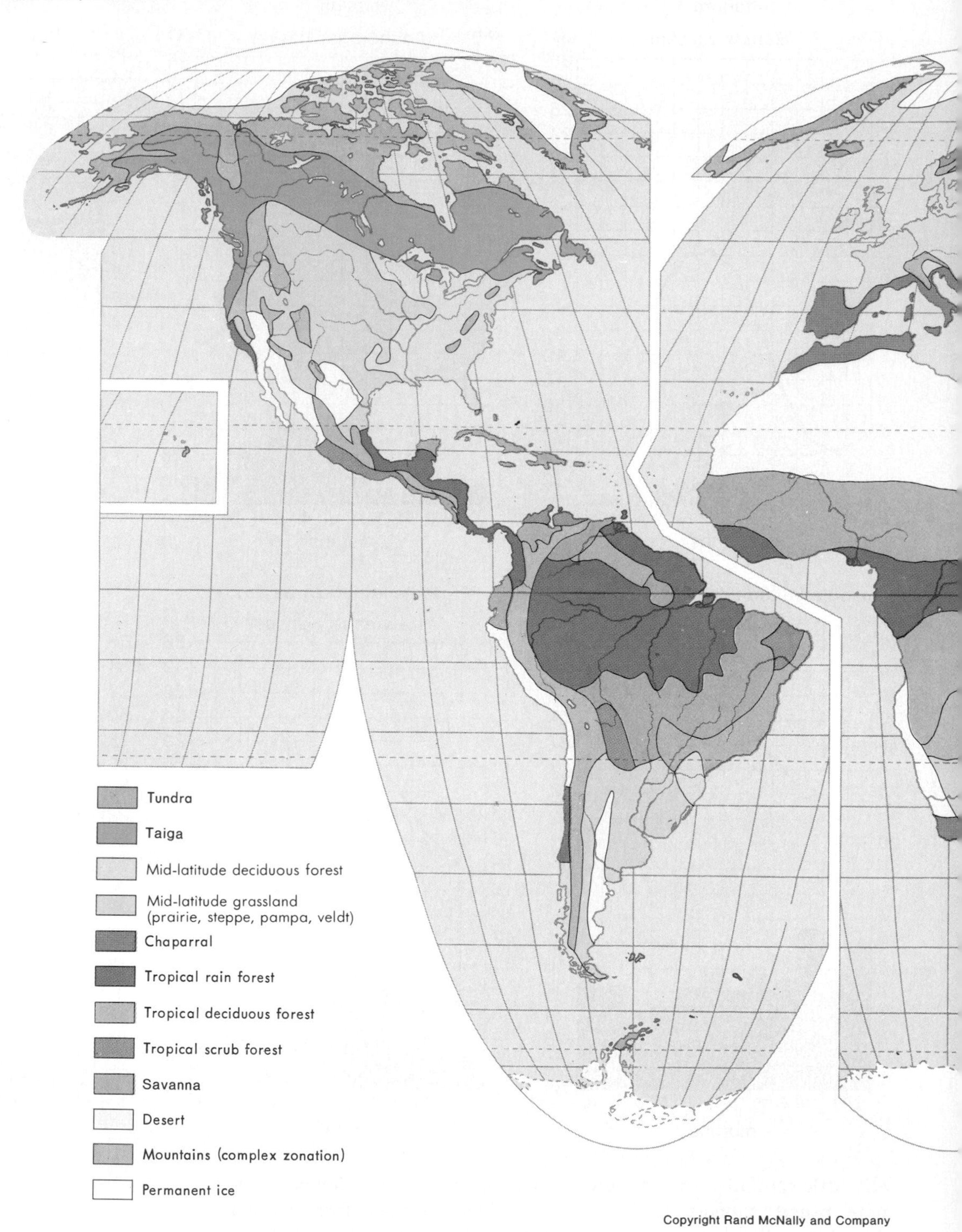

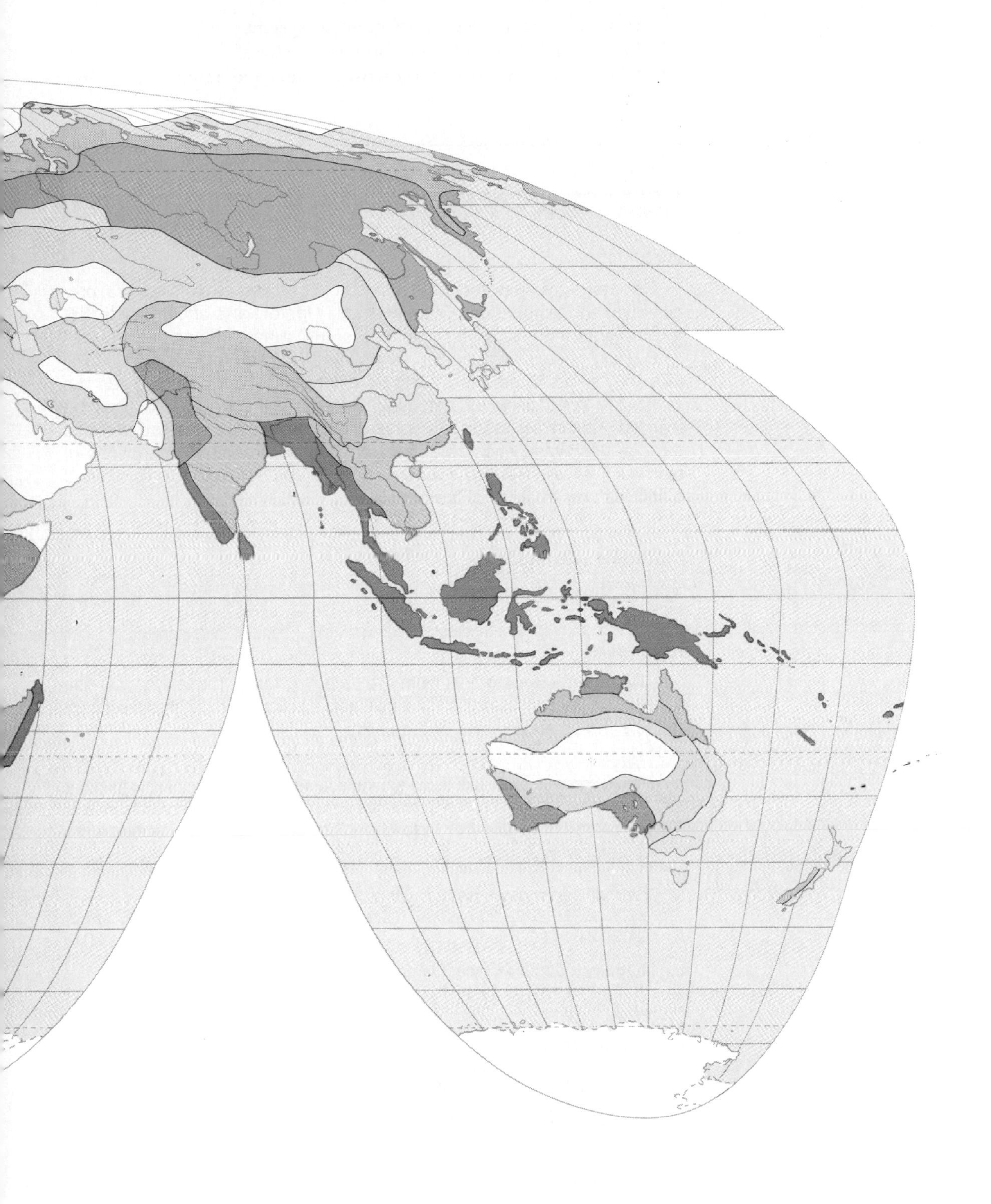

Self-Review

1. How does radiant energy affect an ecosystem?
2. What causes the winter and summer solstices?
3. What determines the characteristic plants and animals found in a biome?

Investigation 22.1 CLIMATOGRAMS

Introduction

Climatograms show monthly variations in only two climatic factors, precipitation and temperature. Of course, other factors also affect climate, but a climatogram does give a rough idea of the climate in a particular area.

By daily observation you can associate the climate of your own locality with the biome found there. Only by extensive travel, however, can the worldwide relationship of particular climates with particular biomes be learned. This investigation is a substitute for such travel. As you proceed through the investigation, refer frequently to pictures and descriptions of biomes. This will help you visualize relationships between the abiotic and biotic features in some of the earth's major ecosystems.

Materials (per student)

3 to 17 sheets graph paper

Procedure

1. Construct climatograms from the data in group 1 (table 22.1). These 4, plus the 6 in figure 22.3, will give you 10 climatograms that represent the major land biomes of the earth.

Table 22.1 Group 1

T = temperature (in degrees Celsius) *P* = precipitation (in centimeters)

	J	F	M	A	M	J	J	A	S	O	N	D
a. Tropical Deciduous Forest: Cuiabá, Brazil												
T	27.2	27.2	27.2	26.7	25.6	23.9	24.4	25.6	27.8	27.8	27.8	27.2
P	24.9	21.1	21.1	10.2	5.3	0.8	0.5	2.8	5.1	11.4	15.0	20.6
b. Chaparral: Santa Monica, California												
T	11.7	11.7	12.8	14.4	15.6	17.2	18.9	18.3	18.3	16.7	14.4	12.8
P	8.9	7.6	7.4	1.3	1.3	0.0	0.0	0.0	0.3	1.5	3.6	5.8
c. Savanna: Moshi, Tanzania												
T	23.2	23.2	22.2	21.2	19.8	18.4	17.9	18.4	19.8	21.4	22.0	22.4
P	3.6	6.1	9.2	40.1	30.2	5.1	5.1	2.5	2.0	3.0	8.1	6.4
d. Tropical Desert: Aden, Aden												
T	24.6	25.1	26.4	28.5	30.6	31.9	31.1	30.3	31.1	28.8	26.5	25.1
P	0.8	0.5	1.3	0.5	0.3	0.3	0.0	0.3	0.3	0.3	0.3	0.3

Table 22.2 Group 2

		J	F	M	A	M	J	J	A	S	O	N	D
a.	*T*	1.1	1.7	6.1	12.2	17.8	22.2	25.0	23.3	20.0	13.9	7.8	2.2
	P	8.1	7.6	8.9	8.4	9.2	9.9	11.2	10.2	7.9	7.9	6.4	7.9
b.	*T*	10.6	11.1	12.2	14.4	15.6	19.4	21.1	21.7	20.0	16.7	13.9	11.1
	P	9.1	8.9	8.6	6.6	5.1	2.0	0.5	0.5	3.6	8.4	10.9	10.4
c.	*T*	25.6	25.6	24.4	25.0	24.4	23.3	23.3	24.4	24.4	25.0	25.6	25.6
	P	25.8	24.9	31.0	16.5	25.4	18.8	16.8	11.7	22.1	18.3	21.3	29.2
d.	*T*	12.8	15.0	18.3	21.1	25.0	29.4	32.8	32.2	28.9	22.2	16.1	13.3
	P	1.0	1.3	1.0	0.3	0.0	0.0	0.3	1.3	0.5	0.5	0.8	1.0
e.	*T*	−3.9	−2.2	1.7	8.9	15.0	20.0	22.8	21.7	16.7	11.1	5.0	−0.6
	P	2.3	1.8	2.8	2.8	3.2	5.8	5.3	3.0	3.6	2.8	4.1	3.3
f.	*T*	19.4	18.9	18.3	16.1	15.0	13.3	12.8	13.3	14.4	15.0	16.7	17.8
	P	0.0	0.0	1.5	0.5	8.9	14.7	12.2	8.1	2.0	1.0	0.3	0.8
g.	*T*	−22.2	−22.8	−21.1	−14.4	−3.9	1.7	5.0	5.0	1.1	−3.9	−10.0	−17.2
	P	1.0	1.3	1.8	1.5	1.5	1.3	2.3	2.8	2.8	2.8	2.8	1.3
h.	*T*	11.7	12.8	17.2	20.6	23.9	27.2	28.3	28.3	26.1	21.1	16.1	12.2
	P	3.6	4.1	4.6	6.9	8.1	6.9	6.4	6.6	8.9	5.1	5.6	4.6
i.	*T*	23.3	22.2	19.4	15.6	11.7	8.3	8.3	9.4	12.2	15.1	18.9	21.7
	P	5.1	5.6	6.6	5.6	2.8	0.9	2.5	4.1	5.8	5.8	5.1	5.3
j.	*T*	17.2	18.9	21.1	22.8	23.3	22.2	21.1	21.1	20.6	19.4	18.9	17.2
	P	0.3	0.5	1.5	3.6	8.6	9.2	9.4	11.4	10.9	5.3	0.8	0.3
k.	*T*	−20.0	−18.9	−12.2	−2.2	5.6	12.2	16.1	15.0	10.6	3.9	−5.6	−15.0
	P	3.3	2.3	2.8	2.5	4.6	5.6	6.1	8.4	7.4	4.6	2.8	2.8
l.	*T*	−0.6	2.2	5.0	10.0	13.3	18.3	23.3	22.2	16.1	10.6	4.4	0.0
	P	1.5	1.3	1.3	1.0	1.5	0.8	0.3	0.5	0.8	1.0	0.8	1.5

2. Obtain monthly averages of precipitation and temperature from the weather station closest to your school. These data might be expressed as inches of precipitation and degrees Fahrenheit. If so, convert the data to centimeters and degrees Celsius, using figure A.1, page 956. From your local data, draw a climatogram.
3. From the data in group 2 (table 22.2), draw the climatograms assigned by your teacher.

Discussion

Compare your local climatogram with the 10 identified ones.

1. Which one does it most closely resemble?
2. What similarities are there between the two?
3. What differences are there?
4. Consider the biotic characteristics of your local area. What characteristics of climate would be a factor in determining these biotic characteristics?
5. Does the local climatogram *exactly* match any of the 10 identified ones?
6. Explain how the differences might affect the biotic characteristics of your biome.

Now compare each unidentified climatogram from group 2 with the 10 identified climatograms. Label each graph with the name of the biome that you think the climatogram represents.

7. Describe the biotic characteristics of each group 2 biome, using the climatic information shown by each of the climatograms.

Your teacher will give you the locations of the group 2 climatograms; you may then check the validity of your reasoning.

Guidepost: How does the vegetation change from north to south?

Biomes Determined by Radiant Energy Supply

22.2 Tundra Is Characterized by Low Vegetation

The **tundra** (TUN druh) biome circles the earth in the northern hemisphere, just south of the ice-covered polar seas. No tundra is found in the southern hemisphere. Can you explain why? A look at the map in figure 22.4 might help.

In the tundra biome the sun is always low in the sky and little radiant energy is received at any given time. In summer, however, the total radiant energy is great because the days are very long—up to 24 hours above the Arctic Circle. The top layer of soil thaws, but the ground beneath, the **permafrost,** always remains frozen. Melting snow cannot drain into permafrost, so water collects on the surface and in the top layers of soil, as can be seen in figure 22.5. For six to eight weeks the tundra is a land of ponds and marshes, even though the yearly precipitation is small.

Figure 22.5 Tundra (Alaska). Note the pond in the foreground and the lack of trees. What climatic factor is primarily responsible for these features?

BSCS

Figure 22.6 A tundra willow. What environmental conditions limit the growth of this woody plant?

David C. Fritts

Figure 22.7 Animals of the arctic tundra: (a) caribou, (b) arctic fox, (c) snowy owl.

a Jim Hassett

b Leonard Lee Rue III/TOM STACK & ASSOCIATES

In this short growing season, plants must synthesize a whole year's food supply. The soils of the tundra are poorly developed and contain very little nitrogen. Microbial decomposition is slow because of the cold temperatures.

Grasses and sedges dominate the tundra. Great areas also are covered by low mats of lichens and mosses. The few woody plants, such as willows (figure 22.6) and birches, grow close to the ground. They seldom become more than a few centimeters tall. Leaves of most plants are small. Many are hairy or have margins rolled inward, thus reducing evaporation of water from the leaf surface. Flowers appear rapidly and seeds develop quickly.

During summer, the tundra teems with animal life. Large flocks of migratory water birds raise their young in the long days that allow around-the-clock food gathering. There are few species of insects in the tundra, but huge numbers of individuals in each species. Great swarms of mosquitoes feed on the caribou, causing them to seek refuge in rivers, only to be plagued again when they leave the water. Caribou graze on grasses and the lichen called "reindeer moss." Ptarmigan, arctic foxes, and snowshoe hares are present in their brown summer coats. Lemmings abound, and when their population is high, predators, such as the snowy

c W. Perry Conway/TOM STACK & ASSOCIATES

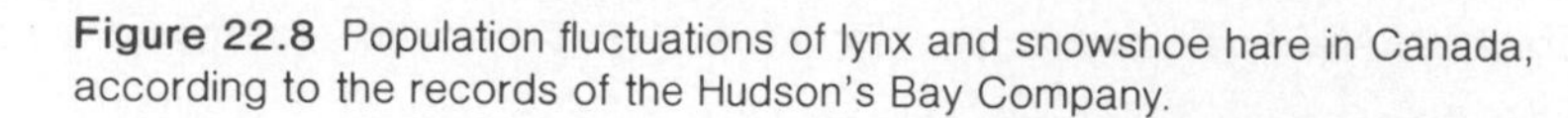

Figure 22.8 Population fluctuations of lynx and snowshoe hare in Canada, according to the records of the Hudson's Bay Company.

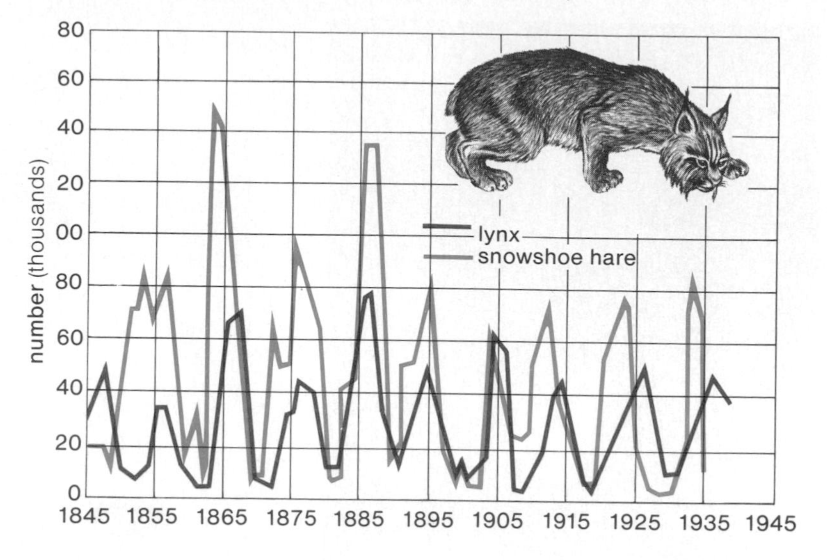

Figure 22.9 Ptarmigan in winter (left) and summer (right). Can you explain the difference in the coloration of the feathers?

owls and the stoat, or ermine, are numerous. Dramatic population cycles, like the one shown in figure 22.8, are common on the tundra because of the harsh climate and variable food supply.

Change from summer to winter is rapid. Lakes and ponds freeze, and the shallower ponds freeze all the way to the bottom. Snowfall is light, only 25 to 30 cm per year, and high winds sweep open areas free of snow. Daylight hours are few, and above the Arctic Circle after the winter solstice there are three months of near darkness.

In the cold and darkness food is scarce. The migratory birds have flown south and some fly deep into the southern hemisphere. Among mammals the chief migrants are caribou, which move south to the forests. Some animals, such as gulls and foxes, migrate to the seashores. When a polar bear kills a seal and has eaten what it needs, the gulls and foxes become scavengers, feeding on the remains. Some animals stay in the tundra all year. Invertebrate animals become dormant or die.

Figure 22.10 Musk ox.

John D. Cunningham / VISUALS UNLIMITED

Figure 22.11 The northern coniferous forests of all continents make up the taiga biome, in which ponds, lakes, and bogs are abundant.

Kirtley-Perkins / VISUALS UNLIMITED

Lemmings avoid the windswept bare ground and burrow under the snow in sheltered spots. There they eat plant roots or seeds they have stored during the summer. Ptarmigan feed on buds of plants that stick out above the shallow snow. Though their feathers provide good insulation, they burrow into the snow during storms. Only musk-oxen face winter's full force. Living on lichens, they seek out uncovered plants or paw away at the snow to uncover the plant material.

22.3 Taiga Is a Coniferous Forest Containing Many Lakes

In the southern reaches of the tundra, scattered groups of dwarf trees appear in sheltered places. Eventually tundra gives way to the great coniferous forest, or **taiga** (TY guh). This forest extends in a broad zone across Europe, Asia, and North America, and it includes many ponds and lakes. There is no similar biome in the southern hemisphere.

Because it is closer to the equator than the tundra, the taiga receives more radiant energy, both daily and annually. Summer days are shorter than those in the tundra, but they are warmer and the ground thaws completely. Winters are not as long as they are on the tundra, although the snow is deeper. Under cover of the trees, snow is not easily blown away, and is kept from melting by the dense shade.

Most coniferous trees are evergreen; they lose their needles a few at a time rather than all at once as broadleaf trees do during the autumn or the dry season. Spruce and fir are the dominant species of trees in the taiga. Throughout the year conifers keep out sunlight, so only mosses, lichens, and a few shrubs can grow near the ground. Most food production, therefore, takes place in the upper parts of trees. Many insects attack the conifers, and a large number of small birds eat the insects. Porcupines eat the tree bark, and deer browse the young leaves.

Figure 22.12 Moose.

Russell C. Dohrmann

The soil tends to be very acid under the coniferous trees and supports few decomposers. Earthworms are uncommon, but large numbers of very small arthropods live in the soil and decompose organic matter.

Until 10,000 to 20,000 years ago, most of this region was covered by a continental ice sheet. Grinding its way slowly across the continents, the ice dug out depressions. As the ice melted, it left piles of dirt and rocks that often formed dams across streams. Many of the ponds and lakes characteristic of taiga were created this way. Today, moose wade into the ponds to eat aquatic vegetation.

During the winter many animals become dormant, or **hibernate.** As winter approaches, they find shelter and their body processes slow down. The energy needed to keep them alive while they are hibernating is derived from the body fat stored during the warmer months. Many other animals migrate southward. The large feet of hares and lynxes serve as snowshoes. Deer and moose wade through the snow on their long legs, browsing on buds and twigs of the trees. Caribou paw away the snow to get at the lichens that form their diet.

22.4 Mid-latitude Deciduous Forest Biomes Have Four Distinct Seasons

South of the coniferous forest are trees with broad leaves rather than needles. These trees are **deciduous** (dee SID joo us)—they shed their leaves each autumn. The shedding is caused by a decrease in three factors: temperature, available soil water, and light. Deciduous trees are common in eastern North America. This biome is not continuous, and in many states much of the forest has been cut and replaced with farmland. Deciduous forest also is found in western Europe and eastern Asia. In the southern hemisphere a similar small forest occurs in southern Chile.

Figure 22.13 Seasons in mid-latitude deciduous forest. All of these pictures show the same area. What effects do these changes have on herbivores such as deer?

Winter

Murray F. Buell

Spring

Murray F. Buell

Summer

Murray F. Buell

Fall

Murray F. Buell

Figure 22.14 The canopy layer of a deciduous forest.

Paul McIver

The summer sun in deciduous forests is much higher in the sky than it is in the taiga or the tundra. The days are long, and there is much radiant energy. In June, at the latitude of Philadelphia, the daily supply of radiant energy is greater than it is in the tropics on all but a few days of the year. Of course, in December, Philadelphia receives little radiant energy. So the *annual* supply of radiant energy is much less in Philadelphia than in the tropics.

Precipitation in the deciduous forest is high (50 to 125 cm per year) and droughts are rare. In winter, snow may be heavy, but it usually melts rapidly and the ground is seldom covered with snow for long. In summer, both temperatures and humidity may be high.

There are many species of deciduous trees, including oaks, hickory, maple, beech, chestnut, and basswood. The tallest ones form a **canopy** (figure 22.14), an upper layer of leaves that catches the full sunlight. Leaves of deciduous trees are rather thin, and much of the radiation filters through them. Thus, there is enough light to provide energy for a lower layer of trees. Even these lower trees do not use all the energy, and enough light filters through to support a layer of shrubs beneath. Finally, mosses and ferns receive the remaining faint light.

This large mass of producers supports a large number of consumers. Squirrels collect nuts and berries from trees. Deer mice climb in the shrubs and search the ground for seeds. White-tailed deer browse on shrubs and the lower branches of trees. In summer, insects are abundant in the soil and in all layers of the forest canopy.

Figure 22.15 Animals and plants of the deciduous forest: (a) squirrel, (b) white-tailed deer, (c) *Trillium,* (d) anemone.

a Carlye Calvin

b William J. Weber / VISUALS UNLIMITED

c Doug Sokell

d Doug Sokell

Figure 22.16 Bird niches in a deciduous forest. Red eyed vireos in the canopy, flycatchers directly below, ovenbirds on the ground, and woodpeckers on the trunks.

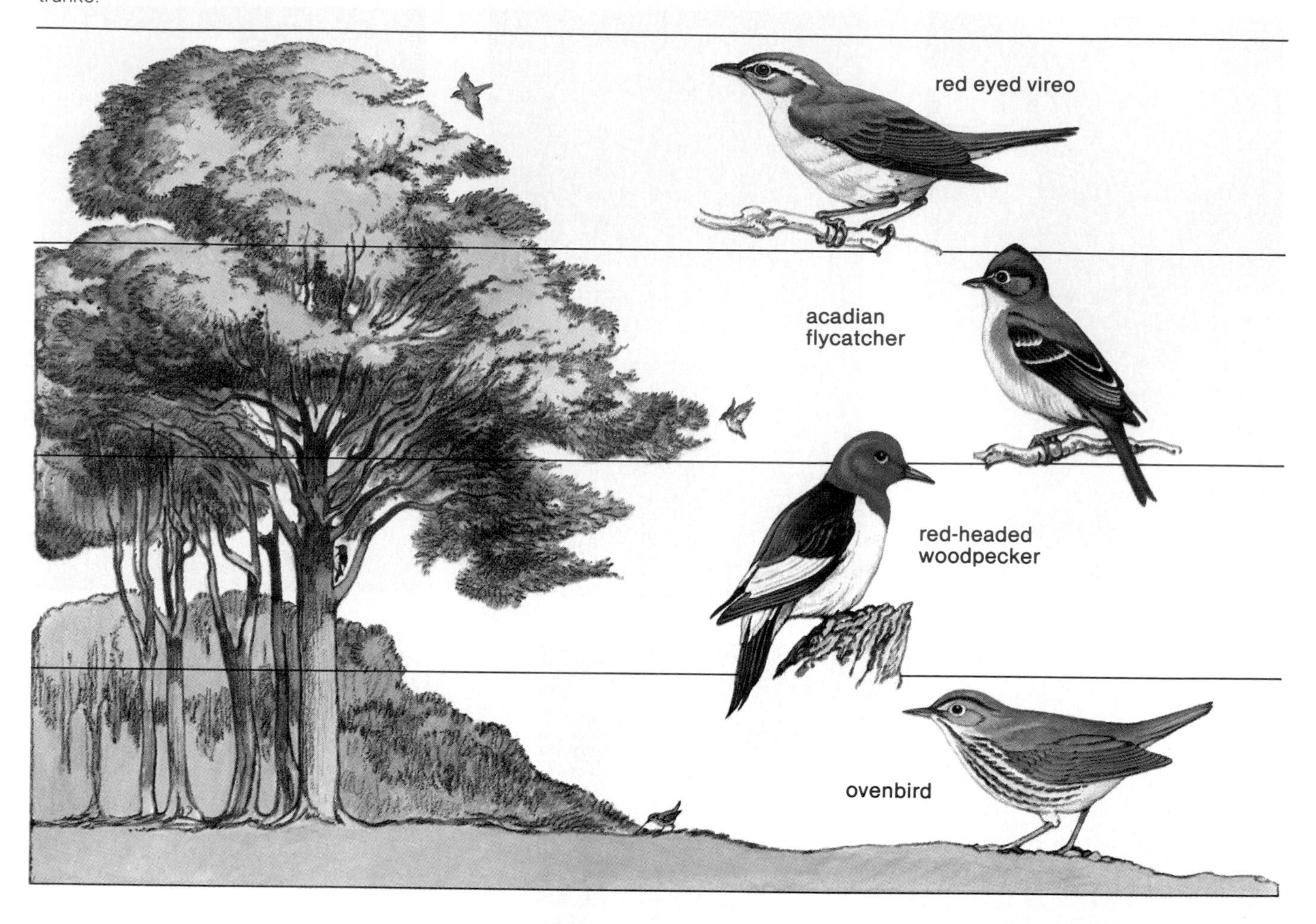

Many birds prey upon insects. In some forests red-eyed vireos consume canopy insects, acadian flycatchers catch insects flying below the canopy, ovenbirds search out insects on the ground, and woodpeckers extract boring insects from the bark of trees. There are few large predators in most of this biome. Foxes, skunks, squirrels, and an occasional black bear are present.

In autumn, the leaves of the deciduous trees turn yellow, orange, red, or brown. The colors appear after the chlorophyll breaks down. The leaves then drift down, covering the ground with a thick mass of organic matter. Nuts and acorns fall, too. Berries cover the lower trees and shrubs. Many mammals fatten themselves on the abundant food, and some store it. Woodchucks form thick layers of fat and then hibernate in burrows. Reptiles, much more abundant here than in the taiga, also hibernate. Many insect-eating birds migrate to the tropics.

Figure 22.17 Leaf litter. This litter serves to enrich the soil through decomposition.

Doug Sokell

In winter, because they have dropped their leaves, the trees use and lose very little water. Many mammals rest during the cold spells. Winter birds are more abundant here than in the coniferous forest. They eat seeds and fruits, and search out dormant insects and insect eggs from the cracks in tree bark.

In spring, activity resumes when masses of warm air move in from the south. Small insects fly in swarms above brooks and ponds. Hibernating animals become active and search for food. Solar radiation becomes strong before air temperatures are high enough to bring the trees to leaf. A great number of nonwoody plants spring up on the forest floor; their leaves and flowers grow quickly. By the time the shade from the trees has closed over them, the nonwoody plants have finished photosynthesis for the year. Food is stored in roots or underground stems; seeds mature and then scatter. The nonwoody plants die back to the ground until the next spring.

22.5 The Tropical Rain Forest Has a Very Uniform Climate

Tropical rain forest (figure 22.18) is found in three separate places along the equator. The biome is named for its location, lying between the Tropic of Cancer and the Tropic of Capricorn. The largest tropical rain forest is in the Amazon Basin of South America. The second largest in size is found in the East Indies, and the smallest is in the Congo Basin of Africa.

Figure 22.18 Amazon basin rainforest.

Brian Parker/TOM STACK & ASSOCIATES

In the tropical rain forest the noon sun is almost directly overhead throughout the year. Thus the amount of radiant energy is high and fairly constant. Rain falls almost every day, and the humidity is always high. The average rainfall is about 2 m a year. Temperatures vary little throughout the year and, beneath the canopy, are nearly constant from day to night. No other terrestrial biome has such a uniform climate.

Vegetation is dense. The canopy reaches an average height of about 50 m. Some individual trees may even grow to 80 m or more. Thus, the trees are taller than those of the temperate deciduous forest (20 to 30 m), the coniferous forest (15 m), or the tundra (0.1 m at most). Beneath the taller trees are shorter ones tolerant of shade. Beneath these are still others even more tolerant of shade. Weaving through the branches are many woody vines.

Along the trunks and branches of the trees and the twisting stems of the vines are many **epiphytes** (EP ih fyts). These plants use the branches on which they perch for support, but not for nourishment. Epiphytes have no contact with the ground, so they have special adaptations for obtaining water and minerals. Some have roots that absorb moisture from the humid atmosphere the way blotting paper soaks up water. Many catch the daily rain in special hollow leaves. Mosquitoes, water beetles, other aquatic insects, and even a species of frog (figure 22.20) live in such treetop puddles.

The dense layers of trees absorb most of the light, so only shade-tolerant plants grow on the forest floor. The trees are supported in the damp soil by huge braces called **buttresses.** Vines coil upward into the dim green of the canopy. Only along rivers or at the edges of clearings does a thick wall of vegetation extend down to the ground, blocking a traveler's way. The way through the forest—once you are in it—is clear.

Figure 22.19 The layering effect in a tropical rainforest. Virtually no sunlight reaches the rainforest floor and comparatively fewer organisms are able to live on the ground than in the trees.

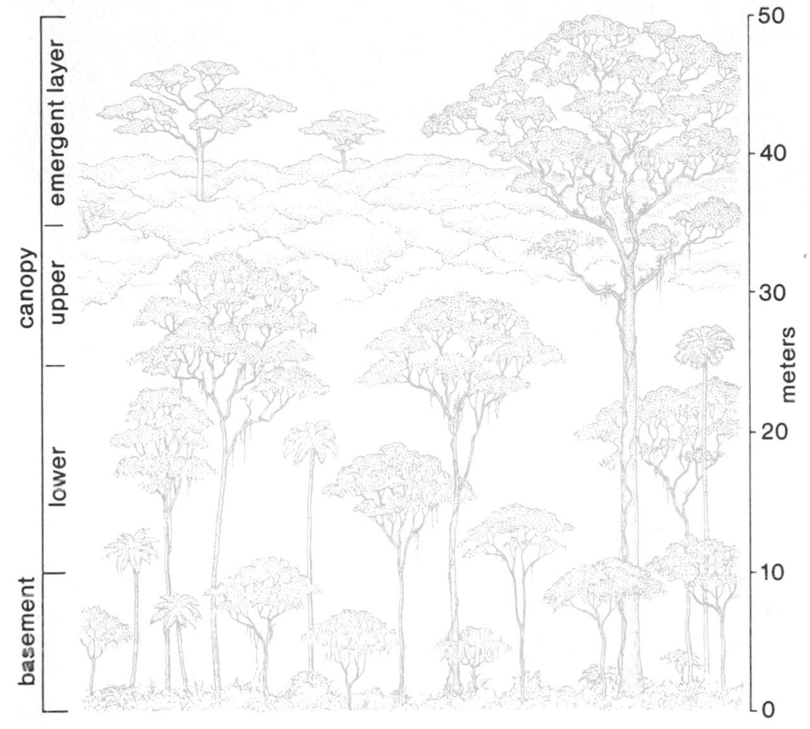

From "*The Canopy of the Tropical Rain Forest*" by Donald R. Perry.

Figure 22.20 An epiphyte with its resident tree frog.

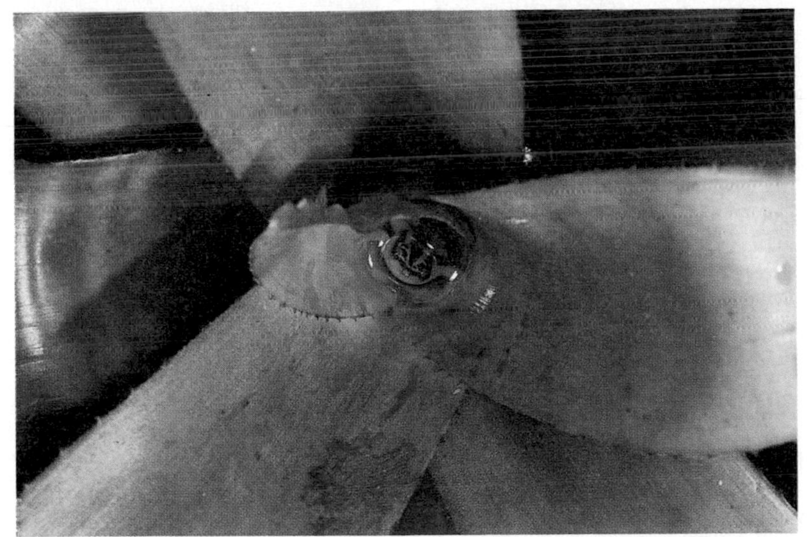

ANIMALS ANIMALS/© Oxford Scientific Films

Figure 22.21 Ground dwellers in a tropical rainforest: (a) long-horned beetle, (b) the collared peccary.

a George-D. Dodge/TOM STACK & ASSOCIATES

b Karlene V. Schwartz

Figure 22.22 Arboreal rainforest animals include (a) the macaw and (b) the spider monkey.

a William J. Weber/VISUALS UNLIMITED

b C. Allan Morgan

Ripe fruits drop to the forest floor and provide a food supply for some ground dwellers. Although the trees are always green, leaves die and fall continuously for most of the year. In the warm, moist environment huge numbers of insects, fungi, and bacteria attack this food supply rapidly. Therefore, organic remains do not build up on the ground. Large herbivores, such as hoofed mammals, are rare or live only near riverbanks. Predators and parasites are abundant at all levels of the forest.

All forests have some **arboreal** animals—animals that live in the trees. In the tropical rain forest many animals live in the canopy. In one study of rain forests 90 percent of the birds were found to feed mostly in the canopy. For birds this may not be surprising. But in this biome a large number of mammals, over 50 percent of the species, also are arboreal.

Since there is more food in the canopy layers than on the ground, it is reasonable to expect a greater diversity of animals in the various canopy layers. There are many tree snakes, tree lizards, tree frogs, and an untold number of arboreal insects.

Many animals, especially birds, lizards, and butterflies, are active in the various canopy layers during the day. At night different animals become active. For example, predators such as owls and leopards or other large cats hunt anything that moves. These differing activity patterns are characteristic of a tropical rain forest.

Self-Review

1. What adaptions of structure and function are found among tundra organisms?
2. What is the most noticeable difference between the tundra and taiga landscapes?
3. Compare the vegetation in a mid-latitude deciduous forest and a tropical rain forest. Explain the differences.
4. Many arboreal animals live in tropical rain forests. What are the reasons for this?
5. How do epiphytes obtain water and minerals?

Biomes with Decreasing Precipitation

Guidepost: How does the vegetation change as the precipitation decreases?

22.6 There Are Three Distinct Types of Grasslands

The principal variable in the biomes we have described is radiant energy. In each biome, precipitation during the growing season was sufficient for the plants that could tolerate the temperatures.

Along the latitudes of deciduous forest however, the precipitation decreases as you travel from east to west in North America. This lack of water is the major factor limiting plant and animal life. Deciduous forests are found in the east, and grasslands are found in the west. Temperature differences, between day and night, and between winter and summer, are greater in the grassland than in the eastern deciduous forest. The principal difference between the two biomes, however, is in the amount of precipitation: it is consistently less in the grassland than in the forest. Grasses can tolerate the frequent droughts that occur in central North America, but the trees cannot.

The tall-grass prairie blends with the western edge of the deciduous forest, and the grasses grow 1.5 to 2 m tall. Mixed-grass prairie is the most characteristic type of grassland of the Great Plains, and supports many species of plants and animals. Grasses here range from 0.5 to 1.2 m in height. The short-grass prairie stretches from the mixed-grass prairie

Figure 22.23 Tall grass prairie.

Brian Parker/TOM STACK & ASSOCIATES

Figure 22.24 Mixed grass prairie.

Soil Conservation Service/USDA

on the east to the Rocky Mountains on the west. These grasses are only about 0.5 m tall. Vegetation in the grasslands, generally, is much less dense than in the forests. Grass leaves grow continuously from their bases. Therefore, as herbivores eat the tops, the grass crop is renewed. Many other nonwoody plants grow among the grasses, but shrubs are rather rare, except along streams. Cactus plants are scattered over the short-grass prairie.

The most conspicuous consumers are hoofed mammals. Once there were many bison and pronghorns in the North American grasslands. Now, nearly all of the bison and most of the pronghorns have been replaced by cattle and sheep. Less conspicuous herbivores are jackrabbits and ground squirrels. Many kinds of insects also feed on vegetation. At times grasshopper populations reach large numbers, devouring the plants down to ground level.

Figure 22.25 Short grass prairie.

BSCS

Figure 22.26 The prairie rattlesnake is an important predator of the grasslands.

John Shaw/TOM STACK & ASSOCIATES

Figure 22.27 Animals of the grassland include meadow larks, black-tailed jackrabbits, and badgers.

Wolves and coyotes were once the chief large predators. Today, wolves have been exterminated almost everywhere in the "lower 48" states, but coyotes survive in many places. Rattlesnakes and badgers are important predators of ground squirrels and prairie dogs. Many insect-eating birds, such as meadowlarks and mountain plovers, nest on the ground under the cactus on the short-grass prairie.

22.7 Mid-latitude Deserts Border the Grasslands

In North America the western edge of the grassland is bordered by desert. The climatic situation is complicated by mountains, but between the western ranges, deserts stretch southward from eastern Washington into Mexico.

Figure 22.28 Hot desert in Arizona. What characteristics do many of the plants have in common?

BSCS by Carlye Calvin

When we think of a desert, we think of an area with little or no precipitation. Just as important in defining a desert, however, is the rate of evaporation. In a desert, evaporation rate is always high compared to precipitation. For example, Tucson, Arizona, receives about 20 cm of rain a year, but is so hot that the evaporation rate exceeds the equivalent of about 195 cm of rain. Latitude and temperature have a profound effect on desert formation. The amount of precipitation that produces a desert at the equator can support a fine grassland at higher latitudes. When precipitation does occur in a desert, it is likely to be heavy but brief and is often the result of thunderstorms or cloudbursts. Much of the water runs off instead of sinking into the soil.

Loss of heat from the earth's surface is greatly slowed by water vapor in the air. Because desert air is very dry, heat that builds up in the soil during the day is quickly lost at night by radiation. Air and soil temperatures at the soil surface vary greatly between day and night. Temperatures underground, however, are much more stable.

There are two types of North American deserts. The northern part of the desert biome is the *cool* desert, and it has an average temperature of about 10 to 12° C in the shade. In the southwestern or *hot* deserts, the temperature averages around 20° to 22° C. Death Valley in the Mojave desert has reached 57° C in the shade.

22.8 Plants Adapt to Desert Conditions in a Variety of Ways

The roots of most desert plants spread far in all directions from the stems and are only a short distance below ground. When rains occur, these widespread, shallow roots soak up the moisture rapidly. These plants are *drought resisters.* Cactus plants are an example, and they store the water in the tissues of their thick stems. In addition, cactus leaves are reduced to spines, which reduces water loss through transpiration.

Figure 22.29 Cool desert. How do these plants differ from those of the hot desert?

Doug Sokell

Figure 22.30 Modification of leaves into spines protects against water loss.

BSCS

Figure 22.31 Mesquite is a drought escaper.

C. Allan Morgan

Drought evaders are plants that conserve water and usually grow very rapidly when conditions are right. The seeds of some of these plants are covered with a chemical that prevents germination during unfavorable conditions. The chemical is washed away during a heavy cloudburst so that germination is possible.

Drought escapers have their root systems far down in the ground in the water table and, therefore, have a continuous supply of water. Mesquite plants (figure 22.31) can have taproots up to 25 to 30 m long and have been seen growing through the ceilings of horizontal mine shafts.

Figure 22.32 This creosote bush in the Tucson Mountains of Arizona is an example of a drought endurer.

C. Allan Morgan

Drought endurers have small leaves that are covered with wax to prevent or at least slow the loss of water. When it is very dry, many plants shed their leaves and, thereby, conserve water. Some plants produce a substance that inhibits the growth of other plants that would otherwise compete for space and water. A good example of this type of plant is the creosote bush (figure 22.32). The aromatic substance of this bush is essentially the same as the creosote derived from coal tar that is used as a preservative for railroad ties.

Few hoofed herbivores live in the mid-latitude deserts, but rodents are numerous. When the day is hot and water is scarce, rodents escape the desert heat by burrowing underground. Here the temperature is cooler and the humidity is higher, and the animal can wait out the hot summer days in a state of sleep called **estivation** (es tih VAY shun). This response to unfavorable environmental conditions is somewhat similar to hibernation. However, estivation is a response to heat and dryness rather than to cold.

Many rodents obtain water from their food or from early morning dew. Kangaroo rats (figure 22.33a), for example, can survive without drinking water. Instead, they use water produced by cellular respiration. Their urine is nearly solid and they lack sweat glands.

Birds in the desert have several ways of coping with the heat and lack of water. First, birds lack sweat glands and, thus, conserve water. Second, bird feathers provide one of the best kinds of insulation found in nature, enabling birds to tolerate the desert heat very well. Third, in flight, the air cools them as it moves over their bodies. Finally, if some insect-eating birds cannot find food in the desert during summer, they can conserve

Figure 22.33 Desert animals include the (a) kangaroo rat and (b) great horned owl.

a

b C. Allan Morgan

their energy by lapsing into a state of **torpor.** During torpor, the body temperature is similar to the environmental temperature, thus reducing the demand on the birds' energy.

As in all terrestrial biomes, there are many herbivores. Many birds and some reptiles, especially lizards, are insect-eaters. Scorpions also prey on insects. Among larger predators are coyotes, hawks, and rattlesnakes, all of which depend primarily on rodents and rabbits as food.

Self-Review

1. Why are there grasslands in the same latitude as forests?
2. What two abiotic factors must be considered together in describing desert climate?
3. How are plants adapted to desert conditions?
4. In what ways are estivation and torpor adaptive behaviors?

Guidepost: What is the effect of variable rainfall and uniform temperature on a biome?

Biomes that Have Variable Precipitation

22.9 Tropical Deciduous Forests Have Distinct Wet and Dry Seasons

The seasonless rain forests with a uniform climate cover a rather small part of the tropics. Most tropical regions have seasons. Instead of being warm and cold seasons, however, they are wet and dry. In the tropics many woody plants lose their leaves during the dry season. Tropical regions with uniform temperatures but wet and dry seasons produce a tropical deciduous forest or tropical seasonal forest. Consult the map in figure 22.4 to locate regions of tropical deciduous forest.

In this biome the canopy is not as dense as that in the rain forest. Light filters all the way to the forest floor. A dense mass of undergrowth thrives during the rainy season. People can penetrate this mass only by cutting their way through. It is this biome that best matches the common idea of a "jungle."

Many animals estivate during the dry season. Insects, reptiles, and amphibians in particular are likely to estivate. In parts of Africa, some species of birds breed twice as a result of the two distinct seasons.

Figure 22.34 Tropical deciduous forest. In what season do you think this picture was taken?

CARIBBEAN COLLECTION/Nancy Sefton

22.10 Savannas Are Tall Grasslands in Tropical Dry Areas

Where tropical dry seasons are long and severe, trees grow far apart. Between the trees the ground is covered with tall grasses. This is the **savanna** (suh VAN uh), a biome that covers large areas in South America and Africa. In less arid climates, fire and soil type are more likely to cause the formation of a savanna than is the climate.

In Africa, the savanna is the home of many large hoofed mammals that graze and browse. Zebras, gazelles, and antelopes are among the many herbivores. These first-order consumers are followed by predators such as lions, leopards, and cheetahs. The kills of these big cats are cleaned up by scavengers such as hyenas and vultures. Very often the carcasses of dead gazelles can be seen draped over the limbs of the acacia trees. These were put there by one of the big cats so that scavengers would not steal the remains of the carcass.

Large herds of zebras, wildebeest, gazelles, and other hoofed animals, as well as elephants and giraffes, are found on the Serengeti Plain of the savanna. At present these herds of animals make up the largest concentration of wild animals to be found on any continent.

Figure 22.35 Tropical savanna in eastern Africa. Elephants, zebras, and giraffes (background); wildebeest and ostrich (foreground). What predators might you find here?

Figure 22.36 Elephants and zebras share a waterhole on the savanna in Kenya.

David L. Pearson/VISUALS UNLIMITED

Figure 22.37 Chaparral (California). At what season do you think this picture was taken?

Dennis Brokaw

22.11 Chaparral Covers Dry Areas that Have Thin Soil

In California most of the precipitation comes in the winter; the summers are very dry. South Africa, western Australia, central Chile, and the region around the Mediterranean Sea have similar climates. The biome characteristic of this kind of climate has several names. In America the term **chaparral** (shap uh RAL) is used to describe the vegetation.

Chaparral is found on thin soil of rather low fertility. The vegetation consists of large shrubs with small, evergreen leaves that are thick and often coated with waxy material. The canopy is very low and often dense. In some cases, no herbs grow under the shrubs. The shrubs have thick underground stems that survive the dry summers and the frequent fires that burn through the chaparral. The fires burn off all the plant structures above the ground, releasing the minerals in the plants and litter. The minerals are thus available for the new plants that sprout from the thick stems that remain alive near the ground. However, when the temporary loss of vegetation is combined with heavy winter rains, soil erosion in the form of mud slides occurs.

Rodents and reptiles are numerous here, and in the chaparral of southern California, there are coyotes living within the city limits of even the largest communities.

Self-Review

1. What climatic factor explains deciduous trees in the tropics?
2. Compare and contrast hibernation and estivation.
3. Describe the savanna biome and the abiotic factors that influence it.
4. What is chaparral?

Investigation 22.2 EFFECTS OF FIRE ON BIOMES

Introduction

Fire is an important ecological factor in terrestrial ecosystems. Some fires start from natural causes. But many are caused by people—deliberately or accidentally. No matter how they begin, fires have many effects on the organisms in their paths. The most easily observed effects are on vegetation.

This investigation considers three different North American biomes and the changes that fire might cause in each biome. Base your answers to the questions on the study of figures 22.38, 22.39, and 22.40.

Procedure

Part A—Fire in Mid-latitude Grassland

Figures 22.38a–d picture a series of events that occur in the southern part of the North American grassland. Two kinds of populations are involved: grasses of various species and mesquite shrubs.

1. Study figures 22.38a and 22.38b. What is happening to the sizes of the populations?
2. Roots of mesquite have been found in mine shafts many meters below the surface of the soil. What competitive advantage might this kind of root growth give mesquite over grasses?

Figure 22.38

a. grasses and mesquite bush

b. same area 10 years later

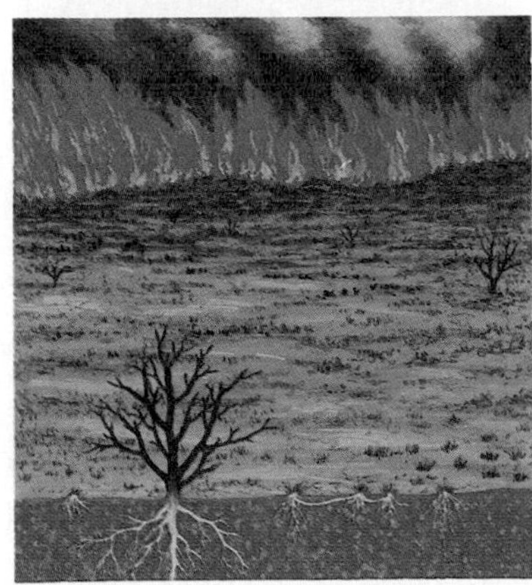

c. fire

d. 2 years after fire

3. If occasional droughts strike the area (as actually happens), what kind of community do you think might result?
4. Now refer to figures 22.38c and 22.38d. In these figures plant parts shown in light color represent unharmed tissue. Do both kinds of plants survive fires?
5. In which kind has more growing tissue been killed?
6. Grasses usually reach maturity and produce seeds in 1 or 2 years; mesquite usually requires 4 to 10 years. Which kind of plant has lost more in terms of growing time?
7. In figure 22.38d which kind of plant occupies most of the land?
8. What might you expect this area to look like 4 or 5 years after a fire?
9. Now you can make a generalization on the effect of fire in this community. Describe the probable landscape if fires did not occur at all.
10. What would be the appearance of the landscape if fires occurred every few years?
11. What seems to be necessary for maintaining grassland in this region?

Part B—Fire in a Forest of the Great Lakes Region

Around the Great Lakes of North America is a region of transition between the coniferous and mid-latitude deciduous forests. In many places much of the forest consists of pines (figure 22.39a). But, early in the settlement of the region, Europeans brought about a great change in the landscape (figure 22.39b).

Figure 22.39

a. before settlement

b. after settlement

c. fire

d. 3 years after fire

1. What was this change?
2. Fires apparently had been rare in this region, but following the change in landscape, they became more frequent. What might have brought about the increase in the number of fires?
3. If fire does not occur, what might the area shown in figure 20.39b look like in later years?
4. Study figures 22.39b, 22.39c, and 22.39d, which picture jack pine. What characteristic of jack pine gives that species a competitive advantage when there is a fire? (Hint: Compare the cones in figures 22.39b and 22.39c.)
5. Describe the probable appearance of the area shown in figure 22.39d 5 or 6 years later.
6. Jack pines produce cones in 8 to 10 years but do not live to a very great age. Their seedlings do not thrive in shade. Suppose no fires occur for 200 years. What changes in appearance might take place in this area during that period?
7. Suppose fires occur about once every 20 years. What might the area look like at the end of 200 years?

Part C—Fire in a Forest of the Southeastern United States

In the southeastern United States are great forests in which longleaf pine is almost the only large tree. Occasionally there may be seedlings and saplings of deciduous trees. Between 3 and 7 years of age longleaf pines look somewhat like clumps of grass (figure 22.40a). While in this grass

Figure 22.40

a. longleaf pines, deciduous saplings and shrubs

b. fire in same area

c. fire in mature pine forest

d. pine forest - no fire for 5 years

stage, the young trees develop deep roots in which food is stored. (See cutaway, lower corner of figure 22.40a.)

Fires in these forests generally are confined to the ground, where they burn grasses and the sparse growth of the deciduous shrubs and saplings (figure 22.40b).

1. What is the effect of fire on young longleaf pines?
2. What is the effect on the deciduous shrubs and saplings?
3. Which plants have a competitive advantage after a fire?
4. After the grass stage, longleaf pines grow rapidly in height and develop a thick, fire-resistant bark. What is the effect of ground fires at this stage in the development of the pines (figure 22.40c)?
5. Which plants have a competitive advantage when fires do not occur (figure 22.40d)?
6. What factor seems to maintain a forest of longleaf pines within the deciduous-forest biome?

Discussion

Knowledge of the ecological effects of fire on biomes can be useful to humans.

1. If you were interested in raising cattle in a mid-latitude grassland, would occasional fires be an advantage or a disadvantage? Why?
2. Jack pine is not as valuable a lumber tree as are other trees of the Great Lakes region. If you were a landowner in that region, would fire be an advantage or a disadvantage? Why?
3. If you were interested in maintaining a longleaf pine forest to obtain turpentine, would ground fires be an advantage or a disadvantage? Why?
4. Suppose you wanted bobwhites (game birds that nest on the ground) in your turpentine forest. What effect might this have on your management of the forest?
5. What things must ecologists know before deciding whether to recommend fire as a method of management to a landowner?

For Further Investigation

Investigation 22.2 is based on case studies of fires in forest and grassland management (originally published in *Scientific American*). Recent controversy over fire as a means to control diseases of forest trees, and as a means to control the replacement of older trees by younger ones, has been discussed in many newspaper articles. A useful and comprehensive reference is T. T. Kozlowski and C. E. Ahlgren, eds., 1974, *Fire and Ecosystems* (New York: Academic Press).

Guidepost: How do mild climates, heavy precipitation, and high altitudes affect biome formation?

Cool, Wet, and Mountain Biomes

22.12 The Coastal Coniferous Forest Has Cool Summers and Mild Winters

Sometimes called the mid-latitude rain forest, this biome is found in a narrow band along the coast from southern Alaska into northern California. It is characterized by cool summers, comparatively mild winters, and abundant precipitation, up to 640 cm per year in some areas.

Figure 22.41 Mid-latitude rainforest. The canopy is much simpler and a fair amount of sunlight reaches the ground. The life on the floor of a mid-latitude rainforest is richer than that of a tropical rainforest.

Linda Kelly-Hassett

The trees are mostly conifers, but they are much larger than those of the taiga. Some even exceed the height of the trees in tropical rain forests. The "coast" redwoods of California are located in the rain forest and may grow to more than 100 m (see figure 13.2, page 438). These redwoods are huge trees with a thick, red bark that resists fire. In addition, chemicals in the bark make the trees nearly insect-proof.

The canopy is much simpler in this biome than in the tropics, and there are relatively few species of trees. Moss, fern, and lichen epiphytes are abundant. Shrubs are fairly numerous, but herbs and vines are few. The ground is covered with deep cushions of moss.

Elk and deer browse on the shrubs. Many birds and rodents live primarily on conifer seeds. Compared with the tropical rain forest, this forest has few arboreal vertebrates, but it has many insects. Small invertebrates live deep in the layers of **humus**, or decomposing plant and animal tissue, on the forest floor. They are food for populations of ground birds.

22.13 Mountain Biomes Resemble Biomes at Higher Latitudes

Air is heated at the earth's surface and becomes cooler at higher altitudes. Temperature drops (on the average) about 2.7° C for each 500 m of elevation. A climb of only a few hundred meters up the side of a mountain gives the same effect as going many kilometers toward the North Pole. This means that at the base of a mountain you may find a climate suitable for grassland, whereas near the top of the mountain only tundra plants can survive. Ecosystems that resemble the biomes of higher latitudes develop as beltlike zones circling mountains.

Figure 22.42 Comparison of effects of altitude and latitude in western North America. Types of vegetation and animal life are affected by both altitude and latitude.

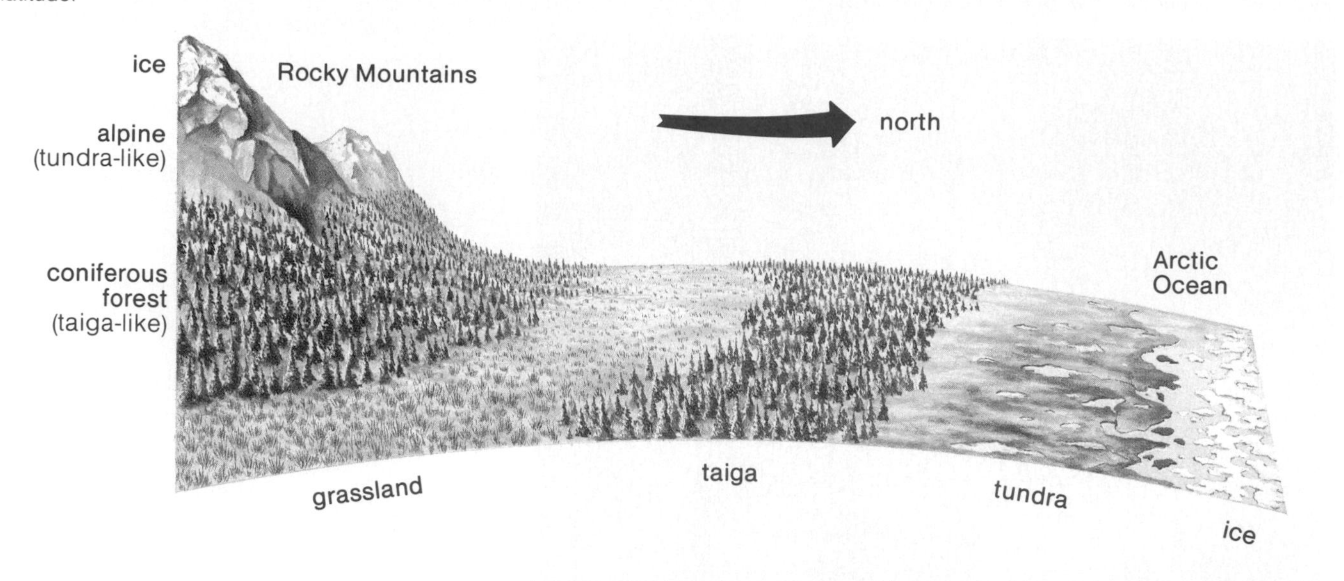

Figure 22.43 The Rocky Mountains of Colorado. What zones seen here can be compared to the biomes you have learned about?

Carlye Calvin

We might attempt to relate these zones to the similar biomes we have read about. The similarities, however, are somewhat superficial. For example, in the upper mountain, or **alpine,** region of the Rocky Mountains, the landscape looks much like the tundra of the north. Many species of organisms are the same in both alpine and tundra biomes. However, there are some differences in the plants due to differences in the amount of light received.

Figure 22.44 Flowers of the alpine tundra.

Doug Sokell

During the summer, arctic tundra plants receive a great deal more light than those of the alpine tundra, even though the light intensity is greater in the alpine tundra. Arctic tundra plants are long-day plants, and alpine tundra plants are short day plants. For this reason there are different species of plants in the two similar biomes.

In the alpine tundra there is usually no permafrost and no long period of darkness in the winter. The amount of radiant energy received here in summer is much greater than that received at any time in the northern tundra. In both biomes the winds blow long and hard, particularly during the winter months. Mount Washington in New Hampshire is about 1830 m high and its alpine tundra has withstood a wind velocity of 385 km per hour.

The amounts of snow are quite different in the two biomes. The northern tundra may get no more than 25 cm during the winter, whereas the top of Mount Rainier, in the state of Washington, receives over 20 m. It seems best, therefore, to think of mountainous regions as often having familiar biomes with certain distinctive characteristics.

Self-Review

1. What vegetation grows in a coastal coniferous forest?
2. How do conditions in an alpine ecosystem on mid-latitude mountains resemble conditions on the arctic tundra?
3. In what ways do the arctic and alpine tundras differ?

Investigation 22.3 A FIELD STUDY OF ANIMAL BEHAVIOR

Introduction

Ethology is the study of an organism's behavior in an ecosystem. This includes its responses to its own species, to other species, and to the nonliving environment. One can learn a great deal about the behavior of an organism by observing it in the field (in its environment) because one will observe the organism under natural conditions. Therefore, the behavior observed is likely to be typical of the species. Usually behaviors observed in the field are responses to the basic needs of the animal, such as food, survival, and reproduction. Your goal in this investigation is to develop a systematic field study of an animal in its natural habitat and then relate the behaviors of the organism you observe to its basic needs without using human values and emotions.

Materials

field notebook

Procedure

1. Select a nondomesticated animal that you feel will be available for your observation. Some animals that should make good field subjects are:
   (a) Arthropods. Any number of insect species such as the dragonfly, bee, beetle, fly, butterfly, or ant are available in almost any environment. Other arthropods such as spiders, sowbugs, or crayfish will do nicely also.
   (b) Birds. A variety of birds such as the sparrow, pigeon, cardinal, dove, robin, and starling live in most neighborhoods. Common in fields or parks are the redwing blackbird, meadowlark, killdeer, crow, duck, and goose.
   (c) Mammals. Squirrels, deer, mice, chipmunks, gophers, muskrats, and otters are very interesting if you are able to observe them.
   (d) Mollusks. Snails and slugs.
   (e) Fish. Aquarium fish are acceptable.
2. Fields, ponds, aquariums, or just a large tree in a park are the homes for many of the organisms listed. The best times of day for observation are just before sunset or just after sunrise because many animals will be feeding at these times. It is not necessary to study the same individual during your observation, because many behavioral characteristics are common to the species.
3. Some good behaviors to focus on are:
   (a) Orientation (change in position) to external stimuli (sunlight, wind, temperature, and moisture)
   (b) Communication with its own species and/or other species
   (c) Feeding
   (d) Courtship
   (e) Interaction with other members of its species
   (f) Defense or protection of itself, its young, or its territory
   (g) Reactions to the presence of other species (including humans)

4. Once you have decided on an animal to study, make a plan for your study and have it approved by your teacher. Your plan should include:
   (a) The name of the organism.
   (b) Where and when you will make your observation.
   (c) What problem or question you will investigate.
   (d) A hypothesis related to your problem.
5. Conduct your observations. Your best observations will be when you are not seen by the animal under study.
6. Take good notes in your field notebook during your observation and refer to these notes when you write your report.

Discussion

1. Organize the data you collected during your observations.
2. Write a report that relates the behaviors of the animal you observed to its basic needs without using human values or emotions.
3. A good report will include the following:
   (a) Title, your name, and date.
   (b) Your original plan sheet with your teacher's approval.
   (c) Your actual procedure (if different from your original plan).
   (d) Your problem and hypothesis.
   (e) Data (notes of your observations): organize your notes by quantifying as much of your data as possible (how many, how large, how often, and so on).
   (f) Conclusions: interpretations and/or explanations of the behaviors observed in light of basic needs of the animal.
   (g) Evaluation of hypothesis: did the data support or refute your hypothesis?
   (h) Recommendations for further study: what you would suggest if someone else were going to do the same study; what you would do differently if doing the study again.

Human Influence on Biomes

Guidepost: How are human activities changing biomes?

22.14 The Need for Land Has Changed Some Biomes

The brief descriptions of the biomes may lead you to conclude that they have changed very little since they were first described many years ago. In fact, many have been altered so they no longer resemble the original biome. What causes these changes, and what are the consequences?

Flying from Cleveland, Ohio, to Nashville, Tennessee, you cross the biome of mid-latitude deciduous forest, yet you see only a few traces of forest. Flying from Chicago, Illinois, to Lincoln, Nebraska, you cross the eastern part of North American grassland. Here, too, you see only traces of the original ecosystem. In fact, in these two flights, the landscapes below appear remarkably similar. Although in both cases the climate remains an important factor, the present landscape has been shaped

Figure 22.45 The rich flat plains of the midwest became the corn and wheat belt of the United States.

John D. Cunningham/VISUALS UNLIMITED

by humans. The changes have been caused by the need for food and homes. In Ohio, for example, only about two percent of the original deciduous forest remains, and the land now supports farms and cities instead. This is the inevitable consequence of a growing population.

Let us examine how biomes are being altered and the consequences of those changes.

22.15 Tropical Rain Forests Will Nearly Be Gone by the Year 2000

The demands of a growing population have placed the tropical rain forests of the world in jeopardy. About 50 percent of the earth's forests are located in the tropics, and it is estimated that the tropical forests will be nearly destroyed by the year 2000. What happens when a forest is destroyed? One of the tragic effects is the loss of habitat for countless numbers of plants and animals, many of which, surely, have yet to be discovered. Perhaps several million species of organisms are being lost. These organisms could create joy just by being seen. Many of them also could have potential use as medicine and food.

One of the reasons for cutting the forest is to clear the land for crops. However, the soil under the trees of the tropical forest is very poor in humus. When the trees are removed, the continual leaching of the plant nutrients by the heavy rainfall leaves the soil infertile and incapable of supporting crops after a few years. The soil becomes almost as hard as concrete and few plants can grow where a magnificent rain forest once stood.

Figure 22.46 This photo dramatically illustrates how overgrazing can affect a grassland.

Soil Conservation Service / USDA

22.16 Desertification Is Increasing Rapidly

Desertification is an ecological change that takes place along the margins of deserts and usually means the loss of grazing land. In other words, a grassland that would support a large herd of livestock becomes unable to support any at all. What are the causes of desertification? No one single factor is responsible for the changes, but several factors appear to be involved in the process of increasing the size of deserts. One is overgrazing by excessive numbers of livestock. Too many sheep, cattle, and goats are eating away the grass and are browsing on the few shrubs and trees.

Another cause of desertification is a change in climate. Drought is caused by the absence of sufficient precipitation needed to make the plants grow. The few plants that remain are soon eaten by the livestock. With the ground cover gone, the winds begin moving the soil of the grazing lands into dunes, and in some places the sands of the deserts encroach on the margins of the grasslands. This is happening in the sub-Saharan region called the Sahel and has caused great misery and death to those nomads who live there. It is estimated that billions of acres of land that border deserts are at risk of becoming deserts by the year 2000.

22.17 Acid Rain Is Destroying Forests

Normal rain has a pH of 5.6. The pH of acid rain ranges from 5.5 to as low as 2.4. In general, the precipitation over much of the world now is thirty times more acid than normal. The burning of fossil fuels adds

Figure 22.47 Trees exposed to acid rain eventually die.

John D. Cunningham / VISUALS UNLIMITED

large amounts of sulfur and nitrogen oxides to the atmosphere. There, these oxides react with water and are transformed into sulfuric and nitric acids, which fall to earth as acid precipitation. What happens to forests that are watered with acid rain?

The soils supporting the forests can no longer buffer, or neutralize, the acid precipitation, which then leaches minerals out of the soil. That deprives the trees of the mineral salts that they require for growth, and they begin to weaken and die. The waxy cuticle on the leaf surface can be directly destroyed by the acid rain. Then needles and leaves turn yellow (figure 22.47) and drop prematurely, and the trees eventually die. Whole forest ecosystems are threatened by acid rain; the forests of the eastern United States, Canada, and Europe show the greatest destruction so far.

Self-Review

1. What has happened to the deciduous forests of the Midwest?
2. How does the cutting of a tropical rain forest affect the soil under the trees?
3. What factors, human and natural, increase the size of deserts?
4. When forest soils can no longer buffer acid rain, what happens to the trees?

Investigation 22.4 A FIELD STUDY OF A PIECE OF THE BIOSPHERE

Introduction

By now you have studied many specific living organisms and have studied ecological relationships between organisms. You also have examined small pieces of the biosphere in the laboratory using climatograms. Now you should study a piece of the biosphere in a natural setting. It need not be a very large piece—just large enough to contain several kinds of organisms that show interrelationships with each other. Different schools have different opportunities for outdoor studies. Therefore, procedures will have to be worked out by your class and your teacher to fit the piece of biosphere that is most convenient to your school setting. Read the following sections carefully to get an overview of what you might do.

Selecting a study area. You may not have many alternatives but let us examine some possibilities. A forest is complex and provides opportunities to collect abundant data, but it is most difficult to picture as a whole. A prairie is almost as complex and is somewhat easier to study. Cultivated areas, such as cornfields and pastures, are relatively simple to study. They are as important as forests and prairies because they now cover a large part of the land area of our country.

Pieces of the biosphere suitable for study can also be found in cities. Many schools have lawns with trees and shrubs. Here there may be fewer kinds of organisms than outside the city, but you can be more thorough in your study. You also can study vacant lots and spaces between buildings. Even cracks in pavement, gutters, and the area around trees often contain a surprising number of organisms.

Organizing the work. After deciding where to make the study, your class must next decide what kinds of data to collect. The questions in the discussion for this investigation should give you some ideas. Different teams should gather different kinds of data. Each team must decide what materials it needs and arrange to obtain them. A team should draw up a form on which data can be recorded quickly. Each team should select a leader to see that all parts of the work are completed as planned by the team. Each individual has special abilities. Use these when deciding on tasks within the team.

All of the procedures in investigation 22.4 can be expanded, depending on the wishes of your class. Additional activities or alternative procedures may be found in many ecology textbooks. Your teacher can suggest additional references.

Collecting the data. It may be easier to handle sheets of paper on a clipboard than to take data books into the field. Paste the sheets into your data book when you return to the laboratory.

No biologist can identify every organism observed. There are two ways to deal with this problem. One is to identify kinds only by general group names such as trees, spiders, grasses, beetles, or turtles. Another method is to collect a specimen—a sample individual or, in the case of large plants, a characteristic part (a leaf, for example). Assign the specimen a letter (A, B, C, and so on), and whenever you need to refer to that kind of organism, refer to its letter. After you return to the classroom, you may be able to identify your specimen by looking it up or showing it to an expert.

Some descriptions of plants you may find in your study area may be useful to you:

1. Tree. Tall, woody plant with a single stem (trunk).
2. Shrub. Woody plant that branches at or near the ground and lacks a trunk.
3. Sapling. Young tree with a trunk 1 to 5 cm in diameter.
4. Herb. Nonwoody plant that dies back at least to ground level in winter.
5. Tree seedling. Very young tree with a trunk less than 1 cm in diameter.

Searching for animal data. This activity should be carried out after the studies of plants have been completed, possibly at a later date. Work in pairs, with one person searching and the other recording. Turn over stones, logs, and other cover to find animals, being sure to return these sheltering objects to their original position. Look on plants, too, especially in flowers. Look for animal droppings.

Make notes of the kinds, numbers, and activities of animals you find. If it is permitted in the area where you are now working, collect specimens of unknown kinds for identification.

Netting insects. In thick forests it may be difficult to catch flying insects, but you can beat the shrubs and saplings with a stout net, holding the open end up. In open fields sweep your net through the plants. If you identify the insect as specifically as you can or wish to, you can release it. Otherwise, you may want to preserve it according to directions by your teacher and take it back to class for further identification.

Studying larger animals. Your searching procedure may uncover toads or snakes. **CAUTION:** *Do not pick up any animals or touch any plants unless you can identify them as harmless.* To study reptiles, birds, and other large animals, you will need to cover larger areas than the ones we have been considering and observe the areas over longer periods of time. It is preferable not to collect these animals.

Birds might not be present or active when your class is collecting data. A few students may want to look for them at different times over a period of several days. Around daybreak and dusk are usually the best times.

The most convenient way to begin studying larger animals, other than birds, is to trap them alive and unharmed. Simple traps can be made using a large coffee can or juice concentrate can. Remove the top and bury the can so that the top rim is level with the soil surface. For bait, mix peanut butter and oatmeal and roll into balls.

Even if you decide not to trap the animals, be sure to look for animal tracks and animal droppings. These can be identified as well. In cities you are likely to see birds, rats, mice, dogs, and cats. And do not forget to look for signs of humans.

Materials (per team)

hammer or mallet
8 stakes, approximately 18 to 25 cm long
about 60 m of rope, twine, heavy string, or plastic clothesline
meterstick or metric tape
trowel or small-bladed garden shovel
white-enameled pan or large sheet of white paper
collection containers such as jars and plastic bags, as anticipated
forceps
wire screen of approximately 5-mm mesh curved into a bowl shape

Procedure

1. Determination of the study area.
   (a) In a forest, study areas for different organisms should be of different sizes. These can be set up as shown in figure 22.48. Square or rectangular study areas are called quadrats.
   (b) In unforested areas, quadrats should be 2 to 4 m on a side without internal divisions.
   (c) In vacant city lots, cultivated fields, and pastures, use smaller teams (of 2 to 3) and more of them. Each team should work on a quadrat 1 m square such as that shown in figure 22.49.
2. Each team should select a site for its quadrat that appears to be representative of the study area. Drive stakes into the ground, measure off the appropriate-sized quadrat, and connect the stakes with your rope. The quadrat should be as square as possible. You may want to subdivide the quadrat to count smaller organisms or to make your counting easier. If so, stake off these areas also and mark them with the rope or clothesline.
3. It will be convenient for most study areas to divide plants into 5 groups: trees, shrubs, saplings, herbs, and seedlings. If you count small organisms in only a subdivision of your quadrat, multiply the number of each different population in that subdivision by a factor that would reflect their abundance in the total area.
4. You also should examine a sample of the surface soil and/or organic littor. This is best done by inserting a trowel or small garden shovel into the ground to a depth of approximately 10 cm and removing a cubic sample of approximately 10 cm × 10 cm × 10 cm. Using the wire screen that has been shaped into a bowl, sift the contents onto a white-enameled pan or onto a large sheet of white paper. Pick through the remaining litter with forceps. Likely organisms present will be a variety of insects (especially beetles), sow or pill bugs, millipedes and centipedes, spiders or other arachnids, worms, and fungi. You may be surprised by the presence of even other organisms.
5. Special problems may arise. In a lawn, for example, there is no need to count blades of grass. However, a count of the weeds might be worthwhile, especially if comparisons are made between well-trodden areas and protected ones.
6. When your field work is completed share your team data with the rest of the class. This can be done by combining data from each team in a large table drawn on the chalkboard. Answer as many of the discussion questions as possible. If different kinds of areas were included, make comparisons wherever possible.

Figure 22.48

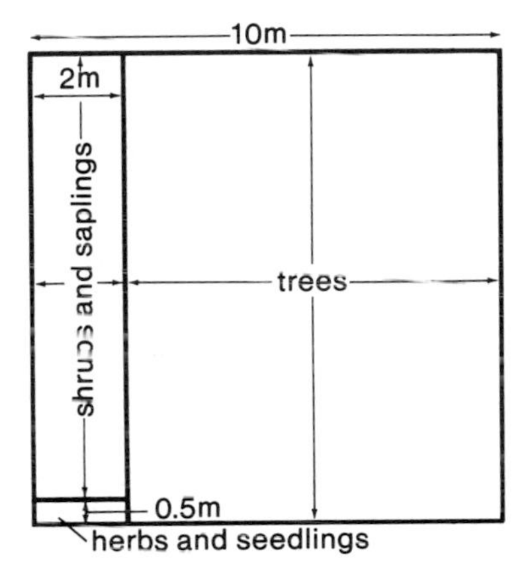

Figure 22.49

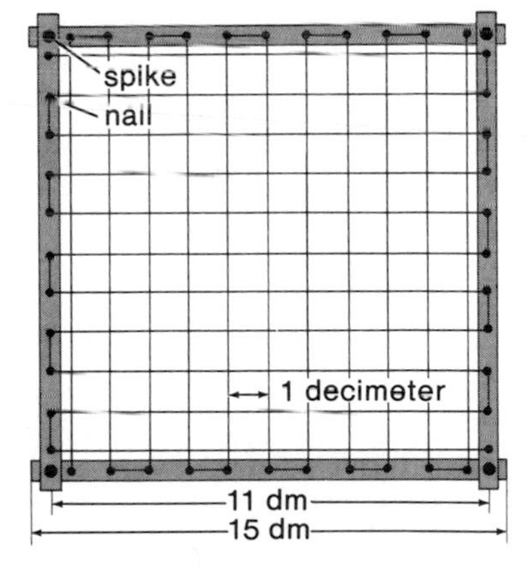

Discussion

1. What producers are in the area? Answer in general terms—trees, shrubs, and so on—or by naming the organisms you were able to identify.
2. Are producers abundant or rare? Explain why.
3. Do you have any evidence that there are seasonal changes in the kinds and numbers of producers?
4. Are there different groups of producers? If so, which one contributes the most toward producing the food that is present in the area?

5. Are there layers of producers? If so, what relationships can you find among the producers in the different layers?
6. Does the area produce all its own food or is food carried in from beyond its boundaries? What evidence do you have for your answer?
7. What consumers are in the community? Answer again in general terms or with the names of organisms you have identified.
8. Which consumers are herbivores and which are carnivores? What evidence supports your answer?
9. What relationships can you find between the numbers of a particular herbivore and the numbers of a carnivore that eats it?
10. Using the information you have, construct an energy-flow diagram for the area.
11. What evidence is there that one kind of organism affects another in ways other than those involving food relationships?
12. What biome type best characterizes the area you studied? Give reasons for your choice.
13. An investigation such as this should raise more questions than it answers. In studying the data, part of your job is to look for questions that need answering. Write several questions concerning the organisms in your area. Although your data from this study is incomplete, you have taken a biologist's first step in describing a study area.

Summary

In each type of climate, a characteristic kind of vegetation develops and maintains itself. That vegetation supports a characteristic variety of animal life. In this chapter we have discussed characteristics of several major biomes. The tundra biome of the northern hemisphere gradually blends with the taiga in a southerly direction. In the middle latitudes of North America are the temperate deciduous forest biome in the east, the grasslands to the west, and the desert biome in the Southwest.

The tropical rain forest biome, located just north and south of the equator, receives abundant rainfall and has warm temperatures all year long. The tropics also support a deciduous forest, but unlike the rain forest, this biome has wet and dry seasons. Still within the tropics is the savanna biome, a grassland that supports a few trees and the world's largest concentration of hoofed animals. Southern California and other scattered areas support evergreen shrubs that make up the chaparral biome.

From southern Alaska into northern California lies a mid-latitude rain forest that includes redwoods, the largest trees in the world. Because of changes in altitude, the mountains have a number of biomes that form bands of vegetation ranging from grasslands at the base to alpine tundra on the top of the tallest peaks.

All biomes around the world are undergoing changes due to the activities of people. The cutting of the tropical rain forests, the loss of grasslands due to desertification, and the acid rain problem in North America and Europe are just a few examples.

Application Questions

1. Explain why the four seasons are more pronounced in the mid-latitudes than in the tropics.
2. What biomes would you encounter if you were to travel from Washington, D.C., to San Francisco?
3. What are some examples of changes in biomes that are caused by human activities?
4. Describe what you think would happen if all human beings left the following places:
   (a) a farm in Nebraska
   (b) a sidewalk in New York
   (c) a swimming pool in Seattle, Washington
   (d) a landscaped park in Las Vegas, Nevada.
5. Make a list of terrestrial organisms that human beings have brought into your locality. Divide the list into two parts: (a) organisms that (in your opinion) survive because of human activities, and (b) organisms that (in your opinion) would survive without human help. Give reasons for your decision on each organism.

Problems

1. Investigate your area and determine the biome in which you live.
2. The prairie dog once was abundant in the prairie ecosystem.
   (a) What is the role of the prairie dog in that ecosystem?
   (b) Why is it being exterminated?
   (c) How will other species be affected by the extermination of the prairie dog?
3. The search for oil in the arctic has ecologists concerned about damage to the tundra.
   (a) What happens to the tundra when heavy equipment is driven over it?
   (b) What might be the effects on migrating herbivores such as the caribou?
4. Find out what different countries are doing to protect their particular ecosystems. Some examples of things that could be explored are:
   (a) national parks
   (b) forest preserves
   (c) wildlife preserves
   (d) city parks
5. Investigate the ecological consequences of forest fires.
6. Before Europeans settled the grasslands of Australia, kangaroos were the ecological equivalents of the bison in North American grasslands. These animals had similar niches in the community structure of their regions—they were the largest grazing herbivores.
   (a) What are the ecological equivalents of these animals in most of the Australian and North American grasslands today?
   (b) What were the ecological equivalents of these animals in the steppes of Asia, the pampas of Argentina, and the veldt of South Africa before these regions were highly modified by humans?
   (c) What are the ecological equivalents of these animals in the tundra?
   (d) In the desert of South Africa, what are the ecological equivalents of the cacti of North American deserts?
   (e) In the tropical forests of the Old World, what are the ecological equivalents of the cacti of North American deserts?
   (f) In the tropical forests of the Old World, what are the ecological equivalents of the hummingbirds of the New World tropical forests?

Suggested Readings

L. R. Brown, W. U. Chandler, and S. Postel, "State of the Earth" *Natural History* (April 1986). Effects of air pollution and acid rain on the forests of central Europe are discussed.

C. Hughes and D. Hughes, "Teeming Life of a Rain Forest" *National Geographic* (January 1983). Many fine illustrations highlight this discussion of this disappearing biome.

C. A. Munn, "Birds of Different Feather Also Flock Together" *Natural History* (November 1984). In the lowland forests of South America, as many as 70 species may forage in a single group.

J. Raloff and J. Silberner, "Saving the Amazon" *Science News* (4 October 1980). Discusses how saving the world's least-known biome will benefit more than its dwellers.

C. Uhl, "You *Can* Keep a Good Forest Down" *Natural History* (April 1983). How much abuse can Amazonian rain forests take and still recover?

P. T. White, "Nature's Dwindling Treasures: Rain Forests" *National Geographic* (January 1983). Many photos accompany this article dealing with Earth's most complex natural habitat.

NASA

The earth is a watery planet, as evidenced in this photo taken from Apollo II.

CHAPTER 23

Aquatic Ecosystems

Introduction

Our planet, when viewed from outer space, is blue with water and water vapor. All this water makes up the **hydrosphere** (HY droh sfir), just as all the air makes up the atmosphere. The hydrosphere is a vast heat reservoir. It absorbs, stores, and circulates the heat that results when radiant energy strikes the earth. It is also a reservoir of chemical elements and compounds. These are continuously dissolved in water that eventually drains into the oceans.

Oceans form the great interconnecting system that surrounds the continents. Tides are clearly evident in oceans, which contain a large amount of dissolved minerals. Inland waters are found on the surface of the land and usually contain very few dissolved minerals. Most inland waters are above sea level, and their water tends to flow downward to the oceans.

Humans are terrestrial organisms, but they have always lived close to a source of fresh water. Throughout the world, villages, towns, and cities have developed close to bodies of water, which have supplied food, transportation, and a waste removal system. In this chapter we will examine the major aquatic ecosystems and the impact human activities have on them.

Standing Fresh Waters

Guidepost: What are the characteristics of ponds and lakes?

23.1 Inland Waters May Be Standing or Flowing

Inland waters are affected in many ways by the surrounding land, but they have distinct environmental characteristics. Puddles around the world contain very similar organisms. The Nile delta is surrounded by desert, and the Mississippi delta by marsh, yet environmental conditions are similar within the slow-moving, warm, muddy waters of both rivers.

Figure 23.1 Part of the Mississippi delta. What major kinds of ecosystems can you see here?

EARTH SCENES/© C. C. Lockwood

Figure 23.2 Cross section through the edge of a natural pond in the northeastern United States.

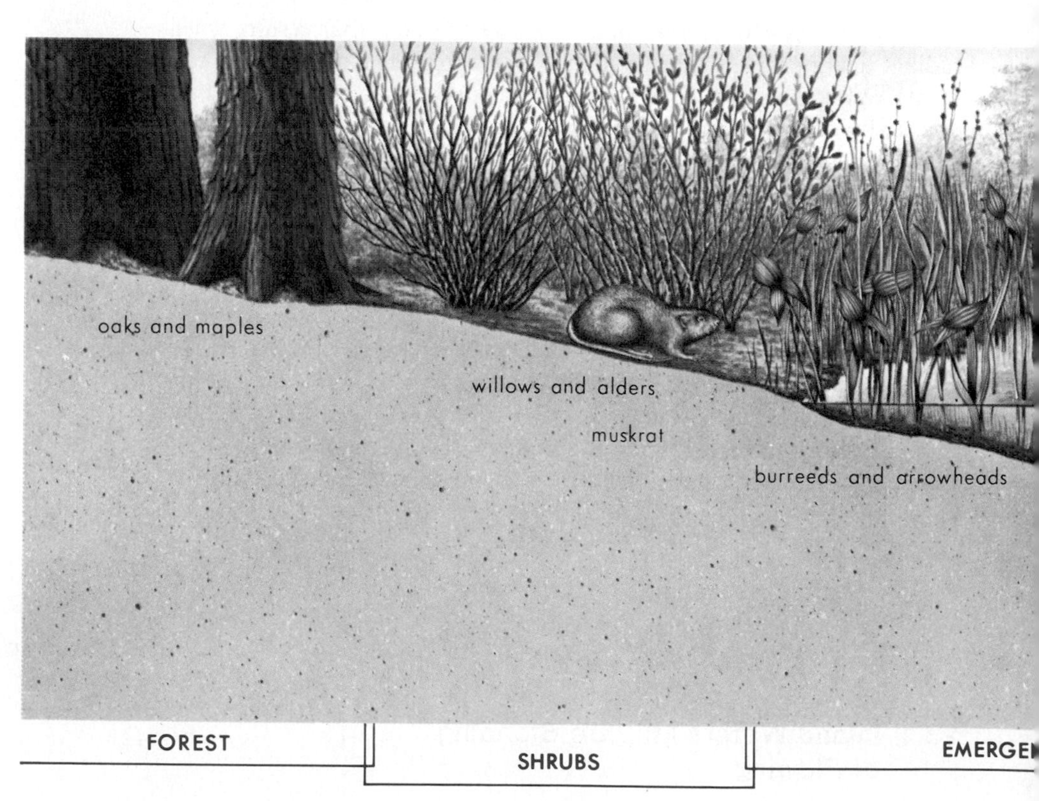

Inland-water ecosystems are grouped as standing waters or flowing waters. As is usual in ecological classification, the boundary between these is not distinct. A pond is an example of standing water, yet some current of water passes through most ponds. Many ponds are fed by springs or brooks, and many have outlets. On the other hand, a river is an example of flowing water, yet in some places a river may have such a slow current that it is difficult to observe any movement of the water.

Standing waters range in size from roadside puddles to the Caspian Sea, which occupies more than 350,000 km^2. Puddles may last for only a few days, whereas ponds may last for a few hundred years. In general, lakes are standing waters that are larger and older than ponds. Standing waters range from very shallow to very deep, from clear to muddy, and from fresh to salty.

23.2 Ponds Are Shallow Enough for Rooted Plants

Ponds are generally defined as small, completely enclosed bodies of water that are shallow enough for light to penetrate to the bottom. Rooted plants can grow throughout, and temperatures from top to bottom are relatively uniform during the warm months of the year. The characteristics of ponds are the same whether they are natural or artificial. As an example, let us look at a natural pond in the northeastern United States.

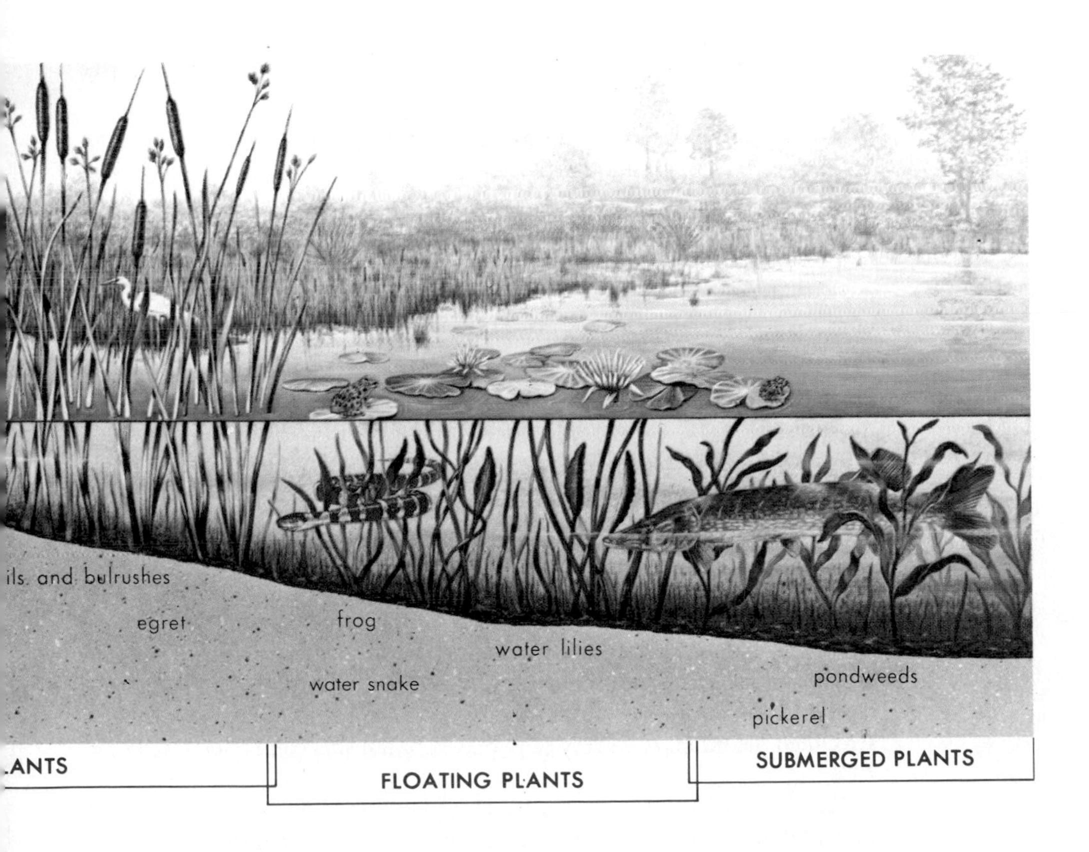

Figure 23.3 A natural pond. It is easy to see the relationship between the forest and aquatic ecosystems.

Paul McIver

We stand on a hill overlooking the pond. As we walk down the tree-covered slope, mosquitoes, which began their life in the pond, start to annoy us and "bite." We walk out of the trees into a tangle of low shrubs. As we push our way through willows and alders, the ground becomes wetter. We leave the last shrubs behind us, and our feet sink into mud. Before us lies a marsh of sedges and cattails, with shallow water lapping about their stems. Dragonflies—newly emerged from the water—dart about. Frogs sit on driftwood and a water snake slithers through the muddy water. A muskrat interrupts its meal of cattail stems and shuffles away. In wading boots we follow the muskrat through the cattails. At last we see the open water surface of the pond. Here and there it is dotted with leaves of water lilies. With our boots in deep mud and with water up to our knees, we are now in the middle of the pond ecosystem.

In studying any ecosystem, an ecologist first looks for its source of energy. In a pond, the most important producers are not the most obvious ones. The large rooted plants such as cattails are conspicuous, but they produce little of the ecosystem's food. Indeed, in some ponds—especially artificial ones—rooted plants may be scarce or absent. We see many plants within the water itself—some floating on the surface and some submerged. Such plants may become so numerous that their thick mass hampers a swimmer. Yet even these are not the most important pond producers.

Figure 23.4 Plankton.

Keith Gillett/TOM STACK & ASSOCIATES

You may have watched specks of dust drifting in a bright beam of sunlight. In a beam of light shining into a pond, you also can see moving specks that look like dust. These specks, however, are living organisms. They may belong to any of the five kingdoms, but all are microscopic or nearly so. Few can swim, but all can stay afloat. They are carried about by the currents in the water. Together all these microscopic organisms are called **plankton.** A variety of plankton organisms can be seen in figure 23.4.

Early ecologists began to realize that plankton make up for their small size by their incredible numbers. Careful studies showed that most food production in all parts of the hydrosphere—not just in ponds—is the result of photosynthesis by plankton.

The plankton producers are collectively called **phytoplankton** (FYT oh PLANK ton). Different kinds of phytoplankton vary in abundance from one body of water to another. Diatoms are usually the most numerous, though not the most conspicuous. Green algae may become so abundant in late summer that a pond's whole surface becomes green.

Because most pond producers are microscopic, you might expect the herbivores to be small, and most of them are. These **zooplankton** (ZOH oh PLANK ton) include a variety of protists, and animals such as rotifers and small crustaceans. Zooplankton are not the only pond herbivores, however. Many young fishes also are herbivores, as are macroscopic bottom dwellers such as mussels. Other pond fishes are carnivores; the larger kinds eat the smaller. Fishes of all sizes eat aquatic insects, many of which are themselves carnivores. Some zooplankton are carnivores. As you can see, pond food chains have many links. Most of the macroscopic carnivores stay near the edge of a pond, where the floating plants provide a hiding place. The larger predatory fishes swim throughout the pond.

Dead organisms sink, so layers of organic matter build up on pond bottoms. Decomposers such as tubifex worms (annelids) reduce the decaying organic matter to smaller bits and pieces, which are then acted on by other decomposers such as fungi and bacteria.

We saw in chapter 3 that it is often difficult to determine the boundaries of an ecosystem. In a pond ecosystem, for example, the surface of the water is not a distinct boundary. Insects are usually flying above and around ponds. Many of them hatch from eggs laid in the water and spend most of their lives there. For example, a mayfly's entire life is spent in the water except for the last few hours, when the adults mate in the air. The females then lay eggs in the water, and the immature mayflies grow there for a year or more. Frogs live primarily on such insects. Water snakes eat fish and frogs. Many kinds of birds and some mammals feed on fish, crayfish, and mussels. Such consumers, though they spend much of their time on land, are actually part of pond ecosystems. Their energy supply can be traced back to phytoplankton.

Figure 23.5 The mayfly lives its entire life in and near the water. Nymph (top) and adult (bottom).

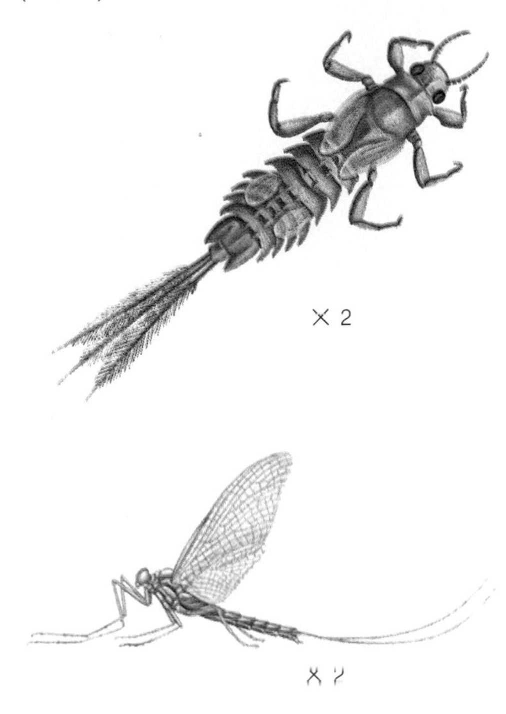

23.3 Lakes Are Larger and Deeper than Ponds

Lakes are larger than ponds and have some depths that are always dark. Most of the world's naturally occurring lakes were formed by the action of glaciers and will eventually change through the process of succession and become terrestrial ecosystems, as shown in figure 23.6. Phytoplankton are the major producers in lakes, as they are in ponds. The phytoplankton of a lake, however, can exist only near the water's surface. In deep lakes, therefore, all the food is produced in the upper part of the water.

In deeper lakes light may penetrate to a depth of about 80 m, depending on the clearness of the water and the cloudiness of the sky. The existence of aquatic consumers, therefore, is limited not by light, but by the amount of oxygen in the water. Surface water constantly receives dissolved oxygen from photosynthesis and from the air. The oxygen diffuses slowly downward from the surface, but before going very far, most of it is used up by zooplankton. The spread of oxygen into deep water thus depends on other factors.

Figure 23.6 An example of lake succession.

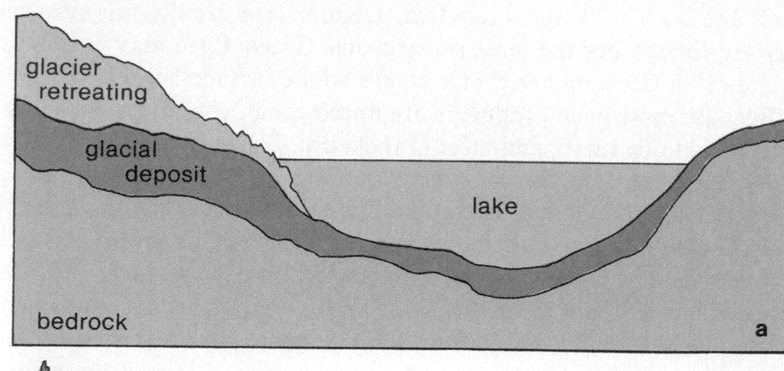

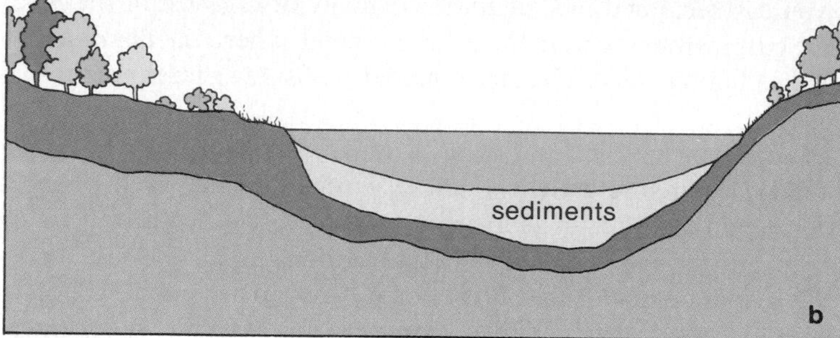

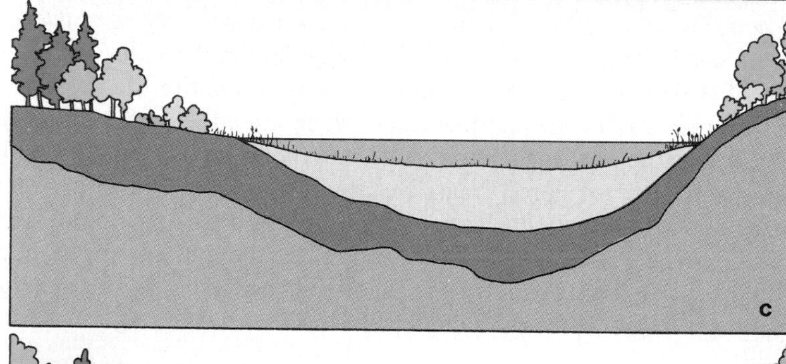

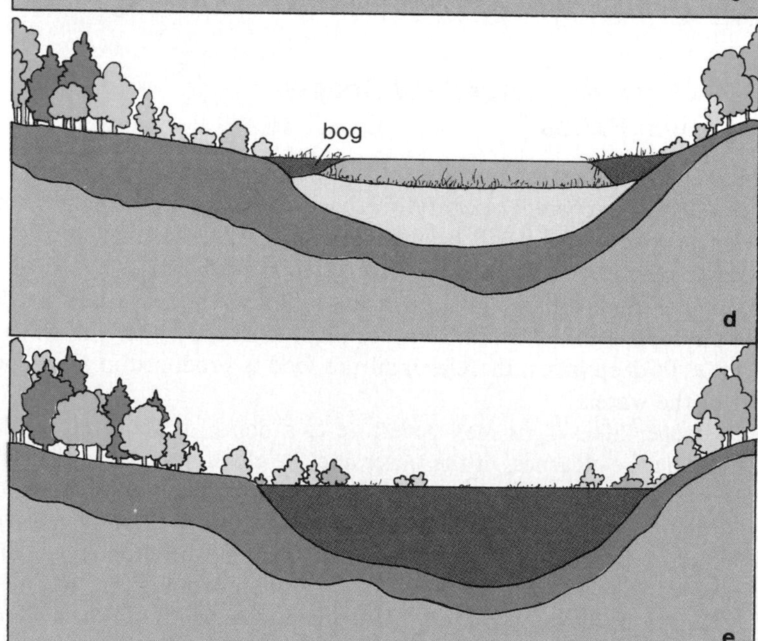

Figure 23.7 A mountain lake. What are the environmental conditions here and what are their effects?

Katherine A. Winternitz

Figure 23.8 The formation of a thermocline in a lake.

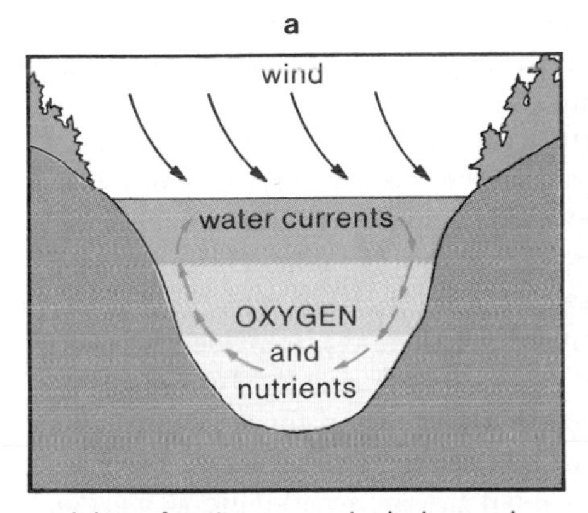

mixing of water currents during spring and fall in a northern lake

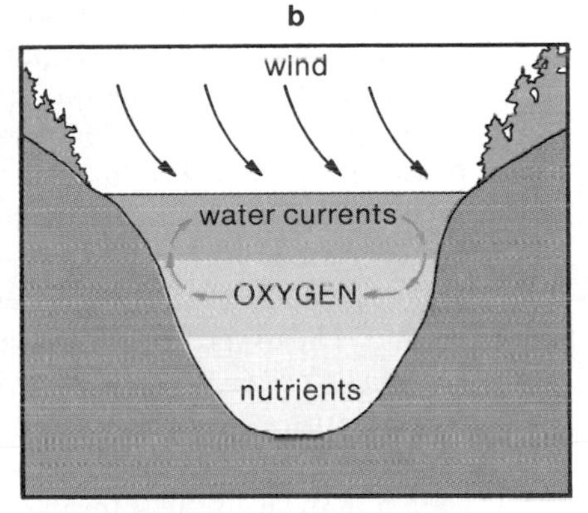

a northern lake in late spring and early summer, and a tropical lake in all seasons

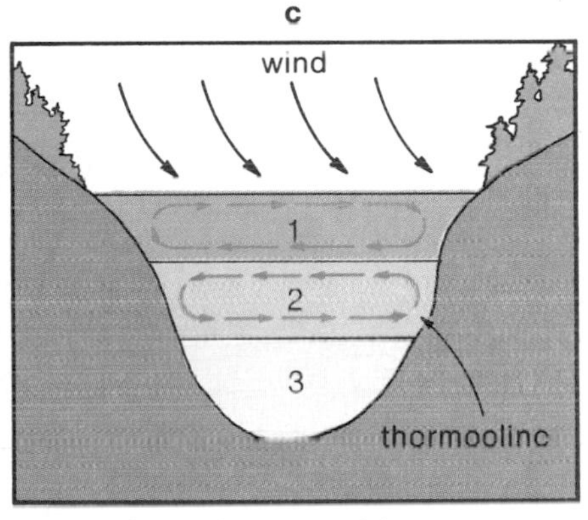

layers formed during midsummer

23.4 A Thermocline Prevents Circulation of Oxygen and Nutrients

During the summer, the sun heats the lake surface and the water expands, becoming lighter or less dense than water at the lake bottom. This forms a warm layer that floats on the colder water below. Separating these two layers is a zone, the **thermocline** (THER moh klyn), across which both temperature and oxygen concentration drop sharply. The thermocline prevents vertical mixing of the upper and lower layers of water, resulting in important differences between these layers. Oxygen concentration remains high in the upper layer because of photosynthesis,

Figure 23.9 Mono Lake in California is another example of the salination of a lake. Salt accumulation is responsible for the large tufa formations on the right. The water is so saline that only brine shrimp live in it.

Catherine L. Case/VISUALS UNLIMITED

but declines in the lower layer as it is used up by consumers. The activities of aerobic decomposers are restricted, so dead bodies of organisms that fall from above are only partly decomposed. Nutrients produced by decomposition remain on the bottom.

In the fall, as the air temperature drops, the surface water becomes denser than the lower level of water. The heavier surface water then sinks, forcing deep water to the top. Wind action aids in mixing the water uniformly and distributing oxygen throughout the lake. During winter, the surface of the lake may freeze, so a warmer layer remains at the bottom. The oxygen concentration declines, but anaerobic decomposers continue to release nutrients from dead organic matter. In the spring, rising temperatures bring about another turnover of the waters, mixing oxygen and nutrients throughout the lake again. Measurements of oxygen content provide useful information about aquatic ecosystems, as you can learn in investigation 23.1.

Lakes in the tropics maintain a thermocline all year, so vertical mixing of water, oxygen, and nutrients does not occur. Tropical lakes such as Tanganyika in Africa, therefore, have no deep water aerobic animals. Outside the tropics, however, lakes have many animals in their deeper water. Animals have been found at a depth of 600 m in Lake Baikal, U.S.S.R., the world's deepest lake.

If a lake has no outlet, minerals washed in from the surrounding land become concentrated in the water, because only water molecules (not minerals) can evaporate from the surface. The **salination** (sayl ih NAY shun), or salt and mineral build up, of a lake takes place faster in arid regions where evaporation is more rapid. The water may become saturated with minerals, the most abundant of which is usually sodium chloride (NaCl), common table salt. The result is an environment unfavorable to most organisms. The Great Salt Lake in Utah contains such a high

Figure 23.10 The water cycle. Water is necessary to life in many ways, as we have seen throughout this book. Land plants absorb water from the soil. Land animals drink water or get it in their foods. Water constantly bathes organisms that live in ponds, lakes, rivers and the oceans. Water also evaporates from the surface of all bodies of water and from land. Plants and animals lose water, too, but by different processes. All the water comes from the nonliving environment. It all returns from the organisms to the nonliving environment. What is the difference between the long and the short cycles?

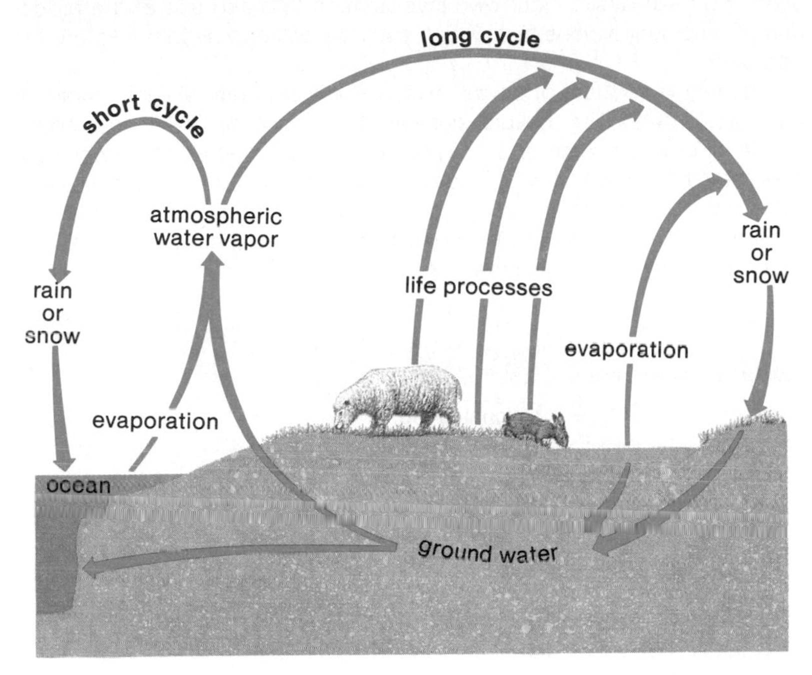

concentration of sodium chloride that only brine shrimp, a few species of cyanobacteria, and two species of brine flies can survive there. Those organisms, however, are present in great numbers.

Some of the water that falls on land runs directly into lakes, ponds, and streams; some evaporates. But most of the water soaks into the ground. This ground water reappears in springs, from which the course to the ocean may be short or long. Thus, water *cycles* in the biosphere.

Self-Review

1. What are the principal types of inland waters?
2. How do phytoplankton affect a pond ecosystem?
3. How is a pond ecosystem linked to surrounding terrestrial ecosystems?
4. How do three layers of water form in a lake?
5. Why are animals found deep in Lake Baikal but not deep in Lake Tanganyika?

Investigation 23.1 DISSOLVED OXYGEN

Introduction

The amount of free oxygen (O_2) dissolved in water is an important abiotic environmental factor in all aquatic ecosystems. Oxygen measurements can be used in studying aquatic productivity and, indirectly, aquatic pollution.

Here you are given a procedure for measuring dissolved oxygen. However, you must design your own investigation to make use of the procedure. Some suggestions from which you may develop hypotheses are the following:

Aquariums. Amount of oxygen with and without artificial light, plants, or aerators; or amount of oxygen early in the morning and in the afternoon.

Standing water. Amount of oxygen in freshly collected rainwater puddles, at various depths in a pond or lake, or in a natural pond compared with that in an artificial pond.

Running water. Amount of oxygen in a sewage-polluted stream at various distances from the source of pollution or in a stream at various times of the year.

Materials (per team)

1 Hach Kit (Kit #1469–00) containing:
- 1 glass-stoppered sample bottle
- 100 dissolved oxygen 1 reagent pillows
- 100 dissolved oxygen 2 reagent pillows
- 100 dissolved oxygen 3 reagent pillows
- 1 plastic measuring tube
- 1 square mixing bottle
- 1 fingernail clipper for opening reagent pillows
- 1 plastic bottle PAO titrant
- instructions for high- and low-range procedures

Water samples from various sources

Procedure (high range)

1. Fill the glass-stoppered sample bottle with the water to be tested by allowing the water to overflow into the bottle without trapping any air bubbles.
2. Add the contents of 1 pillow each of dissolved oxygen 1 reagent powder and dissolved oxygen 2 reagent powder. Stopper the bottle carefully so that no air is trapped in the bottle. Grip the bottle and stopper firmly and shake vigorously to mix. A flocculent (soft flakelike) precipitate will be formed. If O_2 is present, the precipitate will be brownish-orange in color.
3. Allow the sample to stand until the precipitate, or "floc," has settled halfway and leaves the upper half of the bottle clear. Then, again shake the bottle and let it stand a second time until the upper half of the bottle is clear.
4. Remove the stopper and add the contents of 1 pillow of dissolved oxygen 3 reagent powder. Carefully restopper and shake to mix. The floc will dissolve, and a yellow color will develop if oxygen was present. This is the prepared sample.
5. Fill the plastic measuring tube level-full with prepared sample and pour it into the mixing bottle.

6. While swirling the sample to mix, add PAO titrant dropwise, counting each drop, until the sample changes from yellow to colorless. The dropper must be held in a vertical manner. Each drop indicates 1 mg/liter or 1 ppm dissolved oxygen.

Discussion

1. How much oxygen did you find in your water samples (in ppm)?
2. Were your hypotheses supported?
3. How does the oxygen content of your samples compare with that of the water samples of other teams?
4. How do you account for the differences or similarities?
5. Assuming that the chemical materials were properly prepared, what sources of error might there be in the procedure?
6. What factors might cause a difference between the accurate measurement of oxygen present in a sample and the actual amount of oxygen in that sample?

Flowing Waters

Guidepost: How do flowing water ecosystems differ from those of standing water?

23.5 Plankton Are Usually Absent from Brooks

Most springs give rise to small brooks. Such flowing water is usually cool, though some hot springs do exist. Tumbling through rapids and falls, the water traps many air bubbles from which oxygen easily dissolves. Because cool water can hold relatively large amounts of gases in solution, the water in brooks usually contains much oxygen.

In the swift-flowing water of brooks, most plankton are absent because they are swept away. Producers—cyanobacteria, diatoms, and filamentous algae—grow attached to stones. These producers provide some food and much shelter for aquatic insects. The insects, in turn, are food for small fish. Most of the food supply in a brook ecosystem comes from the land around it. Small terrestrial organisms, such as insects, fall in the brook and are eaten by stream inhabitants. Every rain washes in dead organic matter. Anything not used immediately, however, is washed downstream, so there is very little food left for decomposers.

Figure 23.11 A mountain brook. What evidence can you see that this aquatic ecosystem has few producers?

BSCS by Carlye Calvin

23.6 Brooks Join to Form Streams

Brooks meet, forming larger streams with wider beds and more water. Here the water usually moves more slowly. Solid substances that have been carried along by the swift brooks are now deposited as sediments. Bits of organic matter, accumulating among the sediments, provide food for decomposers.

As the stream widens, the relative amount of water surface shaded by trees along its banks decreases. Direct sunlight reaches most of the water surface. Some phytoplankton organisms may live in this slower-moving water, but many still are carried downstream. Rooted plants, such as those in ponds, grow in the sediments of a stream bottom. They, too, may be washed away during floods.

Figure 23.12 Stream consumers. (Top to bottom): dragonfly nymph, freshwater mussel, rainbow trout.

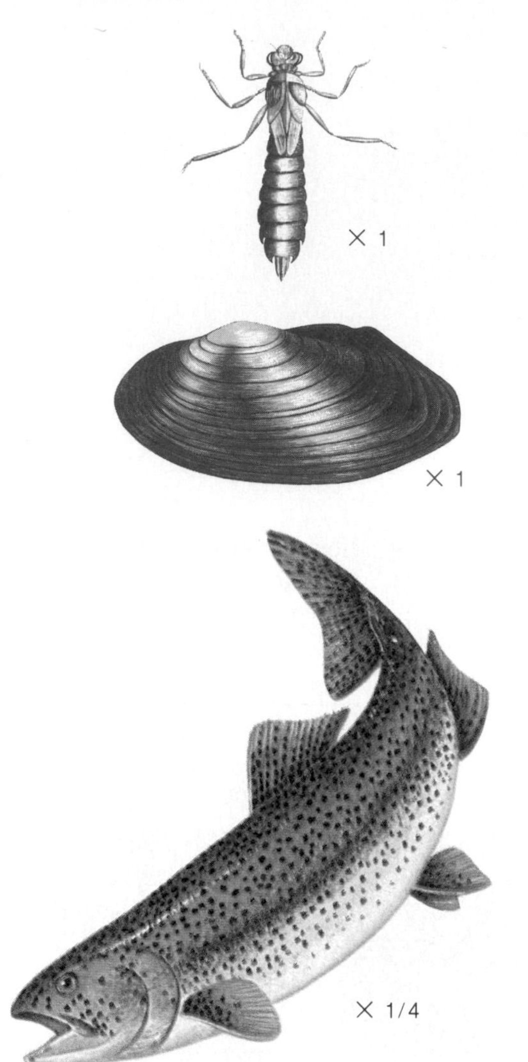

Because it contains more producers, a stream supports a larger number of consumers than does a brook. Mussels, snails, crayfish, and many immature insects inhabit the bottom. Larger consumers, such as turtles and fish, are dependent on these bottom dwellers.

23.7 Rivers Carry Large Amounts of Sediments

Many streams come together to form a river, a large body of flowing water. As a river approaches the sea, it usually moves more slowly and deposits larger amounts of sediments. Thus, near its mouth a river often builds up land instead of eroding it. The river banks may actually become higher than the land behind them. During floods a river often breaks through these natural levees. The water left behind is slow to drain away and forms a swamp. Many rooted and floating plants grow in these swampy lands. Fruits, seeds, and other plant parts that are swept into the river during floods contribute to the food supply of the river ecosystem. Phytoplankton grow well in the unshaded, slow-moving water and provide much of the food for consumers in large rivers.

Consumers in rivers are varied and numerous. Zooplankton are food for bigger predators. Mollusks, crustaceans, and fish often grow to large size. Crocodiles are common in tropical rivers. Many terrestrial birds and mammals obtain their food from rivers, just as many do from ponds. Since ancient times, many humans also have taken advantage of the abundant food in rivers.

Figure 23.13 A river in Alaska.

Doug Sokell

23.8 Flowing Waters Can Serve as a Laboratory

Not all springs give rise to brooks. Some pour forth so much water that large streams flow from them. Many of the short rivers of northwest Florida originated that way. The short Florida rivers are fine outdoor laboratories. Each river has lengths with stable conditions of volume, current, chemical composition, and temperature. Ecologists have used several of these rivers in studies of ecological productivity.

Productivity of any community depends on the photosynthetic rate of its producers. That rate can be measured indirectly. Photosynthesizing organisms give off oxygen in proportion to the amount of organic substances they produce. To calculate productivity, biologists first measure the oxygen given off during a measured period of time. Using that figure, they can calculate the amount of organic substance produced through photosynthesis during that same time period.

Any increase in the amount of oxygen in the spring water as it flows downstream comes largely from photosynthesis. Figure 23.14 shows the oxygen content measured at given places along the river flowing from Rainbow Springs. The ecologists also measured the amount of water that flowed past each point per day. Based on that information, the ecologists calculated the total productivity of the water between its source in the springs and the point of measurement. That was expressed as grams of organic substance produced per square meter of stream surface per day. The investigators found an average productivity of 17.5 g/m^2/day.

In further studies the investigators estimated the **biomass** of each major species in the community. Biomass is the total mass (usually minus water content) of all individuals of a species in a given area. Figure 23.15 shows the result of biomass measurements in the Silver River, another short Florida river. Such measurements provide information that helps ecologists understand the interrelationships in an ecosystem. In investigation 23.2, you can study some of those interrelationships.

Figure 23.14 Diagram of Rainbow Springs (Florida) and the river that flows from them. Ecologists measured the amounts of oxygen in the springs and in the river water at several places downstream. Such measurements are expressed as parts per million (ppm). One ppm = 0.0001 percent.

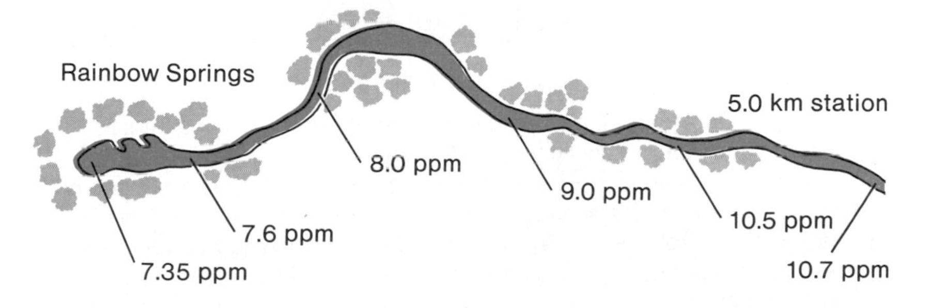

Figure 23.15 Average biomass measurements from Silver River, Florida. Largemouth bass are top carnivores. Compare this with figure 3.15.

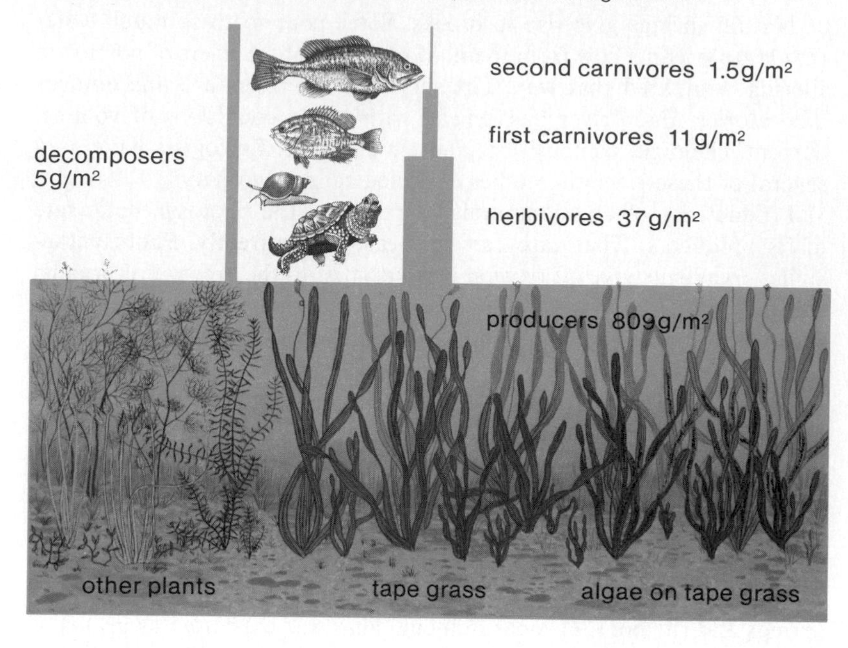

Self-Review

1. How do abiotic conditions in a brook differ from those in a river?
2. What is the source of energy for organisms in a brook?
3. Why is plankton more abundant in a river than in a brook?
4. How do ecologists measure productivity?
5. What usually happens to biomass between one link in a food chain and the next?

Investigation 23.2 ENERGY FLOW IN AN AQUATIC ECOSYSTEM

Introduction

Ecosystems are ecological units of a variety of organisms interacting with each other on a regular basis. A pond, woodland, small section of prairie, or cave is an ecosystem. The African baobab tree is so large and serves as a habitat for so many organisms that it is an ecosystem in itself. Ecosystems are relatively independent and self-sustaining because of the presence of producers, consumers, and decomposers.

The energy in an ecosystem typically begins as sunlight captured by photosynthetic plants. As this energy passes from the plants, through a progressive chain of consumers, and ultimately to decomposers, patterns emerge as to how the energy is utilized and how much is available for use by the various consumers. Although you will investigate only one specific case of energy flow through an ecosystem, the principles you will learn apply to other ecosystems. Your goal in this investigation is to identify some of the major principles dealing with the flow of energy through ecosystems.

Before beginning procedures for this investigation, be sure you understand the following terms: ecosystem, biomass, energy pyramid, food chain, food web, producer, primary consumer, secondary consumer, decomposer, and trophic level.

Materials (per class)

aquarium (at least 10-gallon) containing a variety of primary producers and consumers at different trophic levels or actual samples from a natural aquatic ecosystem (such as a pond) either collected on site or brought freshly into the classroom laboratory.

(per student)
microscope
slide
coverslip
Pasteur pipet

Procedure

1. Sample an ecosystem systematically to estimate the biomass per volume of ecosystem. You should sample several layers (depths) of the ecosystem, including surface and bottom. If you do not know the name of an organism, assign a number or letter to each one you cannot identify. Try to organize your sampling data by trophic levels so the organisms are represented correctly on the food web and energy pyramid that you will construct later. Consider working in groups with other students to divide the labor of counting the organisms in each sample.

   If you do not have sufficient time to count the organisms in your samples, you may wish to judge the relative numbers in qualitative terms, such as abundant, many, some, few, or none. If you follow this strategy, it is important to apply these terms consistently to each sample. Identify representatives from all trophic levels: producers, primary and secondary consumers, and decomposers.
2. Macrobiotic sampling. Identify those organisms that are visible to you without the use of the microscope. There will be few of these organisms, so you can identify the common name of each organism and count the numbers present.
3. Microbiotic sampling. These organisms can only be seen with the microscope. An acceptable and simple technique is to sort all observed organisms into 1 of 4 groups:
   (a) Arthropods. Insects and crustaceans that have obvious eyes, jointed legs, and generally move rapidly.
   (b) Worms. Multicellular worm-shaped organisms. Most will be colorless roundworms.
   (c) Zooplankton. Single or few-celled organisms lacking pigment but usually quite active.
   (d) Phytoplankton. Single or few-celled organisms that contain pigment (usually shades of green).

Use a table similar to the one below for microbiotic data.

Trophic Level	Sample #	Name/ Code	Description Count
	1		
	2		
	etc.		
	1		
	2		
	etc.		
	1		
	2		
	etc.		

4. Construct a food web for your ecosystem. A food web shows the energy relationships of organisms in an ecosystem. If all organisms are not represented, at least all trophic levels should be. Try to show all possible food interactions for each different organism you sample.
5. Construct an energy pyramid for your ecosystem. An energy pyramid illustrates the relative amount of food energy present at any given trophic level of an ecosystem. Actual energy available in an ecosystem is nearly impossible to measure directly. However, because food energy is in the bodies of organisms that may be consumed, a good estimate of energy in any population may be derived from the biomass of those organisms.

   Biomass is closely related to the total number of organisms found in a given population. Base the construction of your energy pyramid on your data, assuming that the samples represent the total environment. When using sampling to determine numbers of a population, be sure to take several samples in different locations and average the numbers. Use the following formula when computing the total population from the average of these samples.

$$\text{total population} = \text{ave. \# in samples} \times \frac{\text{total volume or area of space}}{\text{vol. or area of space sampled}}$$

Discussion

1. What is represented by the food web and food pyramid you constructed?
2. Is the ecosystem you studied a natural one? Give reasons why it might *and* might not be natural.
3. How do a food web and a food pyramid illustrate energy relationships in the biosphere?

Ocean Ecosystems

Guidepost: What factors affect ocean ecosystems?

23.9 Many Abiotic Factors Influence the Ocean

Ocean environments differ in many ways from inland-water environments. The principal difference lies in the chemical composition of the water itself. Seawater—the water of the oceans—is about 3.5 percent dissolved minerals. Because most of the dissolved minerals are salts, the mineral content of seawater is referred to as **salinity** (say LIN it ee). Sodium chloride accounts for more than 75 percent of the dissolved minerals. Salinity varies somewhat at different depths and in different places on the surface. The average mineral content of seawater is shown in table 23.1.

Evidence from rocks and fossils indicates that the ocean has had a high salinity for hundreds of millions of years. It seems, then, that the dissolved substances constantly washed into the ocean from the land have had only a slight effect on the composition of ocean water. Ocean water represents a steady state. Substances are continually added to it, but substances also are continually removed by marine organisms, organisms that live in the ocean. Ocean water is the environment of marine organisms, but it is also a product of their activities. The hydrosphere, like the atmosphere, would undoubtedly have a much different composition if life were absent.

Figure 23.16 The ocean.

Doug Sokell

Table 23.1 Average mineral content of seawater*

Element	Seawater (Parts per Thousand)
Chlorine	18.98
Sodium	10.56
Magnesium	1.27
Sulfur	.88
Calcium	.40
Potassium	.38
Bromine	.065
Carbon	.028
Strontium	.013
Silicon	.003
Fluorine	.001
Aluminum	.0005
Phosphorus	.0001
Iodine	.00005

*These elements occur as parts of compounds.

Figure 23.17 Diagram of an ocean in cross section.

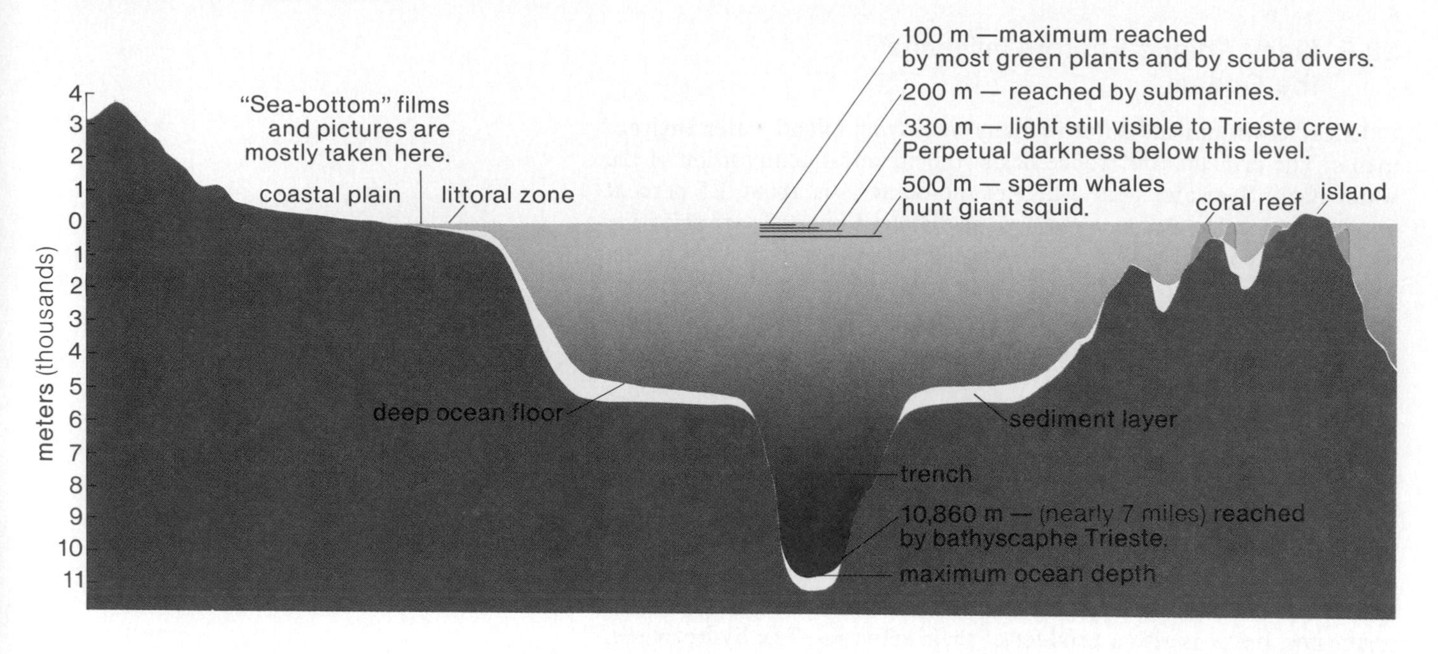

Figure 23.18 Penetration of seawater by sunlight. The water appears blue because blue wavelengths penetrate farthest.

Howard Hall/TOM STACK & ASSOCIATES

Rapid changes of the atmosphere result in great differences in the climates of terrestrial ecosystems. Such rapid changes do not occur in the hydrosphere. Temperature changes between day and night and between the seasons are very small at the ocean surface. Although the surface water at the equator is very different from that of antarctic and arctic waters, those differences diminish with increasing depth. At great depths the oceans have a uniform temperature.

Figure 23.19 The major ocean currents have profound effects on climate. Europe is warmed by the Gulf Stream, the western coast of South America is cooled by the Humboldt Current, and the eastern coast of South America is warmed by water from the equator.

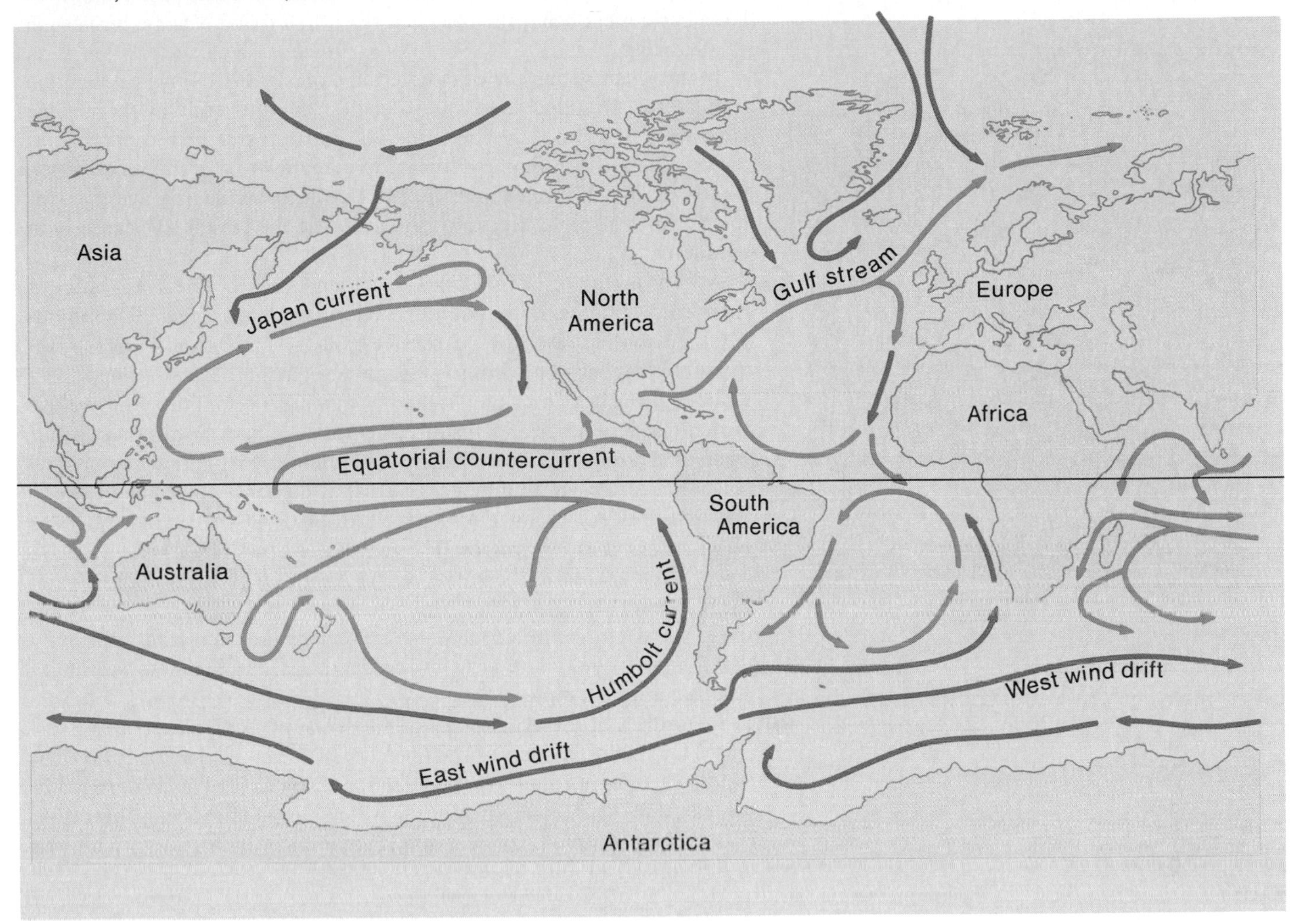

The amount of light energy available to photosynthetic organisms is greatest at the water surface. The extent to which light penetrates into the water depends on several factors. One is the angle at which light strikes the water's surface. Another is whether the surface is smooth or broken by waves. A third is the rate at which light is absorbed by the water. As light passes through the water, longer wavelengths are absorbed most rapidly. That means that red and yellow disappear first, and that blue and violet penetrate farthest. Finally, the rate at which the absorption of light occurs depends on the clarity of the water. The cloudier the water, the faster the rate of light absorption.

Ocean currents distribute chemicals that are useful to organisms. Currents also affect water temperatures and salinities at any given place in the ocean, and they have a profound effect on climate. Currents, in turn, are affected by the world pattern of winds and by the earth's rotation. The major ocean currents are shown in figure 23.19.

Figure 23.20 Plankton net being cast from the *Horizon*, a research vessel of the Scripps Institution of Oceanography, California.

M. Woodbridge Williams

23.10 Productivity Is Limited in the Open Ocean

The chief producers of the open ocean are diatoms, other microscopic algae, and certain flagellates. The zooplankton depend on these phytoplankton directly. Many food chains are based on these producers, with large consumers being the tuna, sharks, whales, and oceanic birds such as albatrosses.

Many scientists have tried to determine the density of marine plankton populations. Detailed results have come from one study at the marine laboratory at Plymouth, England. The ocean water there contains, at the very least, 4.5 million phytoplankton organisms in each liter of water. Biologists do not have enough data to give accurate density averages for the ocean as a whole. But they do know that the oceans vary greatly in productivity.

❶ A limiting factor in the ocean, as on land, may be the availability of chemical elements, especially phosphorus and nitrogen. The phytoplankton continuously use up these elements. Their continued growth, therefore, depends on constant resupply. Elements may be added from sediments washed from the land or from water welling up from below. Upwelling may occur as a result of seasonal changes. It also may occur when offshore winds move surface water and deep water rises to take its place. Because of upwelling, ocean areas at higher latitudes and close to the land are very productive. The North Sea and the Grand Banks of Newfoundland are examples. These areas of upwelling are very small, however, compared to the entire ocean. About 50 percent of all fish and shellfish harvested from the ocean are taken from 0.1 percent of its entire surface. On the other hand, ocean regions far from land, especially those in the tropics, have very low productivity. The Sargasso Sea in the Atlantic is an example.

❶ Regardless of the availability of nutrients, phytoplankton need light. All of the photosynthesis of the open ocean occurs in the upper layer of water, where light penetrates beneath the surface. That layer is very thin compared to the total depth of ocean water. Despite the deep penetration of blue light (550 m near Bermuda), phytoplankton are largely limited to the upper 100 m of water.

23.11 Ocean Depths Support Some Forms of Life

For a long time biologists thought that life could not exist in the dark, cold ocean depths because of the tremendous pressure of the water. The first clear evidence that this idea was wrong came in 1858. One of the telegraph cables lying on the bottom of the Mediterranean Sea broke and was hauled up for repair. It was encrusted with bottom-living animals, mostly sponges. Some had grown at depths as great as 2000 m. Further investigation showed that water pressure has no ill effect on organisms that do not contain body spaces filled with air or other gases. Deep-sea organisms lack such spaces, so pressure is exerted equally from both inside and out, and damage due to pressure does not occur.

❷ The ocean depths are special ecosystems that require unusual adaptations in the organisms that survive there. The depths are cold, dark, and quiet, and food is scarce. In general, life depends on organic substances that settle from the water above. The adaptations of organisms to the pressures of the deep also make their ascent to upper levels fatal. Thus, the consumers in the ocean depths form one of the most isolated communities of the biosphere.

Figure 23.21 Some fishes of the ocean depth and the depths at which they have been caught. All are small; they are shown here actual size.

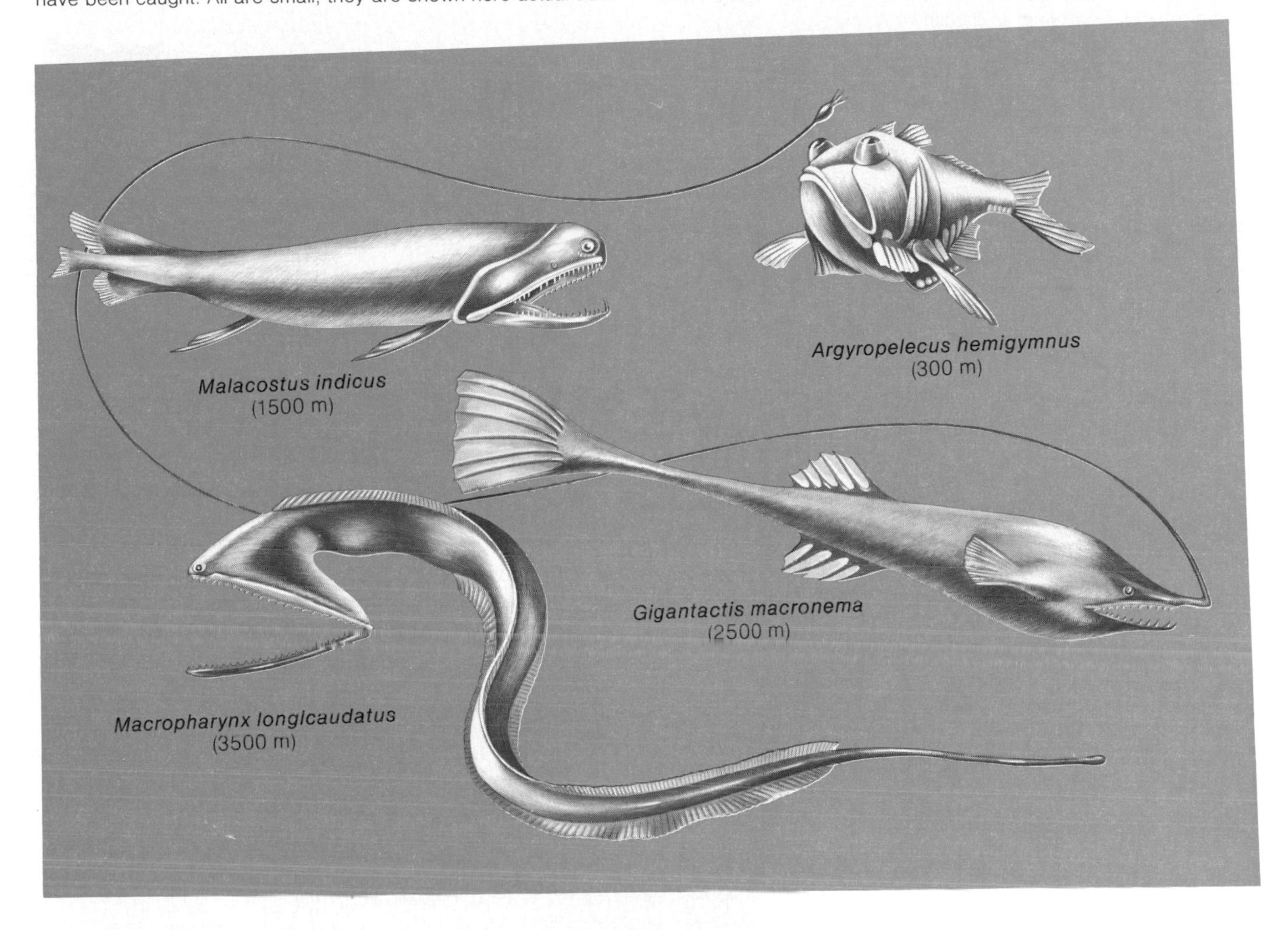

Figure 23.22 An acorn worm on the ocean bottom (South Pacific, depth about 4800 m).

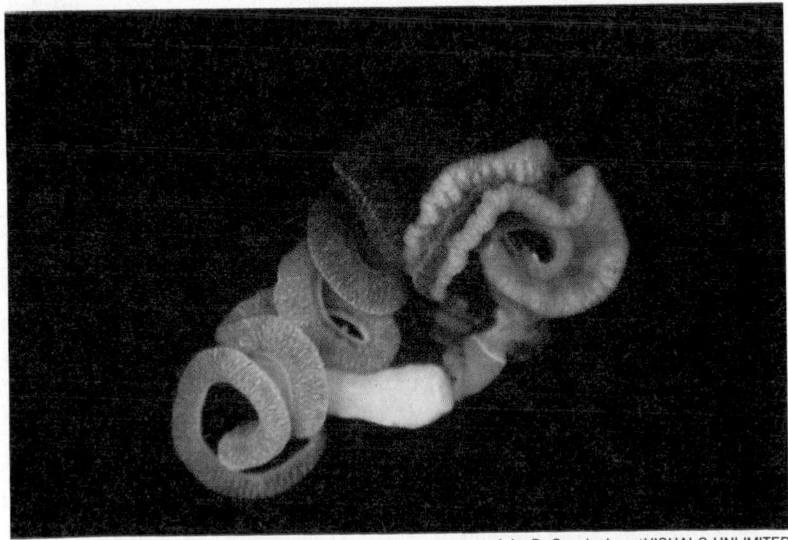

John D. Cunningham/VISUALS UNLIMITED

Figure 23.23 Air-breathing sperm whales descend as much as 500 m to hunt giant squid.

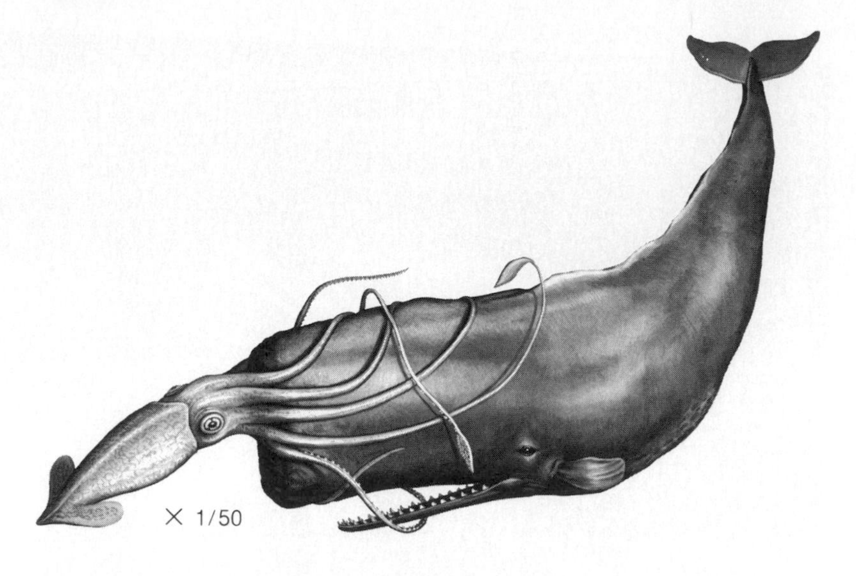

Figure 23.24 The submersible *Alvin.* This deep-sea research laboratory can dive to a depth of 4000 m with a crew of three. *Alvin* is transported to research sites by its mother vessel *Lulu,* a large boat that contains living quarters and a laboratory.

Rod Catanach, Woods Hole Oceanographic Institution

In the eternal night of the ocean depths, most animals are either black or dark red and have very sensitive eyes. Many animals produce their own light; they are **bioluminescent** (by oh loo mih NES ent). The ability to produce light may serve several functions. One species of fish dangles a special luminescent organ in front of its mouth. Apparently this lures unwary victims close enough to be caught and eaten. Deep-sea shrimp escape some predators by secreting clouds of a luminescent substance when disturbed. Patterns of light on an animal's body also may serve as marks of recognition in the depths. That would be similar to the color patterns among many organisms in the world of light.

Development of self-propelled, deep-sea research laboratories has enabled scientists to study ocean bottoms. Some of these labs are built so

Figure 23.25 Deep ocean vent community. The abundant tube worms may measure 1.5 m long.

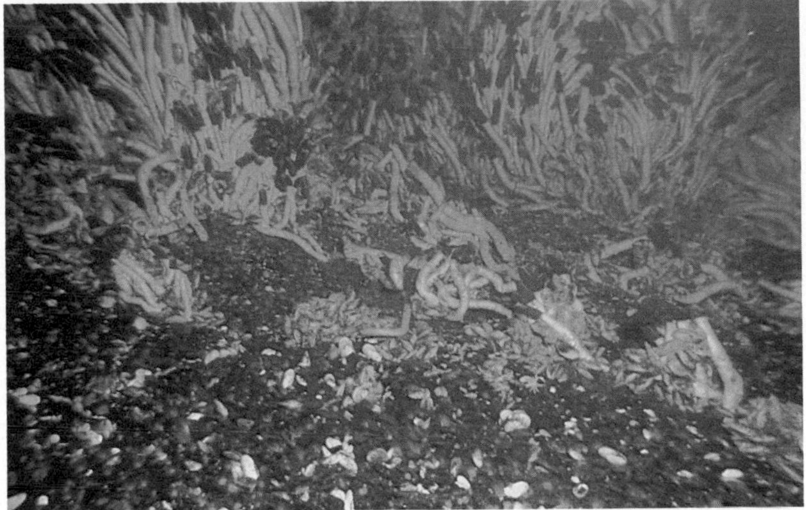

Kathleen Crane, Woods Hole Oceanographic Institution

that several scientists can live in them for weeks at a time without returning to the surface. The labs are equipped with mechanical arms that pick up objects and samples for study. In addition to observing life at great depths, deep-sea research has provided evidence for the theory of plate tectonics discussed in section 21.6.

In 1977 an ecosystem was discovered on the ocean floor northeast of the Galápagos Islands. This unusual ecosystem was characterized by an abundance of consumers, including mussels, giant clams, tube worms, crabs, anemones, and large pink fish. Some of those organisms can be seen in figure 23.25.

The ecosystem derives its energy not from the sun, but from the breakdown of radioactive materials inside the earth. The breakdown releases heat and results in the formation of new oceanic crust. Seawater seeping into the crust reacts with the crustal rock, and large amounts of hydrogen sulfide are released.

The primary producers of this ecosystem are bacteria. At vents in the ocean floor, they absorb the hydrogen sulfide and combine it with oxygen dissolved in the seawater. That reaction releases sufficient energy to support the bacteria, which, in turn, support the other organisms.

23.12 Coastal Waters Are the Source of Much Food for Humans

With few exceptions, oceans are relatively shallow near the continents. These bands of shallow water average less than 200 m in depth. They are widest at the mouths of large rivers and along areas of broad lowlands. Along mountainous coasts, as in California, shallow waters may be almost absent.

In shallow waters some light reaches the bottom. Where there is plenty of light, a luxuriant growth of seaweeds may be found. In middle and higher latitudes the most common and conspicuous seaweeds are brown algae. Among these are kelps (figure 23.26), which may reach lengths of 35 m or more. Nevertheless, here, as elsewhere in aquatic ecosystems, phytoplankton are the principal producers.

Figure 23.26 A diver in a kelp bed.

Howard Hall/TOM STACK & ASSOCIATES

The physical characteristics of the bottom—sand, mud, or rock—determine the kinds of organisms that live there. Plants are not usually abundant on unstable sandy bottoms. However, many kinds of animals burrow into the sand, especially crustaceans, mollusks, and annelid worms. Muddy bottoms have even more burrowers, and most of the species are unlike those adapted to sand. Sea cucumbers, clams, and some crabs plow through the mud. On rocky bottoms and coral reefs, many animals attach themselves permanently to one place. Crabs, octopuses, and fishes hide in nooks and crannies among the rocks.

Because they are shallow and close to land, coastal waters offer more opportunity for human use than does the open ocean. Much of the marine food supply of humans comes from the coastal waters. Underwater farming of kelp, fish, crustaceans, and mollusks is a future possibility. It is unlikely, however, that the ocean will supply all the food we will need in the future. With the exception of coastal waters, the ocean is very limited in some of its dissolved nutrients. Rich fertile soils may contain 0.5 percent nitrogen, an important nutrient for growth. The richest ocean water, in comparison, contains only about 0.00005 percent nitrogen.

23.13 Coral Reefs Support a Great Diversity of Life Forms

Coral reefs are large formations of calcium carbonate laid down by living organisms over thousands of years. They are found only in tropical waters where there is adequate light and oxygen. The reef structure is formed by individual coral polyps that secrete calcium-containing skeletons. Mutualistic green algae live within the tissues of the polyps. These algae carry out most of the photosynthesis of the reef. In addition, they recycle essential minerals such as nitrogen and enhance the ability of the coral to deposit calcium carbonate. Red and brown algae also are part of the reef ecosystem.

Coral reefs are among the most productive and colorful of the ecosystems. They provide food and shelter for a great diversity of sea animals. Numerous species of fishes populate the reef ecosystem. A tremendous variety of invertebrates, such as sponges, sea urchins, and crustaceans, is present in large numbers. In terms of their diversity of life forms, coral reefs have been called the tropical rain forests of the sea.

Figure 23.27 Coral reef showing a variety of corals and sponges with a large starfish.

CARIBBEAN COLLECTION/Nancy Sefton

23.14 The Littoral Zone Is a Difficult Place to Live

Everywhere along the margins of the oceans you can see the effects of waves and tides. In the Bay of Fundy (Nova Scotia) the maxium vertical change between high and low tides is 15.4 m. At the other extreme, the average tidal difference in the Mediterranean is only 0.35 m. Wave action, too, varies depending on the place and time. Some shores, such as those of Maine, are pounded by heavy surf. Others, especially in small, protected bays, may be no more exposed to wave action than the shores of small lakes. High and low tides each occur twice a day. The zone between high and low tides—the **littoral** zone—is a difficult environment for life. Twice a day littoral organisms are submerged in salt water and

Figure 23.28 The ocean shore. Wave action helps to form the pattern of rocks and life along the shore.

Doug Sokell

Figure 23.29 Tide pool. On rocky ocean shores many aquatic organisms live during low tides in pools left above the waterline. Starfish, anemones, and barnacles are visible in this photo.

Doug Sokell

then exposed to air and the bright, hot sun or freezing wind. Between those times the littoral zone is pounded by the advancing or retreating surf.

On rocky coasts, life in the littoral region is surprisingly abundant. In cold water, different species of brown algae cling to the rocks. They are protected from the drying sun by a jelly-like coating. These tangled algae provide protection and support for other algae, protists, and many animals. In addition, barnacles, chitons, and snails cling firmly to rocks or seaweeds, closing up tightly during the periods when they are exposed to air.

On sandy coasts, life in the littoral zone is limited to organisms that can burrow in the sand or skitter over it. There are no attached producers, but phytoplankton may be present when the tide is in. The burrowers, such as small crustaceans, eat food particles brought by the high tides. Shorebirds are a link with land ecosystems. They prey on the sand burrowers or forage in the debris left behind by the retreating tide. Land crabs release their young in the water. Sea turtles crawl out on the beach and bury their eggs. Terrestrial and marine ecosystems merge in the littoral zone.

Wherever ocean meets land, there is constant change. In only a few years sediments deposited at the mouths of rivers stretch the land into the ocean. Elsewhere you can observe the ocean pushing back the land as it carves out sandy beaches with its wave action. Such changes have occurred throughout most of the earth's history.

Self-Review

1. Why do some parts of the oceans have a higher productivity than others?
2. Describe the environment of the ocean depths and the organisms that live there.
3. How do coastal ecosystems differ from those of the open ocean?
4. How do marine organisms affect the amount of dissolved substances in ocean water?
5. Compare variations of temperature in the oceans with those in the atmosphere.
6. What factors determine the amount and color of light beneath the water surface?
7. In what way is a coral reef like a tropical rain forest?

Investigation 23.3 EFFECTS OF SALINITY ON AQUATIC ORGANISMS

Introduction

If you were to move freshwater organisms into the ocean or ocean organisms into fresh water, they would probably die very quickly. Although salmon migrate from the open ocean into freshwater rivers to reproduce, they first spend several days in water with decreasing salinity. In this way, their bodies adjust gradually to the lower salt concentrations.

Small freshwater ponds become salty as the summer sun evaporates the water. Small aquatic organisms that cannot tolerate the change will either die or go into a dormant stage.

In this investigation you will observe the tolerances of some freshwater organisms to various concentrations of salt solutions. Review the procedure and set up an appropriate hypothesis.

Materials (per pair of students)

living specimens of small aquatic organisms
sodium chloride solutions (1%, 3%, and 5%)

elodea or filamentous algae
monocular microscope
3 microscope slides
3 coverslips
dropping pipet
paper towels

Procedure

Part A—Plants and Salinity

1. Take a leaf of elodea from near the tip of the plant. Place the leaf upside down on your microscope slide. Add a drop of fresh water and cover with a coverslip. You may use a filamentous alga such as *Spirogyra* instead.
2. Using the low power of your microscope, find a cell that you can observe clearly.
   (a) Describe the cell contents.
   (b) Does the cell seem to be completely filled with the cell contents?
3. Add a few drops of 5% salt solution to one side of your coverslip. Draw it under the coverslip by applying a paper towel to the opposite side. Watch your cell and describe what you observe.
4. See if the process is reversible by drawing pure water under the coverslip. Record any changes you observe.

Part B—Animals and Salinity

1. Your teacher will have placed several aquatic organisms in containers of water, 1%, 3%, and 5% salt solutions. Using a medicine dropper, place on a slide a drop of the water containing the kind of organism you have chosen to study. Add a coverslip.
2. Using the low power of your microscope, observe the organisms for a few minutes to determine their normal appearance and actions. You can slow down the movement of some kinds of protists by adding protozoa slowing compound, a few wisps of cotton, or a bit of shredded paper towel to the water.
3. Prepare another slide of the same organisms from the 1% salt solution. Observe the organisms, and record any difference in movements and shape.
4. Repeat procedure 3 with the 3% and 5% salt solutions. Which of these is most like ocean water?
5. Replace the 5% salt solution with water as you did in part A, procedure 4. The organisms may be drawn up by the paper towel. If organisms remain on your slide, record any changes in movement or shape that you observe.

Discussion

Individuals of a species usually respond in a variety of ways to an environmental factor. All students who worked with the same organisms should compare their results.

1. Did all individuals of the species react in the same way? If not, what differences were noted?
2. Did the kind of reaction differ with different salt solutions? Try to explain any differences.
3. Compare observations of teams that worked on different kinds of organisms.
   (a) Which kind was most tolerant to changes in salt concentration?
   (b) Which kind was least tolerant?

4. What kind of aquatic habitat do you think each kind of organism normally inhabits?
5. Which of your observations support the hypothesis you set up?
6. Do any of your observations weaken your hypothesis? If so, which ones?
7. Taking all your observations into account, relate your hypothesis in the form of a conclusion to the experiment.

For Further Investigation

All the organisms you studied in this investigation are small. Many larger ones (salmon, for example) regularly move from marine water to fresh water (or vice versa), apparently without harm. Others cannot tolerate much change in salinity. Test the salinity tolerance of macroscopic aquatic animals such as crayfish, goldfish, guppies, or snails, using the principles employed in this exercise. If you use a marine species (for example, a clam worm) in your experiments, how should you modify your procedure? **CAUTION:** *It is not necessary to kill the animals used in your experiments. Whenever they show signs of discomfort, return them to a more tolerable salinity.*

Guidepost: How do human activities affect aquatic ecosystems?

Human Influences on Aquatic Ecosystems

23.15 Drainage of Standing Waters May Have Serious Consequences

Shallow ponds, lakes, and marshes are basins where rich organic matter constantly builds up. This organic matter can be used to grow crops. We need only remove the water from the basins and plow the muck to mix air into it so that crops will thrive.

After the invention of powered pumps, humans could easily drain standing inland water. Throughout the twentieth century the use of such pumps has reduced the number of natural-water areas in many parts of the United States. An unfortunate effect of this drainage has been a decrease in migratory bird populations. The grassland ponds and marshes are the main breeding sites for many migratory bird species (figure 23.30). When a pond or marsh is drained and turned into a wheat field, the area supplies an increased amount of food for humans but no longer supports migratory birds. This is a clear example of one consequence of a growing human population. In the management of farmland and wildlife, as with other resources, we must make choices. These choices are called **trade-offs.** They involve the study of many interacting ecological factors.

Figure 23.30 Migratory birds (Western sandpipers) in wetlands.

Thomas Kitchin/TOM STACK & ASSOCIATES

23.16 Artificial Ponds and Lakes Are Formed by Dams

Although drainage of standing waters has continued, the surface area of inland waters has actually increased during the last 50 years. That has resulted from construction of dams across running waters.

Dams are built to provide a waterfall that will turn electric generators. Most dams, especially in the western states, also form basins in which floodwaters are stored for irrigation and for supplying water to

Figure 23.31 Lower Monument Dam on the Columbia River. What purpose do the structures in the lower right corner of the photo serve?

Bonneville Power Administration

Figure 23.32 A farm pond.

USDA

cities. The result is bodies of standing water where once there were streams and land. Such major changes in environment bring about major changes in communities. A large dam may block the passage of fish that swim up rivers to lay their eggs in headwater streams. On the other hand, it may greatly increase the amount of habitat favorable for other species, such as catfish. Trout and catfish may become trade-offs.

Much of the new inland-water area is made up of small ponds that cover only a few thousand square meters. Some artificial ponds are dug merely to provide a supply of water in case of fire. Other ponds supply a summer source of water for range cattle, deer, and game birds. Still others produce fish for food, sport, or both. In such cases the pond owners must understand something about pond ecosystems so they can make favorable habitats for the fish they want.

23.17 Sewage and Industrial Wastes Affect River Ecosystems

One of the first human uses of flowing water was to float boats for transportation. Today boat and barge traffic, along with industry, have affected stream ecosystems principally by simplifying community structure.

Humans have always used water to flush away unwanted substances. When humans come together in towns and cities, their accumulated biological wastes—sewage—greatly affect nearby river ecosystems. Sewage is mainly organic substances mixed with water. By providing nutrients, sewage increases the growth and reproduction of producers in the water, a process known as **eutrophication** (yoo troh fih KAY shun). If the amount of sewage is large relative to the volume of river water, the producer growth is great. Phytoplankton have short lifespans. When they die, decomposers use up the oxygen in the water as they break down the producers' bodies. An anaerobic condition results, which is deadly for all aerobic organisms. However, as the waters of the river flow on, the sewage

Figure 23.33 Diagram of sewage pollution in a stream. (Organisms are not drawn to scale and distances are greatly decreased.) At the left sewage is attacked by decomposers. The oxygen supply decreases. Aerobic organisms die. Further downstream the amount of sewage decreases. The oxygen supply increases. The phytoplankton and aerobic consumers increase in number.

may be diluted by water from tributary streams. In any case, decomposers eventually use up the sewage materials. River ecosystems once could clean themselves of sewage pollution, as described above. Human populations have increased, however, and cities have been built closer together. Today a river ecosystem seldom can clean itself up before it receives another load of sewage.

From factories and mills, alkalis and chromium, lead, and mercury ions have been dumped into bodies of water. All of these are poisonous to some living things. Industrial processes, particularly the generation of electricity, often result in the discharge of hot water into rivers. Such thermal pollution abruptly changes the abiotic environment and makes it intolerable for many aquatic organisms. The warmer water also may bring about a change in the types of species that can inhabit the area. Nuclear reactors sometimes add small amounts of radioactive substances to streams. Those substances accumulate in the bodies of stream organisms, harming them and the organisms that eat them. All of those pollutants may affect the health of the human populations that depend on the water.

Figure 23.34 A mountain stream such as this one would likely be able to cleanse itself of pollution. Why?

BSCS

23.18 Acid Rain Is Toxic

Acid rain is precipitation that has a pH of less than 5.6. When acidic rain falls into a lake over a period of time, the lake is changed into a body of water that has lost nearly all forms of life normally found in a lake. How does that happen?

We can use the simplified sulfur cycle in figure 23.35 to understand how acid rain forms and gets into lake water. Atmospheric sulfur comes from several sources, including volcanoes, the action of soil microorganisms, and the combustion of fossil fuels such as coal, gas, and oil. When fuel that contains sulfur is burned, oxygen combines with sulfur to form oxides. When the oxides of sulfur reach the atmosphere, they combine with rain water and form sulfuric acid which, in turn, falls to the ground as acid precipitation.

As the pH drops, the organisms that live in or near a lake are affected. Amphibian eggs fail to hatch, snail populations decline, and the diversity of plants and animals diminishes. Bacteria die, and bacterial decomposition of dead plant and animal matter is retarded. The normal reproductive cycle of many fish is disrupted. Toxic metals, such as aluminum, can be leached from the surrounding land or lake bottom, damaging the gills of fish. Mercury can be converted to its organic form and be absorbed by fish. Mammals and birds that depend on aquatic foods are affected because their sources of food are gone.

Figure 23.35 The sulfur cycle.

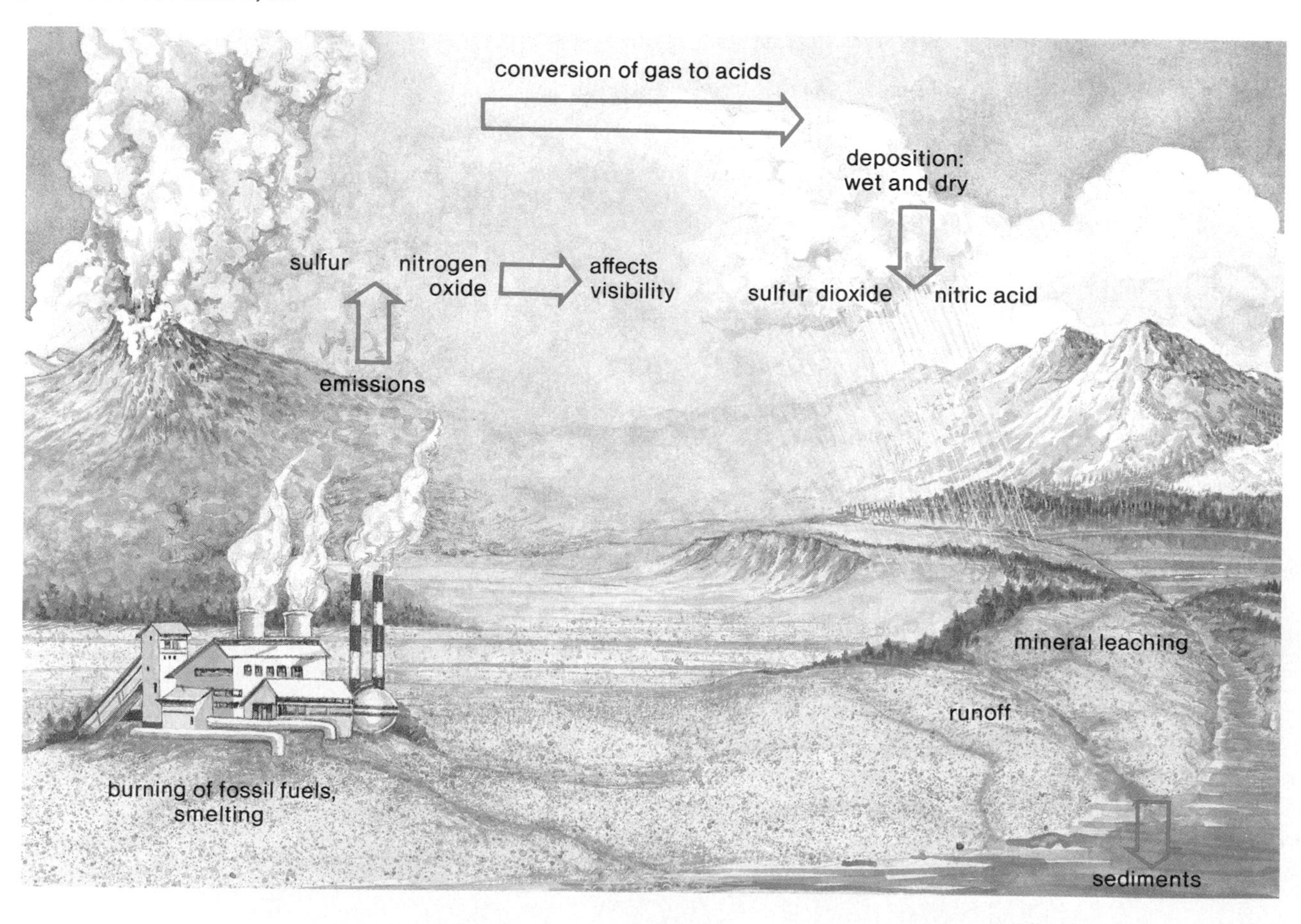

By the time the pH of a lake falls to 4.5, no fish are left. Most of the frogs, insects, and decomposers are gone. The remaining bacteria rapidly use up the available oxygen, and anaerobic bacteria increase. The water becomes beautiful and clear, but the lake is dead. You can observe the effects of acid rain in your area in investigation 23.4.

Investigation 23.4 ACID RAIN IN LOCAL ENVIRONMENTS

Introduction

The degree to which acid rain is destructive differs in the United States from region to region. Many factors influence the probability and the potential damage of acid rain. Most experts agree that the problem begins with the burning of coal, oil, and natural gas. Smokestacks as tall as 300 meters allow winds to carry pollutants far from local sources. In addition, the capacity of the soil or bedrock to buffer the effects of the acid rain varies. Limestone bedrock neutralizes the acid very well. Granite bedrock has no effect at all on the acid rain.

One can study the extent of acid rain in one's own area by starting with a map of the United States that displays several areas of greatest vulnerability. After determining the degree of vulnerability, actual tests of the surroundings can be performed.

Materials (per class)

individual student samples of:
- rainwater
- lake or pond water
- soil
- snow (if possible)

pH meter or pH paper
acid solution—pH 4
boiled distilled water—pH 7
glass or plastic funnel
filter paper
100 ml beaker

Part A—Vulnerability to Acid Rain

Procedure

Examine figure 23.36 showing the areas of the United States with the highest susceptibility to acid rain.

Discussion

1. According to the map, which parts of the country are most susceptible to acid rain?
2. According to the map, is acid rain currently destructive to your area?
3. What causes an area of the country to be more susceptible than another area?

Part B—pH of Your Rainwater Samples

Procedure

Test your rainwater with a pH meter or pH paper and record its pH.

Figure 23.36

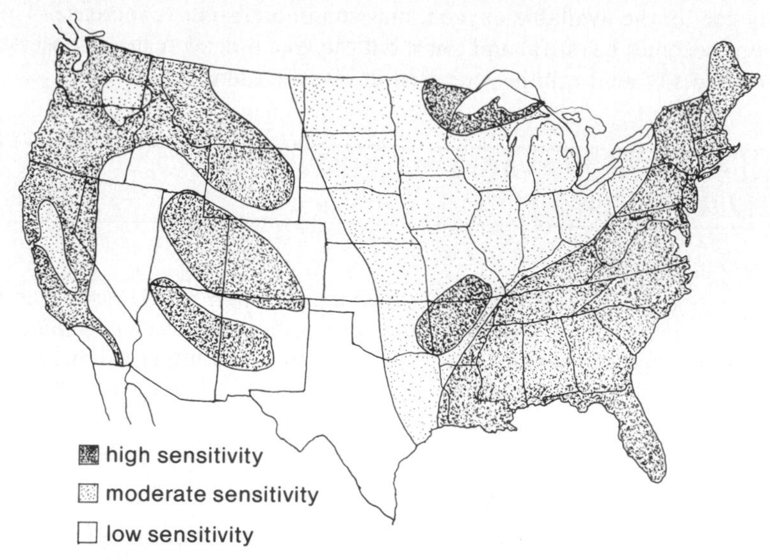

Adapted from E. Johnson and R. Bybee, supervisors, "Acid Rain: Activities for Science Teachers" *The American Biology Teacher* 45:4 (April/May 1983) © National Association of Biology Teachers, Reston, Virginia. Reprinted by permission.

Discussion

1. What is the pH of your rainwater?
2. How does the pH of your rainwater compare to that of normal rainwater (pH 5.6)?
3. Compare the pH of your rainwater to that of 3 other students who live in different neighborhoods. Do you find a difference in pH? Describe these differences.
4. Give some reasons why you think your rainwater is or is not very acidic.

Part C—pH of Soil Samples

Procedure

1. Place filter paper in a funnel and fill the funnel with your soil sample.
2. Hold the end of the funnel over a small beaker and pour 100 ml of boiled distilled water through the soil; dirty water should collect in the beaker.
3. Determine and record the pH of the collected water with the pH meter or pH paper.

Discussion

1. What is the pH of your soil?
2. How does this compare to that of 3 classmates?
3. State 2 reasons why your soil pH might differ from that of your classmates.
4. Consider the data on the pH of the rainwater of your area. In what way, if any, is this rainwater affecting the acidity of your soil?

Part D—Buffering Capacity of Soil Samples

Procedure

1. Set up your funnel and a new sample of soil as you did in part C.
2. Hold the end of the funnel over a small beaker and pour 100 ml of an acid solution (pH 4) through the soil.
3. Determine and record the pH of the collected solution.

Discussion

1. The acid solution had a pH of 4 before it was washed through the soil. What is the pH of the washed-through solution collected in the beaker?
2. Based on the data you just collected, discuss the buffering capacity of your soil.
3. What might cause a soil to have a buffering capacity?
4. Considering the pH of your rainwater, could your soil be healthy without a buffering capacity?

Part E—Acidity of Lake or Pond Water Samples

Procedure

Determine and record the pH of your water sample.

Discussion

1. What is the pH of your pond or lake water sample?
2. Compare the pH of your sample to that of 3 other students who have samples from different lakes or ponds. Do you find a difference in pH? Describe these differences.
3. How does the pH of your sample compare with a healthy pond or lake?
4. Do you think this pond or lake is too acidic?
5. If the pond or lake water is not too acidic and the rainwater is known to be acidic, what might be some factors influencing acidity of the pond or lake water?
6. Consider the characteristics of the area around the pond or lake (for example, forest, farmland, bedrock). How might these factors influence the acidity of pond or lake water?

Part F—pH of Snow Samples

Procedure

1. Melt your snow in a small beaker.
2. Determine and record the pH of the meltwater.

Discussion

1. What is the pH of your melted snow?
2. How does the pH of your meltwater compare with your rainwater investigation in part B?
3. Discuss reasons why snow meltwater might be more or less acidic than rainwater.
4. From your data, what conclusions can you make about what time of the year you might find your lakes and soil the most acidic?

For Further Investigation

Write a letter to your congressional representative explaining the possibilities for a problem with acid precipitation in your area. Include in your letter some suggestions for what we as a nation can do to lessen the threat of acid rain.

This investigation was adapted from E. Johnson and R. Bybee, supervisors, "Acid Rain: Activities for Science Teachers" *The American Biology Teacher* 45:4 (April/May 1983) © National Association of Biology Teachers, Reston, Virginia. Reprinted by permission.

23.19 The Oceans Receive the Major Part of Human Waste

It has been estimated that more than 80 percent of all ocean pollution comes from human activities that are land based. This pollution takes many forms and is found in every ocean, sea, and bay of the world. For example, large amounts of garbage are dumped in the ocean off New York and New Jersey. Everything from plastics to radioactive waste is being dumped in the oceans at an ever increasing rate.

Large rivers that empty into the sea carry sediments from the normal process of erosion. Now, along with the sediments, the rivers carry raw sewage, fertilizers, pesticides, heavy metals, and chemicals, such as dioxin and formaldehyde. What happens to these substances once they have reached the ocean? Some, such as pesticides and mercury, enter the food chains and could eventually end up in the seafood that we eat. The people of Minamata, Japan, learned firsthand what mercury pollution could do. They ate fish with tissues containing high concentrations of methyl mercury, which causes crippling from damage to the brain and nervous system. Between 1953 and the early 60s, 46 persons had died of Minamata disease, and hundreds of others, many of them children, had been affected.

Figure 23.37 New York City garbage being towed to sea for dumping.

EPA

Oil spills are a constant threat to ocean ecosystems and must be constantly monitored. Between 1969 and 1974, there were 500 oil spills and 1 million tons of oil were lost from tankers by accident. On March 16, 1978, the oil tanker *Amoco Cadiz* broke apart off the coast of Brittany in France, spilling 1.6 million barrels of crude oil onto the beaches. More than a million sea birds were killed, and the oyster beds, as well as fish and other sea animals, were destroyed. The tourists avoided the Brittany coast for years after the oil spill because the seawater was nearly devoid of marine life, and the beaches still had a residue of oil in the grains of sand.

The captains of oil tankers often clean the holds of their ships by washing them out with seawater. Most of the pollution comes from these illegal activities. As a result, there are very few beaches in the world that are not affected by oil pollution of this type.

The oceans of the world are like a large basin or tub. Everything that is dumped into a river or stream eventually ends up in the ocean, and many of those pollutants will end up in the food chain. Most pollutants stay in coastal waters, the most productive parts of the ocean. They could very well cause the destruction of important species of fish that many people depend on for food.

Figure 23.38 An oil spill and cleanup crew.

API/VISUALS UNLIMITED

Self-Review

1. What benefits do humans get from draining inland water? From damming flowing waters?
2. How might draining and damming waters be harmful to human interest?
3. What eventually happens to sewage when it is dumped into a river system?
4. What are the effects of acid precipitation on a lake?
5. How did the people of Minamata, Japan, get mercury poisoning?
6. Why is crude oil so destructive to ocean ecosystems?

Summary

Humans always have depended on various sources of water to meet their needs. Inland-water or freshwater ecosystems are grouped as standing or flowing waters. Ponds are generally shallow and smaller than lakes, but phytoplankton are the primary producers in both. Plankton are usually absent in brooks and streams, but may be present in slow-moving rivers. Rivers carry sediments and pollutants into the sea. Drainage, dam building, and pollution may have an adverse effect on the amount, quality, and usage of water by all organisms.

The oceans cover about 70 percent of the earth's surface. The concentration of salt and other minerals remains in a steady state through the action of marine organisms. Temperature, the amount of light available to photosynthetic organisms, and currents also affect ocean waters. There are four major zones in the ocean. The zones blend together, but each one is different in terms of physical factors and biota. All of the zones are affected by human activities, and pollution has become one of the most demanding challenges with which we must deal.

Application Questions

1. Why does the concentration of oxygen in a small pond differ from night to day?
2. How would a cloudy, windy day affect the productivity of phytoplankton in a lake?
3. Is a layer of ice on the surface of a lake harmful to fish? Explain.
4. Compare the sources of oxygen in a brook, a slow-moving river, a pond, and a lake.
5. Would you expect decomposers to be more active on the bottom of a pond or of a lake? Explain.
6. Why is a poisonous substance in a pond—such as a mercury compound—likely to be more concentrated in the flesh of a bass than of a ciliate?
7. A program designed to improve the fishing was introduced in a midwestern pond. First, a fish poison was used to kill all the many small fish that were in the pond. Then the pond was restocked with game fish. Instead of large game fish, the new population contained many stunted individuals. Explain.
8. If you collect 167 snails of a given species from five plots totaling 5 m^2 and find their total mass is 534 g, what would be the biomass of the snail population?

Problems

1. Current is one of the most important limiting factors in a stream ecosystem. Stream organisms must be adapted to maintain a constant position. Cite at least five specific organisms showing five different adaptations to stream currents.
2. Differences in the physical characteristics of water and air are important in understanding the contrast between aquatic and terrestrial environments. Consider questions such as these:
   (a) What land organisms have the most streamlined bodies? With what form of locomotion do you associate this streamlining?
   (b) What water organisms have the most streamlined bodies? What niches in aquatic ecosystems do these organisms occupy?
   (c) Why do most plankton organisms have little or no streamlining?
   (d) How does locomotion by walking on the bottom of the ocean differ from locomotion by walking on land?
3. The Saint Lawrence River in North America is about 1223 km long. Find out what changes have been made in the river in the last 25 years and what those changes have done to the river's ecosystem.
4. Investigate the effects of the current called El Niño.

5. Estuaries, such as Chesapeake Bay and San Francisco Bay, represent a special kind of aquatic environment. Find out what characteristics distinguish estuarine environments from marine and inland-water environments and how these affect aquatic life.
6. Though the seas are very large, pollution of marine waters can occur. Investigate the kinds of oceanic pollution and their effects on the marine ecosystems.
7. Investigate the various kinds of adaptations that allow organisms to survive in the littoral zone.

Suggested Readings

J. F. Grassle, "Hydrothermal Vent Animals: Distribution and Biology" *Science* (23 August 1985). Describes the latest findings on hydrothermal vent communities.

M. M. Littler and D. S. Littler, "Deepest Known Plant Life Discovered on an Uncharted Seamount" *Science* (4 January 1985). Living marine macrophytes found at a record depth of 268 m are investigated.

R. A. Lutz and R. R. Hessler, "Life Without Sunlight" *The Science Teacher* (March 1983). This well-illustrated article explores the biological communities of deep-sea hydrothermal vents.

K. C. Macdonald and B. P. Luyendyk, "The Crest of the East Pacific Rise" *Scientific American* (May 1981). More discussion of sea floor hot spring communities, with emphasis on the undersea exploration used to discover them.

Scientific American, 1980, *Life in the Sea* (San Francisco: W. H. Freeman). A series of reprints from *Scientific American* dealing with oceanic habitats, adaptive living, representative organisms, and human factors.

BSCS

Humans modify the environment in many ways. This is an aerial view of Busch Gardens in Tampa, Florida.

CHAPTER 24

Human-Shaped Ecosystems

Introduction

Seen from the air, the impact of humans on the earth is most apparent where we have built cities. However, we have affected the landscape in less visible ways as well. The varied communities in natural biomes have been largely replaced by agricultural and urban ecosystems.

In previous chapters, you have seen some of the varied ecosystems of the present, how they came to be, and how humans have changed them. Here we will concentrate on how ancient and modern humans have evolved within and spread across the landscape.

The Built Environment

Guidepost: In what ways have humans changed natural ecosystems?

24.1 Early Humans Worked Together within Ecosystems

One reason humans have been so successful in modifying the biosphere is that we cooperate, or work in groups. In other words, we have **social behavior.** Cooperation is an important trait in many animal species. It is probably most apparent in the insects, which are highly adapted for division of labor (figure 24.1). Insects, however, cooperate without reflection on what they do, because they are genetically programmed to do so. Their behavior is involuntary. Human cooperation might or might not be voluntary, and that is a subject of heated debate among biologists. However, we do cooperate, at least much of the time, and we do reflect on the matter.

Figure 24.1 Honeybees. Each of these individuals has specialized behavior. Drones are males; workers are nonreproductive females; queens are egg-layers.

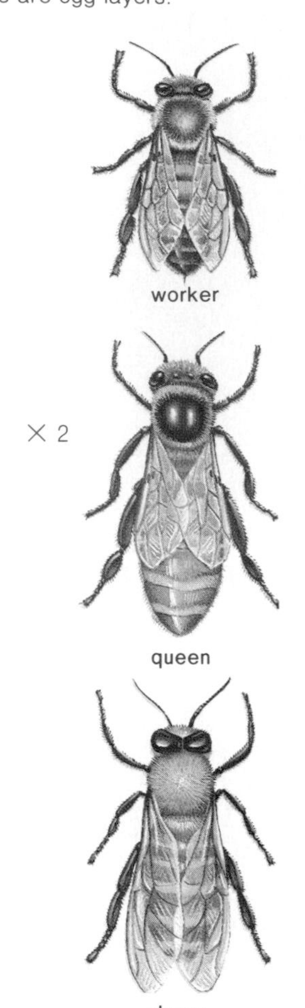

Figure 24.2 A chimpanzee social group.

Stewart Halperin/TOM STACK & ASSOCIATES

There is little cooperation in primitive primates, such as the tarsier. Each tarsier lives a solitary life most of the time. However, in the primates most like us—chimpanzees—evolution has produced much cooperative behavior. Females care for the young, younger males defer to older and stronger ones, adolescent females "baby-sit," and animals sometimes share food and groom each other (figure 24.2).

Like modern apes, the Cro-Magnon men and women who appeared about 25,000 years ago were hunters and food gatherers. Though early humans ate meat, they often gathered berries, fruits, and nuts, and they dug up roots. They were particularly efficient predators because they used tools, were intelligent, and formed social groups. It is likely that men did the hunting, and women did the gathering (and eventually much of the farming). That division of labor probably had little to do with physical differences between men and women: more likely it was that women carrying babies or walking with small children had little freedom of movement.

Among today's few remaining hunting and food-gathering tribes, about 5 km^2 of land are needed to support each person. Based on this figure, the total human population 25,000 years ago must have been small. It also must have been scattered in widely separated groups.

Primitive hominids gathered many plants, preyed on some animals, and sometimes fell prey to other animals. Hominid ecological relationships changed little for most of our history. Indeed, in some remote parts of the world they continued unchanged well into the twentieth century.

Domestication of wolves, 15,000 years ago or more, was important in changing the nomadic way of life. Probably some hunters took wolf cubs home and were later able to take advantage of the growing wolves'

Figure 24.3 Social behavior in wolves. The alpha male of the pack reasserts dominance over his brother. The interaction is ritualized—a fight that does not result in injuries.

Wolf Park, Battle Ground, Indiana 47920

hunting and social behavior. (In a wolf pack, some wolves are subordinate to others, as seen in figure 24.3. A human may be treated as a "top wolf" by wolves.) Eventually dogs (*Canis familiaris*) evolved from the wolf line (*Canis lupus*). With the help of dogs in hunting, and perhaps with the invention of nets for fishing, some human groups began to form permanent settlements.

One early settlement was in the southern USSR, where anthropologists unearthed a large assemblage of mammoth bones and tusks. At first these appeared to be merely the garbage from some early human group, but the scientists found that the mammoth bones and tusks were arranged in certain patterns, not carelessly heaped. It turned out, in fact, that the mammoth bones had been used as construction materials for a small group of human homes (figure 24.4). The homes were used as a winter camp by a band of hunters and gatherers 15,000 years ago. From such beginnings came the earliest villages.

24.2 The Agricultural Revolution Increased the Human Impact on the Biosphere

In early villages, the garbage dump—a by-product of settled life—must have appeared almost at once, and that probably led to deliberate sowing of "crops." Wild plants were gathered for food and brought into the settlement. People may have noticed how a discarded portion of a wild plant sometimes grew into a mature plant on their dumps. They may then have dug up favorite wild plants and transferred them to their settlement.

Figure 24.4 A reconstruction of a mammoth-bone dwelling from a site in the USSR. The structure was about 5 m across at the base. Hides, supported by a wood frame and held in place by bones, may have made the roof.

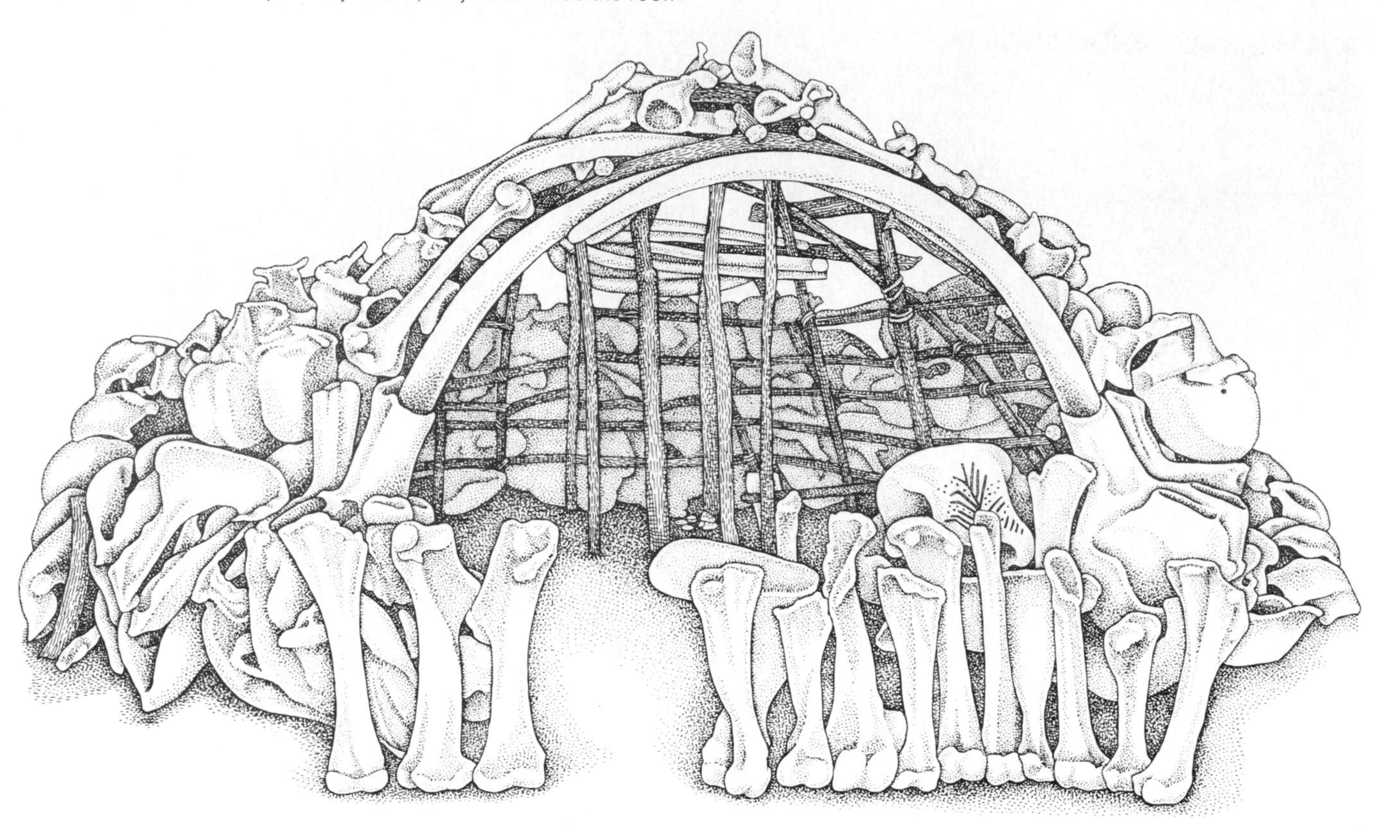

About 7,000 to 10,000 years ago, in Iraq, a series of genetic accidents changed wild wheat into a plant that could be sown and cultivated (figure 24.5). Probably humans already were gathering and using the wild wheat; now they could have wheat fields near their settlements. Similarly, wild rice was gathered in Asia, and eventually it was cultivated for the first time. These events made it possible to obtain more food from a smaller area. When people first assisted the growth of plants and harvested their products, the **agricultural revolution** began. It made human life easier in some ways. It also indirectly increased the size of the human population.

Hunters and gatherers can get by with working three or four days out of each week. But without any way to store food they must sometimes go hungry. Around A.D. 1600, Indians in northern New England were hunters and gatherers. Their population density stayed around 0.16 persons per km^2. Indians in southern New England, however, were farmers. Their population density was 7 times as great, 1.12 persons per km^2.

The Indian farmers used common village grounds for their farms. Use of common areas for grazing and farming tends to lead to what biologist Garrett Hardin has called the "tragedy of the commons:" eventually one of the users tries to use more than his share of the common resource. That problem probably never arose for the Indians, because the available land was vast and they moved villages when resources became scarce.

Figure 24.5 The domestication of wheat. Chance crossing of wild grasses produced an early domesticated wheat. Breeding this with another wild grass gave a plant whose kernels were easily separated from its chaff. This development marked the beginning of the interdependence of humans and wheat. Wheat could not survive without people to cultivate it, as its seeds could no longer be dispersed by wind. Civilization could not grow without this readily available, complete food source. Further crossing gave the common wheat form which now accounts for the majority of modern world wheat production.

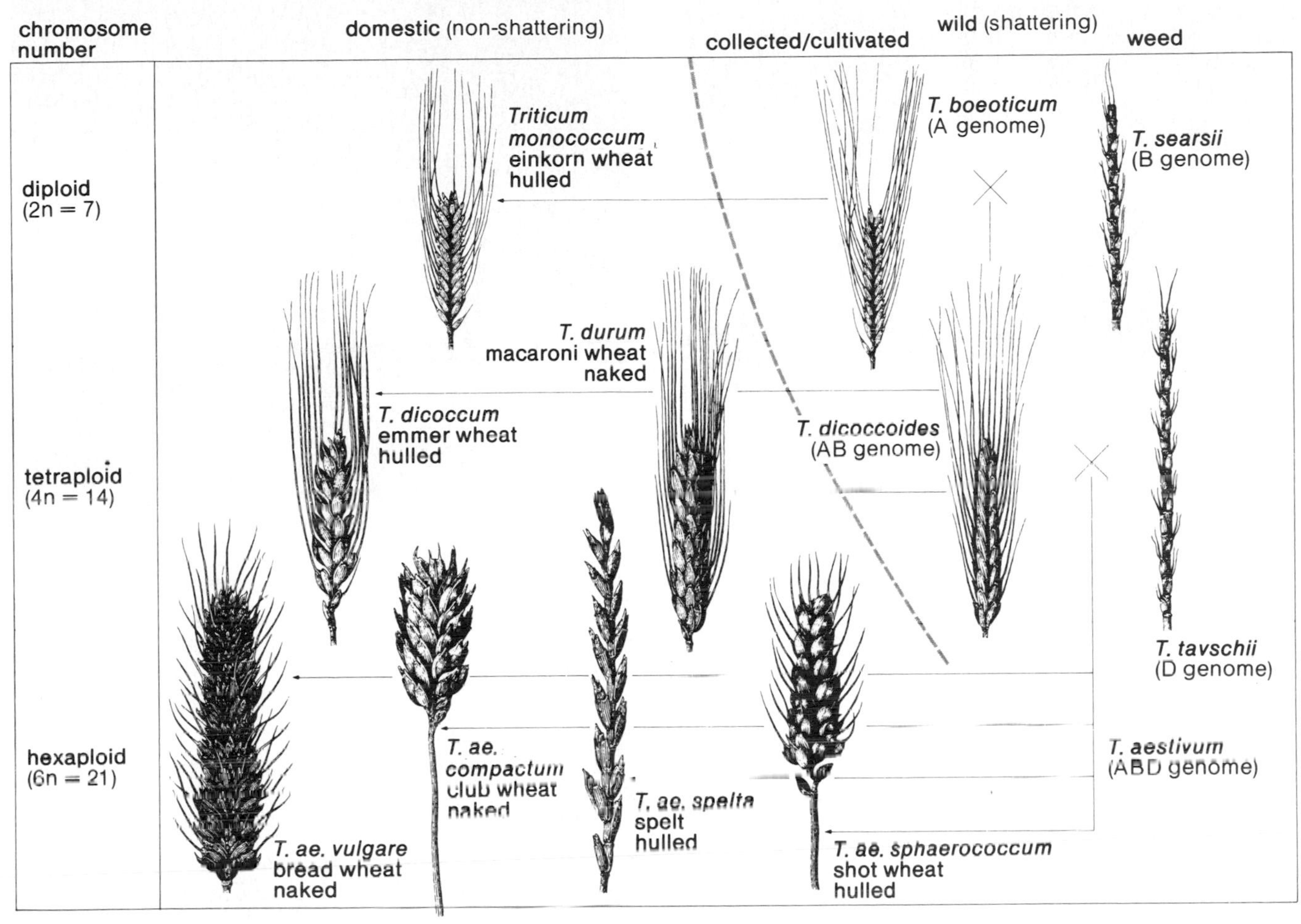

When European settlers arrived, however, they brought along their European ideas of private ownership of property. Again, at first there was plenty of land for all the Europeans. In Plymouth Colony, however, friction developed when pigs wandered into corn fields. Soon the fields were fenced. Eventually, New England was filled with privately owned farms, then factories, and the commons were gone. Today the water and air of New England, common resources of everyone, have been polluted by some users. And much of the forested land has been logged heavily by private owners.

Early hunters had domesticated dogs before the agricultural revolution, but the domestication of other animals apparently came later. Except for dogs, remains of domesticated animals are found only in agricultural communities. Perhaps during times of drought, wild herbivores invaded fields and gardens looking for food. Such animals could be captured, penned up, and used for food later. Some captured animals must have had young, which were then raised by humans. Thus, the domestication of cattle, sheep, and goats may have begun.

Figure 24.6 Animal-powered agriculture. Preparing rice fields with water buffalo in Java, Indonesia. Compare its effects on the biosphere with the effects of the kinds of agriculture shown in figure 24.24b.

Gary Milburn/TOM STACK & ASSOCIATES

Figure 24.7 Primitive village in Mesa Verde National Park, Colorado. Agricultural products were grown in the valleys and on the slopes and mesa tops. These adobe dwellings were occupied between 500 and 1400 A.D.

BSCS by J. B. Thornton

Well after the beginning of the agricultural revolution, primitive farmers discovered that some animals could be put to work. Such animals had to be fed, but that investment paid off in greater food production. That was an early step for humans toward using energy other than their own to change their environment.

Farming required more foresight than hunting did. Farmers had to adjust more of their activities to the changing seasons. They had to store crops between harvests. They had to work hard, and without immediate reward. But farming also provided more leisure time. Once the harvest was in and the surplus stored, farmers usually had enough food for several weeks or months. Hunters had no such extended leisure time.

Surplus agricultural products also supported craftspersons. They gathered with farmers in villages. Eventually the villages became towns, and towns became cities. As the size and complexity of the human-dominated areas grew, the human population grew greatly in size also.

The areas surrounding towns were sources of building materials for the "built environment." Trees were felled for lumber, stones were used for walls and buildings, and straw and clay were mixed for bricks, concrete, and adobe. In investigation 24.1, you will be able to study the changes that have occurred in your ecosystem during the past 20,000 years.

Investigation 24.1 YOUR ECOSYSTEM

Introduction

Since the last glacier retreated from the area that is now the United States, the climate has remained fairly stable. If you are fortunate enough to live near a wilderness area, you can probably see plant communities as they were before the arrival of the first Americans from Asia.

In this investigation you will diagram a food web to show the relationships among the major plants and animals in your area 20,000 years ago. Then you will modify this food web to show how the ecosystem was affected by immigrants from Asia and, later, from Europe and Africa.

Procedure

Part A

1. Using the science and public libraries as well as references provided by your teacher, assemble a list of at least 100 plants and animals found in your area 20,000 years ago. Find the generic and specific names if possible. Include representatives of each of the following groups:
   (a) Plants. Bryophytes, gymnosperms, monocots, and dicots.
   (b) Animals. Insects, other invertebrates, amphibians, reptiles, birds, and mammals.
   (c) Decomposers.
2. The common and scientific names of the organisms should be listed on the chalkboard for reference by the entire class.
3. Your teacher will now assign you to 1 of the groups of organisms. Using field guides and other references, link your organisms to others on the list according to feeding relationships, using a chart such as the following:

Name of Organism	Eats	Is Eaten by
1		
2		
3		
etc.		

   If you can find no information about some organisms, revise the general list after conferring with others in the class.
4. Using butcher or shelf paper, construct a giant food web that includes all 100 organisms.

Part B

Using the same reference materials, modify the food web diagram to include any changes that occurred as a direct result of immigration into the area by peoples from different parts of the world, and at different times over the past 20,000 years. Your teacher will tell you in which year to end your study of the effect of immigration, but generally you do not need to consider changes occurring after about 1880.

Discussion

1. In what biome was your school 20,000 years ago?
2. Is this the same biome that exists today?
3. Briefly describe the changes in the local ecosystem that have occurred in the past 20,000 years.
4. In many parts of the United States, the ecosystem began to change when hunters from Asia followed migrating mammoths and mastodons. How did those elephantine creatures fit into food webs?
5. What effect did early hunters and gatherers have on your ecosystem?
6. How has agriculture changed it?

Figure 24.8 Early copper craftsmanship (Peru; 1100–1400 A.D.).

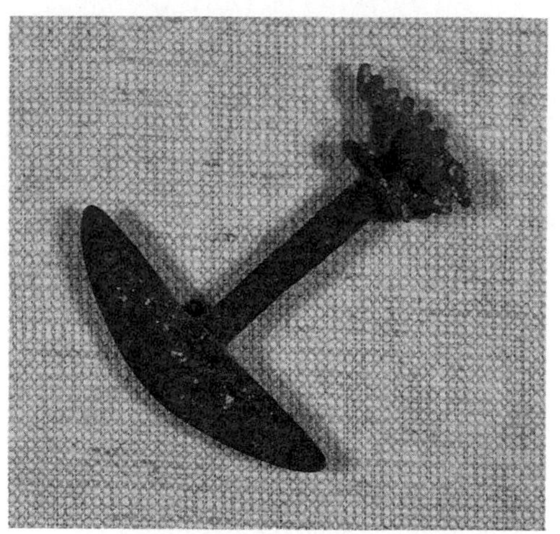

Photograph by Carolina Biological Supply Company

Figure 24.9 Roman aqueducts constructed nearly 2000 years ago.

J. Creager/VISUALS UNLIMITED

24.3 The Built Environment Helped Shape Human Culture

Even the most primitive *Homo sapiens* were skilled toolmakers. The agricultural revolution, however, created a need for many new kinds of tools. As humans shaped their new tools, they began to look at all the things in their environment as **resources,** or things they could use. Stone was originally the toolmakers' basic material. In many parts of the world, people later discovered how to use metal as well. The refining of metals required much heat. Fuels became important for toolmaking, as well as for warmth and for cooking.

All kinds of resources are not found in all places, however. Flint was an especially desirable stone used for toolmaking. Even in the Stone Age, it was traded among different groups of hunters. Trading resources helped tie distant human ecosystems together. Phoenicians from the eastern Mediterranean traded goods for tin in Britain 3000 years ago. Long before Europeans arrived in North America, Indians in what is now Alabama obtained copper from the Lake Superior region. Thus, building settlements helped to bring about travel and trade.

With the growth of trade, villages grew into towns of artisans and traders. Tools and resources made it possible for villagers to erect permanent homes and other buildings. In permanent towns, humans with more leisure time could improve the transmission of knowledge. Manuscripts and books could be preserved for use by many persons and even for many generations. Paintings and maps also could be protected and used for long periods of time. Religious objects, as well as the costumes and sets used in theater, no longer had to be completely portable.

Science, too, could grow in urban surroundings. The tools that made possible better observations could be used only after they were manufactured, and that required permanent buildings and equipment. So, technology and science evolved together.

The built environment and the technology making it possible quickly became more sophisticated. Even today, for example, bridges and aqueducts built by the ancient Romans (figure 24.9) are considered engineering feats. For all such structures, however, more and more materials and energy were taken from the natural environment.

Today, it is hard to find areas having no human-built structures. We have dammed rivers and built bridges over them. We have fenced off land for grazing animals. Mines and hydroelectric plants can be found far from cities. Even in national parks, there may be "rustic" lodges, bathrooms, and other buildings.

Figure 24.10 (a) Medieval planned community and (b) modern unplanned hodgepodge of buildings.

a J. Creager/VISUALS UNLIMITED

b Albert Copley/VISUALS UNLIMITED

In general, growth of the built environment has been unplanned. Here and there a local or national government has decreed that a master plan be used for an area. Usually, however, individuals or small groups have erected their buildings to suit their own preferences, limited only by how much land and materials they could afford. Humans have easily adapted to the built environment, and today few of us would wish to live away from some buildings and other human-made structures.

Self-Review

1. What useful behavioral adaptation is shared by humans and some insects?
2. What is a likely hypothesis concerning the beginning of agriculture?
3. How did even the most primitive built environments change the ecosystems in which they appeared?
4. How did the growth of technology aid the growth of science?

Cities and Suburbs

Guidepost: What advantages and disadvantages do urban environments have for humans?

24.4 Humans Have Created a New "Urban Biome"

Biomes such as grasslands, tundra, and deciduous forest are the products of their geography and climate. At the climax stage, each supports a distinct community of plants and animals. In contrast, a city in any biome has more in common with other cities than with the natural biome

Figure 24.11 Skylines of Denver, Colorado and Tampa, Florida. What were the original natural ecosystems and how have the cities affected those ecosystems?

Carlye Calvin

Florida Image File, Inc.

surrounding it. The skylines of Denver and Tampa (figure 24.11), for example, are much alike. But the natural ecosystems of those two areas are nothing like each other; and the two cities are nothing like their original natural surroundings.

Regardless of geography or climate, the **urban biome** tends to include maple trees and geraniums in wealthier areas and dandelions and trees of heaven (*Ailanthus glandulosa*) in poorer areas. Concrete, glass, and brick surround us; in most cities, even wood is seldom found in newer buildings because of its flammability. In the urban biome there are both more human pathogens and more means to combat them than in natural biomes. On the one hand we are exposed to many infectious diseases because of close proximity to other people, and on the other hand, modern sanitation brings plastic wrappings, insecticides, chlorinated water, germicides, mold inhibitors, and mothballs into our surroundings. These things are found in any urban biome in the United States, with only a little variation in other countries.

Urban ecosystems are largely artificial. Increasingly, building materials are neither wood nor natural stone. Food is shipped in. Garbage is shipped out. Trees are seldom those native to an area. Even weather can be modified by the urban biome. The limited number of trees and other plants allows much sunlight to reach the ground or pavement. Instead of using the sun's energy as plants do and absorbing it as soil does, concrete and glass reflect much of it, heating the air. High buildings interrupt natural air currents and create "wind tunnels." Rain and snow accumulate on concrete until they run off into gutters and sewers. The air is filled with the particles and gases of factories and automobiles.

Figure 24.12 Daily matter and energy inputs and outputs for a large U.S. city.

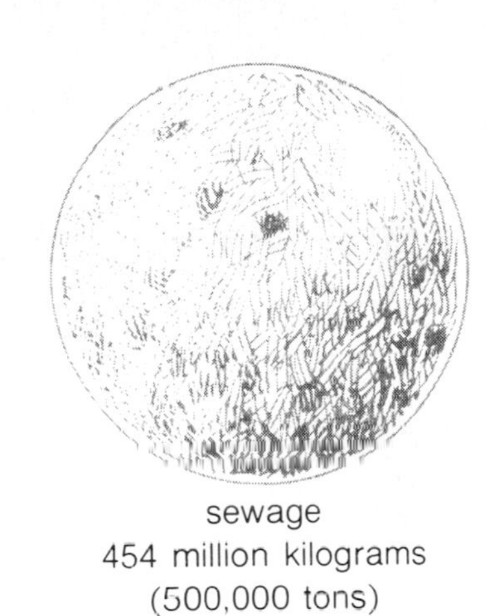

refuse
8.6 million kilograms
(2,000 tons)

Figure 24.13 Golden Gate Park, San Francisco.

Clarence Towers, San Francisco Parks & Recreation Department

Sometimes we prefer an "unnatural" environment. For example, we discourage bears and skunks from wandering into urban areas. The planned surroundings of San Francisco's Golden Gate Park (figure 24.13) probably appeal to more people than would the original sandy area. The park's combination of wooded areas, bicycle paths, museums, and music represent much of what has made cities attractive.

In many cases, however, the artificial human-shaped environment is an unwelcome barrier between humans and the natural ecosystem. In some urban areas, the only plants are unattractive weeds, and the only nonhuman animals are dogs, cats, and pests such as rats and cockroaches. Food in supermarkets may be as nourishing as that found in the country, though not as fresh; urban water supplies are often preferable to those in rural areas. However, many individuals feel that it is important to be in natural surroundings at least some of the time.

24.5 The Quality of Urban Life Has Decreased

Residents of many American cities have felt that the quality of life has declined greatly during their lifetimes. Crime, poverty, and dirt are common. This has happened for a variety of reasons, including economic recessions, poor urban planning, lack of consistent support by taxpayers for public services, and so on. The issue that is most biology related, however, is overpopulation.

Before the industrial revolution in the eighteenth century, only one person in five lived in a city having more than 10,000 residents. Since then, cities have grown quickly. In the past 100 years, especially, more and more persons in all countries have moved to the cities.

When any population reaches a size that nears the area's carrying capacity, competition for the available resources increases greatly. In a city, middle-class residents may begin moving into low-rent districts, forcing the poor to crowd together in slums. Upper-class residents, in turn, may move into middle-class areas. Public parks or golf courses may be turned into housing affordable only by the wealthy. Corner grocery and drug stores disappear, to be replaced by clothing boutiques or expensive bath shops.

As a population increases in size, there is also greater need for basic goods and services. More and more shopping centers appear, providing food and other necessities for residents. Many new shops and homes appear at the edge of the city.

The poor tend to remain in the older inner core of a city, for as a city grows and changes they are unable to move to more desirable areas. The poor are not courted by merchants, who tend to locate new stores in suburbs or near the perimeters of cities. A cycle of urban decay is estabished: the city's core becomes undesirable; wealthier persons move to the outer areas or suburbs and then fail to support services for the urban poor; and the city's core deteriorates further. Some wealthy suburbs become independent cities with their own shopping areas, universities, and other urban advantages. But in time the cycle may begin again in these new cities.

Figure 24.14 The percentage of world population living in cities in the years 1950, 1980, and the estimated percentage in the year 2000. The numbers below the pie graphs indicate total population.

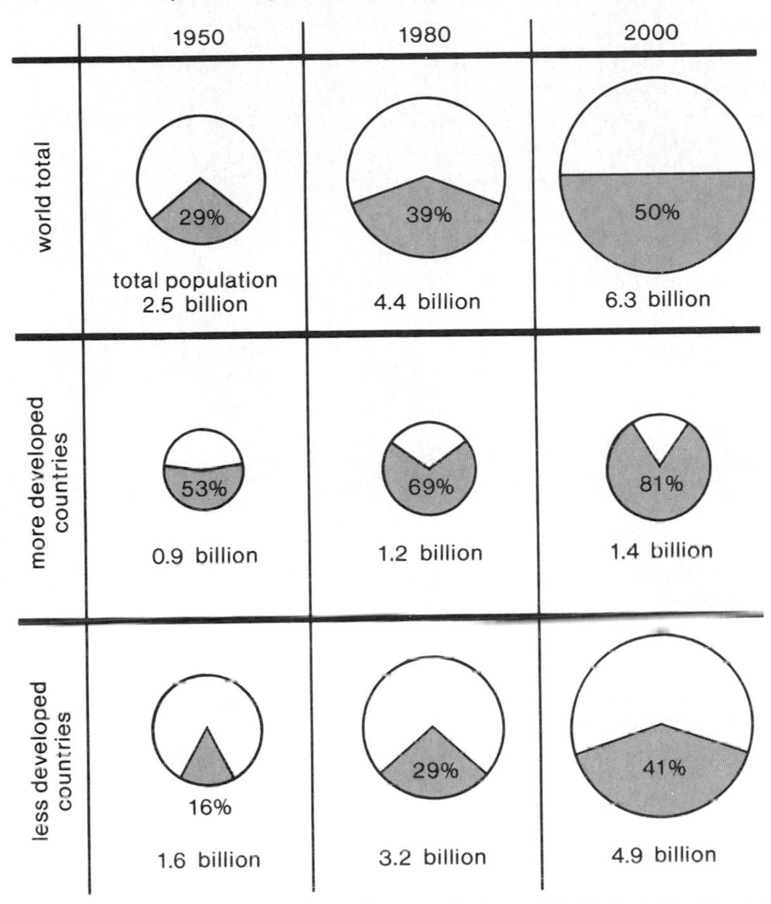

Overpopulation also can contribute to epidemics of contagious diseases. When massive immigration greatly increased the population size of many U.S. cities around 1900, diseases such as tuberculosis also spread. Crowded together in tenements (figure 24.15), people were exposed to new bacteria and often had little money for fuel and healthful food. When sanitation increased, immunizations became widespread, and workers were better paid, the incidence of contagious diseases decreased.

Many cities in other countries are more crowded and have a higher incidence of disease than cities in the United States. A combination of overpopulation and lack of resources has brought about much human misery. For instance, in 1980, about 177 million persons in cities in the developing countries did not have safe drinking water. Sanitation was inadequate for 331 million persons. In such conditions, typhoid and other diseases spread quickly.

Pollution increases with population size also. Pollution of air and water is especially evident in urban areas, where the concentration of people quickly affects the air and water. Is the water in your area polluted? Investigation 24.2 will give you an opportunity to find out.

Figure 24.15 An urban slum c. 1900. What conditions shown in this photo would contribute to the spread of disease?

American Stock Photos/TOM STACK & ASSOCIATES

Investigation 24.2 EVALUATING QUALITY OF NATURAL WATER SOURCES

Introduction

One of the major results of industrialized society and overpopulation of *Homo sapiens* on Earth has been a serious reduction in the availability of quality water sources for human consumption. In addition to preserving the availability of natural water sources, the quality of water to be used must be continuously assessed.

One criterion for evaluating the quality of water from natural sources is based on an examination of the types, variety, and abundance of certain kinds of organisms present. Another is the relative clarity of the sample. Obviously, the abundance of organisms alone can affect the clarity, but significant amounts of impurities of any kind make a sample unsafe for drinking. In this investigation you are to evaluate several water samples from diverse sources and to estimate their potential for human consumption.

Water that would be equivalent to clear mountain streams free of organic debris is considered to be pristine; there is typically diverse algal flora, relative to total biomass, because of relatively low nutrient levels. Water resulting from natural fill-in, sewage input, or fertilizer runoff would be considered to have organic enrichment; here, species diversity is moderate to low, relative to total biomass. Water from acid mine drainage, sulfur springs, or metallic or industrial pollution is said to represent inorganic enrichment; such water may be highly toxic, resulting in low diversity and low to high biomass depending on the total nutrient status. These concepts are useful in discussing the quality of water samples. It should be noted that even pristine water can contain undesirable components, such as *Entomobea histolytica*, whose waste products may give a human amoebic dysentery. Such cases are rare, however.

Materials (per class)

6 labeled water samples (from a variety of natural and human-made habitats)
large pipets in each sample

(per team)
compound microscope
slides
coverslips
6 small test tubes, approx 13 mm × 100 mm
Pasteur pipet
light source

Procedure

Part A—Determining Clarity

1. Pipet a subsample from each of the water samples into a test tube, nearly filling it. Label each test tube by sample source.
2. Estimate the relative clarity of each sample. This is done by lining all the test tubes up against a light source in a holder so that the tubes are between you and the light source. Be sure that the amount of light is the same on each tube. View each sample in a straight line extending from the light source to your eye. Arrange the tubes in order from the clearest to the least clear. Record the results of your clarity analysis.

Part B—Determining Abundance and Diversity of Organisms

The following are guidelines for water quality based on the types, diversity, and relative abundance of organisms in each sample.

As a general rule, when water sources become increasingly enriched organically, they support a greater total biomass.

Low diversity of organisms in a sample suggests contaminated water and high diversity suggests cleaner water.

Four major groups of organisms are important in determining water quality: diatoms, green algae, cyanobacteria, and flagellates.

(a) Green algae and diatoms, in the absence of cyanobacteria and flagellates, suggest clean water.
(b) Cyanobacteria and flagellates (with or without diatoms and green algae) indicate higher levels of organic (nutrient) materials.

1. Use the Catalog of Living Things (appendix 3) and additional materials your teacher will provide to identify the 4 groups of organisms.
2. Depending on available time, use 1 of the following methods to determine the relative abundance of organisms in your sample:
   (a) Qualitative method (if there is very limited time). Examine 3 different drops from each sample (selected at random) and determine using your own criterion whether a given group of organisms in the sample is very abundant, somewhat abundant, present in moderate numbers, or scarce. Make a decision about which of these categories best describes each species present in the sample. A rather loose definition of species can be adopted here, that is, a group of organisms which appear very similar may be considered as 1 species.
   (b) Quantitative method (if there is time to be more precise). Actually count the number of individuals of each species (loosely defined) in 3 different drops of each sample. Average the 3 readings. A sampling procedure such as described in past investigations may be necessary.

Discussion

1. Based on your analysis of the samples, arrange them from what you feel are most to least drinkable.
2. Identify those from which you would probably drink.
3. Name several other factors that also should be considered when estimating water quality.
4. How would those factors be assessed?
5. What methods could be employed to make more accurate estimations of the factors you used here?
6. Most of the factors that influence the suitability of water for human consumption deal with pollutants. To what degree has *Homo sapiens* been responsible for this pollution?
7. In what ways do humans pollute the water on earth?
8. Suggest some ways that we can guarantee that enough water of the quality necessary for human consumption will be available for future generations.

24.6 Similar Cities Are Surrounded by Similar Suburbs

The modern American landscape has been shaped largely by the automobile. Widespread suburbs are possible only because each suburban family has at least one car. Railroads once were the leading movers of food and manufactured goods to city dwellers. Today, trucks deliver food and manufactured goods to widely scattered homes and shopping malls.

The shift from urban to suburban living has caused a demand for a large, complex highway system. That system requires space, as we have seen in chapter 2. Beneath the highways alone lie more than 8 million hectares of land. That land cannot be used to grow crops, although much of it was once prime farmland.

A second consequence of the population shift has been the shift of light industry from the cities to the suburbs. Most of these low, rambling factories (figure 24.17) are built on what was once productive farmland. These industries also must be served by highways.

Figure 24.16 Freeway with heavy traffic. Besides the loss of land on which to build the highways, what other effects does this method of transportation have on the environment?

David M. Doody/TOM STACK & ASSOCIATES

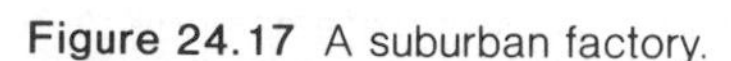

Figure 24.17 A suburban factory.

BSCS by Doug Sokell

Figure 24.18 The sameness of suburban homes.

Linda Kelly Hassett

Like the urban biome, the suburban biome is almost independent of the natural ecosystem around it. "Colonial" and "Californian" suburban homes may be seen anywhere from Oregon to Florida, and nearly all suburban factories look alike. The ecosystem is simplified and modified considerably from the natural biome.

Self-Review

1. In what ways would the urban biome be similar in Chicago and Los Angeles?
2. In what ways do cities affect weather?
3. How can overpopulation contribute to epidemics?
4. How does overpopulation increase pollution?

Agriculture

Guidepost: Compared with other human activities, what is the relative impact of agriculture on natural biomes?

24.7 Agriculture has Reduced the Variety of Plant Species

Like cities and suburbs, modern farms are built environments to some extent. Farm buildings, irrigation pipes, and farm equipment are essential parts of today's agriculture. The agricultural revolution brought about a shift in the role of humans in the biosphere. Before that, humans had been merely members of biotic communities. Since then they began changing and simplifying those communities.

Figure 24.19 Irrigated rice fields in California.

Dennis Paulson/VISUALS UNLIMITED

Figure 24.20 An example of monoculture. Sunflowers are the only crop grown on this Ohio farm.

David Newman/VISUALS UNLIMITED

With the coming of agriculture, natural biomes began to be transformed. Humans removed native plants to make space, and to reduce competition for plants that could be used as food for humans or as fodder for food animals. In some cases the abiotic parts of ecosystems also are modified for agriculture. Rice requires a warm, wet climate. Yet it is grown in some rather dry areas, such as northern California. Water must be piped in for irrigation of the rice fields.

Farmers usually find that marketing one large crop is more profitable than marketing many small ones. All the farmer's resources can be directed to that one crop. By growing only potatoes, for example, a farmer's profit can be maximized; and the farmer's income can be used to buy other foods and manufactured goods. Similarly, the farmer might grow only one variety of crop. Such concentration on a single kind of crop is called **monoculture.** For example, though once there were many varieties of apples for sale, now only a few kinds are available in most stores. The Delicious variety of apple is grown by many farmers because it is attractive and resists plant diseases. Many people find this variety of apple tasteless compared to the older varieties, such as Winesaps and Jonathans. Yet, Winesaps and Jonathans are hard to find, and, because of monoculture, the Delicious is everywhere.

Monoculture presents more serious problems. Fungal and bacterial diseases of plants can spread quickly through large areas where the hosts are available and where the ecosystem has been modified for those hosts and whatever depends on them. Also, many crops use up the soil's nitrates and phosphates quickly. Only if those crops are alternated with others having nitrogen-fixing and other bacteria will those substances be put back in the soil naturally.

Figure 24.21 A cotton crop ready for harvest.

Dick George/TOM STACK & ASSOCIATES

Figure 24.22 The "dust bowl" of the American midwest in the 1930s (Morton County, Kansas).

Soil Conservation Service USDA

24.8 Agriculture Has Affected United States History

At a site in Pennsylvania called Meadowcroft, archaeologists have found squash seeds and popcorn cobs left there in about 350 B.C. The Indians who settled in that area must have done some farming, but it probably affected the natural ecosystem very little. The people hunted deer, wild turkey, and other animals, and they gathered hackberries and nuts. Even that effect on the Meadowcroft environment was temporary, though. By the time Europeans reached the area in the eighteenth century, it was deserted.

European settlers soon began farming the rich lands of the United States. For example, tobacco and cotton have been major crops in the United States throughout its history. However, both crops exhaust the topsoil of its nitrogen. Most topsoil is less than 20 cm thick. If plantings of tobacco and cotton are not alternated with crops of legumes, the soil eventually becomes useless for farming. Much of the topsoil is gone, and **erosion** (wearing away) by wind and water removes the remaining soil. Many small farmers who had worn out their soil by growing tobacco or cotton were forced to move westward before the Civil War.

Farther west, much land was suitable only for grazing, not for farming. In the late nineteenth century, new machinery and new irrigation methods made it possible to use the land for growing crops. Eventually that topsoil, too, began to erode.

In the late 1920s, drought added to the earlier problems, and wind began to blow away the remaining topsoil. Topsoil was blown for hundreds of miles, and finally was washed into the oceans. After a few years the area that was left without its topsoil became a huge "dust bowl" where nothing could grow. Again, many farmers moved farther west, this time to California.

Figure 24.23 (a) "Silicon Valley" California now, and (b) as it was only a few years ago—orchards.

a San Jose Historical Museum

b David Newman/VISUALS UNLIMITED

Some of the land along the West Coast is still wilderness, but much has been converted for agricultural use. Some of the farmland has been further converted to housing developments and shopping malls. In California, what was once one of the most productive orchard areas in the country is now called "Silicon Valley," because it is filled with computer factories, which produce silicon computer chips, and allied businesses.

Federal legislation affecting agriculture was passed during the early years of this century and during the dust bowl years of the 1930s. For example, farmers are often paid not to plant their land if planting will make the soil less fertile, or if an excess of their usual crop has accumulated. Other federal and state laws require inspection of food processing plants for health violations and of farms to ensure the control of diseases of farm animals. Such laws have become even more necessary as small family farms have become huge "agribusinesses." The farms of today may be thousands of acres in area and involve the use of large amounts of energy, water, and other resources.

The progression—natural ecosystem to agricultural land to ruined or paved-over land—continues nearly everywhere on earth. It is the inevitable effect of unchecked human population growth. The progression could be greatly slowed by combining careful use of land with a halt in population growth.

Figure 24.24 Family farms (a) are being replaced by large-scale agribusiness (b), often managed by corporations.

Kevin Magee/TOM STACK & ASSOCIATES

a

BSCS by Doug Sokell

b

Self-Review

1. In what way has agriculture affected natural variation in plant species?
2. What is monoculture, and what are its disadvantages?
3. How have agricultural practices led to loss of topsoil?

Future Ecosystems

Guidepost: What changes are desirable or possible in human-dominated ecosystems?

24.9 Planning Can Help Determine the Quality of Life in Cities

Time for correcting our past mistakes is running out. In many parts of the world, biomes have been permanently changed to deserts or urban wastelands. But there is still some wilderness left; there is still farmland that can be restored or used as is; there are still some livable cities.

One approach to the problem involves *urban planning.* Architects, ecologists, and other specialists can help city officials and urban planners determine the future appearance and functioning of their areas.

Cities can be planned to harmonize with the natural ecosystem, not to be artificial biomes that grow uncontrollably. For example, cities can plant **native trees** (trees found in the area's successional stages or its climax community). Such trees help a city reflect the area's natural biome, give the city an individual character, and resist the problems caused by climate and pollution. Palm trees and tropical plants are appropriate for cities such as Honolulu, but not for many cities in California and Florida.

Figure 24.25 Volunteers planting native trees in a city.

San Francisco Friends of the Urban Forest

Biology Today C

City Forester

Ron Morrow is the city forester for Colorado Springs, a job that includes caring for the city's trees, flower beds and greenhouses. He also is a private forestry consultant and shows homeowners how to care for their trees.

Ron has been interested in the outdoors since he was a child and he majored in forest science in college. His main focus was forest pathology—the study of insects and diseases that affect trees. After obtaining his master's degree he worked in timber management and as an interpreter in the Coronado National Forest in Arizona.

He became city forester 10 years ago and has been responsible for maintaining the trees and flowers in new and existing parks and other city-owned land. He also has developed and implemented many new and innovative plans. The care of trees involves maintenance and disease control. Recently trimmed trees are more vigorous and less susceptible than untrimmed trees to damage from wind and snow loads. It also is necessary to ensure that the trees do not obstruct street signs or interfere with power lines. About 80,000 trees along the city streets and 20,000 trees in the parks are individually maintained. If diseased trees are found, and spraying pesticide is ineffective, the trees (both living and dead) must be cut down and buried. Any trees that die naturally are examined for wildlife nesting signs,

BSCS by Doug Sokell

City of Colorado Springs

and if the tree is not a hazard to people, it is tagged as a "wildlife tree" and allowed to remain in place.

All of the trees on city property are recorded on a computer. Information on the type of tree, its height, diameter, condition, and value is readily available. Soon the computer also will store information concerning the history of the tree and any treatment it has received.

Ron is in charge of 22 full-time employees and 10 to 20 seasonal employees for the forestry and greenhouse divisions. There are four city greenhouses that produce about 120,000 plants and flowers for more than 195 flower beds throughout the city. The greenhouse division also is responsible for the planting and maintenance of a formal garden. Ron personally initiated a native and drought tolerant plant demonstration garden in cooperation with a local horticulture group.

New ordinances Ron has helped develop include one that requires developers to maintain a certain amount of "green space" in each new project. Another ordinance requires that a certain number of trees be planted and maintained in parking lots. The number of trees planted depends on the number of parking spaces.

Ron feels that urban forests and urban parks are very important. Not only do they add to the beauty of a city, but they provide valuable habitat for many different animals, and the trees also serve as wind breaks. Ron feels that a city can grow and still be attractive to people and other animals. He says that trees and parks are important to mental health: "You get out, see open space and wildlife, and you feel better."

Figure 24.26 Small urban park in an apartment complex.

Sybil Shelton/PETER ARNOLD, INC.

Urban planning for new buildings can include reserving some land for parks and other open spaces. In many cities a certain amount of open space must be provided around any new building that is constructed. Even a small park such as the one in figure 24.26 can add greatly to reducing noise, allowing air circulation, and increasing the livability of an area. Larger parks can provide common "lawns" for many people who live in apartments. By sharing facilities in parks, people can use smaller amounts of space and other resources per person.

Even when urban planning limits growth within city borders and creates a livable environment for the city residents, there are problems with the surrounding environment. Suburbs may draw wealthier residents out of the city, beginning the cycle of urban decay described earlier. Suburbs may replace good farmland, and farmland may then replace wilderness.

Transportation is a major problem in most urban areas. Workers may spend hours every day traveling to and from their jobs or visiting customers and clients. Some cities have begun providing better public transportation, making it easier and faster for commuters to get to work. Unfortunately, many persons cannot or will not use public transportation. In some cases, however, new rapid-transit systems are *too* popular: their suburban parking lots fill up early, and many persons who would prefer to use public transportation are forced to drive to work instead.

Figure 24.27 Many urban areas utilize public transportation to ease highway congestion and reduce air pollution. The BART (Bay Area Rapid Transit) system shown here serves the San Francisco metropolitan area.

San Francisco Bay Area Rapid Transit District

Ultimately population growth can override the best plans to live within the environment. If births and immigration bring about a large increase in the human population in any area, something has to give—space for parks, for example. For that reason, urban planning is unlikely to succeed unless it is accompanied by control of population size. The problems of urban populations may increase by the end of the century. At that time two-thirds of the earth's human population will be living in cities or 100,000 or more.

24.10 Agriculture Can Be Integrated with Natural Ecosystems

Agriculture originally fit into natural ecosystems. It did not seriously interrupt the cycles of carbon and other nutrients. Plants were grown where the soil and climate were appropriate for those plants. Yields were fairly small, and not too many of the nutrients in the soil were converted into plant material. Human and animal wastes were used as fertilizer for the soil, returning much of the nitrogen and phosphorous.

As farming has become more widespread and complex, however, those relationships have changed. Intensive farming methods deplete nutrients in the soil. Farming is carried on in dry areas by means of irrigation. When topsoil is not rich enough to produce high yields, artificial fertilizers are added to the soil. Because these are added in large quantities at the soil surface, rain or irrigation water often washes them into nearby waterways, creating water pollution (figure 24.29). We also increase yields by using pesticides to kill insects and plant pathogens, but these may enter food webs. In chapter 3 you saw the effect of DDT on birds' eggshells, and the indirect effect on humans of DDT used in Borneo.

Agriculture has a destructive effect on most biomes, because the ecosystem is modified and simplified greatly. In many tropical areas, slash-and-burn agriculture is destroying thousands of acres of forests. The forests are cut to clear land for planting, and then farming destroys the soil within a few years.

Ecologists have made various suggestions to lessen the impact of agriculture on the biosphere. We can use organic fertilizers, such as cattle manure, instead of artificial ones. We can plant a variety of crops in an area, in place of monoculture. Crops can be chosen to match the natural biome, making less irrigation and fertilization necessary. Consumers can demand fewer out-of-season products and eat "lower on the food chain." The lessened use of pesticides, such as DDT, has already had a beneficial effect on some birds of prey. In 1975, the bald eagle was present in only 39 states; today it can be sighted in every state except Hawaii. Other rare birds of prey, also, have grown in number.

Such measures can help somewhat. Ultimately, though, like urban planning, they cannot offset the demands of a burgeoning human population.

Figure 24.28 Patterns formed by fields watered by center-pivot irrigation systems.

DeKalb-Pfizer Genetics

Figure 24.30 Slash and burn agriculture in the Brazilian rainforest.

G. Prance/VISUALS UNLIMITED

Figure 24.29 Artificial fertilizers containing phosphorus often cause water pollution. Two basins of a lake were separated by a plastic curtain. Phosphorus, carbon, and nitrogen were added to the far basin; only carbon and nitrogen were added to the near basin. Within two months the far basin had developed the heavy algal bloom characteristic of polluted water.

From D. W. Schindler, "Eutrophication and Recovery in Experimental Lakes: Implications for Lake Management." *Science*, Vol. 184, pp. 897–898, 22 October 1974. Copyright 1974 by the AAAS.

Figure 24.31 Wise agricultural practices, such as contour farming, can reduce soil erosion. This farmer has allowed perennial grasses to grow in areas most susceptible to erosion.

Tim McCabe, Soil Conservation Service USDA

Figure 24.32 Unspoiled wilderness. Why is it important that areas such as this be preserved in their natural condition?

Doug Sokell

24.11 Humans Must Act to Preserve the Biosphere

Humans have had a tendency to try to "conquer" nature. As we have learned more about interrelationships in the biosphere, however, we have come to realize the danger of that approach.

We are an integral part of nature. In thoughtlessly trying to subdue it, we ignore all the principles of ecology that are outlined in this book. We cannot ignore those principles forever. Our failure to heed them comes back to haunt us as polluted lakes and rivers, ruined farmland, and overcrowded cities.

Unlike other organisms, humans can and do modify the environment to meet their own needs. That singular ability implies a special obligation. We must remember that we share this fragile planet with countless other organisms. Rather than trying to conquer nature, we must learn to coexist with it. We can cooperate to preserve it, if we understand the basic principles of ecology.

Each one of us is a part of the biosphere, and we are here for only a short time. We can never really "own" any piece of land. We are only *stewards,* caring for the biosphere until someone replaces us. We have an obligation to our successors—of all species—to preserve the environment in which we live.

Self-Review

1. What are the advantages of using native trees in a city?
2. How does agriculture often lead to water pollution?
3. How might we lessen the impact of agriculture on the biosphere?

Summary

The earliest humans changed the biosphere little, living within it much like other primates. With tools and social behavior, however, our ancestors began to adapt environments to make them more hospitable to humans. Renewable and nonrenewable resources were used to make buildings and tools. The agricultural revolution greatly increased the impact of humans on their surroundings, simplifying the variety of plant life and leading to trading of resources between different geographic areas. Today agriculture and the built environment have shaped most of the biosphere to human uses. Because of population growth, many urban areas are crowded, and there is competition for resources. Urban and rural planning may alleviate some problems if population growth is checked also.

Application Questions

1. What social behaviors common to chimpanzees and humans have had an adaptive advantage in the evolution of the two groups, and why?
2. In what ways have automobiles contributed to the human impact on the biosphere?
3. The oldest fossil evidence of humans at the Meadowcroft site (p. 911) is about 19,000 years old. How does that fact contradict some established ideas about human migration to this hemisphere?
4. How does annual crop rotation—the alternation of crops such as corn with leguminous plants such as soybeans—aid the soil?
5. If Americans ate more corn muffins and less corn-fed beef, what would be the effect on corn consumption and production?

Problems

1. Find out about the plant disease called potato blight. How did it help bring about the immigration of many Irish persons to the United States?
2. What native trees might be used in cities in your area? What advantages and disadvantages would each kind have? Should many trees of the same species be used in the same area, or should mixtures of species be used together? Explain your answer.
3. Brackish estuaries are sometimes declared wildlife sanctuaries. They are seldom scenic areas or suitable for picnics, and local industries may find the sanctuary a nuisance. What reasons can you give for saving this kind of habitat?
4. Find out how genetic engineering is being used to produce crops that are resistant to disease, pests, or environmental stress.

Suggested Readings

A. A. Boraiko, "The Pesticide Dilemma" *National Geographic* (February 1980). Examines the dangers to humans of widespread pesticide use.

W. H. Jordan, Jr., "Invasion of the Medfly" *Natural History* (May 1982). Unconventional methods may be necessary to battle this destructive insect.

D. Pimentel and M. Pimentel, "The Risks of Pesticides" *Natural Science* (March 1979). Discusses the possible alternatives to chemical pesticides.

Scientific American (September 1976). The entire issue deals with food and agriculture in North America and worldwide.

A. W. Spirn, 1984, *The Granite Garden: Urban Nature and Human Design* (New York: Basic Books). Interesting discussion of the urban environmental interactions of air, earth, water and energy.

L. Tangley, "The Urban Ecologist" *BioScience* (February 1986). Discusses how ecologists conduct their field research on a variety of organisms living in our cities and suburbs.

G. F. White, "Environment" *Science* (4 July 1980). Contrasts traditional resource management and preservation with the new perspectives that will be necessary in the future.

F. Stuart Westmorland/TOM STACK & ASSOCIATES

Spaceship Earth at Epcot Center, Florida. Will future dwellings look like this?

CHAPTER 25

Humankind in the Future

Introduction

Early in this century, science fiction writers and artists tried to imagine what humans would be like in future stages of evolution. They assumed that humans in the distant future would need tremendous knowledge and calculating ability and, therefore, ever larger brains. Thus humans of the future were sometimes pictured with large, bulging heads on small, wasted bodies. Their uniquely human attributes would increase, and their animal characteristics would decrease.

How have such predictions changed? What have we learned about environmental selection and about human evolution? In this final chapter, we will take a more realistic look at humans of the future not separated from the biosphere, but woven firmly into broad patterns of life.

Figure 25.1 One student's conception of what future humans will look like. What do you think?

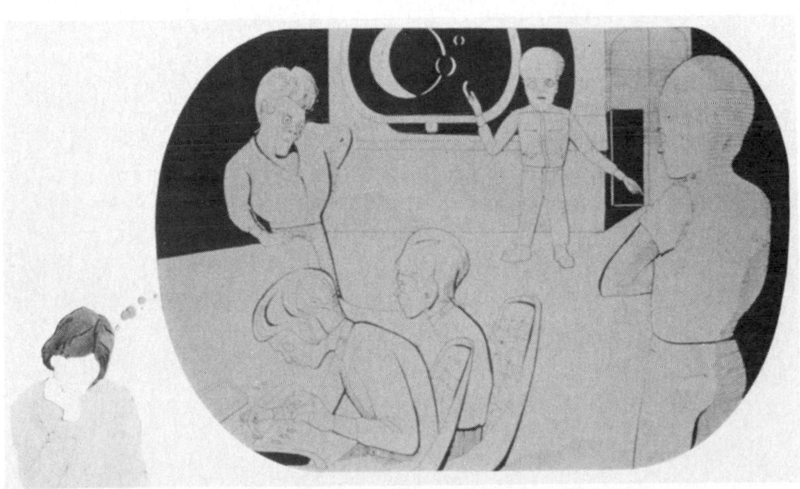

Guidepost: Is our behavior a result of "nature" or "nurture?"

Human Biology and Behavior

25.1 Human Social Behavior May Be Innate

Though the human brain is a most impressive organ, it contains no unique structure that sets it apart from a chimpanzee's. In fact, the basic divisions of all vertebrate brains, from fish to human, are the same as shown here in figure 25.2, and also in figure 17.12 on page 619. The major difference in the human brain is an expansion and greater folding of the cerebrum.

Figure 25.2 Brains of animals in five vertebrate classes. Olfactory bulbs are related to odor. Optic lobes are related to sight. The pituitary is not part of the brain. From these examples, what generalizations about brains in vertebrates can you make? Note the size comparisons. Compare these with the human brain in figure 17.12, page 619.

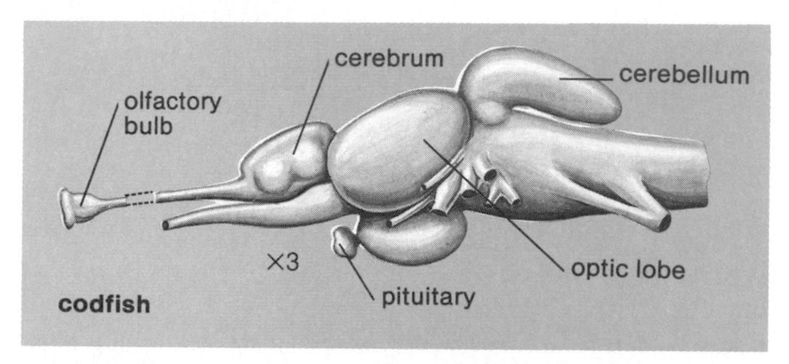

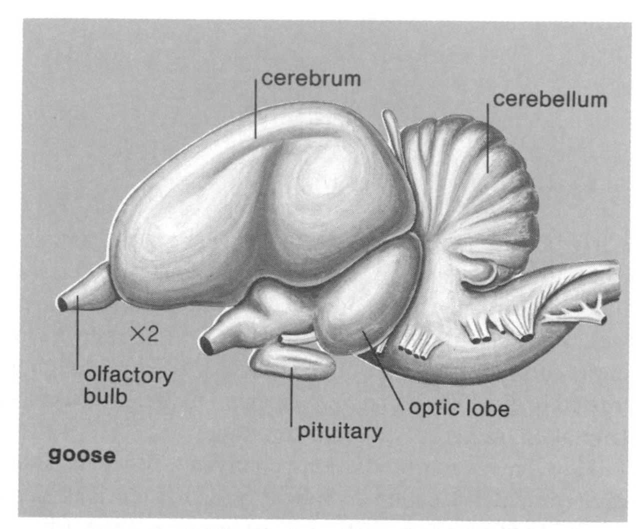

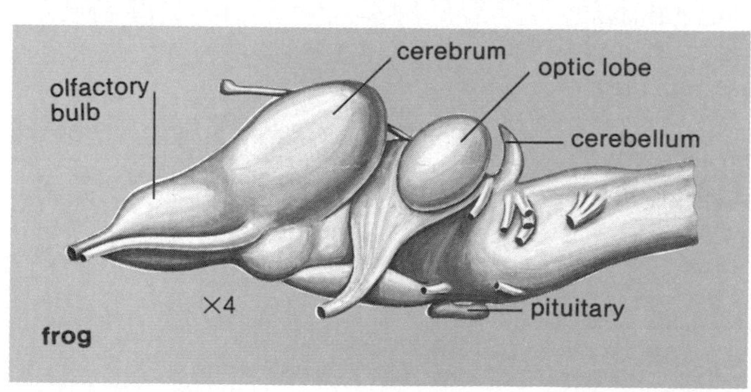

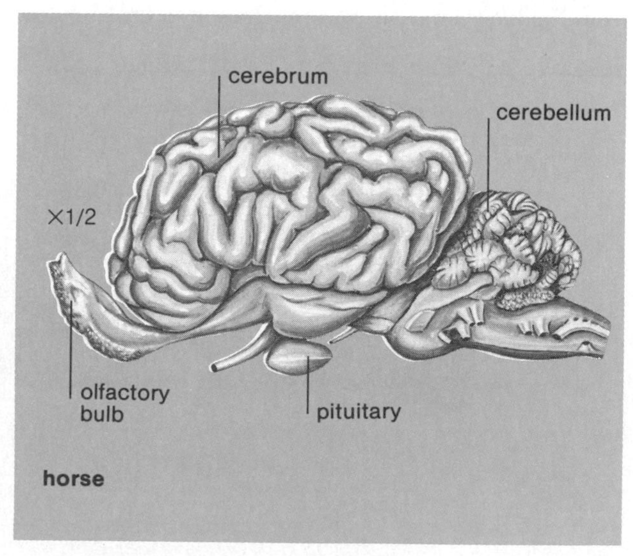

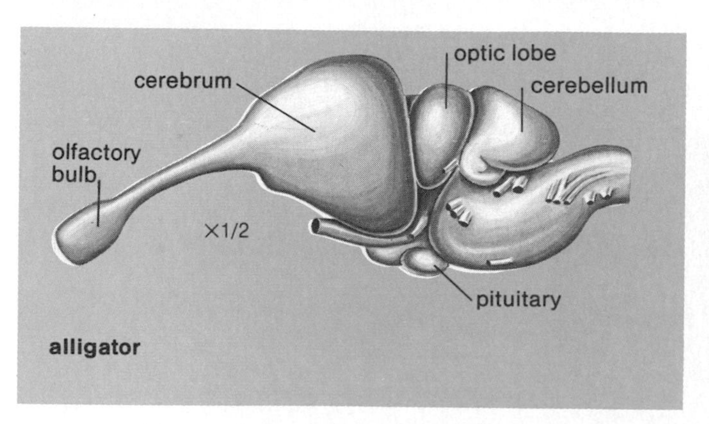

Although humans have the ability to think, and a great deal of our behavior is learned, we probably still have considerable innate (inborn, or genetic) behavior. Studies show that much of animal behavior is innate. Songbirds, for example, sing the songs of their species without ever hearing them. Apparently, only local song "dialects" are learned.

Certainly human babies exhibit some innate behaviors, such as smiling, grasping, and clinging. But no one knows how much of an adult's behavior is innate and how much is learned.

How can we explain **altruistic** (al troo IS tik), or unselfish, behavior that might be harmful to the performer? For example, a female killdeer sensing a predator near her nest will act as if she has a broken wing (figure 25.4). By moving away from the nest (which is on the ground), she lures the predator away from her young. If her "acting" is too realistic she may be caught by the predator. Then both mother and orphaned young will die. Evidently this does not happen often. The altruistic behavior of the mother birds saves more offspring than would survive if killdeer did not possess this innate behavioral drive.

Genes for altruism are selected for if more of the genes survive in offspring than are lost by the death of the mother. Each child shares half of its genes with its mother. For any gene, the evolutionary result of losing two children is the same as losing one mother. If an altruistic gene results in the loss of only one mother per five offspring saved, that gene will be selected for. Thus, the trait of altruism survives.

Figure 25.3 A baby displaying innate behavior.

25.2 Human Social Behavior May Be Learned

Biologists who study mainly social groups, including the effects of selection on them, are called **sociobiologists** (SO see oh by OL uh jists). They think that human behavior is determined largely by our genes.

Figure 25.4 A female killdeer exhibiting altruistic behavior. By pretending to be injured, she can lure a predator away from her nestlings.

Jeff Foott

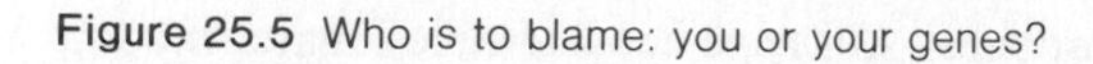

Figure 25.5 Who is to blame: you or your genes?

Other scientists believe that all human behavior is learned. They think that individuals who act altruistically do so because they have been taught that behavior. Similarly, they think selfish individuals have been taught to be selfish. These biologists argue that sociobiology defends **genetic determinism.** That is the idea that an individual's traits (characteristics) are determined mostly by his or her genes, with little or no influence from the environment. Such inherited traits would include intelligence and personality. What might be the results if society were organized on the basis of that assumption?

Which is more important, genes or environment? Many biologists think the debate is somewhat pointless, because it is difficult to separate the two in any meaningful way. That is especially true for complex traits such as intelligence. It is unlikely that an experiment can ever settle the question, because no control can be devised. In this case, a control would be a person who was isolated at birth from contact with other humans. Such an experiment would, of course, violate our rules of **ethics** (ETH iks), or principles of conduct (and ethical behavior itself may be innate or learned).

25.3 Human Social Behavior Has Important Consequences

Whether human altruism is hereditary or learned, we sometimes make great sacrifices for each other. Whether selfish behavior is hereditary or learned, we sometimes behave selfishly. Regardless of its origin, human behavior has certain consequences. If we make war, we are likely to be killed. If we overpopulate the world, we are likely to die in a famine. Even if making war and babies is "in our genes," we can be taught the negative consequences. Even if selfishness is hereditary, we can learn to help other people at some cost to ourselves.

As you have already learned, the consequences of some human activities degrade our environment. If we act without thinking, we may proceed mindlessly to destroy our environment. But we can see the consequences of our actions, and in this case we can see that destroying the human environment is actually self-destruction.

The environment does not "know" *why* we behave in certain ways; it selects organisms according to their adaptations. Psychologist B. F. Skinner has called that process selection by consequences. If we are to survive and pass on our genes to our descendants, we need to assess the consequences of our behavior in terms of selection.

Self-Review

1. Distinguish between innate and learned behavior.
2. How might genes for altruism be selected for?
3. What could be some environmental consequences of "selfish" human behavior?

Investigation 25.1 VIEWS OF EARTH FROM AFAR

Introduction

Aerial photos give the "big picture" of what is happening in an area. In addition, the use of infrared film and computer imaging make it possible to find out about events that are not visible to the naked eye. Infrared film is sensitive to heat. Consequently, photos of objects giving off heat are dark on black-and-white infrared film, or show up as a different color in color infrared photos. Some color prints show warmer areas as green; others show them as red. In either case, the color contrast with cooler areas is striking.

Aerial photos may show a broad view of a city and the surrounding area. Or, sensing devices on a satellite orbiting Earth may provide information about a large portion of the planet. The data collected from many adjoining areas by cameras and other sensing devices on NASA's LANDSAT satellite are transmitted (in a mathematical code) to a land station. There a computer translates the code and draws composite maps showing the temperature or other characteristics of large areas.

In addition to these methods of studying the earth from long distance in space, new methods are being introduced for studying events after long periods of time. For example, some scientists are now examining 19th-century instruments that were used for navigation and other purposes. Because the instruments were tightly sealed, they still contain air from the time when they were sealed. The air can be analyzed for comparison with modern air.

In this investigation you will see how some modern technology is being applied to investigating a current environmental problem.

Figure 25.6

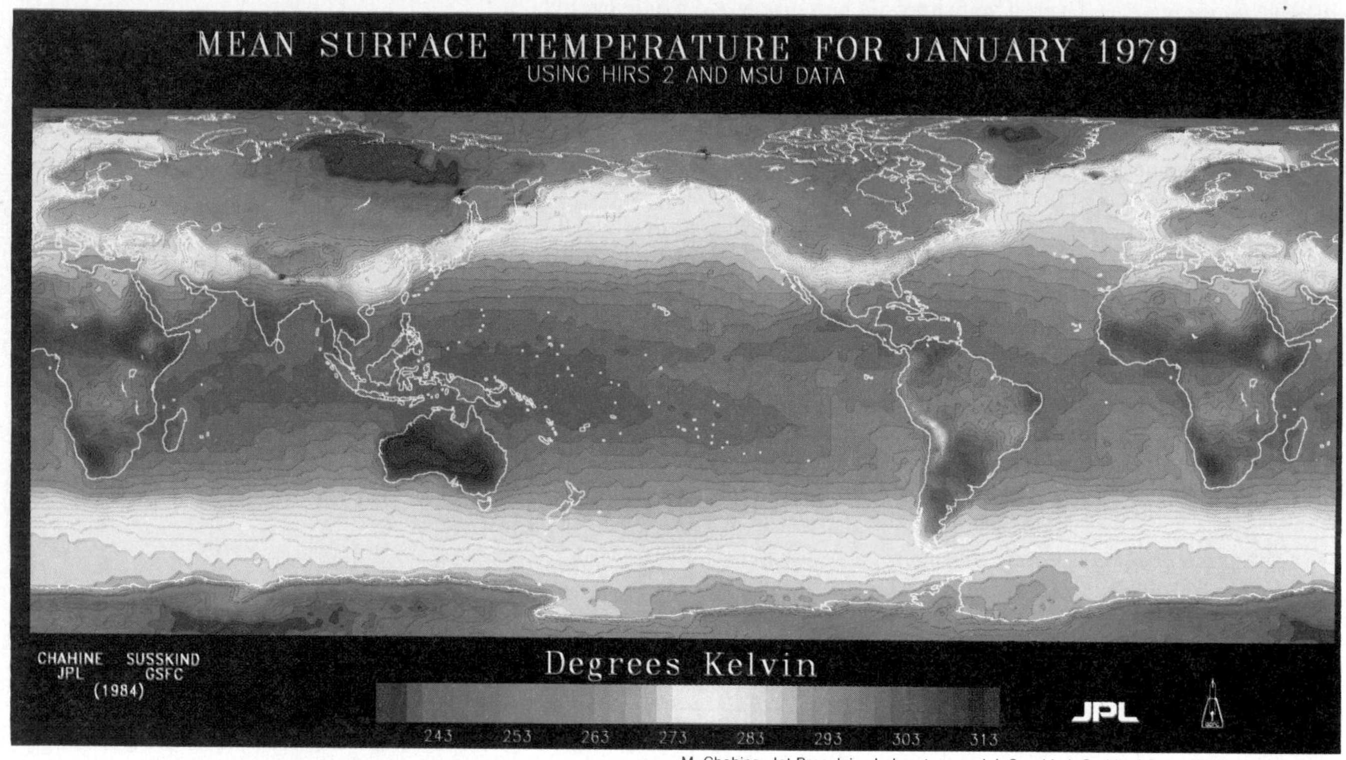

M. Chahine, Jet Propulsion Laboratory, and J. Susskind, Goddard Space Flight Center, NASA.

Table 25.1 Change in atmospheric CO_2 in Hawaii

Year	Average Annual CO_2 Level (ppm)
1958	315
1960	317
1962	318
1964	319
1966	321
1968	322
1970	324
1972	326
1974	331
1976	333
1978	335

Procedure

1. Examination of old "airs" in sealed instruments may show results similar to those given in table 25.1. These data were collected in Hawaii, and similar data have been collected in other areas.
   (a) Between 1958 and 1978, by what percent did the proportion of carbon dioxide in Hawaii's air change, and in which direction did it change?
   (b) If that trend is typical of industrial America in general, by what percent has the atmospheric level of carbon dioxide increased in the last 100 years?
2. Study the maps shown in figure 25.6, which were produced by a computer from satellite data.
   (a) What color has been used for your area for January? For May?
   (b) What do those colors indicate in terms of temperatures?
3. Study the aerial photo of the Vermont forest (figure 25.7). In this film, healthy trees appear green and damaged trees appear red. In areas west of this forest, industries are producing acid rain and other forms of air pollution.

Discussion

1. What is the general trend in atmospheric concentration of carbon dioxide from 1958 to 1978?
2. How might that trend be related to acid rain? To air pollution in general?
3. During the last 100 years, measurements taken around the world show that the mean global temperature has risen 0.4° C. What is the relationship between the level of atmospheric carbon dioxide and temperature?

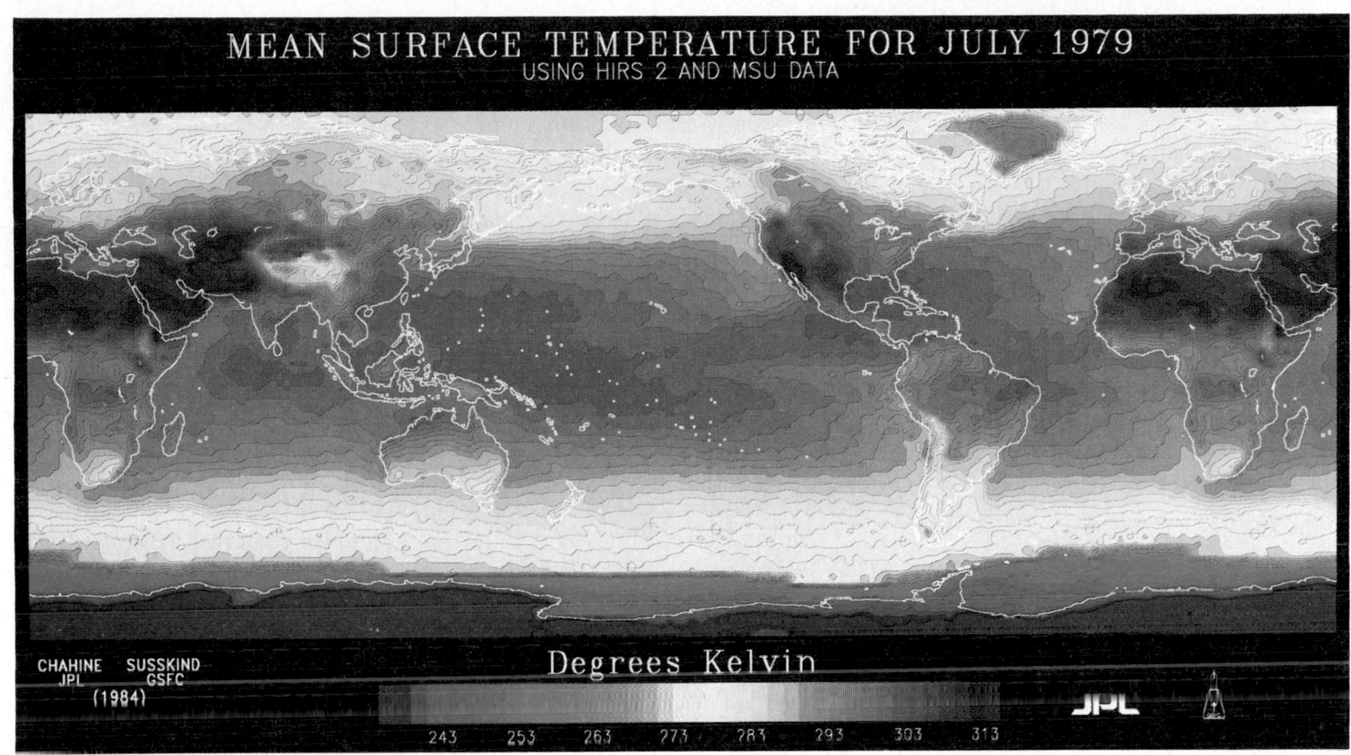

M. Chahine, Jet Propulsion Laboratory, and J. Susskind, Goddard Space Flight Center, NASA.

Figure 25.7

Jet Propulsion Laboratory, California Institute of Technology, under contract with the National Aeronautics & Space Administration.

4. If the trend represented by table 25.1 continues, what colors (temperatures) might be used in a map of your area 100 years from now? How might the food web in your area change as a result of a change in temperature?
5. What cause-and-effect relationship, if any, is demonstrated here?

Guidepost: What kinds of issues may affect the environment?

Major Issues in Human Ecology

25.4 Social Issues Can Affect the Human Environment

Many important and complex issues affect the human environment. Americans have diverse views on those issues. In addition, the opinions of society often change over time. For example, the 1973 *Roe* v. *Wade* Supreme Court decision affirmed that only a woman and her doctor have the right to decide whether the woman may have an abortion during the first six months of pregnancy. That decision has come under increasing attack in the 1980s. Those who oppose the decision feel that the fetus is already a person whose right to life outweighs other considerations. Some people in the "right to life" movement feel that even contraceptive methods that act by destroying the zygote are wrong. Those who support *Roe* v. *Wade* feel that the pregnant woman has a right to decide what will happen with her own body.

Another social issue is the problem of poverty. Though not as critical in the United States as in countries with fewer resources, poverty affects many here as well. A 1985 report by the Physicians Task Force on Hunger stated that up to 20 million Americans are chronically underfed. In recent years, poverty has affected a growing number of young persons. Many children and young adults have too little food, or are undernourished. Experts in child development fear that this might lead to permanent intellectual impairment, especially for very young children.

Can this poverty be relieved in the future? Many persons feel that the vast resources in the United States can be shared and that the answer to poverty is a redistribution of wealth. Others maintain that as the population expands, the ultimate effect of such redistribution would be poverty for everyone.

25.5 Americans Are Trying to Protect the Environment

In the United States, we have gone through several periods of environmental crises. As we have seen the wilderness disappearing, the topsoil eroding, and birds being poisoned by pesticides, we have demanded legislation to govern such waste. Our concern has led to laws such as the Pure Food and Drug Act (1906) and the Soil Conservation Act (1936), and to the establishment of the Environmental Protection Agency in 1970.

Laws have helped to protect the environment, but they have only slowed environmental damage, not stopped it. Despite legislation and voluntary environmental efforts, we still have many problems. These include acid rain (discussed in chapters 22 and 23), offshore drilling for oil, pollution from toxic wastes, and other issues.

Offshore drilling for oil threatens life in the sea. Already water birds have been harmed by oil spills (figure 25.9). If oil spills continue and increase, fish and shellfish probably will be threatened. We are increasingly dependent on those organisms for food.

Figure 25.8 (a) Humans simplifying an ecosystem. (b) Soft egg shells resulting from ingestion of DDT by birds.

a Caterpillar Inc.

b James H. Enderson

Figure 25.9 Oil or gasoline spills can ruin miles of beaches or rivers. Each year thousands of birds are killed by oil or gasoline pollution.

EPA

In the past we simply buried many toxic wastes. (Toxic waste is a phrase used by the media. In fact, *any* waste that affects the cycle of an element may have a toxic effect on organisms in that cycle.) However, "out of sight, out of mind" did not work. In some places, chemical wastes that caused human diseases and birth defects seeped into water supplies. In other places, birds were poisoned by wastes that entered water used by the birds for swimming or drinking.

The EPA has identified 17,000 toxic-waste sites in the United States. More than 500 of these pose a danger to water supplies and have been classified as high priority for cleanup.

25.6 All Environmental Issues Are Connected to Population Growth

What we have accomplished in pollution control is encouraging. However, we need to remember a great insight that came out of the eighteenth-century concern with the survival of democracy: "Eternal vigilance is the price of liberty." The discoveries of our own century make it clear that eternal vigilance is also the price of preserving environmental quality for our children and generations beyond.

Environmental degradation happens slowly, and the early stages are not always obvious. In fact degradation is often disputed by those who stand to profit from exploiting the environment. As population increases, there is more pressure to take more resources from the limited physical and biological environment. That raises a great moral question: to what extent are today's peoples justified in satisfying their needs at the expense of future generations?

In the People's Republic of China, where the population size is more that 1 billion, there is much restriction on individual freedom. To make even a minimum standard of living available to everyone, the Chinese government has set a limit of one child per married couple. Birth-control counseling is mandatory for all citizens. If a woman with one child becomes pregnant, she may be pressured to have an abortion. Social pressure against large families is strong; "only children" are given preferential access to schooling and jobs.

Although the situation in China may seem like a great restriction on the freedom of some individuals, further expansion of the Chinese population would lead to far worse consequences for the entire population. And China is not unique. The U.S. population, for example, is now nearly 239 million. If it doubles just twice, our population size also will be nearly 1 billion.

All our environmental problems are made more severe by our growing population. It is sometimes said that the United States has reached zero population growth because the 1984 birthrate was 1.8 births for every two adults. That sounds as if we are doing less than replacing ourselves, and as if population growth is no longer an issue. But we also are a nation of immigrants. All of our ancestors came here from other countries, and new Americans arrive every day. In 1984, the net gain (immigration minus emigration) was 523,000 persons. That figure takes no account of illegal immigration, which is known to be considerable.

In addition, the age structure of the population is changing. The proportion of older persons in our society is increasing. Of the four factors that determine population size, three are leading to population growth: mortality and emigration are decreasing, and immigration is increasing. Even natality is not decreasing as much as it was during the 1970s, as shown in figure 25.10.

Figure 25.10 Changing age pyramids through the years for the United States population. In 1940, the smaller base reflects the decline in fertility during the Depression. The large base in 1958 represents the post World War II baby boom.

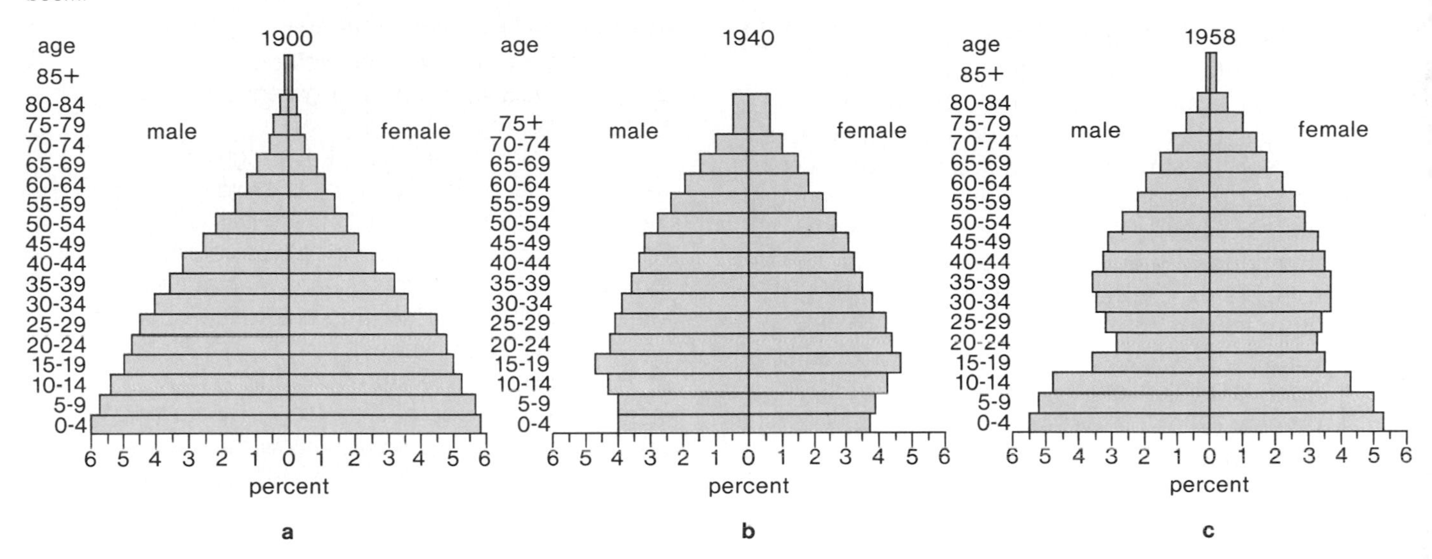

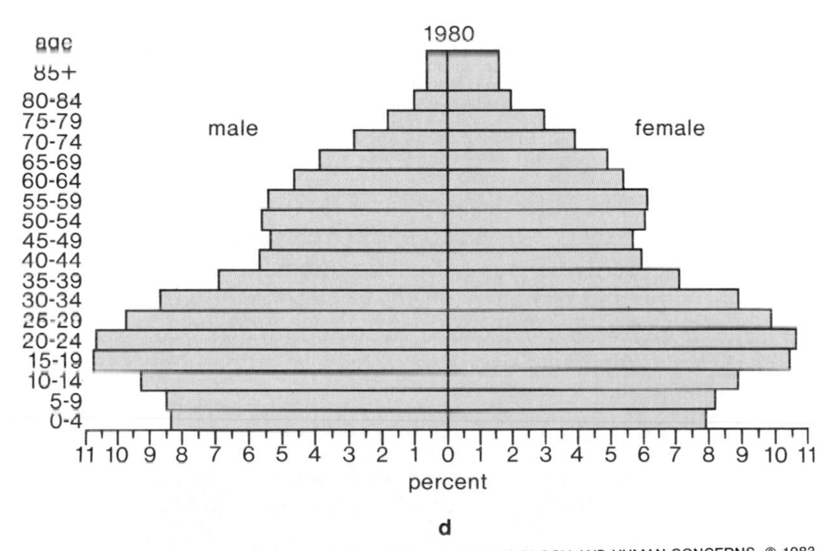

From Volpe, E. Peter, BIOLOGY AND HUMAN CONCERNS. Data from the U.S. Bureau of the Census.

25.7 The Environment Does Not Stop at Political Borders

International cooperation is necessary to solve modern problems. One nation cannot curb worldwide pollution nor ensure preservation of endangered species. To succeed, such efforts require the cooperation of all countries.

Just as ecological problems fail to stop at state borders, they also fail to stop at national boundaries. Air pollution drifts across lakes and oceans into other countries, and water pollution flows into the sea.

Biology Today

Ozone and the Greenhouse Effect

In 1974 two chemists at the University of California at Irvine used computer-model calculations to predict that an important part of the earth's atmosphere, the ozone layer, was in danger of being seriously damaged or even destroyed by chlorofluorocarbons, gaseous compounds widely used in aerosols and refrigerants. Ozone (O_3) forms a layer in the stratosphere about 30 km above the earth's surface. This layer protects plant and animal life from ultraviolet light by screening out about 99 percent of the ultraviolet rays falling on the stratosphere.

The U.S. Government banned the use of chlorofluorocarbons as the propellant gas in aerosol sprays in 1978. However, air conditioners, refrigerators, and insulating foam products also emit chlorofluorocarbons. If emissions continue at today's rate, five to nine percent of the present ozone layer could disappear over the next 50 years; it might be disappearing even faster. Since 1977, British meteorologists have observed that an ozone "hole," in which the ozone is reduced as much as 40 percent, opens up every October over the South Pole.

The thinning of the ozone has led to some dire predictions for the future. Over the lifetime of people alive today in the U.S. there could be a dramatic increase in skin cancer, cataracts, and fatal malignant melanomas. Agricultural crops and aquatic plant communities could be damaged.

Ozone thinning could contribute to the "greenhouse effect" of the gases in the earth's atmosphere. The earth's atmosphere heats up because carbon dioxide and other gases act like the glass walls and roof of a greenhouse, by trapping infrared radiation (heat).

Carbon dioxide, the best known greenhouse gas, is produced in large quantities when fossil fuels (oil, natural gas, or coal) are burned. Destruction of forests also increases carbon dioxide levels in the atmosphere. The increased levels of carbon dioxide, and chlorofluorocarbons, could cause global warming.

The earth's temperature is predicted to increase an average of 5 to 10° C by the year 2030. Global flooding would follow the melting of glaciers and parts of the polar ice caps. Warmer oceans would spawn more powerful and frequent tropical storms, and weather patterns would change. Precipitation would decrease 50 percent in the American grain belt and would increase in the north where less productive soils could not utilize it. Ocean currents would change and the amount of nutrients available to food fish would fall.

What can be done? Emission control is the key. Energy conservation and forest preservation are essential. Banning the use of chlorofluorocarbons on an international level is an option. Efforts to safeguard the ozone layer and reduce the greenhouse gases may result in unforeseen negative side effects. Worldwide cooperation will be needed to solve the problem.

°C	°F
+4.5	+8.1
+3.5	+6.3
+3.0	+5.4
+2.5	+4.5
+1.5	+2.7
+1.0	+1.8

Adapted with permission of Newsweek, Inc. Original illustration by Ib Ohlsson.

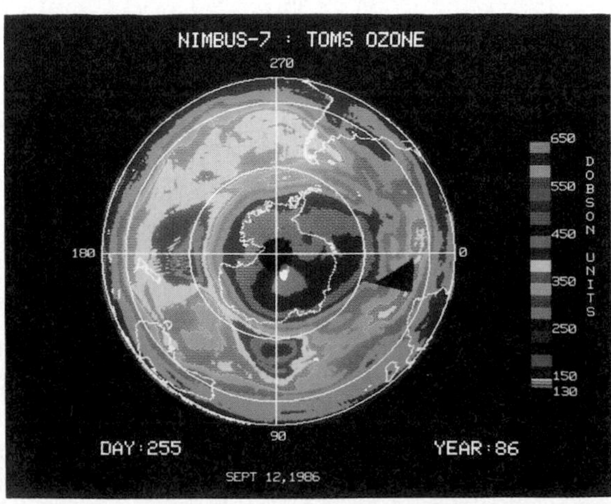

NASA

Figure 25.11 The Chernobyl nuclear power plant. Photo was taken May 9, 1986.

AP/WIDE WORLD PHOTOS

In April 1986, a nuclear power plant in the Ukraine, in the western part of the Soviet Union, exploded and caught fire. The carbon rods used to control the rate of nuclear fission burned for several days. Many deaths and injuries were reported in the U.S.S.R. The effects of the accident were not limited by national boundaries, however. The fire in the reactor released large clouds of radioactive particles, which were carried by the wind to Scandinavia and countries in eastern Europe. Health-care personnel in those countries had to make plans to protect their citizens from the fallout. People were told to stay indoors, and the sale of milk and vegetables was banned in some countries for a short period of time. (Why would milk sales be banned after an accident such as the one described above?)

Another problem with global environmental effects is acid rain, which is carried by wind across national boundaries (figure 25.12). We have discussed some of the effects of acid rain in sections 22.17 and 23.18. Mexican copper smelters produce acid rain that falls on the United States, and U.S. industries produce acid rain that falls on Canada. All three countries must cooperate to solve this problem.

Escalation of the nuclear arms race by the United States, the USSR, and their allies has raised the specter of what some scientists call **nuclear winter.** Scientists have produced computer-generated models of what might happen after a major nuclear war. The nuclear explosions would be followed by a period of darkness lasting from a month to a year, because of the dust and smoke raised by the explosions and the large fires. Because much of the sunlight (up to 95 percent) could not reach the earth, the temperature would fall to as low as $-25°$ C within three weeks,

Figure 25.12 Direction traveled by pollutants responsible for acid rain, and the average acidity of rainfall. Remember that low pH figures indicate high acidity. What other factors should be taken into account when considering damage done by acid rain?

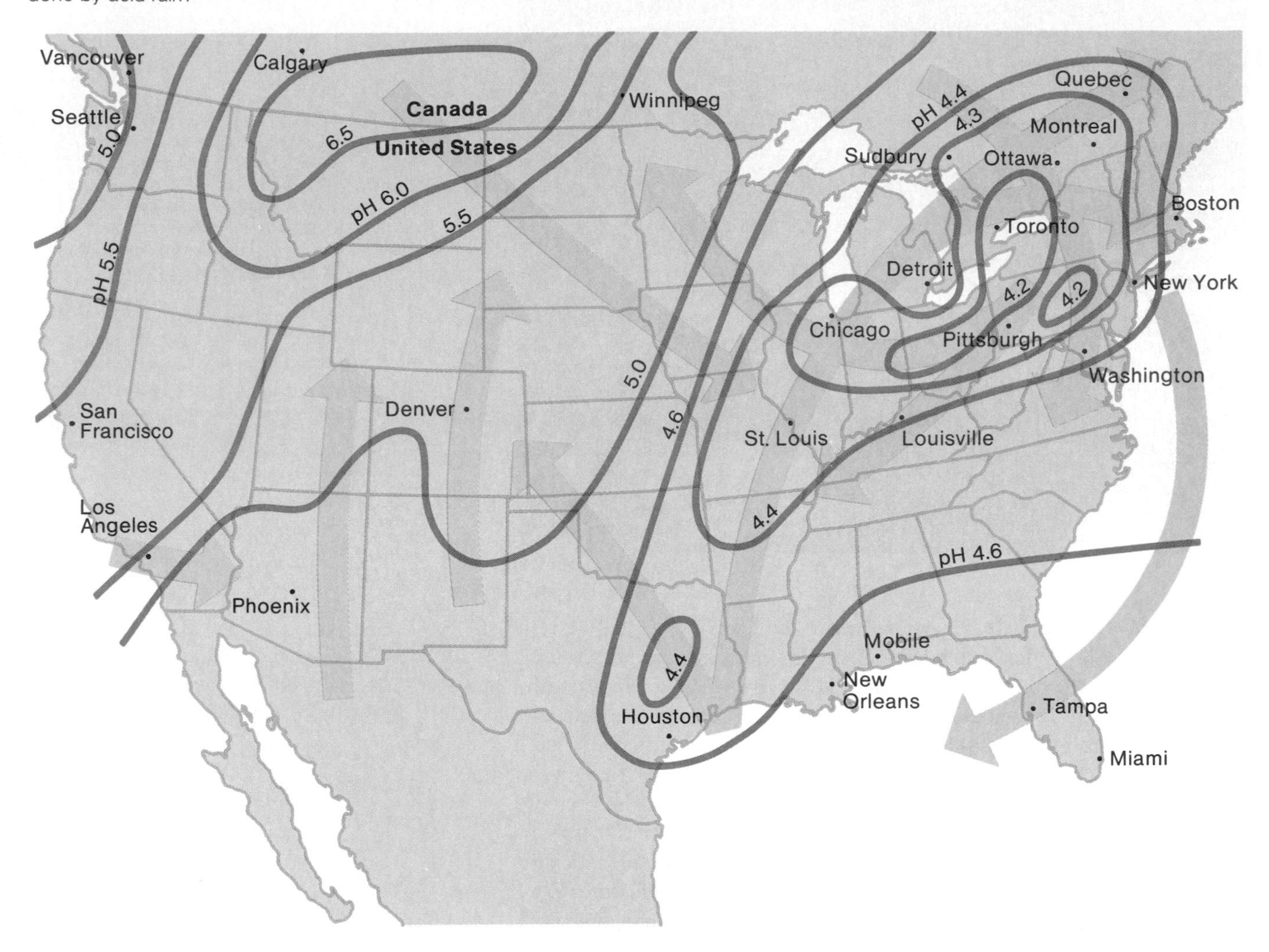

and it would not rise to its usual level for several months. The cold and the darkness would be accompanied by violent windstorms, firestorms, toxic smog, and persistent radioactive particles. The biosphere might never recover.

Self-Review

1. Why cannot toxic wastes simply be buried?
2. What has China done to control population growth?
3. Why is international cooperation necessary to solve the problem of acid rain?
4. How would a nuclear winter affect the biosphere?

Figure 25.13 A patient undergoing kidney dialysis.

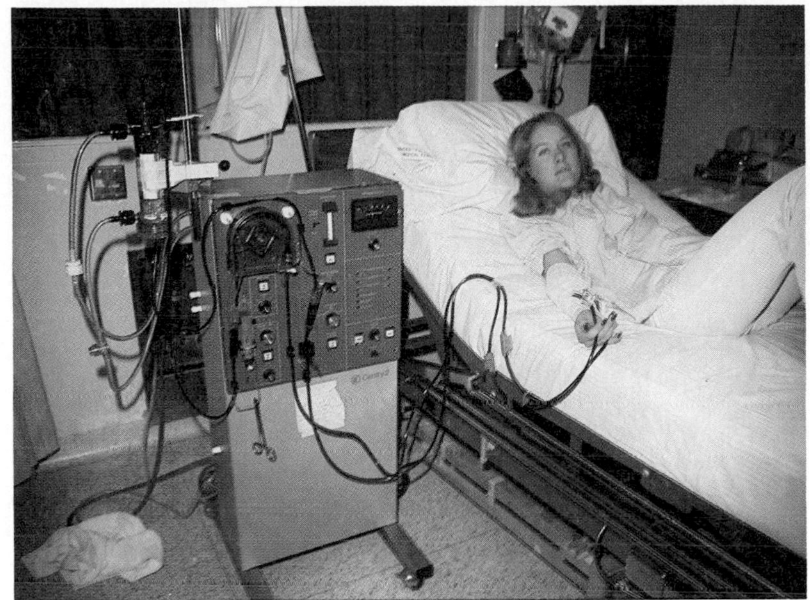

BSCS by Carlye Calvin

Human Technology in the Future

Guidepost: How will we change ourselves and our environment in the future?

25.8 Biotechnology Will Continue to Advance

Science has made spectacular advances during the past 30 years. The basic mechanisms of inheritance are known. The operation of the brain is largely—but still imperfectly—known. The manner in which the immune system works is largely understood—again, however, not completely. Despite this progress, much remains to be done.

A bioengineer is a scientist who combines the talents of a biologist and an engineer. Miniature control systems designed for space research and new materials from industry permit bioengineers to make many artificial organs.

Few persons with poor eyesight complain about wearing eyeglasses or contact lenses. Similarly, anyone who has had a faulty heart corrected with a pacemaker considers that invention significant. Persons unable to walk because of arthritis do not regard plastic hip joints as dangerous inventions. On the contrary, their pain in walking and standing is relieved, and they can once again lead normal lives. Cataract surgery, with the implantation of plastic lenses, has become a routine procedure for many of the elderly.

Disputes arise, however, when lifesaving machines are attached to those who are chronically or terminally ill. Those machines were designed by bioengineers to help people survive brief emergencies that threaten the body's homeostasis. Hearts can now be made to beat by electrical shocks. Several persons have had their diseased hearts replaced with mechanical hearts. A person's blood can be oxygenated in an artificial chamber, or a mechanical respirator can be used. An artificial kidney can be attached to a patient's body to remove metabolic wastes from the blood (figure 25.13). Glucose and other essential nutrients can be added to the circulating blood by means of tubes.

Figure 25.14 (a) A normal EEG and (b) that of a brain-dead person.

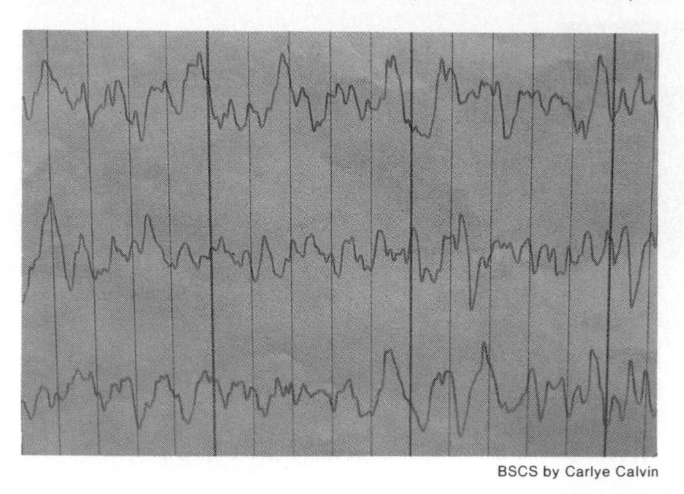

BSCS by Carlye Calvin

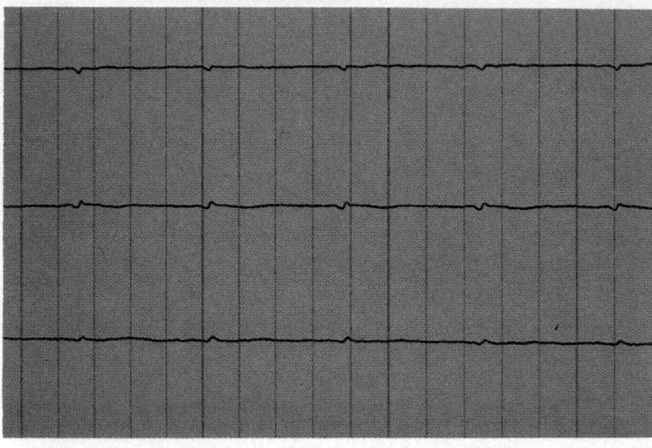

Carlye Calvin

Tragic cases such as that of Karen Ann Quinlan raise **bioethical** questions—ethical questions rooted in biology. After using alcohol and other drugs together, Karen Ann fell into a coma. She lay for 10 years without waking, and she was on an artificial respirator for most of that time. She died in 1985. Should a person in a vegetative state or with a terminal illness be prevented from dying? Should anyone be forced to lie motionless, attached to numerous mechanical devices? Should a family's and society's money be spent to keep someone alive? Does anyone have the right to terminate that life? How do physicians define death? Questions of this kind arise because of our growing technologic ability to manipulate basic life processes. The questions will increase in frequency and complexity as our knowledge and skills increase.

Some answers to these questions have been proposed. None of the answers is completely satisfactory, but all are being debated. We will mention just two. First, terminally ill patients, if they are conscious or have expressed their desires in writing beforehand, may themselves request that all mechanical devices be disconnected. Second, a 24- to 48-hour absence of electrical brain waves (as normally produced by conscious persons) is defined as "brain death." In some courts, brain death is viewed as a justification to allow the still living organs and cells of the rest of the body to die as "the valves are turned off."

Biotechnology in the future will continue to aid us. However, bioethical questions will surely follow. For example, how much effort should be made to keep a newborn baby alive, if the baby has a fatal disorder for which some cure *might* be developed? Have we the right to cause the baby great suffering on the slight chance that a cure might be found? On the other hand, who is to determine what constitutes a "serious" disorder? Perhaps investigation 25.2 will help you deal with some of these problems.

Investigation 25.2 A BIOETHICAL PROBLEM

Introduction

In the usual course of events the scientific inquiry process follows a rather definite series of events. The process begins with a problem. Hypotheses are developed as possible answers to the problem. Then experiments are designed and performed to test the hypotheses. The data that is generated by the experiments is used to evaluate the hypotheses. With the great strides being made in biomedical technology, problems develop that cannot be solved by the inquiry process. They involve situations and values that do not lend themselves to hypotheses and experimentation. Because these problems confront science with unprecedented dilemmas and ethical questions, controversy is a definite part of dealing with these issues. In this investigation you will consider a bioethical problem from two perspectives and then consider some questions raised by the conflicting viewpoints.

In vitro fertilization (fertilization in glass) involves the fertilization of the ovum outside the body. The fertilized egg is then reimplanted in the uterus at the proper time (embryo transfer). Research on in vitro fertilization has been going on for several decades. In 1975, the federal government withdrew support for this type of research. In the fall of 1978, the Ethics Advisory Board—11 men and 2 women—conducted public hearings in 10 regions across the United States. The board heard testimony from 179 people. After analysis of the testimony and the consideration of the benefits and risks of in vitro fertilization, the Ethics Advisory Board concluded that "It is acceptable from an ethical standpoint to undertake research involving human in vitro fertilization and embryo transfer." In January 1980, the first in vitro fertilization clinic in the United States opened at Eastern Virginia Medical School in Norfolk.

Procedure

Carefully read the following excerpts from 2 articles, one defending and the other opposing in vitro fertilization, that are representative of the testimony given at the Ethics Advisory Board's public hearings. Then, with your team, prepare responses to the discussion questions to be presented to the class.

1. The Case Against In Vitro Fertilization—Ruth Hubbard—Biological Laboratories, Harvard University.
   (a) . . . [W]hen it comes to thinking about how a complex organism works, be it as a person in her or his own life, or more especially as a pregnant woman carrying a fetus, I have always felt that one ought to interfere as little as possible, and only when it's absolutely necessary in order to avoid severe pain or death. . . .
   (b) . . . I frankly view with incredulity and horror the notion that one can 'simply' remove an egg from a woman's ovary, put it in a culture medium in a dish, fertilize it and let it go through the first few divisions, and then 'simply' pick it up, reinsert it in a uterus that is at the proper stage of preparedness, and have it implant and go through development, without these many manipulations having some effect on the process of development. I simply do not believe there is no effect . . . there must be an effect, or more likely effects. How or when the effect will express itself is another question, or whether it will be overt and noticed. . . .
   (c) . . . An issue that has been raised is the notion that every women has a right to bear a child . . . it had never occurred to me that every woman has a right to bear a baby any more than that every woman has a 'right' to a 34-inch bustline or a 24-inch waist. . . . I had never thought of circumstances or events that have a strong biological component (as well as, of course, environmental ones) as described in terms of 'rights.' . . .
   (d) . . . [A]cknowledging the genuine hardship and suffering of women who want children and cannot bear them. I question whether there is not some better way to help than to lead them down the garden path of in vitro fertilization, which I believe to be a path of disaster. . . .
   (e) . . . I am also very concerned because this is an extremely complicated technology that involves many steps. . . . There is no way to put this technology into the control of the women who are going to be exposed to it. . . . It really locks the women and their babies into the high-technology medical system. . . . I have read that Drs. Steptoe and Edwards, the men who produced two of the in vitro babies . . . made each woman promise to have an abortion if the doctors felt it should be done. . . .

(f) . . . [T]his is an expensive technology that requires highly skilled professionals and costly equipment . . . as we have heard, poor women with minimal access to minimal health care are being sterilized or otherwise coerced into *not* having babies they want and can have, while women who can pay high prices are encouraged to participate in the expensive and risky technology of in vitro fertilization.

2. In Defense of In Vitro Fertilization—Barbara Menning—Project RESOLVE, Belmont, Massachusetts.

(a) . . . It is estimated that 10 million American women are currently infertile. Of that number, one third of those are problems relating to the Fallopian tubes . . . surgical repair of the Fallopian tubes is successful only 30 percent of the time. This means of every one million women who have serious tubal diseases, 700,000 cannot be helped to become pregnant by *this* means, at this time. . . .

(b) . . . [C]ouples desiring in vitro fertilization are going to be screened so rigorously that there is no danger of inappropriate application of this technology.

(c) . . . [W]e have accepted the following as facts of life: 15 percent of all pregnancies will end in miscarriage; 3 percent of all pregnancies will result in perinatal death, and 5 percent of liveborn children will have a congenital defect. There is no reason to expect the in vitro conception to escape these risk factors. One thing is sure: The couple who are infertile due to hopeless tubal damage run a 100 percent risk of remaining childless if they are not allowed access to in vitro fertilization as a technology. . . .

(d) . . . It hurts to be infertile, to make the conscious and informed choice to have children and then to be denied. . . .

Discussion

1. Some of the excerpts express concern over the risks of in vitro fertilization. Do you think the risks, as stated, are serious enough to consider another moratorium on research of in vitro fertilization?
2. Barbara Menning says, "Let us (the infertile) decide if we want to take the risks."
   (a) Should people be allowed to take such risks?
   (b) Does the government have a responsibility to prevent people from taking a risk?
   (c) Does the government have a right to stop people from putting themselves or others—in this case, the developing embryo—at risk?
3. Do you think every woman has a "right" to have a child? Explain your answer.
4. Ruth Hubbard states, "I simply do not believe that there is no effect [on the process of development]." Do you think she has made an effective argument in support of her position concerning the risks of the procedure? Explain your answer.
5. According to Robert Murray, a member of the Ethics Advisory Board, "There was a clear difference in the positions of witnesses from various regions of the country." In the Northeast ". . . witnesses tended to favor . . . research into in vitro fertilization as well as in vitro fertilization with embryo transfer. On the other hand, in the Midwest and Southeast, witnesses tended to oppose the further development of both technologies."
   (a) To what do you attribute these regional differences?
   (b) What implications do they have for the development of a public consensus on policy issues, such as government funding for in vitro fertilization?

25.9 Genetic Engineering Will Expand into New Areas

Genetic engineering is the process of altering the genes of a living cell by artificial means. The technology is often referred to as recombinant DNA technology, because molecular geneticists can *recombine* genetic material in new sequences as we have seen in section 8.20 and figure 8.30.

Already we can engineer bacteria to suit our purposes. For example, bacteria can be altered to produce insulin or other natural substances. That is done by removing the genes for insulin from human cells. Those genes are then inserted into bacteria. Thus, the genetic material has been recombined. When the bacteria reproduce by fission, they reproduce the gene for human insulin. The gene is active in the bacteria. That is, the bacteria make protein (in this case, insulin) from the directions encoded in the gene. The gene product—insulin—is then harvested for use by diabetics.

Pseudomonas syringae, a bacterial species found on plants, makes a protein that acts as a nucleus for the formation of ice crystals. Genetic engineers have produced a mutant *P. syringae,* which lacks that protein. They want to apply the mutant strain to the surface of potato and strawberry plants. If the mutant crowds out the other form, it will make the plants frost-resistant. Another species of *Pseudomonas* (*P. fluorescens*) has been engineered so that it is a natural pesticide. If it is added to the roots of corn or other plants, it will kill the hornworms, cutworms, and other pests that usually attack the plants.

Both of these engineered bacteria appear to be safe. Scientists, however, want to use caution in introducing any mutants into natural environments. They want to be sure that no beneficial insects are killed by *P. fluorescens,* and that the toxin does not persist in the environment. *P. syringae* is less controversial, because the mutant is similar to some bacteria found in nature. However, there is a possibility that the normal, ice-forming strain is needed for cloud formation and rainfall.

Genetic engineering in humans is still in the future. The hope of molecular geneticists is that specific genes can be transferred to the cells of persons having genetic disorders. The cells with the transferred genes should then produce the protein that the patient lacks. That type of genetic engineering resembles bioengineering. A handicapped individual, having received suitable treatment, could live a more normal life than if untreated. Genetic engineering could help a person with phenylketonuria (PKU), for example. Persons who suffer from PKU have a genetic defect that prevents the formation of an essential enzyme.

Inserting genes into a person's body cells will not correct that person's reproductive cells. His or her offspring would still risk inheriting the faulty gene. To eliminate that risk, the normally functioning gene would have to be transferred into sperm and ova. Some people find the thought of that procedure disturbing. The genes we carry are a random collection of our parent's genes. Some fear that genetic engineering on germ cells might reduce that randomness and change the frequency of genes in the gene pool.

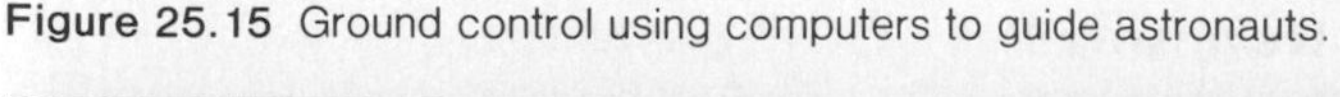

Figure 25.15 Ground control using computers to guide astronauts.

NASA

25.10 Knowledge Will Continue to Expand

Since early members of our species learned to use fire and tools, human evolution has been rapid. As humans continued to use tools, their brains expanded and their tools grew more complex.

For the last 35,000 years, however, human brains have changed little. The Neanderthals' brains were as large as ours. Our brains are limited to their present size because babies with larger heads would not be able to pass through the birth canal. Human knowledge, however, has grown greatly, because of our tools. More complex tools have taken over not only much of our physical labor, but growing amounts of our mental work as well.

When early humans scratched a map in the soil with a stick, or drew an animal on a cave wall with a crayon of ochre (figure 21.31, page 792), the process of storing knowledge outside the brain was beginning. While the human brain can store a great deal of information, its capacity for storage has limits. Except for what is needed often or in emergencies, it is far better to store information permanently as a written record and retrieve it only when needed.

Now we use the keys of computers rather than sticks of wood or ochre. We fill libraries and museums with the accumulating knowledge of our species. We can spend time interpreting and using information, not merely memorizing it or doing arithmetic. With computers as our partners, humankind may learn not only how to live well on earth, but also how to explore the stars.

While this artificial expansion of our brains is occurring, the brain's immediate environment, the body, is improving also. In developed nations, better nutrition, sanitation, and health care have increased both the life span and the health of the average person. New knowledge in medical genetics promises improved treatment and prevention of some genetic disorders. Gene therapy may actually cure some genetic disorders. Such changes in genotypes and phenotypes may even help to direct human evolution.

Evolution of organisms, however, occurs only within environments. Will our enlarged intelligence and ability lead us to understand the environment and live within it for our benefit and that of other organisms? Or will we destroy the environment on which we depend?

There are signs that many persons throughout the world are developing a greater environmental awareness. Since 1975, for the first time in modern history, the growth rate of the world's population has declined (from 2 percent to 1.7 percent). The *total* population of the world is still rising, of course. It is now expected to reach 6.1 billion persons by the year 2000. Population and related issues may gradually be brought under control if there is continued awareness of and action on these problems.

25.11 Individuals Must Participate in Important Decisions about the Environment

Because some issues are international or require expert knowledge, we tend to feel that our individual contributions are meaningless. However, just as evolution at the population level can occur only as the result of selection of individuals, so too are global changes in the environment made up of many interacting specific events.

In addition, in recent years many ecologists have come to see each small environmental issue as the focal point of many interactions. For example, in 1973, a biologist discovered a small population of snail-eating fish, which he called snail darters (figure 25.16), in a river in Tennessee. As far as anyone knew, snail darters could be found nowhere else. Thus, under the Endangered Species Act, which had just been passed, any construction destroying the snail darters' habitat could not proceed. Unfortunately, a massive project, the Tellico Dam, was nearing completion next to the snail darters' habitat. It had already cost $103 million and would provide electricity to heat 20,000 homes. The construction was held up for more than five years while the case was in the courts. Finally, some snail darters were moved to other streams, and the construction of the dam was resumed. Later on, another natural population of the fish was found several miles away, so the lengthy public controversy had not been necessary.

Figure 25.16 Snail darter.

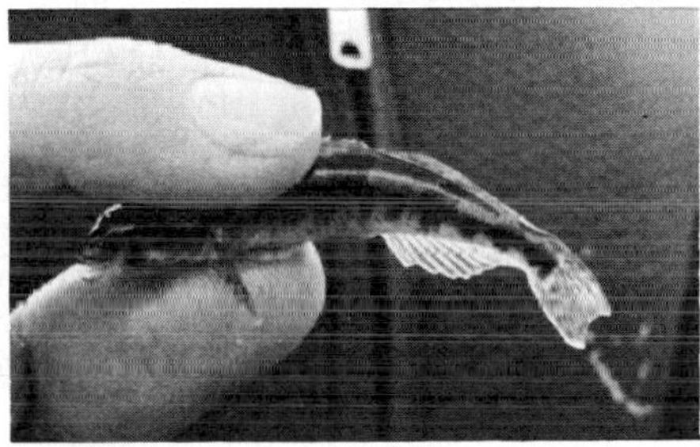

Tennessee Valley Authority

That particular combination of factors was unique to the situation. But each environmental problem has unique, local aspects. In addition, there are biological, physical, and social aspects of each environmental issue. Decisions about specific problems cannot be made from a distance or from a broad level only. They must be made, in part, by those who are close to the situation and who are themselves affected.

Some biologists think that we should not provide food to countries suffering famines unless they agree to control their growing populations, which would help prevent future famines. In contrast, some persons who

Figure 25.17 The power of humans to shape our environment may lead to continuing usefulness, or this power may be directed toward waste, depletion, and ruin. Consider the choices shown here and in the world around you.

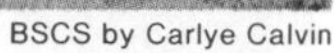

a BSCS by Carlye Calvin

b BSCS by Bob Wilson

c BSCS

d BSCS by Bill Callahan

oppose abortion say that we should not provide any financial aid to countries that promote the use of abortion for population control. Have we the right to interfere in other countries' ethical decisions, even when those decisions affect the global environment?

There are similar difficult bioethical decisions to be made in other areas. Does a childless couple have the right to use fertility drugs that may produce multiple births, for example? Do we have the right to use hominoids as sources of organs for transplants, or as subjects of research that may be painful? Given the threat of "nuclear winter," should we [illegible] nuclear weapons tests even if our enemies continue testing?

e BSCS by Doug Sokell

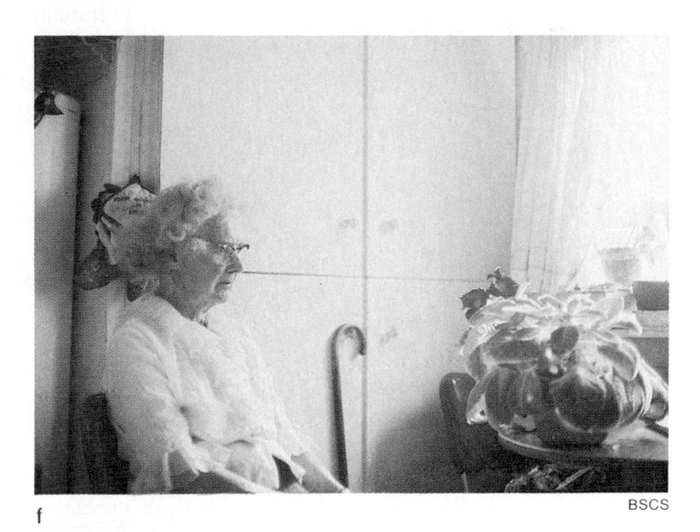
f BSCS

g Kenneth A. Dals

h Jack D. Swenson/TOM STACK & ASSOCIATES

25.12 Decisions Must Be Based on Sound Information and Must Be Reached Logically

The problems that face humankind are varied and complex. Their solutions will require knowledge, creativity, and cooperative effort. The skills of biologists and other scientists will be important. The knowledge stored in computers and the mathematical calculations they make possible will help. But educated citizens are the true key to sound policies that will help ensure a bright future.

You may have no interest in becoming a professional biologist, but you cannot avoid making biological decisions in your own life. Some of your decisions will be personal, but they will affect the environment. You will make other decisions when you vote on environmental issues or face environmental problems in the course of your daily work. We hope that the knowledge and attitudes gained in this year of studying biology will help you to make those decisions.

Self-Review

1. What are some of the issues raised by our increasing use of biotechnology?
2. How can genetic engineering be used to benefit humans?
3. If human brains have not changed in the past 35,000 years, how can we explain the rapid increase of knowledge?
4. What problems resulted from the effort to save snail darters from extinction?

Summary

If someone had tried 100 years ago to predict what humankind and the environment would be like today, the prediction would probably be only a rough approximation of our current situation. Not many people could have foreseen our use of computers, genetic engineering, or nuclear energy.

Now we stand almost at the threshold of a new century. We can see only a fuzzy picture of what the future may hold. Perhaps the only statement we can make with certainty is that many human environmental issues will continue to be important.

In the past, nearly everyone has made mistakes about environmental issues. Now, you have the chance to help determine the future. By knowing something about ecology, and by caring about the earth and the people in it, you can help to bring about a rebirth of our old planet.

Application Questions

1. If humans are "selected by consequences," what human behavioral adaptations are most likely to lead to our future survival?
2. Two children are given an IQ test. If child A has a score of 105, and child B has a score of 110, does that mean that child B inherited genes for greater intelligence?
3. A population map of the United States would show large areas that are barely inhabited. If someone

Problems

1. Demographers are concerned with more than changes in the total numbers of persons. They are also interested in the structure of populations—the relative numbers of individuals of various kinds. For example, two populations of the same size may have different proportions of males and females. Or two populations of the same size may have different proportions of children and adults. Such data often provide much information about a population.

argued that the map showed there is no population problem here, what arguments might you present for another conclusion?

4. Suppose a growth-enhancing form of *Pseudomonas* could be engineered. Would it be a good idea to apply it to food crops to increase production? Why or why not?
5. Research on human gene therapy is likely to begin before the end of the 1980s. Compare gene therapy on somatic cells with gene therapy on germ cells.

(a) The total populations of the United States and Sri Lanka are quite different. More important, the U.S. population has a smaller proportion of children than that of Sri Lanka. What hypotheses can you suggest on the strength of this information?

(b) We can divide the population of the United States into three age groups: (1) persons under 20, most of whom are not self-supporting; (2) persons 20 to 65, most of whom are working; (3) persons over 65, most of whom are retired. In recent years the first and third groups have been increasing more rapidly than the second group. What hypotheses can you suggest to explain this? Can you see a future economic problem in this situation?

(c) In human females reproduction occurs mostly between the ages of 15 and 45. Suppose this age group increases more slowly than the age group over 45 but the number of children per female remains the same. What will happen to the birthrate in the population when expressed as births per 1000 of population?

(d) The average age at which a female has her first child is higher in nation A than in nation B. The average age of death is about the same in both nations. From this information, make a guess about the rate of population growth in the two countries. What additional information would make your guess more reliable?

2. What bacteria are used or are likely to be used in the future in agricultural and industrial microbiology? What foods and pharmaceuticals are the products of bacterial or fungal action? How will microbiology change as a result of future genetic engineering? Much information on this topic is available in the September 1981 issue of *Scientific American.*
3. The term ecology has become a household word, but it is often used as if it were a synonym for pollution or environment. Sometimes it is merely used as a vague indication of something good. How would you explain the scientific meaning of the word ecology to a person who has never studied biology?
4. Identify a local environment problem in your community. Research the biological, physical, and social aspects of the problem.

Suggested Readings

R. P. Ambroggi, "Water" *Scientific American* (September 1980). Examines the future of water resources worldwide.

I. Asimov, "The Union of Genes and Genius" *Science Digest* (March 1983). An interesting discussion concerning the future of biotechnology.

L. R. Brown, W. U. Chandler, and S. Postel, "Stage of the Earth" *Natural History* (April 1985). Various negative aspects and effects of the Earth's rapidly expanding population are examined.

N. Myers, 1984, *GAIA, An Atlas of Planet Management* (Garden City, N.Y.: Anchor Books). Exquisitely illustrated with photos, maps, and diagrams, this book discusses the state of the Earth at a critical point in its history—now, and what the future prospects are.

D. Overbye, "Prophet of the Cold and Dark" *Discover* (January 1985). Discusses how a nuclear war may affect Earth's ecosystem, and the ultimate results of a "nuclear winter."

W. Sassin, "Energy" *Scientific American* (September 1980). Investigates future energy demands and development, focusing on the less-developed countries of the world.

C. H. Southwick, ed., 1983, *Global Ecology* (Sunderland, Mass.: Sinauer Associates). Collection of articles and essays dealing with a full range of environmental problems.

Appendices

APPENDIX 1

Some General Procedures for the Laboratory

Safety Guidelines

The laboratory investigations in this book allow you to experience the methods and thought processes used by the professional biologist. They should be an enjoyable and rewarding learning experience. This goal can be achieved provided you and your classmates make the laboratory a safe place in which to work. Accidents rarely happen when every student is engaged in careful, thoughtful and productive investigative activities. Accidents often happen when someone becomes careless, is apathetic toward the activity, or engages in unacceptable behavior. You, your fellow students, and teacher are responsible for a safe laboratory environment. If an accident does occur, you should know what to do immediately. You are responsible for your fellow students' safety as well as your own.

The following safety guidelines should be observed whenever you are in a biology laboratory:

1. **Preparation:** Study the assigned investigation before you come to class. Clear up any confusion before you begin the investigation.
2. **Organization:** Arrange the materials needed for the investigation in an orderly fashion. Organization helps ensure safety.
3. **Cleanliness:** Maintain a clean, clutter-free work area from beginning to end of the investigation. Wash your hands immediately after handling any living organism or any hazardous materials.
4. **Chemicals:** All chemicals are dangerous, especially if handled without knowledge. Know the 4 hazard classes of chemicals and the safety rules for each class. Know the hazard class of the chemical you are working with. Report all chemical spills to your teacher immediately; *do not attempt to clean up a chemical spill.* Never dispose of any chemical unless specifically instructed to do so by your teacher.

5. **Biological Safety:** Treat all microbiological cultures as pathogenic, or disease-causing. Dispose of all contaminated materials and culture material as your teacher directs. *Never handle microbiological cultures if you have cuts on your hand or are ill.* Report any biological spill immediately to your teacher—do not attempt to clean up a biological spill.

   Wash your hands thoroughly following any experiment, or after handling animals, Do not eat or drink while conducting investigations.
6. **Eye Safety:** Safety goggles must be worn when working with any chemical, or when working with an open flame. *Contact lenses should never be worn while conducting any experiment involving the use of chemicals.* If any solution or substance is splashed into your eye, use the eye wash station *immediately*—flushing the eyes, including under each eyelid, for at least 10 minutes. Make sure your teacher is notified by your partner or classmate.

   Never use reflected sunlight to illuminate your microscope or other optical device. Reflected or direct sunlight can damage your eye's retina and cause serious injury.
7. **Safety Equipment:** Know the location of all safety equipment and be familiar with the use of each piece of equipment. If you witness an accident, report it to your teacher immediately.
8. **Heat:** Use only the source of heat specified by the investigation. When heating a substance in a test tube, do not point the mouth of the tube at another student or yourself.
9. **Glassware:** *Never use cracked or chipped glassware.* Use caution and proper equipment to handle hot glassware; *remember hot glass looks the same as cool glass.* When putting glass tubing into rubber stoppers, moisten the tubing, and protect your hands with heavy cloth. Never force the tubing into the stopper. Broken glassware should be swept up immediately (never picked up with your fingers) and discarded into the special broken glass container.
10. **Neatness:** Keep your work space free of everything except those materials necessary for the assigned investigation. Tie back long hair and remove dangling jewelry. Roll up long loose sleeves, especially when working with chemicals or an open flame.
11. **Cleanup:** Used glassware and instruments should be washed according to the teacher's specific instructions. Disposable materials should be wrapped in paper towels and placed in the proper container. Tables and sinks should be cleaned. Put away all equipment and supplies. Make sure all water, gas, burners, and electrical appliances are turned off. Return all laboratory materials and equipment to their proper place.

It is your responsibility, along with your fellow students and teacher, to ensure that the laboratory is a safe place in which to conduct biological investigations. Make special note of any cautionary statements made in the instructions for your laboratory investigations.

Remember that the laboratory will be safe only if you regard laboratory work as serious work.

Use of Materials

Apparatus. Some kinds of biological work still can be done with a few simple tools. However, as biologists probe deeper, they often find it necessary to use complex apparatus for handling and observing their materials. It is important that you learn how to use each piece of apparatus in order to obtain accurate scientific information.

Living materials. All biologists deal with living things. Though some have no need to handle living things directly in their daily work, no one in a general biology classroom or laboratory can get along without living materials. You, as a biology student, should learn how to care for living organisms.

Animals must be cared for humanely. General rules are as follows:

1. Always follow the teacher's instructions carefully concerning the care of laboratory animals.
2. Provide an escape-proof container suitable for the animal, in a location where the animal will not be constantly disturbed.
3. Keep the container clean. This is necessary for the health of the animal. Cages of small birds and mammals should be cleaned daily. Provide proper ventilation, light and temperature.
4. Provide water at all times.
5. Feed regularly. The frequency of feeding depends on the animals. Small birds and mammals may need to be provided with a continuous food supply.
6. Treat laboratory animals with kindness in all situations. Cruelty has no place in biology.
7. When animals must be disposed of or released, your teacher will provide a suitable method.
8. Plants are just as much living things as are animals; they, too, can be injured or killed. Therefore, handle them carefully and gently. Most plants must be provided with light, soil, and water. Requirements differ a great deal among plants. Therefore, individual students should care for your classroom plants. They will learn the requirements of the particular kinds of plants in their charge.

Record-Keeping

Science deals with verifiable observations. No one—not even the original observer—can check an observation that is hazy, indefinite, or half-remembered. All scientists must keep clear and accurate records of what they have observed, made *at the time of observation.*

Data books. The best method of keeping such records is to jot them down in a data book. This should be a stiff-cover book, permanently bound (not loose-leaf), preferably with square grid pages.

Keep records in a diary form, recording the date first. If you make observations on two or more investigations on the same day, use the numbers or abbreviations of the titles as subheadings.

Data may be recorded in words. In the laboratory, time is short, so you should make these notes brief but to the point. Complete sentences are not necessary, but single words are seldom satisfactory. Phrases are usually most useful.

You may choose to sketch your observations. A drawing often records an observation more easily, completely, and accurately than words can. Your sketches need not be works of art. Their success depends on your ability to observe, not on your artistic talent. Keep them simple, usually without shading, and draw them with a hard pencil—otherwise they might rub off.

Data may be recorded numerically as counts or measurements. Give the units in which measurements are made. Often numerical data are most easily recorded in the form of a table.

Do not jot down your data on other papers, to be copied into the data book later. This might increase neatness, but it will *decrease* accuracy. Both are virtues in a scientist, but neatness is of value only when it increases accuracy. Your data book is *your* record. Your teacher may want to look at it to help you with your work, but he or she is interested in the accuracy of your data, not in the blots and stains that are a normal hazard of field and laboratory work.

Remember to do the following:

1. Record immediately.
2. Record accurately.
3. Record completely.

More and more, science is becoming a cooperative enterprise—a team activity. You will do much of your own laboratory work as a member of a team. Your data book, therefore, will sometimes contain data contributed by other members of your team. Keep track of what you yourself have observed by encircling (or recording in a different color) observations made by others. You should be able to say: "This I know because I saw it; that I believe because I have confidence in my teammates."

Laboratory reports. Discoveries become a part of science only when they are made known to others. Communication, therefore, is a very important part of science. In writing, scientists must express themselves so clearly that another person can repeat their procedures exactly. The reader must know what material was used (in biology this includes the kind of organism) and must be able to understand every detail of the work. Scientists must be free to communicate, but they can use this freedom only if they know how to communicate. For publication, scientific reports are usually written in a rather standard form, somewhat as follows:

1. Title
2. Introduction: section usually stating how the problem arose and often giving a summary of past work
3. Materials and equipment
4. Procedure: complete an exact account of what was done in gathering the data
5. Results: data obtained from the procedure, often in the form of tables and graphs
6. Discussion: part that points up the relationship between the data and the purpose of the work
7. Conclusion: summary of the meaning of the results, often suggesting further work that might be done
8. References: published scientific reports that have been specifically mentioned

If you undertake work on an independent problem, your report should follow this form. For the usual work in this course, however, you do not have to be so elaborate. You are communicating with your fellow students and your teacher, who already know a great deal about the work. Occasionally your teacher may direct you to do a rather complete job of reporting. Usually, however, a much shorter report is all that is required—perhaps merely the answers to the questions in an investigation. In either case, the material in your data book is the basis for your reports.

Measurement

All major countries of the world use the metric system of measurement except the United States. The metric system is a decimal system—that is, it is based on powers of ten, like our system of currency. Scientists in the United States have long used the metric system.

The official name of the internationally standardized metric system is the International System of Units, abbreviated SI (for Système Internationale). Its units of measure are easily manipulated by doing calculations with ten or powers of ten. Among its basic units of measurement are the meter (length), the kilogram (mass), the kelvin (temperature), and the second (time). All lengths are based on that of the meter, and all volumes on a cubic meter. All units of mass are based on the kilogram. Units of temperature, which you will become familiar with as degrees Celsius, are equal to kelvins.

The major exception you will make to SI measure is in the measure of volume. You will use liters and decimals of liters, rather than cubic meters and their decimals. Liter measure is widely used for liquids, and most of your volume measurements in biology will be of liquids. Liter measure is accepted by SI, although not officially as a part of it. Like the cubic meter, the liter is also metric (1 l = 0.001 m^3).

Some of the SI units derived from the basic units for length and mass follow:

1. **Length**

   1 kilometer (km) = 1000 meters
   1 hectometer (hm) = 100 meters
   1 dekameter (dkm) = 10 meters
   1 meter (m)—the basic unit of length
   1 decimeter (dm) = 0.1 meter
   1 centimeter (cm) = 0.01 meter
   1 millimeter (mm) = 0.001 meter
   1 micrometer (μm) = 0.000001 meter
   1 nanometer (nm) = 0.000000001 meter

   Measurements under microscopes are often made in micrometers. Still smaller measurements, as for wavelengths of light used by plants in photosynthesis, are made in nanometers.

   Units of area are derived from units of length by multiplication. One square hectometer is a measure often used for ecological studies; it is commonly called a hectare and equals 10,000 m^2.

Figure A.1 A comparison of Fahrenheit and Celsius (centigrade) temperature scales.

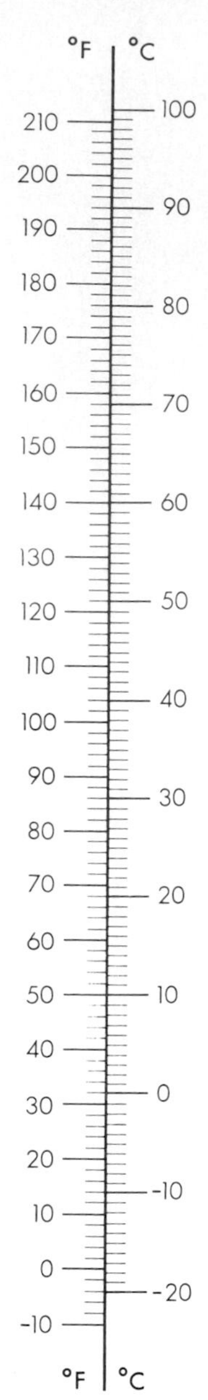

2. **Mass**

1 kilogram (kg) = 1000 grams
1 hectogram (hg) = 100 grams
1 dekagram (dkg) = 10 grams
1 gram (g)—derived from the kilogram, the basic unit
1 decigram (dg) = 0.1 gram
1 centigram (cg) = 0.01 gram
1 milligram (mg) = 0.001 gram
1 microgram (μg) = 0.000001 gram
1 nanogram (ng) = 0.000000001 gram

Measurements of mass in your biology laboratory usually will be made in kilograms, grams, centigrams, and milligrams.

The units you will use for volume and for temperature follow:

3. **Volume**

1 kiloliter (kl) = 1000 liters (or 1 cubic meter)
1 hectoliter (hl) = 100 liters
1 dekaliter (dkl) = 10 liters
1 liter (l)—derived from the cubic meter
1 deciliter (dl) = 0.1 liter
1 centiliter (cl) = 0.01 liter
1 milliliter (ml) = 0.001 liter

Your volume measurements in the laboratory will usually be made in glassware marked for milliliters and liters.

4. **Temperature**

Your laboratory thermometers may read from 0° to 100° Celsius (abbreviated C). Or, since you may be reading temperatures below 0° C, some thermometers may read 30° or 40° below zero.

On the Celsius scale, 0° is the official reading for the triple point of water. At this temperature ice, liquid water, and water vapor pass from any one of these three states to another, staying in equilibrium. Commonly, 0° is known as the freezing point of water. Atmospheric pressure affects this freezing point.

The boiling point of water, commonly, is 100° C. Atmospheric pressure also affects this boiling point.

Figure A.1 illustrates the Celsius scale alongside the Fahrenheit scale that is still used in the United States. On the Fahrenheit scale, 32° F is the freezing point of water and 212° F is the boiling point of water. The figure is useful in converting from one scale to the other.

SI measure includes still other basic units (units of electric current, of force, of amount of substance, and so on) that you will not use in your biology studies.

If you wish to learn more about SI measure, write to the U.S. Department of Commerce, National Bureau of Standards, Washington, D.C. 20234.

APPENDIX 2

Supplementary Investigations

Investigation A.1 CHEMICAL SAFETY

Introduction

Many of the chemicals used in the laboratory can injure you if you are not careful. All chemicals are hazardous in some way. A hazardous chemical is defined as a substance that is likely to cause injury. Chemicals can be placed in 4 hazard categories: flammable substances, corrosive substances, toxic substances, and reactive substances. Their characteristics are summarized in table A.1. This activity will help you become aware of the 4 types of chemical hazards and of how you can reduce the risk of injury when using chemicals.

Part A—Flammable Substances

Flammable substances are solids, liquids, or gases that will burn. The process of burning involves 3 interrelated components: fuel - oxidizer - ignition source. For burning to occur, all 3 sides (components) of the fire triangle (figure A.2) must be present. For practical purposes, there must be sufficient fuel (any substance capable of burning) and oxidizer (usually air) present to form an ignitable mixture. To complete the triangle, an ignition source (energy) must be present. The ignition source need not be in the form of a spark or a flame; temperature alone can supply the energy.

To control the fire hazards of flammable substances, one must remove, or otherwise make inaccessible, at least 1 side of the fire triangle. Removing the oxidizer leg is the most difficult approach. Removing the fuel leg is somewhat easier: Store flammable liquids in an area isolated from reactive substances, such as oxidizers (acids). Removing the ignition source leg is the easiest approach: Store flammable materials in a cool area; eliminate obvious ignition sources, such as flames and sparks; and eliminate those ignition sources that are not so obvious, such as hot plates, sparking electrical equipment, and static electricity.

Figure A.2 The fire triangle.

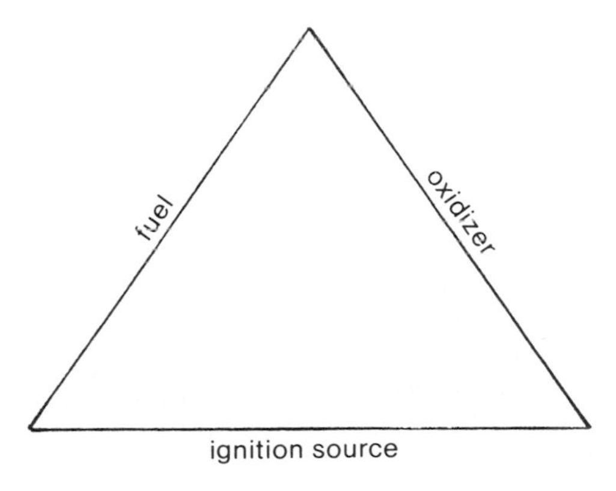

Table A.1 Information and safety guide to hazardous materials

Kind of Material	Categories	**Prevention/Control** Know the hazard class of each chemical or solution you handle or work with in the laboratory. Know all safety precautions for each hazard class. Read and understand all information on the product label. Ask your teacher if you have any questions.
Flammable Substance Common Lab Hazard 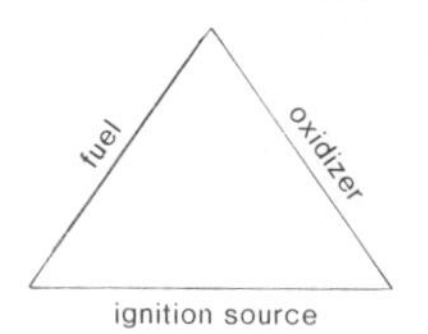	**Flammable Liquid**—Liquid having a flashpoint* less than 100° F (37.8° C). **Combustible Liquid**—Flashpoint* equal to or greater than 100° F (37.8° C) but less than 200° F. *Flashpoint—the lowest temperature at which a liquid gives off vapor which forms an ignitable mixture with air near the surface. **Flammable Solid**—Causes fire through friction, absorption of moisture, or spontaneous chemical change. Ignites readily; burns vigorously. **Flammable Gas**—Forms a flammable mixture with air at ambient temperature and pressure.	Store away from oxidizers and reactives. Store in approved, grounded containers and in safety cabinets. Store no more than one-half gallon in glass containers. Store in cool area (under 80° F). Transport in metal or other approved containers. Store in cool area (under 80° F). Transport in metal or other approved containers. Ground all metal containers when dispensing. Report all chemical spills to your teacher immediately.
Reactive Chemical Violent reaction under certain ambient or induced conditions. Spontaneous generation of great heat, light, and flammable and non-flammable gases or toxicants.	**Acid-Sensitive**—Reacts with acids or acid fumes to generate heat, flammable or explosive gases, or toxicants. **Water-Sensitive**—Reacts with moisture to generate heat and/or flammable or explosive gases. **Oxidizer**—Promotes combustion in other materials through release of oxygen or other gases.	Isolate compounds of a given hazard class from other hazard classes. Protect reactives from physical shock. Provide a ready water source for dilutions not involving water sensitives. Keep water away from water sensitives. Store reactives in a cool, dry area away from sunlight. Never pour *any* chemical or chemical solution down any drain. Ask your teacher for correct disposal method.
Corrosive Chemical Injures body tissue and corrodes metal by direct chemical action. 	**Corrosive Liquid, Solid, Gas**—Causes visible destruction or irreversible alterations in living tissue. **Irritant**—Causes reversible inflammation in living tissue. **Sensitizer**—Causes allergic reaction in normal tissue of a substantial number of individuals after repeated exposure.	Never mix any two chemicals or solutions together unless told to do so by your teacher. Store in approved containers away from sunlight and rapid temperature changes. Wear protective equipment: eye goggles, gloves, and lab apron. Know the *exact* location of the eyewash station near you. Never handle any chemical directly.
Toxic Chemical Injures by direct action with body systems when tolerable limits are exceeded. Exposure routes: direct contact, inhalation, ingestion, and penetration. 	**Inhalation**—Toxic gases may pass rapidly into capillary beds of lungs and be carried to all parts of the body via circulatory system. **Ingestion**—Toxics may damage tissues of mouth, throat and gastrointestinal tract; produce systemic poisoning if absorbed through these tissues. **Skin/Eye Contact**—Hair follicles, sweat glands, as well as cuts and abrasions are the main portals of entry. Eyes are acutely sensitive to chemical irritants as well as corrosives. **Injection/Penetration**—Exposure to toxics by injection seldom occurs; however wounds by broken glass or metal are frequent avenues for circumstances of injected chemicals.	Treat all chemicals as toxic until you are certain they are otherwise. Wear protective equipment over exposed skin and eyes. Handle contaminated metal and glassware carefully.

Courtesy of Ward's Natural Science Establishment

Procedure

1. Use your knowledge to draw fire triangles with the correct leg removed to represent the following control measures.
   (a) Isolate flammable materials from reactive chemicals.
   (b) Do not store more than 1 gallon of flammable material in glass in the laboratory.
   (c) Transfer flammable liquids in a working fume hood whenever possible.
   (d) Eliminate sources of ignition.
   (e) Store flammable substances in a cool area, at a maximum temperature of 27° C (80° F).
   (f) Use special sorbent materials to reduce vapor pressure when wiping up spills.
   (g) Transport flammable liquids in metal or other protective containers.
2. Use your knowledge to circle the leg of the fire triangle that is most vulnerable to these common safety problems.
   (a) Improperly stored glass containers of flammable solvents.
   (b) A lack of adequate grounding to prevent sparking (by static electricity) generated by flowing liquids.
   (c) Mixed flammable liquids in a waste disposal can with other chemicals.
   (d) Open flames on a laboratory bench near flammable liquids.
   (e) Transporting glass containers containing flammable liquids on top of cart.
   (f) Flammable substances stored on shelf with acids and other reactive chemicals.

Part B—Corrosive Substances

Corrosive chemicals are solids, liquids, or gases that, by direct chemical action, are injurious to body tissue and corrosive to metal. Corrosive injury may range from irritation to actual physical destruction of body tissues. Below are typical corrosive substances that you may encounter in the laboratory.

Type	Chemical	Phase
Mineral Acid	Hydrochloric acid (HCl)	Liquid
Mineral Acid	Sulfuric acid (H_2SO_4)	Liquid
Organic Acid	Acetic acid (CH_3COOH)	Liquid
Strong Base	Sodium hydroxide ($NaOH$)	Solid or Liquid
Strong Base	Potassium hydroxide (KOH)	Solid or Liquid
Strong Base	Ammonium hydroxide (NH_4OH)	Solid or Liquid

I. Mineral acids. Everyone knows that mineral acids can cause burns. Few people realize, however, the extent to which they can damage body tissues. Sulfuric acid vapor is more toxic than hydrogen cyanide (HCN). The corrosive and toxic effects of sulfuric acid are listed below.

(a) Physical properties: Dense, corrosive liquid. Very strong oxidizer. Liberates large amounts of heat when mixed with water. Dissolves most metals with release of hydrogen gas.
(b) Flammability: Non-flammable, but highly reactive. Heat of reaction sometimes great enough to ignite flammable gases generated by reactions.

(c) Effects: Destruction of skin and eye tissues. Vapors can cause destruction of lung and other respiratory tissues. Ingestion of a corrosive liquid can cause teeth to dissolve and destroy tissues of mouth, throat and abdomen.

Materials

1 pint concentrated red food dye
glass beakers, 100 ml
white paper
2 dropping pipets

Procedure

Every student has heard the admonishment "Do as you oughta . . . add acid to water." The following investigation will demonstrate why this rule is critical to chemical safety.

1. For illustration purposes, the red food coloring will represent hydrochloric acid. Cut and position 7-cm white paper strips around the top edge of two beakers. Fill 1 beaker with the red dye, the other with tap water. Fill beakers to the same height, about 2 cm from the lip.
2. To the beaker containing the acid (red dye), use a pipet to add 5 to 10 drops of water from a normal dispensing height (15 to 20 cm).
3. To the beaker containing the water, use a pipet to add 5 to 10 drops of acid from a normal dispensing height.
4. Remove the paper and check the white paper wrapped around each beaker for signs of splashing. What can you conclude from the evidence (the color of the splash marks) about acid dilution?

II. Corrosive solids. Corrosive solids may appear relatively harmless because they can be removed more easily than liquids, and because they might not cause an immediate destructive effect. The effect is largely dependent on their solubility in skin moisture and even more rapid solubility in the moisture present in the respiratory and intestinal tracts.

Caustic alkalies (sodium or potassium hydroxides) are perhaps the greatest potential hazard because of their wide use in general science laboratories. The hazards of corrosive solids include the following.

(a) Solutions of corrosive solids are readily absorbed through the skin.
(b) Caustic alkalies and other corrosive solids might not produce immediate, painful reactions.
(c) Many corrosive solids dust easily, thus increasing the hazard through other exposure routes (inhalation).
(d) Molten corrosive solids greatly increase the threat of exposure by acting as liquid corrosives.

The most serious hazard associated with corrosives is from materials in the gaseous state. In this state, corrosives are rapidly absorbed into the body by dissolution in skin moisture and by inhalation. Remember, many corrosives give off dangerous vapors whether by themselves or during spills or chemical reactions.

Procedure

Your teacher will set up a demonstration that shows the action of corrosive solids. Agar is used to represent body tissue.

5. Observe the effects of each substance on the agar over the next 1 to 2 hours, especially within the first 1/2 hour.
6. Which solid(s) had the greatest corrosive effect? Which solid(s) the least corrosive effect?

7. What factor present in the agar is responsible for initiating the corrosive effect?
8. Which solid took the longest time to exhibit a corrosive effect?
9. (a) Are some substances non-corrosive?
   (b) Why, based on what observed characteristics?
10. Based upon your observations, what can you conclude about those solids that are corrosive?

Part C—Toxic Substances

One gram of table salt will kill a rat, if administered in the right manner. All chemicals are toxic in excess, that is, if they exceed tolerable limits. Chemicals can injure a body system via one or more exposure routes: direct contact, inhalation, ingestion, and penetration.

Materials

Paramecium culture
concentrated biological stain
dilute biological stain
microscope slides
coverslips
dropping pipets
protozoa slowing agent (DETAIN)
pond or distilled water

Procedure

1. Prepare a wet mount with 1 drop each *Paramecium* culture, concentrated biological stain, and DETAIN (protozoa slowing agent). Label the slide A.
2. Prepare a 2nd wet mount in the same way, but this time use dilute biological stain. Label this slide B.
3. Prepare a control with *Paramecium* and DETAIN but no stain. Label the control C.
4. Observe each of the 3 slides for 15 to 20 minutes under various magnifications of a compound microscope.
   (a) Which preparation concentration is toxic to *Paramecium?*
   (b) What observations would form the criteria to measure cell toxicity of the stain?

Part D—Reactive Substances

Reactive chemicals promote violent reactions under certain conditions. They are placed in categories that reflect their common reactive hazard.

(a) Acid-sensitives: chemicals that react with acids (or acid fumes) to generate heat, hydrogen, or flammable gases and toxicants.

Type	Example
alkali hydroxides	sodium hydroxide
carbonates	potassium carbonate
nitrites	
sulfides	

(b) Oxidizers: chemicals that promote or start combustion in other materials through the release of oxygen or other gases.

Type	Example
oxygen	hydrochloric acid
mineral acids	hydrogen peroxide
peroxides	potassium nitrite
nitrites	sodium nitrate
nitrates	potassium dichromate
dichromates	zinc oxide
oxides	

(c) Water-sensitives: chemicals that react with water, steam, and moisture to generate heat and/or flammable or explosive gases.

Type	Example
Strong acids	sulfuric acid
Strong bases	sodium hydroxide

Always read the container label for any listed incompatibilities for any chemical that you are working with.

Materials

baking soda (sodium bicarbonate)
vinegar (acetic acid)
small glass beaker
spatula

Procedure

1. Pour a small amount of vinegar in the glass beaker.
2. Add a pinch of baking soda to the vinegar. What happens?
3. What reaction category did this chemical reaction demonstrate?
4. Can you write the chemical equation for this reaction?
5. Would you expect this reaction to proceed at a quicker rate if sulfuric acid were used?

Investigation A.2 INTRODUCTION TO THE MICROSCOPE

Introduction

There are many different kinds of microscopes. The compound microscope often used in biology laboratories is an instrument made up of two groups of glass lenses, one at each end of a tube. With the monocular microscope you use only one eye in viewing an object, so the image you see has length and width but little depth. Most objects examined under a monocular microscope must be so small or thin that light can pass through them. You can see form and structure in such objects because some of their parts absorb more light than others. Things seen in this way are said to be observed by transmitted light.

Materials (per student or pair of students)

monocular microscope
microscope slide
coverslip
forceps
dropping pipet
finger bowl or beaker containing water
lens paper
paper towels
strips of newspaper
scissors
transparent plastic millimeter rule
pieces cut from magazine photograph

Procedure

1. **Setting up a microscope.**
   Remove your microscope from its case or storage cabinet. Grasp the arm of the instrument with one hand. Place your other hand under the

base. Always use two hands to carry a microscope. Set it down gently on the laboratory table, with the arm toward you and the stage away from you. The base should be a safe distance from the edge of the table.

Your teacher will help you identify each part of the microscope (figure A.3) and explain its use. Become familiar with each part before proceeding.

Figure A.3 Two styles of monocular compound microscope.

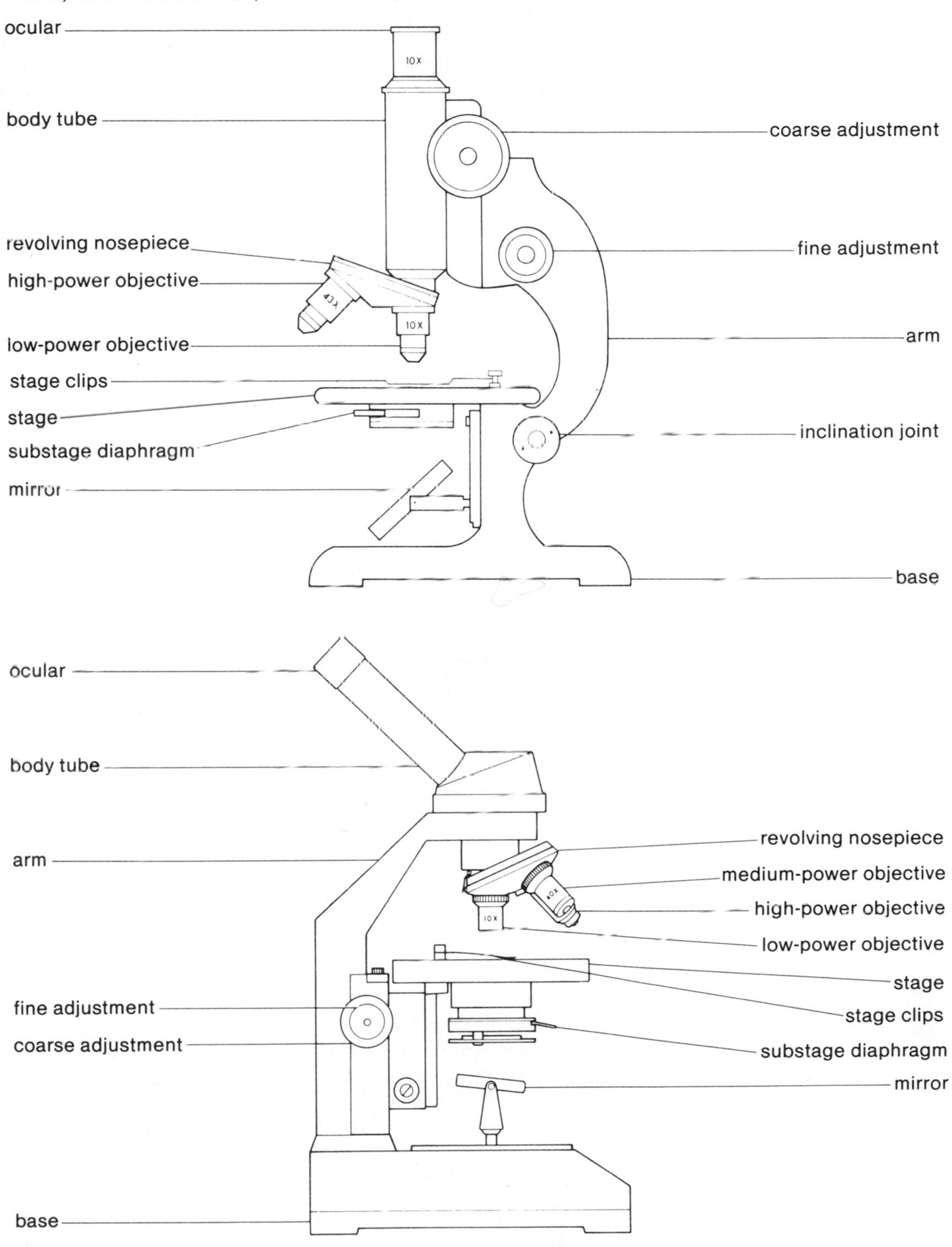

2. **Preliminary adjustments.**
Use the coarse-adjustment knob to raise the body tube so that the objectives do not hit the stage when you rotate the revolving nosepiece. Turn the nosepiece so that the low-power (shorter) objective is in line with the body tube. You will hear a click when the objective moves into position. Adjust the substage diaphragm to the largest possible opening. Adjust the mirror so that it reflects light upward through the opening in the stage. Never let direct sunlight strike the mirror. Look into the ocular. Make final adjustment of the mirror so that the circular field of view is evenly illuminated. Adjust the diaphragm to eliminate any glare.
If the lenses of the ocular or the objective are cloudy or dusty, wipe them gently with a piece of lens paper. Use a circular motion and light pressure. Never use any other kind of paper or cloth. When a piece of lens paper has been used once, discard it. If this procedure does not clean the lenses, consult your teacher.
3. **Preparation of materials.**
Material to be studied under a microscope is usually placed on a piece of glass called a microscope slide. In most cases the material is covered with a small, thin piece of glass called a coverslip. Both slide and coverslip should be as clean as possible. Always handle them by the edges.
To clean a slide, hold it by the edges, between index finger and thumb, and dip it into water. Then wipe dry, using a piece of soft, clean cloth or paper towel.
Coverslips are much more fragile than slides. To clean a coverslip, hold it by the edges, using the index finger and thumb of one hand, and dip it into water. Fold a piece of thin, soft cloth or lens paper. Hold it between the index finger and thumb of the other hand. Insert the coverslip in the fold and apply pressure to both surfaces at the same time by bringing thumb and finger together (figure A.4). A gentle, circular motion is most effective.

Figure A.4 Cleaning a coverslip.

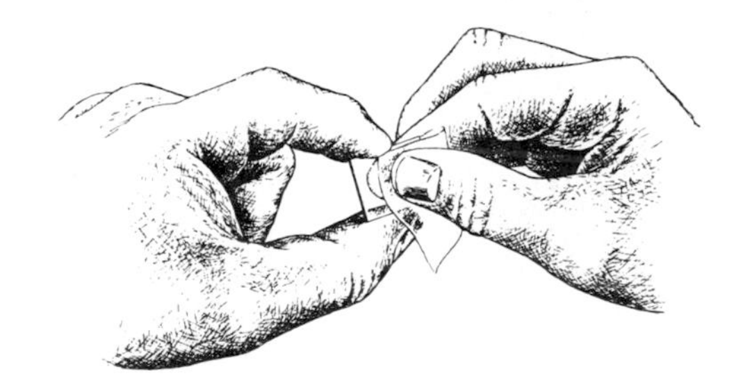

4. **Preparing a wet mount.**
Using scissors, cut out a piece of newspaper that includes at least one letter *e*. The piece should be not more than 3 to 5 mm^2. If possible, find a piece that has printing on only one side. Place the piece of newspaper in the center of a slide, printed side up. Put a single drop of water on the newspaper. Some of the water will soak into the paper, but some should remain surrounding it. If necessary, add another drop of water. Place a coverslip over the paper. The water will spread out in a thin, even layer between coverslip and slide.
Some skill is required to place the coverslip on the slide so that no air bubbles are included in the mount. The best method is to hold the coverslip at an angle of about 45° to the slide. Bring the cover slip down to the slide until the lower edge touches the drop of water. Continue to lower the slip slowly until it is parallel to the surface of the slide (figure A.5). Remaining bubbles may be moved by gently tapping the coverslip with the eraser of a pencil.
5. **Focusing.**
Using the coarse adjustment, raise the body tube until there are about 2 cm between the low-power objective and the stage. Place the wet-mount slide on the stage. Position it so that a letter *e* is in the center of the stage opening and is right side up. Use the stage clips to hold the slide in position. Look at the microscope from the side and use the coarse adjustment to slowly lower the body tube. The lower end of the objective should be about 1 mm above the coverslip. Never allow the objective to touch the coverslip.

Look through the ocular. Slowly raise the body tube until the print on the newspaper becomes visible. If you see no image after you have raised the object more than I cm, you have missed the position for correct focus. Refocus—look at the microscope from the side, lower the objective to its original position, and try again. Never lower the tube with the coarse adjustment while you are looking into the ocular. When you see an image of the printed material, rotate the fine-adjustment knob to obtain the best possible focus. Adjusting the diaphragm may improve clearness.

(a) Compare the position of the image of the letter *e* in the ocular with the position of the printed *e* (the object) on the slide. Is the image in the same position as the object seen with the unaided eye? If not, describe its position.
(b) While looking into the ocular, slowly move the slide from right to left. Which way does the image move?
(c) Move the slide away from you. Which way does the image move?

6. **Using high power.**
Rotate the revolving nosepiece so that the high-power (longer) objective is in line with the body tube. Make sure that the lower end of the objective does not touch the coverslip. If this happens, you will have to repeat the entire sequence, beginning with focusing the low-power objective. Use only the fine adjustment to bring the image into focus. Usually less than one full turn (in either direction) is needed.
(a) Is the field of view now larger or smaller?
(b) Does the switch from low power to high power change the position of the image?
(c) Is the illumination more or less bright than it is with low power?
Use the coarse adjustment to raise the body tube. Remove the slide and save it for later use.

7. **Magnification.**
If an object is magnified 50 diameters (50×), the image you see is 50 times longer and wider than if the object were viewed with the unaided eye at a distance of 25.4 cm.
The degree of magnification provided is engraved on each objective and ocular. The magnification of combined ocular and objective equals the product of these numbers. If, for example, the number on the ocular is 5× and that on the low-power objective is 12×, the combined magnification is 5 × 12, or 60, diameters. Using the same ocular and high-power objective that magnifies 45× will produce a magnification of 5 × 45, or 225, diameters.
(a) Find the magnification numbers on your microscope.
(b) Calculate the magnification with low power.
(c) With high power.

8. **Measuring with a microscope.**
Because objects examined with a microscope are usually quite small, biologists use units of length smaller than centimeters or millimeters for microscopic measurement. One such unit is the micrometer, which is one thousandth of a millimeter. The Greek letter μ (called mu) followed by m, thus μm, is the symbol for micrometer.
You can estimate the size of a microscopic object by comparing it with the size of the circular field of view. To determine the size of the field, place a plastic mm rule on the stage. Use the low-power objective to obtain a clear image of the divisions on the rule. Carefully move the rule until its marked edge passes through the exact center of the field of view. Now, count the number of divisions that you can see in the field of view. The marks on the rule will appear quite wide; 1 mm is the distance from the center of one mark to the center of the next.
(a) What is the diameter, in millimeters, of the low-power field of your microscope?

Figure A.5 Making a wet mount.

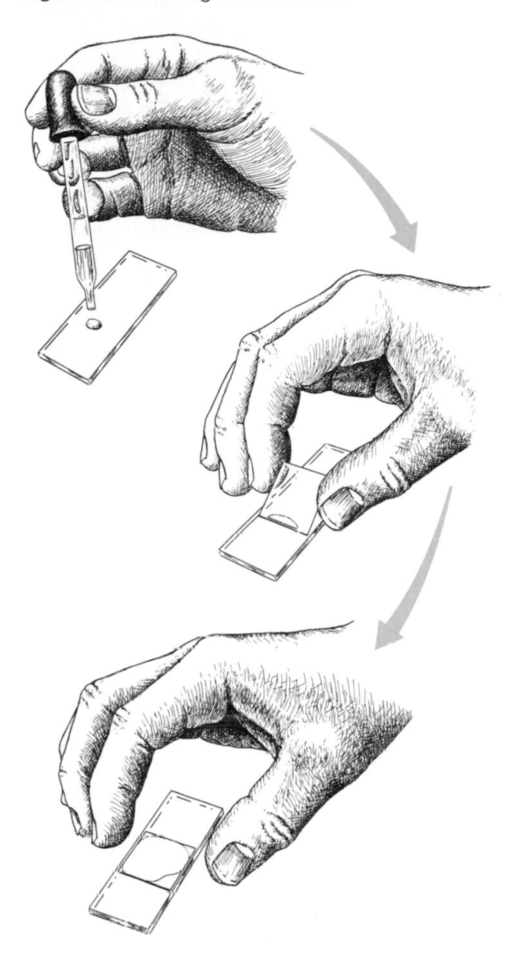

(b) What is it in micrometers?

To measure the diameter of the high-power field, use the following procedure: First, divide the magnification number of the high-power objective by that of the low-power objective. Then divide the diameter of the low-power field of view by this quotient. The result is the diameter of the high-power field of view. For example, if the magnification of your low-power objective is 12× and that of your high-power objective is 48×, the quotient is 4. If the diameter of the low-power field of view is 1600 μm, the diameter of the high-power field of view is 1600 ÷ 4, or 400 μm.

(c) Calculate the diameter of your high-power field in micrometers.

Remove the plastic rule and replace it with the wet mount of the letter *e*. (If the mount has dried, add water.) Using low power, compare the height of the letter with the diameter of the field of view.

(d) Estimate as accurately as possible the actual height of the letter in millimeters.

(e) In micrometers.

9. **Resolving power.**

Remove the slide from the stage and carefully lift off the coverslip. Discard the piece of paper. Dry the slide and the coverslip. Prepare another wet mount, using a small piece of a magazine photograph. Examine this mount under low power.

(a) How does the magnified image compare with the photograph as seen with the unaided eye?

You have just seen an example of a microscope's resolving power, its ability to clearly separate details. With the unaided eye most people cannot see two separate objects that are less than 0.1 mm apart. A microscope permits us to detect space between objects that are much closer together than this.

A microscope actually does two things: it provides magnifying power, and it provides resolving power.

10. **Care of a microscope.**

Microscopes, like all other laboratory instruments, must be given proper care. At the end of the class, turn the revolving nosepiece until the low-power objective is in place. Adjust the body tube so that the lower end of the objective is about 1 cm above the stage. If you tilted the instrument at the inclination joint, return it to its untilted position. Turn the stage clips so that they do not extend beyond the side of the stage. Do not leave a slide on the stage. Return the microscope to its storage space. Clean and dry all slides and coverslips.

For Further Investigation

If you have a stereoscopic microscope in your laboratory, explore its use. This instrument is used most often to view whole objects by reflected rather than by transmitted light.

Investigation A.3 USE OF A MICROSCOPE: BIOLOGICAL MATERIAL

Materials (per student or pair of students)

small piece of white potato
iodine-potassium-iodide (I_2KI) solution in dropper bottle
yeast culture
monocular microscope
glass slide
coverslip
dropping pipet
beaker or finger bowl containing water
lens paper
paper towel

Procedure

For setting up the microscope, cleaning slides and coverslips, and preparing wet mounts, follow the directions given in investigation A.2.

1. Place a *small* piece of potato in the center of a clean slide. Place the slide on your laboratory table and carefully press the potato with a finger until some juice is forced out. Distribute the juice evenly over the center of the slide by moving the piece of potato in a circle. Discard the potato. Add 1 drop of water and a coverslip. Avoid getting air bubbles in the mount.
2. Examine the mount under low power. Decrease the size of the opening in the substage diaphragm. This increases contrast between the starch grains and the water surrounding them. Move the slide on the stage until you locate a field in which you see well-separated grains. Center a group of these grains in the field and switch to high power.
   (a) Describe the shape of an individual starch grain.
   (b) Can you see any internal structure in these grains? If you can, describe what you observe.
3. Turn again to low power. Stain the starch grains by placing a small drop of the iodine-potassium-iodide (I_2KI) solution on the slide at one side of the coverslip (figure A.6). Tear off a small piece of paper towel. Place the torn edge in contact with the water at the opposite edge of the coverslip. As water is absorbed by the paper towel at one edge, I_2KI solution will be drawn under the coverslip at the opposite edge. Continue until the I_2KI solution covers half the space under the coverslip. I_2KI solution will continue to spread slowly throughout the mount.
4. Examine various regions of the mount to observe the effects of different concentrations of I_2KI on starch grains. Examine under low power, then under high power.
   (a) What changes occur in the starch grains exposed to relatively high concentrations of I_2KI?
   (b) What differences do you see between these grains and others exposed to lower concentrations of I_2KI?
   (c) Can you see internal structures in the stained grains? If so, describe them.
   (d) Using the method given in investigation A.2, estimate the size (in micrometers) of the larger starch grains.
5. Remove the slide, lift off the coverslip, and dip both into water. Dry them. Carefully wipe off any liquid from the microscope stage.
6. Place 1 drop of yeast culture on a clean slide. Add a coverslip. Examine first under low power, then under high power. Describe the shape of the yeast organisms.

Figure A.6 Putting a liquid under a coverslip.

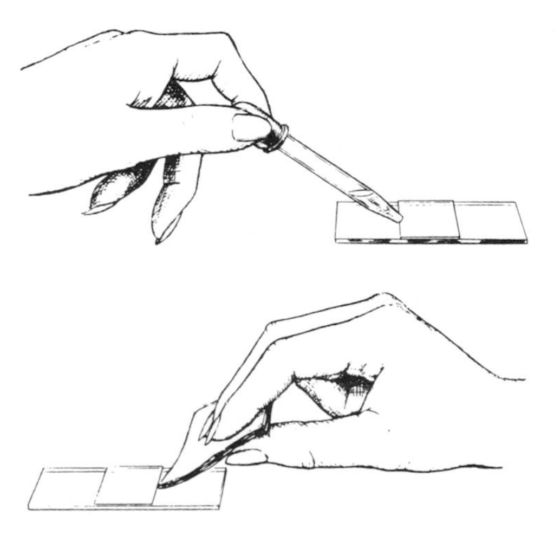

7. Study the arrangement of small groups of these organisms.
   (a) From your observations, can you come to any conclusions about how new yeast organisms develop?
   (b) Sketch any internal structures you see.
8. Using I_2KI solution, stain the yeast as you stained the starch grains.
   (a) Compare the effects of the solution on the yeast organisms with its effects on starch grains.
   (b) Can you see any structures that were not visible in the unstained yeast organisms? If so, describe them.
9. Using the method previously described, estimate the size (in micrometers) of an average yeast organism.

APPENDIX 3

A Catalog of Living Things

This appendix shows one way taxonomists arrange the major groups of living organisms. It does not take into account the many extinct groups known to us only from fossils.

In general the classification is not carried below class level. In two groups—insects and mammals—a more detailed classification at the order level is given. In some cases, examples are given at the family level. To show how complicated classification can become at lower levels, the primate order of mammals is carried to the family level.

In examples, common names of groups are used wherever appropriate, as, for example, phylum Chlorophyta: green algae. The illustrated organisms are identified by common names if they have them. If not, names of genera rather than of individual species are usually given. References to figures in the text are provided to supplement the appendix illustrations, thus providing a greater diversity of examples.

A Catalog of Living Monerans

All are prokaryotic, lacking membrane-bounded organelles; DNA a naked strand, usually circular. Extremely minute (usually 1 to 5 μm). Single cell, chains, colonies, or slender branched filaments. Great diversity in metabolic pathways: many anaerobic, many photosynthetic. Photosynthetic species may use H_2, H_2O, or other substances. Reproduction by fission; exchange of genetic material occurs in some species. Bacteria are prevalent in all environments; more than 5000 species described; 2 major groups; classification to phyla difficult. (Figures 11.1, 11.2, 11.3, 11.6)

Archaebacteria

Biochemically, this group appears to fall between the eubacteria and the eukaryotes; composition of cell walls and plasma membranes differs from that of eubacteria; transfer RNA and ribosomal RNA also unique. These may have been among the very first organisms. They are adapted to extreme conditions. 3 major groups: methanogens, thermoacidophiles, extreme halophiles. (Figures 11.8, 11.9, 11.10)

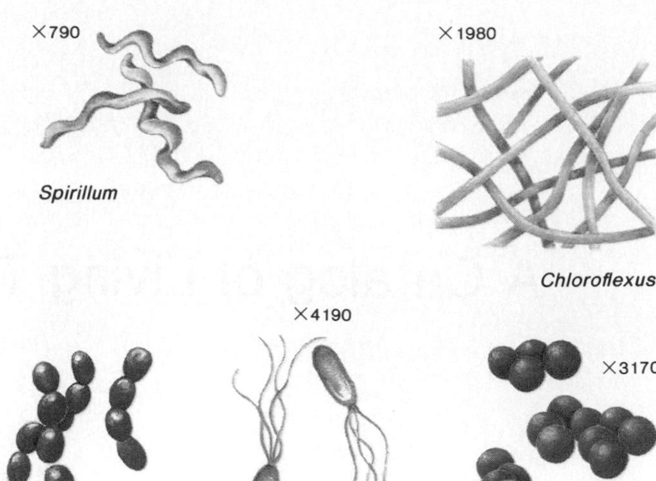

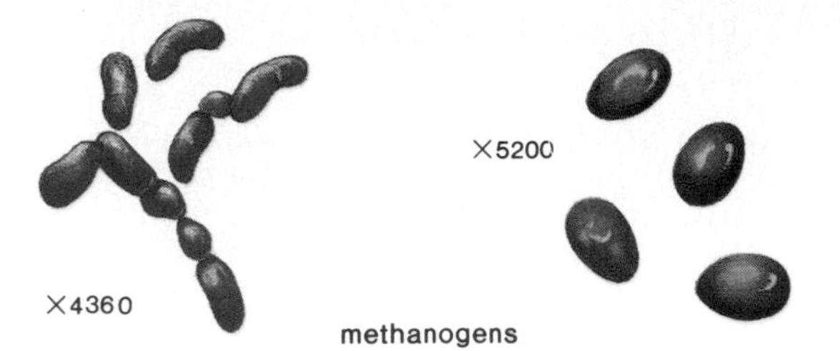

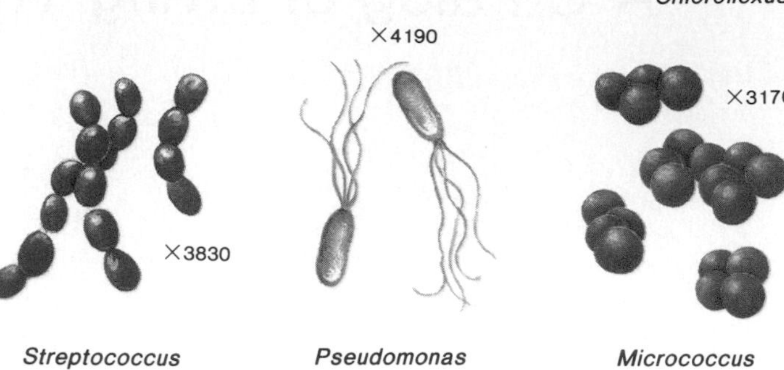

Eubacteria

Distinguishing characteristics include shape; nutritional patterns; waste materials produced; reactions to stains; size, shape, and color of colonies; and means of locomotion. Bacterial flagella are different in structure from those of eukaryotes. Major groups include cyanobacteria, anaerobic photosynthetic bacteria, chemoautotrophic bacteria, spirochetes, enteric bacteria, fermenting bacteria, aerobic nitrogen fixers, gram-positive bacteria. (Figures 6.1, chapter 11 opener, 11.1, 11.2, 11.3, 11.4, 11.5, 11.12, 11.13, 11.15, 11.16, 11.18, 11.19, 11.26, 11.34, 11.38)

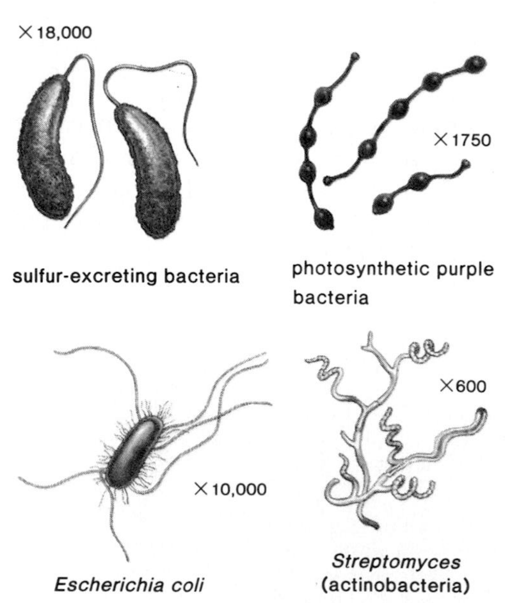

Continued at top of next column.

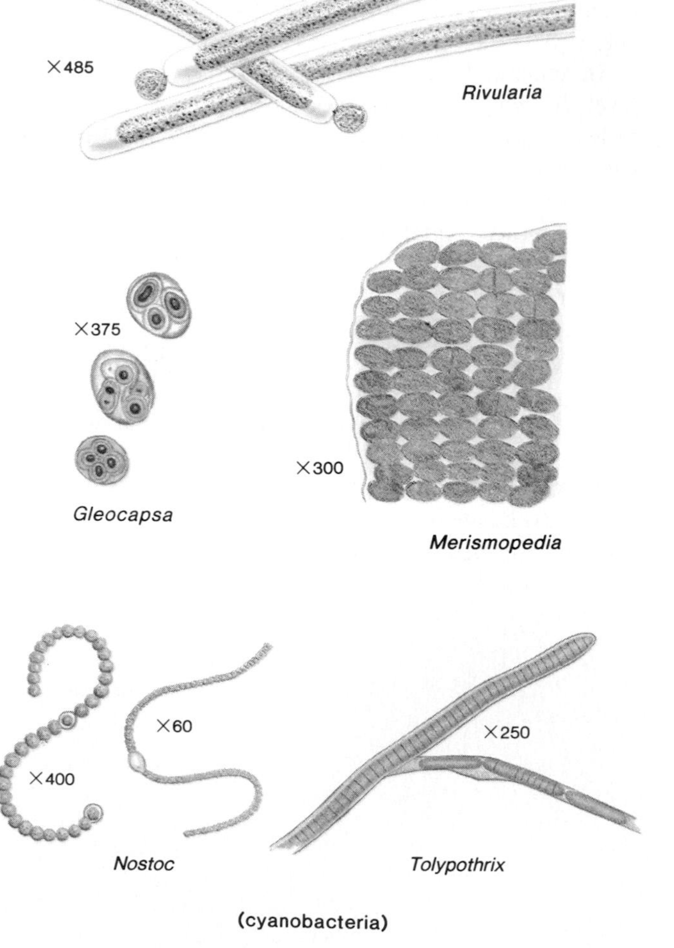

A Catalog of Living Protists

Eukaryotic, with membrane-bounded nuclei and organelles; DNA organized into chromosomes complexed with protein. Size ranges from microscopic to 100 m. Unicellular, colonial, or multicellular. Great variability in cell organization, chromosome structure, mitosis, meiosis, and life cycles.

Reproduction asexual, by fission; or sexual, by conjugation or fertilization; often involving complex life cycles. Nutrition autotrophic or heterotrophic; many can switch from one form to the other.

Algae, protozoa, slime molds, slime nets, water molds, and others; more than 100,000 species. (Figures 10.23a,b,c)

Flagellates (several phyla) [Latin: *flagellatus*, whipped]

Microscopic or almost so. Locomotion by whiplike flagella. They occur singly or as colonies. Some contain chlorophyll. Includes euglenoids, dinoflagellates; many parasitic, mutualistic, and commensalistic forms. About 2000 species. (Figures 1.11b, 12.7)

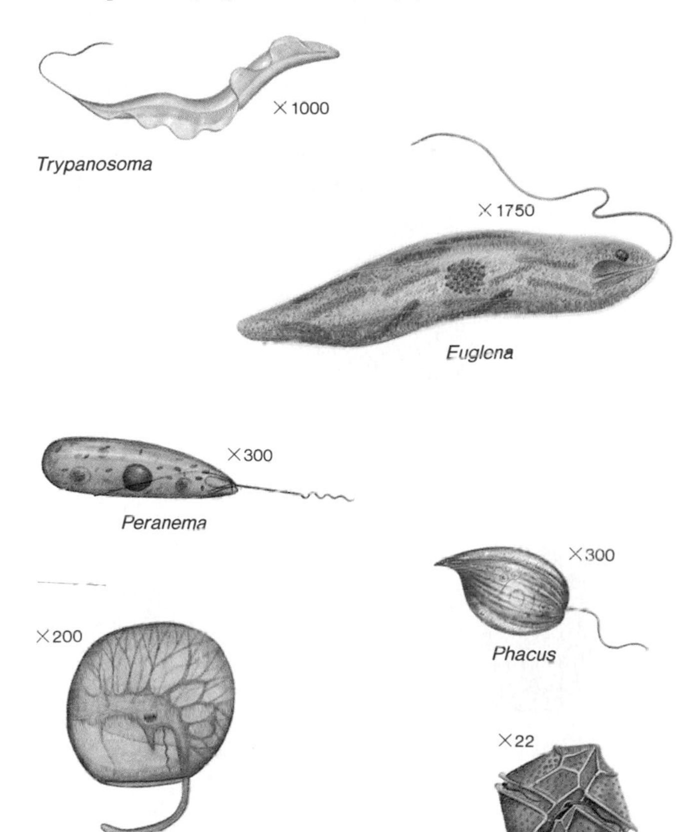

Sarcodines (several phyla) [Greek: *sarx*, flesh, + *eidos*, form]

Microscopic or almost so. Locomotion by pseudopods. Many produce intricate shells or skeletal structures; others are naked. About 8000 species. (Figures 10.23b, 10.33a, 12.2, 12.8, 12.9)

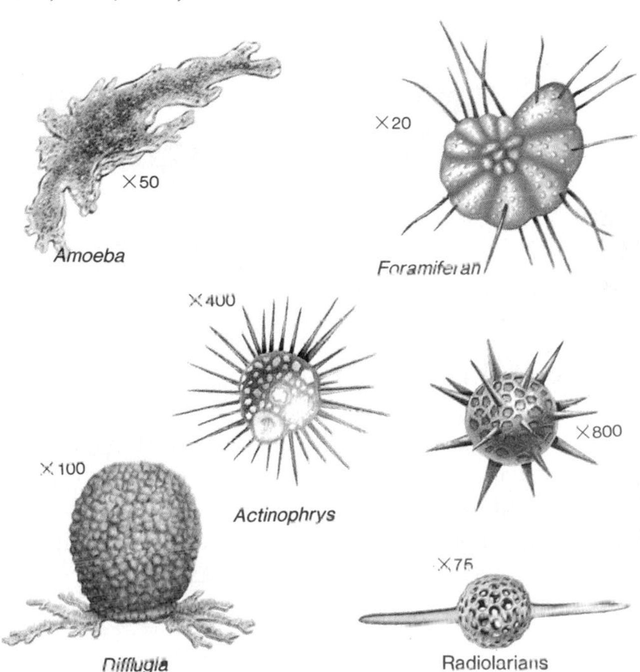

Sporozoans (Phylum Apicomplexa) [Latin: *apex*, summit, + *complexus*, an embrace]

Microscopic. Usually no locomotion, but pseudopods or flagella may occur in certain stages of some species. Parasites with complex life histories. About 2000 species. (Figure 12.10)

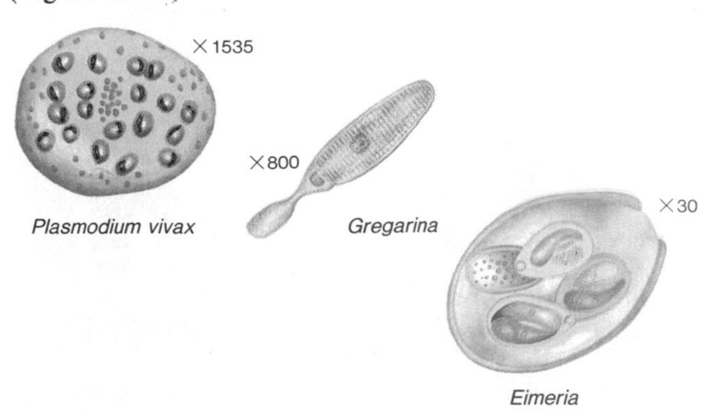

Ciliates (Phylum Ciliophora) [Latin: *cilium*, eyelash, + Greek: *phoros*, carrying or bearing]

Microscopic or almost so. Characterized by presence of macro- and micro-nuclei. Locomotion by cilia. About 5000 species. (Figures 1.11a, 12.1b, 12.11, 12.12)

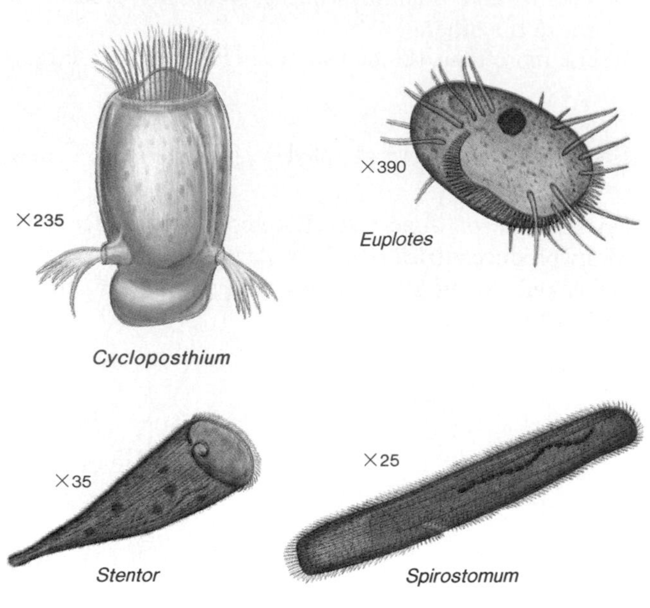

Slime Molds (Phylum Myxomycota) [Greek: *myxa*, mucus, slime, + *myketes*, fungus]

Macroscopic masses of living substance with hundreds of nuclei inside 1 membrane. Each mass moves about and engulfs food like a giant amoeba. Reproduction by spores, as in fungi. Found on decaying vegetation in damp habitats. About 450 species. (Figure 10.23a, 12.5)

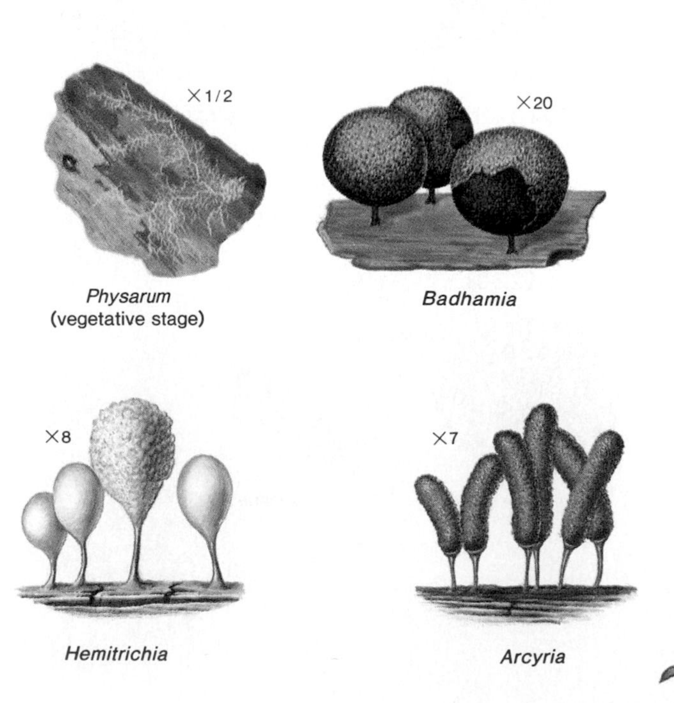

Golden Algae (Phylum Chrysophyta) [Greek: *chrysos*, gold, + *phyton*, plant]

Mostly microscopic. Many with shells of silicon. Chlorophyll usually masked by yellow pigments. Food often stored as oil. Some 10,000 species of diatoms alone. (Figure 12.15)

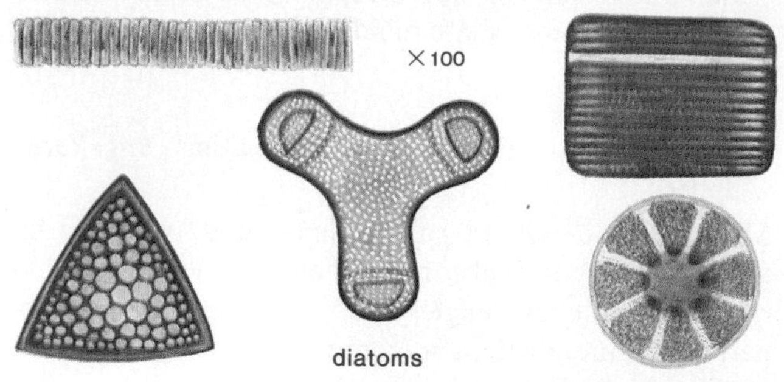

Green Algae (Phylum Chlorophyta) [Greek: *chloros*, green, + *phyton*]

Single cells, filaments, ribbons, sheets, tubes, or irregular masses. Chlorophyll seldom masked by other pigments. Food usually stored as starch. Probably ancestral to plants. About 7000 species. (Figures 12.14, 12.16, 12.17, 13.1, 13.5, 19.9)

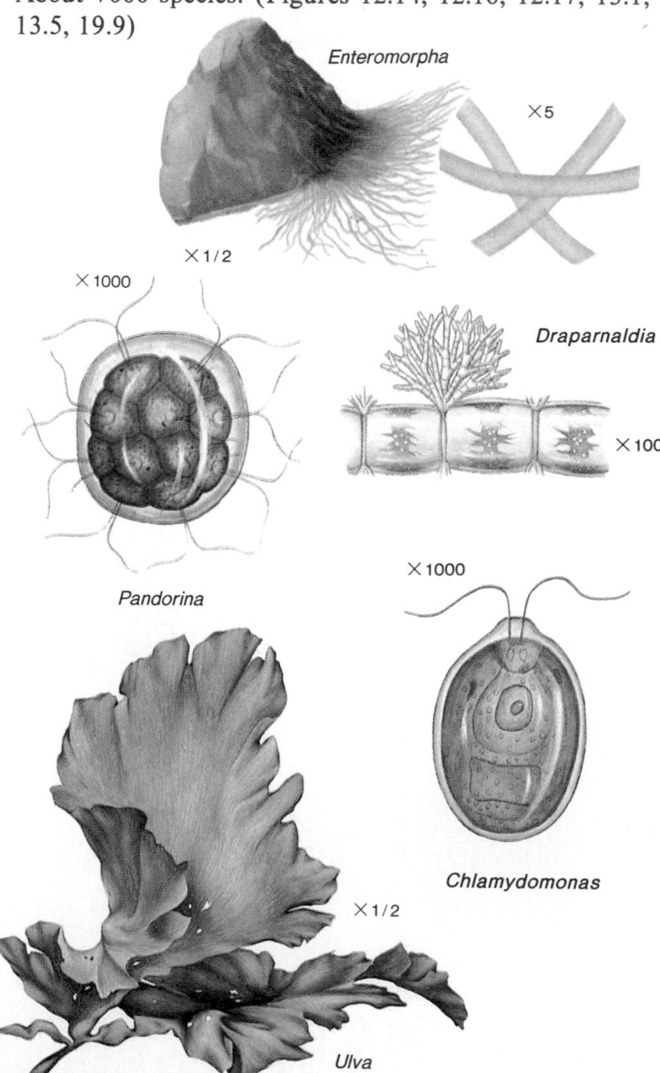

Brown Algae (Phylum Phaeophyta) [Greek: *phaios,* brown, + *phyton*]

Almost all macroscopic (up to 100 m) and marine. Chlorophyll usually masked by brownish pigments. Food stored as carbohydrates, but not as starch. About 1500 species. (Figures 12.18a, 12.18b)

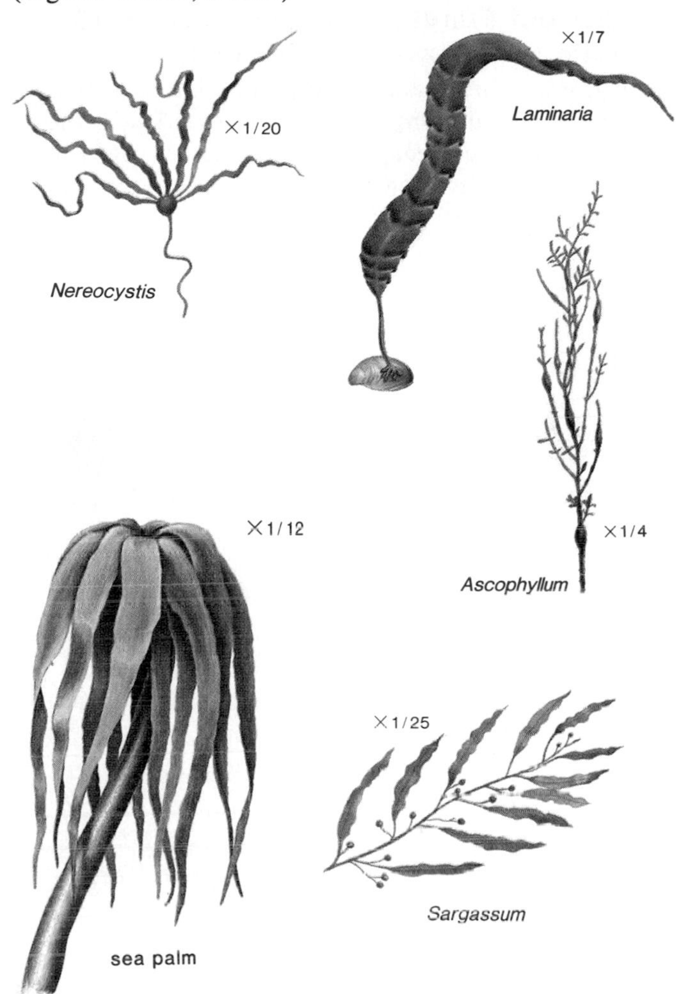

Red Algae (Phylum Rhodophyta) [Greek: *rhodon,* a rose, + *phyton*]

Almost all macroscopic and marine. Chlorophyll usually masked by red pigments. Complex life histories. Reproductive cells not capable of locomotion. Food stored as carbohydrates, but not as starch. About 4000 species. (Figure 12.18c)

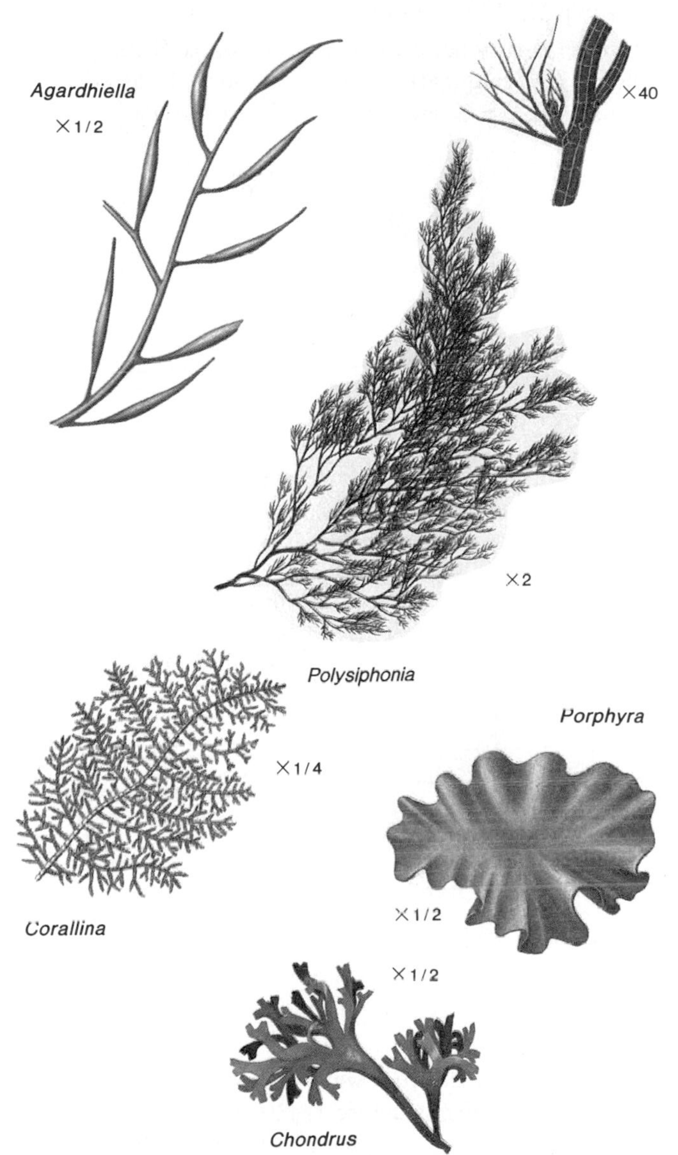

A Catalog of Living Fungi

Eukaryotic; nonmotile; heterotrophic; develop from spores. No chlorophyll. No vascular tissues. Structure primarily a system of threadlike cell groups, or hyphae. Mostly saprophytic, but many are parasitic on plants or animals. More than 100,000 species. (Figure 10.22)

Conjugation Fungi (Phylum Zygomycota) [Greek: *zygon,* pair, + *myketes*]

Hyphae usually not divided by cross walls. Sexual reproduction by conjugation and formation of thick-walled zygospores. About 600 species. (Figure 12.20)

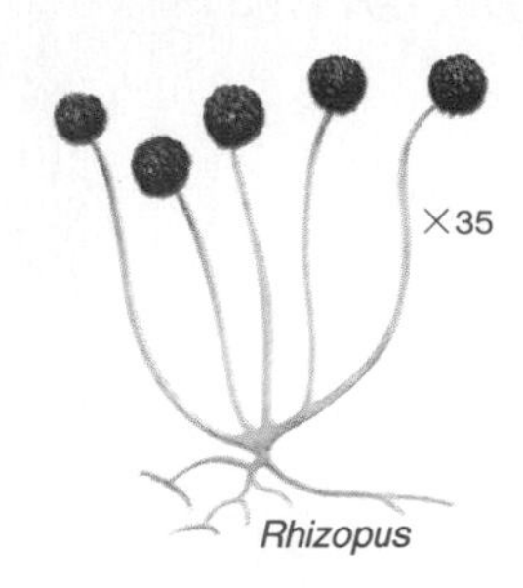

Sac Fungi (Phylum Ascomycota) [Greek: *askos,* bag, bladder, + *myketes*]

Hyphae divided by cross walls. A few unicellular species. Spores of a definite number (usually 8). Sexual spores produced in a saclike structure, the ascus. Many form lichen partnerships with green algae or cyanobacteria. About 25,000 species. (Figures 2.14, 8.19, 12.22, 12.24)

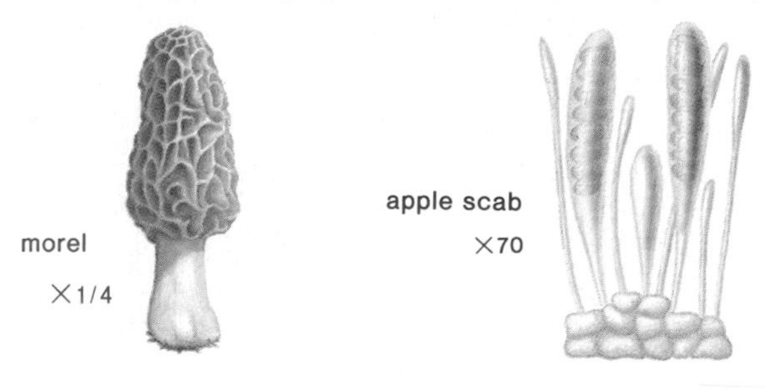

Club Fungi (Phylum Basidiomycota) [Greek: *basis,* base, + *myketes*]

Hyphae divided by cross walls. Spores produced on the surface of a clublike structure, the basidium. About 25,000 species. (Figures 1.8, chapter 12 opener, 12.25, 12.27)

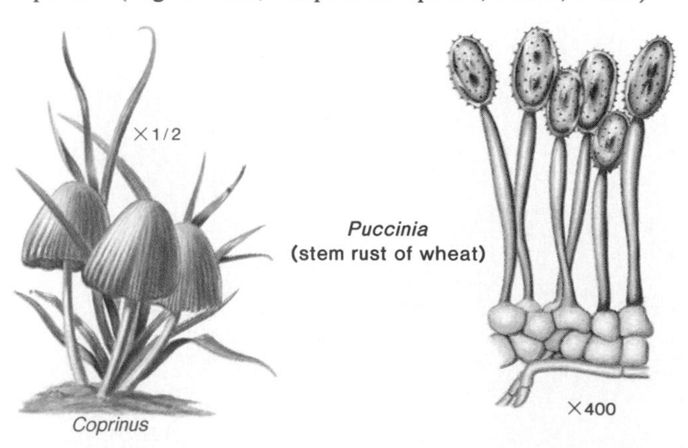

Imperfect Fungi (Phylum Deuteromycota) [Greek: *deuteros,* second, secondary, + *myketes*]

Fungi whose life histories are so little known that they cannot be placed in any of the other classes. This is, therefore, a taxonomic grouping of convenience, not of relationship. Includes members of the genus *Penicillium.* About 25,000 species. (Figures 12.28, 12.30)

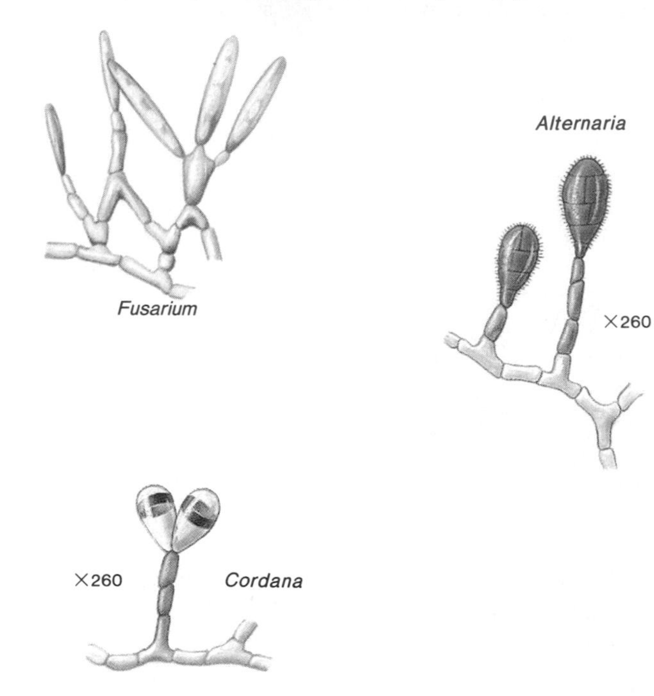

Lichens (Phylum Mycophycophyta) [Greek: *myketes,* + *phykos,* seaweed, + *phyton*]

Symbiotic relationship between a fungus and an alga. Extremely slow-growing. Reproduction often involves the formation of ascospores by meiosis. About 25,000 species. (Figures 3.9, 12.32, 12.33, 12.34)

A Catalog of Living Plants

Eukaryotic; multicellular; autotrophic; develop from a multicellular embryo that does not have a blastula stage. All have cellulose-containing cell walls and chloroplasts containing chlorophylls *a* and *b* plus other pigments. Reproduction sexual, with alternation of generations; in some cases asexual, by vegetative means. 500,000 species.

Bryophytes (Division Bryophyta) [Greek: *bryon,* moss, + *phyton*]

Small (less than 40 cm tall). Mostly terrestrial. Many bear structures resembling stems and leaves, but lack vascular (conducting) tissue. Well-developed alternation of generations. Gametophyte generation is the more conspicuous; sporophyte is more or less dependent on it. About 24,000 species.

Class Hepaticae (liverworts) [Greek: *hepatikos,* liverlike (from the shape of the leaves)]

Gametophytes flat; often simple, branching masses of green tissue, sometimes with leaflike structures. About 8500 species.

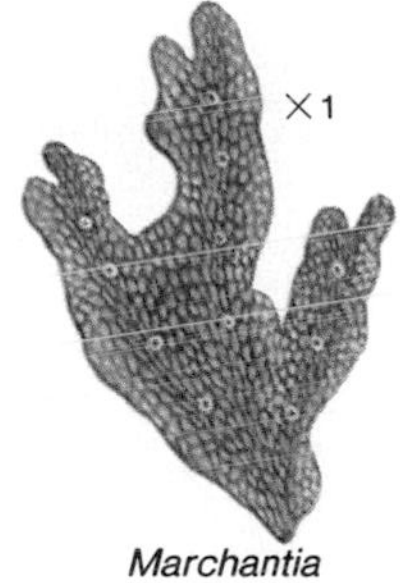

Marchantia

Class Anthocerotae (Hornworts) [Greek: *anthos,* flower, + *keras,* horn]

Gametophytes similar to those of liverworts. Sporophytes live longer and are capable of continuous growth. About 50 species.

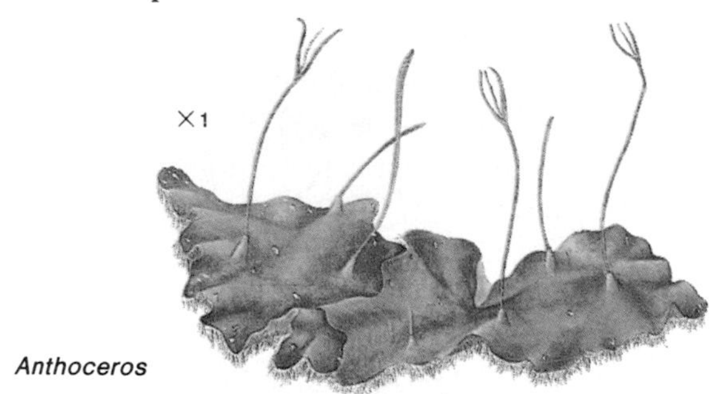

Anthoceros

Class Musci (true mosses) [Latin: *muscus,* moss]

Gametophytes developed from algalike masses of green threads. Plants usually erect (not flat) with leaflike structures arranged in radial symmetry around a stalk. About 15,000 species. (Figure 13.12)

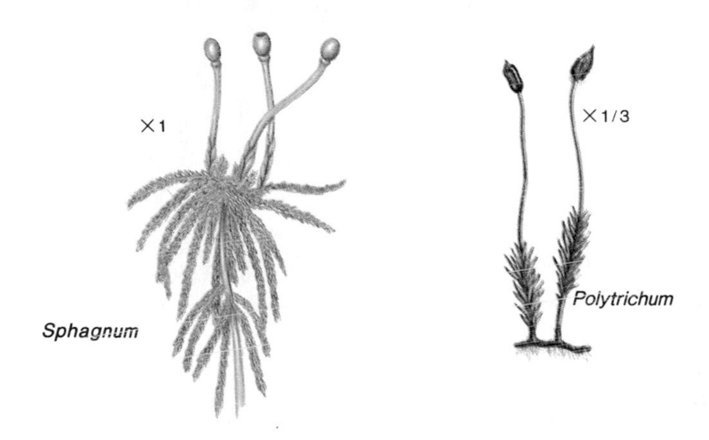

Sphagnum *Polytrichum*

Psilophytes (Division Psilophyta) [Greek: *psilos,* bare, + *phyton*]

Vascular plants with alternation of generations and conspicuous sporophyte. No roots. Forking stems, with spore cases at the tips of short branches. Oldest fossil land plants. 3 species. (Figure 13.12)

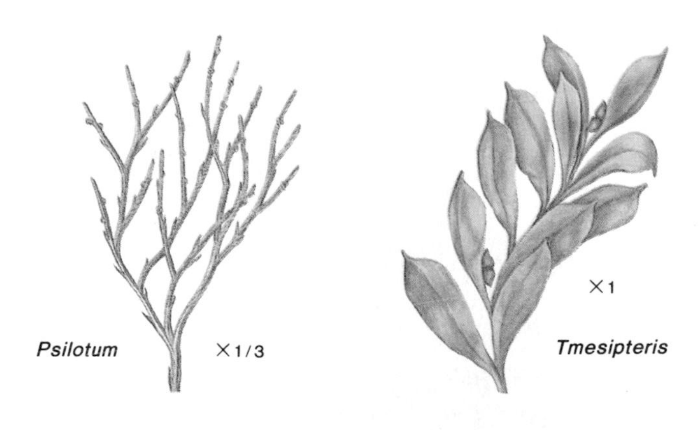

Psilotum *Tmesipteris*

Horsetails (Division Sphenophyta) [Greek: *sphen,* a wedge (from the shape of the leaves), + *phyton*]

Vascular; roots and hollow, jointed stems. Small scalelike leaves arranged in a circle around each stem joint. Spore cases borne on stem structures resembling cones. 32 species. (Figure 13.27, chapter 13 opener)

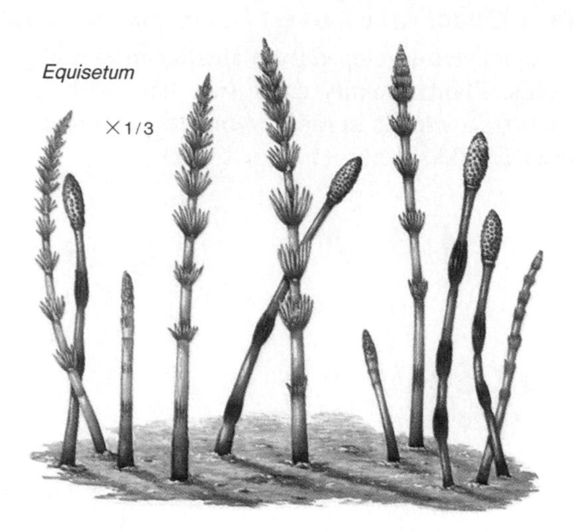

Club Mosses (Division Lycophyta) [Greek: *lycos,* wolf, + *phyton* (so named because the roots of a lycopod were thought to resemble a wolf's claw)]

Low-growing evergreen vascular plants with roots, horizontal stems, and small leaves. Spore cases borne in various ways, usually on modified leaves grouped to form structures something like cones. About 1100 species.

Ferns (Division Pterophyta) [Greek: *pteron,* feather, + *phyton*]

Most have roots, stems, and leaves. Compound leaves grow from underground stems. Sporophytes dominant generation, but gametophytes independent. Free-swimming sperm cells. About 12,000 species. (Figures 10.20a, 13.32)

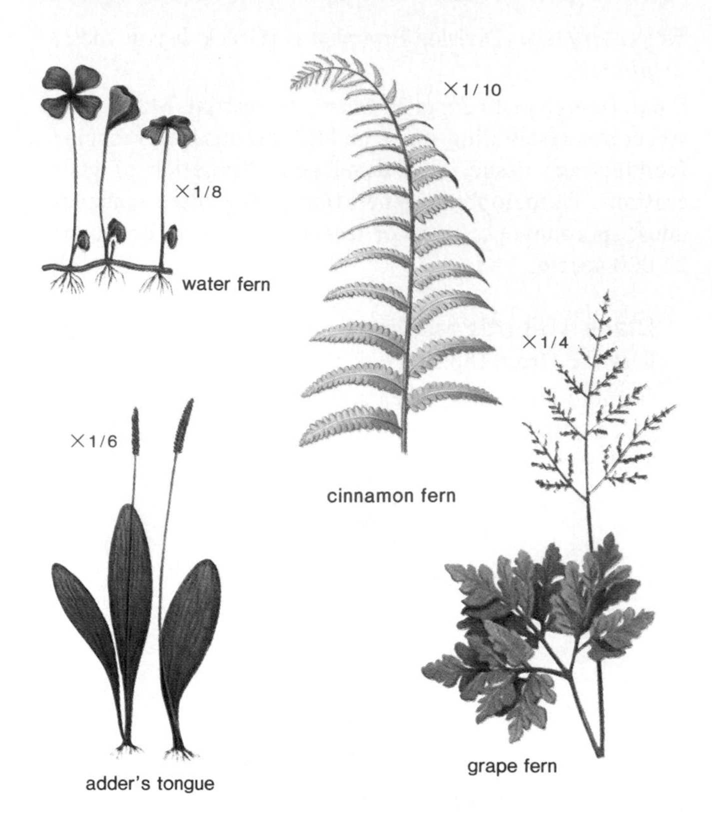

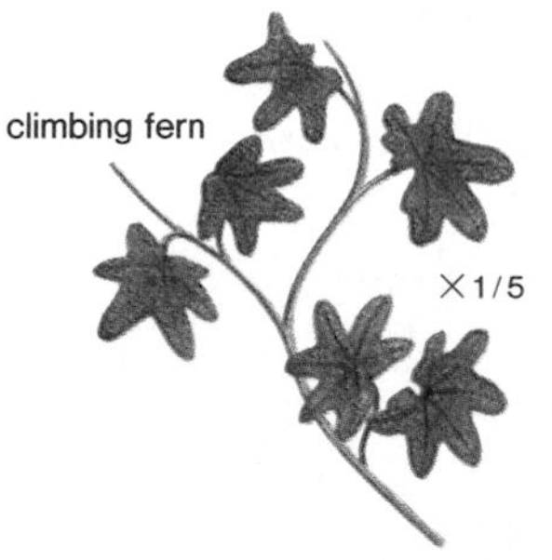

Cycads (Division Cycadophyta) [Greek: *kyos*, a palm, + *phyton*]

Tropical and subtropical vascular plants with palmlike or fernlike compound leaves. Naked seeds borne in cones; unbranched stems. About 100 species. (Figure 13.33b)

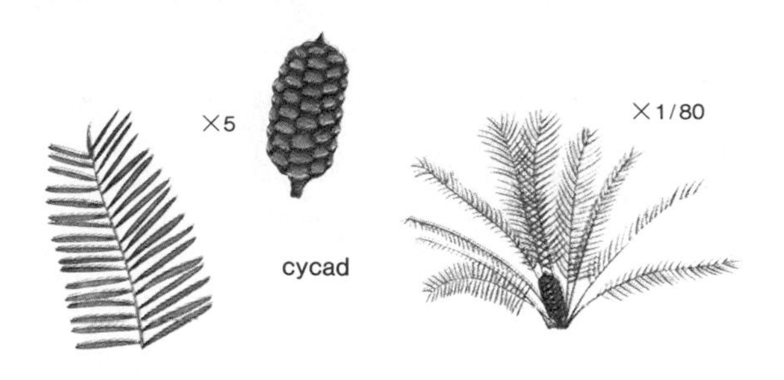

Ginkgoes (Division Ginkgophyta) [Japanese: *gingkyo*, silver apricot, + Greek: *phyton*]

Ancient division of vascular plants with naked seeds, flagellated sperm, fan-shaped leaves; cultivated world-wide. (Figure 13.33c)

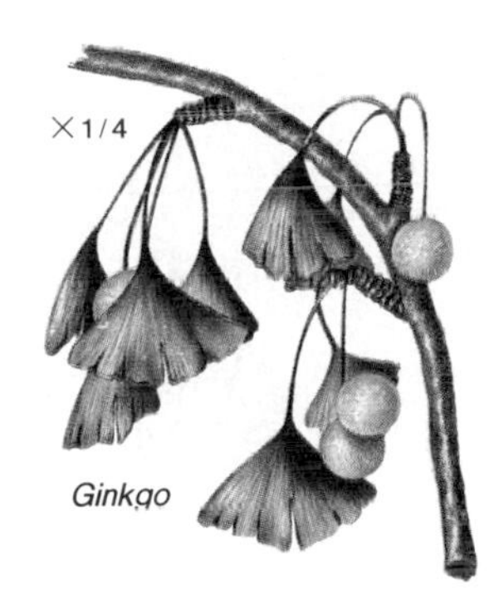

Gnetophytes (Division Gnetophyta) [Latin: *gnetum* from Moluccan Malay *ganemu*, a gnetophyte species found on the island of Ternate, + Greek: *phyton*]

Vascular plants with naked seeds borne in cones; some characteristics like those of flowering plants. 70 species.

Conifers (Division Coniferophyta) [Latin: *conus*, cone, + *ferre*, to bear, + Greek: *phyton*]

Gametophytes microscopic, within tissues of sporophytes. Seeds naked (not enclosed in a fruit), attached to the surface of a modified leaf. Most have needle-shaped leaves; many are evergreen. About 700 species. (Figures 2.3, 2.5, 2.12, 13.2, 13.33a, 13.34)

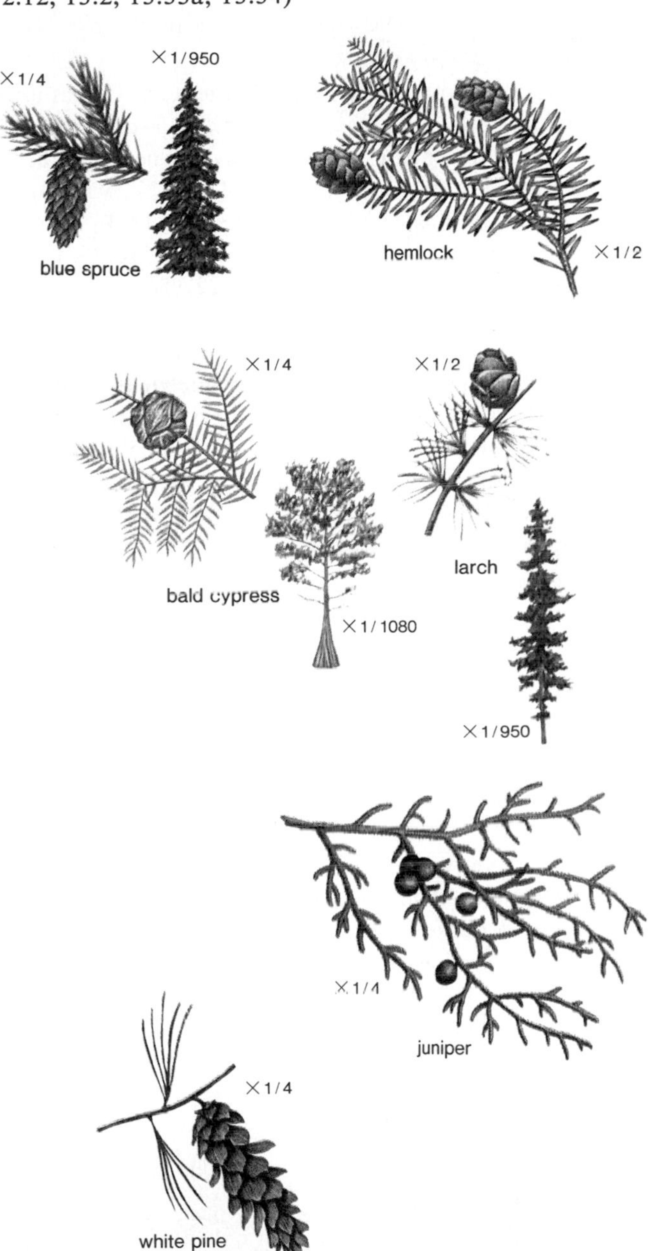

Flowering Plants (Division Anthophyta)

Gametophytes microscopic, within tissues of sporophytes. Seeds enclosed in a fruit. Sperm cells in pollen tubes. About 200,000 species. (There are more than 300 families in the division Anthophyta. A few of the common families are given in the following classes. Orders are omitted.)

Dicots (Class Dicotyledoneae) [Greek: *dis,* two, double, + *cotyledon,* a cavity]

Flowering plants. 2 cotyledons in the seed. Leaves usually have veins that form a network. Flower parts usually in fours or fives or multiples of these numbers. About 166,000 species. (Figures 1.3, 1.17, 3.23, 3.25, 6.1, 10.5, 10.20c, 13.14, 13.37c, 13.37d, 13.38, 13.42a, 13.42b, 13.43b, 17.23, chapter 18 opener, 18.25, 18.27, 19.5, 19.29, 20.29a, 22.6, 22.15c, 22.15d)

Family Caprifoliaceae (Honeysuckle Family). Flowers radially or bilaterally symmetrical, with 4 or 5 sepals, 4 or 5 petals (united), 4 or 5 stamens, 1 pistil, and an inferior ovary. (An ovary is the enlarged base of the pistil. It contains the ovules. An inferior ovary is one that is located *below* the attachment of the sepals, petals, and stamens.)

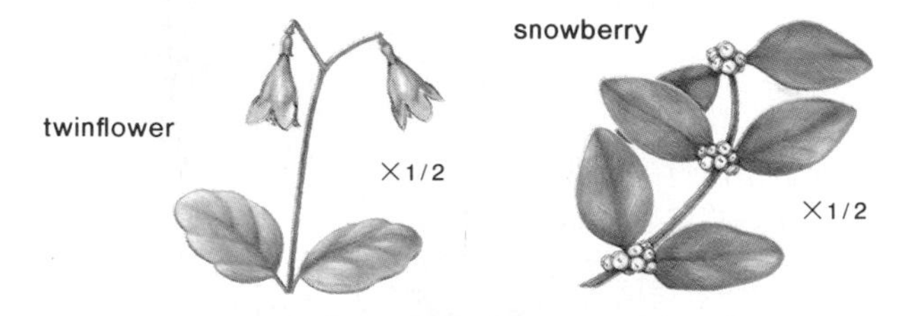

Family Compositae (Composite Family). Small flowers in dense groups. Each group appears to be a single, large flower. Individual flowers radially or bilaterally symmetrical, with sepals reduced to bristles or scales, 5 petals (united), 5 stamens, 1 pistil, and an inferior ovary. (Figures 13.37b, 13.42b, 19.29c)

Family Cruciferae (Mustard Family). Herbaceous. Flowers radially symmetrical, with 4 sepals, 4 petals, 2 sets of stamens (4 long and 2 short), 1 pistil, and a superior ovary. (A superior ovary is one that is located *above* the attachment of sepals, petals, and stamens.) They often have a turniplike or cabbagelike odor.

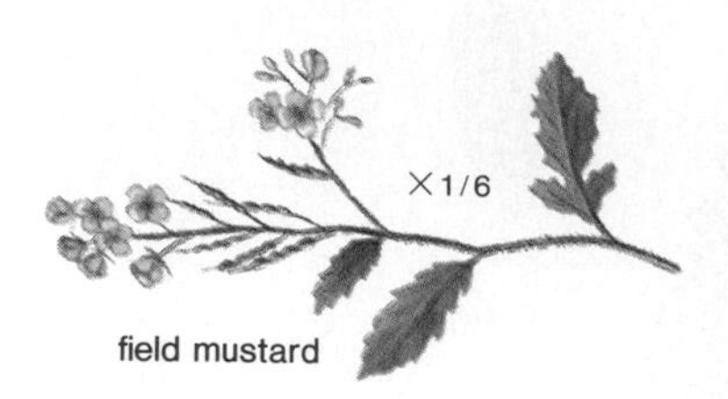

Family Fagaceae (Oak Family). Trees and shrubs. Pistils and stamens in separate flowers. Flowers radially symmetrical, with 4 to 7 sepals, no petals, few to many stamens, 1 pistil, and an inferior ovary.

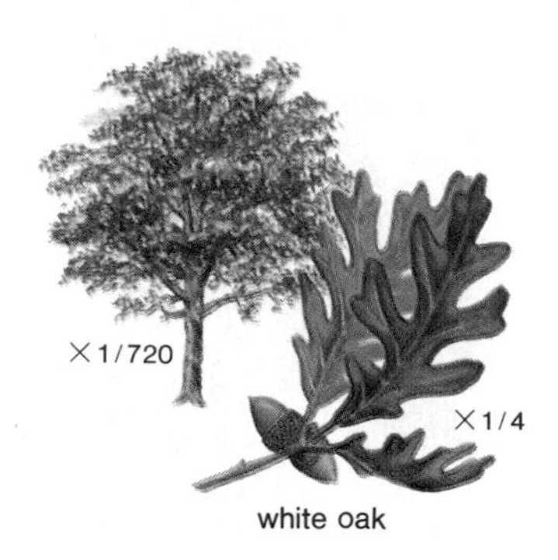

Family Labiatae (Mint Family). Flowers bilaterally symmetrical, with 5 sepals (united), 5 petals (united), 2 or 4 stamens, 1 pistil, and a superior ovary. Stems usually square in cross section. (Figure 19.5)

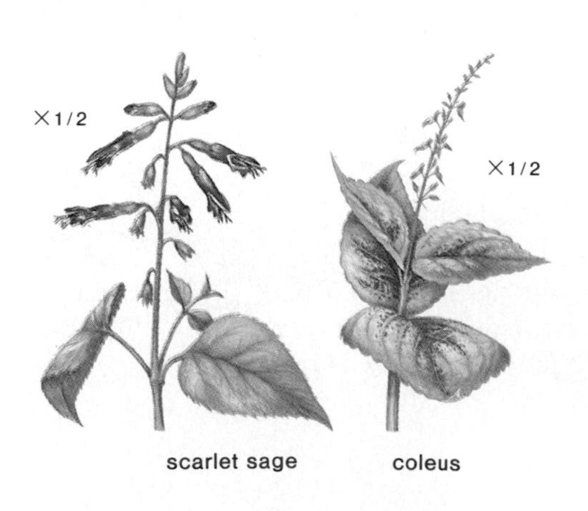

Family Leguminosae (Bean Family). Flowers bilaterally symmetrical, with 5 sepals, 5 petals, 10 stamens, 1 pistil, and a superior ovary. (Figure 19.21)

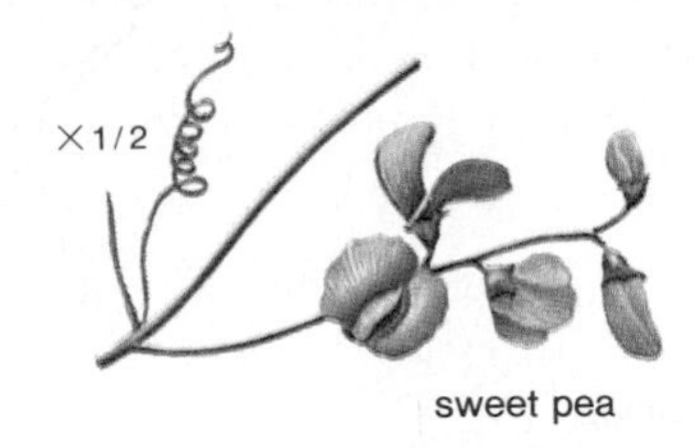

Family Polemoniaceae (Phlox Family). Flowers radially symmetrical, with 5 sepals (united), 5 petals (united), 5 stamens, 1 pistil, and a superior ovary.

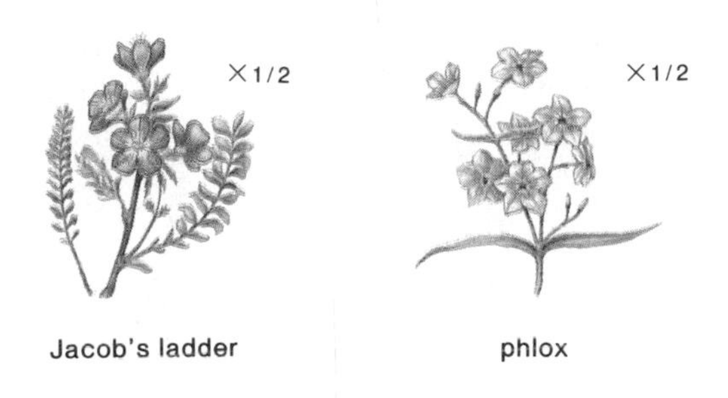

Family Ranunculaceae (Buttercup Family). Herbaceous. Flowers radially symmetrical, with few to many sepals and petals, many stamens and pistils, and a superior ovary. (Figure 13.14)

Family Rosaceae (Rose Family). Flowers radially symmetrical, with 5 sepals, 5 petals, numerous stamens, 1 to many pistils, and either a superior or partially inferior ovary. (Figure 19.29b)

Family Scrophulariaceae (Snapdragon Family). Flowers bilaterally symmetrical, with 5 sepals, 5 petals (2 forming an upper lip and 3 forming a lower lip), 4 stamens (in 2 unlike pairs), 1 pistil, and a superior ovary.

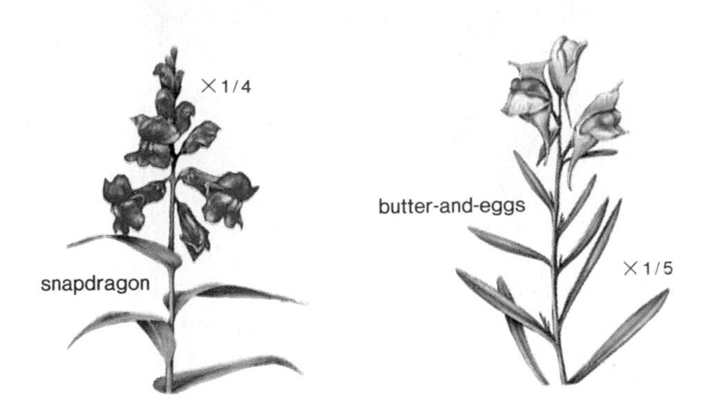

Family Umbelliferae (Parsley Family). Herbaceous. Flowers radially symmetrical, with 5 small sepals, 5 petals, 5 stamens, 1 pistil, and an inferior ovary.

Monocots (Class Monocotyledoneae) [Greek: *monos*, one, single, + *cotyledon*]

Flowering plants. One cotyledon in the seed. Leaves usually have parallel veins. Flower parts usually in threes or multiples of three. About 34,000 species. (Figures 13.9, 13.43a, chapter 20 opener)

Family Alismataceae (Water Plantain Family). Herbaceous. Aquatic or marsh plants. Flowers radially symmetrical, with 3 sepals, 3 petals, 6 to many stamens, 6 to many pistils, and a superior ovary.

Family Amaryllidaceae (Amaryllis Family). Herbaceous. Flowers radially symmetrical, with 3 sepals, 3 petals, 6 stamens, 1 pistil, and an inferior ovary.

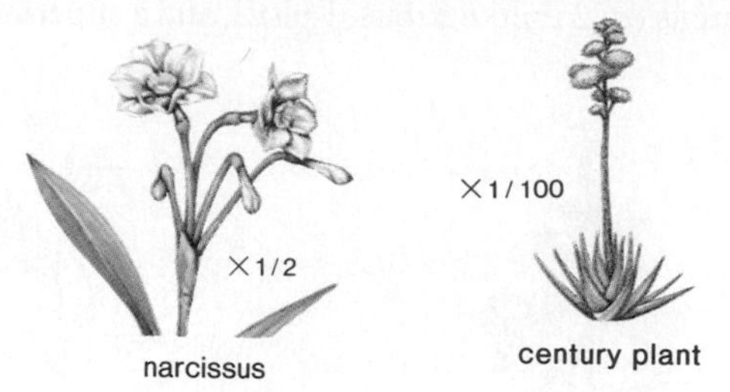

Family Commelinaceae (Spiderwort Family). Herbaceous. Flowers radially or somewhat bilaterally symmetrical, with 3 sepals, 3 petals, 3 or 6 stamens, 1 pistil, and a superior ovary.

Family Cyperaceae (Sedge Family). Herbaceous. Stems usually solid. Flowers radially symmetrical, with no sepals or petals (but scalelike structures present), 1 to 3 stamens, 1 pistil, and a superior ovary. Leaves sheath the stem.

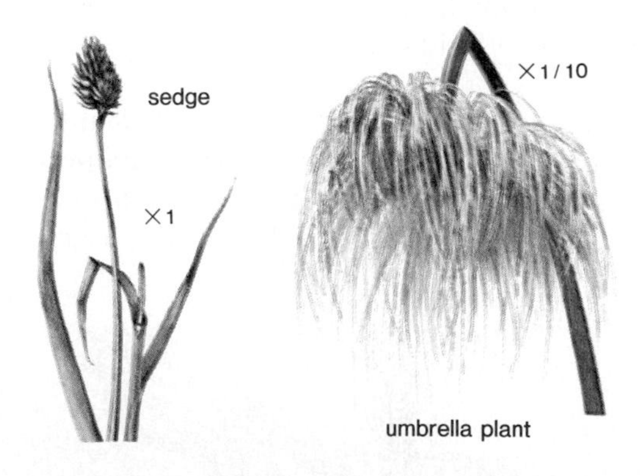

Family Gramineae (Grass Family). Stems usually hollow. Flowers radially symmetrical, with no sepals or petals (but scalelike structures present), 1 to 6 stamens, 1 pistil, and a superior ovary. Leaves sheath the stem.

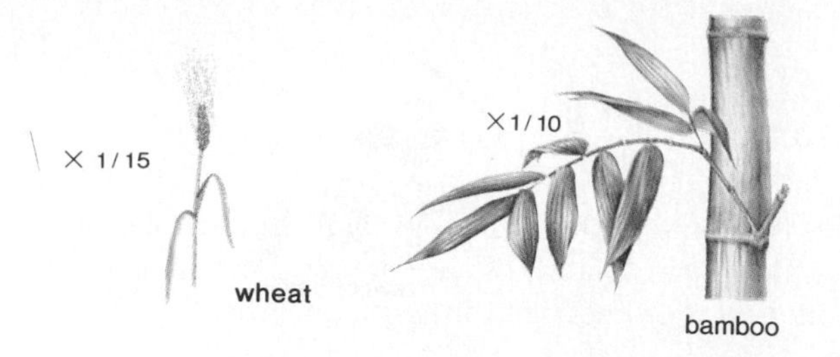

Family Iridaceae (Iris Family). Herbaceous. Flowers radially or somewhat bilaterally symmetrical, with 3 sepals, 3 petals, 3 stamens, 1 pistil, and an inferior ovary.

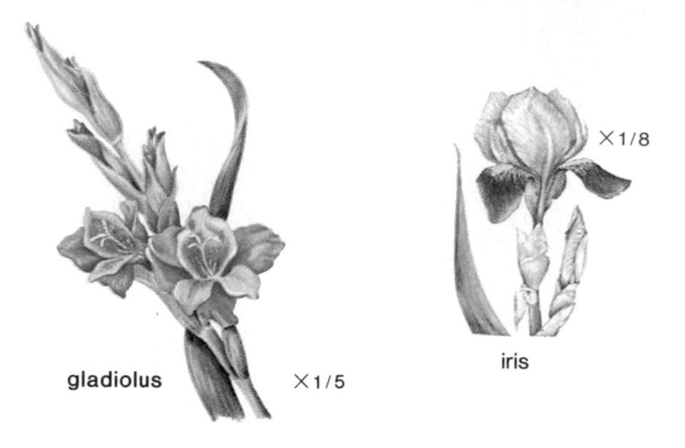

Family Liliaceae (Lily Family). Flowers radially symmetrical, with 3 sepals, 3 petals (sepals and petals often colored alike, thus appearing to be 6 petals), 3 or 6 stamens, 1 pistil, and a superior ovary. (Figures 13.9, chapter 20 opener)

Family Orchidaceae (Orchid Family). Herbaceous. Flowers bilaterally symmetrical, with 3 sepals, 3 petals (united), 1 or 2 stamens, 1 pistil, and an inferior ovary. (Figure 13.37a)

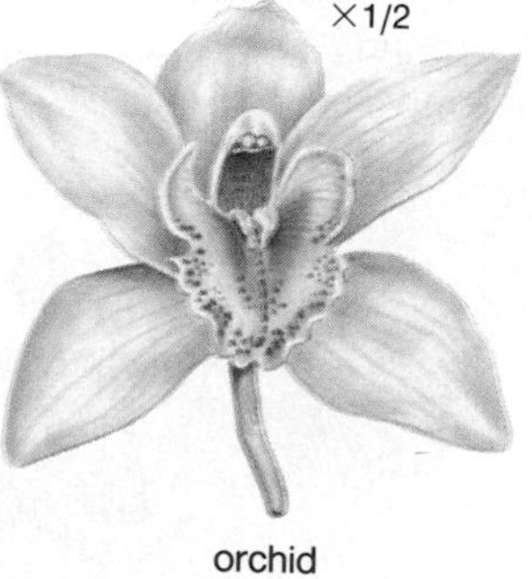

A Catalog of Living Animals

Eukaryotic, multicellular heterotrophs; most are motile at some stage in the life cycle. Reproduction usually sexual, with organisms developing from an embryo that has a blastula stage. More than 1 million species.

Sponges (Phylum Porifera) [Latin: *porus,* pore, + *ferre*]

Mostly marine. Adults always attached to some solid object. Body wall consists of 2 cell layers. Pores in body wall connected to an internal canal system. About 10,000 species. (Figure 14.5)

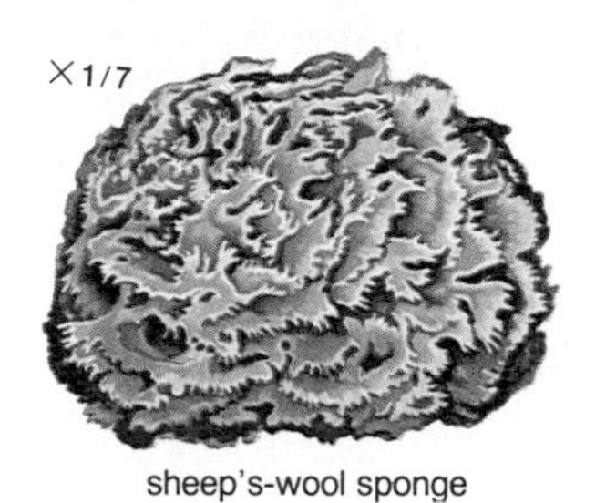

sheep's-wool sponge

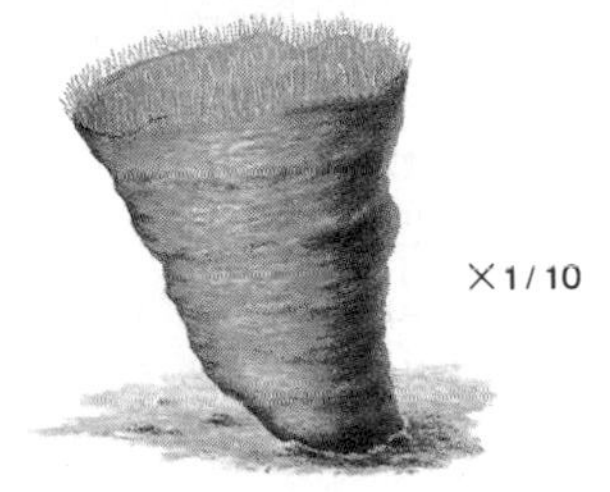

fringed basket

Grantia

bath sponge

Coelenterates (Phylum Cnidaria) [Greek: *knide,* nettle]

Mostly marine. Body wall consists of 2 cell layers and jellylike material between. Saclike digestive cavity with a single opening. Radially symmetrical. Tentacles with stinging cells, nerve network. About 9500 species. (Figure 14.7)

Class Hydrozoa (hydras) [Greek: *hydor,* water, + *zoion,* animal]

Single individuals or colonies. Digestive cavity undivided. Simple sense organs. About 3100 species. (Figures 6.1, 12.4a, 14.40)

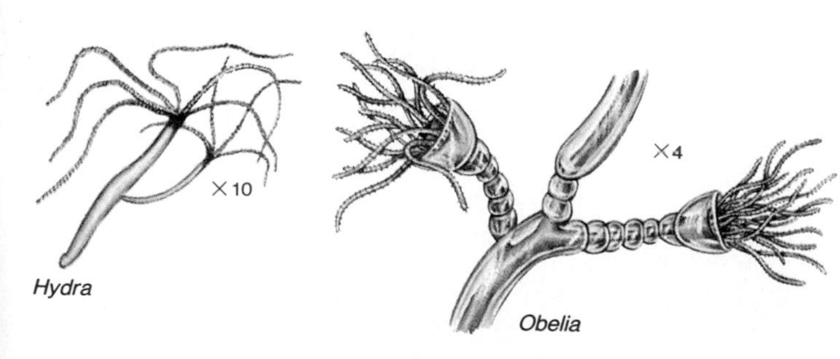

Hydra *Obelia*

Class Scyphozoa (jellyfish) [Greek: *skyphos,* a cup, can, + *zoion*]

Single individuals that float or swim. A few species have attached stages in the life history. Digestive cavity divided. Rather complex sense organs. About 200 species. (Figures 14.7b, 20.2)

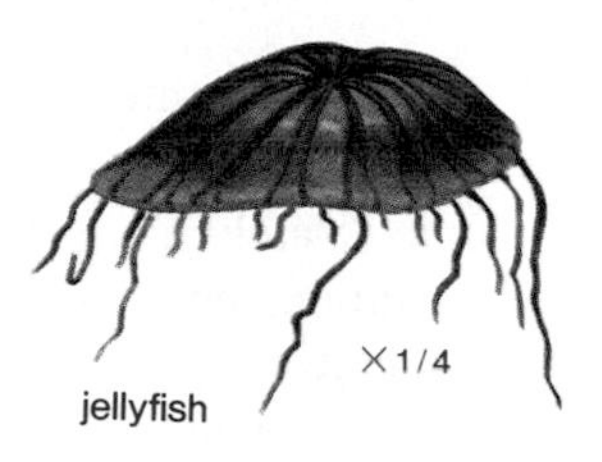

jellyfish

Class Anthozoa (corals and sea anemones) [Greek: *anthos* + *zoion*]

Single individuals or massive colonies. Many species produce limy skeletons. No floating or swimming stages. Digestive cavity divided. About 6200 species. (Figures 14.7a, 14.7c)

sea anemone

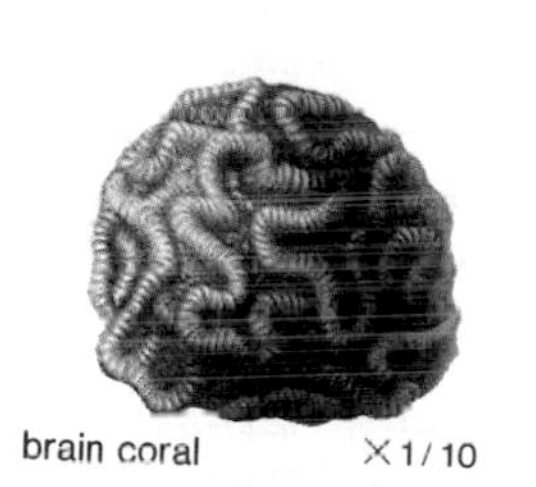

brain coral

Comb Jellies (Phylum Ctenophora) [Greek: *ktenos,* comb, + phoros]

Marine. Somewhat resembling jellyfish, but without stinging cells. Free-swimming, by means of 8 rows of cilia. About 100 species.

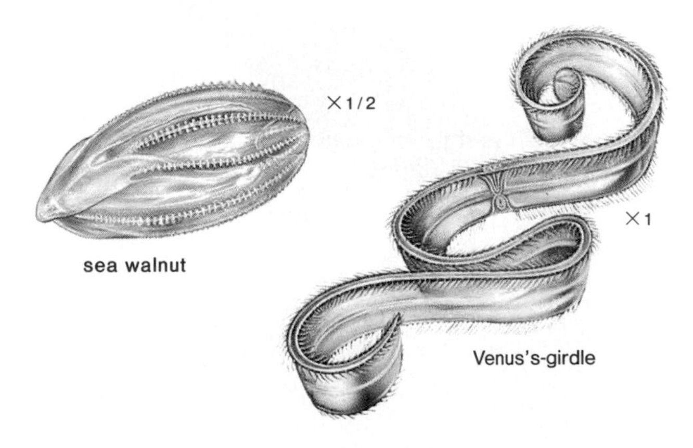

sea walnut

Venus's-girdle

Mesozoans (Phylum Mesozoa) [Greek: *mesos*, middle, + *zoion*]

Parasitic in flatworms, mollusks, and annelids. Minute; worm-shaped. Simple structure; 2 tissue layers; no digestive system. About 45 species.

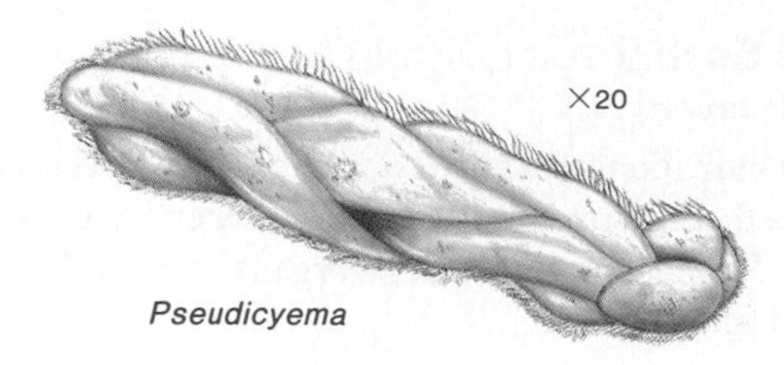

Pseudicyema

Flatworms (Phylum Platyhelminthes) [Greek: *platys*, flat, + *helmins*, worm]

Free-living or parasitic. Usually flat and bilaterally symmetrical. Branched or unbranched digestive cavity with a single opening, or no digestive cavity. Excretion by flame cells. Bodies consist of 3 cell layers. About 15,000 species. (Figure 14.9)

Class Turbellaria (planarians) [Latin: *turba*, disturbance (so named because the cilia cause tiny currents in the water)]

Mostly marine, but some freshwater or terrestrial species. Free-living. Usually have cilia on the outside. (Figures 6.1, 14.9a)

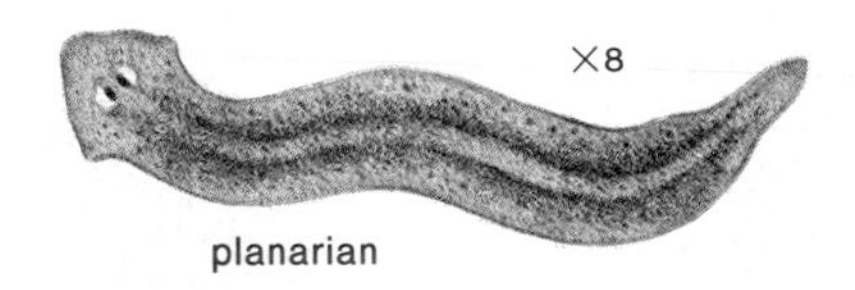

planarian

Class Trematoda (flukes) [Greek: *trematodes*, having holes]

Parasitic. No external cilia. Usually possess hooks and suckers. Digestive system present. (Figures 14.9b, 14.41)

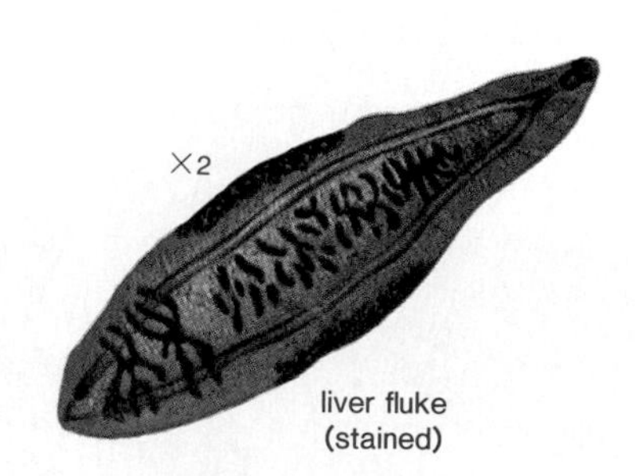

liver fluke (stained)

Class Cestoda (tape worms) [Greek: *kestos*, girdle]

Internal parasites of animals; complex life cycles involving alternate hosts. No digestive system. (Figure 14.9c)

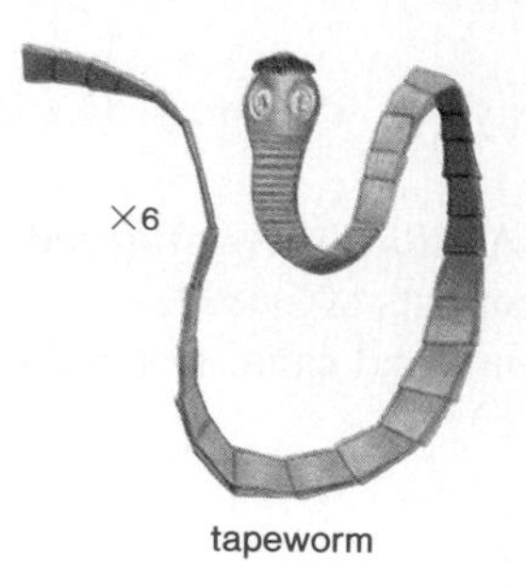

tapeworm

Ribbon Worms (Phylum Nemertina) [Greek: *Nemertes* (the name of a water nymph in mythology)]

Mostly marine. Flat and unsegmented. Digestive tube with 2 openings (mouth and anus). Circulatory system. About 750 species.

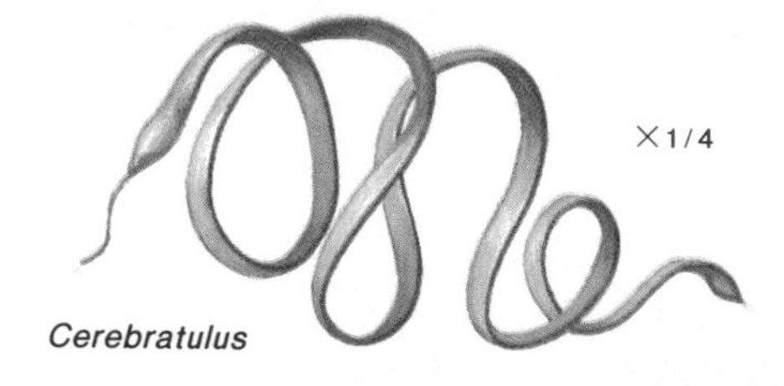

Cerebratulus

Rotifers (Phylum Rotifera) [Latin: *rota*, wheel, + *ferre*]

Microscopic. Freshwater or marine. Bilaterally symmetrical. Internal organs lie in a body cavity developed between endodermal and mesodermal cell layers. Gut with opening. No circulatory system. Cilia form a wheel around mouth. About 2000 species.

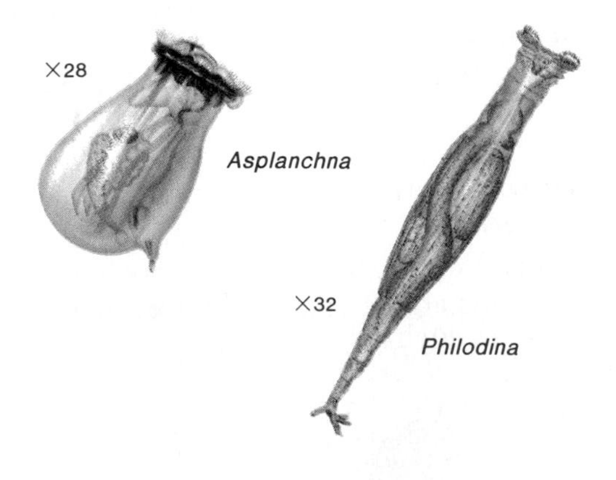

Gastrotrichs (Phylum Gastrotricha) [Greek: *gaster,* belly, + *thrix,* hair]

Freshwater and marine. Free-living. Microscopic. Cilia on ventral surface. Surface of body covered with cuticular scales. 400 species.

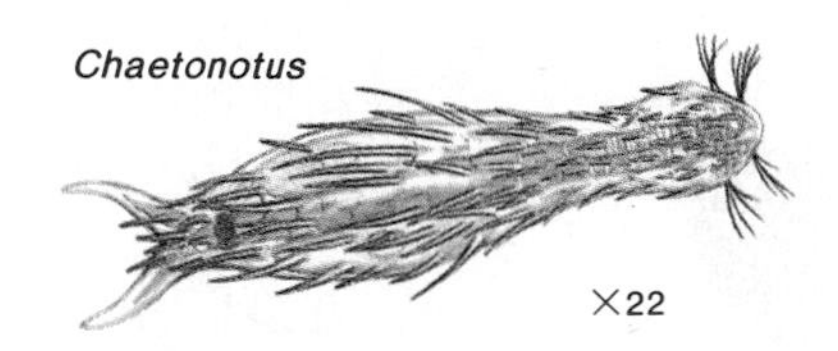

Kinorhynchs (Phylum Kinorhyncha) [Greek: *kinein,* to set in motion, + *rhynchos,* snout or beak]

Marine. Minute. Protrusible spiny snout. Outer surface of body covered with cuticular plates arranged in rings. 100 species.

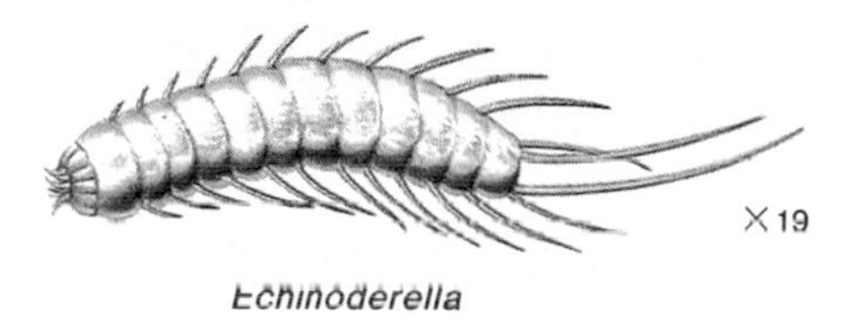

Spiny-headed Worms (Phylum Acanthocephala) [Greek: *akantha,* spine, + *kephale,* head]

Young parasitic in arthropods. Adults parasitic in intestine of vertebrates. No digestive system. About 600 species.

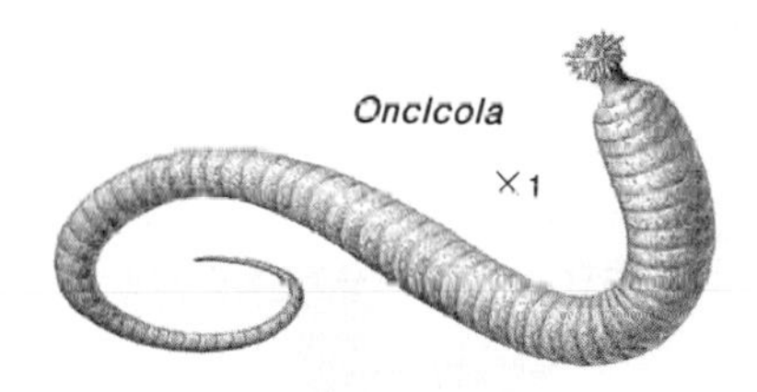

Horsehair Worms (Phylum Nematomorpha) [Greek: *nema,* thread, + *morphe,* form]

Young are parasitic in arthropods. Adults are free-living and have much reduced digestive tubes. About 230 species.

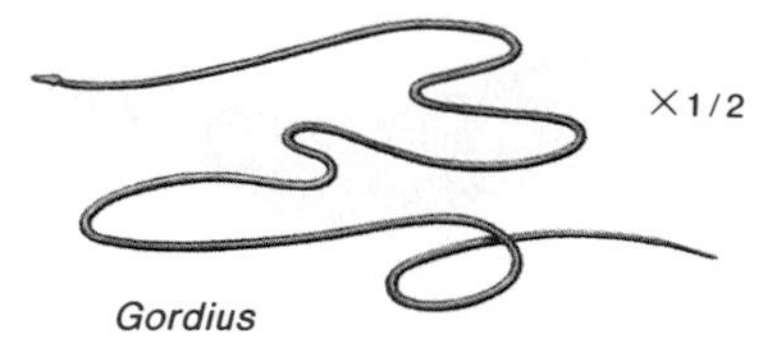

Roundworms (Phylum Nematoda) [Greek: *nema*]

Free-living or parasitic, especially on roots of plants. About 30 species known to live in humans. Cylindrical bodies, bilaterally symmetrical. Digestive tube with mouth and anus. No circulatory system. Many species are decomposers. More than 80,000 species. (Figure 14.11)

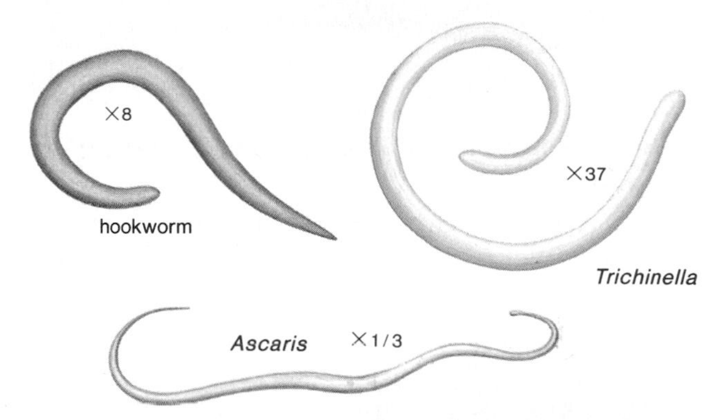

Mollusks (Phylum Mollusca) [Latin: *mollis,* soft]

Marine, freshwater, or terrestrial. Bilaterally symmetrical or asymmetrical. The mantle is a fold of tissue over the body that secretes a hard, limy shell in most species. No segmentation; true body cavity. Well developed digestive, circulatory, and nervous systems. About 110,000 species. (Figure 14.13)

Class Monoplacophora [Greek: *monos,* solitary, + *plax,* tablet, flat plate, + *phoros*]

Marine. Single shell with a curved apex. Broad, flattened foot. Found in deep ocean trenches. 10 species.

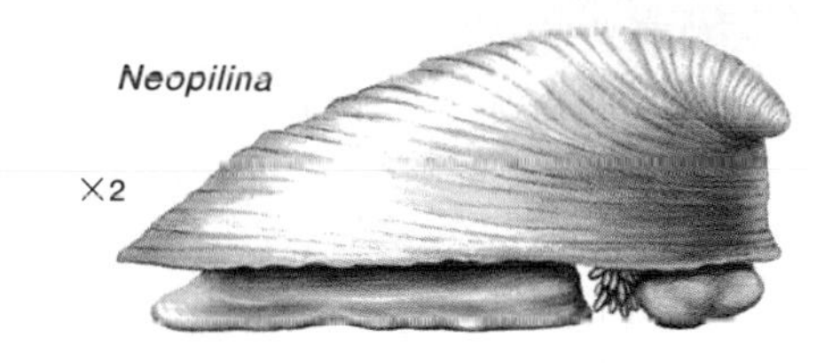

Class Polyplacophora (chitons) [Greek: *poly,* many, + *plax* + *phoros*]

Marine. Shell composed of 8 overlapping plates (exposed or hidden). No distinct head.

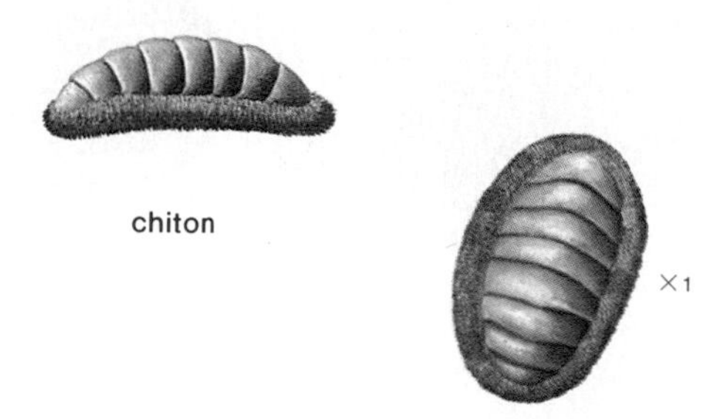

Class Scaphoda (tooth shells) [Greek: *skaphe*, boat, + *pous*, foot]

Marine. Shells form a tapering tube. Food-catching tentacles on head.

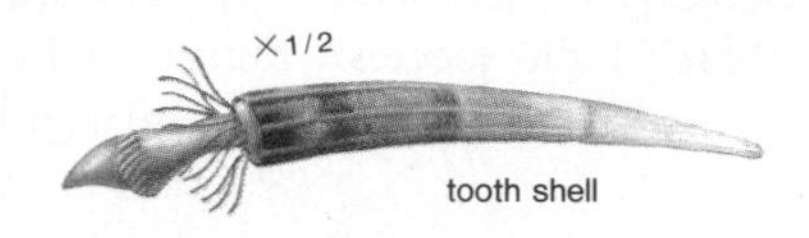

Class Gastropoda (slugs and snails) [Greek: *gastros*, stomach, + *pous*]

Marine, freshwater, or terrestrial. Shell (if present) coiled. Head usually distinct. (Figures 3.4, 10.21a, 14.13a)

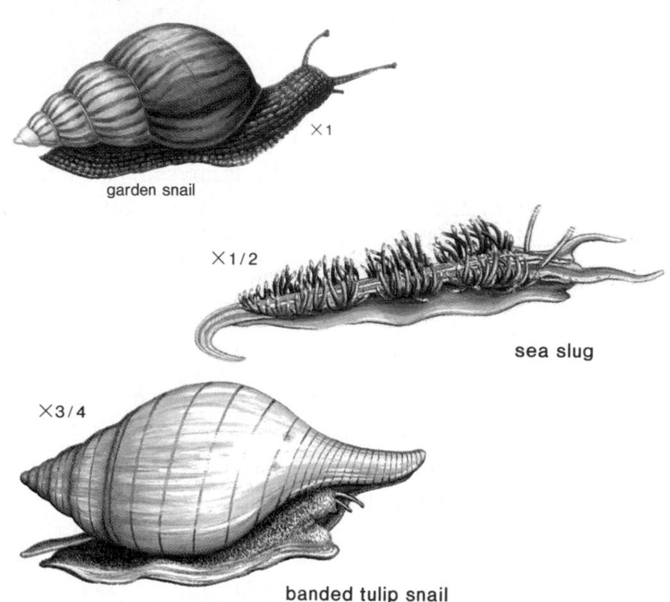

Class Bivalvia (bivalves)

Marine or freshwater. Some attached; others burrow in mud or sand. Shells in 2 parts, hinged. (Figure 14.13b)

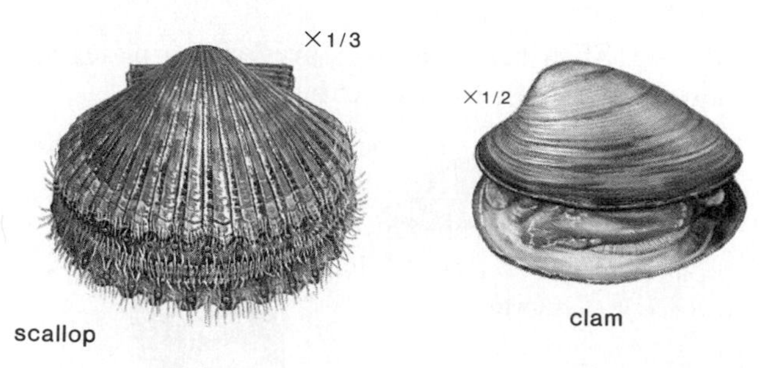

Class Cephalopoda (octopus and squid) [Greek: *kephale* + *pous*]

Marine. Small, internal shell. In a few cases shell is external, coiled, and internally divided. Several tentacles on head. Locomotion by jet of water. (Figure 14.13c)

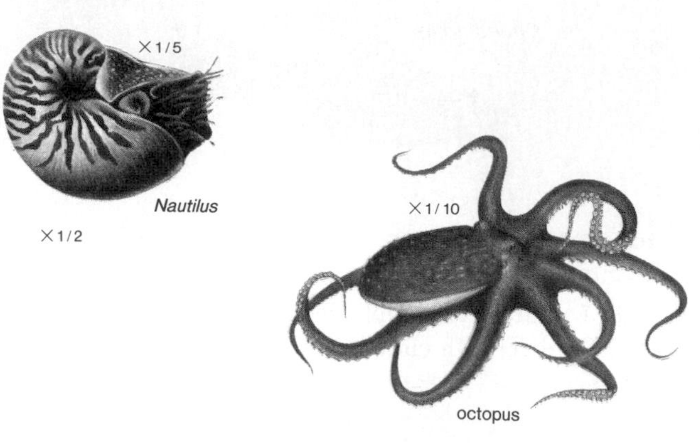

Segmented Worms (Phylum Annelida) [Latin: *anulus*, a ring]

Marine, freshwater, or terrestrial. Bilaterally symmetrical. Body internally and externally segmented. Appendages either not jointed or lacking. Main nerve cord ventral. About 8700 species. (Figure 14.15)

Class Oligochaeta (earthworms) [Greek: *oligos*, few, + *chaite*, hair]

Mostly freshwater or terrestrial. Appendages small or lacking. (Figure 14.15a)

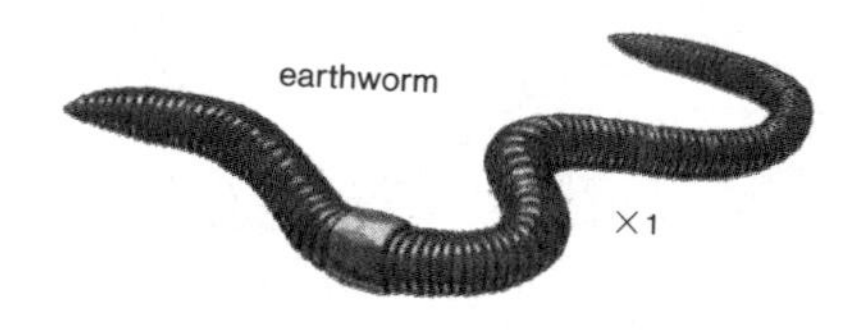

Class Hirudinea (leeches) [Latin: *hirudo*, leech]

Rather flat. Appendages lacking. Suction disks at each end. (Figure 14.15c)

Class Polychaeta [Greek: *poly,* many, + *chaite*]
Mostly marine. Burrowers or tube-builders. Usually with paddlelike appendages on each body segment. (Figure 14.15b)

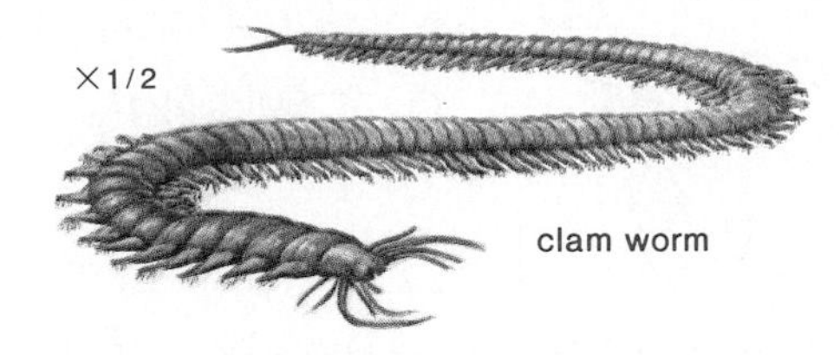

Arthropods (Phylum Arthropoda) [Greek: *arthron,* joint, + *pous*]

Marine, freshwater, or terrestrial. Bilaterally symmetrical. Body segmented, but segments often fused. Jointed appendages. Body and appendages covered with a jointed exoskeleton. Main nerve cord ventral. About 800,000 described species; there may be as many as 10 million insect species alone.

Subphylum Chelicerata [Greek: *chele,* a claw]

1st pair of appendages modified to grasp food. 4 pairs of legs; no antennae; 2 body parts (head-thorax and abdomen).

Class Arachnida (spiders, ticks, and mites) [Greek: *arachne,* spider]
No antennae. Segmentation reduced. 4 pairs of legs. No jaws (feeding appendages may resemble claw-bearing legs). (Figure 1.2, 14.17)

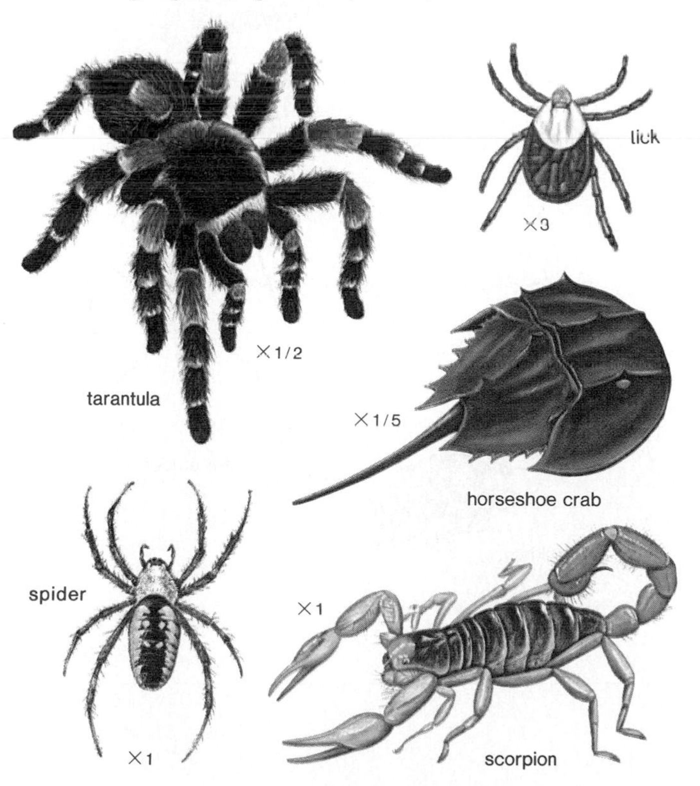

Subphylum Mandibulata [Latin: *mandibula,* to chew]

Head with 2 pairs of antennae; jaws.

Class Crustacea (crayfish, lobsters) [Latin: *crusta,* rind]
2 pairs of antennae. Mostly aquatic; respiration by gills. (Figures 14.2a, 14.18)

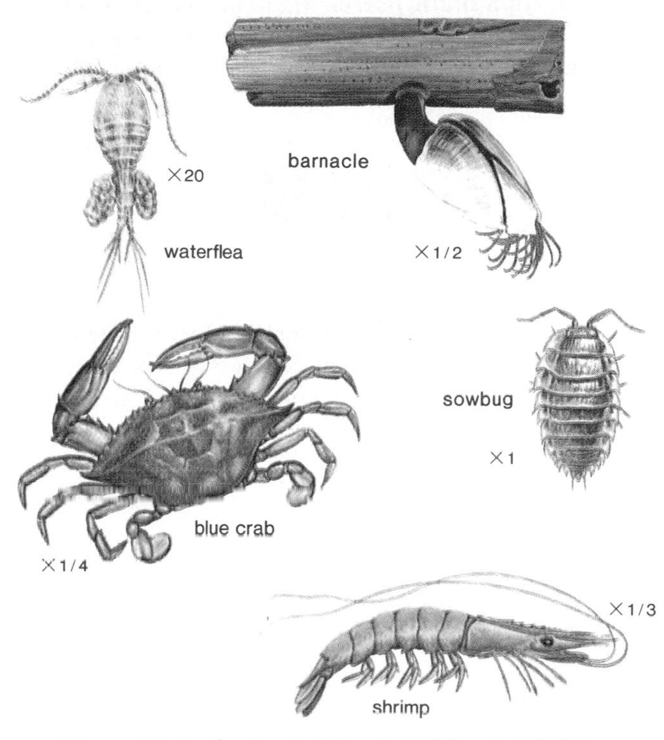

Class Diplopoda (millipedes) [Greek: *diplos,* two, double, + *pous*]
1 pair of short antennae. Entire body segmented; round in cross section. 2 pairs of legs on each segment. Important forest decomposers.

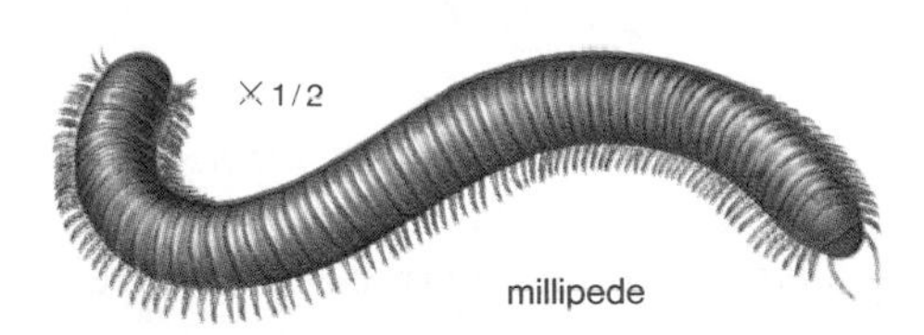

Class Chilopoda (centipedes) [Greek: *cheilos,* lip, + *pous*]
1 pair of long antennae. Entire body segmented; flat. 1 pair of legs on each segment. Predators that mostly prey on insects.

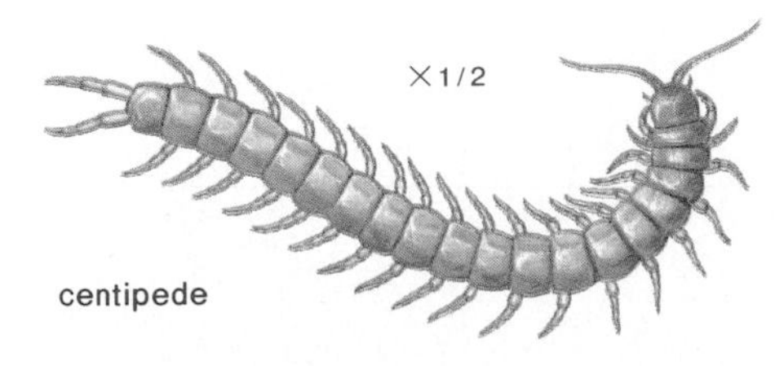

Class Insecta (insects) [Latin: *in,* into, + *secare,* to cut, divide (from the segmented bodies)]
1 pair of antennae. Body divided into head, thorax, and abdomen. 3 pairs of legs on thorax. (Figures chapter 2 opener, 14.19)

The following are the more common orders in the class Insecta.

Order Thysanura [Greek: *thysanos,* tassel, + *oura,* tail]. Small; wingless; soft scales on the body. 3 long bristles at posterior end.

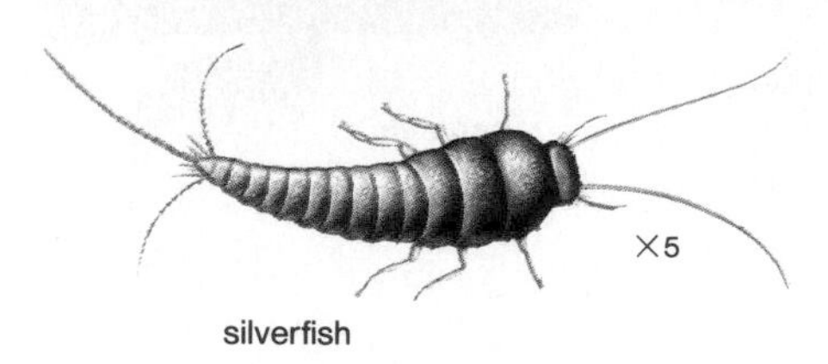

Order Ephemeroptera [Greek: *ephemeros,* temporary (literally, existing but one day), + *pteron*]. 2 pairs of transparent wings; hind wings smaller. 2 or 3 long tails. Immature forms aquatic. (Figure 23.5)

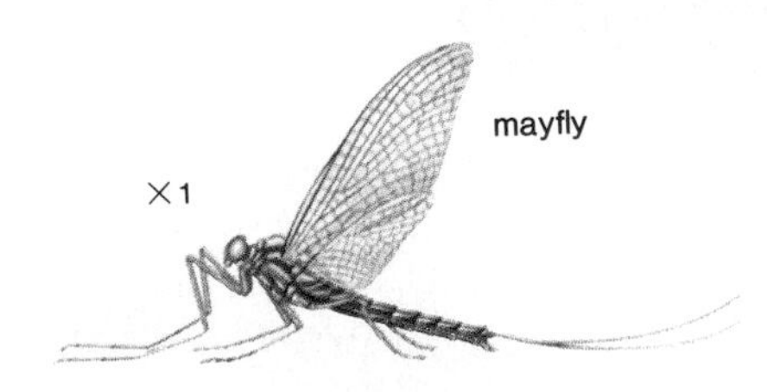

Order Odonata [Greek: *odous,* tooth]. 2 similar pairs of long wings. Antennae short. Abdomen long and slender. Immature forms aquatic. (Figure 10.21b)

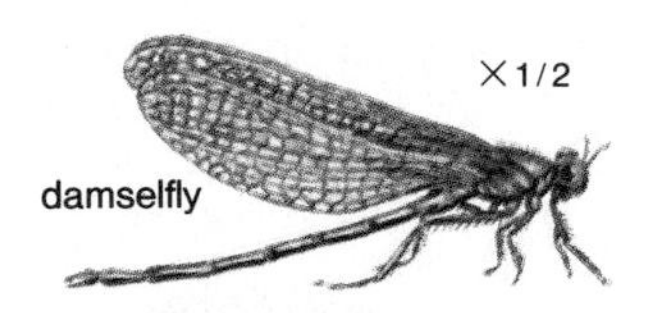

Order Orthoptera [Greek: *orthos,* straight, + *pteron*]. Terrestrial. Front wings leathery; hind wings folded, fanlike. Chewing mouth parts. (Figure 1.1)

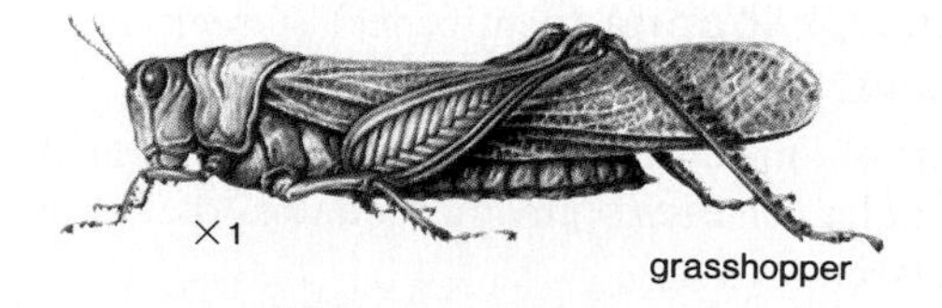

Order Isoptera [Greek: *isos,* equal, + *pteron*]. 4 wings alike in size, with many fine veins, or wings lacking. Chewing mouth parts. Social.

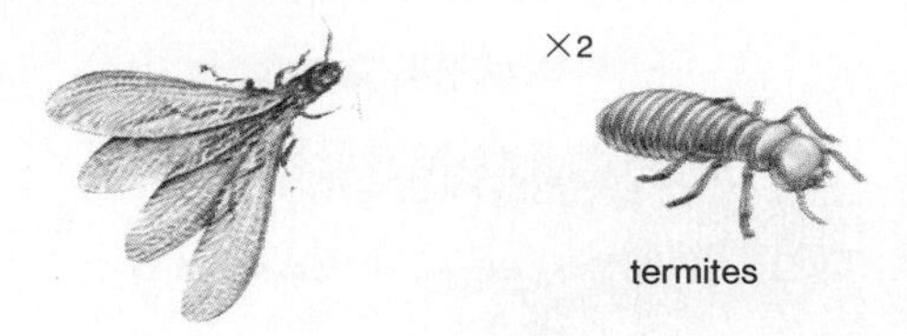

Order Anoplura [Greek: *anoplos,* unarmed, + *oura*]. Wingless; flat. Sucking or piercing mouth parts. Parasitic on mammals.

Order Homoptera [Greek: *homos,* alike, + *pteron*]. 2 pairs of wings, arched above the body, or wings lacking. Jointed sucking beak at base of head. (Figure 14.19d)

Order Hemiptera [Greek: *hemi,* half, + *pteron*]. Front wings thick at the base, thin at the tips; hind wings thin. Jointed beak on front of head.

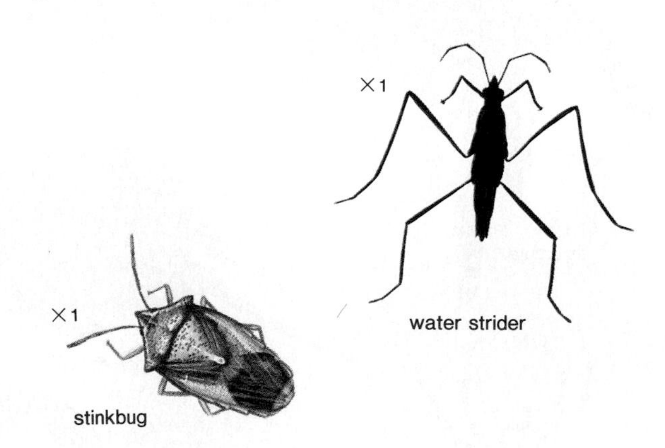

Order Lepidoptera [Greek: *lepidos,* scale, + *pteron*]. 2 pairs of wings covered with soft scales. Coiled sucking mouth parts in adults. Young are wormlike (caterpillars). (Figures 1.4, chapter 14 opener, 14.19c)

Order Diptera [Greek: *dis,* twice, + *pteron*]. 1 pair of wings (hind wings reduced to small rods). Antennae short. Sucking mouth parts. Young are wormlike and either terrestrial (maggots) or aquatic. (Figures 8.10, 9.29, 14.19a, 20.5, 20.31)

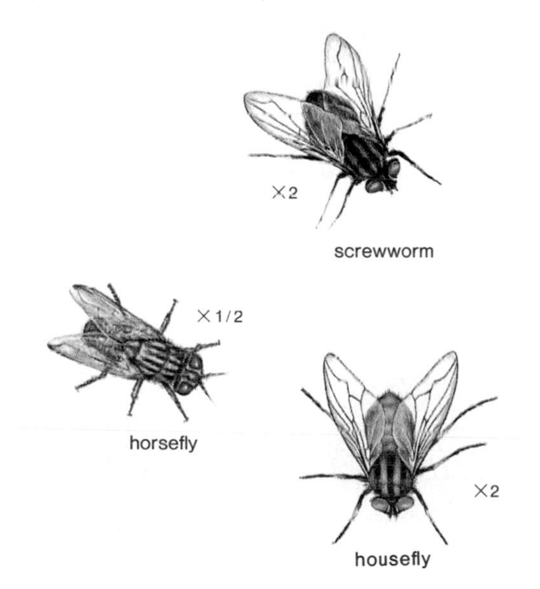

Order Coleoptera [Greek: *koleos,* a sheath, + *pteron*]. Front wings form a hard sheath; hind wings folded beneath them. Chewing mouth parts. Young usually wormlike (grubs). (Figures 14.19e)

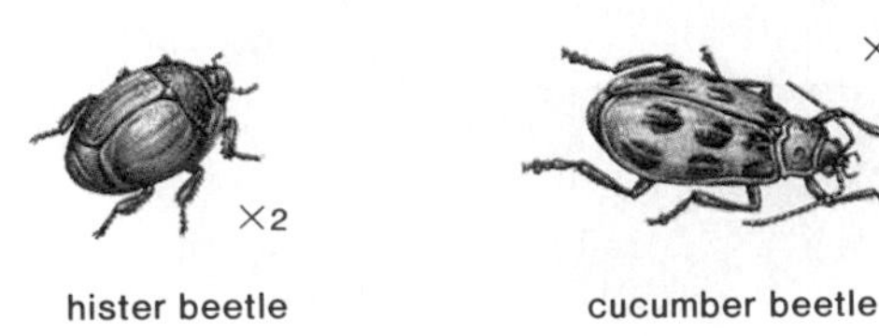

Order Hymenoptera [Greek: *hymen,* membrane, + *pteron*]. Front wings much larger than hind wings, with the 2 pairs hooked together, or wings lacking. Chewing or sucking mouth parts. Young are wormlike. Many social species. (Figures 1.17, 14.19b, 20.29b, 24.1)

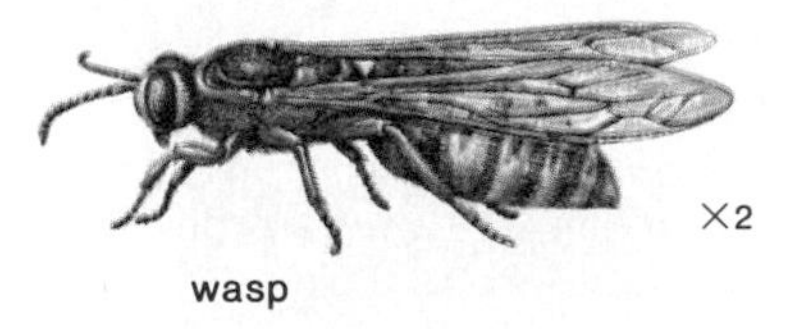

Priapulids (Phylum Priapulida) [Greek: *Priapos* (a god of gardens and vineyards)]

Marine. Free-living. Mouth region with spines. Body covered with rings of cuticle. About 5 species.

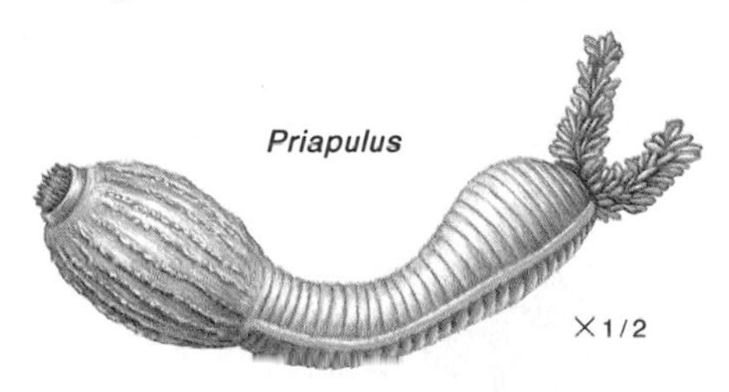

Velvet Worms (Phylum Onychophora) [Greek: *onyx,* nail, claw, + *phoros*]

Terrestrial; tropical. Wormlike. Paired legs. Poorly developed segmentation. Combine many annelid and arthropod characteristics. About 80 species.

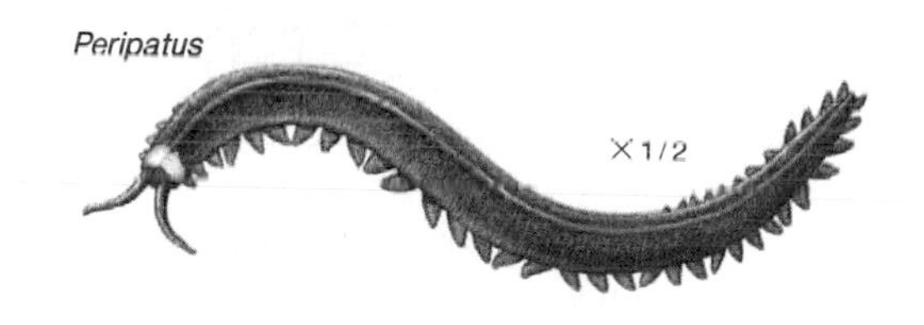

Phoronids (Phylum Phoronida) [Greek: *Phoronis* (the name of a mythological character)]

Marine. Living in tubes in mud. A pair of arms bearing tentacles. U-shaped digestive tube. About 15 species.

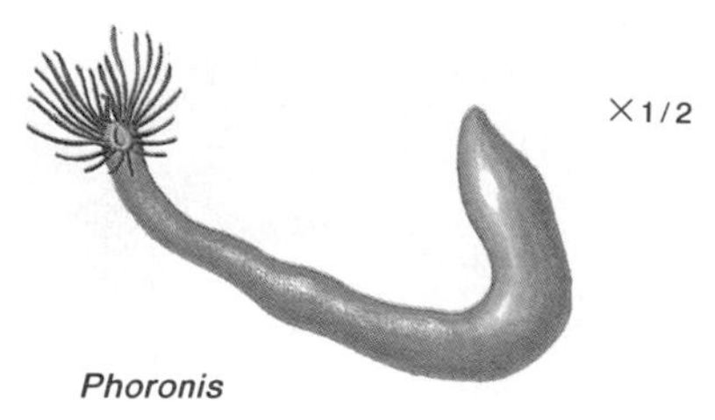

Bryozoans (Phylum Ectoprocta) [Greek: *ektos,* outside + *proktos,* anus]

Mostly marine, living in attached colonies. U-shaped digestive tube. Mouth encircled in a crown of tentacles. About 3000 species.

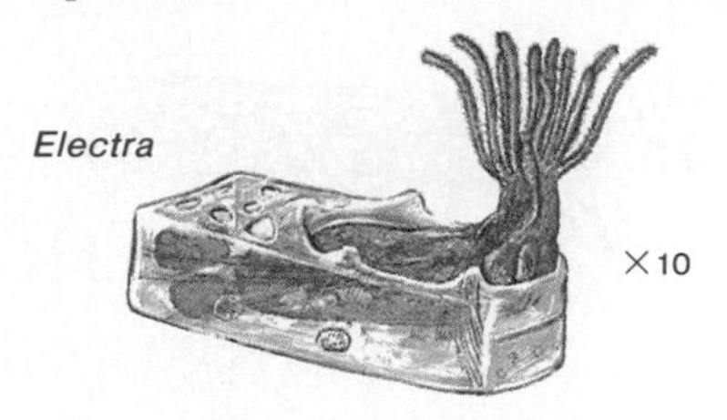

Brachiopods (Phylum Brachiopoda) [Greek: *brachion,* arm, + *pous*]

Marine. Symmetrical, 2-piece shell, enclosing a pair of arms bearing tentacles. About 120 species. (Figure 21.9)

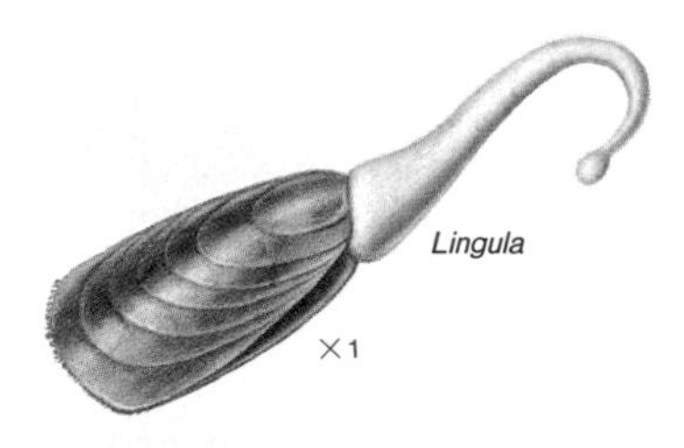

Echinoderms (Phylum Echinodermata) [Greek: *echinos,* hedgehog, + *derma,* skin]

All marine. Adults radially symmetrical. Radiating sections (when present) are called arms. Larvae bilaterally symmetrical and chordatelike. Internal, limy skeleton, usually with many projecting spines. A system of water-filled tubes, acting on the suction principle, catches food and assists in locomotion. About 6000 species.

Class Crinoidea (crinoids) [Greek: *krinon,* lily, + *eidos,* appearance]

Attached (at least when young). Many highly branched arms.

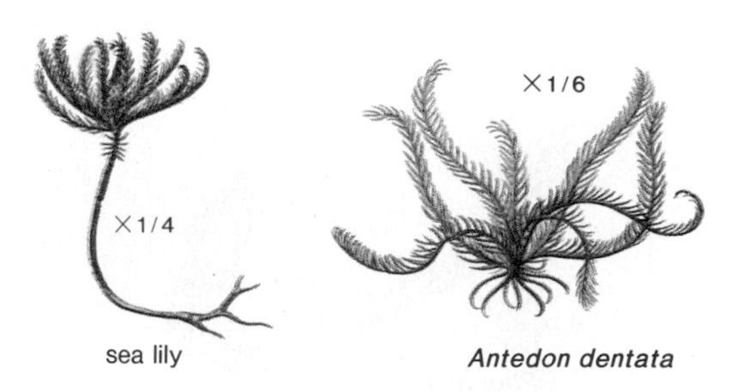

Class Asteroidea (starfish) [Greek: *aster,* star, + *eidos,* form]

Usually 5 arms, joined to the body at broad bases. (Figure 6.4)

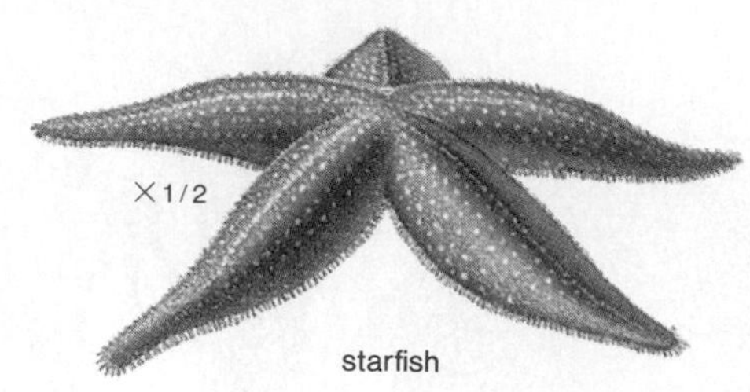

Class Ophiuroidea (brittle stars) [Greek: *ophis,* serpent, + *oura* + *eidos*]

Usually 5 long, slim arms (sometimes branched), clearly distinguished from the body.

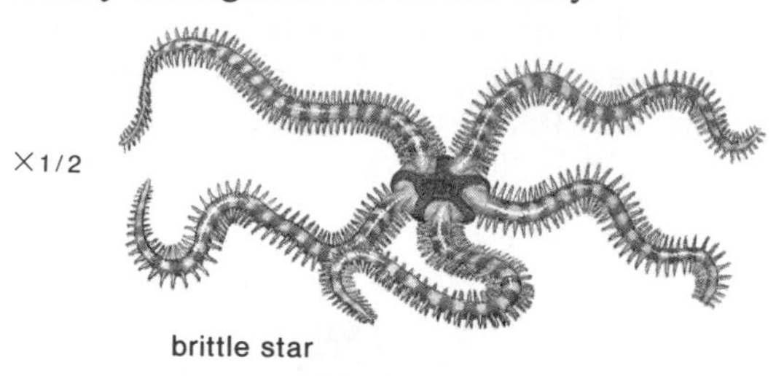

Class Echinoidea (sand dollars) [Greek: *echinos* + *eidos*]

Spherical or disk-shaped. No arms; long spines or short, hairlike projections from body. Skeleton of interlocking plates.

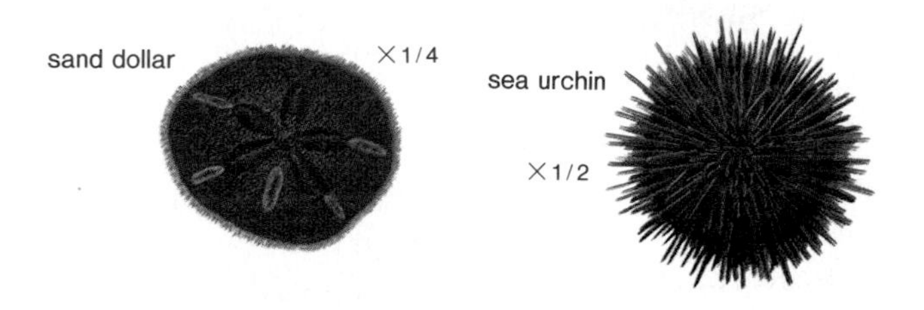

Class Holothuroidea (sea cucumbers) [Greek: *holothourion,* a kind of water animal]

Somewhat cylindrical. No arms. Tentacles around mouth. No spines. Skeleton consists of particles embedded in the leathery skin.

Arrowworms (Phylum Chaetognatha) [Greek: *chaite* + *gnathos,* jaw]

Marine; free-swimming or floating. Bilaterally symmetrical. Straight digestive tube. About 50 species.

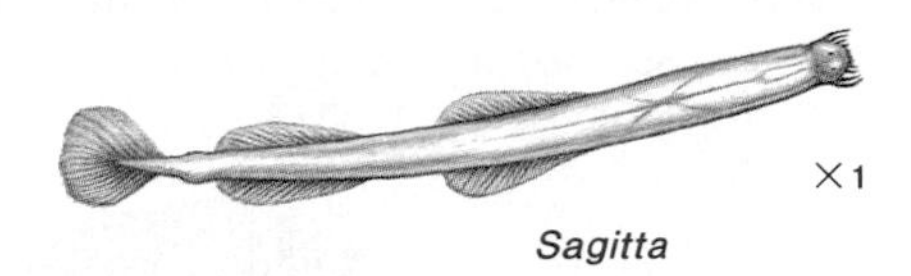

Acorn Worms (Phylum Hemichordata) [Greek: *hemi,* + *chorde,* string of a musical instrument]

Marine; wormlike. Conspicuous proboscis used for burrowing in mud and sand. Dorsal nerve cord and pharyngeal slits. Presence of notochord doubtful. About 65 species. (Figure 23.22)

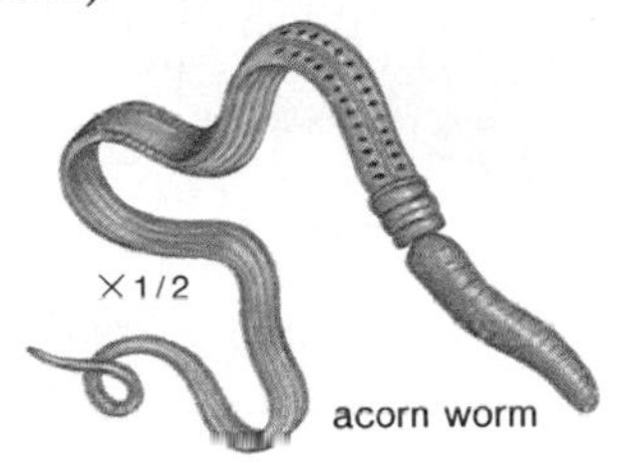

Chordates (Phylum Chordata) [Greek: *chorde*]

Marine, freshwater, or terrestrial. Bilaterally symmetrical. Hollow dorsal nerve tube and a stiff notochord beneath it (may be lost or replaced during development). Several pairs of pharyngeal pouches in the throat region. (These may become perforated during development, forming slits.) Some segmentation, especially in arrangement of muscles and nerves. About 45,000 species.

Subphylum Urochordata (Tunicates) [Greek: *oura* + *chorde*]

Marine; larvae free-swimming, adults usually attached. Notochord and part of nervous system usually disappear during development.

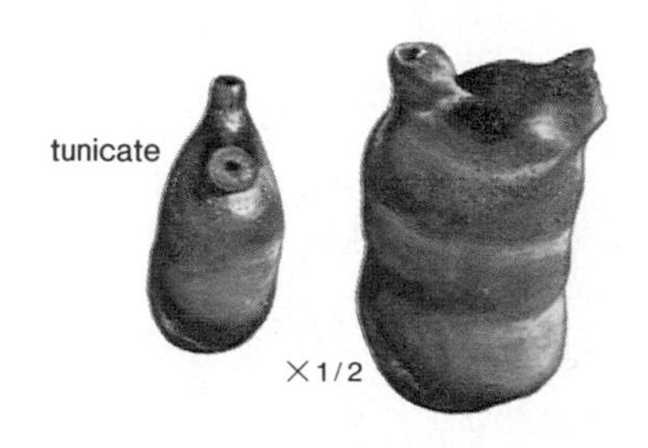

Subphylum Cephalochordata (Lancelets) [Greek: *kephale* + *chorde*]

Marine; free-swimming. Translucent. Well-developed hollow dorsal nerve cord, notochord, and pharyngeal slits in adults.

Subphylum Vertebrata (vertebrates) [Latin: *vertebra,* joint]

Notochord replaced by a backbone of vertebrae during development. Enlarged anterior end of the nerve cord (brain) protected by cartilage or bone. Most species have appendages in pairs.

Class Agnatha (jawless fish) [Greek: *a,* without, + *gnathos*]

No jaws. No paired fins. Skeleton of cartilage. Heart with 1 ventricle.

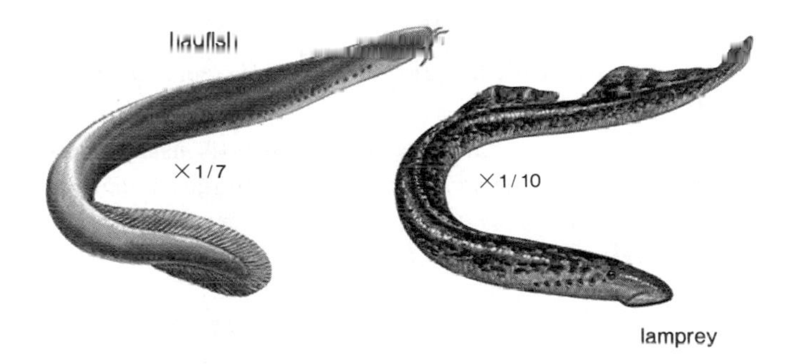

Class Chondrichthyes (Cartilaginous fishes) [Greek: *chondros,* cartilage, + *ichthyes,* fish]

Skeleton of cartilage. 5 or more pharyngeal slits externally visible. Ventral mouth and nostrils. Heart with 1 ventricle. (Figures 3.8, 14.22)

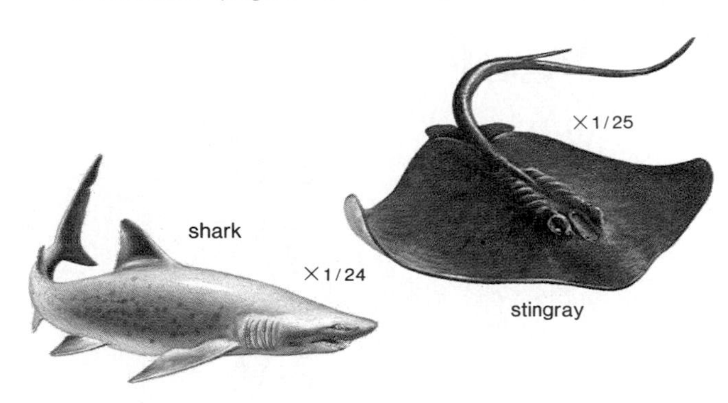

Class Osteichthyes (Bony Fishes) [Greek: *osteon,* bone, + *ichthyes*]

Skeleton of bone (at least in part). Pharyngeal slits covered (not externally visible). Heart with 1 ventricle. (Figures 3.3, 9.25, 14.23, 14.39, 21.21, 25.16)

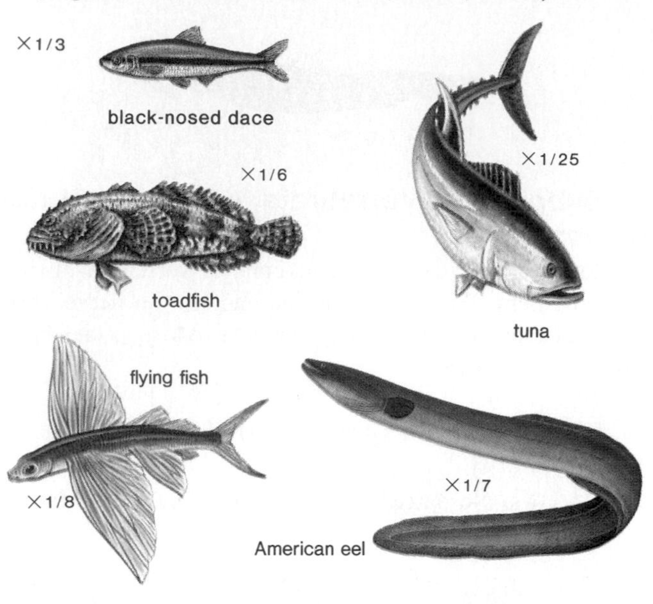

Class Amphibia (amphibians) [Greek: *amphis,* + *bios,* life]

Larvae usualy aquatic, with gills. Adults usually terrestrial, with lungs. 2 pairs of appendages (small or lacking in some species). No claws. Heart with 1 ventricle. (Figures chapter 6 opener, 9.18, 9.26, 14.24)

Class Reptilia (reptiles) [Latin: *repere,* to creep]

Both young and adults breathe by lungs. Eggs with leathery shells; membrane in egg encloses water. 2 pairs of appendages (lacking in some species) with claws. Scales on skin. Heart with 2 ventricles but with an opening in wall separating them (in most species). (Figures 3.3, 3.4, 7.9, 14.25, 16.25)

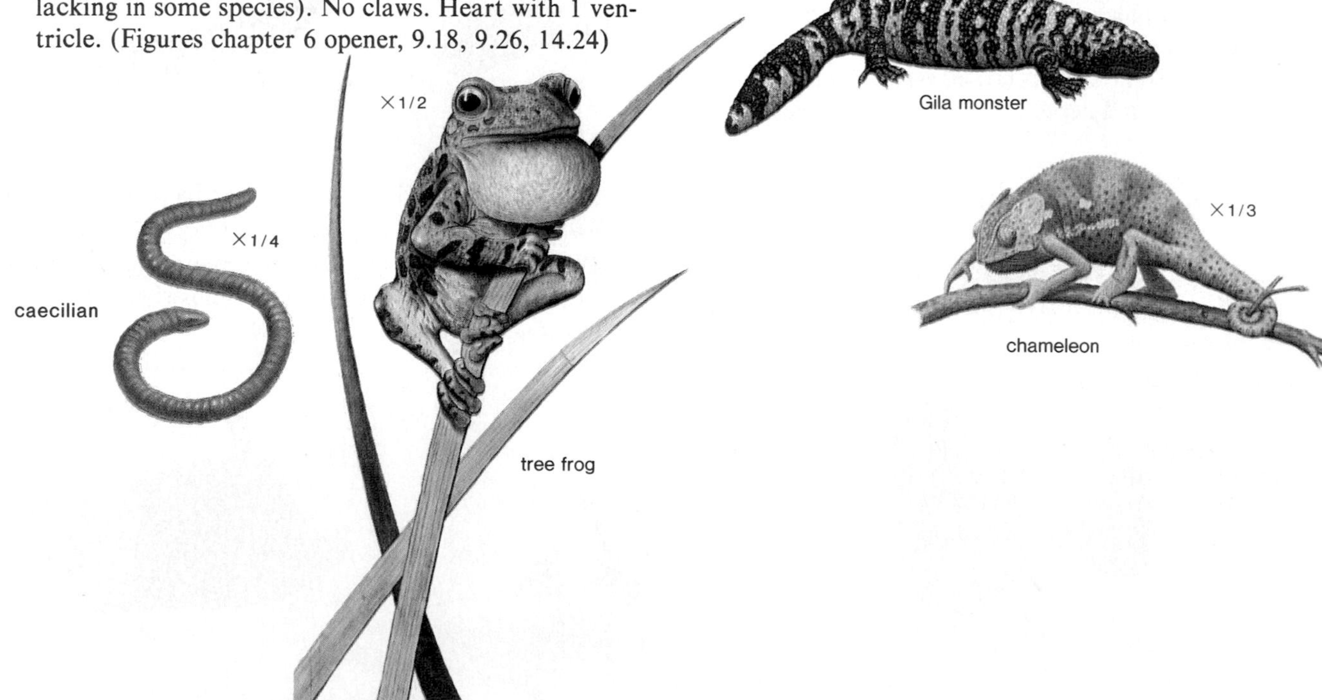

Class Aves (birds) [Latin: *avis,* bird]

Scales modified as feathers. Eggs as in reptiles, but shell always hard. Front appendages usually modified as wings. Heart with 2 ventricles. (Figures 1.5, 1.16, 2.2, 3.3, 3.5, 3.7, 3.23, 9.1, 9.3, 9.4, 9.9, 9.21, 9.23, 10.1, 10.21c, 13.39, 14.26, 14.44, 20.4, 20.11, 20.18, 20.21, 22.7c, 22.9, 22.16, 22.33b, 23.30, 25.4)

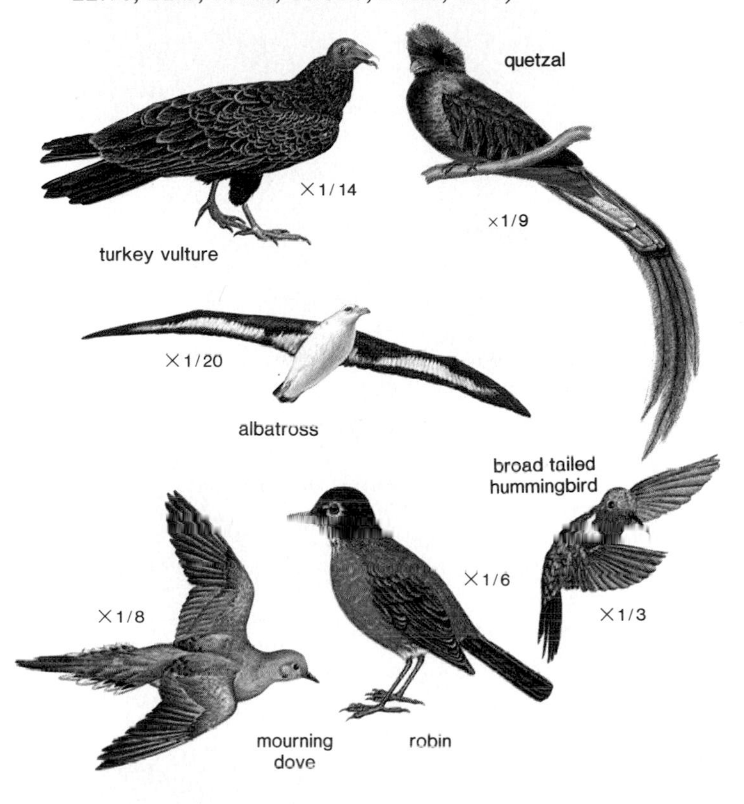

Class Mammalia (mammals) [Latin: *mamma,* breast]

Scales modified as hairs. Mammary glands of females secrete milk. Fewer bones than in reptiles. Teeth usually of 4 well-defined types (incisors, canines, premolars, molars). Heart with 2 ventricles. About 5000 species. (Figures 1.16, 14.27, 21.10)

Order Monotremata [Greek: *monos,* one, + *trema,* hole]. Egg-laying. Mammary glands without nipples. 5 species.

Order Marsupialia [Greek: *marsypos,* pouch, bag]. Young born in undeveloped state and transferred to a pouch, where they remain tightly attached to the nipples. About 250 species. (Figure 14.27e)

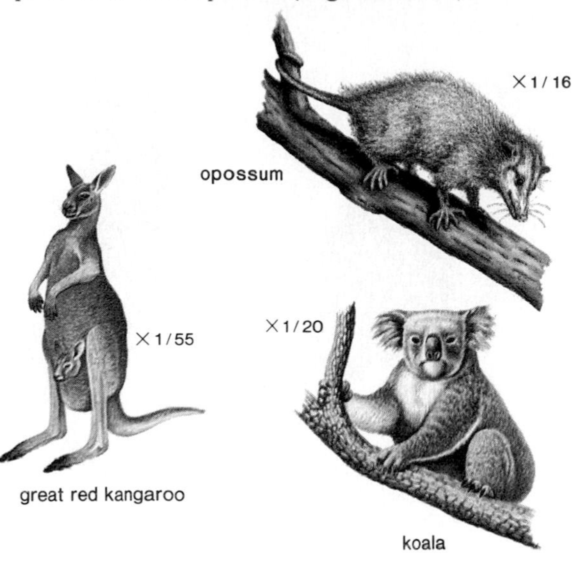

Order Insectivora [Latin: *insectum,* insect, + *vorare,* to eat]. Numerous teeth of all 4 mammalian kinds; none highly specialized. About 400 species.

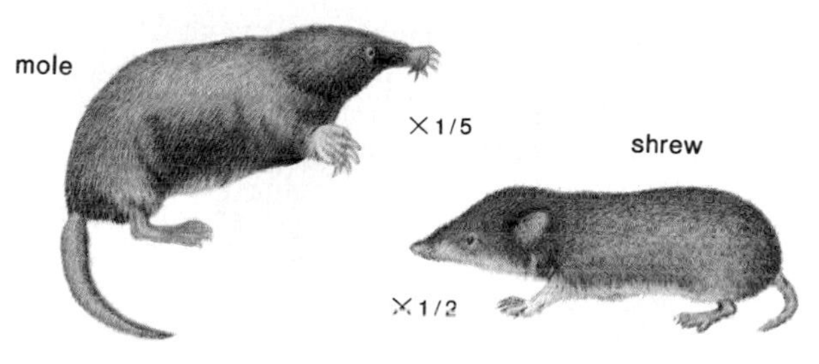

Order Chiroptera [Greek: *cheir,* hand, + *pteron*]. Bats. Web of skin between fingers and between front limbs and hind limbs, allowing flight. About 900 species.

Order Primates [Latin: *primus,* first]. Eyes usually directed forward. Nails usually present instead of claws. Teeth much like those of insectivores. About 200 species. (Figures chapter 17 opener, 17.21, 21.27, 24.2)

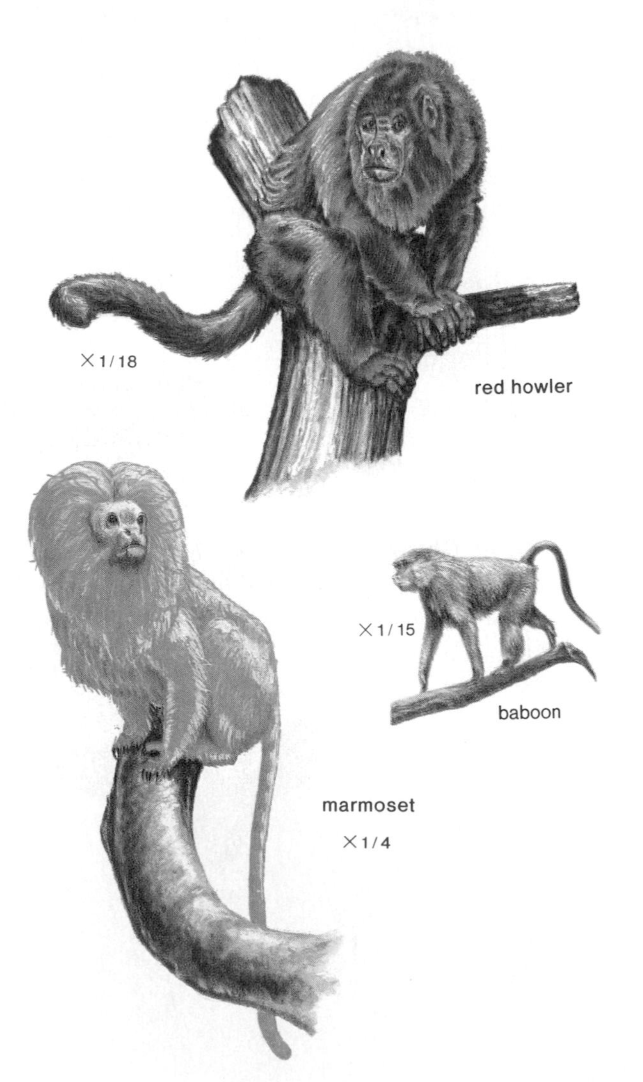

To show how complex classification can become, a complete classification of the order Primates is given below.

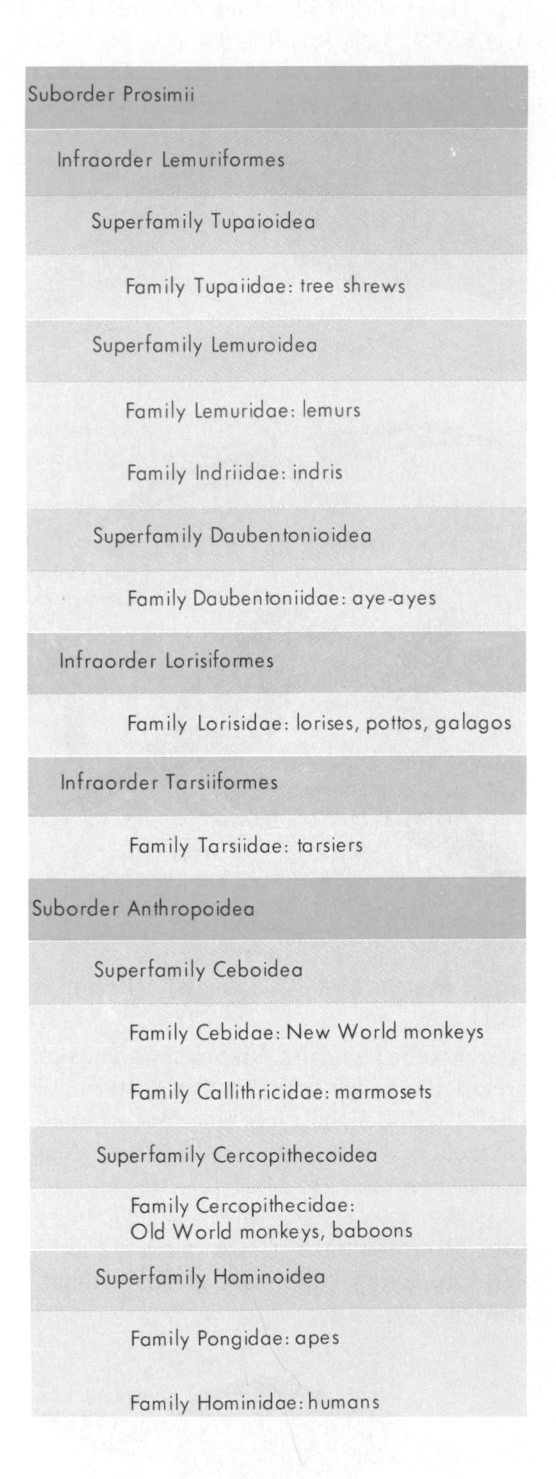

Suborder Prosimii
Infraorder Lemuriformes
Superfamily Tupaioidea
Family Tupaiidae: tree shrews
Superfamily Lemuroidea
Family Lemuridae: lemurs
Family Indriidae: indris
Superfamily Daubentonioidea
Family Daubentoniidae: aye-ayes
Infraorder Lorisiformes
Family Lorisidae: lorises, pottos, galagos
Infraorder Tarsiiformes
Family Tarsiidae: tarsiers
Suborder Anthropoidea
Superfamily Ceboidea
Family Cebidae: New World monkeys
Family Callithricidae: marmosets
Superfamily Cercopithecoidea
Family Cercopithecidae: Old World monkeys, baboons
Superfamily Hominoidea
Family Pongidae: apes
Family Hominidae: humans

Order Edentata [Latin: *edentare,* to make toothless]. No front teeth; molars in some species. About 30 species.

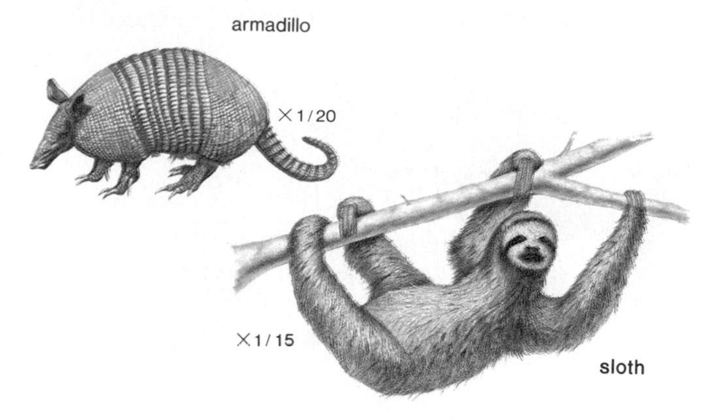

Order Pholidota (pangolins) [Greek: *pholis,* scale]. No teeth. Body encased in scales formed from modified hairs. 8 species.

Order Tubulidentata (aardvarks) [Latin: *tubulus,* small tube, + *dens,* tooth]. Teeth few in adults but numerous in embryos. Toes ending in nails that are intermediate between claws and hoofs.

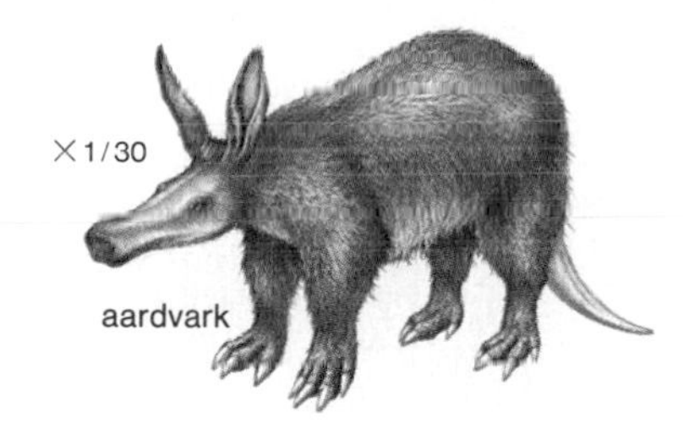

Order Rodentia [Latin: *rodere,* to gnaw]. Chisel-like incisors, growing continually from the roots; no canines; broad molars. About 1700 species. (Figures chapter 1 opener, 9.24, 10.21d, 20.16, 20.17, 20.28, 22.15a, 22.33a)

Order Lagomorpha [Greek: *lagos,* hare, + *morphe*]. Harelike mammals. Teeth similar to those of rodents, but with 4 upper incisors instead of 2. Tail very short. About 60 species.

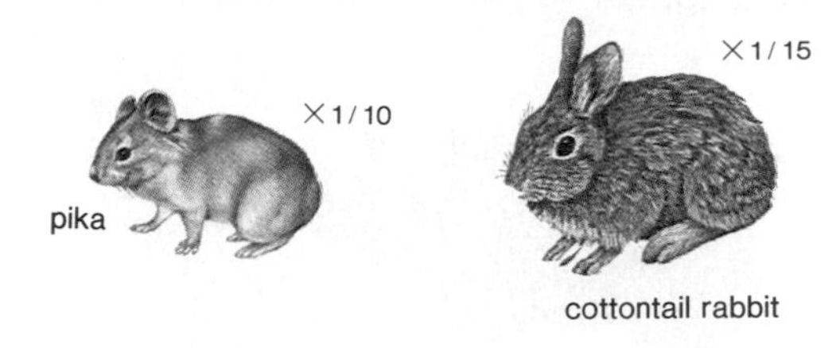

Order Cetacea [Greek: *ketos,* whale]. Marine. Front limbs modified as flippers; hind limbs absent. No hair on adults. Eyes small. Head very large. About 80 species. (Figure 14.27d)

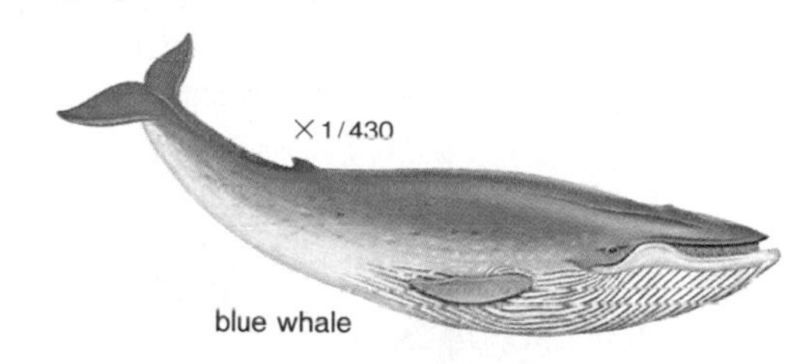

Order Carnivora [Latin: *carnis,* flesh, + *vorare,* to eat]. Incisors small, canines large, premolars adapted for shearing. Claws usually sharp. About 280 species. (Figures 3.3, 9.22, 10.2, 10.4, 14.27a, 14.27f, 20.20, 22.7b, 24.3)

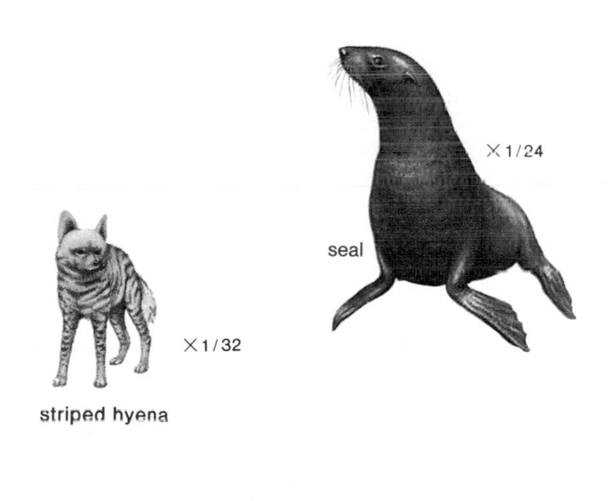

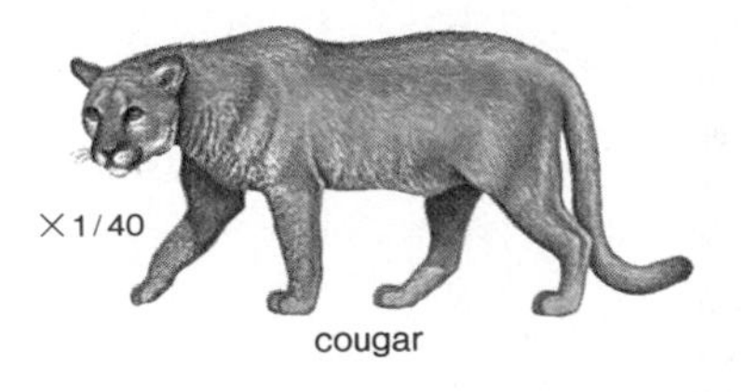

Order Proboscidea [Greek: *pro,* before, in front of, + *boskein,* to feed, graze]. Herbivorous. Upper incisors modified as tusks; molars produced 2 to 4 at a time as older ones wear out. Nose and upper lip modified as a trunk. 2 species. (Figure 22.36)

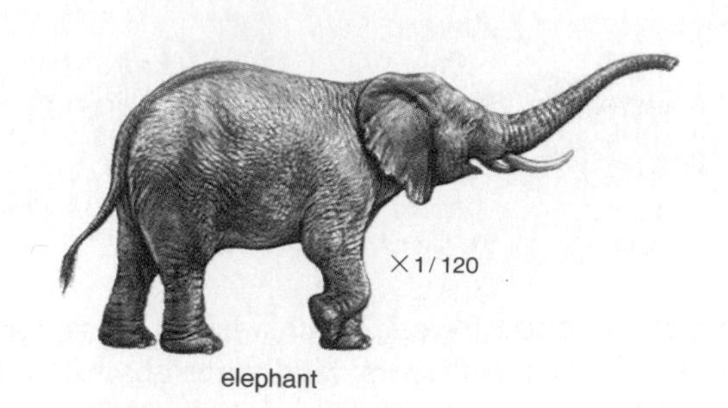

Order Sirenia [Latin: *siren,* a kind of mermaid]. Aquatic. Herbivorous. No hind limbs. Broad, flat tail, expanded as a fin. Few hairs. 5 species.

Order Perissodactyla [Greek: *perissos,* uneven, + *daktylos,* finger or toe]. Odd-toed, hoofed mammals. 1, 3, or 5 toes, modified as hooves. Herbivorous. Well-developed molars. About 15 species. (Figures 10.3, 22.36)

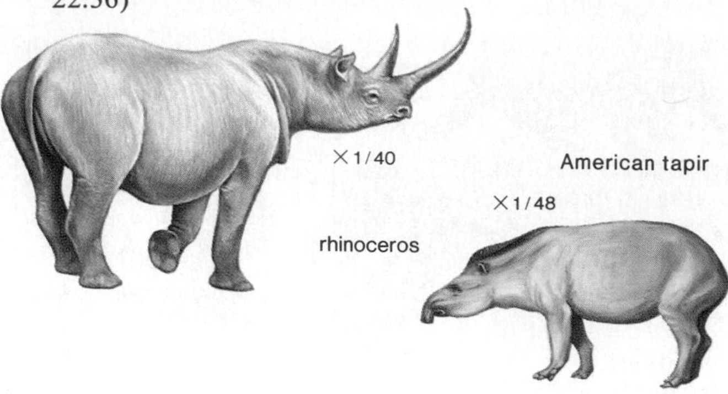

Order Artiodactyla (Greek: *artios,* even, + *daktylos*]. Even-toed, hoofed mammals, 2 or 4 toes, modified as hooves. Herbivorous. Most have complex stomachs. Many have horns or antlers. About 170 species. (Figures 2.29, chapter 8 opener, 8.1, 9.5, 14.27b, 22.7a, 22.10, 22.12, 22.15b)

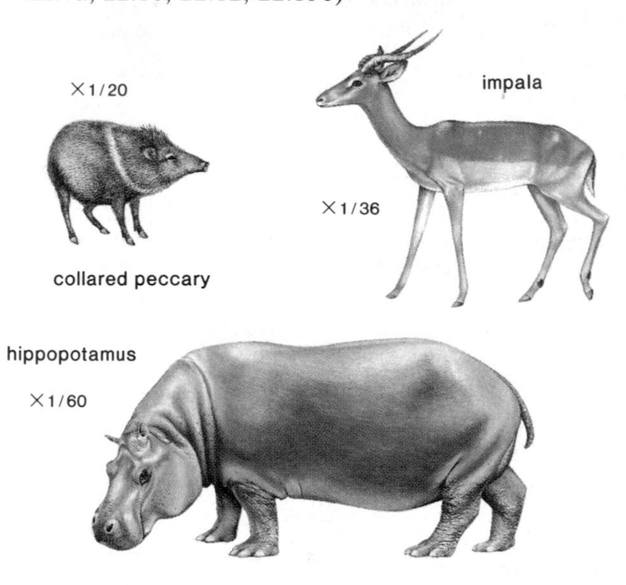

Glossary

a

abiotic (AY by OT ik)
not biotic; nonliving.

abscisic acid (ab SIS ik)
a plant hormone that acts to protect a plant in unfavorable environmental conditions, by promoting dormancy in buds and seeds, and the closing of stomates.

absorption
in photosynthesis, the interception of light wavelengths by chlorophyll; in digestion, the passage of digested food molecules from the food tract into the circulatory system.

absorption spectrum
(ab SORP shun SPEK trum)
a graph showing the percentage of light absorbed by a pigment at each wavelength of visible light.

acidic (uh SID ik)
having a pH of less than 7, reflecting more dissolved hydrogen ions than hydroxide ions.

action spectrum (SPEK trum)
a representation of the rate of an activity, in particular photosynthesis, under different wavelengths of light at a given light intensity.

active site
the part of a large biological molecule, particularly an enzyme, most directly involved in its characteristic chemical functions.

active transport
a process in which a cell expends energy to move substances, often against a diffusion gradient. A steep diffusion gradient that is maintained is indirect evidence that a cell is actively transporting a substance.

adaptation
in natural selection, a hereditary characteristic of some organisms in a population that improves their chances for survival and reproduction in their environment, compared with other organisms in the population.

adaptive convergence (uh DAP tiv kun VER jents)
evolution of similar species in similar environments, but from different ancestors.

adaptive radiation (uh DAP tiv rayd ee AY shun)
evolution of a variety of adaptations in descendants of a common ancestor, leading to their dispersal into many differing environments. In this way, different families, genera, and species arise from common ancestors.

adenosine diphosphate (uh DEN oh seen dy FOS fayt)
ADP, the compound that remains when a phosphate group is transferred from ATP to a cell reaction site requiring an energy input.

adenosine triphosphate
(uh DEN oh seen try FOS fayt)
ATP, a compound used by cells to store energy. ATP has three phosphate groups.

ADP
see adenosine diphosphate.

adventitious root (ad ven TISH us)
a root that forms in an unusual place, as on a cut stem placed in water.

aerobic (ehr ROH bik)
occurring or living in the presence of free or dissolved oxygen.

agglutinate (uh GLOOT in ayt)
to unite in a mass; to combine. A transfusion with the wrong type of blood causes red blood cells to agglutinate.

agricultural revolution
the pattern of permanent human settlements that began with fishing villages but grew widespread only when selected plants were raised and harvested, requiring extended occupation of the cropland.

alkaline (AL kuh lin)
basic; having pH greater than 7, reflecting more dissolved hydroxide ions than hydrogen ions.

allantois (uh LANT oh wis)
one of four embryonic membranes of vertebrate embryos.

allele (uh LEEL)
one of two or more possible forms of a gene, each affecting the hereditary trait somewhat differently.

alpine (AL pyn)
an environment above timberline on mountains that is roughly similar to arctic tundra.

alternate hosts
organisms of different species that are hosts to the same parasites or pathogens at different stages in the latter's life cycles. *Anopheles* mosquitoes and humans are alternate hosts for malarial parasites.

alternation of generations
in plants, the production of a diploid sporophyte generation, followed by a haploid gametophyte generation, then a diploid sporophyte generation again, and so on.

altruistic (al troo IS tik)
unselfish; having deep regard for the welfare of one's offspring, mate, the young of other members of the group, and sometimes one's peers in the group.

alveolus (al VEE oh lus)
one of the millions of tiny air sacs in the lungs; its membranous wall contains a network of blood capillaries.

amino acid (uh MEE noh)
a biological compound that forms a subunit of peptides and proteins; it contains carbon, hydrogen, oxygen, nitrogen, and sometimes sulfur.

amniocentesis (AM nee oh sen TEE sus)
removal and analysis of a sample of the amniotic fluid surrounding a fetus; followed by culture and study of the cells (and their chromosomes) found in the fluid. Many types of genetic disorders and birth defects can be detected through amniocentesis.

amnion (AM nee on)
one of four embryonic membranes of vertebrate embryos. It surrounds and holds the embryo in a cushioned, fluid environment.

anaerobic (an eh ROH bik)
occurring or living in conditions without free oxygen.

anaphase (AN uh fayz)
the stage in mitosis in which chromosome strands on the spindle separate and are pulled toward opposite ends of the cell.

animalia (an ih MAYL yuh)
the kingdom of animals.

annual
occurring each year; in plants, a herbaceous species that must produce new individuals each year from seed, because plants of that species live for only one growing season.

annual ring
the ring of xylem cells added each year to a plant stem.

anorexia (an oh REK see uh)
abnormal loss of appetite, usually partly induced by self-starvation to reduce body weight.

anterior (an TIR ee er)
situated toward the front; having a head end, as in most animals.

anther
the enlarged, pollen-producing end of a stamen in a flower.

anthropologist (an throh POL uh jist)
a scientist who specializes in the study of human groups, their evolution, and their culture.

antibiotic (ant ih by OT ik)
a substance produced by organisms (usually microorganisms) that kills or inhibits the growth of other microorganisms; or, a synthetically-produced substance identical to, or closely related to, such a biologically-produced substance.

antibody
a substance produced by specialized cells of the immune system to neutralize or destroy an antigen, antibody, or toxin.

antigen (ANT ih jen)
a substance that the body detects as foreign and that activates a response by the immune system.

anus (AY nus)
the opening, controlled by a sphincter muscle, from the large intestine to the outside of the body.

apex
the highest point; in plants, the tip of a growing stem or root.

appendage (uh PEN dij)
a structure attached to the main part of the body; in animals, a tentacle, a leg, a flipper, a wing, a fin, etc.

appendicular skeleton
(ap en DIK yuh lar)
the shoulder and hip girdles and the appendage bones (arm, wing, flipper, leg) of a vertebrate.

arboreal
living in trees.

archaebacteria (ar kee bak TIR ee uh)
descendants of ancient bacteria that differ from other bacteria today in the nucleotide sequence of their RNAs, in certain lipids in their transfer RNA, in certain lipids in their plasma membranes, and in other ways.

artery
a large blood vessel that receives blood from the heart or from a still larger artery and transports it (1) to the lungs or gills where oxygen and carbon dioxide are exchanged, or (2) to smaller blood vessels that serve body cells and tissues.

articulation (ar tik yoo LAY shun)
the manner of coming together at a skeletal joint in animals, or at a node in plants. In particular, articulation applies to movable skeletal joints and how they work.

artificial selection
selection by humans, usually plant and animal breeders, of other organisms with prized characteristics for reproduction. Similar organisms under the breeders' control usually are prevented from reproducing.

ascus (AS kus)
a reproductive structure formed by sac fungi when two hyphae conjugate. Spores (ascospores) are formed in the ascus.

asexual reproduction
reproduction by a single parent, not involving a gamete; a clone is produced. Some organisms reproduce asexually from buds, others by dividing, and still others by other means.

associative neuron (NYOO rahn)
a nerve cell that transmits impulses from a sensory to a motor neuron, or from a sensory neuron to a part of the brain.

assumption (uh SUMP shun)
provisional acceptance of an unproved relationship; or, acceptance of an oversimplified relationship in a model. Examples: an animal population probably has some pattern of mating preferences (first case) but is represented as mating at random in a simplified model (second case).

atherosclerosis
(ATH uh roh skleh ROH sis)
deposition of fatty plaque on the inner walls of blood vessels, restricting the flow of blood.

atom (AT um)
the smallest particle of an element; in turn, an atom is made of smaller particles that do not separately have the properties of the element.

ATP
see adenosine triphosphate.

atrium (AY tree um)
a receiving chamber of the heart; it receives blood from major veins, releasing it into a ventricle when the ventricle's muscular walls relax.

autoimmune disease
a disorder in which antibodies are produced against some of the body's own cells.

autonomic nervous system
a division of the nervous system that controls unconscious activities of the body such as blood pressure, body temperature, and other functions necessary to the maintenance of homeostasis.

autosome (AWT oh sohm)
any chromosome other than a sex chromosome.

autotroph (AWT oh trohf)
a producer; a photosynthetic or other organism that takes its food materials and energy from the nonliving environment.

auxin (AWK sin)
a plant hormone produced in an actively growing region of a plant and transported to another part of the plant, where it produces a growth effect related to the concentration of the auxin and characteristic of the target cells.

axial skeleton (AK see ul)
the skull, backbone, and ribs of a vertebrate.

b

bacteriophage (bak TIR ee oh fayj)
a virus that infects bacteria.

barrier
an obstacle to the dispersal of individuals of a population of species. An example is a hostile climate or an ocean or mountain range.

basic
alkaline; having a pH greater than 7, reflecting more dissolved hydroxide ions than hydrogen ions.

basidium (buh SID ee um)
a spore-bearing structure between the gills under a mushroom cap, or between the gills of the reproductive bodies of other club fungi.

B cell lymphocyte (LIM foh syt)
a type of lymphocyte that produces antibodies. Memory B cells protect against repeated invasions by the same antigen; along with memory T cells, they are the key cells in acquired immunity.

bilateral symmetry (by LAT er ul SIM eh tree)
correspondence in size, shape, and position of parts on each side; close similarity of the two halves of the body on each side of an imaginary midline drawn from one end to the other.

bile
a secretion of the liver, stored in the gall bladder and released through a duct to the small intestine. Bile breaks large fat droplets into smaller ones that enzymes can act upon more efficiently.

binomial nomenclature (by NOH mee ul NOH men klay chur)
the two-word naming system used in biology to name each species.

biocide (BY oh syd)
a poisonous substance produced and used to kill forms of life that are considered pests to humans or that spread diseases or attack food crops.

bioethical (by oh ETH ih kul)
considerations of right and wrong with respect to issues raised by biological knowledge or technology.

biological distance
the degree of similarity or dissimilarity in genetic makeup between two species, or in gene frequencies between two populations.

biologist (by OL uh jist)
a scientist trained in the study of one or more of the life sciences; for example, a botanist, ecologist, geneticist, microbiologist, ornithologist, pathologist, paleontologist.

bioluminescent (by oh loo mih NES ent)
producing light as a specialized body process. Fireflies on land and many animals of the ocean depths provide examples.

biomass (BY oh mass)
the amount of matter, usually less the water content, in organisms under study; the dry mass of organisms.

biome (BY ohm)
the distinctive plant cover, and the rest of the community of organisms, associated with a particular physical environment. Often the biome is named for its plant cover, for example, grassland or deciduous forest.

biosphere (BY oh sfir)
the outer portion of the earth—air, water, and soil—where life is found.

biosynthesis (by oh SIN thuh sis)
the process of putting together or building up the large molecules characteristic of a particular type of cell or tissue.

biotic (by OT ik)
alive or only recently dead, or produced by the living.

blade
the flattened portion of a leaf in grasses and deciduous trees.

blastocyst (BLAS toh sist)
the mammalian embryonic stage that corresponds to the blastula of other animals.

blastula (BLAS chuh luh)
an animal embryo after the cleavage stage, when a pattern of cell movements toward the outside of the ball of cells results in a fluid-filled cavity inside.

bolt
to produce flowers, seed, and fruit prematurely; also, in horses, to become startled and run.

botanist (BOT un ist)
a biologist who specializes in the study of plants.

Bowman's capsule
the cup of a nephron, containing a ball of blood capillaries.

buffer
a substance that modifies the pH of a solution by its interactions with hydrogen or hydroxide ions; buffers help regulate or stabilize pH during reactions that release large numbers of these ions.

bulimarexia (byoo lih muh REK see uh)
alternate overeating and self-starvation, a dietary disorder reflecting unbalanced attempts to control body weight.

bulimia (byoo LIM ee uh)
an abnormal craving for food beyond the body's needs; frequently expressed as gorging followed by forced vomiting.

buttress
a support. In trees, buttresses are thickened vertical parts of the trunk that help support the tree in the soil.

C

callus (KAL us)
thickened or hardened tissue on skin or bark, around a break in a bone, and so on; also, in tissue culture, a mass of undifferentiated plant tissue that is grown from identical cells, then induced by plant hormones to develop into a complete plant.

calorie (KAL oh ree)
the amount of energy required to raise the temperature of one gram of water one degree Celsius. The larger food Calorie, or kilocalorie, is equal to 1000 calories.

Calvin cycle
the cycle (named for its discoverer) in which 3-carbon, 5-carbon, and 6-carbon sugars of photosynthesis are made. Light is not required, because light energy has already been converted to chemical energy in two kinds of molecules that take part in the cycle.

cambium (KAM bee um)
a layer of living cells near the outer surface of plant stems and roots, which produces new phloem and xylem cells.

canopy
an overhead covering, usually provided by deciduous trees in a dense forest.

capillary (KAP ih lair ee)
a tiny, thin-walled blood vessel between an artery and a vein. Food and oxygen molecules diffuse through the capillary walls to body cells, and carbon dioxide and wastes diffuse from the body cells into the capillaries.

carbohydrate (kar boh HY drayt)
an energy-rich biological compound in which the hydrogen and oxygen atoms that occur with the carbon are found in the same ratio as in water—twice as many hydrogens as oxygens. Sugars and starches are examples.

carbon cycle
the biological cycle in which carbon compounds made by some organisms are digested and decomposed by others, releasing the carbon in small inorganic molecules that can be used again by more organisms to synthesize carbon compounds.

cardiac muscle (KARD ee ak)
muscle tissue of the heart in vertebrates—a specialized type of nonskeletal, striated muscle.

cardiovascular
(KARD ee oh VAS kyoo ler)
relating to the heart (cardio) and blood vessels (vascular).

cardiovascular fitness
(KARD ee oh VAS kyoo ler)
the relative state of health or fitness of the lungs, heart and blood vessels, especially with regard to their ability to deliver oxygen to the cells.

carnivore (KAR nih vor)
a meat-eating animal, or another consumer organism that feeds on fellow consumers rather than on plants or other producers.

carrier
an organism that transmits a pathogen without acquiring a disease; also a molecule or molecular ion that transmits an electron or hydrogen atom in the energy-transferring of a cell.

carrying capacity
the greatest number of individuals of a given species that an environment can support with its available resources.

cartilage (KAR tih lej)
a tough, elastic connective tissue that makes up the skeleton of a cartilaginous fish, but that in other vertebrates is mostly replaced by bone as the animals mature.

catalyst (KAT uh list)
a compound that speeds up a specific kind of chemical reaction by taking part in the critical step; afterward it is restored to its original condition.

cell body
enlarged part of a nerve cell that contains the nucleus.

cell cycle
a cycle of events from cell division to normal growth and metabolism between divisions, to the next cell division.

cellular respiration (SEL yoo ler res pih RAY shun)
the series of chemical reactions by which a living cell breaks down food molecules and obtains energy from them; the energy is used in the cell's life processes, including restructuring other molecules.

cellulose (SEL yoo lohs)
a major plant carbohydrate, and the most abundant carbohydrate of living things. Among its functions is semi-rigid support for plant stems for as long as the stems are normally supplied with water.

cell wall
a covering enclosing the cells of plants, many algae, and certain bacteria. It is located outside the plasma membrane, and is made of materials secreted by each cell through its membrane.

central nervous system
the brain and spinal cord in vertebrates.

centriole (SEN tree ohl)
one of a pair of small, tubular structures present in animal and protist cells. The centrioles duplicate before mitosis or meiosis and form organizing centers for the spindle fibers.

centromere (SEN troh meer)
the specialized region of a chromosome that holds two replicated chromosomal strands together and that attaches to the spindle in mitosis.

cerebellum (ser eh BEL um)
the part of the brain in vertebrates that is associated with regulating muscular coordination, balance, and similar functions.

cerebral cortex (seh REE brul KOR teks)
the neuron-rich outer layers, or "gray matter," of the cerebrum.

cerebrum (seh REE brum)
the largest portion of the brain in humans and many other animals; it controls the higher mental functions, including learning.

chaparral (shap uh RAL)
a type of plant cover in a temperate region with summer-long droughts. Typically the plants are dense and sometimes large shrubs with small, waxy, evergreen leaves.

chemical bond
the chemical interaction between atoms that leads to the formation of molecules and ionic compounds.

chemical energy
energy stored in the structure of molecules, particularly organic molecules.

chemoautotrophic bacteria (kee moh aut oh TROH fik)
bacteria that obtain their energy from inorganic molecules in the environment.

chitin (KYT in)
a horny carbohydrate found in cell walls of many fungi and in the exoskeletons of insects, crustaceans, and certain other arthropods.

chlorophyll (KLOR uh fil)
green pigments of plants and many microorganisms; electrons in chlorophyll absorb light energy and escape, but are captured in biological reactions before they can lose (or re-emit) their absorbed energy.

chloroplast (KLOR oh plast)
a cell organelle that carries on photosynthesis in producer organisms with eukaryotic cells; it contains chlorophyll, the enzymes of electron transfer, and the enzymes for synthesis of sugars.

cholesterol (koh LES ter ol)
a lipid associated particularly with animal cells and linked to deposits in blood vessels and corresponding heart disorders.

chorion (KOR ee on)
one of four embryonic membranes of vertebrate embryos. In mammals, it forms the embryonic part of the placenta.

chromatid (KROH muh tid)
either of the two strands of a replicated chromosome before separation at the centromere.

chromosome (KROH moh sohm)
in eukaryotes, a long structure of DNA, with some protein, that contains genetic information organized in linear sequence.

cilia (SIL ee uh)
short hairlike cell extensions of many microorganisms and of certain body cells of animals (including humans). Cilia are used for movement or to create a current.

class
in biological classification, the next-larger grouping above order.

cleavage
the earliest cell divisions, usually without growth, in an animal embryo. A solid ball of cells is produced.

climatogram
a graph of temperature and precipitation for a given area by month, during a year.

climax community
a stable, self-perpetuating community established by succession and considered semi-permanent. It persists until interrupted or destroyed by fire, flood, volcanic activity, human activity, or change in climate.

clone
an organism genetically identical to the donor of the cell from which it was produced; or, any of a group of organisms produced from genetically identical cells.

closed population
a population with no entering immigrants and no departing emigrants; a completely isolated population.

coacervate (koh AS er vayt)
a cluster of proteins or proteinlike substances held together in small droplets within a surrounding liquid and used as a model for a precell to investigate the formation of the first life on earth.

codominant
genes that show complete expression of both alleles in the heterozygote, as in the AB blood type in humans, which is produced by the expression of the I^A and I^B alleles.

codon
a sequence of three nucleotides in messenger RNA that codes for a single amino acid.

coevolution
in two interacting groups or species, the evolution of each with the other as a factor in natural selection. The result is an ever-increasing interdependence between the two—for example, between hummingbirds and plants with red flowers of long, tubular shape.

cohesion
attraction between similar or identical molecules, or other similar particles.

cohesion transpiration
the theory that water molecules may be strongly enough attracted to one another (cohesion) to be pulled up through a plant from its roots by the continuous loss of water from the leaves (transpiration). Root pressure (absorbed water from the soil) and adherence of water to plant cell surfaces may also contribute.

coleoptile (koh lee OP til)
the first leaf in germination of grasses, which forms a sheath around the other developing leaves.

commensalism (kuh MEN suh liz um)
an association between two unlike organisms in which one benefits and the other is unaffected. An example is a remora that attaches itself to a shark and benefits by a "free ride" and "free food" (small bits of the shark's food as they float by).

community
the populations of different organisms that live and interact in the same place or ecosystem at a given time; a biological neighborhood.

competition
interaction between organisms for the same food source, or for the same mate, and so on.

complement (KOM pleh ment)
a protein in blood plasma that destroys antigens held in an antigen-antibody complex.

complete proteins
proteins that contain all the essential amino acids in the proportions needed by humans. The essential amino acids are those that the body cannot synthesize from other food substances, or cannot synthesize in the required amounts.

compound (KOM pownd)
a substance composed of chemically bonded atoms of two or more elements. Unlike a simple mixture of these elements, it is a single substance with unique chemical properties.

conifer (KON ih fer)
cone-bearing plant that usually grow as evergreen trees and shrubs. Pines, spruces, firs, and junipers are examples.

conjugation (kon joo GAY shun)
the process by which sexual exchange and reproduction take place in many microscopic organisms, principally protists and fungi.

consumer
an organism that obtains its food materials and energy by feeding on other organisms or their wastes or remains.

continental drift
change in distance between continents and in their positions relative to each other, caused by introduction of new crustal material in sea-floor spreading and in land rifts.

control
the norm (unchanged subject or group) in an experiment; it is selected to be like the experimental subject or group except for one characteristic or variable being tested. A control helps an investigator link a planned change with an effect in the experimental group (or discover that it produced no effect by comparison with the control).

corpus luteum (KOR pus LOOT ee um)
in female mammals, a hormone-producing mass of tissue that develops in a ruptured ovarian follicle after release of an egg.

cortex
the outer layers of the cerebrum in the brain of a vertebrate; also, a layer of cells under the epidermis or bark of some plant stems.

cotyledon (kot ih LEE dun)
a seed leaf, often modified to store large amounts of food; it also may carry on photosynthesis until the first true leaves develop. Among flowering plants, the monocots have one seed leaf in the embryo, the dicots two.

creatine phosphate (KREE uh tin FOS fayt)
an energy storage compound used by muscle cells of vertebrates to replenish ATP supplies; when the cells are not contracting, they break down glycogen to replenish both the creatine phosphate and ATP.

cuticle
a waxy, waterproof coating present in differing amounts on the leaves of plants of different species; also, certain living or dead tissue around the nails or claws of vertebrates.

cyanobacteria
(SY uh noh bak TIR ee uh)
the blue-green bacteria, which carry on oxygen-producing photosynthesis much like plants, but without membrane-bounded chloroplasts to isolate their chlorophyll.

cytokinesis (syt oh kih NEE sus)
cell division following mitosis (in which two cell nuclei have been produced from one).

cytokinin (syt oh KY nin)
one of a group of plant hormones that promote cell division, stem and root growth, chlorophyll synthesis, and chloroplast development.

cytoplasm (SYT oh plaz um)
the contents of a cell between, but not including, the nucleus and the plasma membrane; cell organelles and cytosol.

cytosol (SYT oh sol)
the partly gel, partly fluid portion of cell cytoplasm in which cell organelles are suspended.

cytotoxic (syt oh TOKS ik)
poisonous or injurious to cells. The human body produces cytoxic lymphocytes that help destroy diseased cells.

d

data (DAY tuh)
observations and experimental evidence bearing on a biological question or problem. The singular is **datum** (DAY tum), for a single observation.

deciduous (dee SID joo us)
characterized by loss of leaves each autumn, followed by new leaf growth the following spring.

decomposer (de kum POHZ er)
an organism that feeds on the wastes or decaying remains of other organisms, breaking down these wastes or remains for food energy and materials.

decomposition (de kom poh ZISH un)
the process of taking molecules apart. Heat and chemical reactions are the chief agents; organisms employ the latter.

deletion
in genetics, a missing piece of a chromosome with the genes that it carries.

denitrifying bacteria
(dee NY trih fy ing)
bacteria that break down nitrogen compounds in the soil and release nitrogen gas to the air.

density
number of individuals in a population in proportion to the size of their environment or living space.

deoxyribonucleic acid
(dee OK sih RY boh noo KLEE ik)
DNA; the biological molecules that carry hereditary instructions from parents to offspring during reproduction. Viruses similarly employ either DNA or RNA.

deoxyribose (dee OK sih RY bohs)
a sugar used in the structure of DNA; it has one fewer oxygen atoms than ribose.

development
cell division, growth, and differentiation of cells from the embryonic germ layers into all the tissues and organs of the body; also, later changes with age, as the organism continues to grow, reaches reproductive maturity with its effects on appearance and body functions, and so on.

diabetes (dy uh BEET eez)
a disease that results from insufficient insulin secretion or impairment of insulin receptors on cells of the body; normal absorption and use of glucose from the bloodstream is then impossible.

diaphragm (DY uh fram)
a sheet of muscle in the body cavity of mammals that divides the cavity into a chest cavity and an abdominal cavity.

diatom (DY uh tom)
any of a large group of golden algae that have intricate, patterned shells made in two halves, and containing silica. Unusually shaped pores create the patterns.

dicot (DY kot)
a seed plant whose embryo has two cotyledons, or seed leaves.

differentiation
(dif er en CHEE AY shun)
the process by which different specialized cells—gland, muscle, skin, and so on—develop from less-specialized parental cells that are descendants of the same egg cell.

diffusion (dih FYOO zhun)
random motion of molecules, resulting overall in dispersal from a place of concentration. An odor escaping from a bottle is an example.

diffusion gradient
a difference in concentration of certain molecules between two places. The steepness of the gradient, if maintained, indicates either an impassable barrier or an active mechanism that returns the molecules to one place as rapidly as they diffuse to the other.

digestion (dih JES chun)
the chemical process of breaking food down into nutrients an organism's cells can use.

digit
a finger or toe.

dihybrid cross (dy HY brid)
a cross or mating of two individuals that are purebred for unlike genotypes in each of two different traits being studied. The cross extends to a mating of their offspring to produce an F_2 generation.

dipeptide (DY PEP tyd)
two amino acid molecules bonded to one another; the dipeptide may be the start of a chain for a protein or a product of digestion of a protein or polypeptide.

diploid (DIP loyd)
containing all the pairs of chromosomes—the full genome—characteristic of a sexually reproducing species.

disaccharide (DY SAK uh ryd)
a double sugar, composed of two chemically bonded simple sugars. In solution, a disaccharide forms a double-ring structure.

discontinuous distribution (dis kun TIN yuh wus dis trih BYOO shun)
populations of a species isolated from one another without "corridors" of migration and interbreeding. Isolation may be on separate continents, although at one time the range of the species was continuous.

dispersal
the spreading of organisms from a place of concentration; also, the scattering of spores and seeds that promotes dispersal of otherwise nonmotile organisms.

DNA
see deoxyribonucleic acid.

dominant
in genetics, exerting a controlling influence on the expression of a trait; in social behavior, exerting a controlling influence over other individuals.

dormant
inactive but alive or viable. Grasses are dormant during long droughts or cold winters, spores and seeds during unfavorable conditions, and microorganisms and even certain animals when conditions are too inhospitable.

dorsal (DOR sul)
in animals, situated toward the top or back side.

duration
the time span of an activity, event, or environmental condition.

e

ecologist (ee KOL uh jist)
a scientist trained in the study of the interactions of each kind of organism with others of its kind, with others of unlike kinds, and with nonliving parts of its environment.

ecology (ee KOL uh jee)
the study of the living and nonliving parts of the environment and of their interactions in affecting life for each biological species.

ecosystem (EE koh sis tum)
a biological community in its abiotic environment.

ectoderm (EK toh derm)
the outer layer of cells in the gastrula stage of an animal embryo.

effector
a muscle or a gland, activated by nerve impulses or hormones.

egg cell
an ovum; a female gamete.

electroencephalograph
(ee LEK troh en SEF uh loh graf)
a complex electronic instrument that monitors brain waves.

electron (ee LEK trahn)
negatively-charged atomic particle found outside the nucleus of atoms.

electron transport system
the process in which electrons are transferred from one carrier molecule to another in photosynthesis and in cellular respiration. Some of the energy is stored in ATP molecules.

element (EL uh ment)
a substance whose atoms are all chemically identical. Each atom has the same number and arrangement of protons and electrons; only the number of neutrons may vary.

embryo (EM bree oh)
an early stage in the development of an animal from the fertilized egg, or of a plant from the fertilized egg nucleus.

emigration (em uh GRAY shun)
departure by migration; out-migration.

endocast (EN doh kast)
a plaster or plastic cast of the inside surface, or the contents, of a covering or enclosing structure. Examples are endocasts of a skull's braincase, a plant's spore case, or a marine microorganism's glasslike shell.

endocrine gland (EN doh krin)
a ductless gland that secretes one or more hormones into the bloodstream.

endoderm (EN doh derm)
the inner layer of cells in the gastrula stage of an animal embryo.

endoplasmic reticulum (en do PLAZ mik reh TIK yoo lum)
a complex membrane network within the cell cytoplasm; many ribosomes are found along its membranes.

endoskeleton (EN doh SKEL eh ton)
a skeleton that is inside the body, as in vertebrates.

endosperm (EN doh sperm)
food-storage cells in a plant ovule, later enclosed with an embryo plant in a seed.

endospore (EN doh spor)
a thick-walled spore of a particular type, like that produced by the anaerobic bacterium that causes botulism.

energy
the active ingredient of all atoms; the characteristic of matter that can change it. Organisms utilize the readily available energy associated with an atom's outer electrons; however, far greater potential energy is associated with an atom's nucleus.

environment (en VY run ment)
everything in the surroundings of an organism; living and nonliving surroundings and factors including light, temperature, air, soil, water, and organisms.

enzyme (EN zym)
a catalyst produced by an organism and used to speed up a specific kind of chemical reaction.

enzyme-substrate complex
an enzyme molecule together with the molecules on which it acts, correctly arranged at the active site of the enzyme.

epicotyl (EP ih kot il)
the embryonic shoot of a developing plant, made up of a stem tip and tiny leaves.

epidermis (ep ih DER mis)
the outer layer of cells in many organisms, including leaves and younger stems of plants.

epididymis (ep ih DID ih mus)
in mammals, a coiled duct near a testis, where sperm are held after they mature.

epinephrine (ep ih NEF rin)
an adrenal hormone, also called adrenalin, that speeds up heart rate and raises blood sugar level and blood pressure; the "fight or flight" hormone that is secreted during a sudden fright or emergency.

epiphyte (EP ih fyt)
a plant that takes its moisture and nutrients from the air and from rainfall and that is usually supported by growing on a branch of another plant. It is not a parasite.

ER
see endoplasmic reticulum.

erosion
displacement of soil or rock material by wind and water action and by temperature/humidity cycles.

esophagus (ee SOF uh gus)
in humans, the tube through which food, when swallowed, is passed to the stomach in a series of wavelike muscular contractions (peristalsis); in other vertebrates and many invertebrates, a tube identical or at least similar in function.

essential nutrient
a nutrient that an organism cannot synthesize, or not in the quantities it requires. Plants must obtain such a nutrient from the soil; animals from the food they ingest.

estivation (es tih VAY shun)
a state of partial dormancy in which certain animals survive the summer heat in their burrows or in the mud of drying ponds.

estrogen (ES troh jen)
a hormone active in the reproductive cycles of female mammals, promoting development of the inner tissues of the uterus.

ethics (ETH iks)
principles dealing with what is right or wrong.

ethylene (ETH ih leen)
a gaseous plant hormone that promotes fruit ripening, while inhibiting further plant growth in stems and roots.

eubacteria (yoo bak TIR ee uh)
"true bacteria;" they include the cyanobacteria but not the archaebacteria. Eubacteria differ from archaebacteria in their ribosomal RNA, transfer RNA, and in other ways.

eukaryote (yoo KAIR ee oht)
an organism whose cells have a membrane-bounded nucleus and membrane-bounded organelles such as mitochondria, chloroplasts, and lysosomes; a protist, fungus, plant, or animal.

eutrophication (yoo troh fih KAY shun)
nutrient enrichment of a body of water, as by sewage, leading to population explosions first of photosynthetic organisms, then of decomposers that deplete the dissolved oxygen, causing fish and other aquatic animals to die.

evolution
change through time that results from natural selection acting on genetic variations present among individuals of a species. That process results in the development of new species.

excretion (ek SKREE shun)
the elimination of wastes, especially by-products of body metabolism, by organisms.

exocrine gland (EK soh krin)
a gland that delivers its secretion externally through a tube or duct. A tear gland and a sweat gland are examples.

exon (EKS on)
a segment of chromosomal DNA that is transcribed into mRNA and translated in protein synthesis. Exons make up the known genes.

exoskeleton (EK soh SKEL eh ton)
a skeleton on the outside of the body, or separated by a cell layer from the outside of the body. Insects and other arthropods are the principal animals with exoskeletons.

extinct (ek STINKT)
no longer surviving as a species.

extracellular (ek struh SEL yoo lar)
outside a cell, or taking place outside body cells. Often, secretions from cells are responsible for an extracellular process, as in digestion in most animals.

f

family
in biological classification, the next-larger grouping above genus.

famine (FAM in)
severe shortage of food, causing widespread hunger and starvation within a population.

feces (FEE seez)
undigested food remnants that are eliminated from the large intestine through the anus. Mixed with the food remnants are mucus, bacteria, and dead intestinal cells.

female
an animal with ovaries but not testes; also, a plant that produces egg cells but not sperm, or a plant part that produces egg nuclei.

fermentation (fer men TAY shun)
the incomplete breakdown of food molecules, especially sugars, in the absence of oxygen.

fertile (FERT il)
capable of reproducing.

fertilization
the production of the first cell of a new individual by the union of a sperm with an ovum; also, the enrichment of soil by the addition of plant nutrients.

fetus (FEET us)
a vertebrate embryo in later stages of development, when it has attained the recognizable structural plan and features of its kind.

fibrin (FY brin)
an insoluble blood protein that forms a network of fibers around which a clot develops.

fibrinogen (fy BRIN oh jen)
a soluble blood protein that is changed into its insoluble form as fibrin during the blood-clotting process.

fibrous-root system
a root system consisting of many branching roots of various sizes, with no one root easily identifiable as the original plant root.

flagellum (fluh JEL um)
a whiplike organelle of many bacteria, protists, and certain cells of animals such as sponges and hydras.

flame cell
in planarians, a cell with cilia in a network connected by tubules; flame cells absorb fluid and wastes and move the fluid through the tubules, using their cilia to create a current. Excess water is removed in this way and eliminated from the body through pores.

fluctuation (fluk shoo AY shun)
change in numbers or values in both directions—up and down.

follicle
in mammals, any of several different structures—an ovarian sac from which an egg is released; a thyroid tissue that produces and stores a hormone; and a tiny skin cavity from which a hair grows. Other structures named follicles also exist.

food
a substance containing energy-rich organic compounds made by organisms, and used by them and other organisms for the energy and materials for life.

food chain
a food relationship beginning with a producer, eaten by a consumer, in turn eaten by another consumer, and so on. The producer is eaten or fed upon by a herbivore, which is eaten by a carnivore, which is eaten by still another carnivore; eventually, decomposers end the chain.

food web
a food scheme of overlapping and interlinking food chains used to complete a picture of "who eats what" for a community of organisms.

foramen magnum
(foh RAY men MAG num)
the large opening in the base of the skull, through which the spinal cord maintains its continuity with the brain.

fossil
a cast of an organism preserved in rock that formed where it died, or the organism itself in ice or volcanic glass, or its tracks, seeds, or skeleton preserved in deposits.

fungi (FUN jy)
a kingdom of eukaryotic organisms that develop from spores but not from embryos, often form many-celled structures, and live as consumers (often decomposers); molds, yeasts, mushrooms, living rusts, smuts, bracket fungi, and related organisms.

fungicide (FUN jih syd)
a poison produced and used to kill fungi that attack food crops and ornamental plants.

g

gamete (GAM eet)
a sexual reproductive cell or nucleus; in animals, a sperm cell or an egg cell, and in flowering plants, a sperm nucleus or egg nucleus.

gametophyte (guh MEET oh fyt)
a plant of the gamete-producing generation in a plant species that undergoes alternation of generations. In many species—the flowering plants, for example—the male and female gametophytes are reduced to small dependent structures that develop in flowers of the sporophyte plants.

ganglion (GAN glee un)
a mass of nerve tissue, or of nerve cell bodies from which the nerve fibers extend.

gastric juice
mixed secretions of the glands in the stomach wall—in humans, principally mucus, hydrochloric acid, and protein-fragmenting enzymes.

gastrula (GAS truh luh)
an animal embryo after the blastula stage, when an infolding of the cells from one side of the embryo occurs, replacing the blastula cavity with a new gastrula cavity bounded by two layers of cells.

gene (JEEN)
a portion of DNA that codes for one hereditary characteristic and occupies a specific place on a chromosome.

gene pool
all the genes in a population of interbreeding individuals.

generalization
a statement summarizing a pattern observed from an accumulation of separate observations.

genetic determinism (jeh NET ik de TER mih niz um)
the belief that an individual's traits, including behavioral traits, are primarily determined by the genes rather than by environmental influence.

genome (JEE nohm)
the total genetic content or complement of a cell, other than a gamete, from any given species.

genotype (JEE noh typ)
the genetic makeup of an organism, as distinguished from its observable traits.

genus (JEE nus)
in biological classification, the next-larger grouping above species.

germ layer
the ectoderm, mesoderm, and endoderm cell layers of an early animal embryo. By differentiation, cells in these layers give rise to all the different tissues of the body.

gibberellin (jib uh REL en)
one of a group of plant hormones that promote seed germination, plant growth in height, and certain other growth-related changes.

glomerulus (glah MER yoo lus)
the ball of blood capillaries in the cup, or Bowman's capsule, of a nephron in a kidney

glucagon (GLOO kuh gahn)
a pancreatic hormone that acts to raise the blood glucose level.

glycogen (GLY koh jen)
the chief carbohydrate made and used by animals for energy storage. In mammals, excess sugar (glucose) is removed from the blood in liver and muscle tissues and converted to glycogen.

glycolysis (gly KAWL uh sis)
the initial breakdown of a carbohydrate, usually glucose, into smaller molecules at the beginning of the cellular respiration process.

golgi complex (GOHL jee)
a cell organelle that is involved in packaging cell products in vesicles.

gonad (GOH nad)
an animal organ that produces sperm or ova; a testis or an ovary.

granum (GRAY num)
a stack of thylakoids within a chloroplast.

gravitropism (grav ih TROH piz um)
the response of a plant to the earth's gravitational pull. Roots usually react positively, growing downward, but stems may react negatively.

gross primary productivity
the total amount of food energy stored during a unit of time by photosynthesis in an ecosystem.

guard cells
a pair of cells that surround a stomate in a plant leaf's epidermis. Turgor pressure in the guard cells regulates the opening and closing of a stomate.

h

habitat (HAB ih tat)
the place where an organism lives. Even in the same ecosystem, different organisms differ in their habitats.

half-life
the time required for half a quantity of a radioactive element to break down. The time is independent of how little or how much of the element is present.

haploid (HAP loyd)
containing only one member of each pair of chromosomes characteristic of a sexually reproducing species. Gametes are haploid.

hemoglobin (HEE moh gloh bin)
the oxygen-carrying pigment in the blood of vertebrates and certain invertebrates; in vertebrates it is found in red blood cells.

herbaceous (her BAY shus)
herblike; without woody tissues.

herbicide (HER bih syd)
a plant poison produced and used to kill unwanted plants, usually weeds in lawns or food crops.

herbivore (HER bih vor)
a plant-eating consumer, one of the class of consumers most closely associated with producers.

hermaphrodite (her MAF roh dyt)
an animal that has both ovaries and testes.

heterotroph (HET eh roh trohf)
a consumer; an organism that obtains its food materials and energy by feeding on other organisms or their wastes or remains.

heterotroph hypothesis
(HET eh roh trohf hy POTH uh sis)
the hypothesis that the first life on earth fed on "leftovers"—naturally occurring organic compounds like those from which the life evolved. Thus, the first living things would have been consumers or heterotrophs.

heterozygous (het eh roh ZY gus)
having different alleles for a trait in a pair of alleles inherited one from each parent; hybrid.

hibernate (HY ber nayt)
to go into a state of dormancy, in which body processes and metabolism, including heartbeat and breathing, slow to a point ordinarily considered near death. Hibernating animals may breathe as infrequently as once or twice in five minutes and exist for long periods on body fat.

homeostasis (hoh mee oh STAY sis)
the tendency for an organism, or a population of organisms, to remain relatively stable under the range of conditions to which it is subjected; a complex process of self or population regulation.

hominid (HOM ih nid)
an upright-walking primate. Humans are the only survivors of this group of several former species.

hominoid (HOM ih noyd)
a primate of the group that includes humans, apes, and monkeys.

homolog (HOH moh log)
in genetics, either chromosome of a pair that bear similar genes in identical sequences.

homology (hoh MOL uh jee)
correspondence in structure, biochemical make-up, or other features suggesting a relationship.

homozygous (hoh moh ZY gus)
having identical alleles for a trait in a pair of alleles inherited one from each parent.

hormone (HOR mohn)
a substance secreted by a cell or gland that has a regulatory effect on cells and organs elsewhere in the body; a chemical messenger.

host
an organism that serves as a habitat or living food source, or both, for another organism.

human culture
a way of life in human populations that is the outgrowth of intelligence, toolmaking, speech, written language, and social communication and cooperation.

humus
decomposing plant and animal tissues in soil.

hybrid (HY brid)
having different alleles for a trait in a pair of alleles inherited one from each parent; heterozygous.

hydrosphere (HY droh sfir)
the bodies of water and the atmospheric water vapor that give earth its blue color when viewed from space.

hyphae (HY fee)
threadlike growths of a fungus. In an irregular mass they make up the mycelium of many fungi; in an orderly and tightly-packed arrangement they make up the body of a mushroom or a bracket fungus.

hypocotyl (HY poh kot il)
the embryonic root of a developing plant.

hypoglycemia (hy poh gly SEE mee uh)
low blood sugar level.

hypothalamus (hy poh THAL uh mus)
a specialized part of the base of the brain that in humans combines neuron and hormone activity. It links the autonomic nervous system with the endocrine system in regulating many body functions.

hypothesis (hy POTH uh sis)
a statement suggesting an explanation for an observation or an answer to a scientific problem. The hypothesis must fit the existing data and, if possible, predict more data that can be tested in experiments.

i

immigration (im uh GRAY shun)
arrival by migration; in-migration.

immune (im YOON)
protected against; in humans the protection is provided by the various components of the immune system, including specialized proteins (antibodies) and cells.

immunity (im YOO nit ee)
disease-resistance, usually specific for one disease or the pathogen that causes it.

impermeable (im PER mee uh bull)
impassable; impenetrable. A membrane, for example, may be impermeable to some molecules and ions but not others.

infectious (in FEK shus)
caused by viruses or microorganisms that can be transmitted directly from an affected individual to a healthy one, affecting that individual in turn.

ingestion (in JES chun)
the process of taking a substance from the environment, usually food, into the body.

innate (in AYT)
genetically determined, as in behavior that is uniform for a species but is not learned.

inorganic compound (IN or GAN ik)
a compound containing no carbon, or only one carbon atom per molecule. Inorganic compounds do not depend on living things for their formation; however, living things can make some inorganic as well as organic compounds.

insecticide (in SEK tih syd)
an insect poison produced and used to control insect populations that are pests to humans or that carry disease organisms or damage food crops.

insulin (IN suh lin)
a pancreatic hormone that promotes cell absorption and use of glucose; impairment of its secretion or its action results in diabetes.

interphase (INT er fayz)
a normal interval between successive cell divisions when the only evidence of future division is that genes begin to be replicated; in general, a cell at work, rather than a cell dividing.

intestinal juice
secretions of glands in the small intestinal wall; they contain enzymes that act on dipeptides and disaccharides.

intracellular (in truh SEL yoo lar)
inside a cell, or taking place inside cells.

intron
a segment of chromosomal DNA that is transcribed into precursor mRNA but then removed before the mRNA leaves the nucleus. Thus, introns are not translated into protein.

inversion
in genetics, part of a chromosome that has undergone breakage, end-over-end turning, and reattachment, reversing its gene sequence.

ion (EYE un)
an atom or molecule that has gained or lost one or more electrons, acquiring a net negative or positive charge.

ionize (EYE uh nyz)
in an atom, to form an ion by adding or removing one or more electrons; in an ionic compound, to separate the ions, as in solution.

j

joint
a point of movement, or of fixed calcium deposits preventing movement, marking where two bones meet in the skeleton.

k

karyotype (KAIR ee oh typ)
a photomicrograph of an organism's chromosomes arranged and labeled in homologous pairs.

kingdom
in biological classification, the next-larger grouping above phylum or division; the largest grouping used.

Krebs citric acid cycle
the cycle in cellular respiration that completes the breakdown of intermediate products of glycolysis, releasing electrons and hydrogen to the cell's electron-transport system. The cycle also is a source of carbon skeletons for use in biosynthesis reactions.

kwashiorkor (kwah shee OR kor)
a disease of malnourishment from too much starch and not enough protein.

l

larva (LAR vuh)
an immature stage of development in offspring of many kinds of animals.

learning
behavior that is modified by experience; or, new behavior that is determined by experience.

lenticel (LENT ih sel)
an opening in the surface of a plant stem through which air can diffuse.

lichen (LY ken)
an alga and a fungus living together in a mutualistic relationship as an apparent "single" kind of organism, often found on rocks.

life cycle
the events from appearance of new individuals in a species to their reproduction of other new individuals, over the span of each generation.

light-dependent reactions
the energy-capturing reactions in photosynthesis; also, reactions in the human skin leading to production of vitamin D.

limiting factor
an environmental condition such as food, temperature, water, and so on that restricts types of organisms and population numbers an environment can support.

linked
genes that are located on the same chromosome.

lipid (LIP id)
an energy-rich organic compound formed of carbon, hydrogen, and small amounts of oxygen. Lipids are important components of the cell's plasma membrane. Fats, oils, and waxes are examples.

littoral zone
the zone between high and low tides on a seashore, submerged part time and exposed to air part time.

lymph (LIMF)
tissue fluid, similar to blood plasma but with lesser amounts of plasma proteins and greater amounts of cell wastes. Lymph leaving the intestinal area also carries great amounts of digested food molecules.

lymphatic system (lim FAT ik)
a system of vessels through which body lymph flows, eventually entering the bloodstream where the largest lymph duct joins a blood vein.

lymph node
a tiny, twisted portion of a lymph vessel in which white blood cells attack any pathogenic organisms in the lymph and engulf any foreign particles.

lymphocyte (LIM foh syt)
a small white blood vessel that produces antibodies or regulates an immune response. Lymphocytes are the typical cellular elements of lymph.

lymph vessel
a vessel in which lymph from body tissues, or from villi in the intestine, flows until it enters the largest lymph duct, which empties into a blood vein.

lysosome (LY soh zohm)
a cell vesicle that contains digestive enzymes. The membrane of the vesicle protects vital parts of the cell from digestion by the enzymes.

m

macronucleus (MAK roh NOO klee us)
the larger of two types of nuclei in many one-celled protists. One or more macronuclei may be present in each organism.

macronutrient
a nutrient required in large amounts by a plant or other organism.

macrophage (MAK roh fayj)
a large white blood cell that engulfs and digests antigen.

male
an animal with testes but not ovaries; also, a plant that produces sperm but not egg cells, or a plant part that produces sperm nuclei.

malnourished (mal NUR isht)
undersupplied with certain essential nutrients; the food supply may be adequate for energy and some nutrients, but not others.

mantle (MANT el)
in mollusks, two extended lobes of the body wall that line the two halves of the shell and create a body cavity.

mass
the amount of matter in organisms or objects being studied.

medium
in a laboratory culture, the nutrient broth that sustains the organisms placed in it.

meiosis (my OH sis)
the distribution of chromosomes, following replication, through a reduction cell division and a second cell division, yielding gametes with the haploid chromosome number.

menstrual cycle (MEN stroo ul)
the monthly cycle of ovarian and uterine events in human females—a biological preparation for reproduction.

menstruation (men stroo AY shun)
the loss of blood and tissue from the uterus in human females when no pregnancy has occurred in a menstrual cycle.

meristem tissue (MER ih stem)
plant cells at growing tips of roots and stems, and in buds and cambium, that divide and produce new cells that can differentiate into various plant tissues.

mesoderm (MEZ oh derm)
the middle cell layer that forms between the ectoderm and the endoderm of an early animal embryo.

mesophyll (MEZ oh fil)
green leaf cells between the upper and lower epidermis of a leaf; the primary site of photosynthesis in leaves.

metabolism (meh TAB oh liz um)
a term for all chemical reactions in a cell or organism considered in their total.

metamorphosis (met uh MOR phuh sus)
in the life cycles of many animals, marked changes in body form and functions from the newly-hatched young to the adults. The young and the adults may differ so greatly that they could be mistaken for different species.

metaphase (MET uh fayz)
the stage in mitosis in which replicated chromosomes move to the center of the spindle and become attached to it.

micronucleus (MY kroh NOO klee us)
the smaller of two types of nuclei in many one-celled protists. One or more micronuclei may be present in each organism.

micronutrient
a nutrient required in only small or trace amounts by a plant or other organism.

microorganism
(my kroh OR guh niz um)
an organism too small to be seen with the unaided eye.

microsphere (MY kroh sfir)
a cooling droplet from a hot water solution of polypeptides; the droplet forms its own double-layered boundary as it cools. Microspheres are used as a model for precells to investigate the formation of the first life on earth.

microtubule (MY kroh TOO byool)
a tiny hollow tube made of protein, part of a cell's "skeletal" network.

microvillus (my kroh VIL us)
a microscopic projection on the surface membrane of an intestinal villus.

mitochondrion (my toh KON dree un)
a cell organelle in eukaryotic cells that carries on cellular respiration, releasing energy from food molecules and storing it in ATP.

mitosis (my TOH sis)
the replication of chromosomes and formation of two identical cell nuclei in one cell. Usually mitosis is followed by cell division.

model
a mental picture, or an actual three-dimensional construction, representing a situation in its essential terms.

molecule (MOL uh kyool)
a particle of matter formed by bonds between atoms. A molecule may be formed from a single element, or from different elements, as in a compound.

monera (moh NEHR uh)
a kingdom of prokaryotic organisms, the bacteria.

monocot (MON oh kot)
a seed plant whose embryo has one cotyledon, or seed leaf.

monoculture
in farming, single-crop agriculture. Also, the usual condition of a laboratory culture in medical research—a single variety of organism from a single species, nourished by nutrients artificially supplied.

monosaccharide (MON oh SAK uh ryd)
a simple sugar, with seven or fewer carbon atoms to which hydrogen and oxygen are bonded. In solution, its structure is single-ring.

mortality (mor TAL ih tee)
death rate, measured as the proportion of deaths to total population over a given time period; often expressed as number of deaths per 1000 or 10,000 individuals.

motile (MOH til)
capable of movement from place to place, a characteristic of most animals.

motor neuron (NYOO rahn)
a specialized neuron that receives impulses from a sensory or associative neuron and transmits them to a muscle or gland.

multicellular (mul tih SEL yoo ler)
many-celled; composed of dozens to billions of cells.

multiple alleles (uh LEELZ)
three or more different alleles for the same genetic trait. An individual usually can have only two of these alleles—one on each chromosome of a pair.

muscle tone
a state of partial muscle contraction, or readiness, in healthy organisms.

mutation (myoo TAY shun)
a chemical change in a gene, resulting in a new allele; or, a change in the portion of a chromosome that regulates the gene. In either case the change is hereditary.

mutualistic (myoo choo uh LIS tik)
mutually beneficial in a close biological association, as between the algae and the fungi that make up lichens.

mycelium (my SEE lee um)
an irregular mass of fungal hyphae.

mycologist (my KOL oh jist)
a biologist who specializes in the study of fungi.

mycorrhiza (my koh RY zuh)
a mutualistic association between fungal hyphae and a seed plant's roots.

n

NAD^+
see nicotinamide adenine dinucleotide.

$NADP^+$
see nicotinamide adenine dinucleotide phosphate.

natality (nay TAL ih tee)
birthrate, measured as the proportion of new individuals to total population over a given time period; often expressed as number of new individuals per 1,000 or 10,000 in the population.

native trees
trees that occur naturally in some stage of plant succession in a given place.

natural history
the descriptive history of organisms and their ways of life in their respective environments.

natural selection
the tendency of members of a population with the most successful adaptations to their environment to be the surviving members and parents of the next generation.

nectar
a secretion, mainly a sugar solution, produced by small glands in the petals of many flowers.

nephron (NEF rahn)
a working unit of a kidney in vertebrates; a long, coiled tubule surrounded by blood capillaries. Each kidney has about a million nephrons.

nerve
a bundle of nerve fibers. The cell bodies from which the fibers extend usually are located together at one end of the fibers.

nerve fiber
an extension from the cell body of a neuron, ranging from less than one millimeter to almost one meter in length, that transmits nerve impulses.

nerve impulse
a wave of chemical and electrical changes that passes along a nerve fiber in response to a stimulus.

net primary productivity
the amount of food energy available to consumers from the total produced by photosynthesis.

neuron (NYOO rahn)
a nerve cell; a name usually reserved for nerve cells in animals that have a complex brain and specialized associative, sensory, and motor nerves.

neurotransmitter
(NYOOR oh trans MIT er)
a chemical messenger, often similar to or identical with a hormone, that diffuses across a nerve synapse and transmits a nerve impulse from one neuron to another.

neutral solution
neither acidic nor basic; having a pH of 7, reflecting approximately equal numbers of hydrogen and hydroxide ions.

neutron (NOO trahn)
a particle with no electric charge, found in the nucleus of most atoms.

niche (NITCH)
in ecology, the way of life of an organism or its role in the community, including its habitat, manner of obtaining food, and so on.

nicotinamide adenine dinucleotide
(nik uh TEE nuh myd AD uh neen DY NOO klee oh tyd)
NAD^+, a hydrogen-carrier molecule that forms NADH in gylcolysis.

nicotinamide adenine dinucleotide phosphate (nik uh TEE nuh myd AD uh neen DY NOO klee oh tyd FOS fayt)
$NADP^+$, a hydrogen-carrier molecule that forms NADPH in the light-dependent reactions of photosynthesis.

nitrifying bacteria (NY trih fy ing)
bacteria that use ammonium ions to produce nitrite and nitrate ions.

nitrogen-fixing bacteria
bacteria that take free nitrogen from the air and use it to produce ammonia; subsequent reactions by other bacteria produce ammonium ions and nitrates, from which plants can obtain their nitrogen.

nodule (NOD yool)
a rounded growth of tissue that usually contains microorganisms or some other agent associated with the growth. In certain plants, nitrogen-fixing bacteria live in nodules on the plant roots.

nondisjunction
a failure in chromosome separation during meiosis, putting an extra chromosome in one gamete and omitting it from a second.

notochord (NOH toh kord)
in chordates, a flexible, dorsal, rodlike structure that extends the length of the body; in vertebrates it is replaced in later stages of development by the vertebrae, which make up the backbone.

nuclear envelope
the membrane enclosing a cell nucleus.

nuclear winter
the prediction by some scientists of the biological conditions that would follow nuclear war—sunless cold, violent windstorms, toxic smog, persistent radioactivity, and extinction of populations of many species.

nucleic acid (noo KLEE ik)
DNA or RNA; an organic compound comprised of nucleotides and important in coding instructions for cell processes.

nucleotide (NOO klee oh tyd)
a subunit or building block of DNA or RNA; it is chemically constructed of a 5-carbon sugar, a nitrogen base, and a phosphate group.

nucleus (NOO klee us)
a membrane-bounded organelle in a eukaryotc cell that contains the DNA and controls the cell's activities; also the central body of an atom, composed of protons and neutrons.

nutrition
the ways in which an organism obtains, processes, and uses nutrients.

O

observation
an item of knowledge obtained experimentally or by use of one or more of the senses in the natural environmental situation.

omnivore (OM nih vor)
a consumer organism that feeds partly as a herbivore and partly as a carnivore; it eats both plants and animals, and often fungi as well.

open population
a population that gains members by immigration or loses them by emigration, or both.

optimum
best; most favorable to an individual or a population.

oral cavity
in vertebrates, the entrance chamber to the digestive tract; the cavity inside the mouth.

order
in biological classification, the next-larger grouping above family.

organ
a body structure of different tissues that work together in a major function. Examples are the heart, the stomach, a plant leaf, and a flower.

organelle (or guh NEL)
an organized structure within a cell, with a specific function; a chloroplast and a mitochondrion are examples.

organic compound (or GAN ik)
a compound characteristically containing a multiple number of carbon atoms per molecule; the number may vary from two to thousands.

organism (OR guh niz um)
a living thing.

organ system
an organized, connected group of organs and tissues that carry on a "whole body" function. For example, the brain, spinal cord, nerves, and the sensory organs and receptors make up the nervous system.

osmosis (os MOH sis)
movement of water through a differentially permeable membrane.

ovary
an organ in which eggs or egg nuclei are produced.

oviduct (OH vih dukt)
in vertebrates, a tube through which eggs pass after their release from an ovary. The tube leads to the uterus in mammals, or to an enlarged duct opening outside the body of egg-laying vertebrates.

ovulation (ohv yoo LAY shun)
in vertebrates, the release of one or more eggs from an ovary.

ovule (OHV yool)
a female spore- and egg-producing structure in the ovary of a pistil, within a flower.

ovum (OH vum)
a female gamete, or egg cell.

P

paleoecology
(pay lee oh ee KOL uh jee)
the study of organisms of the past, their interactions, and their environments from fossil evidence.

paleoecosystem
(pay lee oh EE koh sis tum)
an ecosystem of the earth's past, reconstructed from fossil evidence in rock strata.

paleontologist (pay lee un TOL uh jist)
a biologist who specializes in the study of life in the past, as represented by fossils.

pancreatic juice (pan kree AT ik)
secretions from the pancreas to the small intestine, delivered through a duct; the secretions contain enzymes that act on polypeptides, polysaccharides, and fats.

parasite (PAIR uh syt)
an organism that lives and feeds on another, host organism.

parasitism (PAIR uh sih tiz um)
an ecological niche in which one organism is the habitat and the food for another, which lives and feeds on the host organism (usually without killing it).

parthenogenesis
(par thuh noh JEN eh sis)
reproduction by development of an unfertilized egg.

pasteurized (PAS tyoor ized)
treated by heating in a specified method to kill unwanted microorganisms.

pathogen (PATH oh jen)
a disease-producing organism.

pathology (path OL uh jee)
the study of diseases and the changes they produce in organisms.

pelvis
in vertebrates, the basin-shaped structure formed by the bones of the hip girdle growing together.

penis
in vertebrates, the male organ through which sperm are passed to the female, and through which nitrogenous wastes from the kidneys—in the form of urine—are discharged outside the body.

perennial (peh REN ee ul)
a herbaceous plant that lives from year to year, becoming dormant after one growing season ("dying back to the ground") and sending up new shoots the next growing season.

peristalsis (per ih STAWL sis)
wavelike contractions of smooth muscle that move the contents of a tubelike part or organ in the direction of the wavelike motion.

permafrost
frozen sublayers of soil that remain frozen through the summer thaw in the tundra of northern latitudes.

permeable (PER mee uh bul)
penetrable by molecules below a certain size.

petal
one of the leaflike, often brightly colored, structures within the ring of green sepals in a developing flower. In the mature flower the petals may form their own ring, or fuse to form a cuplike or tubular structure.

petiole (PET ee ohl)
the slender structure at the base of a leaf that attaches the leaf to a plant stem.

petrified (PEH trih fyd)
mineralized and hardened, as in parts of organisms replaced by minerals in fossils.

PGAL
see phosphoglyceraldehyde.

phenotype (FEE noh typ)
the observable traits produced in an individual, as distinguished from the alleles that determined it.

phloem (FLOH em)
conducting tissue that transports sap or dissolved sugars in a vascular plant.

phosphoglyceraldehyde
(fos foh glis uh RAL deh hyd)
PGAL, a 3-carbon sugar phosphate formed in the Calvin cycle of photosynthesis.

photoperiodism
(foh toh PIH ree ud iz um)
the responses of plants to seasonal differences in length of daylight, light intensity, and shorter or longer periods of darkness. Different species show differences in their most favorable periods for flowering, fruiting, and so on.

photosynthesis (foh toh SIN thuh sis)
the process by which organisms that contain chlorophyll convert light energy to chemical energy to synthesize sugars and other organic molecules.

phototropism (foh toh TROH piz um)
the response of a plant to a source of light. Usually the plant grows toward the light source, but a shade-tolerant plant might not if the light intensity is too great.

pH scale (PEE AYTCH)
a scale from 0 to 14 reflecting the concentration of hydrogen ions. The lower numbers denote acidic conditions, 7 is neutral, and the upper numbers denote basic or alkaline conditions.

phylogenetic (fy loh jen NET ik)
based on evolutionary relationships as studied in the body form and structure of fossils and living species, or genetic evidence of chromosome changes, or biochemical comparisons of living descendants of different past species.

phylum (FY lum)
in biological classification, the next-larger grouping above class. (However, for plants the term used at this level is division, not phylum.)

phytochrome (FYT oh krohm)
a plant pigment involved in photoperiodism. Its responses to light and darkness affect the activities of the plant.

phytoplankton (FYT oh PLANK tun)
very small aquatic organisms, many microscopic, that carry on photosynthesis.

pistil (PIS til)
a female reproductive structure in a flower. The enlarged base of the pistil encloses an ovary.

pith
cells at the center of young stems of many plants. In some plants the pith disappears as the stems age.

pituitary gland (pih TYOO ih ter ee)
an endocrine gland at the base of the brain that, along with the hypothalamus, regulates and coordinates the work of other endocrine glands; it also produces hormones with specific effects on body tissues.

placenta (pluh SENT uh)
in a pregnant mammal, a structure formed from uterine and embryonic tissue. The developing embryo obtains nourishment from its mother and disposes of wastes through the placenta.

plankton (PLANK tun)
very small aquatic organisms, many microscopic, that usually float or feebly swim near the surface.

plantae (PLAN tee)
the kingdom of plants.

plant physiology (fiz ee OL uh jee)
study of the internal functioning, as contrasted to the anatomy, of plants.

plasma (PLAZ muh)
the liquid portion of the blood, in which blood cells, plasma proteins, and other substances are suspended and still other substances are dissolved.

plasma membrane
the membrane that encloses a cell; it is made of two layers of lipid molecules, with protein molecules on, and embedded in, the lipid layers.

plasmid (PLAZ mid)
in prokaryotes, a circular strand of DNA that has become separate from the overall strand or chromosome.

plasmodium (plaz MOHD ee um)
the malarial parasite; also, the motile, sheetlike stage of life formed by fusion of many amoebalike slime molds.

platelet (PLAYT let)
a small plate-shaped blood factor that contributes to blood clotting at the site of a wound. The platelet releases substances that begin formation of a network in which it and other platelets are caught, forming a clot.

plate tectonics (PLAYT tek TON iks)
the theory and study of the great plates in the earth's crust and their movements, which produce earthquakes, sea-floor spreading, continental drift, and often mountain building.

polar bodies
tiny cells formed during meiosis in development of an egg cell or ovum. A polar body contains one of the nuclei derived from the first or second division of meiosis, but almost no cell cytoplasm, most of which goes to the one cell that becomes the ovum.

pollen grain
a haploid spore produced by a flowering plant; it gives rise to sperm nuclei.

pollen tube
a tube that develops from a germinating pollen grain and penetrates the pistil until it reaches the ovary; sperm nuclei pass through the tube.

pollination
the transfer of pollen from a stamen to the tip of a pistil in a flower, or between different flowers on one or more plants of the same species.

polypeptide (POL ee PEP tyd)
a long chain of amino acids; the basic structure found in a protein molecule, which usually contains two or more such chains.

polysaccharide (POL ee SAK uh ryd)
a biological molecule made of many simple sugars (monosaccharides) chemically bonded in a chain; starch, glycogen, and cellulose are examples.

population
a group of organisms of one species that live in the same place or ecosystem at the same time.

population biologist
a biologist who specializes in the characteristics and activities of populations, such as their geographic range, migration, breeding habits, food cycles, diseases, climatic adaptations, and so on.

population cycle
fluctuation in population numbers, measured from one peak or trough on a graph to the next.

posterior (pah STIR ee er)
situated toward the rear, or coming last; a tail end, in most animals.

predation (preh DAY shun)
the killing of consumer organisms for food, by other consumer organisms.

predator (PRED uh tor)
a consumer organism that feeds on other consumer organisms that it kills for its food.

pressure-flow
the hypothesis that the rate of flow of dissolved plant food through the living tissue of phloem cells is accounted for by pressure differences; dissolved sugars flow from an area of higher pressure to one of lower pressure.

prey (PRAY)
a consumer organism that is a food organism for another consumer.

primary growth
growth in length of plant roots and stems.

primary succession
a succession of communities beginning in an undisturbed rock or bare soil area and proceeding without major interruption.

prion (PREE ahn)
a protein particle believed to be the disease agent in certain animal diseases. How the particle is multiplied is not known; no nucleic acids have so far been found associated with it.

probability
the investigation and expression of uncertain events in mathematical ratios, which are used for prediction.

producer
an organism that makes it own food using materials and energy from the nonliving environment.

progesterone (proh JES teh rohn)
a hormone active in the reproductive cycles of female mammals, promoting build-up of the inner tissues of the uterus and maintenance of these tissues in the built-up condition.

prokaryote (pro KAIR ee oht)
an organism whose cells do not have membrane-bounded nuclei or membrane-bounded organelles such as mitochondria and chloroplasts; a moneran (bacteria).

prophase (PROH fayz)
the stage in mitosis during which replicated strands of chromosomes condense to become shorter and thicker, the nuclear envelope begins to disappear, and a spindle forms.

protein (PROH teen)
a biological molecule composed of one or more—usually two or more—chains of amino acids.

prothrombin (proh THROM bin)
a blood protein that is converted by an activator substance to thrombin whenever a bleeding tissue wound occurs; the thrombin acts as an enzyme to convert fibrinogen to a network of fibrin on which a blood clot forms.

protista (proh TIST uh)
a kingdom of eukaryotes that are mostly aquatic, mostly microscopic, either autotrophs or heterotrophs, with or without a method of locomotion, and varied in still other respects.

proton (PROH tahn)
a positively charged particle within the nucleus of an atom.

protoplast fusion
(PROH toh plast FYOO zhun)
production of a hybrid plant from cells of two different species by chemically removing the cell walls of the "parent" cells and inducing the naked cells (protoplasts) to fuse.

pseudopod (SOO doh pod)
an extension of an amoebalike cell that is used for both movement and feeding. The cell may continue to flow into the pseudopod, or two pseudopods may surround food particles and pull them into the cell.

psychoactive (sy koh AK tiv)
affecting mental functions or behavior.

punctuated equilibrium
a hypothesis suggested by long periods in the fossil record in which there is little change, followed by shorter periods of rapid change. According to the hypothesis, new species arise as a result of major genetic changes that occur in small, isolated populations in relatively short periods of time (thousands of years). These changes are separated by long periods (hundreds of thousands or millions of years), during which very little change occurs.

pyramid of biomass (BY oh mass)
a graphic representation of producers and consumers, in their mass, as a pyramid: at the bottom, with greater total mass, are the producers, with herbivores (of less total mass) above them, and carnivores (of still less total mass) above the herbivores.

pyramid of numbers
a graphic representation of producers and consumers, in their total numbers, as levels of a pyramid: at the bottom, with greater total number, are the producers, with herbivores (of smaller total number) above them, and carnivores (of still smaller total number) above the herbivores.

r

radial symmetry (RAYD ee ul SIM eh tree)
correspondence in size, shape, and position of parts as though they all radiated equally from a center point, or from a center line or axis.

radioactive (rayd ee oh AK tiv)
emitting nuclear radiation, as in certain heavier elements and particular isotopes of some of the lighter elements.

random genetic drift
change in a population's gene pool by chance, as in the loss of an allele with low frequency because no fertilizations of gametes bearing this allele happen to occur, or as in the increase of frequency of nonadaptive alleles that happen to be linked to adaptive ones.

range
all the habitats of a given species, or all the area in which a given population may sometimes be found; also, the span of temperatures, or the variations in other factors, tolerable to a population.

rate
change per unit of time; the amount of change measured over a period of time, divided by the length of time.

ray cells
thin-walled cells that form horizontal rays in larger stems of plants.

receptor
a specialized sensory cell, as in the eye or the skin, that is sensitive to a particular type of stimulus.

recessive
exerting little or no influence on the determination of a trait, in the presence of an unlike allele.

recombinant DNA
DNA to which a new gene has been spliced in the laboratory. Microorganisms have been given new genetic capabilities by this process.

recombination
exchange of parts of two homologous chromosomes, resulting in new linkages of alleles for both chromosomes.

relative humidity
the moisture content of the air, expressed as a percentage of the maximum amount of moisture the air could hold at that temperature.

replication (rep lih KAY shun)
the process of making a copy of the chromosome in a cell nucleus, and of other genes in certain organelles outside the nucleus—particularly chloroplasts and mitochondria. The process is unlike duplication in that each gene and each chromosome in the double set is partly new but also includes part of the old gene or chromosome, as a result of the way the process occurs.

resistance
relative immunity; the ability of a host organism to destroy a pathogen or prevent the disease symptoms it causes.

resource
in ecology, an environmental supply of one or more of an organism's nutritional or other requirements (light energy, food energy, water, oxygen or carbon dioxide, living space, protective cover, and so on). In human society, a resource may have a broader definition—anything useful.

respiration (res phi RAY shun)
the overall process of exchanging gases with the environment, to obtain oxygen and release carbon dioxide.

rhizoid (RY zoyd)
threadlike structure that in nonvascular plants absorbs water and minerals from the soil and helps hold the plants in place.

rhizome (RY zohm)
an underground vascular stem, usually horizontal and enlarged with stored food; it produces shoots above and roots below. The oldest vascular plant fossils show rhizomes.

ribonucleic acid (RY boh noo KLEE ik)
RNA; the biological molecules that carry instructions for the majority of cell processes. DNA codes RNA with the instructions.

ribose (RY bohs)
a sugar used in the structure of RNA; it has one more oxygen atom than deoxyribose.

ribosome (RY boh sohm)
a cell organelle on which the polypeptides of proteins are synthesized; messenger RNA carries the code for the synthesis from a chromosome to the ribosome.

RNA
see ribonucleic acid.

root cap
a layer of protective cells that covers the growing tip of a plant root.

root hair
a thin-walled extension into the soil from a single epidermal cell on a plant root, greatly increasing the cell surface and promoting absorption of water and minerals.

rumen (ROO men)
an enlargement of the digestive tract of many herbivorous mammals, in which microorganisms that can digest cellulose live.

S

salination (sayl ih NAY shun)
salt and mineral buildup in a body of water, as evaporation occurs.

salinity (say LIN it ee)
salt content, as in seawater.

sampling
determination of characteristics of a population from a portion of the population selected as representative.

saturated fat
a fat containing fatty acids with no double-bonded carbon atoms; the single-bonded carbon chains have other single bonds to hydrogen atoms at every carbon position. Saturated fats usually are solids at room temperature.

savanna (suh VAN uh)
a dry tropical or subtropical grassland with tall grasses and few trees, typical of large areas in South America and Africa and of smaller areas in Florida.

scapula (SKAP yoo luh)
a shoulder blade in a vertebrate.

scavenger (SKAV en jer)
a consumer organism that feeds on the dead carcasses of other consumer organisms that it did not kill.

scrotum
in male mammals, an outgrowth from the lower abdominal wall, forming a pouch into which the testes descend.

secondary growth
growth in girth or diameter of plant roots and stems.

secondary succession
a succession of communities in an area where a previous succession was interrupted or destroyed.

seed
an embryo plant, along with food-storage tissue (endosperm), both enclosed within protective coatings formed of tissues from an ovule in the parent plant.

seed coat
a protective covering around the embryonic plant and stored food in a seed.

selective breeding
sexual breeding in plants and animals that is restricted to individuals having particular characteristics in appearance, food production, tolerance of a specific climate, or disease resistance.

semen (SEE men)
in mammals, a whitish fluid produced by male glands, and in which sperm are transported to the female during sexual intercourse.

sensory neuron (NYOO rahn)
a neuron that receives impulses from a sensory organ or receptor and transmits these impulses toward the central nervous system.

sepal (SEEP ul)
one of the leaflike structures that enclose and protect a flower bud; in the mature flower they are on the underside, next to the stem. They often are green.

sessile (SES il)
not free to move about in the environment. Sessile animals usually are attached by the base to an object in the environment.

sex chromosomes
the chromosomes that are associated with sex determination; in particular, the X and Y chromosomes of animals.

sexual reproduction
reproduction that involves male and female gametes, usually produced by different parents. The central event is fertilization of an egg or egg nucleus by a sperm or sperm nucleus.

small intestine
a digestive organ of vertebrates and some invertebrates; in vertebrates it is located between the stomach and the large intestine and is the organ in which the digestive processes are completed.

smooth muscle
muscle tissue in many invertebrates, and of the walls of inner organs except the heart in vertebrates.

social behavior
animal behavior that shows evidence of differing individual roles in the organization of a group, and of cooperation or division of labor in tasks.

sociobiologist (SO see oh by OL uh jist)
a biologist who specializes in the study of animal societies and the genetic and evolutionary influences on them.

solute (SOL yoot)
a dissolvable substance, usually in water or the cytosol of a cell.

solvent
a substance, usually liquid, in which other substances can be dissolved.

speciation (spee shee AY shun)
emergence of species by natural selection and by reproductive isolation from pre-existing species.

species (SPEE sheez)
all individuals and populations of a particular kind of organism, maintained by biological mechanisms that result in their breeding only with their kind.

specimen
a sample, or some part or all of an organism as the specified example.

sperm cell
a male gamete, usually motile in swimming movements. Its motility increases its chance of encountering and fertilizing an egg.

sphincter (SFINK ter)
a circular muscle whose contraction or relaxation closes or opens a tubelike passage in an animal.

sporangium (spoh RAN jee um)
in many organisms (but not animals), a spore-producing structure formed in one stage of the life cycle.

spore (SPOR)
a one-celled reproductive body, usually thick-walled and able to resist harsh environmental conditions (during which it is dormant). Some organisms form asexual spores, others sexual spores that must unite to complete reproduction, still others zygospores after the union of sexual nuclei.

sporophyte (SPOR oh fyt)
a plant of the spore-producing generation in a plant species that undergoes alternation of generations. In some species—mosses, for example—the sporophyte is reduced to a dependent structure that grows from the gametophyte plant.

stamen (STAY men)
a male reproductive structure in a flower. Its enlarged end, the anther, is a mass of specialized pollen-producing cells.

sterile (STEHR il)
not capable of reproducing.

sternum (STER num)
the breastbone in a vertebrate.

stigma
the tip of a pistil in a flower. It secretes a sticky substance that traps pollen.

stimulus (STIM yoo lus)
a change or signal in the internal or external environment that causes an adjustment or reaction by an organism.

stomach
an organ of the digestive tract that has specialized functions in digestion—in humans, the churning of food by peristalsis and the fragmenting of proteins into shorter segments of their polypeptides.

stomate (STOH mayt)
an opening between two guard cells in the epidermis of a plant leaf. Gases are exchanged with the air through stomates.

stratum (STRAYT um)
a layer, usually of deposited earth sediments from erosion. Many strata become mineralized and transformed into rock layers.

striated muscle (STRY ayt ed)
muscle tissue that is banded by cross striations where thick and thin filaments overlap; in particular, skeletal and certain other muscle in vertebrates.

stroma (STROH muh)
the pale, semi-liquid substance in a chloroplast in which the chlorophyll-containing thylakoids and grana occur. The enzymes of the Calvin cycle are also in the stroma.

subspecies
a variety of organisms distinguished from other varieties of the same species. Often an incomplete tendency toward reproductive isolation is a factor in designating and naming a subspecies.

substrate (SUB strayt)
a molecule on which an enzyme acts.

succession
replacement of one community by another in a progression to a climax community.

succulent (SUK yoo lent)
a plant with large amounts of stored water in fleshy or juicy tissues; or, the plant characteristic of having fleshy or juicy tissues that store water.

synapse (SIN aps)
an open junction between neurons, across which an impulse is transmitted by a chemical messenger, a neurotransmitter.

synthesis (SIN thuh sis)
the process of putting together or building up ideas, chemical compounds, and so on.

t

taiga (TY guh)
northern coniferous forests mainly of spruces and firs, bordering the tundra.

taproot system
a root system consisting of one long, vertical root with short, slender side branches.

taxonomy (tak SAHN uh mee)
the classification of fossil and living organisms according to knowledge of their evolutionary relationships.

T cell lymphocyte (LIM foh syt)
one of a team of lymphocytes that include cytotoxic or "killer" T cells, helper T cells that activate B and T cells, memory T cells that are specific for a particular antigen, and suppressor T cells that help terminate B and T cell activity.

telophase (TEL oh fayz)
the final stage in mitosis: two new cell nuclei are completed as nuclear envelopes form around the two clusters or chromosomes at opposite ends of the cell, and the cell itself divides.

tendril
a modified stem or leaf that grows as a whiplike structure; it helps support a plant by growing around any nearby upright object.

testis (plural, testes)
in animals, a male gonad in which sperm are produced.

theory
in nonscientific usage, a suggested explanation or conjecture; but in science, a well-tested hypothesis that organizes knowledge in a field, fits existing data, explains how events or processes are thought to occur, and successfully predicts future discoveries and events.

thermal pollution
pollution by heat, as in a lake whose water is used for an industrial cooling process, then recirculated into the lake.

thermocline (THER moh klyn)
a layer in a thermally stratified body of water that separates upper, oxygen-rich and nutrient-poor warm water from lower, oxygen-poor and nutrient-rich cold water.

thrombin (THROM bin)
a blood protein that is important in the clotting process.

thrombus
a blood clot that forms in a blood vessel and remains attached where it formed.

thylakoid (THY luh koyd)
a flattened sac in a chloroplast. Many of the thylakoids are arranged in stacks known as grana. The pigments and enzymes for the light-dependent reactions of photosynthesis are embedded in the sac membrane.

thyroxin (thy ROK sin)
a hormone that regulates the rate of cell metabolism; it is produced in the thyroid gland.

tissue
a sheet or group of organized cells of the same type that perform the same function. Skin tissue covers and protects; muscle tissue contracts; vascular tissue conducts fluids; mesophyll tissue in a leaf carries on photosynthesis; and so on.

tissue culture
the controlled production of a body tissue outside the organism; also, in plants, the production of a tissue or callus that is treated with hormones to induce growth into a complete plant.

tolerance
the ability to withstand or survive a particular environmental condition.

torpor
a state of decreased body metabolism and activity, usually as an adaptation to an environmental condition such as heat.

toxin (TOK sin)
a substance produced by one organism and poisonous to another.

trachea (TRAY kee uh)
the windpipe of an air-breathing vertebrate, connecting the air passage in the throat with the lungs; in insects, a tube in the tracheal system, similarly used in obtaining oxygen from air.

trade-off
a "no win" dilemma; an action that produces both a benefit and a loss. For example, drainage of marshlands adds to croplands (the benefit) but eliminates migratory birds and other habitats (the loss).

transpiration (trans pih RAY shun)
the loss of water to the atmosphere by a plant, through the stomates in its leaves.

tripeptide (TRY pep tyd)
three amino acid molecules bonded in a short chain; the tripeptide may be the start of a chain for a protein or a product of digestion of a protein or polypeptide.

tropism (TROH piz um)
a change in orientation of a plant, or part of a plant, in response to light, gravity, or other environmental factors.

tundra (TUN druh)
arctic land with permanently frozen subsoil and only low-growing plants. Only the soil surface thaws in summer.

turgor pressure (TER ger)
pressure exerted by plant cells against their cell walls whenever the plant is adequately supplied with water.

U

umbilical cord (um BIL ih kul)
a tube that connects a mammalian embryo with the placenta in the mother's uterus. The tube is formed from embryonic membranes and encloses blood vessels.

undernourished
undersupplied with food or food energy.

unicellular (yoo nih SEL yoo ler)
one-celled.

unsaturated fat
a fat containing fatty acids with one or more double-bonded carbon atoms; each double bond in the carbon chains reduces by one the number of hydrogen atoms that can be bonded to the carbons. Unsaturated fats usually are liquid at room temperature.

urban biome
the largely artificial community of humans, other animals, plants, and microorganisms in and surrounding a city.

urea
a nitrogen-containing waste product of animal metabolism; the principal nitrogenous waste product of adult amphibians and of mammals.

ureter (YOOR et er)
a tube that transports urine from a kidney to the bladder.

urethra (yoo REE thruh)
a tube that transports urine from the urinary bladder to outside the body.

uric acid (YOOR ik)
a nitrogen-containing waste product of animal metabolism; the principal nitrogenous waste product of insects, reptiles, and birds.

uterus
the mammalian organ in which liveborn young develop.

V

vacuole (VAK yoo ohl)
a membrane-enclosed, usually fluid-filled cell organelle. In plant cells it stores nutrients and waste materials; in animal cells it often functions in digestion.

vagina
in mammals, the muscular passageway that connects the uterus to the outside of the body, and in which sperm are deposited during sexual intercourse.

variable (VAIR ee uh bul)
a condition that varies from one organism to another (size, shape, color) or is subject to change for an individual organism (humidity, temperature, light intensity, fatigue).

vascular (VAS kyoo ler)
specialized in conducting fluids through a channel or vessel. Phloem and xylem in plants, and arteries and veins in animals, are vascular tissues.

vas deferens (VAS DEF eh renz)
in male mammals, a duct through which sperm, protected in semen added by glands, pass from the epididymis into the urethra and penis.

vector (VEK tor)
in disease transmission, an organism that carries a pathogen from an infected to an uninfected individual. Mosquitoes are the vectors of malaria in humans.

vegetative reproduction
asexual reproduction by plants that also may reproduce sexually. Examples are reproduction of potato plants from potato "eyes" and reproduction of grass plants from runners.

vein
in many animals, a blood vessel that carries blood to the heart, or toward the heart; in plants, a fluid-transmitting bundle of xylem and phloem tissues in a leaf.

ventral (VEN trul)
in animals, situated toward the lower or belly side.

ventricle (VEN trih kul)
a pumping chamber of the heart; it receives blood from an atrium and pumps the blood into a large artery.

vertebra (VER teh bruh)
an articulated bone; the vertebrae make up the backbone, or spinal column, of vertebrates.

vesicle (VES ih kul)
a membrane-enclosed "package" of cell supplies or cell products. Materials frequently make their way from one compartment of the cytoplasm to another in vesicles.

villus (VIL us)
a fingerlike projection of cells from the chorion of a mammalian embryo into the wall of its mother's uterus; also, a microscopic bulge of the intestinal wall into the cavity of the intestine, facilitating food absorption.

viroid (VY roid)
a naked particle of RNA similar to the RNA of many plant-infecting viruses, and capable of causing certain plant diseases.

virulence (VIR uh lents)
the relative ability of a pathogen to overcome body defenses and cause disease.

x

x-linked trait
a trait determined by alleles that are carried by X chromosomes but are absent from Y chromosomes. Recessive X-linked traits can be produced in males (XY) by a single recessive allele.

xylem (ZY lem)
conducting tissue that transports water with dissolved minerals in vascular plants.

yolk sac
one of four embryonic membranes of vertebrate embryos. It encloses stored food (yolk).

z

zoologist (zoh OL uh jist)
a biologist who specializes in the study of animals.

zooplankton (ZOH oh PLANK tun)
very small, feebly swimming aquatic organisms that are herbivorous or carnivorous or both.

zygospore (ZY goh spor)
a zygote that forms a spore. This type of spore is produced in some fungi and many plants following the union of sexual cells or nuclei.

zygote (ZY goht)
a fertilized egg, the first cell of a new individual.

Index

C

D

E

F

G

H

I

J

K

N

O

P

Q

R

S

T

V

W

X

Y

Z